CW00407683

Miroslav Lovrić
McMaster University

VECTOR CALCULUS

Addison-Wesley Publishers Limited

Don Mills, Ontario • Reading, Massachusetts • Menlo Park, California • New York
Wokingham, England • Amsterdam • Bonn • Sydney • Singapore • Tokyo • Madrid
San Juan • Paris • Seoul • Milan • Mexico City • Taipei

PUBLISHER: Ron Doleman
MANAGING EDITOR: Linda Scott
EDITOR: Santo D'Agostino
COVER AND INTERIOR DESIGN: Anthony Leung
PAGE LAYOUT: Nelson Gonzalez
PRODUCTION COORDINATOR: Wendy Moran
MANUFACTURING COORDINATOR: Sharon Latta Paterson

Canadian Cataloguing in Publication Data

Lovrić, Miroslav
   Vector calculus

Includes index.
ISBN 0–201–42797–4

1. Vector analysis.   I. Title.

QA433.L68 1997   515′.63   C97–930125–4

ISBN 0–201–42797–4

Printed and bound in Canada

A B C D E F – BB – 01 00 99 98 97

For the past three years my words, sentences and ideas have been creating pages of this book — and, at the same time, this book has shaped my thoughts, my experience and my life. As I was trying to build a path through vector calculus woods my muses guided, inspired and advised me. They helped me find a way out of a nightmare of re-editing and proofing the text and pictures. And now, when I am about to finish the last sentence, save the file and e-mail it to my publisher, they are here, sitting on my shoulder. To all of them — those living, and those in the skies — I dedicate this book.

Contents

Preface

Into vector calculus . . .
You will be absorbed. Resistance is futile.
Borg

What Is Vector Calculus and What Does This Book Have to Do with It?

Vector calculus is a branch of mathematics that is dedicated to a study of functions whose values belong to $\mathbb{R}^2$, $\mathbb{R}^3$ (or $\mathbb{R}^n$, $n \geq 2$, in general), and can, therefore, be thought of as vectors — hence the name *vector-valued functions*. The most common vector-valued functions are paths and vector fields. Important concepts of calculus of real-valued functions (limit, continuity and derivative) are expanded to such functions and their properties are studied. Attempts to generalize the definite integral result in a construction of path and surface integrals. The integration theorems of Green, Gauss and Stokes, which relate the concepts of derivative and integral, preserve the spirit of the Fundamental Theorem of Calculus for real-valued functions of one variable.

This book gives a comprehensive and thorough introduction to ideas and some major results of the theory of functions of several variables and of modern vector calculus in two and three dimensions. It provides a clear and rigorous, yet not too technical or "dry," exposition of the theory. Vector calculus lives through its applications — and one of the strengths of this text lies in its applied side, in the richness and variety of examples and applications, taken mostly from physics and engineering, that illustrate all concepts and results that are introduced and discussed.

A Note on the History of Vectors and Vector Calculus

Two traditions have been associated with the development of the concepts of a vector and vector operations. Since the time of the Babylonians and Egyptians, there have been attempts to extend the notion of a (natural) number. (Natural numbers are numbers like 1, 2, 3, 4, etc.) Successive generalizations have added negative numbers, zero, fractions and irrational numbers, forming what is now known as the set of real numbers. An attempt to solve the equation $x^2 + 1 = 0$ led to the discovery of complex numbers, and their geometric interpretation in a two-dimensional coordinate system to the discovery of a vector.

The second tradition relates to an eternal search for (mathematical) entities that could best describe physical phenomena. It suffices to use a single number (and a unit of measurement) to describe the distance between two cities, the area of a lake or the temperature on the surface of the Earth. However, to convey information on the velocity of a wind or on the attractive force of a planet, one needs to specify not only a number, but also a direction. Although, for instance, temperature is a scalar (scalar, in our context, is a synonym for a real number), the way it *changes* cannot be described using a number only — if we fly south from Toronto we will experience an increase in the air temperature; but the temperature will decrease if we fly north. The need to describe a *direction* in a plane or in space, combined with the idea of using *geometry* to approach physical problems (a good example is a parallelogram of forces) brought forth the concept of a vector.

In the second half of the 19th century, basic concepts and principles that form the foundations of vector calculus were formalized (for example, parallelogram law, which talks about "addition of lines with a direction," formalized a parallelogram of forces). The first vector calculus book, E.B. Wilson's *Vector Calculus: A Text Book for the Use of Students of Mathematics and Physics Founded upon the Lectures of J.W. Gibbs,* published in 1901, was the first book entirely devoted to modern vector calculus. Nowadays, every branch of classical physics, modern physics, geometry, engineering, astronomy and numerous other disciplines makes extensive use of the language, ideas and results of vector calculus.

What Is in This Book

This book begins with a review of relevant topics from linear algebra: vectors, dot and cross products, matrices and determinants. This material is spiced with numerous applications, ranging from parametric equations of a line and the center of mass to the work of a force and torque.

Chapter 2 provides a detailed and concise review of basic concepts of calculus of functions of several variables. The bad news is that proofs of some theorems (especially differentiation theorems) tend to be hard, messy and technically involved (and not really revealing). In order to keep the text flowing, most of the proofs are skipped and are presented in Appendix A. Great care is given to examples, comments and remarks that enhance our understanding of the material; for example, instead of insisting on proving differentiability using a (fairly abstract) definition, the book explains how to relate differentiability to a more intuitive (and geometric, hence "visual") concept of a linear approximation. Or, instead of sweating out the proof of equality of mixed second partials (for an interested reader, actual sweating out is done in Appendix A), the book goes through a number of important situations (not only in vector calculus, but also in applications in electromagnetism and elsewhere) where this result is used.

Chapters 3 and 4 are devoted to a study of the two most popular classes of vector-valued functions: paths and vector fields. A vector-valued function of one variable is called a path, and its image, visualized as a geometric object, is a curve. Various ways of constructing paths (so-called parametrizations) are discussed. We learn how to extract information (like length, velocity and acceleration) from a parametrization and discover a close relationship between acceleration and curvature. Serret-Frenet formulas enable us to peek into the world of the differential geometry of curves.

A vector field is a function that assigns a vector to a point in a plane or in space (think of a river — every water molecule (a "point") has its own direction of motion (i.e., a "vector" that is associated with it) — and you see a vector field). In Chapter 4, with the help of partial derivatives, we develop the tools (gradient, curl and divergence) that are instrumental in the investigation of properties of vector fields. In the spirit of the text, emphasis is placed on interpretations and applications of these operators in various physical situations. We end Chapter 4 by introducing differential forms, the importance of which is understood best in the context of vector integral theorems in Chapter 8.

Chapters 5–7 are devoted to the development of generalizations of the definite integral to various regions in two and three dimensions. We learn how to integrate functions along curves, over two-dimensional regions in a plane and over surfaces and three-dimensional solids. With the help of a parametrization, a path integral is reduced to the definite integral of a function of one variable. The work of a force and the circulation of a vector field are presented as main applications. A vector field is called a gradient vector field if it is the gradient of some real-valued function. We end Chapter 5 with an investigation of remarkable properties of such vector fields with respect to integration.

Next, we move one dimension higher: our goal is to define integrals over surfaces. The construction proceeds in a way analogous to the one for curves: first, we describe a surface in analytic terms (this is again called a parametrization), and then we use this description to reduce a surface integral to a double integral over a region in a plane. Chapter 6 is devoted to the construction and techniques of evaluation of double integrals. Taking advantage of the machinery available, we end the chapter by a short study of triple integrals.

In Chapter 7 we investigate parametrizations of surfaces and define surface integrals. Related applications include surface area and flux of a vector field. In the last section we unify various types of integration into a single concept and discuss further examples, properties and physical applications.

The Fundamental Theorem of Calculus states that the definite integral of the derivative of a function depends not on the whole interval of integration but only on its endpoints (that is, only on the boundary points of the interval). In Chapter 8 we investigate further the relation between the concepts of integration and differentiation. The results, contained in the theorems of Green, Gauss and Stokes (the so-called Classical Integration Theorems of Vector Calculus), are all variations on the same theme applied to different types of integration. Green's Theorem relates the path integral of a vector field along an oriented, simple closed curve in the xy-plane to the double integral of its derivative (to be precise, of the *curl*) over the region enclosed by that curve. Gauss' Divergence Theorem extends this result to closed surfaces and Stokes' Theorem generalizes it to simple closed curves in space. The last section of this chapter is completely devoted to a discussion of applications of vector calculus in electromagnetism. The emphasis is placed not on explaining the details of the theory of electromagnetism but on identifying physical quantities involved as mathematical objects and showing how to use calculus in manipulating them to obtain meaningful results. The guiding idea is to explain, line by line, all details and intricacies of the mathematical arguments, so that, when studying a text in electromagnetism, the reader will be prepared to go over the mathematical side smoothly and concentrate on understanding the physics of it.

Examples and Exercises

This text contains a large number of fully solved examples that are designed to help and to enhance the understanding of the theory, to illustrate methods and concepts introduced in the text and to give a routine in technical intricacies of computations. The end of each section contains numerous exercises ranging from basic and routine to hard and thought-provoking. Every chapter ends with a review section that is divided into three parts: *review questions, computer projects* and *further exercises. Review questions* ask students to relate various concepts, rephrase or quote a definition or a theorem and discuss their statements. *Further exercises* consist of harder, thought-provoking questions; on a few occasions, related theoretical concepts are introduced. *Computer projects* present a new feature for textbooks on this level and deserve a heading of their own — see below.

The appendices at the back of the book contain proofs of technical differentiation theorems, statements of several results that are used throughout the text and answers to odd-numbered exercises. The front endpapers contain a list of symbols; derivatives, integrals and other useful formulas appear on the back endpapers.

Detailed solutions to odd-numbered exercises are contained in the students' version of the Solutions Manual. Solutions to all exercises will appear in the Instructor's Solutions Manual.

Computer Projects

Whether we like it or not, we have to accept the realities of modern times — and might put our computer to good (and productive) use in mathematics. In this book we suggest projects that are platform-free (i.e., can be done on any computer using any math software that has symbolic and graphical capabilities) and do not require any programming knowledge. They are designed to illustrate important ideas and results introduced in the text and to further deepen our understanding of basic concepts. For example, one project discusses the relation between the flow lines of a conservative vector field and the level curves of its potential function. In another project we investigate the isoperimetric ratio — that is, the relation between the surface area and the volume for various geometric objects. A project in Chapter 7 teaches us how to write the formulas (parametrizations) that generated pictures of a torus and a Möbius band that are shown in the text. Moreover, the projects promote the point that, although we have a pretty powerful machine at our disposal, it is totally helpless and useless without our guidance. We are not in a science-fiction story — here, computers compute and we do the thinking.

What Is Not in This Book: Prerequisites

It is assumed that students have taken a course on the calculus of real-valued functions of one variable, and are familiar with elementary functions (polynomials, rational functions, trigonometric functions and their inverses, $\ln x$, e^x, and the absolute value), limits, continuity, derivatives (basic differentiation formulas, including the chain rule) and integrals (antiderivatives, definite integrals, substitution and integration by parts). Part of the material mentioned above is reviewed at appropriate places in the text. Relevant concepts from linear algebra are covered in Chapter 1.

A Note on Notation

The front endpapers contain a list of symbols introduced and used in this book, together with a brief description and the page number of the first appearance of each symbol. Let us say a few more words about some of them, recall interval notation and mention a few other things.

The set of real numbers is denoted by $\mathbb{R}$. In general, we use $\{a \mid p\}$ to define a set of all elements a that satisfy the property p. For example, the set $\mathbb{R}^+ = \{x \text{ is a real number} \mid x > 0\}$ contains all positive real numbers. Sometimes we identify a set by listing its elements, as in $A = \{0, 13, \pi\}$. We use $x \in A$ if we want to say that an element x belongs to a set A. Using the symbol $\in$, we write $\mathbb{R}^+ = \{x \in \mathbb{R} \mid x > 0\}$. We say that a set A is a subset of a set B, and write $A \subseteq B$, if every element that belongs to A also belongs to B. For example, $\mathbb{R}^+ \subseteq \mathbb{R}$. The difference $A - B$ of sets A and B is the set of all elements of A that are not in B. For example, $\mathbb{R} - \mathbb{R}^+$ contains all negative real numbers and zero. If we want to remove the origin from $\mathbb{R}^2$, we write $\mathbb{R}^2 - \{(0, 0)\}$.

Let a and b be real numbers and $a < b$. The closed interval $[a, b]$ contains all real numbers between a and b, including both a and b; i.e., $[a, b] = \{x \in \mathbb{R} \mid a \leq x \leq b\}$. The open interval (a, b) is defined by $(a, b) = \{x \in \mathbb{R} \mid a < x < b\}$; similarly, $[a, b) = \{x \in \mathbb{R} \mid a \leq x < b\}$, etc.

When we want to say that a function f has the domain A and the range B, we use $f: A \to B$. The composition of functions f and g (f is applied first) is denoted by $g \circ f$. f^{-1} is a symbol for the inverse function of f.

The end of a definition, the end of a statement of a theorem and the end of its proof are marked by ∎ and the end of an example by ◄.

Acknowledgments

First of all, I would like to thank my teachers — professors at the University of Zagreb, Croatia, and at the Ohio State University, Columbus, U.S.A.; in particular, Šime Ungar and Ernst Ruh — who taught me not only how to read definitions and theorems but also how to read between the lines to capture their messages: concepts, guiding principles and ideas of mathematics. That is the approach I have incorporated into my teaching and into the lines of this book. I am grateful to my colleagues at McMaster University — Mark Chamberland, Jean-Pierre Gabardo and Maung Min-Oo — for their valuable comments and suggestions that materialized through numerous improvements in the text. Thanks to my colleagues from other places: John Blanchard, Lakshmi Narayani and Willem Sluis. I thank my teaching assistants and my students — Whitney Black,

Derek DiFilippo, Daniel Egloff, Jeff Hooper, Fadil Khouli and Rouset Shaikhi-Adeh —
for their help, persistence and dedication in various stages of this project. My colleagues

  Robert Adams (University of British Columbia)

  Adel Boules (University of North Florida)

  Daniel Norman (Queen's University)

  Josef Paldus (University of Waterloo)

  Edgar Pechlaner (Simon Fraser University)

  David Royster (University of North Carolina at Charlotte)

  E.J. Janse von Rensburg (York University)

have read the manuscript, reviewed it and provided valuable comments. I thank them
all for their thoroughness, patience and literally hundreds of suggestions. My thanks
to Jacqueline Gallet for her assessment of the exercise sets and Santo D'Agostino for
extremely useful criticism, both mathematical and linguistic.

I am grateful to my publisher, Ron Doleman of Addison-Wesley (Canada), for his
help and assistance from the first days of this project. I also thank Abdulqafar Abdullahi,
Michelle Bish and Linda Scott of Addison-Wesley for their help, and Nelson Gonzalez
for producing excellent pictures and for dealing with all sorts of computer-related issues.
Many thanks to others who have contributed in various ways and whose names I am not
aware of.

Finally, I would like to thank my parents, Vilma and Ivan Lovrić, my wife Marija
Dalbello-Lovrić, the rest of my family and my friends for all their support and encour-
agement.

Epilogue

Like any other book, a math textbook is a communication between the author and the
reader — and I would be really glad if we can make it a two-way communication. If
you find an error, or have a comment, a question or a suggestion for improvement, or
there is something you would like to discuss with me, please write me at

  Department of Mathematics and Statistics

  McMaster University

  Hamilton, Ontario, Canada L8S 4K1

or send me an e-mail at

  lovric@icarus.math.mcmaster.ca

or visit my WWW home page at

  http://icarus.math.mcmaster.ca/lovric/lovric.html

and follow the links. I will create a list (and will keep updating it) of corrections,
comments and suggestions regarding the material in this book. If you would like a copy,
please write me or send me an e-mail and I will be glad to mail/e-mail it to you. A copy
of the list will be available on the WWW at the above URL.

I thank you for choosing to use this book and hope that you will like it (even when
you will have to cram for that vector calculus exam) and benefit from it. Maybe, just
maybe, you might admit that math isn't that bad after all.

Miroslav Lovrić

December 1996

Chapter 1
VECTORS, MATRICES AND APPLICATIONS

It suffices to use a single real number (together with a unit of measurement) to describe the average temperature on the surface of the Sun, the mass of a molecule, the distance between two cities or the surface area of a lake. Quantities such as temperature, mass, distance or area are called *scalars* or *scalar quantities*. On the other hand, the description of a wind on a weather report contains not only its magnitude but the direction as well (for example, "northwesterly"). The attractive force of a planet on a satellite is specified by its magnitude and direction ("radially towards the center of the planet"). Quantities such as force and motion are called *vectors* or *vector quantities*.

This chapter begins with the construction of rectangular coordinate systems, the definition of a vector and a discussion of basic vector operations. Numerous applications, ranging from parametric equations of lines and planes to relative velocity, physical forces and center of mass are discussed in the following section. The two types of vector multiplication, the dot product and the cross product, are defined and their algebraic and geometric aspects are studied in detail. Related examples introduce physical applications such as the work of a force, angular and tangential velocities of a rotating body and torque. Since matrices and determinants will appear in a number of situations in this book, a brief review covering only the relevant topics is presented in a separate section.

1.1   VECTORS

In this section we will review the definition and basic properties of vectors. Although we will concentrate on dimensions 2 and 3 (for reasons of convenience), all statements and results remain valid for vectors in n dimensions, where $n \geq 2$.

One way to identify points in a plane is to use a two-dimensional *Cartesian* (or *rectangular*) *coordinate system*: we first select a point of reference (usually denoted by O and called the *origin*) and two perpendicular number lines that intersect at O and are placed so that O represents the number zero for both of them. Their orientation (i.e., the direction of increasing values) is indicated by an arrow. The two lines (called the *coordinate axes*) are usually visualized as the horizontal line, called the *x-axis* and the vertical line, called the *y-axis*. To describe the location of a point A we have to specify two numbers: the (directed) distance from A to the *x*-axis (called the *y-coordinate* of A) and the (directed) distance from A to the *y*-axis (called the *x-coordinate* of A). "Directed distance" means that the *y*-coordinates of points below the *x*-axis and the *x*-coordinates of points to the left of the *y*-axis are negative. We write $A(a_1, a_2)$, where a_1 is the *x*-coordinate and a_2 is the *y*-coordinate of A. A plane together with the coordinate system just constructed is called the *xy-plane* and is denoted by $\mathbb{R}^2$ (sometimes by E^2). Using set notation, $\mathbb{R}^2$ can be described as

$$\mathbb{R}^2 = \{(x, y) \mid x \in \mathbb{R}, y \in \mathbb{R}\},$$

where curly braces {} are used to denote a set, (x, y) is called an ordered pair, the vertical bar is read "such that", and $\in$ means "belongs to" or "is an element of." In this new language, the formula written above can be translated as: $\mathbb{R}^2$ is the set of all ordered pairs (x, y) (that are visualized as points in the *xy*-plane) such that x and y are real numbers. Similarly,

$$\mathbb{R}^3 = \{(x, y, z) \mid x, y, z \in \mathbb{R}\}$$

describes all points in three-dimensional space. To give meaning to the numbers x, y and z we construct a three-dimensional *Cartesian* (or *rectangular*) *coordinate system* in much the same way as a two-dimensional system: choose a reference point O and three mutually perpendicular directed number lines that intersect at O (and O represents the number zero for all three of them). The three axes are called the *coordinate axes* and are identified as the *x-axis*, the *y-axis* and the *z-axis*; they are usually visualized as in Figure 1.1.

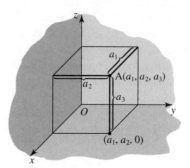

Figure 1.1   Three-dimensional rectangular coordinate system.

The coordinate axes define the three coordinate planes: the *xy-plane*, the *yz-plane*, and the *xz-plane*. The location of a point A in space can now be specified by listing the following three real numbers: the (directed) distance a_1 from A to the *yz*-plane (called the *x-coordinate* of A), the (directed) distance a_2 from A to the *xz*-plane (called the *y-coordinate* of A), and the (directed) distance a_3 from A to the *xy*-plane (called the *z-coordinate* of A). We say that the point A has coordinates (a_1, a_2, a_3) and write $A(a_1, a_2, a_3)$. Since it takes three real numbers to uniquely determine A, we say that the space is three-dimensional, and denote it (and we have done so already) by $\mathbb{R}^3$. Notice that the correspondence between the points and the coordinates is one-to-one. This means that every point in $\mathbb{R}^2$ ($\mathbb{R}^3$) is described by one ordered pair (triple) of real numbers and every ordered pair (triple) of real numbers represents one point in $\mathbb{R}^2$ ($\mathbb{R}^3$).

Analogously, we define

$$\mathbb{R}^n = \{(x_1, \ldots, x_n) \mid x_i \in \mathbb{R}, i = 1, \ldots, n\}.$$

In words, $\mathbb{R}^n$, $n \geq 2$, is the set of ordered n-tuples of real numbers, interpreted as points in n-dimensional space. Very soon we will come across another common interpretation of $\mathbb{R}^n$.

In the description of $\mathbb{R}^2$ and $\mathbb{R}^3$ (and, in general, $\mathbb{R}^n$ for $n \geq 1$) using the rectangular coordinate system all coordinates are given the same meaning — that of a distance. However, there are other ways of describing the location of a point, such as using a combination of angles and distances, as in polar, cylindrical or spherical coordinates. We will define polar coordinates in a moment, but will postpone the discussion of cylindrical, spherical and other coordinate systems until the end of Chapter 2.

Sometimes more information than just distances is built into coordinates. For example, an ordered quadruple (x, y, z, t) (assume that t represents time) gives not only the location of a point in space, but also the time when something of interest occurred at that location.

A statement such as "the place you are looking for is three kilometers southwest of here" represents another common way of describing the location of a point. It uses "polar coordinates," that will now be constructed.

Choose a point in a plane, label it O (and name it the *pole*), and then choose a half-line starting at O (use an arrow to indicate its direction and call it the *polar axis*), as shown in Figure 1.2(a). The location of any point A in the plane is determined by the following two numbers: the distance r ($r \geq 0$) from O to A and the angle θ ($0 \leq \theta < 2\pi$) between the polar axis and the segment $\overline{OA}$. By convention, θ is measured in radians counterclockwise from the polar axis. We say that r and θ are the *polar coordinates* of A and write $A(r, \theta)$. The correspondence between the points and the polar coordinates is one-to-one, except in one case (the pole can be represented as $(0, \theta)$, for any θ, $0 \leq \theta < 2\pi$).

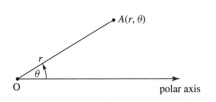   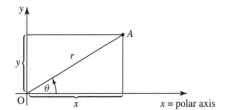

Figure 1.2 Polar coordinate system in a plane.
(a) Polar coordinates of a point.   (b) Comparison with Cartesian coordinates.

To compare polar and rectangular coordinate systems in a plane, we place the pole at the origin and the polar axis over the positive direction of the x-axis, as in Figure 1.2(b) (this is how the polar coordinate system is usually visualized). From $\cos\theta = x/r$ and $\sin\theta = y/r$ we obtain the formulas

$$x = r\cos\theta, \qquad y = r\sin\theta$$

for the Cartesian coordinates of a point if its polar coordinates are known. If x and y are known, then the formulas

$$r = \sqrt{x^2 + y^2}, \qquad \tan\theta = y/x, \quad 0 \le \theta < 2\pi$$

give corresponding polar coordinates.

From now on (unless stated otherwise) we use rectangular coordinate systems in $\mathbb{R}^2$ and $\mathbb{R}^3$.

Recall that the distance between two points $A(a)$ and $B(b)$ on a number line (points A and B are identified with the real numbers a and b) is given by $|b-a|$. We can generalize this formula to any dimension: the distance $d(A, B)$ between points $A(a_1, \dots, a_n)$ and $B(b_1, \dots, b_n)$ in $\mathbb{R}^n$ is given by

$$d(A, B) = \sqrt{(b_1 - a_1)^2 + \dots + (b_n - a_n)^2}. \tag{1.1}$$

In low dimensions, this formula takes on the familiar forms

$$d(A, B) = \sqrt{(b_1 - a_1)^2 + (b_2 - a_2)^2},$$

if $A(a_1, a_2)$ and $B(b_1, b_2)$ are in $\mathbb{R}^2$, and

$$d(A, B) = \sqrt{(b_1 - a_1)^2 + (b_2 - a_2)^2 + (b_3 - a_3)^2},$$

if $A(a_1, a_2, a_3)$ and $B(b_1, b_2, b_3)$ are in $\mathbb{R}^3$. The proof of formula (1.1) for $n = 2$ and $n = 3$ uses the Pythagorean Theorem and is left as an exercise.

Example 1.1   Find the equation of the circle in $\mathbb{R}^2$ of radius r centered at $C(c_1, c_2)$, and the equation of the sphere in $\mathbb{R}^3$ of radius r whose center is located at the point $C(c_1, c_2, c_3)$.

Solution   The circle consists of all points (x, y) in the xy-plane whose distance from $C(c_1, c_2)$ is constant and equal to r. Therefore, $\sqrt{(x - c_1)^2 + (y - c_2)^2} = r$, and hence the equation (square both sides)

$$(x - c_1)^2 + (y - c_2)^2 = r^2$$

represents the given circle. Similarly, we obtain

$$(x - c_1)^2 + (y - c_2)^2 + (z - c_3)^2 = r^2$$

for the equation of the sphere of radius r with center at $C(c_1, c_2, c_3)$.   ◀

A vector is a quantity characterized by both magnitude and direction. We will now give a precise definition.

Definition 1.1   Vector in 2, 3 and n Dimensions.

An *n-dimensional vector* (or a *vector in* $\mathbb{R}^n$) is an ordered n-tuple $\mathbf{v} = (v_1, \ldots, v_n)$ of real numbers, $n \geq 2$. In particular, a *two-dimensional vector* (or a vector in $\mathbb{R}^2$) is an ordered pair $\mathbf{v} = (v_1, v_2)$, and a *three-dimensional vector* (or a vector in $\mathbb{R}^3$) is an ordered triple $\mathbf{v} = (v_1, v_2, v_3)$. The real numbers $v_1, v_2, \ldots, v_n$ are called the *components* or the *coordinates* of $\mathbf{v}$.

We often visualize a two-dimensional vector $\mathbf{v} = (v_1, v_2)$ as a line segment joining the origin and the point (v_1, v_2), with the direction (indicated by an arrow) from the origin towards (v_1, v_2). It is important to notice that the *same set* (namely $\mathbb{R}^2$) is viewed both as a set of points and as a set of vectors; i.e., an ordered pair $(v_1, v_2) \in \mathbb{R}^2$ can be interpreted either as a point $A(v_1, v_2)$ or as a two-dimensional vector $\mathbf{v} = (v_1, v_2)$. Similarly, elements of $\mathbb{R}^3$ (or $\mathbb{R}^n$, $n \geq 2$ in general) are visualized either as points or as vectors in a three-dimensional (or n-dimensional) space. What we defined as a vector is sometimes called a *position vector* or a *directed line segment* (whose initial point is at the origin), or a *"bound" vector*. For convenience, we would like to have a vector that can be "moved around;" i.e., that can "start" at any point, not necessarily at the origin. We now proceed by precisely defining this concept.

A *line segment* $\overline{AB}$ is the collection of points on the line joining A and B that lie between A and B (including the endpoints A and B). Once the direction has been specified (for example, "from A to B"), we obtain the *directed line segment* $\overrightarrow{AB}$. In other words, $\overrightarrow{AB}$ is a line segment $\overline{AB}$ with the initial point (or the tail) A and the terminal point (or the tip) B. Now let $\mathbf{v} = (v_1, v_2)$ be a vector in $\mathbb{R}^2$ and pick any point $A(a_1, a_2)$. A *representative* of the vector $\mathbf{v}$ with initial point A is the directed line segment $\overrightarrow{AB}$, where B is the point $(a_1 + v_1, a_2 + v_2)$. Similarly, the directed line segment $\overrightarrow{AB}$, where $A(a_1, a_2, a_3)$ and $B(a_1 + v_1, a_2 + v_2, a_3 + v_3)$ is the representative of a vector $\mathbf{v} = (v_1, v_2, v_3)$ in $\mathbb{R}^3$ that starts at A. Figure 1.3 shows several representative directed line segments of a vector $\mathbf{v} = (v_1, v_2)$ in $\mathbb{R}^2$. The choice of a directed line segment that will represent a vector is determined from context. What we usually label as $\mathbf{v}$ is that chosen representative directed line segment. The representative of $\mathbf{v}$ that starts at the origin is called the *position vector*. Sometimes, representative directed line segments of a vector are called *"free" vectors*.

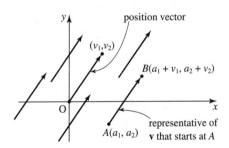

Figure 1.3   Several representatives of a vector $\mathbf{v} = (v_1, v_2)$ in $\mathbb{R}^2$.

Take two points $A(a_1, a_2, a_3)$ and $B(b_1, b_2, b_3)$ in $\mathbb{R}^3$ and consider the directed line segment $\overrightarrow{AB}$. Let us construct the vector $\mathbf{v} = (v_1, v_2, v_3)$ that is represented by $\overrightarrow{AB}$ (i.e., we want to find the "vector from A to B"). By definition, if $\overrightarrow{AB}$ represents $\mathbf{v}$, then $a_1 + v_1 = b_1$, $a_2 + v_2 = b_2$ and $a_3 + v_3 = b_3$; i.e., $v_1 = b_1 - a_1$, $v_2 = b_2 - a_2$ and $v_3 = b_3 - a_3$, and therefore, $\mathbf{v} = (b_1 - a_1, b_2 - a_2, b_3 - a_3)$. We have just proved the following theorem.

■ **Theorem 1.1** Vector Defined by the Representative Directed Line Segment $\overrightarrow{AB}$.

The vector $\mathbf{v} \in \mathbb{R}^3$ represented by the directed line segment $\overrightarrow{AB}$, where the coordinates of A and B are $A(a_1, a_2, a_3)$ and $B(b_1, b_2, b_3)$, is given by

$$\mathbf{v} = (b_1 - a_1, b_2 - a_2, b_3 - a_3).$$

■

By removing the last component, we obtain the corresponding statement for vectors in $\mathbb{R}^2$.

Example 1.2 This example illustrates the relationship between a vector and its representative directed line segments.

(a) Find the representative $\overrightarrow{AB}$ of the vector $\mathbf{v} = (3, 0, 4) \in \mathbb{R}^3$ that starts at the point $A(-2, 6, 2)$.

(b) Find the vector $\mathbf{v} \in \mathbb{R}^2$ that is represented by $\overrightarrow{AB}$, where $A = (3, 2)$ and $B = (-1, 4)$.

Solution

(a) By definition, the representative of $\mathbf{v} = (3, 0, 4)$ is the directed line segment $\overrightarrow{AB}$, where $A = (-2, 6, 2)$. If $B = (b_1, b_2, b_3)$, then $b_1 = a_1 + v_1 = -2 + 3 = 1$, $b_2 = a_2 + v_2 = 6 + 0 = 6$ and $b_3 = a_3 + v_3 = 2 + 4 = 6$. Hence $B = (1, 6, 6)$.

(b) By Theorem 1.1 the vector $\mathbf{v} = (-1 - 3, 4 - 2) = (-4, 2)$ has the given directed line segment $\overrightarrow{AB}$ as its representative.

◀

The fact that all representatives of a vector are parallel translates of each other characterizes a Cartesian coordinate system. We will see in Sections 2.7 and 2.8 that representatives of unit coordinate vectors in other coordinate systems depend on their location and no longer satisfy this property.

Consider a vector $\mathbf{v} = (v_1, v_2, v_3)$ and its representative directed line segment $\overrightarrow{AB}$, where $A = (a_1, a_2, a_3)$ and $B = (b_1, b_2, b_3)$ are points in $\mathbb{R}^3$ (this means that $v_1 = b_1 - a_1$, $v_2 = b_2 - a_2$ and $v_3 = b_3 - a_3$). The distance between A and B is computed by (1.1) to be

$$d(A, B) = \sqrt{(b_1 - a_1)^2 + (b_2 - a_2)^2 + (b_3 - a_3)^2} = \sqrt{v_1^2 + v_2^2 + v_3^2}.$$

We have just shown that the length of a representative $\overrightarrow{AB}$ of $\mathbf{v}$ does *not* really depend on the coordinates of the points A or B, but only on the components of $\mathbf{v}$. In other words, all representatives of $\mathbf{v}$ have the same length, equal to $\sqrt{v_1^2 + v_2^2 + v_3^2}$. Based on this observation we will now define the *length* (or the *magnitude* or the *norm*) of a vector. It will be denoted by $|\mathbf{v}|$, or more often by $\|\mathbf{v}\|$.

■ **Definition 1.2**   Length of a Vector.

The length of a vector is equal to the length of any of its representatives. In particular, if $\mathbf{v} = (v_1, v_2)$ is a vector in $\mathbb{R}^2$, then

$$\|\mathbf{v}\| = \sqrt{v_1^2 + v_2^2}.$$

If $\mathbf{v} = (v_1, v_2, v_3)$ is a vector in $\mathbb{R}^3$, then
$$\|\mathbf{v}\| = \sqrt{v_1^2 + v_2^2 + v_3^2}.$$

The vectors $\mathbf{v} = (0, 0, 0) \in \mathbb{R}^3$ and $\mathbf{v} = (0, 0) \in \mathbb{R}^2$ are called the *zero vectors* and are denoted by $\mathbf{0}$. The representative of the zero vector starting at A is the (degenerate) directed line segment $\overrightarrow{AA}$. Clearly, $\|\mathbf{0}\| = 0$.

■ **Definition 1.3**   Addition of Vectors and Multiplication by Scalars.

(a) The sum $\mathbf{v}+\mathbf{w}$ and the difference $\mathbf{v}-\mathbf{w}$ of two vectors $\mathbf{v} = (v_1, v_2)$ and $\mathbf{w} = (w_1, w_2)$ in $\mathbb{R}^2$ are the vectors given by

$$\mathbf{v} + \mathbf{w} = (v_1 + w_1, v_2 + w_2) \qquad \text{and} \qquad \mathbf{v} - \mathbf{w} = (v_1 - w_1, v_2 - w_2).$$

If $\mathbf{v} = (v_1, v_2, v_3)$ and $\mathbf{w} = (w_1, w_2, w_3)$ are in $\mathbb{R}^3$, then

$$\mathbf{v}+\mathbf{w} = (v_1+w_1, v_2+w_2, v_3+w_3) \qquad \text{and} \qquad \mathbf{v}-\mathbf{w} = (v_1-w_1, v_2-w_2, v_3-w_3).$$

(b) If $\mathbf{v} = (v_1, v_2) \in \mathbb{R}^2$ and $\alpha \in \mathbb{R}$, then $\alpha\mathbf{v}$ is the vector in $\mathbb{R}^2$ defined by

$$\alpha\mathbf{v} = (\alpha v_1, \alpha v_2).$$

If $\mathbf{v} = (v_1, v_2, v_3)$ then

$$\alpha\mathbf{v} = (\alpha v_1, \alpha v_2, \alpha v_3)$$

for any real number α.

The addition of vectors can be visualized as the Triangle Law or as the Parallelogram Law; see Figures 1.4 and 1.5. The details of the verification (similar triangles argument) are left as exercises.

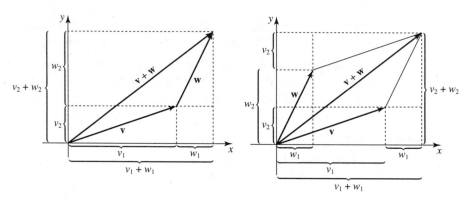

Figure 1.4 Triangle Law.   **Figure 1.5** Parallelogram Law.

■ **Theorem 1.2**   Properties of Addition and Multiplication by Scalars.

Let $\mathbf{u}$, $\mathbf{v}$ and $\mathbf{w}$ be vectors in $\mathbb{R}^2$ or $\mathbb{R}^3$ and let α and β be real numbers. The addition of vectors is *commutative*

$$\mathbf{v} + \mathbf{w} = \mathbf{w} + \mathbf{v},$$

associative

$$\mathbf{u} + (\mathbf{v} + \mathbf{w}) = (\mathbf{u} + \mathbf{v}) + \mathbf{w}$$

and, if $\mathbf{0}$ denotes the zero vector,

$$\mathbf{v} + \mathbf{0} = \mathbf{v}.$$

The *distributive laws*

$$\alpha(\mathbf{v} + \mathbf{w}) = \alpha\mathbf{v} + \alpha\mathbf{w} \qquad \text{and} \qquad (\alpha + \beta)\mathbf{v} = \alpha\mathbf{v} + \beta\mathbf{v}$$

hold for the multiplication of scalars and vectors. Moreover,

$$(\alpha\beta)\mathbf{v} = \alpha(\beta\mathbf{v})$$

and

$$1 \cdot \mathbf{v} = \mathbf{v}.$$ ■

The product $(-1)\mathbf{v}$ is written as $-\mathbf{v}$. One could define the difference as $\mathbf{v} - \mathbf{w} = \mathbf{v} + (-\mathbf{w})$.

To show any of the identities we have to write vectors in terms of their components, use the appropriate definitions of vector operations and properties of real numbers. For example, let us prove the first distributive law for vectors $\mathbf{v}$ and $\mathbf{w}$ in $\mathbb{R}^2$. Write $\mathbf{v} = (v_1, v_2)$ and $\mathbf{w} = (w_1, w_2)$ and compare the two sides. The left side is

$$\alpha(\mathbf{v} + \mathbf{w}) = \alpha((v_1, v_2) + (w_1, w_2)) = \alpha(v_1 + w_1, v_2 + w_2) = (\alpha(v_1 + w_1), \alpha(v_2 + w_2)).$$

Since the right side is

$$\alpha\mathbf{v} + \alpha\mathbf{w} = \alpha(v_1, v_2) + \alpha(w_1, w_2) = (\alpha v_1, \alpha v_2) + (\alpha w_1, \alpha w_2) = (\alpha v_1 + \alpha w_1, \alpha v_2 + \alpha w_2),$$

it follows that the two sides are equal (by the distributive property of real numbers). The proof of the rest of the theorem is left as an exercise.

Theorem 1.2 shows that, as far as the operations of addition and multiplication by scalars are concerned, vectors behave in the same way as real numbers.

From the interpretation of the sum $\mathbf{v} + \mathbf{w}$ of $\mathbf{v}$ and $\mathbf{w}$ given by the Triangle Law (see Figure 1.4) and the fact that the sum of lengths of any two sides in a triangle is at least as large as the length of the third side, we get the *Triangle Inequality*

$$\|\mathbf{v} + \mathbf{w}\| \leq \|\mathbf{v}\| + \|\mathbf{w}\|.$$

We say that the vectors $\mathbf{v}$ and $\mathbf{w}$ are *parallel* if there is a non-zero real number α such that $\mathbf{w} = \alpha\mathbf{v}$. The length of a vector $\alpha\mathbf{v}$ is computed to be

$$\|\alpha\mathbf{v}\| = |\alpha|\,\|\mathbf{v}\|.$$

If $\alpha > 0$, then $\mathbf{v}$ and $\alpha\mathbf{v}$ have the *same direction,* and if $\alpha < 0$, then they are of *opposite directions.* A vector whose length is 1 is called a *unit vector.* If $\mathbf{v}$ is a non-zero vector, then the vector $\mathbf{v}/\|\mathbf{v}\| = (1/\|\mathbf{v}\|)\mathbf{v}$ is the unit vector in the same direction as $\mathbf{v}$.

A vector $\mathbf{v} = (v_1, v_2, v_3)$ in $\mathbb{R}^3$ can be written as

$$\mathbf{v} = (v_1, v_2, v_3) = v_1(1, 0, 0) + v_2(0, 1, 0) + v_3(0, 0, 1) = v_1\mathbf{i} + v_2\mathbf{j} + v_3\mathbf{k},$$

where $\mathbf{i} = (1, 0, 0)$, $\mathbf{j} = (0, 1, 0)$ and $\mathbf{k} = (0, 0, 1)$ are the *standard unit vectors* in $\mathbb{R}^3$. The set $\{\mathbf{i}, \mathbf{j}, \mathbf{k}\}$ is called the *standard basis of $\mathbb{R}^3$* (the word *basis* refers to the fact that every vector in $\mathbb{R}^3$ can be expressed in terms of $\mathbf{i}$, $\mathbf{j}$ and $\mathbf{k}$). When the *order* of the basis vectors is specified (for example, $\mathbf{i}$, $\mathbf{j}$, $\mathbf{k}$), we say that the space $\mathbb{R}^3$ is *oriented.* Similarly, if $\mathbf{v} \in \mathbb{R}^2$ then

$$\mathbf{v} = (v_1, v_2) = v_1(1, 0) + v_2(0, 1) = v_1\mathbf{i} + v_2\mathbf{j},$$

where $\mathbf{i} = (1, 0)$ and $\mathbf{j} = (0, 1)$ are the standard unit vectors in $\mathbb{R}^2$. Vectors $\mathbf{i}$ and $\mathbf{j}$ (in that order) define an *orientation* of $\mathbb{R}^2$.

Example 1.3 Find the unit vector in the direction of $\mathbf{v} = \mathbf{i} - 2\mathbf{j} + \mathbf{k}$.

Solution The length of $\mathbf{v}$ is $\|\mathbf{v}\| = \sqrt{6}$, and therefore the vector

$$\frac{\mathbf{v}}{\|\mathbf{v}\|} = \frac{1}{\sqrt{6}}\mathbf{i} - \frac{2}{\sqrt{6}}\mathbf{j} + \frac{1}{\sqrt{6}}\mathbf{k}$$

is the required unit vector. ◀

Example 1.4 Find the vector $\mathbf{v}$ in $\mathbb{R}^2$ of length 4 whose direction makes an angle of $\pi/3$ radians (measured counterclockwise) with respect to the positive x-axis.

Solution See Figure 1.6. Since $\|\mathbf{v}\| = 4$, it follows from $\cos(\pi/3) = v_1/\|\mathbf{v}\|$ that $v_1 = \|\mathbf{v}\| \cos(\pi/3) = 4(1/2) = 2$. Similarly, $v_2 = \|\mathbf{v}\| \sin(\pi/3) = 4(\sqrt{3}/2) = 2\sqrt{3}$. Hence $\mathbf{v} = (2, 2\sqrt{3}) = 2\mathbf{i} + 2\sqrt{3}\mathbf{j}$. ◀

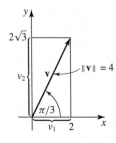

Figure 1.6   Vector **v** of Example 1.4.

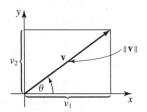

Figure 1.7   Quantities $\|\mathbf{v}\|$ and θ define the polar form of a vector.

Let $\mathbf{v} = v_1\mathbf{i} + v_2\mathbf{j}$ be a non-zero vector in $\mathbb{R}^2$. Then $\|\mathbf{v}\| \neq 0$, and (multiply and divide by $\|\mathbf{v}\|$)

$$\mathbf{v} = \|\mathbf{v}\| \left(\frac{v_1}{\|\mathbf{v}\|}\mathbf{i} + \frac{v_2}{\|\mathbf{v}\|}\mathbf{j} \right).$$

Now (see Figure 1.7) $v_1/\|\mathbf{v}\| = \cos\theta$ and $v_2/\|\mathbf{v}\| = \sin\theta$, where θ is the angle (measured counterclockwise) between the positive x-axis and the direction of **v**. Consequently, **v** can be expressed in terms of $\|\mathbf{v}\|$ and θ as

$$\mathbf{v} = \|\mathbf{v}\|(\cos\theta\mathbf{i} + \sin\theta\mathbf{j}).$$

This formula is called the *polar form of a vector*, since the components of **v** are expressed in polar coordinates with $r = \|\mathbf{v}\|$. If **v** is a unit vector, then $\|\mathbf{v}\| = 1$ and

$$\mathbf{v} = \cos\theta\mathbf{i} + \sin\theta\mathbf{j}.$$

EXERCISES 1.1

1. Find two vectors **v** and **w** in $\mathbb{R}^3$ such that $\|\mathbf{v} + \mathbf{w}\| = \|\mathbf{v}\| + \|\mathbf{w}\|$. Find two vectors **v** and **w** in $\mathbb{R}^2$ such that $\|\mathbf{v} + \mathbf{w}\| < \|\mathbf{v}\| + \|\mathbf{w}\|$, and find two other vectors **v** and **w** in $\mathbb{R}^2$ such that $\|\mathbf{v} + \mathbf{w}\| < (\|\mathbf{v}\| + \|\mathbf{w}\|)/2$.

2. Using the definition of the length of a vector, show that $\|\alpha\mathbf{v}\| = |\alpha| \, \|\mathbf{v}\|$ for $\mathbf{v} \in \mathbb{R}^3$, and $\alpha \in \mathbb{R}$.

3. Show that $\|\mathbf{v}\| = 0$ if and only if $\mathbf{v} = \mathbf{0}$ (in words, the only vector whose length is zero is the zero vector).

4. Find the Cartesian coordinates of points whose polar coordinates are $(0, \pi/2)$, $(10, \pi/2)$, $(2, 3\pi/4)$, $(1, \pi/6)$ and $(12, 3\pi/2)$.

5. Find the polar coordinates of points whose Cartesian coordinates are $(2, 2)$, $(-2, 2)$, $(2, -2)$, $(-2, -2)$.

6. Find the polar coordinates of points whose Cartesian coordinates are $(0, -3)$, $(1, \sqrt{3})$, $(-\sqrt{3}, -1)$ and $(-2, 0)$.

7. Using the Triangle Inequality show that $\|\mathbf{v} - \mathbf{w}\| \geq \|\mathbf{v}\| - \|\mathbf{w}\|$ for **v** and **w** in $\mathbb{R}^2$ (or in $\mathbb{R}^3$). Give a geometric interpretation of this inequality.

8. Find two vectors $\mathbf{v}$ and $\mathbf{w}$ in $\mathbb{R}^2$ such that $\|\mathbf{v} - \mathbf{w}\| = \|\mathbf{v}\| - \|\mathbf{w}\|$.

9. Let $\mathbf{v}, \mathbf{w} \in \mathbb{R}^2$ be vectors such that $\|\mathbf{v}\| = \|\mathbf{w}\| = 1$. What are the largest and the smallest possible values of $\|\mathbf{v} + \mathbf{w}\|$?

10. The sum of distances from the point (x, y) on an ellipse to the points $(-e, 0)$ and $(e, 0)$ (where $e > 0$) is constant and equal to ϵ. Use this characterization of the ellipse to show that its equation in the xy-plane is $x^2/a^2 + y^2/b^2 = 1$, where $a^2 = (\epsilon/2)^2$ and $b^2 = (\epsilon/2)^2 - e^2$.

Exercises 11 to 14: Find the length of the vector $\mathbf{v}$.

11. $\mathbf{v} = (0, 2, -1)$.

12. $\mathbf{v} = \sin\theta\mathbf{i} + \cos\theta\mathbf{j} + \mathbf{k}$.

13. $\mathbf{v} = \mathbf{w}/\|\mathbf{w}\|$, $\mathbf{w} = 3\mathbf{i} + 4\mathbf{j}$.

14. $\mathbf{v} = \mathbf{w}/\|\mathbf{w}\|^2$, $\mathbf{w} = \mathbf{i} - \mathbf{j} + 2\mathbf{k}$.

15. Using the Pythagorean Theorem, derive the formulas (1.1) for the distance between two points in $\mathbb{R}^2$ and $\mathbb{R}^3$.

16. Provide the details of the arguments (use similar triangles) that the formula for the sum of two vectors can be interpreted geometrically as the Triangle Law or as the Parallelogram Law.

17. Find the representatives of the vector $\mathbf{v} = (0, 2, -1)$ whose tails are located at $(0, 1, 1)$, $(0, 3, 0)$, $(8, 9, -4)$ and $(10, -1, 4)$.

18. Find the vector represented by the directed line segment $\overrightarrow{AB}$, where $A(3, 4)$ and $B(-1, 0)$. Find its representatives with tails located at $(0, 2)$, $(1, 1)$ and $(-4, -2)$.

19. Let $\mathbf{a} = 2\mathbf{i} - \mathbf{j} + \mathbf{k}$, $\mathbf{b} = \mathbf{k} - 3\mathbf{i}$ and $\mathbf{c} = 2\mathbf{i}$. Find vectors $\mathbf{a} - 2\mathbf{b}$, $\mathbf{a} - \mathbf{c}/\|\mathbf{c}\|$, $3\mathbf{a} + \mathbf{c} - \mathbf{j} + \mathbf{k}$ and the unit vector in the direction of $\mathbf{b} + 2\mathbf{a}$.

20. Find all vectors $\mathbf{v}$ of length 10 whose directions make an angle of $2\pi/3$ radians with respect to the positive x-axis.

21. Represent the vectors $-3\mathbf{i}$, $\mathbf{i}/2 - \mathbf{j}$ and $\mathbf{i} - 4\mathbf{j}$ in polar form.

22. Let $\mathbf{a} = 2\mathbf{i} + \mathbf{j}$ and $\mathbf{b} = -\mathbf{j} - 2\mathbf{k}$. Find the vector $\mathbf{x}$ such that $\mathbf{a} + 2(\mathbf{x} - \mathbf{b}) = 3\mathbf{x} + 2(\mathbf{a} - \mathbf{b})$.

23. Show that if $\mathbf{v} \in \mathbb{R}^3$ and $\alpha, \beta \in \mathbb{R}$, then $(\alpha + \beta)\mathbf{v} = \alpha\mathbf{v} + \beta\mathbf{v}$ and $(\alpha\beta)\mathbf{v} = \alpha(\beta\mathbf{v})$.

24. Explain how to construct geometrically the difference $\mathbf{v} - \mathbf{w}$ of two given vectors $\mathbf{v}$ and $\mathbf{w}$ in $\mathbb{R}^2$ (or in $\mathbb{R}^3$).

1.2 APPLICATIONS IN GEOMETRY AND PHYSICS

Vectors and vector operations introduced in the previous section will now be applied in a number of geometric and physical situations. We will start by computing equations of lines in $\mathbb{R}^2$ and $\mathbb{R}^3$. To make our exposition as clear as possible we will not make a distinction between a vector and its representative. For example, when we say "a vector from A to B" or "a vector with initial point A" or "a tip of a vector $\mathbf{v}$" we are actually talking about the directed line segment (i.e., the "arrowed line") $\overrightarrow{AB}$ that is the representative of that vector. We should also keep in mind that it is often useful to identify vectors and points: to be more precise, a vector $\mathbf{v} = (v_1, v_2)$ in $\mathbb{R}^2$ can be thought of as a point (v_1, v_2) in a plane, and vice versa.

Let $\mathbf{v} = (v_1, v_2)$ be a non-zero vector in $\mathbb{R}^2$. Draw the line ℓ that contains the origin O and the point (v_1, v_2); see Figure 1.8(a) (in other words, the line ℓ "contains" $\mathbf{v}$, or the vector $\mathbf{v}$ "lies" on ℓ). Pick any point P on ℓ and consider the vector $\mathbf{w}$ determined by O and P.

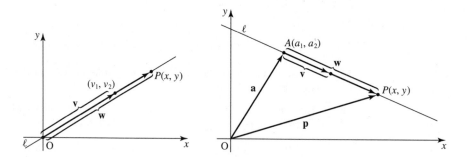

Figure 1.8   Line ℓ determined by a point and a vector.
(a) ℓ goes through the origin.   (b) ℓ goes through $A(a_1, a_2)$.

Since $\mathbf{w}$ is parallel to $\mathbf{v}$ ($\mathbf{w}$ and $\mathbf{v}$ could be in the same direction or in opposite directions), there is a real number t such that $\mathbf{w} = t\mathbf{v}$. In this way, for every point P on the line ℓ we can find a unique scalar multiple $t\mathbf{v}$ of $\mathbf{v}$ whose tip is located at that point (the real number t is called a *parameter*). The line ℓ is "built" of all possible scalar multiples of $\mathbf{v}$,

$$\ell = \{t\mathbf{v} \mid t \in \mathbb{R}\}$$

(remember that we have identified a vector $t\mathbf{v}$ with its tip). Now pick a point $A(a_1, a_2)$ and a vector $\mathbf{v} = (v_1, v_2)$ and visualize it as its representative directed line segment that starts at A; see Figure 1.8(b). Let $P(x, y)$ be a point on the line ℓ that contains A and whose direction is the same as $\mathbf{v}$. By the Triangle Law, $\mathbf{p} = \mathbf{a} + \mathbf{w}$, where $\mathbf{p} = (x, y)$, $\mathbf{a} = (a_1, a_2)$ and $\mathbf{w}$ is the vector from A to P. Since $\mathbf{w}$ is parallel to $\mathbf{v}$, $\mathbf{w} = t\mathbf{v}$ for some $t \in \mathbb{R}$ and therefore

$$\mathbf{p} = \mathbf{a} + t\mathbf{v}, \quad t \in \mathbb{R}.$$

We have thus derived a *vector form of a parametric equation* of the line ℓ. As the parameter t takes on different values in $\mathbb{R}$, tips of vectors $\mathbf{p}$ describe points on the line. This equation is usually written as

$$\ell(t) = \mathbf{a} + t\mathbf{v}, \quad t \in \mathbb{R},$$

or, in components as

$$\ell(t) = (a_1 + tv_1, a_2 + tv_2), \quad t \in \mathbb{R},$$

or as

$$x = a_1 + tv_1, y = a_2 + tv_2, \quad t \in \mathbb{R}.$$

Any of the above forms is called a *parametric equation* (or *parametric equations*) *of a line*.

Similarly, we compute parametric equations of the line ℓ in $\mathbb{R}^3$ that contains a point $A(a_1, a_2, a_3)$ and whose direction is that of a vector $\mathbf{v} = (v_1, v_2, v_3)$ to be

$$\ell(t) = \mathbf{a} + t\mathbf{v} = (a_1 + tv_1, a_2 + tv_2, a_3 + tv_3), \quad t \in \mathbb{R}.$$

The equation of a line can easily be memorized as "line equals point plus parameter times direction."

Example 1.5   Find parametric equations of the line ℓ in $\mathbb{R}^3$ that passes through $(3, 2, -2)$ in the direction of the vector $\mathbf{i} - \mathbf{j} + 2\mathbf{k}$.

Solution   An equation of this line is $\ell(t) = \mathbf{a} + t\mathbf{v}$, where $\mathbf{a} = (3, 2, -2)$ and $\mathbf{v} = (1, -1, 2)$. Hence

$$\ell(t) = (3, 2, -2) + t(1, -1, 2) = (3 + t, 2 - t, -2 + 2t), \quad t \in \mathbb{R}$$

gives a possible form for the needed parametric equations.   ◄

Example 1.6   Find an equation of the line in $\mathbb{R}^2$ that contains $(1, 3)$ and $(0, -2)$.

Solution   To determine an equation of a line we need a point and a direction vector $\mathbf{v}$. Two points are given — choose one, say $\mathbf{a} = (1, 3)$. The direction is that of the vector from $(1, 3)$ to $(0, -2)$. Consequently, $\mathbf{v} = (-1, -5)$ and an equation is

$$\ell_1(t) = (1, 3) + t(-1, -5) = (1 - t, 3 - 5t), \quad t \in \mathbb{R}.$$

We made some choices along the way. Now let us recompute the equation using $(0, -2)$ as the point and keeping the same direction $\mathbf{v} = (-1, -5)$ (we could have taken the opposite direction $\mathbf{v} = (1, 5)$ as well). This time,

$$\ell_2(t) = (0, -2) + t(-1, -5) = (-t, -2 - 5t), \quad t \in \mathbb{R}.$$

The equations are not the same! For example, $\ell_1(0) = (1, 3)$ and $\ell_2(0) = (0, -2)$. However, $\ell_2(-1) = (1, 3)$, i.e., the point $(1, 3)$ does belong to both ℓ_1 and ℓ_2 (it is generated by different parameter values, but that is not important). Moreover, $\ell_1(1) = (0, -2)$, so $(0, -2)$ also belongs to both ℓ_1 and ℓ_2. Since ℓ_1 and ℓ_2 have two points in common, they must be the same line!

To get a better feel for parametrizations, pick another point on the line ℓ_1, say, $\ell_1(3) = (-2, -12)$. Now try to find the value of t so that $\ell_2(t) = (-2, -12)$. Since $\ell_2(t) = (-t, -2 - 5t) = (-2, -12)$, we get $t = 2$. Hence $\ell_2(2) = (-2, -12)$, so $(-2, -12)$ belongs to both lines.

Another way of proving that ℓ_1 and ℓ_2 represent the same line is to convert them to an explicit form: since $\ell_1(t) = (1 - t, 3 - 5t)$ it follows that $x = 1 - t$ and $y = 3 - 5t$. Computing t from the first and substituting into the second equation we get $y = 3 - 5(1 - x)$, i.e., $y = 5x - 2$. Similarly, from $\ell_2(t) = (-t, -2 - 5t)$ we get $x = -t$, $y = -2 - 5t$, and, after eliminating t, $y = -2 - 5(-x) = 5x - 2$.   ◄

We have just seen that the same line can be represented in many different ways (as a matter of fact, there are infinitely many parametric equations that represent the same line). Parametric equations of various curves will be studied in detail in later sections.

Example 1.7   Let us compute yet another form of parametric equations of the line in the previous example. Take $(1, 3)$ as the point and $\mathbf{v} = (1, 5)$ as the direction vector. By eliminating the parameter, compute an explicit equation of the line.

Solution   A parametric equation is

$$\ell(t) = \mathbf{a} + t\mathbf{v} = (1, 3) + t(1, 5) = (1 + t, 3 + 5t), \quad t \in \mathbb{R}.$$

Eliminating t from $x = 1 + t$, $y = 3 + 5t$ we get $y = 3 + 5(x - 1)$ and $y = 5x - 2$.

Example 1.8   Find an equation of the line in $\mathbb{R}^3$ that contains $(1, 2, 0)$ and $(0, -2, 4)$.

Solution   As we have just seen, we might get different parametrizations, depending on our choices of the point and of the direction vector. However, they will all represent the same line. Choosing $(1, 2, 0)$ as the point and taking the direction to be determined by the vector from $(1, 2, 0)$ to $(0, -2, 4)$, we get

$$\ell_1(t) = (1, 2, 0) + t(-1, -4, 4) = (1 - t, 2 - 4t, 4t), \quad t \in \mathbb{R}.$$

Using $(0, -2, 4)$ as the point and taking the direction to be the vector from $(0, -2, 4)$ to $(1, 2, 0)$, we get

$$\ell_2(t) = (0, -2, 4) + t(1, 4, -4) = (t, -2 + 4t, 4 - 4t), \quad t \in \mathbb{R}$$

as another possible form of the parametric equations.

Let $\mathbf{v}$ and $\mathbf{w}$ be non-zero, non-parallel vectors, visualized as directed line segments starting at the same point A. The point A and the tips of $\mathbf{v}$ and $\mathbf{w}$ determine the unique plane π, called the *plane (through A) spanned by $\mathbf{v}$ and $\mathbf{w}$*. We will now compute its parametric equation(s). Pick a point $P(x, y, z)$ on π and, drawing parallels to $\mathbf{v}$ and $\mathbf{w}$, construct the parallelogram whose diagonal is $\overline{AP}$, as shown in Figure 1.9.

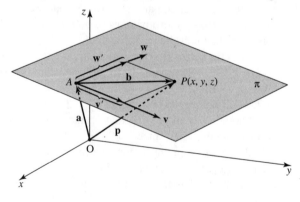

Figure 1.9 Plane through A spanned by $\mathbf{v}$ and $\mathbf{w}$.

The vector $\mathbf{b}$ that is represented by the directed line segment $\overrightarrow{AP}$ can be written as $\mathbf{b} = \mathbf{v}' + \mathbf{w}'$, where $\mathbf{v}'$ is parallel to $\mathbf{v}$ (and therefore $\mathbf{v}' = t\mathbf{v}$ for some real number t) and $\mathbf{w}'$ is parallel to $\mathbf{w}$ (hence $\mathbf{w}' = s\mathbf{w}$ for some s in $\mathbb{R}$). Consequently, $\mathbf{b} = t\mathbf{v} + s\mathbf{w}$, and since $\mathbf{p} = \mathbf{a} + \mathbf{b}$, it follows that the equation

$$\mathbf{p} = \mathbf{a} + t\mathbf{v} + s\mathbf{w}, \quad t, s \in \mathbb{R} \tag{1.2}$$

(where $\mathbf{a}$ is the vector from O to A) represents points in the plane π. The equation (or equations, if written in components) is (are) called *parametric equation(s) of the plane through A*, spanned by $\mathbf{v}$ and $\mathbf{w}$. This time, a single point is specified by assigning numerical values to *two* parameters, t and s.

Example 1.9 Find parametric equation(s) of the plane that contains the points $(0, 1, 0)$, $(2, 1, -3)$ and $(1, -1, 4)$.

Solution   We have to pick a point and two vectors. Depending on the choices we make, we will get different equations. However, the equation obtained from parametric equations by eliminating the parameters will be the same in all cases. Pick $(0, 1, 0)$ as the point, and let $\mathbf{v}$ be the vector from $(0, 1, 0)$ to $(2, 1, -3)$ (hence $\mathbf{v} = (2, 0, -3)$) and let $\mathbf{w}$ be the vector from $(0, 1, 0)$ to $(1, -1, 4)$ (hence $\mathbf{w} = (1, -2, 4)$). It follows that the parametric equations

$$\mathbf{p} = \mathbf{a} + t\mathbf{v} + s\mathbf{w} = (0, 1, 0) + t(2, 0, -3) + s(1, -2, 4) = (2t + s, 1 - 2s, -3t + 4s),$$

for $t, s \in \mathbb{R}$ represent the given plane.

To obtain the equation in x, y and z we have to eliminate the parameters t and s from $x = 2t + s$, $y = 1 - 2s$ and $z = -3t + 4s$. From the second equation, $s = (1 - y)/2$. Substitute this into the first equation to get $x = 2t + (1 - y)/2$, and hence $t = (2x - 1 + y)/4$. Finally, substituting the expressions for t and s into the equation for z we get $z = (-3)(2x - 1 + y)/4 + 4(1 - y)/2$, i.e., $6x + 11y + 4z - 11 = 0$, or $z = (-6x - 11y + 11)/4$ as the explicit form. The reader is encouraged to try some other choices, compute the parametric equations and check that they give the same explicit form. ◄

Next, we will illustrate the use of vectors in various physical situations. Although we will concentrate on the dimension 2 (sometimes 3), all conclusions and arguments will remain valid for any dimension.

Example 1.10 Displacement (Position) and Relative Position.

Suppose that we are located at the point $A(a_1, a_2)$ in the xy-plane and are walking towards $B(b_1, b_2)$ along a straight line. The vector $\mathbf{v} = (b_1 - a_1, b_2 - a_2)$, represented by the directed line segment $\overrightarrow{AB}$, gives the direction of our motion, and its magnitude $\|\mathbf{v}\|$ measures the distance we have to cover. The vector $\mathbf{v}$ is called the *displacement vector*. For example, suppose that $(2, 1)$ is the initial point and $(4, 4)$ the terminal point of our travel. The direction of our motion is given by $\mathbf{v} = (4 - 2, 4 - 1) = (2, 3)$, and the distance we have to cover is $\|\mathbf{v}\| = \sqrt{4+9} = \sqrt{13}$ units.

Now suppose that a cat and a dog approach the same point H (see Figure 1.10), and that, at a particular moment, their displacements from H are given by the vectors $\mathbf{c}$ and $\mathbf{d}$. Their *relative position* at that moment is given by the vector $\mathbf{v}$ that joins the tails of $\mathbf{c}$ and $\mathbf{d}$. By the Triangle Law, $\mathbf{v} + \mathbf{d} = \mathbf{c}$, i.e., the difference

$$\mathbf{v} = \mathbf{c} - \mathbf{d}$$

is the vector giving their relative position (the distance between them is equal to $\|\mathbf{v}\|$). We could have taken $\mathbf{v}$ as the vector joining the tail of $\mathbf{d}$ with the tail of $\mathbf{c}$, in which case $\mathbf{v} = \mathbf{d} - \mathbf{c}$. Anyway, a relative position is always computed as the difference of displacement vectors.

◀

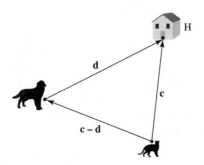

Figure 1.10   Relative position of the cat and the dog from Example 1.10.

Example 1.11   Velocity and Speed.

The velocity of an object moving with constant speed along a straight line can be represented as a vector: its direction is the direction of the motion and its magnitude is the speed.

(a) A particle moves along the line $y = 2x$ in the first quadrant away from the origin with speed 10 units/s. Find its position (i.e., the displacement) two seconds later.

(b) A particle initially located at $(3, -2, -1)$ starts moving along the line specified by the velocity $\mathbf{v} = \mathbf{i} + 2\mathbf{j} + \mathbf{k}$ units/s. Find its position five seconds later.

(c) A particle initially at $(1, 4)$ starts moving with speed 3 m/s in the direction of $3\mathbf{i} - 4\mathbf{j}$. Find its position ten seconds later.

Solution

(a) We have to find the velocity vector $\mathbf{v}$ first. Pick any point (other than the origin) on the line $y = 2x$, say, $(1, 2)$. Then $\mathbf{w} = \mathbf{i} + 2\mathbf{j}$ is a vector parallel to $\mathbf{v}$, but with magnitude $\|\mathbf{w}\| = \sqrt{5}$. Since the speed is 10 units/s, i.e., $\|\mathbf{v}\| = 10$, we must take

$$\mathbf{v} = \frac{10}{\sqrt{5}}\mathbf{w} = \frac{10}{\sqrt{5}}\mathbf{i} + \frac{20}{\sqrt{5}}\mathbf{j}$$

(check: $\|\mathbf{v}\| = |10/\sqrt{5}| \ \|\mathbf{w}\| = (10/\sqrt{5})\sqrt{5} = 10$). Using the formula

$$\textbf{displacement} = \textbf{velocity} \cdot \text{time} \tag{1.3}$$

we finally get that the displacement $\mathbf{d}$ of the particle two seconds later is

$$\mathbf{d} = 2\mathbf{v} = \frac{20}{\sqrt{5}}\mathbf{i} + \frac{40}{\sqrt{5}}\mathbf{j},$$

i.e., the particle is located at the point $(20/\sqrt{5}, 40/\sqrt{5})$.

(b) The equation of the line $\ell(t)$ (that is the trajectory of the motion of the particle) is given by $\ell(t) = \mathbf{a} + t\mathbf{v}$, where $\mathbf{a} = (3, -2, -1)$ and $\mathbf{v} = (1, 2, 1)$. Hence

$$\ell(t) = (3, -2, -1) + t(1, 2, 1) = (3 + t, -2 + 2t, -1 + t).$$

Now, $\ell(0) = (3, -2, -1)$ is the initial position. Five seconds later the particle is located at $\ell(5) = (8, 8, 4)$.

Here is another way of solving this problem: given the velocity $\mathbf{v}$, the displacement vector (five seconds later) of the particle is $\mathbf{d} = 5\mathbf{v} = (5, 10, 5)$. Since the particle is initially at $(3, -2, -1)$, its location five seconds later will be

$$\textbf{initial point} + \textbf{displacement} = (3, -2, -1) + (5, 10, 5) = (8, 8, 4).$$

(c) The velocity vector $\mathbf{v}$ of the particle has to be parallel to $\mathbf{w} = 3\mathbf{i} - 4\mathbf{j}$ (hence $\mathbf{v} = \alpha\mathbf{w}$ for some real number α) and $\|\mathbf{v}\| = 3$. Since $\|\mathbf{w}\| = 5$, it follows that $\mathbf{v} = (3/5)\mathbf{w} = (3/5)(3\mathbf{i} - 4\mathbf{j}) = (9/5)\mathbf{i} - (12/5)\mathbf{j}$ is the velocity vector. The displacement 10 s later (see (1.3)) is $\mathbf{d} = 10\mathbf{v} = 18\mathbf{i} - 24\mathbf{j}$, and the position of the particle is

$$\mathbf{p} = \textbf{initial point} + \textbf{displacement} = (\mathbf{i} + 4\mathbf{j}) + (18\mathbf{i} - 24\mathbf{j}) = 19\mathbf{i} - 20\mathbf{j}.$$

As in (b), we could have computed the equation of the line of motion (with $\mathbf{a} = \mathbf{i} + 4\mathbf{j}$ and $\mathbf{v} = (9/5)\mathbf{i} - (12/5)\mathbf{j}$), thus getting

$$\mathbf{p}(t) = (\mathbf{i} + 4\mathbf{j}) + t\left(\tfrac{9}{5}\mathbf{i} - \tfrac{12}{5}\mathbf{j}\right) = \left(1 + \tfrac{9}{5}t\right)\mathbf{i} + \left(4 - \tfrac{12}{5}t\right)\mathbf{j},$$

and then substituted $t = 10$ to get the position $\mathbf{p}(10) = 19\mathbf{i} - 20\mathbf{j}$ of the particle ten seconds later.

◀

Example 1.12   A wind is blowing towards the northeast direction at a constant speed of 80 km/h. Find the vector in $\mathbb{R}^2$ that describes the velocity of the wind.

Solution   Assume that the y-axis points to the north and the x-axis to the east. In this case, the northeast direction is described by the angle of $\pi/4$ radians with respect to the positive x-axis. Using the polar form of a vector introduced in the previous section, we get $\mathbf{v} = \|\mathbf{v}\|(\cos(\pi/4)\mathbf{i} + \sin(\pi/4)\mathbf{j}) = 80((\sqrt{2}/2)\mathbf{i} + (\sqrt{2}/2)\mathbf{j})$. Consequently, the vector $\mathbf{v} = 40\sqrt{2}\mathbf{i} + 40\sqrt{2}\mathbf{j}$ describes the velocity of the wind.

◀

Example 1.13   Relative Speed and Relative Velocity.

Suppose that two cars, V and W, move along the same straight line with constant speeds v and w. At time t, V and W have covered the distances vt and wt respectively, and the change in their (directed) distance as seen by the driver of V (i.e., measured from V to W) is $wt - vt$. It follows that the driver of V sees the car W moving with the speed (called the *relative speed of W with respect to V*)

$$\frac{wt - vt}{t} = w - v$$

(we have used the fact that speed = distance/time).

Now assume that the motions take place along the x-axis. The velocities of V and W are $\mathbf{v} = v\mathbf{i}$ and $\mathbf{w} = w\mathbf{i}$, and the *relative velocity of W with respect to V* is

$$w\mathbf{i} - v\mathbf{i} = \mathbf{w} - \mathbf{v}.$$

In general, by analyzing each component of the velocity vectors $\mathbf{v}$ and $\mathbf{w}$ of V and W in this way we will get that the difference $\mathbf{w} - \mathbf{v}$ represents the relative velocity of W with respect to V (or the relative velocity of W as seen (experienced) by V).

Example 1.14   Physical Forces.

A force of constant magnitude and direction can be thought of as a vector. Suppose that the vectors $\mathbf{F}_1, \ldots, \mathbf{F}_n$ define a system of n concurrent forces (i.e., all are applied at the same point A). The action of this system of n forces can be represented as the single force

$$\mathbf{F} = \mathbf{F}_1 + \ldots + \mathbf{F}_n$$

acting at A, called the *resultant force* of the system. If the resultant force is $\mathbf{0}$, we say that the system $\mathbf{F}_1, \ldots, \mathbf{F}_n$ of concurrent forces is in *equilibrium*.

Assume that the forces $\mathbf{F}_1$, $\mathbf{F}_2$ and $\mathbf{F}_3$ of magnitudes 2 N, 3 N and 4 N (N denotes newton, a unit of force) are applied at the origin in the directions of $\pi/3$, $-\pi/2$ and $2\pi/3$ radians respectively with respect to the positive x-axis. Find the force $\mathbf{F}_4$ needed to keep the system $\mathbf{F}_1, \mathbf{F}_2, \mathbf{F}_3$ in equilibrium.

Solution   We have to express $\mathbf{F}_1, \mathbf{F}_2, \mathbf{F}_3$ as vectors first. Using the polar form from Section 1.1 we get

$$\mathbf{F}_1 = \|\mathbf{F}_1\| \left(\cos \tfrac{\pi}{3}\mathbf{i} + \sin \tfrac{\pi}{3}\mathbf{j}\right) = 2\left(\frac{1}{2}\mathbf{i} + \frac{\sqrt{3}}{2}\mathbf{j}\right) = \mathbf{i} + \sqrt{3}\mathbf{j},$$

$$\mathbf{F}_2 = \|\mathbf{F}_2\| \left(\cos \left(-\tfrac{\pi}{2}\right)\mathbf{i} + \sin \left(-\tfrac{\pi}{2}\right)\right)\mathbf{j} = -3\mathbf{j}$$

and

$$\mathbf{F}_3 = \|\mathbf{F}_3\| \left(\cos \tfrac{2\pi}{3}\mathbf{i} + \sin \tfrac{2\pi}{3}\mathbf{j}\right) = 4\left(-\frac{1}{2}\mathbf{i} + \frac{\sqrt{3}}{2}\mathbf{j}\right) = -2\mathbf{i} + 2\sqrt{3}\mathbf{j}.$$

The resultant force of this system is

$$\mathbf{F} = \mathbf{F}_1 + \mathbf{F}_2 + \mathbf{F}_3 = (\mathbf{i} + \sqrt{3}\mathbf{j}) + (-3\mathbf{j}) + (-2\mathbf{i} + 2\sqrt{3}\mathbf{j}) = -\mathbf{i} + (-3 + 3\sqrt{3})\mathbf{j}.$$

Therefore, the force $\mathbf{F}_4 = \mathbf{i} - (-3 + 3\sqrt{3})\mathbf{j} = \mathbf{i} + (3 - 3\sqrt{3})\mathbf{j}$ has to be applied at the origin in order to keep the system $\mathbf{F}_1, \mathbf{F}_2, \mathbf{F}_3$ in equilibrium (see Figure 1.11).

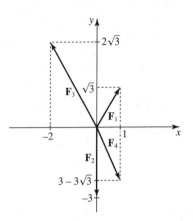

Figure 1.11 System of concurrent forces $\mathbf{F}_1, \mathbf{F}_2, \mathbf{F}_3, \mathbf{F}_4$ of Example 1.14.

Example 1.15

Principle of Superposition.

Coulomb's Law in electrostatics says that the electrostatic force on a charge q due to a charge Q is given by

$$\mathbf{F} = \frac{1}{4\pi\epsilon_0} \frac{Qq}{d(q, Q)^2}\mathbf{u},$$

where $d(q, Q)$ is the distance between q and Q, $\mathbf{u}$ is the unit vector in the direction from Q to q and ϵ_0 is a constant (called the *permittivity of vacuum*; in the SI system it can be determined from $\epsilon_0 = 10^7/(4\pi c^2)$, where c is the speed of light in vacuum).

Now assume that $\mathbf{F}_1$ is the force on q due to a charge Q_1 with no other charges present and $\mathbf{F}_2$ is the force on q due to a charge Q_2 with no other charges present. The *Principle of Superposition* (which is one of the basic principles in electrostatics) states that the total force $\mathbf{F}$ on q when both Q_1 and Q_2 are present is the sum $\mathbf{F}_1 + \mathbf{F}_2$ of the forces $\mathbf{F}_1$ and $\mathbf{F}_2$. Let us explain this: with only Q_1 present, the force is $\mathbf{F} = \mathbf{F}_1$. When another charge Q_2 is included, it does not *change* the effect of the force $\mathbf{F}_1$ on q. Instead, its contribution to the total force is contained in a separate term $\mathbf{F}_2$, that is vectorially *added* to $\mathbf{F}_1$.

Example 1.16

Center of Mass.

For a particle of mass M located at the point (a_1, a_2, a_3) we define the three moments: the *moment about the xy-plane* is the scalar Ma_3, the *moment about the yz-plane* is the scalar Ma_1 and the *moment about the xz-plane* is the scalar Ma_2. Now assume that n particles of mass m_i are located at (x_i, y_i, z_i), $i = 1, \ldots, n$, in space in such a way that their relative positions do not change (for example, m_i could be the parts of a rigid body rotating in space). When some aspects of the system $m_1, \ldots, m_n$ are considered, it turns out that its behavior is the same as that of the single mass $M = m_1 + \ldots + m_n$ located at the point $C_M(x_M, y_M, z_M)$ called the *center of mass* (or the *centroid*), which is defined as follows: the moment of M about any plane is equal to the sum of the moments of m_i with respect to the same plane. Applying this definition to the xy-plane, we get

$$M z_M = m_1 z_1 + \ldots + m_n z_n.$$

Similarly (considering moments about the xz-plane),

$$M y_M = m_1 y_1 + \ldots + m_n y_n$$

and (considering moments about the yz-plane)

$$M x_M = m_1 x_1 + \ldots + m_n x_n$$

(recall that $M = m_1 + \ldots + m_n$). The coordinates of the center of mass C_M are therefore

$$(x_M, y_M, z_M) = \left(\frac{m_1 x_1 + \ldots + m_n x_n}{M}, \frac{m_1 y_1 + \ldots + m_n y_n}{M}, \frac{m_1 z_1 + \ldots + m_n z_n}{M} \right).$$

The position vector $\mathbf{c}_M$ of the center of mass C_M is then

$$
\begin{aligned}
\mathbf{c}_M &= x_M \mathbf{i} + y_M \mathbf{j} + z_M \mathbf{k} \\
&= \frac{1}{M} \left((m_1 x_1 + \ldots + m_n x_n) \mathbf{i} + (m_1 y_1 + \ldots + m_n y_n) \mathbf{j} + (m_1 z_1 + \ldots + m_n z_n) \mathbf{k} \right) \\
&= \frac{1}{M} \left(m_1 (x_1 \mathbf{i} + y_1 \mathbf{j} + z_1 \mathbf{k}) + \ldots + m_n (x_n \mathbf{i} + y_n \mathbf{j} + z_n \mathbf{k}) \right) \\
&= \frac{1}{M} \left(m_1 \mathbf{r}_1 + \ldots + m_n \mathbf{r}_n \right),
\end{aligned}
\tag{1.4}
$$

where $\mathbf{r}_i = (x_i, y_i, z_i)$ is the position vector of the mass m_i, $i = 1, \ldots, n$.

◀

Example 1.17   Three stones of mass 2 kg, 4 kg and 3 kg are placed at $(2, 1, 0)$, $(-1, -1, 5)$ and $(0, 0, 3)$ respectively. Where should a fourth stone of mass 1 kg be placed so that the center of mass of the system is at the origin?

Solution   Denote the masses by $m_1 = 2$, $m_2 = 4$, $m_3 = 3$ and $m_4 = 1$ and their positions by $\mathbf{r}_1 = (2, 1, 0)$, $\mathbf{r}_2 = (-1, -1, 5)$, $\mathbf{r}_3 = (0, 0, 3)$ and $\mathbf{r}_4 = (x_4, y_4, z_4)$. Using (1.4) with $M = 2 + 4 + 3 + 1 = 10$, we get

$$
\begin{aligned}
(0, 0, 0) &= \frac{1}{10} \left(2(2\mathbf{i} + \mathbf{j}) + 4(-\mathbf{i} - \mathbf{j} + 5\mathbf{k}) + 3(3\mathbf{k}) + 1(x_4 \mathbf{i} + y_4 \mathbf{j} + z_4 \mathbf{k}) \right) \\
&= \frac{1}{10} \left((x_4) \mathbf{i} + (-2 + y_4) \mathbf{j} + (29 + z_4) \mathbf{k} \right).
\end{aligned}
$$

Hence $(x_4 = 0, y_4 = 2, z_4 = -29)$ is the location of the fourth stone.

◀

EXERCISES 1.2

1. Compute another form of a parametric equation of the line in Example 1.6: take $(1, 3)$ as the point and the multiple $3\mathbf{v}$ of $\mathbf{v} = (-1, -5)$ as the direction (clearly, $3\mathbf{v}$ and $\mathbf{v}$ have the same direction). Explain how to get infinitely many parametric equations of the line.

2. Find a parametric equation of the line that contains the points $(3, 2, 0)$ and $(0, -1, -1)$.

3. Find a parametric equation of the line that contains the points $(1, 1)$ and $(-2, 4)$. What values of the parameter should be used to describe the half-line starting at $(1, 1)$ and going through $(-2, 4)$? What values of the parameter should be used to describe the line segment between $(1, 1)$ and $(-2, 4)$, including both endpoints?

4. Compute a parametric equation of the line ℓ that contains the points $(2, -2, 0)$ and $(1, 1, 4)$. In this case, the parameter can be any real number. By restricting its values, describe the set of all points on the line segment defined by the two given points (that includes both of them).

5. Compute a parametric equation of the line ℓ that contains the points $(2, 1)$ and $(-1, 5)$. By restricting the values of the parameter, describe the half-line ℓ' with the initial point at $(2, 1)$ in the direction towards $(-1, 5)$.

6. Compute another set of parametric equations of the plane in Example 1.9: take $(1, -1, 4)$ as the point and the vectors from $(1, -1, 4)$ to $(2, 1, -3)$ and from $(1, -1, 4)$ to $(0, 1, 0)$ as spanning vectors. Compute the explicit form of the equation. Explain how to get infinitely many parametric equations of the plane.

7. Consider the rectangle which has three vertices located at $(1, 1)$, $(4, 1)$ and $(1, 2)$. By imitating parts of the construction of parametric equations of the plane obtain a vector description of all points that belong to that rectangle (i.e., that are either inside the rectangle or on its boundary).

8. The tips of vectors $\mathbf{v} = (1, 4, 2)$ and $\mathbf{w} = (-2, 0, 3)$ (whose initial point is the origin) and the origin define a parallelogram (called the parallelogram spanned by $\mathbf{v}$ and $\mathbf{w}$). By adjusting the construction of parametric equations of the plane obtain the vector description of all points that belong to this parallelogram.

9. Find the distance and relative position of two cars approaching the same intersection A if their displacement vectors from A are $\mathbf{i} + 3\mathbf{j} - \mathbf{k}$ and $\mathbf{j} + 2\mathbf{k}$.

10. A particle is ejected in the direction of $\mathbf{i} + 2\mathbf{j} - 2\mathbf{k}$ with speed 12 units/s. Find its position one minute later.

11. A particle moves from the point $(3, 2, 4)$ with the constant velocity $3\mathbf{i} - \mathbf{k}$. When and where is it going to cross the xy-plane?

12. A particle moves from the point $(-2, 1)$ in the direction of $\pi/3$ radians with respect to the positive x-axis at a speed of 3 units/s. Find its velocity and location 10 s later.

13. Find the vector $\mathbf{F}$ that describes a force of magnitude 10 N acting on an object located at the origin having an angle of $\pi/6$ with respect to the positive x-axis.

14. A car A is moving north with speed 100 km/h and a car B is moving northeast with speed 80 km/h. Find the relative velocity of B as seen by the driver of A.

15. Find the center of mass of a system of four masses of 2 kg each located at the vertices of the parallelogram (one vertex is at the origin) spanned by $\mathbf{i} - 2\mathbf{j}$ and $\mathbf{i} + \mathbf{j}$.

16. Three forces of 3 N, 4 N and 6 N are applied at the origin in the directions towards the points $(1, 1)$, $(0, -4)$ and $(10, 1)$ respectively. Find the resultant force of this system.

17. Three objects of mass 1 kg are placed at the vertices of an equilateral triangle with sides of length 2 m. Find the center of mass of the system.

18. Two cats walk away from each other along perpendicular paths with speeds of 10 km/h and 12 km/h. Find the relative velocity of the faster cat as seen by the slower cat.

19. Find the resultant force of a system of four forces, each of magnitude 5 N, applied at the origin at angles $\pi/10$, $\pi/5$, $\pi/2$ and $13\pi/10$ with respect to the positive x-axis.

1.3 THE DOT PRODUCT

We are going to define two more operations with vectors that produce meaningful quantities and are used in mathematics and various applications. In this section we introduce the dot product, and in Section 1.5 we introduce the cross product.

■ **Definition 1.4**   Dot Product.

Let $\mathbf{v} = (v_1, \ldots, v_n)$ and $\mathbf{w} = (w_1, \ldots, w_n)$ be vectors in $\mathbb{R}^n$, $n \geq 2$. The *dot product* of $\mathbf{v}$ and $\mathbf{w}$ is the real number $\mathbf{v} \cdot \mathbf{w}$ defined by

$$\mathbf{v} \cdot \mathbf{w} = v_1 w_1 + \ldots + v_n w_n.$$

In particular, if $\mathbf{v}, \mathbf{w} \in \mathbb{R}^2$, then

$$\mathbf{v} \cdot \mathbf{w} = (v_1 \mathbf{i} + v_2 \mathbf{j}) \cdot (w_1 \mathbf{i} + w_2 \mathbf{j}) = v_1 w_1 + v_2 w_2$$

and

$$\mathbf{v} \cdot \mathbf{w} = (v_1 \mathbf{i} + v_2 \mathbf{j} + v_3 \mathbf{k}) \cdot (w_1 \mathbf{i} + w_2 \mathbf{j} + w_3 \mathbf{k}) = v_1 w_1 + v_2 w_2 + v_3 w_3$$

if $\mathbf{v}$ and $\mathbf{w}$ are vectors in $\mathbb{R}^3$.

Let us emphasize that the dot product of two vectors is a *real number*. This is the reason why it is also called the *scalar product* (sometimes the term *inner product* is used). Other notation for the dot product $\mathbf{v} \cdot \mathbf{w}$ include angle brackets, $\langle \mathbf{v}, \mathbf{w} \rangle$, or (unfortunately) parentheses $(\mathbf{v}, \mathbf{w})$. Applying the definition we compute the dot products of the standard basis vectors $\mathbf{i}$, $\mathbf{j}$ and $\mathbf{k}$ to be $\mathbf{i} \cdot \mathbf{i} = 1, \mathbf{j} \cdot \mathbf{j} = 1, \mathbf{k} \cdot \mathbf{k} = 1, \mathbf{i} \cdot \mathbf{j} = \mathbf{j} \cdot \mathbf{i} = 0, \mathbf{i} \cdot \mathbf{k} = \mathbf{k} \cdot \mathbf{i} = 0$, and $\mathbf{j} \cdot \mathbf{k} = \mathbf{k} \cdot \mathbf{j} = 0$.

■ **Theorem 1.3**   Properties of the Dot Product.

Assume that $\mathbf{u}$, $\mathbf{v}$ and $\mathbf{w}$ are vectors in $\mathbb{R}^n$ (for $n \geq 2$), and α is a real number. The dot product is *commutative*

$$\mathbf{v} \cdot \mathbf{w} = \mathbf{w} \cdot \mathbf{v}$$

and *distributive* with respect to addition

$$\mathbf{u} \cdot (\mathbf{v} + \mathbf{w}) = \mathbf{u} \cdot \mathbf{v} + \mathbf{u} \cdot \mathbf{w}$$

and scalar multiplication

$$(\alpha \mathbf{u}) \cdot \mathbf{v} = \alpha (\mathbf{u} \cdot \mathbf{v}) = \mathbf{u} \cdot (\alpha \mathbf{v}).$$

Moreover,

$$\mathbf{0} \cdot \mathbf{v} = 0$$

(**0** is the zero vector) and

$$\mathbf{v} \cdot \mathbf{v} = \|\mathbf{v}\|^2.$$

If **v** and **w** are parallel, then

$$\mathbf{v} \cdot \mathbf{w} = \|\mathbf{v}\| \, \|\mathbf{w}\| \tag{1.5}$$

if **v** and **w** have the same direction, and

$$\mathbf{v} \cdot \mathbf{w} = -\|\mathbf{v}\| \, \|\mathbf{w}\| \tag{1.6}$$

if they have opposite directions. ∎

The proof of the theorem is left as an exercise. All identities can be checked by writing the vectors involved in terms of their components, using the definitions of vector operations and the properties of real numbers. As an illustration, let us verify the last two statements for vectors $\mathbf{v} = (v_1, v_2, v_3)$ and $\mathbf{w} = (w_1, w_2, w_3)$ in $\mathbb{R}^3$ (the same proof works in any dimension; we choose $\mathbb{R}^3$ for convenience). Since **v** and **w** are parallel, there exists $\alpha \in \mathbb{R}$ such that $\mathbf{w} = \alpha \mathbf{v}$. Then $w_1 = \alpha v_1$, $w_2 = \alpha v_2$ and $w_3 = \alpha v_3$ and

$$\mathbf{v} \cdot \mathbf{w} = (v_1 \mathbf{i} + v_2 \mathbf{j} + v_3 \mathbf{k}) \cdot (\alpha v_1 \mathbf{i} + \alpha v_2 \mathbf{j} + \alpha v_3 \mathbf{k}) = \alpha(v_1^2 + v_2^2 + v_3^2).$$

We have used the distributivity (that allowed us to multiply each term in the first factor with each term in the second factor) and the results on dot products of standard basis vectors **i**, **j** and **k**. On the other hand (since $\sqrt{\alpha^2} = |\alpha|$),

$$\|\mathbf{v}\| \, \|\mathbf{w}\| = \sqrt{v_1^2 + v_2^2 + v_3^2} \cdot \sqrt{(\alpha v_1)^2 + (\alpha v_2)^2 + (\alpha v_3)^2} = |\alpha| \, (v_1^2 + v_2^2 + v_3^2).$$

If **v** and **w** have the same direction, then $\alpha > 0$, and consequently, $|\alpha| = \alpha$ and $\mathbf{v} \cdot \mathbf{w} = \|\mathbf{v}\| \, \|\mathbf{w}\|$. Otherwise, if **v** and **w** have opposite directions, then $\alpha < 0$, $|\alpha| = -\alpha$ and hence $\mathbf{v} \cdot \mathbf{w} = -\|\mathbf{v}\| \, \|\mathbf{w}\|$.

Our next theorem gives a geometric interpretation of the dot product, from which a number of useful consequences follow. Before introducing the theorem we have to define the angle between vectors. Let **v** and **w** be vectors in $\mathbb{R}^2$ or in $\mathbb{R}^3$ represented by the directed line segments $\overrightarrow{AB}$ and $\overrightarrow{AC}$ that start at the same point A; see Figure 1.12.

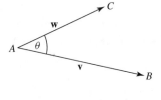

Figure 1.12 Angle between vectors.

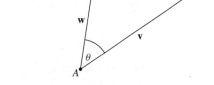

Figure 1.13 Triangle ABC from the proof of Theorem 1.4.

The angle θ between **v** and **w** is defined as the smaller of the two angles (in the plane through A spanned by $\mathbf{v}$ and $\mathbf{w}$) defined by the directed line segments $\overrightarrow{AB}$ and $\overrightarrow{AC}$. From our definition it follows that $0 \leq \theta \leq \pi$. If $\mathbf{v}$ and $\mathbf{w}$ are parallel, then $\theta = 0$ (if they have the same direction) or $\theta = \pi$ (if they have opposite directions).

■ **Theorem 1.4**   Geometric Version of the Dot Product.

Let $\mathbf{v}$ and $\mathbf{w}$ be vectors in $\mathbb{R}^2$ or $\mathbb{R}^3$. Then

$$\mathbf{v} \cdot \mathbf{w} = \|\mathbf{v}\| \, \|\mathbf{w}\| \, \cos\theta, \tag{1.7}$$

where θ is the angle between $\mathbf{v}$ and $\mathbf{w}$.

Proof

If either $\mathbf{v} = \mathbf{0}$ or $\mathbf{w} = \mathbf{0}$ (or both), then both sides of (1.7) are zero. If $\theta = 0$ then $\mathbf{v}$ and $\mathbf{w}$ are parallel and have the same direction. In this case, $\cos\theta = 1$ and (1.7) follows from (1.5). If $\theta = \pi$, then $\mathbf{v}$ and $\mathbf{w}$ are parallel and have opposite directions, $\cos\theta = -1$ and (1.6) implies (1.7). Having verified all trivial cases, we must now consider the case $\mathbf{v} \neq \mathbf{0}$, $\mathbf{w} \neq \mathbf{0}$ and $0 < \theta < \pi$. Represent the vectors $\mathbf{v}$ and $\mathbf{w}$ by the directed line segments $\overrightarrow{AB}$ and $\overrightarrow{AC}$ starting at the same point A, as in Figure 1.13, and apply the Law of Cosines to the triangle ABC (the sides of the triangle are $\overline{AB} = \|\mathbf{v}\|$, $\overline{AC} = \|\mathbf{w}\|$ and $\overline{BC} = \|\mathbf{v} - \mathbf{w}\| = \|\mathbf{w} - \mathbf{v}\|$):

$$\|\mathbf{v} - \mathbf{w}\|^2 = \|\mathbf{v}\|^2 + \|\mathbf{w}\|^2 - 2\|\mathbf{v}\| \, \|\mathbf{w}\| \cos\theta.$$

Using the properties of the dot product we transform the left side as

$$\|\mathbf{v} - \mathbf{w}\|^2 = (\mathbf{v} - \mathbf{w}) \cdot (\mathbf{v} - \mathbf{w}) = \mathbf{v} \cdot \mathbf{v} - \mathbf{w} \cdot \mathbf{v} - \mathbf{v} \cdot \mathbf{w} + \mathbf{w} \cdot \mathbf{w} = \|\mathbf{v}\|^2 - 2\mathbf{v} \cdot \mathbf{w} + \|\mathbf{w}\|^2.$$

Now substitute the right side of the previous equation into the Law of Cosines formula above to get

$$\|\mathbf{v}\|^2 - 2\mathbf{v} \cdot \mathbf{w} + \|\mathbf{w}\|^2 = \|\mathbf{v}\|^2 + \|\mathbf{w}\|^2 - 2\|\mathbf{v}\| \, \|\mathbf{w}\| \cos\theta.$$

Thus $-2\mathbf{v} \cdot \mathbf{w} = -2\|\mathbf{v}\| \, \|\mathbf{w}\| \cos\theta$ and

$$\mathbf{v} \cdot \mathbf{w} = \|\mathbf{v}\| \, \|\mathbf{w}\| \cos\theta,$$

which is the formula (1.7).   ■

Let us note two important consequences of this theorem. Non-zero vectors $\mathbf{v}$ and $\mathbf{w}$ are called *orthogonal* (or *perpendicular*) if the angle between them is $\pi/2$.

■ **Theorem 1.5**   Test for Orthogonality of Vectors.

Let $\mathbf{v}$ and $\mathbf{w}$ be non-zero vectors in $\mathbb{R}^2$ or $\mathbb{R}^3$. Then $\mathbf{v} \cdot \mathbf{w} = 0$ if and only if $\mathbf{v}$ and $\mathbf{w}$ are orthogonal.

Proof

From $\mathbf{v} \cdot \mathbf{w} = 0$ it follows that $\|\mathbf{v}\| \, \|\mathbf{w}\| \cos\theta = 0$, i.e.; $\cos\theta = 0$ (since $\mathbf{v}, \mathbf{w} \neq \mathbf{0}$ their magnitudes are non-zero as well) and hence $\theta = \pi/2$. Conversely, if $\theta = \pi/2$, then

$\mathbf{v} \cdot \mathbf{w} = \|\mathbf{v}\| \, \|\mathbf{w}\| \cos(\pi/2) = 0.$ ∎

Definition 1.5   Orthonormal Set of Vectors.

Vectors $\mathbf{v}_1, \ldots, \mathbf{v}_k$ (where $k \geq 2$) in $\mathbb{R}^n$, $n \geq 2$ are said to form an *orthonormal set* if they are of unit length and each vector in the set is orthogonal to the others. ▨

Sometimes the vectors that form an orthonormal set are referred to as *orthonormal vectors*. For example, the standard unit vectors $\mathbf{i}$, $\mathbf{j}$, $\mathbf{k}$ form an orthonormal set in $\mathbb{R}^3$. More sophisticated examples will be provided in the discussion of various coordinate systems in Sections 2.7 and 2.8.

Theorem 1.6   Angle Between Vectors.

Let $\mathbf{v}$ and $\mathbf{w}$ be non-zero vectors in $\mathbb{R}^2$ or $\mathbb{R}^3$. Then

$$\cos \theta = \frac{\mathbf{v} \cdot \mathbf{w}}{\|\mathbf{v}\| \, \|\mathbf{w}\|},$$

where θ is the angle between $\mathbf{v}$ and $\mathbf{w}$.

Proof

All we have to do is to solve (1.7) for θ and notice that the denominator cannot be zero (since $\mathbf{v}$ and $\mathbf{w}$ are assumed to be non-zero vectors). ∎

Example 1.18   This example illustrates the use of Theorems 1.5 and 1.6.

(a) Find the angle between $\mathbf{v} = 4\mathbf{i} - \mathbf{j} + \mathbf{k}$ and $\mathbf{w} = \mathbf{j} + 3\mathbf{k}$ in $\mathbb{R}^3$.

(b) Show that the line ℓ_1 that goes through $(1, 0)$ and $(3, 4)$ is perpendicular to the line ℓ_2 that contains $(3, -1)$ and $(1, 0)$.

Solution

(a) From $\|\mathbf{v}\| = \sqrt{4^2 + (-1)^2 + 1^2} = \sqrt{18}$, $\|\mathbf{w}\| = \sqrt{1 + 9} = \sqrt{10}$ and $\mathbf{v} \cdot \mathbf{w} = (4\mathbf{i} - \mathbf{j} + \mathbf{k}) \cdot (\mathbf{j} + 3\mathbf{k}) = 2$, using Theorem 1.6, we get

$$\cos \theta = \frac{\mathbf{v} \cdot \mathbf{w}}{\|\mathbf{v}\| \, \|\mathbf{w}\|} = \frac{2}{\sqrt{10}\sqrt{18}} = \frac{1}{3\sqrt{5}}$$

and $\theta = \arccos(1/3\sqrt{5}) \approx 1.42$ radians.

(b) The direction of ℓ_1 is that of the vector $\mathbf{v}' = (2, 4)$, and the direction of ℓ_2 is $\mathbf{v}'' = (-2, 1)$. Since their dot product $\mathbf{v}' \cdot \mathbf{v}'' = (2, 4) \cdot (-2, 1) = 0$, it follows that ℓ_1 and ℓ_2 are perpendicular. (It makes no difference if we take $(-2, -4)$ as the direction of ℓ_1 or $(2, -1)$ as the direction for ℓ_2.) ◀

We have already seen that every vector in $\mathbb{R}^2$ can be expressed in terms of the standard unit vectors $\mathbf{i}$ and $\mathbf{j}$. As a matter of fact, a vector in $\mathbb{R}^2$ can be expressed in terms of any pair of orthogonal vectors. That is the point of the next theorem.

■ Theorem 1.7   Vector Expressed in Terms of Orthogonal Vectors.

Let $\mathbf{v}$ and $\mathbf{w}$ be (non-zero) orthogonal vectors in $\mathbb{R}^2$ and let $\mathbf{a}$ be any vector in $\mathbb{R}^2$. Then

$$\mathbf{a} = a_{\mathbf{v}}\mathbf{v} + a_{\mathbf{w}}\mathbf{w},$$

where $a_{\mathbf{v}} = \mathbf{a} \cdot \mathbf{v}/\|\mathbf{v}\|^2$ is the component of $\mathbf{a}$ in the direction of $\mathbf{v}$ and $a_{\mathbf{w}} = \mathbf{a} \cdot \mathbf{w}/\|\mathbf{w}\|^2$ is the component of $\mathbf{a}$ in the direction of $\mathbf{w}$ (or in the direction orthogonal to $\mathbf{v}$).

Proof

From linear algebra we know that every vector in $\mathbb{R}^2$ can be written as a linear combination (i.e., expressed in terms) of two mutually orthogonal vectors. Hence $\mathbf{a} = a_{\mathbf{v}}\mathbf{v} + a_{\mathbf{w}}\mathbf{w}$ for some real numbers $a_{\mathbf{v}}$ and $a_{\mathbf{w}}$. Computing the dot product of $\mathbf{a} = a_{\mathbf{v}}\mathbf{v} + a_{\mathbf{w}}\mathbf{w}$ with $\mathbf{v}$, we get

$$\mathbf{a} \cdot \mathbf{v} = a_{\mathbf{v}}\|\mathbf{v}\|^2 + a_{\mathbf{w}}\mathbf{w} \cdot \mathbf{v}.$$

Since $\mathbf{v}$ and $\mathbf{w}$ are orthogonal, $\mathbf{w} \cdot \mathbf{v} = 0$ and $\mathbf{a} \cdot \mathbf{v} = a_{\mathbf{v}}\|\mathbf{v}\|^2$. Hence $a_{\mathbf{v}} = \mathbf{a} \cdot \mathbf{v}/\|\mathbf{v}\|^2$. Repeating the same argument (this time, computing the dot product of $\mathbf{a}$ and $\mathbf{w}$) we obtain the formula for the component $a_{\mathbf{w}}$ of $\mathbf{a}$.   ■

An analogous statement holds in three dimensions: if $\mathbf{u}$, $\mathbf{v}$ and $\mathbf{w}$ are non-zero and mutually orthogonal vectors (i.e., $\mathbf{u} \cdot \mathbf{v} = \mathbf{u} \cdot \mathbf{w} = \mathbf{v} \cdot \mathbf{w} = 0$) and $\mathbf{a} \in \mathbb{R}^3$, then

$$\mathbf{a} = a_{\mathbf{u}}\mathbf{u} + a_{\mathbf{v}}\mathbf{v} + a_{\mathbf{w}}\mathbf{w},$$

where $a_{\mathbf{u}} = \mathbf{a} \cdot \mathbf{u}/\|\mathbf{u}\|^2$, $a_{\mathbf{v}} = \mathbf{a} \cdot \mathbf{v}/\|\mathbf{v}\|^2$ and $a_{\mathbf{w}} = \mathbf{a} \cdot \mathbf{w}/\|\mathbf{w}\|^2$.

Example 1.19   Check that $\mathbf{u} = (1, 2, 0)$, $\mathbf{v} = (2, -1, 1)$ and $\mathbf{w} = (-2, 1, 5)$ are mutually orthogonal vectors and express $\mathbf{a} = (0, 1, 1)$ in terms of $\mathbf{u}$, $\mathbf{v}$ and $\mathbf{w}$.

Solution   Since $\mathbf{u} \cdot \mathbf{v} = (1, 2, 0) \cdot (2, -1, 1) = 0$, $\mathbf{u} \cdot \mathbf{w} = (1, 2, 0) \cdot (-2, 1, 5) = 0$ and $\mathbf{v} \cdot \mathbf{w} = (2, -1, 1) \cdot (-2, 1, 5) = 0$, the vectors $\mathbf{u}$, $\mathbf{v}$ and $\mathbf{w}$ are mutually orthogonal. Now $\mathbf{a} \cdot \mathbf{u} = (0, 1, 1) \cdot (1, 2, 0) = 2$, $\mathbf{a} \cdot \mathbf{v} = (0, 1, 1) \cdot (2, -1, 1) = 0$ and $\mathbf{a} \cdot \mathbf{w} = (0, 1, 1) \cdot (-2, 1, 5) = 6$; $\|\mathbf{u}\| = \sqrt{5}$, $\|\mathbf{v}\| = \sqrt{6}$, and $\|\mathbf{w}\| = \sqrt{30}$, and therefore

$$\mathbf{a} = \frac{\mathbf{a} \cdot \mathbf{u}}{\|\mathbf{u}\|^2}\mathbf{u} + \frac{\mathbf{a} \cdot \mathbf{v}}{\|\mathbf{v}\|^2}\mathbf{v} + \frac{\mathbf{a} \cdot \mathbf{w}}{\|\mathbf{w}\|^2}\mathbf{w} = \tfrac{2}{5}\mathbf{u} + \tfrac{0}{6}\mathbf{v} + \tfrac{6}{30}\mathbf{w} = \tfrac{2}{5}\mathbf{u} + \tfrac{1}{5}\mathbf{w}. \quad ◀$$

Example 1.20   Express the vector $\mathbf{a} = 3\mathbf{i} + \mathbf{j}$ as the sum $\mathbf{a} = a_{\mathbf{v}}\mathbf{v} + a_{\mathbf{w}}\mathbf{w}$, where $\mathbf{v}$ and $\mathbf{w}$ are unit vectors, $\mathbf{v}$ is parallel to the line $y = x$, $\mathbf{w}$ is perpendicular to it and both have positive $\mathbf{j}$ components.

Solution   Picking two points on the line $y = x$, say $(1, 1)$ and $(2, 2)$, we compute its direction to be $(1, 1) = \mathbf{i} + \mathbf{j}$. The vector $\mathbf{v}$ has to be of unit length in that direction and hence $\mathbf{v} = (\mathbf{i}+\mathbf{j})/\|\mathbf{i}+\mathbf{j}\| = (\mathbf{i}+\mathbf{j})/\sqrt{2}$. The vector $\mathbf{w}$ has to be orthogonal to $\mathbf{v}$ and of unit length. So, first take any vector whose dot product with $\mathbf{v}$ is zero, (and whose $\mathbf{j}$ component is positive) and then adjust its length. For example, $(-\mathbf{i} + \mathbf{j}) \cdot (\mathbf{i}/\sqrt{2} + \mathbf{j}/\sqrt{2}) = 0$, so take $\mathbf{w} = (-\mathbf{i} + \mathbf{j})/\|\mathbf{i} - \mathbf{j}\| = (-\mathbf{i} + \mathbf{j})/\sqrt{2}$. Although there are infinitely many vectors orthogonal to $\mathbf{v}$, only two (namely $\mathbf{w}$ and $-\mathbf{w}$) are of unit length; the requirement that its $\mathbf{j}$ coordinate be positive uniquely determines $\mathbf{w}$. Now $\mathbf{a} = a_\mathbf{v}\mathbf{v} + a_\mathbf{w}\mathbf{w}$, where $a_\mathbf{v} = \mathbf{a} \cdot \mathbf{v}/\|\mathbf{v}\|^2 = (3\mathbf{i} + \mathbf{j}) \cdot (\mathbf{i}/\sqrt{2} + \mathbf{j}/\sqrt{2}) = 4/\sqrt{2}$, (since $\|\mathbf{v}\| = 1$) and $a_\mathbf{w} = \mathbf{a} \cdot \mathbf{w}/\|\mathbf{w}\|^2 = (3\mathbf{i} + \mathbf{j}) \cdot (-\mathbf{i}/\sqrt{2} + \mathbf{j}/\sqrt{2}) = -2/\sqrt{2}$, (since $\|\mathbf{w}\| = 1$). Hence

$$\mathbf{a} = \frac{4}{\sqrt{2}} \left(\frac{1}{\sqrt{2}}\mathbf{i} + \frac{1}{\sqrt{2}}\mathbf{j} \right) - \frac{2}{\sqrt{2}} \left(-\frac{1}{\sqrt{2}}\mathbf{i} + \frac{1}{\sqrt{2}}\mathbf{j} \right)$$

is the required decomposition.

We are going to give a geometric meaning to the vectors $a_\mathbf{v}\mathbf{v}$ and $a_\mathbf{w}\mathbf{w}$ in the expression $\mathbf{a} = a_\mathbf{v}\mathbf{v} + a_\mathbf{w}\mathbf{w}$, where $\mathbf{v}$ and $\mathbf{w}$ are orthogonal vectors in $\mathbb{R}^2$.

Take the representatives of $\mathbf{a}$ and $\mathbf{v}$ that start at the same point A, and draw the line ℓ through A in the direction $\mathbf{v}$; see Figure 1.14. The line perpendicular to ℓ that goes through the tip A' of $\mathbf{a}$ intersects ℓ at the point B. The vector represented by the directed line segment $\overrightarrow{AB}$ is called the *orthogonal projection* (or the *orthogonal vector projection*) of $\mathbf{a}$ onto $\mathbf{v}$, and is denoted by $pr_\mathbf{v}\mathbf{a}$. Its magnitude $\|pr_\mathbf{v}\mathbf{a}\|$ is called the *scalar projection*.

Let θ be the angle between $\mathbf{a}$ and $\mathbf{v}$. From the triangle ABA' we get $\cos\theta = \|pr_\mathbf{v}\mathbf{a}\|/\|\mathbf{a}\|$, and hence $\|pr_\mathbf{v}\mathbf{a}\| = \|\mathbf{a}\| \cos\theta$. Combining this with the formula $\cos\theta = \mathbf{a} \cdot \mathbf{v}/\|\mathbf{a}\| \|\mathbf{v}\|$ of Theorem 1.6 we get the expression for the scalar projection

$$\|pr_\mathbf{v}\mathbf{a}\| = \|\mathbf{a}\| \cos\theta = \|\mathbf{a}\| \frac{\mathbf{a} \cdot \mathbf{v}}{\|\mathbf{a}\| \|\mathbf{v}\|} = \frac{\mathbf{a} \cdot \mathbf{v}}{\|\mathbf{v}\|}. \tag{1.8}$$

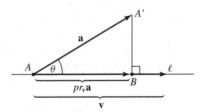

Figure 1.14 Projection of $\mathbf{a}$ onto $\mathbf{v}$.

To obtain the vector projection, we multiply the scalar projection by the unit vector $\mathbf{v}/\|\mathbf{v}\|$ in the direction of $\mathbf{v}$ (we need the direction of $\mathbf{v}$, but cannot multiply by $\mathbf{v}$ only as this would mess up the length of the projection). Hence

$$pr_\mathbf{v}\mathbf{a} = \frac{\mathbf{a} \cdot \mathbf{v}}{\|\mathbf{v}\|} \frac{\mathbf{v}}{\|\mathbf{v}\|} = \frac{\mathbf{a} \cdot \mathbf{v}}{\|\mathbf{v}\|^2} \mathbf{v}. \tag{1.9}$$

Repeating this argument will give

$$pr_\mathbf{w}\mathbf{a} = \frac{\mathbf{a} \cdot \mathbf{w}}{\|\mathbf{w}\|^2} \mathbf{w}.$$

Comparing these formulas with Theorem 1.7, we get that $pr_\mathbf{v}\mathbf{a} = a_\mathbf{v}\mathbf{v}$ and $pr_\mathbf{w}\mathbf{a} = a_\mathbf{w}\mathbf{w}$. In other words, the decomposition $\mathbf{a} = a_\mathbf{v}\mathbf{v} + a_\mathbf{w}\mathbf{w}$ is the sum $\mathbf{a} = pr_\mathbf{v}\mathbf{a} + pr_\mathbf{w}\mathbf{a}$ of orthogonal projections of $\mathbf{a}$ onto $\mathbf{v}$ and $\mathbf{w}$ (keep in mind that $\mathbf{v}$ and $\mathbf{w}$ are (non-zero) orthogonal vectors).

Similarly, the decomposition

$$\mathbf{a} = a_{\mathbf{u}}\mathbf{u} + a_{\mathbf{v}}\mathbf{v} + a_{\mathbf{w}}\mathbf{w}$$

in $\mathbb{R}^3$ is the sum of orthogonal projections of $\mathbf{a}$ onto $\mathbf{u}$, $\mathbf{v}$ and $\mathbf{w}$ (and $\mathbf{u}$, $\mathbf{v}$ and $\mathbf{w}$ are mutually orthogonal (non-zero) vectors).

Example 1.21   Compute the scalar and vector orthogonal projections of $\mathbf{a} = (2, 1, 4)$ onto $\mathbf{v} = (0, 2, 3)$.

Solution   Since $\mathbf{a} \cdot \mathbf{v} = (2, 1, 4) \cdot (0, 2, 3) = 14$ and $\|\mathbf{v}\| = \sqrt{13}$, it follows that

$$pr_{\mathbf{v}}\mathbf{a} = \frac{\mathbf{a} \cdot \mathbf{v}}{\|\mathbf{v}\|^2}\mathbf{v} = \tfrac{14}{13}(0, 2, 3) = (0, \tfrac{28}{13}, \tfrac{42}{13})$$

is the vector projection, and

$$\|pr_{\mathbf{v}}\mathbf{a}\| = \|\tfrac{14}{13}\mathbf{v}\| = \tfrac{14}{13}\|\mathbf{v}\| = 14/\sqrt{13}$$

is the scalar projection.

◀

Example 1.22   **Work.**

Assume that a constant force $\mathbf{F}$ acts on an object located initially at $A(a_1, a_2)$ as the object moves along the straight line to the point $B(b_1, b_2)$. The *work* W done by the force $\mathbf{F}$ on the object is defined to be the product of the component of $\mathbf{F}$ in the direction of the motion (we now know that this is just the orthogonal projection) and the distance moved.

The distance moved is equal to the length $\|\mathbf{d}\|$ of the displacement vector $\mathbf{d} = (b_1 - a_1, b_2 - a_2)$. The component of $\mathbf{F}$ needed is the scalar projection $\|pr_{\mathbf{d}}\mathbf{F}\|$ of $\mathbf{F}$ onto $\mathbf{d}$, and is given by (apply (1.8)) $\mathbf{F} \cdot \mathbf{d}/\|\mathbf{d}\|$; see Figure 1.15. Therefore,

$$W = \frac{\mathbf{F} \cdot \mathbf{d}}{\|\mathbf{d}\|}\|\mathbf{d}\| = \mathbf{F} \cdot \mathbf{d},$$

i.e., the work is the dot product of the force and the displacement vectors.

◀

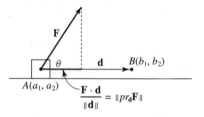

Figure 1.15   The work of a force $\mathbf{F}$ on an object is the dot product of $\mathbf{F}$ and the object's displacement vector $\mathbf{d}$.

Example 1.23   A force $\mathbf{F}$ of 5 N acts on an object as the object moves from the origin to the point $(3, 2)$ along a straight line. In what direction with respect to the displacement should the force act to produce maximum work? Explain why $\mathbf{F}$ does zero work if applied in the direction perpendicular to the displacement.

Solution   According to the previous example the work of $\mathbf{F}$ is $W = \mathbf{F} \cdot \mathbf{d} = \|\mathbf{F}\| \, \|\mathbf{d}\| \cos \theta$, where $\mathbf{d} = 3\mathbf{i} + 2\mathbf{j}$ is the displacement vector and θ is the angle between $\mathbf{F}$ and $\mathbf{d}$. Since $\|\mathbf{F}\| = 5$ and $\|\mathbf{d}\| = \sqrt{13}$, it follows that $W = 5\sqrt{13} \cos \theta$. The work is maximum when $\cos \theta = 1$, i.e., when $\theta = 0$. Hence maximum work is obtained by applying $\mathbf{F}$ in the direction of motion. Since $\cos(\pi/2) = 0$, the work is zero if $\mathbf{F}$ is applied in the direction perpendicular to the motion.

◀

Example 1.24   Equation of a Plane in Space.

As an application of the dot product, we will compute the equation of the plane in space containing the point $A(x_0, y_0, z_0)$ and perpendicular to the vector $\mathbf{n} = (a, b, c)$ (here we depart from our standard use of the subscripts for the components of a vector; using a, b and c instead will produce a familiar form of the equation). Visualize $\mathbf{n}$ as the directed line segment starting at A and pick any point $P(x, y, z)$ in the plane. The vector $\mathbf{v} = (x - x_0, y - y_0, z - z_0)$ defined by the directed line segment $\overrightarrow{AP}$ is perpendicular to $\mathbf{n}$, and consequently $\mathbf{n} \cdot \mathbf{v} = 0$; i.e.,

$$(a, b, c) \cdot (x - x_0, y - y_0, z - z_0) = 0.$$

This expression, written as

$$a(x - x_0) + b(y - y_0) + c(z - z_0) = 0$$

represents the equation of the plane that contains the point (x_0, y_0, z_0) and is perpendicular to the vector $\mathbf{n} = (a, b, c)$. The vector $\mathbf{n}$ is called a *normal vector* to the plane; see Figure 1.16.

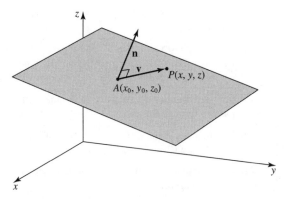

Figure 1.16   Plane through a point A with a normal vector $\mathbf{n}$.

EXERCISES 1.3

1. Show that the dot product is commutative; i.e., $\mathbf{v} \cdot \mathbf{w} = \mathbf{w} \cdot \mathbf{v}$ for $\mathbf{v}, \mathbf{w} \in \mathbb{R}^n$.

2. Explain why $\mathbf{u} \cdot (\mathbf{v} \cdot \mathbf{w}) \neq (\mathbf{u} \cdot \mathbf{v}) \cdot \mathbf{w}$ for vectors $\mathbf{u}$, $\mathbf{v}$ and $\mathbf{w}$ in $\mathbb{R}^2$ (or in $\mathbb{R}^3$).

3. Prove that, for vectors $\mathbf{u}$, $\mathbf{v}$ and $\mathbf{w}$ in $\mathbb{R}^3$ and any $\alpha \in \mathbb{R}$, $\mathbf{u} \cdot (\mathbf{v} + \mathbf{w}) = \mathbf{u} \cdot \mathbf{v} + \mathbf{u} \cdot \mathbf{w}$, $(\alpha\mathbf{u}) \cdot \mathbf{v} = \alpha(\mathbf{u} \cdot \mathbf{v})$ and $\mathbf{u} \cdot (\alpha\mathbf{v}) = \alpha(\mathbf{u} \cdot \mathbf{v})$.

4. Prove that $\mathbf{v} \cdot \mathbf{v} = \|\mathbf{v}\|^2$ for any vector $\mathbf{v} \in \mathbb{R}^n$.

5. Show that if $\mathbf{u}$, $\mathbf{v}$ and $\mathbf{w}$ are non-zero and mutually orthogonal vectors in $\mathbb{R}^3$ and $\mathbf{a} \in \mathbb{R}^3$, then $\mathbf{a} = a_u\mathbf{u} + a_v\mathbf{v} + a_w\mathbf{w}$, where $a_u = \mathbf{a} \cdot \mathbf{u}/\|\mathbf{u}\|^2$, $a_v = \mathbf{a} \cdot \mathbf{v}/\|\mathbf{v}\|^2$ and $a_w = \mathbf{a} \cdot \mathbf{w}/\|\mathbf{w}\|^2$.

6. Find the angle between $2\mathbf{j} - \mathbf{k}$ and $\mathbf{i} + \mathbf{j} - 3\mathbf{k}$.

7. Find the angles in the triangle with vertices $(0, 3, 4)$, $(0, 3, 0)$ and $(12, 0, 5)$.

8. Determine whether the vectors $(3, 2, 4)$ and $(1, 2, 7)$ are parallel or orthogonal or neither. Do the same for $\mathbf{i} - \mathbf{j} - \mathbf{k}$ and $\mathbf{i} + \mathbf{j}$.

9. Let $\mathbf{v}$ and $\mathbf{w}$ be non-zero vectors in $\mathbb{R}^2$. Show that the vectors $\mathbf{w} - (\mathbf{v} \cdot \mathbf{w}/\|\mathbf{v}\|^2)\mathbf{v}$ and $\mathbf{v}$ are orthogonal.

10. Prove the *Cauchy-Schwarz Inequality* $|\mathbf{v} \cdot \mathbf{w}| \leq \|\mathbf{v}\| \|\mathbf{w}\|$ for vectors in $\mathbb{R}^2$ (and then for vectors in $\mathbb{R}^3$). When does the equality hold?

11. Find the angles between the diagonal of a cube and its three adjacent edges.

12. Find the angle between the diagonals of the parallelogram three of whose vertices are located at $(0, 2, -3)$, $(1, 1, 0)$ and $(-1, 0, 1)$.

13. Let $\mathbf{v}$ and $\mathbf{w}$ be non-zero vectors such that $\|\mathbf{v}\| = \|\mathbf{w}\|$ and let $\mathbf{a} = \|\mathbf{v}\|\mathbf{w} + \|\mathbf{w}\|\mathbf{v}$. Show that the angles between $\mathbf{v}$ and $\mathbf{a}$ and $\mathbf{w}$ and $\mathbf{a}$ are the same.

14. Find the work of the force of magnitude 10 N acting at an angle of $\pi/3$ on an object located at $(1, 1)$ as the object moves from $(1, 1)$ to $(3, -2)$.

15. Write the vector $\mathbf{i} + 2\mathbf{j}$ as the sum of its orthogonal projections onto $\mathbf{i} + \mathbf{j}$ and $\mathbf{i} - \mathbf{j}$.

16. Check that the vectors $(\mathbf{i}+\mathbf{j}-\mathbf{k})/\sqrt{3}$, $(\mathbf{i}-\mathbf{j})/\sqrt{2}$ and $(\mathbf{i}+\mathbf{j}+2\mathbf{k})/\sqrt{6}$ form an orthonormal set.

17. Find the equation of the plane that contains the point $(0, -2, 2)$ that is orthogonal to the vector $(3, 0, -1)$.

18. Fix a non-zero vector $\mathbf{v}$ in $\mathbb{R}^3$ and consider the dot products $\mathbf{v} \cdot \mathbf{u}$, where $\mathbf{u}$ is a unit vector in $\mathbb{R}^3$. Find all $\mathbf{u}$ such that $\mathbf{v} \cdot \mathbf{u}$ is the largest. Find all $\mathbf{u}$ such that $\mathbf{v} \cdot \mathbf{u}$ is the smallest. Describe geometrically all directions $\mathbf{u} \in \mathbb{R}^3$ that satisfy $\mathbf{v} \cdot \mathbf{u} = 0$.

19. Find the equation of the plane in $\mathbb{R}^3$ that contains the origin and is orthogonal to the line passing through the points $(3, 2, -1)$ and $(0, 0, 7)$.

20. Compute the scalar projection of the vector $3\mathbf{i} - 2\mathbf{j}$ onto the line passing through the points $(2, -1)$ and $(0, 4)$.

21. Show that the work done by a constant force $\mathbf{F}$ on an object that moves around any closed polygon is zero.

22. Find all unit vectors parallel to the yz-plane and perpendicular to the vector $\mathbf{i} + \mathbf{j} - 2\mathbf{k}$.

23. Check that the vectors $\mathbf{u} = \mathbf{i} + \mathbf{j} - 2\mathbf{k}$, $\mathbf{v} = 2\mathbf{j} + \mathbf{k}$ and $\mathbf{w} = 5\mathbf{i} - \mathbf{j} + 2\mathbf{k}$ are mutually orthogonal and express the vector $\mathbf{i}$ in terms of $\mathbf{u}$, $\mathbf{v}$ and $\mathbf{w}$.

24. The vectors $\mathbf{u} = (\mathbf{i} - 2\mathbf{j} + \mathbf{k})/\sqrt{6}$ and $\mathbf{v} = -(\mathbf{i} + \mathbf{j} + \mathbf{k})/\sqrt{3}$ are orthogonal and of unit length. Find all vectors $\mathbf{w}$ so that $\mathbf{u}$, $\mathbf{v}$ and $\mathbf{w}$ form an orthonormal set in $\mathbb{R}^3$.

25. Assume that $\mathbf{u}$, $\mathbf{v}$ and $\mathbf{w}$ are mutually orthogonal (non-zero) vectors in $\mathbb{R}^3$. Show that there does not exist a non-zero vector in $\mathbb{R}^3$ orthogonal to all three of them.

1.4   MATRICES AND DETERMINANTS

In this section we introduce two new mathematical objects: matrices and determinants. Our discussion will not be exhaustive, but will rather concentrate on those topics that will be used in this book.

■ **Definition 1.6**   Matrix.

An $m \times n$ *matrix* A is a rectangular table of real numbers, arranged in m rows and n columns:

$$A = \begin{bmatrix} a_{11} & a_{12} & \dots & a_{1n} \\ a_{21} & a_{22} & \dots & a_{2n} \\ \vdots & \vdots & & \vdots \\ a_{m1} & a_{m2} & \dots & a_{mn} \end{bmatrix}.$$

An $m \times n$ matrix is also called a *matrix of type $m \times n$* or of *order $m \times n$*. The elements $a_{i1}, a_{i2}, \dots, a_{in}$ form the *i-th row* of A, $i = 1, \dots, m$. The elements $a_{1j}, a_{2j}, \dots, a_{mj}$ form the *j-th column* of A, $j = 1, \dots, n$. Sometimes the i-th row of A is written as a $1 \times n$ matrix

$$[\, a_{i1} \quad a_{i2} \quad \dots \quad a_{in} \,]$$

(and called a *row vector*) and the j-th column of A is written as an $m \times 1$ matrix

$$\begin{bmatrix} a_{1j} \\ a_{2j} \\ \vdots \\ a_{mj} \end{bmatrix}$$

(and called a *column vector*). A 1×1 matrix $a = [a_{11}]$ is identified with its entry a_{11}. Matrices are usually denoted by uppercase letters A, B, C, etc. and their elements (or entries) by corresponding lowercase letters together with two subscripts that define their location in the matrix. For example, the element in the i-th row and the j-th column of A is denoted by a_{ij}. Sometimes we use the notation $A = [a_{ij}]$.

For our purpose, we have to extend this (classical) definition of a matrix: we will allow the entries of a matrix to be real-valued functions of several variables, not only real numbers. All the properties that we will discuss will hold for these more general matrices (we still call them matrices, or matrices of functions).

Example 1.25   Consider the 3×4 matrix

$$A = \begin{bmatrix} 9 & 0 & -5 & 5 \\ 2 & -5 & 9 & 1 \\ -4 & 0 & 2 & -7 \end{bmatrix}.$$

Let us list a few entries: $a_{12} = 0$, $a_{33} = 2$, $a_{21} = 2$, $a_{31} = -4$, $a_{24} = 1$, etc. The elements 2, -5, 9 and 1 form the second row and 5, 1 and -7 form the fourth column of A. We can also write them as matrices: the second row is the 1×4 matrix (or a row vector)

$$[2 \quad -5 \quad 9 \quad 1]$$

and the fourth column is the 3×1 matrix

$$\begin{bmatrix} 5 \\ 1 \\ -7 \end{bmatrix}$$

(also called a column vector).

◀

The $m \times n$ matrix all of whose entries are 0 is called a *zero matrix* (of type $m \times n$) and is denoted by 0. A matrix $A = [a_{ij}]$ of type $n \times n$ (i.e., A has the same number of rows and columns) is called a *square matrix of order n*. Its elements $a_{11}, a_{22}, \ldots, a_{nn}$ are said to form the *(main) diagonal* of A, and all other elements are called *off-diagonal elements*. The square matrix of order n whose diagonal elements are 1 and all off-diagonal elements are 0 is called an *identity matrix* (of order n) and is denoted by I or I_n (if its order needs to be specified).

Two matrices $A = [a_{ij}]$ and $B = [b_{ij}]$ are said to be *equal* (denoted by $A = B$) if and only if they are of the same type (say, $m \times n$) and all corresponding elements are equal; i.e., $a_{ij} = b_{ij}$ for all $i = 1, \ldots, m$ and $j = 1, \ldots, n$.

▨ **Definition 1.7**   Elementary Operations With Matrices.

Let $A = [a_{ij}]$ and $B = [b_{ij}]$ be matrices of type $m \times n$, and let α be a real number. The *sum* of A and B is the $m \times n$ matrix $C = A + B$ whose elements are defined by $c_{ij} = a_{ij} + b_{ij}$. The *difference* of A and B is the $m \times n$ matrix $C = A - B$ whose elements are defined by $c_{ij} = a_{ij} - b_{ij}$. The product of a scalar α and a matrix A is the $m \times n$ matrix $C = \alpha A$, where $c_{ij} = \alpha a_{ij}$.

▨

In words, only matrices of the same type can be added or subtracted. The ij-th entry in $A + B$ ($A - B$) is the sum (difference) of the corresponding entries in A and B. In order to multiply a matrix by a real number α, we multiply all of its entries by α.

■ **Theorem 1.8**   Properties of Matrix Addition and Multiplication by a Scalar.

Assume that A, B and C are matrices of type $m \times n$ and let α and β be real numbers.

Matrix addition is *commutative*

$$A + B = B + A,$$

associative

$$(A + B) + C = A + (B + C),$$

and if 0 is the $m \times n$ zero matrix, then

$$A + 0 = A.$$

The *distributive* laws

$$\alpha(A + B) = \alpha A + \alpha B \qquad \text{and} \qquad (\alpha + \beta)A = \alpha A + \beta A$$

hold for multiplication by scalars. Finally,

$$1 \cdot A = A. \qquad\qquad\blacksquare$$

By definition, $(-1) \cdot A$ is denoted by $-A$. One could define the difference $A - B$ as $A + (-B)$.

Theorem 1.8 states that, as far as addition (subtraction) and multiplication by scalars are concerned, matrices behave in the same way as real numbers. Proofs of all parts of Theorem 1.8 consist of checking that the corresponding entries in the matrices on both sides of the above identities are equal. For example, let us check the first distribution law: the ij-th entry in the matrix on the left side is $\alpha(a_{ij} + b_{ij})$, and the corresponding entry on the right side is $\alpha a_{ij} + \alpha b_{ij}$. By the properties of real numbers, the two entries are equal.

Example 1.26   This example illustrates the matrix operations just defined.

(a) Let

$$A = \begin{bmatrix} 2\sin^2 x & x^2 \\ 1 & 0 \end{bmatrix} \qquad \text{and} \qquad B = \begin{bmatrix} -\cos^2 x & y^2 \\ xy & 2 \end{bmatrix}.$$

Compute $A - 2B + I_2$, where I_2 is the identity matrix of order 2.

(b) Let

$$A = \begin{bmatrix} 1 & 1 & 2 \\ 7 & -2 & 0 \end{bmatrix} \qquad \text{and} \qquad B = \begin{bmatrix} 0 & 2 & -1 \\ 6 & 2 & 4 \end{bmatrix}.$$

Find the 2×3 matrix X such that $3A + X = 2(B - X)$.

Solution

(a) A straightforward computation gives

$$A - 2B + I_2 = \begin{bmatrix} 2\sin^2 x & x^2 \\ 1 & 0 \end{bmatrix} - 2\begin{bmatrix} -\cos^2 x & y^2 \\ xy & 2 \end{bmatrix} + \begin{bmatrix} 1 & 0 \\ 0 & 1 \end{bmatrix}$$

$$= \begin{bmatrix} 2\sin^2 x + 2\cos^2 x + 1 & x^2 - 2y^2 + 0 \\ 1 - 2xy + 0 & 0 - 4 + 1 \end{bmatrix}$$

$$= \begin{bmatrix} 3 & x^2 - 2y^2 \\ 1 - 2xy & -3 \end{bmatrix}.$$

(b) One way to solve for X is to substitute its entries and those of A and B into the given equation in order to obtain equations for the entries x_{ij} of X. There is an easier alternative: we will use the properties of matrix operations and the fact that $A = B$ implies that $A + C = B + C$ (for any matrix C of the same size as A and B) and $\alpha A = \alpha B$ (for any real number α). Using the distributive property, we write the given equation as $3A + X = 2B - 2X$. Now add $2X$ to both sides and then subtract $3A$ from both sides to get $3X = 2B - 3A$. To find X, multiply both sides by $1/3$

$$X = \tfrac{1}{3}(2B - 3A)$$

$$= \tfrac{1}{3}\left(\begin{bmatrix} 0 & 4 & -2 \\ 12 & 4 & 8 \end{bmatrix} - \begin{bmatrix} 3 & 3 & 6 \\ 21 & -6 & 0 \end{bmatrix} \right)$$

$$= \begin{bmatrix} -1 & 1/3 & -8/3 \\ -3 & 10/3 & 8/3 \end{bmatrix}.$$

Let us repeat that, as long as only addition, subtraction and multiplication by scalars are involved, there is no difference between the properties of matrices and real numbers. In this case, we solved the matrix equation in exactly the same way as an equation in real numbers would have been solved.

◀

■ Definition 1.8   Matrix Multiplication.

The *product* $C = A \cdot B$ of an $m \times n$ matrix A and an $n \times p$ matrix B is the $m \times p$ matrix $C = [c_{ij}]$, where

$$c_{ij} = a_{i1}b_{1j} + a_{i2}b_{2j} + \ldots + a_{in}b_{nj}, \qquad (1.10)$$

$i = 1, \ldots, m$ and $j = 1, \ldots, p$.

■

The product $A \cdot B$ (also written without the dot, as AB) of two matrices is defined only if the number of columns of the first factor A is equal to the number of rows of the second factor B. In that case, the product $A \cdot B$ is the matrix C that has the same number of rows as A and the same number of columns as B. Let us look a bit more closely at formula (1.10) that gives the general element in the product matrix. The first factors in all terms are $a_{i1}, a_{i2}, \ldots, a_{in}$; i.e., the elements of the i-th row of A. Think of them as a row vector

$$[a_{i1} \quad a_{i2} \quad \ldots \quad a_{in}].$$

The second factors in all terms are $b_{1j}, b_{2j}, \ldots, b_{nj}$; i.e., the elements of the j-th column of B. Put them together in a column vector

$$\begin{bmatrix} b_{1j} \\ b_{2j} \\ \vdots \\ b_{nj} \end{bmatrix}.$$

If we interpret both the row and column vectors as vectors in $\mathbb{R}^n$, we recognize the expression in (1.10) as their dot product! Therefore, the ij-th entry in the product matrix AB is computed as the dot product of the i-th row of A and the j-th column of B.

Example 1.27   Let

$$A = \begin{bmatrix} 1 & 0 & 4 \\ 3 & 2 & -1 \end{bmatrix} \quad \text{and} \quad B = \begin{bmatrix} 4 & 1 \\ 7 & 6 \\ 0 & 0 \end{bmatrix}.$$

Compute (if defined) $A \cdot B$ and $B \cdot A$.

Solution   The matrix A is of type 2×3 and B is of type 3×2. The product $A \cdot B$ is defined (since the number of columns of A = the number of rows of $B = 3$) and is a 2×2 matrix. The product $B \cdot A$ is also defined (the number of columns of B = the number of rows of $A = 2$), but is a 3×3 matrix. We have just detected the first big difference between real numbers and matrices. Since $A \cdot B$ and $B \cdot A$ are of different types, they certainly cannot be equal. Hence, in general, $A \cdot B \neq B \cdot A$ (and it gets worse, as we can easily imagine and will witness soon: in many cases one of the two products $A \cdot B$ or $B \cdot A$ will not be defined).

Let us compute $C = A \cdot B$. The entry c_{11} is the dot product of the first row of A and the first column of B:

$$c_{11} = \begin{bmatrix} 1 & 0 & 4 \end{bmatrix} \cdot \begin{bmatrix} 4 \\ 7 \\ 0 \end{bmatrix} = 1 \cdot 4 + 0 \cdot 7 + 4 \cdot 0 = 4$$

(although we use row and column vectors, we think of them as vectors in $\mathbb{R}^3$). Similarly,

$$c_{12} = \begin{bmatrix} 1 & 0 & 4 \end{bmatrix} \cdot \begin{bmatrix} 1 \\ 6 \\ 0 \end{bmatrix} = 1 \cdot 1 + 0 \cdot 6 + 4 \cdot 0 = 1,$$

$$c_{21} = \begin{bmatrix} 3 & 2 & -1 \end{bmatrix} \cdot \begin{bmatrix} 4 \\ 7 \\ 0 \end{bmatrix} = 3 \cdot 4 + 2 \cdot 7 + (-1) \cdot 0 = 26$$

and

$$c_{22} = \begin{bmatrix} 3 & 2 & -1 \end{bmatrix} \cdot \begin{bmatrix} 1 \\ 6 \\ 0 \end{bmatrix} = 3 \cdot 1 + 2 \cdot 6 + (-1) \cdot 0 = 15.$$

Hence

$$A \cdot B = \begin{bmatrix} 4 & 1 \\ 26 & 15 \end{bmatrix}.$$

Similarly, we compute

$$D = B \cdot A = \begin{bmatrix} 4 & 1 \\ 7 & 6 \\ 0 & 0 \end{bmatrix} \cdot \begin{bmatrix} 1 & 0 & 4 \\ 3 & 2 & -1 \end{bmatrix} = \begin{bmatrix} 7 & 2 & 15 \\ 25 & 12 & 22 \\ 0 & 0 & 0 \end{bmatrix}.$$

Let us check a few entries in D. For example, d_{12} is obtained as the dot product of the first row of B and the second coulmn of A,

$$d_{12} = \begin{bmatrix} 4 & 1 \end{bmatrix} \cdot \begin{bmatrix} 0 \\ 2 \end{bmatrix} = 4 \cdot 0 + 1 \cdot 2 = 2.$$

Similarly,

$$d_{33} = \begin{bmatrix} 0 & 0 \end{bmatrix} \cdot \begin{bmatrix} 4 \\ -1 \end{bmatrix} = 0 \cdot 4 + 0 \cdot (-1) = 0,$$

$$d_{23} = \begin{bmatrix} 7 & 6 \end{bmatrix} \cdot \begin{bmatrix} 4 \\ -1 \end{bmatrix} = 7 \cdot 4 + 6 \cdot (-1) = 22,$$

etc.

As we have already seen, the product of matrices is not commutative; i.e., in general $AB \neq BA$. However, our next theorem will show that some properties of ordinary multiplication are preserved.

■ **Theorem 1.9**   Properties of Matrix Multiplication.

Let A, B and C be three matrices. Matrix multiplication is *associative*

$$(AB)C = A(BC)$$

and *distributive*

$$(A + B)C = AC + BC \quad \text{and} \quad A(B + C) = AB + AC,$$

whenever the operations on both sides of these identities are defined. ■

The associativity property tells us that in order to compute the product of three matrices (if defined) ABC we can either compute AB first and then multiply by C from the right, or compute BC first and then multiply by A from the left. Since the product of matrices is not commutative, we have to make precise the order of factors in the product. That is the reason why there are two distributive laws: one will not suffice, since neither one implies the other. The proofs are straightforward (the associativity part is fairly messy) and will be omitted.

Next, we give a useful interpretation of one case of matrix multiplication. Let $A = [a_{ij}]$

be a square matrix of order n (i.e., of type $n \times n$) and let $\mathbf{v}$ be an $n \times 1$ matrix

$$\begin{bmatrix} v_1 \\ v_2 \\ \vdots \\ v_n \end{bmatrix}$$

($\mathbf{v}$ has only one column, so instead of using double subscripts $v_{11}, v_{21}, \ldots v_{n1}$ for its elements, we supress the second subscript). We think of $\mathbf{v}$ as a vector in $\mathbb{R}^n$. The product $A \cdot \mathbf{v}$ of A and $\mathbf{v}$ is an $n \times 1$ matrix, that can again be visualized as a vector. In this way, we have defined a function (call it $\mathbf{F}_A$) that, for a given fixed matrix A, assigns the vector $A \cdot \mathbf{v}$ to a vector $\mathbf{v}$. The function $\mathbf{F}_A$ is called a *linear function* on $\mathbb{R}^n$.

Visualizing $\mathbf{v}$ and $A \cdot \mathbf{v}$ as points rather than vectors, we get another interpretation: $\mathbf{F}_A$ maps points in $\mathbb{R}^n$ to points in $\mathbb{R}^n$ (i.e., "moves points in $\mathbb{R}^n$ around"). There is one more interpretation: think of $\mathbf{v}$ as a point in $\mathbb{R}^n$ and think of $A \cdot \mathbf{v}$ as a vector in $\mathbb{R}^n$: thus, $\mathbf{F}_A$ assigns a vector in $\mathbb{R}^n$ to a point in $\mathbb{R}^n$. This function is an example of a vector field, called a *linear vector field*. Vector fields will be formally introduced in Section 2.1 and will be one of the major subjects of our study.

Example 1.28   Let

$$A = \begin{bmatrix} 3 & 2 \\ 1 & 1 \end{bmatrix}$$

and consider the linear map $\mathbf{F}_A$ just defined.

(a) Find the image of the vector $\mathbf{j}$ under the map $\mathbf{F}_A$.

(b) Compute $\|\mathbf{F}_A(\mathbf{v})\|$ if $\mathbf{v} = -2\mathbf{i} + 4\mathbf{j}$.

Solution   The matrix A is of type 2×2; i.e., the map $\mathbf{F}_A$ is defined on vectors in $\mathbb{R}^2$.

(a) Think of $\mathbf{j}$ as a column vector $\begin{bmatrix} 0 \\ 1 \end{bmatrix}$. Then

$$\mathbf{F}_A(\mathbf{j}) = \mathbf{F}_A\left(\begin{bmatrix} 0 \\ 1 \end{bmatrix}\right) = \begin{bmatrix} 3 & 2 \\ 1 & 1 \end{bmatrix} \cdot \begin{bmatrix} 0 \\ 1 \end{bmatrix} = \begin{bmatrix} 2 \\ 1 \end{bmatrix}.$$

Hence, the image of $\mathbf{j}$ is the vector $\begin{bmatrix} 2 \\ 1 \end{bmatrix} = 2\mathbf{i} + \mathbf{j}$.

(b) Since

$$\mathbf{F}_A(-2\mathbf{i} + 4\mathbf{j}) = \mathbf{F}_A\left(\begin{bmatrix} -2 \\ 4 \end{bmatrix}\right) = \begin{bmatrix} 3 & 2 \\ 1 & 1 \end{bmatrix} \cdot \begin{bmatrix} -2 \\ 4 \end{bmatrix} = \begin{bmatrix} 2 \\ 2 \end{bmatrix} = 2\mathbf{i} + 2\mathbf{j},$$

it follows that $\|\mathbf{F}_A(-2\mathbf{i} + 4\mathbf{j})\| = \|2\mathbf{i} + 2\mathbf{j}\| = \sqrt{8}$.   ◄

To any square matrix we can assign a real number, called the determinant of the matrix. Since we will need only the determinant of matrices of order 2 and 3, we will not give a general definition.

■ **Definition 1.9**   Determinant of a Matrix.

Let A be a square matrix of order 2. The *determinant* of A is the real number

$$\det(A) = \det \begin{bmatrix} a_{11} & a_{12} \\ a_{21} & a_{22} \end{bmatrix} = \begin{vmatrix} a_{11} & a_{12} \\ a_{21} & a_{22} \end{vmatrix}$$

defined by

$$\begin{vmatrix} a_{11} & a_{12} \\ a_{21} & a_{22} \end{vmatrix} = a_{11}a_{22} - a_{21}a_{12}.$$

If A is a square matrix of order 3, then its determinant $\det(A)$ is defined by

$$\begin{vmatrix} a_{11} & a_{12} & a_{13} \\ a_{21} & a_{22} & a_{23} \\ a_{31} & a_{32} & a_{33} \end{vmatrix} = a_{11} \begin{vmatrix} a_{22} & a_{23} \\ a_{32} & a_{33} \end{vmatrix} - a_{12} \begin{vmatrix} a_{21} & a_{23} \\ a_{31} & a_{33} \end{vmatrix} + a_{13} \begin{vmatrix} a_{21} & a_{22} \\ a_{31} & a_{32} \end{vmatrix},$$

and the 2×2 determinants are computed as above.   ■

The determinant of a 2×2 matrix is easy to compute: it is the difference of the product of the diagonal elements and the product of the off-diagonal elements. The determinant of a 3×3 matrix has three terms: each term is the product of the element a_{1j} from the first row and the j-th column of A and the 2×2 determinant obtained from A by removing the first row and the j-th column. The minus sign is put in front of the a_{12} term, and then all three terms are added up.

Example 1.29   Compute the determinant of the matrix $\begin{bmatrix} 2 & 3 \\ 1 & 0 \end{bmatrix}$.

Solution   By definition,

$$\begin{vmatrix} 2 & 3 \\ 1 & 0 \end{vmatrix} = 2 \cdot 0 - 1 \cdot 3 = -3.$$ ◄

Example 1.30   Compute

$$\begin{vmatrix} 3 & -2 & 0 \\ 1 & -7 & -2 \\ 6 & 0 & 6 \end{vmatrix}.$$

Solution   By definition, a determinant of order 3 is reduced to three order 2 determinants:

$$\begin{vmatrix} 3 & 2 & 0 \\ 1 & -7 & -2 \\ 6 & 0 & 6 \end{vmatrix} = 3 \begin{vmatrix} -7 & -2 \\ 0 & 6 \end{vmatrix} - 2 \begin{vmatrix} 1 & -2 \\ 6 & 6 \end{vmatrix} + 0 \begin{vmatrix} 1 & -7 \\ 6 & 0 \end{vmatrix}$$

$$= 3(-42) - 2(18) + 0(42) = -162.$$ ◄

We finish this section by listing properties of determinants. They can all be checked by using the definition and are left as exercises. Assume that A is a square matrix of order 2 or 3.

(a) If A contains a row or column of zeros, then $\det(A) = 0$.

(b) If B is a matrix obtained from A by multiplying *one* of its rows or columns by a real number α, then $\det(B) = \alpha \det(A)$.

(c) If B is a matrix obtained from A by interchanging two of its rows or columns, then $\det(B) = -\det(A)$.

(d) If A has two equal rows or columns, then $\det(A) = 0$.

EXERCISES 1.4 **Exercises 1 to 9:** Let

$$A = \begin{bmatrix} 2 & -1 & 1 \\ 0 & -5 & 4 \end{bmatrix}, \qquad B = \begin{bmatrix} 0 & 5 \\ 4 & 0 \end{bmatrix}, \qquad C = \begin{bmatrix} -1 & 0 \\ 1 & 2 \\ 3 & -1 \end{bmatrix}$$

and let I_2 and I_3 denote the identity matrices of order 2 and 3. Compute the following expressions (or else say that they are not defined). The symbol X^2 denotes the product $X \cdot X$.

1. $2B - 16I_2$ **2.** $B^2 - 16I_2 + AC$ **3.** $CB - BA$

4. $I_3 - 3CA$ **5.** $AC + I_2$ **6.** $A(I_3 + CA)$

7. $C(BA)$ **8.** $(CA)B$ **9.** $(AC)^2 + 4B^2$

10. Let A, B and C be matrices of the same type. Show that $A = B$ implies that $A + C = B + C$, and if α is a real number, then $A = B$ implies $\alpha A = \alpha B$.

Exercises 11 to 15: Let

$$A = \begin{bmatrix} 2 & -1 \\ 4 & 0 \end{bmatrix}, \qquad B = \begin{bmatrix} 10 & 1 \\ 0 & 0 \end{bmatrix}, \qquad C = \begin{bmatrix} 0 & 1 \\ 1 & 0 \end{bmatrix},$$

and let I_2 denote the identity matrix of order 2.

11. Solve the equation $3A - X = I_2 + 4(C - X)$ for X.

12. Solve the equation $X = 4BC - X$ for X.

13. Find the matrix X such that $AX = B$.

14. Find the images of the vector $4\mathbf{i} - 3\mathbf{j}$ under the linear maps $\mathbf{F}_A$, $\mathbf{F}_B$ defined in the text.

15. Describe in words the maps $\mathbf{F}_C$ and $\mathbf{F}_{I_2}$.

16. Consider the 2×2 matrices

$$A = \begin{bmatrix} 0 & 1 \\ 0 & 0 \end{bmatrix} \quad \text{and} \quad B = \begin{bmatrix} 4 & 7 \\ 0 & 0 \end{bmatrix}.$$

Show that $A^2 = A \cdot A$ and $A \cdot B$ are zero matrices. This is another big difference between matrices and real numbers: the product of non-zero matrices can be zero, whereas the product of two non-zero numbers is always non-zero. Find another pair A, B with this property.

Exercises 17 to 22: Compute the determinants of the following matrices.

17. $\begin{bmatrix} 3 & 4 \\ 4 & 3 \end{bmatrix}$

18. $\begin{bmatrix} -1 & 9 \\ 0 & 1 \end{bmatrix}$

19. $\begin{bmatrix} \cos\theta & \sin\theta \\ -r\sin\theta & r\cos\theta \end{bmatrix}$

20. $\begin{bmatrix} e^x & e^{-x} \\ e^{-x} & e^x \end{bmatrix}$

21. $\begin{bmatrix} 2 & 1 & 4 \\ 0 & 6 & 5 \\ 0 & 2 & 0 \end{bmatrix}$

22. $\begin{bmatrix} \cos t & 0 & \sin t \\ 0 & 1 & 0 \\ -\sin t & 0 & \cos t \end{bmatrix}$

23. Let A and B be 2×2 matrices. Prove that $\det(AB) = \det(A)\det(B)$. We know that, in general, $AB \neq BA$. However, is it true that $\det(AB) = \det(BA)$?

24. Show that if A contains a row or column of zeros, then $\det(A) = 0$.

25. Let A be a 2×2 matrix. Define the matrix B as follows: the first row of B is the first row of A, and the second row of B is the first row of A multiplied by a real number α. Show that $\det(B) = 0$.

26. Show that if B is a 2×2 or 3×3 matrix obtained from A by interchanging two of its rows or columns, then $\det(B) = -\det(A)$.

27. Let A be a 3×3 matrix and let B be the matrix obtained from A by switching the first and the third rows of A and then by switching the second and the third columns. What is the relation between $\det(B)$ and $\det(A)$?

28. Prove that if A is a square matrix of order 3 with two equal rows then $\det(A) = 0$.

29. Show that if B is a 3×3 matrix obtained from A by multiplying one of its rows by a real number α, then $\det(B) = \alpha \det(A)$.

30. Let A be an $n \times n$ matrix ($n \geq 2$) and let $\mathbf{F}_A$ be the linear function $\mathbf{F}_A(\mathbf{v}) = A \cdot \mathbf{v}$. Show that $\mathbf{F}_A(\alpha\mathbf{u} + \beta\mathbf{v}) = \alpha\mathbf{F}_A(\mathbf{u}) + \beta\mathbf{F}_A(\mathbf{v})$, for $\mathbf{u}, \mathbf{v} \in \mathbb{R}^n$ and $\alpha, \beta \in \mathbb{R}$ (this fact justifies the use of the word "linear").

31. Let A and B be $n \times n$ matrices ($n \geq 2$) and let $\mathbf{F}_A$ and $\mathbf{F}_B$ be the corresponding linear vector fields (or linear functions, as defined in this section). Express the linear vector fields corresponding to $A + B$, $2AB$ and $7B$ in terms of $\mathbf{F}_A$ and/or $\mathbf{F}_B$.

32. Let A and B be $n \times n$ matrices ($n \geq 2$) and let $\mathbf{F}_A$ and $\mathbf{F}_B$ be the corresponding linear functions defined in this section. Show that $\mathbf{F}_{AB} = \mathbf{F}_A \circ \mathbf{F}_B$, where $\circ$ denotes the composition of functions $\mathbf{F}_A$ and $\mathbf{F}_B$ and AB on the left side is the product of matrices A and B.

1.5   THE CROSS PRODUCT

The cross product of two vectors is an operation that assigns a vector (that is why it is sometimes called the *vector product*) to two given vectors. Unlike the dot product, it is defined only for vectors in $\mathbb{R}^3$.

Definition 1.10   Cross Product.

The *cross product* of two vectors $\mathbf{v} = v_1\mathbf{i} + v_2\mathbf{j} + v_3\mathbf{k}$ and $\mathbf{w} = w_1\mathbf{i} + w_2\mathbf{j} + w_3\mathbf{k}$ is the vector $\mathbf{c} = \mathbf{v} \times \mathbf{w}$ in $\mathbb{R}^3$ defined by

$$\mathbf{c} = (v_2w_3 - v_3w_2)\mathbf{i} - (v_1w_3 - v_3w_1)\mathbf{j} + (v_1w_2 - v_2w_1)\mathbf{k}$$

There is no need to memorize this formula. We will now give an easy way of computing the cross product with the help of the determinant. Construct a 3×3 determinant in the following way: put vectors $\mathbf{i}$, $\mathbf{j}$ and $\mathbf{k}$ in the first row, the components of $\mathbf{v}$ in the second row, and the components of $\mathbf{w}$ in the third row. Strictly speaking, this is not a determinant as we defined it in the previous section, since some of its entries are vectors. However, neglecting that fact and using the definition of the determinant anyway, we get

$$\begin{vmatrix} \mathbf{i} & \mathbf{j} & \mathbf{k} \\ v_1 & v_2 & v_3 \\ w_1 & w_2 & w_3 \end{vmatrix} = \mathbf{i}\begin{vmatrix} v_2 & v_3 \\ w_2 & w_3 \end{vmatrix} - \mathbf{j}\begin{vmatrix} v_1 & v_3 \\ w_1 & w_3 \end{vmatrix} + \mathbf{k}\begin{vmatrix} v_1 & v_2 \\ w_1 & w_2 \end{vmatrix}$$

$$= (v_2w_3 - v_3w_2)\mathbf{i} - (v_1w_3 - v_3w_1)\mathbf{j} + (v_1w_2 - v_2w_1)\mathbf{k},$$

which is precisely the definition of the cross product!

Example 1.31   Let $\mathbf{v} = \mathbf{i} - 2\mathbf{k}$ and $\mathbf{w} = -2\mathbf{i} + 3\mathbf{j} - 4\mathbf{k}$. Compute $\mathbf{v} \times \mathbf{w}$ and $\mathbf{w} \times \mathbf{v}$.

Solution   We will form the cross product determinants and evaluate them.

$$\mathbf{v} \times \mathbf{w} = \begin{vmatrix} \mathbf{i} & \mathbf{j} & \mathbf{k} \\ 1 & 0 & -2 \\ -2 & 3 & -4 \end{vmatrix}$$

$$= \mathbf{i}\begin{vmatrix} 0 & -2 \\ 3 & -4 \end{vmatrix} - \mathbf{j}\begin{vmatrix} 1 & -2 \\ -2 & -4 \end{vmatrix} + \mathbf{k}\begin{vmatrix} 1 & 0 \\ -2 & 3 \end{vmatrix} = 6\mathbf{i} + 8\mathbf{j} + 3\mathbf{k}.$$

Similarly,

$$\mathbf{w} \times \mathbf{v} = \begin{vmatrix} \mathbf{i} & \mathbf{j} & \mathbf{k} \\ -2 & 3 & -4 \\ 1 & 0 & -2 \end{vmatrix}$$

$$= \mathbf{i}\begin{vmatrix} 3 & -4 \\ 0 & -2 \end{vmatrix} - \mathbf{j}\begin{vmatrix} -2 & -4 \\ 1 & -2 \end{vmatrix} + \mathbf{k}\begin{vmatrix} -2 & 3 \\ 1 & 0 \end{vmatrix} = -6\mathbf{i} - 8\mathbf{j} - 3\mathbf{k}.$$

In the previous example, $\mathbf{v} \times \mathbf{w} = -\mathbf{w} \times \mathbf{v}$. The next theorem confirms that this property holds in general.

Theorem 1.10   Properties of the Cross Product.

Let $\mathbf{u}$, $\mathbf{v}$ and $\mathbf{w}$ be vectors in $\mathbb{R}^3$ and let α be any real number. The cross product is *anticommutative*

$$\mathbf{v} \times \mathbf{w} = -\mathbf{w} \times \mathbf{v}$$

and *distributive* with respect to the sum

$$\mathbf{u} \times (\mathbf{v} + \mathbf{w}) = \mathbf{u} \times \mathbf{v} + \mathbf{u} \times \mathbf{w} \qquad \text{and} \qquad (\mathbf{u} + \mathbf{v}) \times \mathbf{w} = \mathbf{u} \times \mathbf{w} + \mathbf{v} \times \mathbf{w}.$$

Moreover,

$$\mathbf{v} \times \mathbf{v} = \mathbf{0}$$

($\mathbf{0}$ is the zero vector in $\mathbb{R}^3$) and

$$\alpha(\mathbf{v} \times \mathbf{w}) = (\alpha \mathbf{v}) \times \mathbf{w} = \mathbf{v} \times (\alpha \mathbf{w}). \qquad \blacksquare$$

The proofs of all parts of Theorem 1.10 consist of writing the vectors involved in terms of components and using relevant definitions. As an illustration, let us prove that

$$\mathbf{u} \times (\mathbf{v} + \mathbf{w}) = \mathbf{u} \times \mathbf{v} + \mathbf{u} \times \mathbf{w}.$$

Let $\mathbf{u} = (u_1, u_2, u_3)$, $\mathbf{v} = (v_1, v_2, v_3)$ and $\mathbf{w} = (w_1, w_2, w_3)$. Then

$$\mathbf{u} \times (\mathbf{v} + \mathbf{w}) = \begin{vmatrix} \mathbf{i} & \mathbf{j} & \mathbf{k} \\ u_1 & u_2 & u_3 \\ v_1 + w_1 & v_2 + w_2 & v_3 + w_3 \end{vmatrix}$$

$$= \mathbf{i} \begin{vmatrix} u_2 & u_3 \\ v_2 + w_2 & v_3 + w_3 \end{vmatrix} - \mathbf{j} \begin{vmatrix} u_1 & u_3 \\ v_1 + w_1 & v_3 + w_3 \end{vmatrix} + \mathbf{k} \begin{vmatrix} u_1 & u_2 \\ v_1 + w_1 & v_2 + w_2 \end{vmatrix}$$

$$= (u_2(v_3 + w_3) - u_3(v_2 + w_2))\mathbf{i} - (u_1(v_3 + w_3) - u_3(v_1 + w_1))\mathbf{j}$$
$$+ (u_1(v_2 + w_2) - u_2(v_1 + w_1))\mathbf{k}.$$

The right side is computed to be

$$\mathbf{u} \times \mathbf{v} + \mathbf{u} \times \mathbf{w} = \begin{vmatrix} \mathbf{i} & \mathbf{j} & \mathbf{k} \\ u_1 & u_2 & u_3 \\ v_1 & v_2 & v_3 \end{vmatrix} + \begin{vmatrix} \mathbf{i} & \mathbf{j} & \mathbf{k} \\ u_1 & u_2 & u_3 \\ w_1 & w_2 & w_3 \end{vmatrix}$$

$$= \mathbf{i} \begin{vmatrix} u_2 & u_3 \\ v_2 & v_3 \end{vmatrix} - \mathbf{j} \begin{vmatrix} u_1 & u_3 \\ v_1 & v_3 \end{vmatrix} + \mathbf{k} \begin{vmatrix} u_1 & u_2 \\ v_1 & v_2 \end{vmatrix}$$

$$+ \mathbf{i} \begin{vmatrix} u_2 & u_3 \\ w_2 & w_3 \end{vmatrix} - \mathbf{j} \begin{vmatrix} u_1 & u_3 \\ w_1 & w_3 \end{vmatrix} + \mathbf{k} \begin{vmatrix} u_1 & u_2 \\ w_1 & w_2 \end{vmatrix}$$

$$= (u_2 v_3 - u_3 v_2)\mathbf{i} - (u_1 v_3 - u_3 v_1)\mathbf{j} + (u_1 v_2 - u_2 v_1)\mathbf{k}$$
$$+ (u_2 w_3 - u_3 w_2)\mathbf{i} - (u_1 w_3 - u_3 w_1)\mathbf{j} + (u_1 w_2 - u_2 w_1)\mathbf{k}.$$

Clearly, both sides are equal. $\qquad \blacksquare$

Example 1.32   Find all cross products of the standard unit vectors $\mathbf{i}$, $\mathbf{j}$ and $\mathbf{k}$.

Solution Since the cross product of a vector with itself is a zero vector, we get $\mathbf{i} \times \mathbf{i} = \mathbf{0}$, $\mathbf{j} \times \mathbf{j} = \mathbf{0}$ and $\mathbf{k} \times \mathbf{k} = \mathbf{0}$. From the definition it follows that

$$\mathbf{i} \times \mathbf{j} = \begin{vmatrix} \mathbf{i} & \mathbf{j} & \mathbf{k} \\ 1 & 0 & 0 \\ 0 & 1 & 0 \end{vmatrix} = \mathbf{i} \begin{vmatrix} 0 & 0 \\ 1 & 0 \end{vmatrix} - \mathbf{j} \begin{vmatrix} 1 & 0 \\ 0 & 0 \end{vmatrix} + \mathbf{k} \begin{vmatrix} 1 & 0 \\ 0 & 1 \end{vmatrix} = \mathbf{k},$$

and then, by anticommutativity, $\mathbf{j} \times \mathbf{i} = -(\mathbf{i} \times \mathbf{j}) = -\mathbf{k}$. Similarly, $\mathbf{k} \times \mathbf{i} = \mathbf{j}$, $\mathbf{i} \times \mathbf{k} = -\mathbf{j}$ and $\mathbf{j} \times \mathbf{k} = \mathbf{i}$, $\mathbf{k} \times \mathbf{j} = -\mathbf{i}$.

A way to memorize these results is to write down the sequence $\mathbf{i}\,\mathbf{j}\,\mathbf{k}\,\mathbf{i}\,\mathbf{j}$ and read it from left to right: the cross product of two adjacent vectors is the next one in the sequence.

◀

Consider the expression $\mathbf{u} \cdot (\mathbf{v} \times \mathbf{w})$, where $\mathbf{u} = (u_1, u_2, u_3)$, $\mathbf{v} = (v_1, v_2, v_3)$ and $\mathbf{w} = (w_1, w_2, w_3)$ are vectors in $\mathbb{R}^3$; it is the dot product of vectors $\mathbf{u}$ and $\mathbf{v} \times \mathbf{w}$, and therefore a scalar. Let us compute it: since

$$\mathbf{v} \times \mathbf{w} = \begin{vmatrix} \mathbf{i} & \mathbf{j} & \mathbf{k} \\ v_1 & v_2 & v_3 \\ w_1 & w_2 & w_3 \end{vmatrix} = (v_2 w_3 - v_3 w_2)\mathbf{i} - (v_1 w_3 - v_3 w_1)\mathbf{j} + (v_1 w_2 - v_2 w_1)\mathbf{k},$$

it follows that

$$\begin{aligned} \mathbf{u} \cdot (\mathbf{v} \times \mathbf{w}) &= (u_1 \mathbf{i} + u_2 \mathbf{j} + u_3 \mathbf{k}) \cdot ((v_2 w_3 - v_3 w_2)\mathbf{i} - (v_1 w_3 - v_3 w_1)\mathbf{j} + (v_1 w_2 - v_2 w_1)\mathbf{k}) \\ &= u_1(v_2 w_3 - v_3 w_2) - u_2(v_1 w_3 - v_3 w_1) + u_3(v_1 w_2 - v_2 w_1). \end{aligned}$$

Once again, with the help of determinants we will be able to make sense of this mess. Form a 3×3 determinant whose rows consist of components of vectors $\mathbf{u}$, $\mathbf{v}$ and $\mathbf{w}$ (in that order). Then

$$\begin{vmatrix} u_1 & u_2 & u_3 \\ v_1 & v_2 & v_3 \\ w_1 & w_2 & w_3 \end{vmatrix} = u_1(v_2 w_3 - v_3 w_2) - u_2(v_1 w_3 - v_3 w_1) + u_3(v_1 w_2 - v_2 w_1),$$

and hence

$$\mathbf{u} \cdot (\mathbf{v} \times \mathbf{w}) = \begin{vmatrix} u_1 & u_2 & u_3 \\ v_1 & v_2 & v_3 \\ w_1 & w_2 & w_3 \end{vmatrix}$$

(this is a "real" determinant, unlike the one coming from the cross product). The expression $\mathbf{u} \cdot (\mathbf{v} \times \mathbf{w})$ is called the *scalar triple product* of $\mathbf{u}$, $\mathbf{v}$ and $\mathbf{w}$.

We now turn to the geometric side of the cross product.

■ **Theorem 1.11**   Geometric Properties of the Cross Product.

Let $\mathbf{v}$ and $\mathbf{w}$ be vectors in $\mathbb{R}^3$. Then

(a) the cross product $\mathbf{v} \times \mathbf{w}$ is a vector orthogonal to both $\mathbf{v}$ and $\mathbf{w}$.

(b) the magnitude of $\mathbf{v} \times \mathbf{w}$ is

$$\|\mathbf{v} \times \mathbf{w}\| = \|\mathbf{v}\| \, \|\mathbf{w}\| \, \sin\theta,$$

where θ denotes the angle between $\mathbf{v}$ and $\mathbf{w}$. ∎

Proof

(a) The dot product $\mathbf{v} \cdot (\mathbf{v} \times \mathbf{w})$ of $\mathbf{v}$ and $\mathbf{v} \times \mathbf{w}$ is the scalar triple product of $\mathbf{v}$, $\mathbf{v}$ and $\mathbf{w}$. It is computed as the determinant whose first and second rows contain the components of $\mathbf{v}$ and the third row consists of components of $\mathbf{w}$. Since this determinant has two equal rows, it is equal to zero. Hence $\mathbf{v} \cdot (\mathbf{v} \times \mathbf{w}) = 0$ and, consequently, $\mathbf{v} \times \mathbf{w}$ is orthogonal to $\mathbf{v}$. An analogous argument proves that $\mathbf{v} \times \mathbf{w}$ is orthogonal to $\mathbf{w}$.

(b) Using the definition of the cross product and the formula for the length of a vector, we get

$$\|\mathbf{v} \times \mathbf{w}\|^2 = (v_2 w_3 - v_3 w_2)^2 + (v_1 w_3 - v_3 w_1)^2 + (v_1 w_2 - v_2 w_1)^2.$$

Now add zero, written as $v_1^2 w_1^2 + v_2^2 w_2^2 + v_3^2 w_3^2 - v_1^2 w_1^2 - v_2^2 w_2^2 - v_3^2 w_3^2$, to the right side and rearrange terms as follows:

$$\|\mathbf{v} \times \mathbf{w}\|^2 = v_1^2 w_1^2 + v_1^2 w_2^2 + v_1^2 w_3^2 + v_2^2 w_1^2 + v_2^2 w_2^2 + v_2^2 w_3^2 + v_3^2 w_1^2 + v_3^2 w_2^2 + v_3^2 w_3^2$$
$$- (v_1^2 w_1^2 + v_2^2 w_2^2 + v_3^2 w_3^2 + 2 v_1 w_1 v_2 w_2 + 2 v_1 w_1 v_3 w_3 + 2 v_2 w_2 v_3 w_3).$$

Combine the first nine and the last six terms to get

$$\|\mathbf{v} \times \mathbf{w}\|^2 = (v_1^2 + v_2^2 + v_3^2)(w_1^2 + w_2^2 + w_3^2) - (v_1 w_1 + v_2 w_2 + v_3 w_3)^2$$
$$= \|\mathbf{v}\|^2 \|\mathbf{w}\|^2 - (\mathbf{v} \cdot \mathbf{w})^2.$$

Using Theorem 1.4 we simplify the right side as follows:

$$\|\mathbf{v}\|^2 \|\mathbf{w}\|^2 - (\mathbf{v} \cdot \mathbf{w})^2 = \|\mathbf{v}\|^2 \|\mathbf{w}\|^2 - \|\mathbf{v}\|^2 \|\mathbf{w}\|^2 \cos^2\theta = \|\mathbf{v}\|^2 \|\mathbf{w}\|^2 \sin^2\theta.$$

therefore,

$$\|\mathbf{v} \times \mathbf{w}\|^2 = \|\mathbf{v}\|^2 \|\mathbf{w}\|^2 \sin^2\theta.$$

Computing the square root of both sides ($\sqrt{\sin^2\theta} = |\sin\theta| = \sin\theta$, since $0 \le \theta \le \pi$, and therefore $\sin\theta \ge 0$) we get the formula in (b). ∎

We can now describe geometrically the cross product $\mathbf{c} = \mathbf{v} \times \mathbf{w}$. By the previous theorem, $\mathbf{c}$ is orthogonal to both $\mathbf{v}$ and $\mathbf{w}$ and its length is given by $\|\mathbf{c}\| = \|\mathbf{v}\| \, \|\mathbf{w}\| \, \sin\theta$. This narrows down our search to two candidates (see Figure 1.17), $\mathbf{c}_1$ and $\mathbf{c}_2$, where $\mathbf{c}_2 = -\mathbf{c}_1$ and $\|\mathbf{c}_1\| = \|\mathbf{c}_2\|$. Consider an example first: let $\mathbf{v} = \mathbf{i}$ and $\mathbf{w} = \mathbf{j}$; then $\mathbf{c} = \mathbf{i} \times \mathbf{j} = \mathbf{k}$, and therefore $\mathbf{c}_1$ should represent $\mathbf{i} \times \mathbf{j}$. This example illustrates the following general rule. The direction of $\mathbf{v} \times \mathbf{w}$ is determined by the *"right-hand rule:"* place your right hand in the direction of $\mathbf{v}$, and curl your fingers from $\mathbf{v}$ to $\mathbf{w}$ through the angle θ (remember that θ is the smaller of the two angles formed by the lines with directions $\mathbf{v}$ and $\mathbf{w}$). Your thumb then points in the direction of $\mathbf{v} \times \mathbf{w}$. Applying this rule to vectors $\mathbf{v}$ and $\mathbf{w}$ of Figure 1.17, we get that $\mathbf{c}_1 = \mathbf{v} \times \mathbf{w}$. Another common interpretation is the following: when driving an ordinary screw, turning the screwdriver from $\mathbf{v}$ to $\mathbf{w}$ advances the screw in the direction of $\mathbf{v} \times \mathbf{w}$.

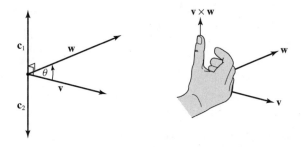

Figure 1.17   Candidates for the cross product of $\mathbf{v}$ and $\mathbf{w}$. By the "right-hand rule," $\mathbf{c}_1 = \mathbf{v} \times \mathbf{w}$.

Example 1.33   Find all unit vectors orthogonal to both $\mathbf{v} = \mathbf{i} + \mathbf{k}$ and $\mathbf{w} = \mathbf{j} - 2\mathbf{k}$.

Solution   The vector

$$\mathbf{c} = \mathbf{v} \times \mathbf{w} = \begin{vmatrix} \mathbf{i} & \mathbf{j} & \mathbf{k} \\ 1 & 0 & 1 \\ 0 & 1 & -2 \end{vmatrix} = -\mathbf{i} + 2\mathbf{j} + \mathbf{k}$$

is orthogonal to both $\mathbf{v}$ and $\mathbf{w}$. Now, cut it to make it of unit length: $\mathbf{c}/\|\mathbf{c}\| = (-\mathbf{i} + 2\mathbf{j} + \mathbf{k})/\sqrt{6}$. This is one desired vector. There is another one, $-(-\mathbf{i} + 2\mathbf{j} + \mathbf{k})/\sqrt{6}$, in the opposite direction.

◀

Example 1.34   **Velocity Vector of a Rotating Body.**

Assume that a particle P rotates with constant angular speed w (units could be radians per second, for example) about an axis ℓ in space (its trajectory, thus, is a circle of radius a). The information on the motion of P is summarized by the *angular velocity vector* $\mathbf{w}$: its magnitude $w = \|\mathbf{w}\|$ is the angular speed and its direction is parallel to the axis of rotation and determined by the "right-hand rule" (when the fingers of the right hand are curled in the direction of rotation, the thumb points in the direction of $\mathbf{w}$). Assume (for convenience) that ℓ contains the origin O and visualize $\mathbf{w}$ as the directed line segment starting at O, as in Figure 1.18. Denote by π the plane through O spanned by $\mathbf{w}$ and $\mathbf{p}$, where $\mathbf{p}$ is the vector represented by $\overrightarrow{OP}$. The *tangential velocity vector* $\mathbf{v}$ is defined as the vector orthogonal to this plane, with magnitude $\|\mathbf{v}\| = \|\mathbf{w}\| a$ (since arc = angle · radius, it follows that (tangential) speed = arc/time = (angle/time) · radius = (angular) speed · radius), whose direction indicates the direction of motion. Let θ be the angle between $\mathbf{w}$ and $\mathbf{p}$. From $\sin\theta = a/\|\mathbf{p}\|$, we get $a = \|\mathbf{p}\| \sin\theta$ and hence $\|\mathbf{v}\| = \|\mathbf{w}\| \|\mathbf{p}\| \sin\theta$. Since $\mathbf{v}$ is orthogonal to $\mathbf{w}$ and $\mathbf{p}$, by the definition of $\mathbf{w}$ (the "right-hand rule") it follows that $\mathbf{v} = \mathbf{w} \times \mathbf{p}$. In words, the tangential velocity vector is the cross product of the angular velocity vector and the position vector of a particle.

◀

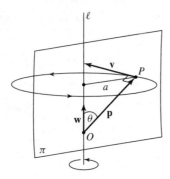

Figure 1.18   Angular and tangential velocity vectors.

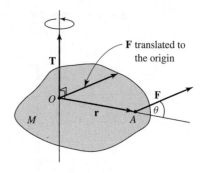

Figure 1.19   Torque of a force.

Example 1.35   Torque.

Suppose that a constant force $\mathbf{F}$ acts at a point $A(x, y, z)$ on a rigid body M that is fixed at the origin (and capable of rotating only). The *torque* $\mathbf{T}$ (with respect to the origin) is defined as the cross product $\mathbf{T} = \mathbf{r} \times \mathbf{F}$ of the position vector $\mathbf{r} = x\mathbf{i} + y\mathbf{j} + z\mathbf{k}$ of A and the force vector $\mathbf{F}$. By Theorem 1.11, $\mathbf{T}$ is orthogonal to both $\mathbf{r}$ and $\mathbf{F}$ and its magnitude is $\|\mathbf{T}\| = \|\mathbf{r}\| \, \|\mathbf{F}\| \, \sin\theta$, where θ is the angle between the force applied and the position vector of A (see Figure 1.19). If $\mathbf{F}$ acts parallel to $\mathbf{r}$, there will be no rotation ($\mathbf{F}$ just tries to pull A in the radial direction away from O) and the torque is zero. If the torque is non-zero, $\mathbf{F}$ tends to cause a rotation whose axis is parallel to $\mathbf{T}$. This is why we say that torque measures the tendency of a force to cause a rotation of a rigid body.

■ Theorem 1.12   Test for Parallel Vectors.

Non-zero vectors $\mathbf{v}$ and $\mathbf{w}$ in $\mathbb{R}^3$ are parallel if and only if $\mathbf{v} \times \mathbf{w} = \mathbf{0}$.

Proof

Non-zero vectors $\mathbf{v}$ and $\mathbf{w}$ are parallel if and only if the angle θ between them is 0 or π. In either case, $\sin\theta = 0$, and therefore $\|\mathbf{v} \times \mathbf{w}\| = \|\mathbf{v}\| \, \|\mathbf{w}\| \, \sin\theta = 0$, and hence $\mathbf{v} \times \mathbf{w} = \mathbf{0}$. Conversely, if $\mathbf{v} \times \mathbf{w} = \mathbf{0}$, then $\|\mathbf{v} \times \mathbf{w}\| = 0$ and (since $\|\mathbf{v}\|, \|\mathbf{w}\| \neq 0$) it follows that $\sin\theta = 0$. Hence $\theta = 0$ or $\theta = \pi$.   ■

Let $\mathbf{v}$ and $\mathbf{w}$ be non-parallel vectors in $\mathbb{R}^3$ represented by the directed line segments $\overrightarrow{AB}$ and $\overrightarrow{AC}$ respectively, that start at the same point, as shown in Figure 1.20. By drawing parallels to $\overline{AB}$ and $\overline{AC}$ we obtain the parallelogram $ABDC$, called the parallelogram *spanned by* $\mathbf{v}$ *and* $\mathbf{w}$. Let h be its height drawn from C perpendicular to $\overline{AB}$, and denote the angle between $\mathbf{v}$ and $\mathbf{w}$ by θ. Then $\sin\theta = h/\|\mathbf{w}\|$, so $h = \|\mathbf{w}\| \sin\theta$, and the area of the parallelogram is equal to $\|\mathbf{v}\| \, h = \|\mathbf{v}\| \, \|\mathbf{w}\| \, \sin\theta$, which is precisely the magnitude of $\mathbf{v} \times \mathbf{w}$! We have thus demonstrated the following theorem.

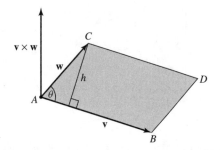

Figure 1.20 The magnitude of the cross product of **v** and **w** equals the area of the parallelogram spanned by **v** and **w**.

■ **Theorem 1.13** Area of the Parallelogram Spanned by Two Vectors.

Let **v** and **w** be non-zero, non-parallel vectors in $\mathbb{R}^3$. The magnitude $\|\mathbf{v} \times \mathbf{w}\|$ is the real number equal to the area of the parallelogram spanned by **v** and **w**.   ■

Since **v** and **w** are non-parallel, $0 < \theta < \pi$ and therefore $\sin\theta > 0$, and $\|\mathbf{v}\| \, \|\mathbf{w}\| \, \sin\theta > 0$; this is reasonable, since areas are positive.

Example 1.36 Compute the area of the parallelogram in the xy-plane with three of its vertices located at $(1, 1)$, $(3, 2)$ and $(0, 2)$.

Solution   Labelling the vertices as points $A(1, 1)$, $B(3, 2)$ and $C(0, 2)$, we compute the vectors determined by the directed line segments $\overrightarrow{AB}$ and $\overrightarrow{AC}$ to be $\mathbf{v} = 2\mathbf{i} + \mathbf{j}$ and $\mathbf{w} = -\mathbf{i} + \mathbf{j}$. Now think of **v** and **w** as vectors in $\mathbb{R}^3$ whose **k** components are zero (a useful trick). The area of the parallelogram in question is

$$\|\mathbf{v} \times \mathbf{w}\| = \left\| \begin{vmatrix} \mathbf{i} & \mathbf{j} & \mathbf{k} \\ 2 & 1 & 0 \\ -1 & 1 & 0 \end{vmatrix} \right\| = \|3\mathbf{k}\| = 3.$$

In the solution to this problem, we made choices in labelling the points, and hence in the vectors that span the parallelogram. The reader is invited to check that other combinations (producing possibly different spanning vectors) give the same result.   ◀

Now let **u**, **v** and **w** be non-zero vectors in $\mathbb{R}^3$ (represented by directed line segments with the same initial point) such that **v** and **w** are not parallel (so that they span a parallelogram) and such that **u** does not belong to the plane spanned by **v** and **w**.

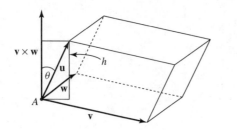

Figure 1.21   Parallelepiped spanned by **u**, **v** and **w**.
(a) $\theta < \pi/2$.   (b) $\theta > \pi/2$.

Construct the parallelepiped with adjacent sides **u**, **v** and **w** (i.e., *spanned* by **u**, **v** and **w**) as shown in Figure 1.21, and consider the scalar triple product $\mathbf{u} \cdot (\mathbf{v} \times \mathbf{w}) = \|\mathbf{u}\| \|\mathbf{v} \times \mathbf{w}\| \cos\theta$, where θ is the angle between **u** and $\mathbf{v} \times \mathbf{w}$ ($0 \le \theta \le \pi$, and $\theta \ne \pi/2$). By the previous theorem, $\|\mathbf{v} \times \mathbf{w}\|$ is the area of the parallelogram spanned by **v** and **w**. If $\theta < \pi/2$, the height h of the parallelepiped is $h = \|\mathbf{u}\| \cos\theta$; see Figure 1.21(a). If $\theta > \pi/2$, then $h = \|\mathbf{u}\| \cos(\pi - \theta) = -\|\mathbf{u}\| \cos\theta$; see Figure 1.21(b). In either case, $h = \|\mathbf{u}\| |\cos\theta|$, and consequently, the absolute value

$$|\mathbf{u} \cdot (\mathbf{v} \times \mathbf{w})| = \|\mathbf{v} \times \mathbf{w}\| \|\mathbf{u}\| |\cos\theta|$$

represents the volume of the parallelepiped spanned by **u**, **v** and **w**.

Example 1.37   Find the volume of the parallelepiped spanned by **i**, $\mathbf{i} - 2\mathbf{j}$ and $\mathbf{i} - \mathbf{j} + \mathbf{k}$.

Solution   The scalar triple product of the given vectors is

$$\mathbf{i} \cdot ((\mathbf{i} - 2\mathbf{j}) \times (\mathbf{i} - \mathbf{j} + \mathbf{k})) = \begin{vmatrix} 1 & 0 & 0 \\ 1 & -2 & 0 \\ 1 & -1 & 1 \end{vmatrix} = -2.$$

The volume of the parallelepiped is 2.   ◀

EXERCISES 1.5

1. Let $\mathbf{v} = 2\mathbf{i} - 3\mathbf{k}$ and $\mathbf{w} = 4\mathbf{j} + \mathbf{i} + \mathbf{k}$. Compute $\mathbf{v} \times \mathbf{w}$, $(\mathbf{v} + \mathbf{w}) \times \mathbf{k}$, $(2\mathbf{v} - \mathbf{w}) \times (\mathbf{v} + \mathbf{w})$ and $\mathbf{i} \cdot (\mathbf{v} \times \mathbf{w})$.

2. Prove that for any two vectors **v** and **w** in $\mathbb{R}^3$, $\mathbf{v} \times \mathbf{w} = -\mathbf{w} \times \mathbf{v}$. Use this fact to prove that $\mathbf{v} \times \mathbf{v} = \mathbf{0}$.

3. Show that $(\mathbf{u} + \mathbf{v}) \times \mathbf{w} = \mathbf{u} \times \mathbf{w} + \mathbf{v} \times \mathbf{w}$ for **u**, **v** and **w** in $\mathbb{R}^3$.

4. Prove that $\alpha(\mathbf{v} \times \mathbf{w}) = (\alpha\mathbf{v}) \times \mathbf{w}$, for any real number α and $\mathbf{v}, \mathbf{w} \in \mathbb{R}^3$.

5. Find all unit vectors orthogonal to both $\mathbf{i} + \mathbf{j} - 2\mathbf{k}$ and **k**.

6. Describe all vectors orthogonal to both $4\mathbf{i} + \mathbf{k}$ and $\mathbf{j} - \mathbf{i} + 2\mathbf{k}$. Find all unit vectors orthogonal to the given vectors.

7. Find vectors $\mathbf{u}$, $\mathbf{v}$ and $\mathbf{w}$ such that $(\mathbf{u} \times \mathbf{v}) \times \mathbf{w} \neq \mathbf{u} \times (\mathbf{v} \times \mathbf{w})$. In other words, show that the cross product is not associative. (Hint: try standard unit vectors $\mathbf{i}$, $\mathbf{j}$ and $\mathbf{k}$.)

8. Find the volume of the parallelepiped spanned by $\mathbf{i}$, $\mathbf{i} + \mathbf{k}$ and $\mathbf{i} - \mathbf{j} + \mathbf{k}$.

9. Find the volume of the parallelepiped spanned by $3\mathbf{i} + \mathbf{j} - \mathbf{k}$, $-\mathbf{i} - \mathbf{j}$ and $\mathbf{j} + \mathbf{k}$.

10. Using the properties of the determinant, show that $\mathbf{u} \cdot (\mathbf{v} \times \mathbf{w}) = \mathbf{v} \cdot (\mathbf{w} \times \mathbf{u}) = \mathbf{w} \cdot (\mathbf{u} \times \mathbf{v})$, and $\mathbf{u} \cdot (\mathbf{v} \times \mathbf{w}) = -\mathbf{u} \cdot (\mathbf{w} \times \mathbf{v})$.

11. Let us go back to Example 1.36. Draw the parallelogram spanned by the vectors $\mathbf{v}$ and $\mathbf{w}$ chosen in the solution. Now choose another pair of vectors determined by the given points, draw the parallelogram that they span and compute its area.

12. Let $\mathbf{u}$, $\mathbf{v}$ and $\mathbf{w}$ be non-zero vectors in $\mathbb{R}^3$. Show that $\mathbf{u}$ lies in the plane spanned by $\mathbf{v}$ and $\mathbf{w}$ if and only if $\mathbf{u} \cdot (\mathbf{v} \times \mathbf{w}) = 0$. Use this fact to check that the vectors $2\mathbf{i} + \mathbf{j}$, $-\mathbf{i} + 2\mathbf{k}$ and $3\mathbf{i} + 2\mathbf{j} + 2\mathbf{k}$ lie in the same plane.

13. Using the statement of Exercise 12 check whether the points $(1, 0, 0)$, $(1, 2, -1)$, $(0, 2, -4)$ and $(2, -1, 0)$ lie in the same plane.

14. Find the area of the triangle with vertices $(0, 2, 1)$, $(3, 3, 3)$ and $(-1, 4, 2)$.

15. Use the cross product to show that the points $(1, 0, 0)$, $(-3, 2, 2)$ and $(3, -1, -1)$ lie in the same line.

16. Find an equation of the plane that passes through $(3, 2, -1)$ and contains the line $\ell(t) = (-t, 2, 3 + t)$, $t \in \mathbb{R}$.

17. Find an equation of the plane that contains the lines $\ell_1(t) = (-t, 1, 1 + t)$, $t \in \mathbb{R}$ and $\ell_2(t) = (3t, 1, 1 - t)$, $t \in \mathbb{R}$.

18. Describe geometrically all solutions $\mathbf{x} \in \mathbb{R}^3$ of the equation $\mathbf{x} \times \mathbf{a} = \mathbf{b}$, where $\mathbf{a}$ and $\mathbf{b}$ are given non-zero vectors in $\mathbb{R}^3$.

19. Find the (perpendicular) distance between the point $(3, 2, 0)$ and the plane through the origin spanned by $\mathbf{v} = (2, 4, 0)$ and $\mathbf{w} = (0, 1, -1)$.

20. Find the torque $\mathbf{T}$ of a force of 10 N acting parallel to the xy-plane at an angle of $\pi/6$ rad with respect to the positive x-axis, at the point $(3, -2, -2)$ on a rigid body M in $\mathbb{R}^3$.

21. Let M be a sphere of radius 1 whose center is fixed at the origin (so that M is capable of rotating only). Describe the points on M where the torque of $\mathbf{F} = 2\mathbf{k}$ has the largest and the smallest magnitude.

22. A rigid body is rotated about the z-axis at an angular speed of 5π rad/s. Find the angular velocity vector and the tangential velocity vector at the point $(1, 2, 1)$.

23. A disk in the xy-plane of radius 1, centered at the origin, is rotated counterclockwise as seen from above about the z-axis at an angular speed of 10 rad/s. Identify the points on the disk where the magnitude of the tangential velocity vector is the largest and the smallest.

CHAPTER REVIEW

Review Questions

Answer/discuss the following questions:

1. Give an analytic and a geometric description of a vector in $\mathbb{R}^3$. Explain how to identify vectors and points.

2. Explain how to find an equation of the plane in space that contains three given points.

3. Is it true that the cross product of two unit vectors is a unit vector? Find an example to show that the cross product is not associative.

4. Although we defined a vector in $\mathbb{R}^n$ as an ordered n-tuple of real numbers, other objects were (for various reasons) identified as vectors. List all of them.

5. What is the largest number of elements in an orthonormal set of vectors in $\mathbb{R}^2$, $\mathbb{R}^3$ (and in $\mathbb{R}^n$, in general)? Find a formula that expresses a vector $\mathbf{a} \in \mathbb{R}^3$ in terms of three orthonormal vectors $\mathbf{u}$, $\mathbf{v}$ and $\mathbf{w}$ in $\mathbb{R}^3$.

6. Explain how to find a vector projection of a vector onto a given vector. Write down the formula for the angle between two vectors. State the method(s) that you can use to check whether two vectors are parallel or not.

7. Consider two unit vectors $\mathbf{v}$ and $\mathbf{w}$ in $\mathbb{R}^3$. When does their cross product have a maximum magnitude? Minimum magnitude? When is it zero?

8. List the differences between matrix multiplication and ordinary multiplication of real numbers. Find two 2×2 non-zero matrices A and B such that $AB = 0$.

9. Explain how it is possible to use vectors and vector operations to determine whether a given line and a given plane are parallel ("parallel" means that they do not intersect each other).

Computer Project

1. **Distance Between Two Cars.**
   A car A, initially located at the point $(10, 0)$ (assume that the units are km), moves in the negative direction of the x-axis (i.e., towards the origin) with the constant speed of 50 km/h. A car B, initially located at the origin, moves in the positive direction of the y-axis with the constant speed of 80 km/h.

   (a) Find their positions at time t (hours).

   (b) Find an expression for the distance between A and B in terms of t.

   (c) Plot the distance as a function of t.

   (d) When is the distance between A and B the smallest? What is that distance?

   (e) When will the distance between A and B be 200 km?

Further Explorations

1. Let $\mathbf{v}$ and $\mathbf{w}$ be non-zero vectors. Prove that $\|\mathbf{v} - \mathbf{w}\|^2 + \|\mathbf{v} + \mathbf{w}\|^2 = 2(\|\mathbf{v}\|^2 + \|\mathbf{w}\|^2)$ and give a geometric interpretation.

2. Let $\mathbf{v}$ and $\mathbf{w}$ be non-zero vectors in $\mathbb{R}^3$, where $\mathbf{v} \neq \mathbf{w}$. Show that $\mathbf{v}$ and $(\mathbf{v} \times \mathbf{w}) \times \mathbf{v}$ are orthogonal. Prove that

$$\mathbf{w} = \frac{\mathbf{v} \cdot \mathbf{w}}{\|\mathbf{v}\|^2} \mathbf{v} + \frac{(\mathbf{v} \times \mathbf{w}) \times \mathbf{v}}{\|\mathbf{v}\|^2}.$$

3. Let $\mathbf{v} \in \mathbb{R}^3$ be a non-zero vector. The direction angles of $\mathbf{v}$ are the angles α, β and γ $(0 \leq \alpha, \beta, \gamma \leq \pi)$ between $\mathbf{v}$ and the positive x-axis, y-axis and z-axis respectively. Express the so-called *direction cosines* $\cos \alpha$, $\cos \beta$ and $\cos \gamma$ in terms of $\mathbf{v}$ and the unit vectors $\mathbf{i}$, $\mathbf{j}$ and $\mathbf{k}$, and show that $\cos^2 \alpha + \cos^2 \beta + \cos^2 \gamma = 1$. Express a non-zero vector $\mathbf{v}$ in $\mathbb{R}^3$ in terms of its norm and its direction cosines.

4. Prove the Triangle Inequality using the Cauchy-Schwarz Inequality $|\mathbf{v} \cdot \mathbf{w}| \leq \|\mathbf{v}\| \|\mathbf{w}\|$ of Exercise 10 in Section 1.3 and the properties of the dot product. (Hint: start by expanding $\|\mathbf{v} + \mathbf{w}\|^2 = (\mathbf{v} + \mathbf{w}) \cdot (\mathbf{v} + \mathbf{w})$.)

5. Compute an equation of the plane Π that contains the points $(1, 2, 0)$, $(2, 0, 4)$ and $(-1, -1, 2)$. Find an equation representing all planes perpendicular to Π that contain the point $(1, 2, 0)$.

6. Let D be the 3×3 matrix whose only non-zero elements lie on the main diagonal. Is it true that $DA = AD$ for any 3×3 matrix A?

7. Let A be a 3×3 matrix and let α and β be two real numbers. Define the matrix B as follows: the first row of B is the first row of A, the second row of B is the second row of A and the third row of B is the sum of the first row of A multiplied by α and the second row of A multiplied by β. Show that $\det(B) = 0$. Give a geometric reason why $\det(B) = 0$.

8. Show that the (perpendicular) distance from the point (x_0, y_0) to the line $ax + by + c = 0$ in $\mathbb{R}^2$ is given by $d = |ax_0 + by_0 + c| / \sqrt{a^2 + b^2}$.

9. Let A be a 2×2 matrix and let $\mathbf{F}_A$ be the corresponding linear function $\mathbf{F}_A(\mathbf{v}) = A \cdot \mathbf{v}$, $\mathbf{v} \in \mathbb{R}^2$.

   (a) Find an example of a non-zero matrix A and a non-zero vector $\mathbf{v}$ such that $\mathbf{F}_A(\mathbf{v}) = \mathbf{0}$.

   (b) Assume that $\det(A) \neq 0$. Prove that $\mathbf{F}_A(\mathbf{v}) = \mathbf{0}$ implies that $\mathbf{v} = \mathbf{0}$.

10. Let $\mathbf{a}$ and $\mathbf{b}$ be non-zero vectors in $\mathbb{R}^3$. Find all vectors $\mathbf{x} \in \mathbb{R}^3$ such that $\mathbf{x} \times \mathbf{a} = \mathbf{b}$ and $\mathbf{x} \cdot \mathbf{a} = 1$. Use geometric arguments to determine the number of solutions.

Chapter 2
CALCULUS OF FUNCTIONS OF SEVERAL VARIABLES

The aim of this chapter is to generalize concepts of calculus of real-valued functions of one variable (limit, continuity and, in particular, differentiability) to real-valued and vector-valued functions of several variables. Since the properties of continuity and differentiability of a vector-valued function depend on those of its components (which are real-valued), our study will focus on real-valued functions.

This chapter opens with the definition and examples of various functions of several variables. Different ways of visualizing such functions are discussed, the emphasis being not so much on the ways of constructing graphs but on understanding what they represent. In other words, we will discuss the ways to "read" the information on the function contained in its visual interpretation. The discussion of the limit is presented on a more intuitive level and covers only those aspects that will be needed in this book. A full and rigorous approach would require a lot of time, space and patience (from both the writer and the reader), and is certainly beyond the scope of this book. The definition of continuity is a straightforward generalization of the definition for real-valued functions of one variable, and the results presented in this section are the extensions of known results for such functions.

An exhaustive discussion of derivatives and differentiability is given. In order to preserve the theorem "differentiability implies continuity" we need a new definition of differentiability for functions of several variables. An interpretation (linear approximation) will make a rather abstract definition more transparent and understandable. We proceed by discussing properties of differentiable functions, in particular the chain rule.

Next, the higher order derivatives are discussed for a number of important examples. The theorem on equality of mixed second partial derivatives is stated and its proof is presented.

In the last two sections cylindrical, spherical and generalized curvilinear coordinate systems are introduced and studied.

2.1 REAL-VALUED AND VECTOR-VALUED FUNCTIONS OF SEVERAL VARIABLES

We need three pieces of data in order to describe a function: two sets (called the domain and the range of a function) and a rule that assigns to each element of the domain a unique element in the range. In this section we will give a definition and investigate examples of functions of several variables and also introduce special classes of such functions that will be studied extensively in this book.

Definition 2.1   Real-Valued and Vector-Valued Functions of Several Variables.

A function whose domain is a subset U of $\mathbb{R}^m$ and whose range is contained in $\mathbb{R}^n$ is called a *real-valued function of m variables* if $n = 1$, and a *vector-valued function of m variables* if $n > 1$.

Real-valued functions are also called *scalar-valued* or just *scalar functions*. A *vector function* is a synonym for a vector-valued function. We use the notation $f: U \subseteq \mathbb{R}^m \to \mathbb{R}$ (the symbol $\subseteq$ denotes a subset) to describe a scalar function, and $\mathbf{F}: U \subseteq \mathbb{R}^m \to \mathbb{R}^n$ (with $n > 1$) to describe a vector function. Instead of listing variables as an m-tuple of coordinates $(x_1, \ldots, x_m)$, we take advantage of a vector notation $\mathbf{x} = (x_1, \ldots, x_m)$. For functions with a low number of variables, we use $\mathbf{x} = (x, y)$, $\mathbf{x} = (x, y, z)$ and the like, instead of naming the variables by subscripts. Let us rephrase the definition: a scalar function assigns a unique *real number* $f(\mathbf{x}) = f(x_1, \ldots, x_m)$ to each element $\mathbf{x} = (x_1, \ldots, x_m)$ in its domain U, whereas a vector function assigns a unique *vector* (or *point*, depending on the interpretation) $\mathbf{F}(\mathbf{x}) = \mathbf{F}(x_1, \ldots, x_m) \in \mathbb{R}^n$ to each $\mathbf{x} = (x_1, \ldots, x_m) \in U$ (the symbol $\in$ is read "in" or "belong(s) to"). We write $\mathbf{F}(x_1, \ldots, x_m) \in \mathbb{R}^n$ as

$$\mathbf{F}(x_1, \ldots, x_m) = (F_1(x_1, \ldots, x_m), \ldots, F_n(x_1, \ldots, x_m))$$

or as $\mathbf{F}(\mathbf{x}) = (F_1(\mathbf{x}), \ldots, F_n(\mathbf{x}))$, where $F_1, \ldots, F_n$ are the *components* (or the *component functions*) of $\mathbf{F}$. Notice that $F_1, \ldots, F_n$ are *real-valued* functions of $x_1, \ldots, x_m$. Sometimes, instead of writing $\mathbf{F}(x, y, z) = (F_1(x, y, z), F_2(x, y, z))$ for a function $\mathbf{F}: U \subseteq \mathbb{R}^3 \to \mathbb{R}^2$ we will use vector notation $\mathbf{F}(x, y, z) = F_1(x, y, z)\mathbf{i} + F_2(x, y, z)\mathbf{j}$. On a few occasions we will take advantage of matrix notation in order to keep track of the components of a function; for example,

$$\mathbf{F}(x, y, z) = \begin{bmatrix} F_1(x, y, z) \\ F_2(x, y, z) \end{bmatrix}$$

for $\mathbf{F}: U \subseteq \mathbb{R}^3 \to \mathbb{R}^2$.

Example 2.1   The function $f(x, y) = y \ln x$ is a real-valued function of two variables whose domain U consists of all pairs (x, y) such that $x > 0$. Using the curly braces {} to denote a set and a vertical bar $|$ to say "such that", we write $U = \{(x, y) \mid x > 0\}$.

The *distance function* $f(x, y, z) = \sqrt{x^2 + y^2 + z^2}$ (that measures the distance from the point (x, y, z) to the origin) is a real-valued function of three variables defined on $U = \mathbb{R}^3$. A *projection* $\mathbf{F}(x, y, z) = (x, y)$ is a vector-valued function of three variables that assigns to every vector (x, y, z) in $\mathbb{R}^3$ its projection (x, y) onto the xy-plane; see Figure 2.1.

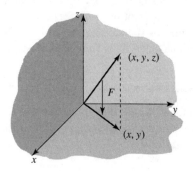

Figure 2.1   A projection function $\mathbf{F} \colon \mathbb{R}^3 \to \mathbb{R}^2$, $\mathbf{F}(x, y, z) = (x, y)$.

Example 2.2   Find the domain and the range of the function

$$f(x, y) = \frac{x - 3y^2}{x^2 - y}.$$

Solution   The domain U is a subset of $\mathbb{R}^2$, not $\mathbb{R}^3$, since f is a function of two variables. The domain is determined by the requirement that the denominator $x^2 - y$ be non-zero. Consequently, U consists of all points (x, y) in the xy-plane except those lying on the parabola $y = x^2$. Using set notation we write $U = \{(x, y) \mid y \neq x^2\}$.

The collection of values of f for all $(x, y) \in U$ forms the range of f. Notice that $f(0, y) = 3y$ if $y \neq 0$; in other words, any real number $c \neq 0$ can be obtained as a value of f, since $f(0, c/3) = c$. Since $f(3, 1) = 0$, the range of f consists of all real numbers.

Definition 2.2   Vector Field.

A vector-valued function $\mathbf{F} \colon U \subseteq \mathbb{R}^m \to \mathbb{R}^m$ defined on a subset U of $\mathbb{R}^m$ is called a *vector field on U*.

Although the domain and the range of a vector field belong to the same set $\mathbb{R}^m$, we often visualize them in a different way: elements of the domain are thought of as points, whereas the elements of the range are viewed as vectors. For example, a vector field on $\mathbb{R}^3$ is a function that assigns a *vector* $\mathbf{F}(x, y, z)$ to every *point* (x, y, z) in the three-dimensional space $\mathbb{R}^3$. This interpretation helps us graph a vector field: its value $\mathbf{F}(x, y, z)$ at (x, y, z) is represented as a vector $\mathbf{F}(x, y, z)$ whose initial point is (x, y, z). Similarly, a vector field $\mathbf{F}$ on $\mathbb{R}^2$ assigns the vector $\mathbf{F}(x, y) \in \mathbb{R}^2$ to a point (x, y) in its domain (and (x, y) is taken as the initial point of $\mathbf{F}(x, y)$). The graphs of the vector fields $\mathbf{F}_1(x, y) = (-y, x) = -y\mathbf{i} + x\mathbf{j}$ in Figure 2.2(a) and $\mathbf{F}_2(x, y, z) = (0, y, 0) = y\mathbf{j}$ in Figure 2.2(b) were constructed in that way.

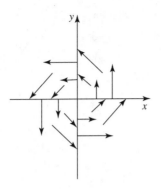

Figure 2.2 Graphs of vector fields.
(a) $\mathbf{F}_1(x, y) = (-y, x)$ in $\mathbb{R}^2$.   (b) $\mathbf{F}_2(x, y, z) = (0, y, 0)$ in $\mathbb{R}^3$.

We can think of a vector field as a "field of arrows", one "arrow" emerging from every point. By analogy to this definition, a scalar function (i.e., an assignment of a real number to each point) is sometimes called a *scalar field*.

There are situations when it is more convenient to visualize a vector-valued function $\mathbf{F}: U \subseteq \mathbb{R}^m \to \mathbb{R}^m$ as a mapping of points. This useful way of thinking about $\mathbf{F}$ will be discussed and used in later sections, for example in the change of variables technique (for integration) and in the definitions of path and surface. Yet another interpretation of maps $\mathbf{F}: \mathbb{R}^m \to \mathbb{R}^m$ (for $m = 3$) in the context of transformation of coordinates will be discussed in the last two sections of this chapter.

Example 2.3   A *rotational vector field* in the xy-plane is illustrated by the function $\mathbf{F}: \mathbb{R}^2 \to \mathbb{R}^2$, $\mathbf{F}(x, y) = (-y, x)$. The *unit rotational vector field* is a vector field

$$\mathbf{F}(x, y) = (-y/\sqrt{x^2 + y^2}, x/\sqrt{x^2 + y^2}),$$

defined on $U = \mathbb{R}^2 - \{(0, 0)\}$ (the symbol "$-$" denotes that U is obtained from $\mathbb{R}^2$ by removing the origin; it is read "without"). Rotational vector fields will appear again in various examples and applications.

◄

Example 2.4   Gravitational Force and Gravitational Potential.

A mass M is placed at the origin of the coordinate system. According to *Newton's Law of Gravitation* the force of attraction or the *gravitational force* on a small mass m located at $(x, y, z) \neq (0, 0, 0)$ is given by

$$\mathbf{F}(\mathbf{r}) = -\frac{GMm}{\|\mathbf{r}\|^2} \frac{\mathbf{r}}{\|\mathbf{r}\|}, \tag{2.1}$$

where $\mathbf{r} = x\mathbf{i} + y\mathbf{j} + z\mathbf{k}$, $\|\mathbf{r}\| = \sqrt{x^2 + y^2 + z^2}$ and G is the *gravitational constant*, $G = 6.67 \cdot 10^{-11}$ Nm²kg⁻². The function $\mathbf{F}(\mathbf{r})$ can be thought of as a vector field (called the *gravitational force field*), whose value at a point $\mathbf{r} \neq \mathbf{0}$ is given by (2.1); see

Figure 2.3. The *gravitational potential* is the scalar field

$$V(\mathbf{r}) = -\frac{GMm}{\|\mathbf{r}\|} \tag{2.2}$$

defined on $U = \mathbb{R}^3 - \{\text{origin}\}$.

◀

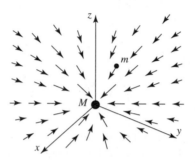

Figure 2.3 Gravitational force field $\mathbf{F}(\mathbf{r}) = -\frac{GMm}{\|\mathbf{r}\|^2}\frac{\mathbf{r}}{\|\mathbf{r}\|}$.

Example 2.5

Find the range of the vector field $\mathbf{F}(x, y) = (\sin x, \sin y)$.

Solution   Since $-1 \le \sin x, \sin y \le 1$, the range consists of all vectors whose components lie between -1 and 1. Geometrically, the range is the square with vertices at $(1, 1)$, $(-1, 1)$, $(-1, -1)$ and $(1, -1)$, together with the line segments that form its boundary.

◀

Consider a vector-valued function $\mathbf{F}: U \subseteq \mathbb{R}^m \to \mathbb{R}^n$. Its value $\mathbf{F}(x_1, \ldots, x_m)$ at a point $(x_1, \ldots, x_m)$ in U is a vector in $\mathbb{R}^n$ that can be expressed in terms of its coordinates (or components) as

$$\mathbf{F}(x_1, \ldots, x_m) = (F_1(x_1, \ldots, x_m), F_2(x_1, \ldots, x_m), \ldots, F_n(x_1, \ldots, x_m)).$$

Each component F_i $(i = 1, \ldots, n)$ is a scalar-valued function, $F_i: U \subseteq \mathbb{R}^m \to \mathbb{R}$.

Example 2.6

The components of the vector-valued function $\mathbf{F}: \mathbb{R}^3 \to \mathbb{R}^2$ defined by $\mathbf{F}(x, y, z) = (e^x - yz, y - 2)$ are the functions $F_1(x, y, z) = e^x - yz$ and $F_2(x, y, z) = y - 2$. The components of the gravitational force field given by (2.1) are $F_1(x, y, z) = -GMm(x^2 + y^2 + z^2)^{-3/2}x$, $F_2(x, y, z) = -GMm(x^2 + y^2 + z^2)^{-3/2}y$ and $F_3(x, y, z) = -GMm(x^2 + y^2 + z^2)^{-3/2}z$.

◀

The domain of a vector-valued function is the common domain of its components. Let us consider an example.

Example 2.7   Find the domain U of the function $\mathbf{F}: U \subseteq \mathbb{R}^2 \to \mathbb{R}^3$ defined by

$$\mathbf{F}(x, y) = \left(\frac{y}{x^2 + y^2}, \frac{x}{x^2 + y^2}, \sqrt{xy} \right).$$

Solution   The domains of the first two components consist of all pairs (x, y) of real numbers, except $(0, 0)$. The function $\sqrt{xy}$ is defined whenever $xy \geq 0$; i.e., when $x \geq 0$ and $y \geq 0$ or when $x \leq 0$ and $y \leq 0$. Therefore, U consists of all pairs (x, y) such that either both x and y are positive or 0 or both are negative or 0, but such that x and y are not simultaneously 0. In other words, U consists of all points in the first and the third quadrants (including the x-axis and the y-axis), with the origin removed. ◀

Example 2.8   **Electrostatic Force and Electrostatic Potential.**

The electrostatic force on a charge q placed at a point $\mathbf{r} = (x, y, z) \neq (0, 0, 0)$ due to a charge Q located at the origin is given by *Coulomb's Law*

$$\mathbf{F}(\mathbf{r}) = \frac{1}{4\pi \epsilon_0} \frac{Qq}{\|\mathbf{r}\|^2} \frac{\mathbf{r}}{\|\mathbf{r}\|}, \tag{2.3}$$

where (in the SI system) $1/4\pi \epsilon_0 = c^2 \cdot 10^{-7} = 8.99 \cdot 10^9$ Nm^{2}C^{-2} (C denotes coulomb, a unit of charge, N is the newton, a unit of force and m is the meter), and c denotes the speed of light in a vacuum. The constant ϵ_0 is called the *permittivity of vacuum*. The *electrostatic force field* is a vector field whose value at a point $\mathbf{r}$ in $\mathbb{R}^3 - \{\text{origin}\}$ is given by (2.3). The scalar field defined by

$$V(\mathbf{r}) = \frac{1}{4\pi \epsilon_0} \frac{Qq}{\|\mathbf{r}\|} \tag{2.4}$$

is called the *electrostatic potential*. ◀

Note the similarity between the forces given by (2.1) and (2.3) — both are inverse-square-law forces — but there is also an important difference. Gravitational masses M and m are always positive, so the gravitational force is always attractive. The interaction between charges of opposite sign is attractive, but it is repulsive if charges of the same sign are involved. Experiments confirm that (2.3) remains valid even if the charge q moves with large velocities (and the charge Q remains at rest).

In physics, the potential functions introduced in formulas (2.2) and (2.4) are called the *gravitational potential energy* and the *electrostatic potential energy*.

Example 2.9   **Electrostatic and Magnetic Fields.**

Assume that the charge q is at rest. The *electrostatic field* $\mathbf{E}(\mathbf{r})$ at the point $\mathbf{r} \neq \mathbf{0}$ due to a charge Q placed at the origin is given by the equation

$$\mathbf{E}(\mathbf{r}) = \frac{1}{4\pi \epsilon_0} \frac{Q}{\|\mathbf{r}\|^2} \frac{\mathbf{r}}{\|\mathbf{r}\|}.$$

By comparing this equation with equation (2.3) we can see that the force exerted by charge Q on another charge q located at $\mathbf{r}$ can be written as

$$\mathbf{F}(\mathbf{r}) = q\mathbf{E}(\mathbf{r}).$$

Alternatively, suppose that there is no charge Q and the charge q is acted upon by a *magnetic field* $\mathbf{B}(\mathbf{r})$. Then the force that the magnetic field exerts on q is

$$\mathbf{F}(\mathbf{r}) = q\,\mathbf{v} \times \mathbf{B}(\mathbf{r}),$$

where $\mathbf{v}$ is the velocity of q. Notice that the electrostatic force depends only on the location of q, not on how q is moving when it is at a particular location. However, the magnetic force on q depends on both its location and its velocity; in particular, note that the magnetic force on a charge at rest ($\mathbf{v} = \mathbf{0}$) is zero.

If both electrostatic *and* magnetic fields act on a charge q, then the total force acting on q (called the *electromagnetic* or *Lorentz force*) is

$$\mathbf{F}(\mathbf{r}) = q\big(\mathbf{E}(\mathbf{r}) + \mathbf{v} \times \mathbf{B}(\mathbf{r})\big). \qquad (2.5)$$

This is an extension of the Principle of Superposition introduced in Example 1.15 in Section 1.2.

◄

Example 2.10   Wind Chill Temperature.

The *wind chill temperature* is the scalar field W defined on some subset $U \subseteq \mathbb{R}^2$ by

$$W(T, v) = 91 + (0.44 + 0.325\sqrt{v} - 0.023v)(T - 91),$$

where T denotes the temperature (in °F) without wind and v is the wind speed (in mph), $5 \leq v \leq 45$.

◄

Example 2.11   Pressure in an Ideal Gas.

The pressure in an ideal gas is the scalar field $P\colon U \subseteq \mathbb{R}^3 \to \mathbb{R}$ given by

$$P(n, T, V) = \frac{RnT}{V},$$

where V is the volume occupied by the gas, T is the absolute temperature (in °K), n is the number of moles of gas and R is a constant.

◄

Example 2.12   Motion of a fluid through a channel can be described by a function $\mathbf{F}\colon U \subseteq \mathbb{R}^3 \to \mathbb{R}^2$, where $\mathbf{F}(x, y, t)$ denotes the velocity vector of the fluid at a point (x, y) at time t; see Figure 2.4. The domain U consists of ordered triples (x, y, t) where (x, y) denotes the coordinates of points in the channel and $t \geq 0$ represents time.

◄

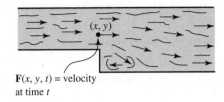

$\mathbf{F}(x, y, t) = $ velocity
at time t

Figure 2.4 Motion of a fluid through a channel.

The following example introduces an important class of functions that will be studied extensively in this book.

Example 2.13 Consider a function $\mathbf{c}: [a, b] \to \mathbb{R}^3$ defined on an interval $[a, b]$ of real numbers. The value of $\mathbf{c}$ at $t \in [a, b]$ can be interpreted as a point $\mathbf{c}(t) = (x(t), y(t), z(t))$ in space; as t changes from a to b, the values $\mathbf{c}(t)$ describe a curve in $\mathbb{R}^3$. Similarly, a function $\mathbf{c}: [a, b] \to \mathbb{R}^2$ defines a curve in the xy-plane. For example, the function $\mathbf{c}: [0, 2\pi] \to \mathbb{R}^2$, $\mathbf{c}(t) = (\cos t, \sin t)$ describes the circle of radius 1 centered at the origin, since its components (or coordinates) $x(t) = \cos t$ and $y(t) = \sin t$ satisfy $x^2(t) + y^2(t) = 1$. In general, a function $\mathbf{c}: [a, b] \to \mathbb{R}^n$ is called a *path* in $\mathbb{R}^n$, and its graph, or image (i.e., the geometric object that is its range) is called a *curve* in $\mathbb{R}^n$.

EXERCISES 2.1

Exercises 1 to 13: Find the domain and the range of the functions given below.

1. $f: \mathbb{R}^2 \to \mathbb{R}, \ f(x, y) = 3x + y - 7$ 2. $f: \mathbb{R}^3 \to \mathbb{R}, \ f(x, y, z) = e^{x^2 + y^2 + z^2}$

3. $f: \mathbb{R}^4 \to \mathbb{R}, \ f(u, v, t, z) = \tan(u + v) + t^3 z^3$

4. $f: \mathbb{R}^3 \to \mathbb{R}, \ f(x, y, z) = 3/(x + y)$ 5. $f: \mathbb{R}^2 \to \mathbb{R}, \ f(x, y) = 3x^2/(x^2 + y^2)$

6. $f: \mathbb{R}^2 \to \mathbb{R}, \ f(x, y) = (x^2 + y^2 + 1)^{-1}$ 7. $\mathbf{F}: \mathbb{R}^2 \to \mathbb{R}^2, \ \mathbf{F}(x, y) = (\ln x, (\ln y)^2)$

8. $f: \mathbb{R}^2 \to \mathbb{R}, \ f(x, y) = \sqrt{xy}$ 9. $f: \mathbb{R}^2 \to \mathbb{R}, \ f(x, y) = |x| + |y|$

10. $f: \mathbb{R}^3 \to \mathbb{R}, \ f(x, y, z) = 4x^{-1}y^{-1}$ 11. $f: \mathbb{R}^2 \to \mathbb{R}, \ f(x, y) = \sqrt{4 - 4x^2 - y^2}$

12. $f: \mathbb{R}^2 \to \mathbb{R}, \ f(x, y) = \arctan(x^2 + y^2)$ 13. $f: \mathbb{R}^2 \to \mathbb{R}, \ f(x, y) = y/|x|$

14. Describe geometrically the range of the function $\mathbf{F}: \mathbb{R}^2 \to \mathbb{R}^2$ defined by $\mathbf{F}(\alpha, \beta) = (\sin \alpha, \cos \beta)$.

15. Visualizing a vector as a directed line segment starting at the origin, describe the range of the unit rotational vector field defined in Example 2.3.

16. Write a formula for a vector field in two dimensions whose direction at (x, y) makes an angle of $\pi/4$ with respect to the positive x-axis and whose magnitude at (x, y) equals the distance from (x, y) to the origin.

17. Write a formula for a real-valued function f of three variables whose value at (x, y, z) is

inversely proportional to the square of the distance from (x, y, z) to the origin, and is such that $f(1, 2, 3) = 3$.

18. Write a formula for a unit vector field in three dimensions whose direction at (x, y, z) is parallel to the line joining (x, y, z) and $(1, 2, -2)$ and points away from $(1, 2, -2)$.

19. What could be the domain of the wind chill temperature function of Example 2.10?

Exercises 20 to 25:   Find and sketch (or describe in words) the domain of the functions given below.

20. $f: \mathbb{R}^2 \to \mathbb{R}, \ f(x, y) = x(x^2 + y^2 - 1)^{-1}$ **21.** $f: \mathbb{R}^3 \to \mathbb{R}, \ f(x, y, z) = 5/xyz$

22. $f: \mathbb{R}^2 \to \mathbb{R}, \ f(x, y) = \ln(x/y) + \ln(y/x)$ **23.** $\mathbf{F}: \mathbb{R}^2 \to \mathbb{R}^2, \ \mathbf{F}(r, \theta) = (r \cos\theta, r \sin\theta)$

24. $f: \mathbb{R}^2 \to \mathbb{R}, \ f(x, y) = \arctan(x/y)$ **25.** $f: \mathbb{R}^2 \to \mathbb{R}, \ f(x, y) = \sqrt{x^2 - y^2 - 1}$

26. The norm of a vector-valued function $\mathbf{c}(t) = (x(t), y(t), z(t)): \mathbb{R} \to \mathbb{R}^3$ is given by

$$\|\mathbf{c}(t)\| = \sqrt{x(t)^2 + y(t)^2 + z(t)^2}.$$

(a) Compute $\|\mathbf{c}(t)\|$ if $\mathbf{c}(t) = (e^t \cos t, e^t \sin t, e^t)$.

(b) Let $f: \mathbb{R} \to \mathbb{R}$ be any function. Show that $\|f(t)\mathbf{c}(t)\| = |f(t)| \cdot \|\mathbf{c}(t)\|$.

(c) Show that $\|\mathbf{c}(t)\| = 0$ for all t if and only if $\mathbf{c}(t)$ is identically zero; i.e., $\mathbf{c}(t) = (0, 0, 0)$.

(d) Find an example to show that $\|\mathbf{c}_1(t) + \mathbf{c}_2(t)\| \neq \|\mathbf{c}_1(t)\| + \|\mathbf{c}_2(t)\|$ for $\mathbf{c}_1, \mathbf{c}_2: \mathbb{R} \to \mathbb{R}^3$.

(e) Show that the norm of $\mathbf{c}(t)/\|\mathbf{c}(t)\|$ is 1 for any t such that $\mathbf{c}(t) \neq \mathbf{0}$.

2.2   GRAPH OF A FUNCTION OF SEVERAL VARIABLES

The graph of a real-valued function $y = f(x)$ of one variable is a curve in the xy-plane. Each point (x, y) on that curve carries two pieces of data: the value x of the independent variable and the corresponding value $y = f(x)$ of the function. Alternatively, we can describe the graph of f as the set

$$\text{Graph}(f) = \{(x, f(x)) | x \in U\} \subseteq \mathbb{R}^2,$$

where $U \subseteq \mathbb{R}$ is the domain of f. Generalizing this description we obtain the following definition.

Definition 2.3   Graph of a Real-Valued Function.

The *graph* of a real-valued function $f: U \subseteq \mathbb{R}^m \to \mathbb{R}$ of m variables is the set

$$\text{Graph}(f) = \{(x_1, \ldots, x_m, f(x_1, \ldots, x_m)) \mid (x_1, \ldots, x_m) \in U\} \subseteq \mathbb{R}^{m+1},$$

where $U \subseteq \mathbb{R}^m$ denotes the domain of f.

In other words, both the values of all variables $(x_1, \ldots, x_m)$ in the domain and the corresponding value $f(x_1, \ldots, x_m)$ of the function are encoded as a point on the graph.

For example, the graph of a real-valued function $z = f(x, y)$ of two variables is the subset

$$\text{Graph}(f) = \{(x, y, f(x, y)) | (x, y) \in U\}$$

of $\mathbb{R}^3$ (U, as usual, denotes the domain of f) called a *surface* in $\mathbb{R}^3$; see Figure 2.5.

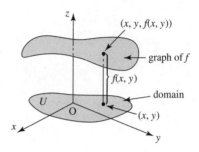

Figure 2.5   Graph of a function $z = f(x, y)$ is a surface in $\mathbb{R}^3$.

To graph a real-valued function $y = f(x)$ we need two dimensions (i.e., two coordinate axes): one for x and one for y. The graph of a real-valued function $z = f(x, y)$ has to be placed in three dimensions: two coordinate axes are needed for the domain (i.e., for the independent variables x and y) and the third one for the values of f (i.e., for the range). To construct a graph of $w = f(x, y, z)$ we would need four dimensions, so there are limitations on the visual representation of functions, even if they have a small number of variables.

However, there is another way of visualizing graphs that uses two dimensions to represent the graph of the function $z = f(x, y)$ of two variables. It consists of drawing *level curves* (or *contour curves*), and uses "two-dimensional data" to obtain "three-dimensional information." This idea has been used quite often. In technical documentation, instead of drawing a complicated three-dimensional object, we draw its projections onto different planes (thus the two-dimensional drawings convey information on the three-dimensional features of the object in question). A contour curve on topographic maps indicates points of the same (integer-valued) elevation. Not only can we find the elevation (or at least, approximate elevation) at various locations (and thus form a mental three-dimensional image of the hill), but we can also draw various conclusions: for example, the closer the contour curves are, the steeper the hill; the further apart they get, the smaller the slopes are. Figure 2.6 shows some (computer generated) contour curves of part of the Himalayan Mountains north of Mt. Everest.

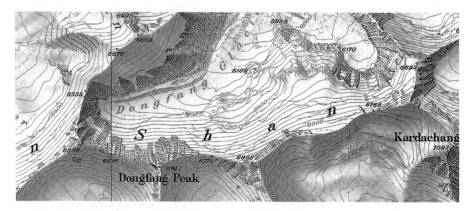

Figure 2.6   Contour curves of part of the Himalayan Mountains north of Mt. Everest.

On a weather forecast map, contour curves are used to label points with the same air temperature. We can also draw isobars, by connecting points with the same barometric pressure (looking at the isobars we get information on the wind: for example, the closer the isobars are, the stronger the wind).

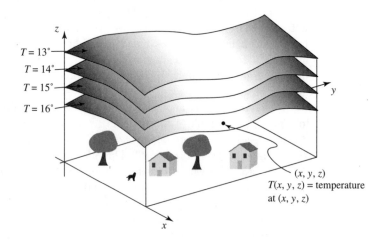

Figure 2.7   Isothermal surfaces of the temperature $T(x, y, z)$.

Contour curves are known under different names that usually have a prefix *iso* or *equi* (meaning "(of) equal" in Greek and Latin, respectively). We have already mentioned isobars. Isotherms are the contour curves of the temperature function and isomers are the curves connecting points having the same monthly or seasonal precipitation. Equipotential curves are curves along which a potential function is constant.

To visualize a function $w = f(x, y, z)$ of three variables we can use a three-dimensional analogue of level curves, namely the *level surfaces* (or *contour surfaces*). Figure 2.7 shows several isothermal surfaces for air temperature. Later on we will show that the equipotential surfaces for the gravitational potential of a point mass (2.2) (and, consequently, for the electrostatic potential of a point charge (2.4)) are concentric spheres.

■ Definition 2.4   Level Set.

Let $f : U \subseteq \mathbb{R}^m \to \mathbb{R}$ be a real-valued function of m variables and let $c \in \mathbb{R}$. The *level set of value c* is the set of all points in the domain U of f on which f has a constant value; i.e.,

level set of value $c = \{(x_1, \ldots, x_m) \in U \mid f(x_1, \ldots, x_m) = c\}$. ■

In particular, for $m = 2$ the level set

$$\{(x, y) \in U \subseteq \mathbb{R}^2 \mid f(x, y) = c\}$$

is called a *level curve (of value c)*, and for $m = 3$ the level set

$$\{(x, y, z) \in U \subseteq \mathbb{R}^3 \mid f(x, y, z) = c\}$$

is called a *level surface (of value c)*. In other words, a level curve of value c is the curve that contains all points where the value of a function of two variables is equal to c. Similarly, a level surface of value c contains all points where a function of three variables is constant and equal to c. By definition, level curves and level surfaces are always contained in the domain of a function. Sometimes we do not draw a level curve of value c in the xy-plane, but in the plane $z = c$. In that case, we refer to it as the *level curve "lifted" to the surface*, or as the *cross-section* at (height) $z = c$.

Example 2.14   Describe the level curves of $z = 9 - x^2 - y^2$.

Solution   Setting $z = c$ we get $9 - x^2 - y^2 = c$, and

$$x^2 + y^2 = 9 - c.$$

Since $x^2 + y^2 \geq 0$ there are no level curves for $9 - c < 0$, i.e., for $c > 9$. In the case $c = 9$ the level curve consists of a single point, and for $c < 9$ it is a circle of radius $\sqrt{9 - c}$. Figure 2.8 shows several cross-sections identified by the value of c and the three-dimensional graph of the surface.

Here is another way of thinking about level curves. Imagine that we have a scanning device capable of detecting horizontal cross-sections, placed parallel to the xy-plane, and that we move it up and down. Suppose that we start scanning from the point 10 units above the xy-plane. As the scanner moves downward, it does not show anything until it reaches $z = 9$, when a single point is detected. From that moment on, the circles (of radius $\sqrt{9 - c}$) appear on the scanner, and their size keeps increasing as we continue moving the scanner further down. Hence we can say that the surface in question is built of circles (smaller circles are placed on top of bigger ones) that shrink to a point when $z = 9$.

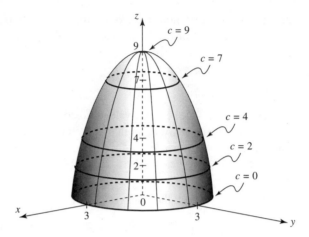

Figure 2.8 Several cross-sections of the surface $z = 9 - x^2 - y^2$.

The next example presents another situation when the level curves are conveniently visualized as cross-sections (i.e., as "lifted" from the xy-plane to the surface).

Example 2.15 Let $H(x, y)$ give the height of a hill above the point (x, y) in the xy-plane, that represents sea level. The level curve of value h connects all points whose height above sea level is h; see Figure 2.9. ◀

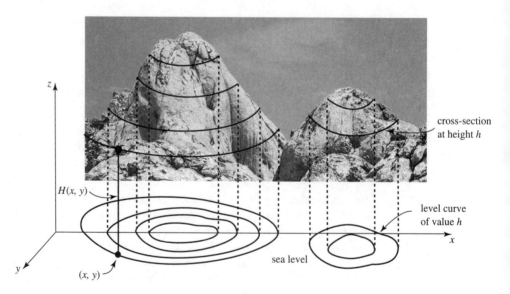

Figure 2.9 Several cross-sections and the corresponding level curves of the height function $H(x, y)$ of Example 2.15.

Example 2.16   Compute the level curves of the graph of $f(x, y) = e^{-x^2-2y^2}$.

Solution   The fact that e^x is always positive implies that there are no level curves for $c \leq 0$. If $c > 0$ then $e^{-x^2-2y^2} = c$ gives

$$x^2 + 2y^2 = -\ln c.$$

Moreover, since $x^2 + 2y^2 \geq 0$, there are no level curves when $\ln c > 0$; i.e., when $c > 1$. The level curve of value $c = 1$ consists of a single point (the origin, since $x^2 + 2y^2 = -\ln 1 = 0$ implies $x = y = 0$). It follows that the whole graph is contained in the region above the xy-plane and below the plane $z = 1$. For $0 < c < 1$ (for such a value of c, $-\ln c$ is positive) the level curve $x^2 + 2y^2 = -\ln c$ is the ellipse

$$\frac{x^2}{-\ln c} + \frac{y^2}{(-\ln c)/2} = 1$$

with axes $\sqrt{-\ln c}$ and $\sqrt{(-\ln c)/2}$; see Figure 2.10.

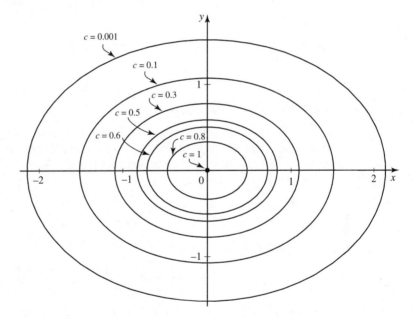

Figure 2.10   Level curves of the function $f(x, y) = e^{-x^2-2y^2}$.

It follows that the surface $z = e^{-x^2-2y^2}$ is built of ellipses whose size increases as we move from $z = 1$ towards $z = 0$. Figure 2.11 shows a computer-generated plot of the function, together with the cross-sections corresponding to the level curves in Figure 2.10.

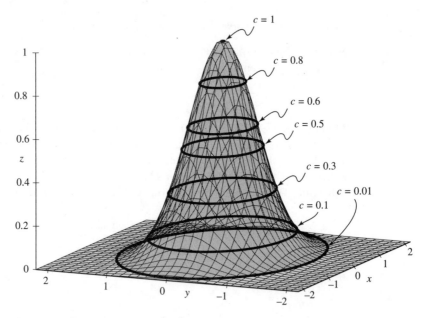

Figure 2.11   Graph of $f(x, y) = e^{-x^2 - 2y^2}$ with the cross-sections corresponding to the level curves in Figure 2.10.

Example 2.17   Equipotential Curves of an Electric Dipole.

An electric dipole is a configuration consisting of two point charges of the same magnitude q and of opposite signs placed at $(0, \ell/2)$ (the positive charge) and $(0, -\ell/2)$ (the negative charge), where $\ell > 0$. The potential at the point (x, y) due to the dipole is, for $\ell \to 0$ and $q \to \infty$, given by

$$\Phi(x, y) = \frac{1}{4\pi \epsilon_0} \frac{q\ell y}{(x^2 + y^2)^{3/2}},$$

or, in polar coordinates ($x = r \cos\theta$, $y = r \sin\theta$):

$$\Phi(r, \theta) = \frac{q\ell}{4\pi\epsilon_0} \frac{r \sin\theta}{(r^2)^{3/2}} = \frac{q\ell}{4\pi\epsilon_0} \frac{\sin\theta}{r^2}.$$

It follows that $\Phi(r, \theta) > 0$ if $0 < \theta < \pi$ (since then $\sin\theta > 0$) and $\Phi(r, \theta) < 0$ if $\pi < \theta < 2\pi$. The level curves (or equipotential curves) are given by

$$\Phi(r, \theta) = \frac{q\ell}{4\pi\epsilon_0} \frac{\sin\theta}{r^2} = c;$$

i.e., (after solving for r)

$$r = d\sqrt{\frac{\sin\theta}{c}}, \qquad \text{where} \quad d = \sqrt{\frac{q\ell}{4\pi\epsilon_0}}$$

and $0 < \theta < \pi$ if $c > 0$ and $\pi < \theta < 2\pi$ if $c < 0$. Several level curves (with $d = 2$) are drawn in Figure 2.12.

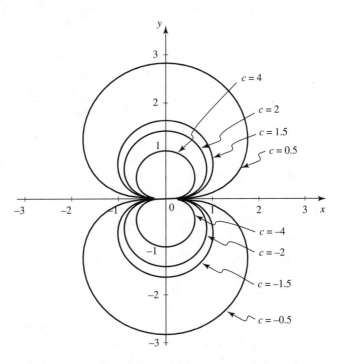

Figure 2.12 Equipotential curves of the electric dipole of Example 2.17.

Example 2.18   Find the level curves of $f(x, y) = 1 - (x^2 + y^2 - 1)^2$.

Solution   Setting $f(x, y) = c$ for a constant c we get $1 - (x^2 + y^2 - 1)^2 = c$ and

$$x^2 + y^2 = 1 \pm \sqrt{1 - c}. \tag{2.6}$$

There are no level curves if $1 - c < 0$, i.e., for $c > 1$. If $c = 1$ the level curve is the circle $x^2 + y^2 = 1$ of radius 1. If $0 < c < 1$ both $1 + \sqrt{1 - c}$ and $1 - \sqrt{1 - c}$ are positive and the corresponding level curve consists of two circles centered at the origin of radii $\sqrt{1 + \sqrt{1 - c}}$ and $\sqrt{1 - \sqrt{1 - c}}$. When $c = 0$, (2.6) reduces to $x^2 + y^2 = 1 \pm 1$, that is, the level curve of value 0 consists of the circle $x^2 + y^2 = 2$ *and* the point $(0, 0)$ (obtained from $x^2 + y^2 = 0$). If $c < 0$ then $1 + \sqrt{1 - c}$ is positive but $1 - \sqrt{1 - c}$ is negative, so this time the level curve consists only of the circle of radius $\sqrt{1 + \sqrt{1 - c}}$. Figure 2.13 shows the surface and several cross-sections.

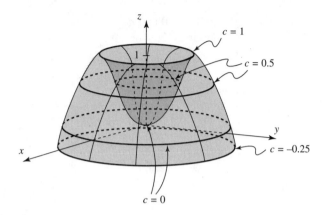

Figure 2.13   The surface $f(x, y) = 1 - (x^2 + y^2 - 1)^2$ and several cross-sections.

Example 2.19   Find the level surfaces of the functions $f(x, y, z) = \ln(x^2 + y^2 + z^2)$ and $g(x, y, z) = 5x + y - z$.

Solution   In this case it is impossible to draw the graphs, but we can still describe them by analyzing level surfaces. For any $c \in \mathbb{R}$, $f(x, y, z) = c$ implies that $\ln(x^2 + y^2 + z^2) = c$, i.e., $x^2 + y^2 + z^2 = e^c$. The level surfaces of f are spheres centered at the origin of radii $\sqrt{e^c}$.

From $5x + y - z = c$ it follows that the level surfaces of g are parallel planes (since they all have the same normal vector $(5, 1, -1)$).   ◀

Example 2.20   **Equipotential Surfaces of a Gravitational Potential.**

Consider the gravitational potential (see Example 2.4) $V(\mathbf{r}) = -GMm/\|\mathbf{r}\|$. If $V(\mathbf{r}) = c$ (for some constant $c \neq 0$) then

$$-\frac{GMm}{\|\mathbf{r}\|} = -\frac{GMm}{\sqrt{x^2 + y^2 + z^2}} = c,$$

(c has to be negative for the above to make sense) and therefore

$$x^2 + y^2 + z^2 = \frac{G^2M^2m^2}{c^2}.$$

In other words, level surfaces for this gravitational potential (also called equipotential surfaces) are spheres centered at the origin with radii $GMm/|c|$.   ◀

Let us now discuss ways of graphing vector fields. A vector field $\mathbf{F}: U \subseteq \mathbb{R}^2 \to \mathbb{R}^2$ can be interpreted as a function that assigns a *vector* $\mathbf{F}(x, y)$ to each *point* (x, y) in U. One way to visualize it is to draw the vector $\mathbf{F}(x, y)$ using the directed line segment whose tail is located at (x, y). We have already used this convention in drawing Figures 2.2, 2.3 and 2.4 in the previous section; see also Figure 2.14. The graph of a vector field $\mathbf{F}: U \subseteq \mathbb{R}^3 \to \mathbb{R}^3$ is constructed in the same way.

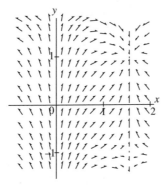

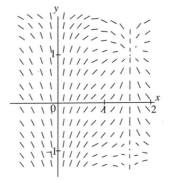

Figure 2.14 The graph of the vector field
$\mathbf{F}(x, y) = (\sin(2x), \cos(xy))$.

Figure 2.15 Slope lines of the vector field
$\mathbf{F}(x, y) = (\sin(2x), \cos(xy))$.

Another way of visualizing a vector field consists of drawing the slope lines of $\mathbf{F}$, as in Figure 2.15. This method conveys only the information on the direction of $\mathbf{F}$, unlike the previous one which shows both the direction and the magnitude of $\mathbf{F}$. Sometimes we describe a vector field by drawing its flow lines, as explained in Section 3.6.

Unlike the graphs we have discussed so far (where both the domain and the range were shown) the graph of a vector-valued function $\mathbf{c}(t)$ of one variable is drawn by representing the range only. The graph does not contain the information on t; i.e., if we choose a point on the curve, we cannot read off the value of t that generated it. Sometimes we add to the graph the values of t corresponding to some points on the curve (as shown in Figure 2.16) and indicate with an arrow in which direction t increases.

Example 2.21

Sketch the graph of the function $\mathbf{c} \colon [0, 3] \to \mathbb{R}^2$ given by $\mathbf{c}(t) = (t^2, 1 - t)$.

Solution We interpret the values of $\mathbf{c}(t)$ as the coordinates $x(t) = t^2$ and $y(t) = 1 - t$ of a point in $\mathbb{R}^2$. If $t = 0$, then $x(0) = 0$ and $y(0) = 1$. For $t = 1$, we get $x(1) = 1$ and $y(1) = 0$, and similarly, $x(2) = 4$, $y(2) = -1$ and $x(3) = 9$, $y(3) = -2$. Continuing this process and connecting all points thus obtained gives us a curve that is the graph of $\mathbf{c}$ (alternative graphing techniques will be discussed later). See Figure 2.16.

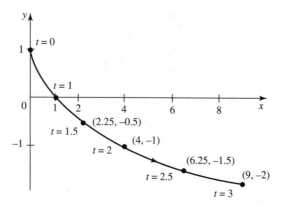

Figure 2.16   Graph of the curve $\mathbf{c}(t) = (t^2, 1 - t)$ for $t \in [0, 3]$.

Example 2.22   Construct the graph of the function $\mathbf{c}: [0, 2\pi] \to \mathbb{R}^3$ defined by $\mathbf{c}(t) = (\cos t, \sin t, 2t)$.

Solution   Since $x^2(t) + y^2(t) = 1$ for every t, the projections of points of the curve onto the xy-plane describe a circle of radius 1. When $t = 0$, $\mathbf{c}(0) = (1, 0, 0)$, and as t increases from 0 to 2π, the z-coordinate (= height) increases from 0 to 4π. The graph is a circular helix in $\mathbb{R}^3$; see Figure 2.17.

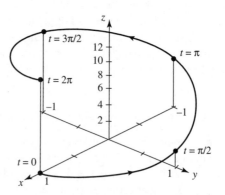

Figure 2.17   Graph of $\mathbf{c}(t) = (\cos t, \sin t, 2t)$ is a circular helix in $\mathbb{R}^3$.

We will end this section by explaining how computers generate plots of functions. In order to request a plot of a function $y = f(x)$ of one variable we have to input the formula for f and the interval where the plot will be constructed. The computer computes the values $y = f(x)$ at a certain number of equally spaced values x within the interval, plots the points (x, y) thus obtained and joins them with straight line segments. Some better graphing programs select extra points in those subintervals where there is a large difference in the values of the function to obtain a more precise plot. The same principle is used to plot paths in $\mathbb{R}^2$ and in $\mathbb{R}^3$. The plot of a function $z = f(x, y)$ of two variables is obtained in the following way: a computer chooses a number of equally spaced points in the given interval for x and in the given interval for y (thus obtaining a grid of elements (x, y) of the domain). Then it computes the values $z = f(x, y)$, plots all points (x, y, z) and connects them with line segments, forming a "net" as shown in Figures 2.18, 2.19 and 2.20.

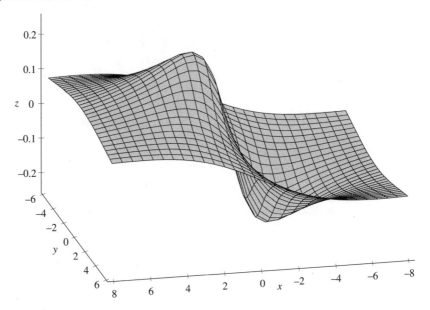

Figure 2.18 Plot of the function $f(x, y) = x/(x^2 + y^2 + 4)$.

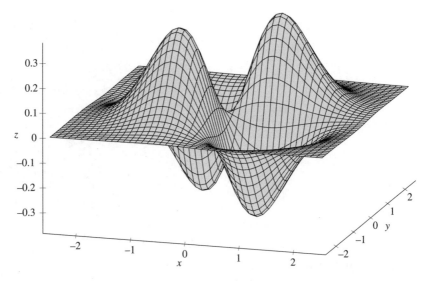

Figure 2.19 Plot of the function $f(x, y) = 2xye^{-x^2-y^2}$ with higher resolution.

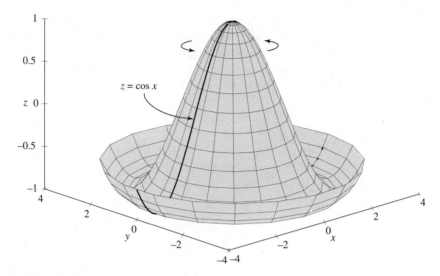

Figure 2.20 Plot of the function $z = \cos \sqrt{x^2 + y^2}$. This surface is an example of a *surface of revolution*: it is obtained by rotating the curve $z = \cos x$ in the xz-plane about the z-axis.

However, "seeing is not always believing" when considering computer-generated plots. Important features of the graph could be hidden or not shown at all. Figure 2.21 represents the function $f(x, y) = x^2y/(x^2 + y)$, and the graph of the function $g(x, y) = \arctan(0.2y/x)$ is shown in Figure 2.22. The complicated behavior of f near $(0, 0)$ (we will see in the next section that f does not have a limit there) cannot be detected from

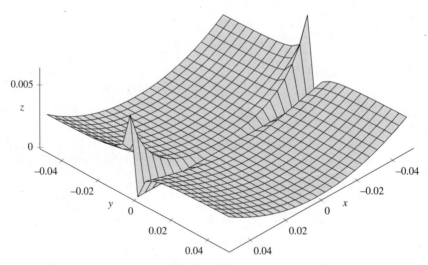

Figure 2.21 Plot of the function $f(x, y) = x^2y/(x^2 + y)$.

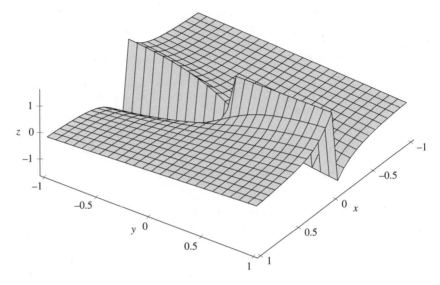

Figure 2.22   Plot of the function $f(x, y) = \arctan(0.2y/x)$.

the plot. The graph given in Figure 2.22 is incorrect: there should be a break along points on the y-axis, since g is not continuous there (this will also be discussed in the next section; see Figure 2.30).

EXERCISES 2.2

1. A level set of a function $f: \mathbb{R}^2 \to \mathbb{R}$ does not have to be a curve (it is called a level curve anyway). We have already seen that a level set can degenerate to a point. What are the "level curves" of the function $f(x, y) = 1$?

Exercises 2 to 11:   Describe the level curves of the graphs of the functions given below.

2. $f(x, y) = 2x - 3y - 5$

3. $f(x, y) = 3 - x^2 - y^2$

4. $f(x, y) = -3y(x^2 + y^2 + 1)^{-1}$

5. $f(x, y) = e^{xy}$

6. $f(x, y) = \sqrt{x^2 - y}$

7. $f(x, y) = x/y$

8. $f(x, y) = (3x - y)/(x + 2y)$

9. $f(x, y) = y - \sin x$

10. $f(x, y) = 3x^2 - y^2 + 4$

11. $f(x, y) = x^2 - y^2$

12. Find the level curves of the function $f: \mathbb{R}^2 \to \mathbb{R}$ defined by

$$f(x, y) = \begin{cases} 1 - x^2 - y^2 & \text{if } x^2 + y^2 < 1 \\ 0 & \text{if } x^2 + y^2 \geq 1 \end{cases}$$

Exercises 13 to 18:   Describe the level surfaces of the graphs of the functions of three variables given below.

13. $f(x, y, z) = y - x^2$

14. $f(x, y, z) = e^{x^2 + y^2 + z^2}$

15. $f(x, y, z) = 4x^2 + 4y^2 + z^2 + 1$

16. $f(x, y, z) = x - 2y + z + 3$

17. $f(x, y, z) = 3x + 4$ **18.** $f(x, y, z) = x^2 + y^2$

19. The function $T(x, y) = 50(1 + x^2 + 3y^2)^{-1}$ describes the temperature of a metal plate at the point $(x, y) \in \mathbb{R}^2$. Describe the level curves (isotherms) of T.

20. The voltage at a point (x, y) on a metal plate placed in the xy-plane is given by the function $V(x, y) = \sqrt{1 - 9x^2 - 4y^2}$. Sketch the equipotential curves (i.e., the curves of constant voltage).

21. What is the graph of the equation:

    (a) $x = a$ in $\mathbb{R}^2$? In $\mathbb{R}^3$?   **(b)** $y = b$ in $\mathbb{R}^2$? In $\mathbb{R}^3$?

22. Graph the following surfaces in $\mathbb{R}^3$.

    (a) $y = ax + b$ **(b)** $z = ax + b$ **(c)** $z = ay + b$

23. Describe in words each graph (assume that $a > 0$).

    (a) $x^2 + y^2 + z^2 = a^2$ **(b)** $(x - m)^2 + (y - n)^2 + (z - p)^2 = a^2$

Exercises 24 to 33:   Sketch (and/or describe in words) the following surfaces in $\mathbb{R}^3$. In each case, describe the level curves and compute the traces in the xz- and the yz-planes (a trace is the intersection of the surface and a coordinate plane).

24. $x + 2y + 3z - 6 = 0$ **25.** $z = \sqrt{2 - x^2 - y^2}$

26. $x^2 + 3y^2 + 9z^2 = 9$ **27.** $x^2 + y^2 = 9$

28. $y - x^2 = 3$ **29.** $z = 4$

30. $z = x^2 + y^2$ **31.** $z = 2 - x^2 - y^2$

32. $z^2 = x^2 + y^2$ **33.** $z = \sqrt{x^2 + y^2}$

Exercises 34 to 41:   Sketch the vector field $\mathbf{F}$ in $\mathbb{R}^2$.

34. $\mathbf{F}(\mathbf{x}) = \mathbf{x}$ **35.** $\mathbf{F}(\mathbf{x}) = \mathbf{x}/\|\mathbf{x}\|$

36. $\mathbf{F}(\mathbf{x}) = \mathbf{x} - \mathbf{x}_0$, where $\mathbf{x}_0 = (1, 2)$ **37.** $\mathbf{F}(\mathbf{x}) = (\mathbf{x} - \mathbf{x}_0)/\|\mathbf{x} - \mathbf{x}_0\|$, where $\mathbf{x}_0 = (1, 2)$

38. $\mathbf{F}(x, y) = \frac{1}{2}\mathbf{i} - \frac{1}{2}\mathbf{j}$ **39.** $\mathbf{F}(x, y) = x^2\mathbf{i} + \mathbf{j}$

40. $\mathbf{F}(x, y) = \mathbf{i} + 2\mathbf{j}/y$ **41.** $\mathbf{F}(x, y) = x\mathbf{i} - y\mathbf{j}$

2.3   LIMITS AND CONTINUITY

In the introduction to this section we recall the definition of the limit of a real-valued function of one variable. Consider the function (see Figure 2.23) defined by

$$f(x) = \begin{cases} x^2 + 1 & \text{if } x < 1 \\ 2x + 1 & \text{if } x \geq 1. \end{cases}$$

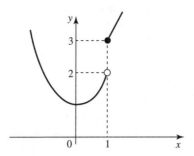

Figure 2.23   Graph of the function $f(x)$ defined above.

The small empty circle means that the point $(1, 2)$ does not belong to the graph. The filled circle at $(1, 3)$ denotes the fact that $f(1) = 3$. Let us try to describe the behavior of f for values of x that are close to $a = 1$. We start at, say, $x = 0.5$, and, as we walk along the x-axis towards $a = 1$, we compute the corresponding values of the function (keeping in mind that for $x < 1$, $f(x) = x^2 + 1$). If $x = 0.5$, then $f(0.5) = 0.5^2 + 1 = 1.25$. If $x = 0.9$, then $f(0.9) = 0.9^2 + 1 = 1.81$. Similarly, $f(0.99) = 1.9801$, $f(0.999) = 1.998001$, etc. We see that the values of the function approach 2 as x gets closer and closer to 1. For example, if we need that $f(x)$ be closer to 2 than 1.9999, we can choose any x (just substitute $y = 1.9999$ into $y = x^2 + 1$ and solve for x) such that $x > 0.99995$ (and $x < 1$). Let us check a few values: $f(0.99996) = 1.99992$, $f(0.99998) = 1.99996$, etc. The fact that f can be made as close to 2 as needed by choosing $x < 1$ close enough to 1 is written as

$$\lim_{x \to 1^-} f(x) = 2,$$

and is called the *left limit of $f(x)$ as x approaches* 1 or the *limit of $f(x)$ as x approaches* 1 *from the left* (the symbol $x \to 1^-$ denotes the fact that x gets closer and closer to 1, but is always smaller than 1). A similar investigation shows that $f(x)$ can be made as close to 3 as needed by choosing $x > 1$ to be close enough to 1. This fact is written as

$$\lim_{x \to 1^+} f(x) = 3,$$

and represents the *right limit of $f(x)$ as x approaches* 1, or the *limit of $f(x)$ as x approaches* 1 *from the right* (the symbol $x \to 1^+$ is used to denote the fact that x gets close to 1 and $x > 1$). In a situation like this one, when different approaches give different values for the right and the left limits, we say that the *limit* or the *two-sided (or both-sided) limit* does not exist, and write

$$\lim_{x \to 1} f(x) \quad \text{does not exist.}$$

The left and the right limits are also referred to as the *one-sided* limits. An analogous examination of the behavior of f near $a = 0$ (where $f(x) = x^2 + 1$) would show that

$$\lim_{x \to 0^+} f(x) = 1 \qquad \text{and} \qquad \lim_{x \to 0^-} f(x) = 1.$$

This time, the one-sided limits agree, and we say that the *two-sided (or both-sided) limit* of $f(x)$ as x approaches 0 exists and is equal to 1, and write

$$\lim_{x \to 0} f(x) = 1.$$

Notice that in our investigation of limits the value of f at $a = 1$ or at $a = 0$ did not play any role. Let us remember this important fact: when doing limits (as x approaches a), what matters is not the value of the function at $x = a$ (it may not even be defined) but the values of $f(x)$ "near" a. Figure 2.24 illustrates this point. In all three cases $\lim_{x \to a} f(x) = L$. In the first, f is not defined at a, in the second it is defined but the value $f(a)$ differs from the limit, and in the third the value $f(a)$ and the limit L are equal.

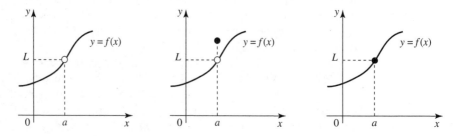

Figure 2.24 In all three cases, $\lim_{x \to a} f(x) = L$.

Next, we will give precise meaning to phrases like "x approaches a" and "$f(x)$ can be made as close to L as needed". Take an interval $(a - \delta, a + \delta)$ around a, where $\delta > 0$. The phrase "x approaches a" means that no matter what $\delta > 0$ is chosen, we can always find a value x that is inside $(a - \delta, a + \delta)$, and is such that $x \neq a$. Recalling the fact that the absolute value $|A - B|$ gives the distance between real numbers A and B on the x-axis, we can rephrase the above statement as: "x approaches a" means that no matter what δ is chosen, we can always find an $x \neq a$ whose distance from a is smaller than δ, i.e., $|x - a| < \delta$. Since $x \neq a$, the distance between x and a cannot be zero, (hence $|x - a| > 0$) and we write the above as $0 < |x - a| < \delta$.

Here is one way of visualizing this process of "approaching." Assume that "x approaches 5;" i.e., let $a = 5$. Select a sequence of values for δ, like $\delta = 10^{-1}$, 10^{-2}, 10^{-3}, etc. This sequence defines a sequence of intervals of the form $(a - \delta, a + \delta)$; specifically, the intervals are $(4.9, 5.1)$, $(4.99, 5.01)$, $(4.999, 5.001)$, etc. The phrase "x approaches 5" describes a process of selecting a number x from every interval in this sequence.

The phrase "$f(x)$ can be made as close to L as needed" means that, for any $\epsilon > 0$ the value $f(x)$ lies inside the interval $(L - \epsilon, L + \epsilon)$; i.e., the distance $|f(x) - L|$ between $f(x)$ and L is less than ϵ. Let us go back to our previous example and illustrate what we have just said. We claim that $\lim_{x \to 0} f(x) = \lim_{x \to 0} (x^2 + 1) = 1$ (i.e., $a = 0$ and $L = 1$). Take, for example, $\epsilon = 0.2$ and consider the interval $(L - \epsilon, L + \epsilon) = (0.8, 1.2)$.

We should be able to find an interval $(a - \delta, a + \delta) = (-\delta, \delta)$ such that, no matter what non-zero x is selected from that interval, the corresponding value $f(x)$ lies inside $(0.8, 1.2)$. From $|f(x) - 1| < \epsilon = 0.2$ we get $|x^2 + 1 - 1| < 0.2$, so $x^2 < 0.2$; hence, δ can be taken to be $\sqrt{0.2}$. In other words, for any $x \in (-\sqrt{0.2}, \sqrt{0.2})$, $f(x)$ is in $(0.8, 1.2)$. The fact that the limit is 1 means that the above construction of the interval $(a - \delta, a + \delta) = (-\delta, \delta)$ can be carried out for any choice of $\epsilon > 0$.

In the same example we demonstrated that $\lim_{x \to 1} f(x)$ does not exist. Let us think a bit about it: we will show that, for example, $L = 2$ cannot be the limit. Let $\epsilon = 0.1$; i.e., consider the interval $(L - \epsilon, L + \epsilon) = (1.9, 2.1)$. Any interval $(a - \delta, a + \delta) = (1 - \delta, 1 + \delta)$, no matter how small, contains a number (call it x_0) to the right of 1. The corresponding value $f(x_0) = 2x_0 + 1$ is greater than 3 (since $x_0 > 1$) and certainly does not belong to $(1.9, 2.1)$; see Figure 2.25. This violates the definition of the limit, and therefore $L = 2$ is not the limit of $f(x)$ as x approaches 1. A similar discussion would rule out any other real number as a candidate for the limit.

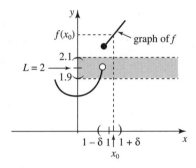

Figure 2.25 Limit of $f(x)$ as x approaches 1 does not exist.

Example 2.23

Let us relate this "closeness" and "approaching" to a problem most of us have encountered in some version in a computer science class. Suppose that we have to find a real number x such that $x^2 = 2$ (the solutions are infinite non-periodic decimal numbers $x = \pm\sqrt{2} = \pm 1.4142...$).

A bad computer program might try to solve the problem as follows:

choose an(other) x
if $x^2 = 2$ then done, else choose another x

The phrase "choose an(other) x" means that we have a way of selecting a new try for x based on the outcomes of previous passes through the loop (how this is done is not our concern). A program like this has a good chance of never ending! The computer might, for example, get $x^2 = 1.999999$ or $x^2 = 2.000001$ for some choices of x and continue trying with new choices, since neither of the two results is equal to 2. To fix the program, we change it to the following:

choose an(other) x
if x^2 is "close enough to 2" then done, else choose another x

In this case, the computer will stop when it hits a number x whose square is close to two, for example $x^2 = 1.999999$, and will return that x as a solution. Clearly, the result will be an approximation of the solution. If we require that x^2 be even "closer to 2", the approximation will be even better. More precisely, the program

> let $\epsilon = 0.00001$
> choose an(other) x
> if $|x^2 - 2| < \epsilon$ then done, else choose another x

will return an approximate solution. To find a better approximation, all we have to do is to choose a smaller interval (restrict the "tolerance"); i.e., take, for example, $\epsilon = 10^{-10}$.

◀

We are now ready for the definition of the limit.

■ **Definition 2.5**   Limit of a Function.

A function $f : \mathbb{R} \to \mathbb{R}$ has limit L as x approaches a, in symbols

$$\lim_{x \to a} f(x) = L,$$

if and only if for any given number $\epsilon > 0$ there is a number $\delta > 0$ such that

$$0 < |x - a| < \delta \qquad \text{implies} \qquad |f(x) - L| < \epsilon.$$

■

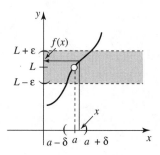

Figure 2.26 L is the limit of a function $y = f(x)$ as $x \to a$.

In other words, given the "tolerance" $\epsilon > 0$ we can find an interval $(a - \delta, a + \delta)$ (with $\delta > 0$) around a so that for every $x \neq a$ inside $(a - \delta, a + \delta)$ the corresponding value $f(x)$ lies within the allowed "tolerance" interval $(L - \epsilon, L + \epsilon)$; see Figure 2.26.

We are on our way to generalizing the definition of a limit. Since the limit (and continuity) of a vector-valued function is based on the limits (continuity) of its components, it suffices to generalize limits to real-valued functions of several variables. In order to accomplish this task, we have to come up with an analogue of our concept of "closeness:" we have to explain what is meant by phrases like "$\mathbf{x} = (x, y)$ approaches $\mathbf{a} = (a, b)$" or "$\mathbf{x} = (x, y, z)$ approaches $\mathbf{a} = (a, b, c)$," etc. Since "closeness" was defined using open intervals, what we need now is their generalization to higher dimensions.

■ **Definition 2.6**   Open Balls in $\mathbf{R}^m$.

The *open ball* $B(\mathbf{a}, r) \subseteq \mathbb{R}^m$ with center $\mathbf{a} = (a_1, \ldots, a_m)$ and radius r $(r > 0)$ is the set of all points $\mathbf{x}$ in $\mathbb{R}^m$ whose distance from a fixed point $\mathbf{a}$ is smaller than r. In symbols,

$$B(\mathbf{a}, r) = \{\mathbf{x} \in \mathbb{R}^m \mid \|\mathbf{x} - \mathbf{a}\| < r\},$$

where $\mathbf{x} = (x_1, \ldots, x_m)$ and $\|\mathbf{x} - \mathbf{a}\| = \sqrt{(x_1 - a_1)^2 + \cdots + (x_m - a_m)^2}$.

For example, the open ball $B((1, 2), 3) \subseteq \mathbb{R}^2$ consists of all points in $\mathbb{R}^2$ whose distance from $(1, 2)$ is strictly smaller that 3; i.e., $\sqrt{(x - 1)^2 + (y - 2)^2} < 3$. It is the inside of the circle of radius 3 centered at the point $(1, 2)$. Similarly, the open ball $B((0, 0, 0), 2) \subseteq \mathbb{R}^3$ consists of the region inside the sphere of radius 2 centered at the origin. The open ball $B(3, 2) \subseteq \mathbb{R}$ contains all real numbers whose distance from 3 is less than 2; i.e., $|x - 3| < 2$. It is the interval $(1, 5)$. The last example shows that, as subsets of $\mathbb{R}$, open balls coincide with open intervals. In particular, the statement $|x - a| < \delta$ (translated as "the distance from x to a is less than δ") can be written as $x \in B(a, \delta)$.

In the case of a function of one variable, the limit as $x \to a$ was determined by investigating two special approaches, namely the right and the left limits. If the two limits were equal, we said that the function had a (two-sided) limit, and its value $\lim_{x \to a} f(x)$ was equal to the common value of the one-sided limits. Consider now the function of two variables (this is a choice of convenience: everything said holds for a function of any number of variables). It is impossible to investigate all possible ways of approaching a selected point $\mathbf{a} = (a, b)$ in $\mathbb{R}^2$: there are infinitely many of them! See Figure 2.27.

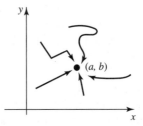

Figure 2.27 Point (a, b) can be approached in infinitely many ways.

There is some good news here: the limit should be (and is) independent of the way we approach $\mathbf{a} = (a, b)$. Therefore, if two different approaches give two different candidates for the limit, we can be sure that the limit does not exist. However, if several approaches to (a, b) all give the same number this does not prove anything yet: all it says is that, if the limit exists, it is equal to that number.

Let us now imitate the one-variable case and define the limit of a function $f: U \subseteq \mathbb{R}^m \to \mathbb{R}$ as $\mathbf{x}$ approaches $\mathbf{a}$. The definition (applied to functions of two variables) says that if we can force the values $f(x, y)$ to move arbitrarily close to L as (x, y) gets close to (a, b), the function f has limit L (see Figure 2.28).

Definition 2.7   Limit of a Real-Valued Function of Several Variables.

Let $f: U \subseteq \mathbb{R}^m \to \mathbb{R}$ be a real-valued function of m variables. We say that the limit of $f(\mathbf{x}) = f(x_1, \ldots, x_m)$ as $\mathbf{x} = (x_1, \ldots, x_m)$ approaches $\mathbf{a} = (a_1, \ldots, a_m)$ is L, in symbols

$$\lim_{\mathbf{x} \to \mathbf{a}} f(\mathbf{x}) = L \qquad \text{or} \qquad \lim_{(x_1, \ldots, x_m) \to (a_1, \ldots, a_m)} f(x_1, \ldots, x_m) = L,$$

if and only if for every $\epsilon > 0$ there is a number $\delta > 0$ such that $\mathbf{x} \in U$ and

$$0 < \|\mathbf{x} - \mathbf{a}\| < \delta \qquad \text{implies} \qquad |f(\mathbf{x}) - L| < \epsilon. \tag{2.7}$$

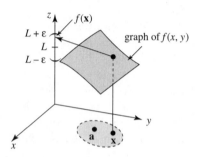

Figure 2.28   Limit of a function of two variables.

The condition $\|\mathbf{x} - \mathbf{a}\| > 0$ in (2.7) guarantees that $\mathbf{x} \neq \mathbf{a}$. Notice that there is no mention on the way $\mathbf{x}$ is supposed to approach $\mathbf{a}$. The requirement in (2.7) is that the *distance* $\|\mathbf{x} - \mathbf{a}\|$ between $\mathbf{x}$ and $\mathbf{a}$ gets smaller and smaller and therefore the definition includes every possible path that brings $\mathbf{x}$ close to $\mathbf{a}$. A convenient way of thinking about the requirement that $\|\mathbf{x} - \mathbf{a}\| < \delta$ is to think of a process of selecting a point $\mathbf{x}$ (of course, $\mathbf{x}$ has to belong to the domain U of the function) from the sequence of open balls (all centered at $\mathbf{a}$) that shrink in size (their radii δ becoming smaller and smaller). Now let $\mathbf{x} = (x, y)$, $\mathbf{a} = (a, b)$, and consider the expression

$$\|\mathbf{x} - \mathbf{a}\| = \sqrt{(x - a)^2 + (y - b)^2}.$$

If $\mathbf{x} \to \mathbf{a}$, then the distance $\|\mathbf{x} - \mathbf{a}\|$ can be made as small (i.e., as close to 0) as needed. But that means that the square root, and hence the expression $(x - a)^2 + (y - b)^2$ can be made as close to 0 as needed. Since both summands are positive, it follows that each of $x - a$ and $y - b$ can be made as close to 0 as needed (but only one can actually be made equal to 0). In other words, if $\mathbf{x} \to \mathbf{a}$, then $x \to a$ and $y \to b$. An analogous statement holds in general; i.e., if $\mathbf{x} \to \mathbf{a}$, where $\mathbf{x} = (x_1, \ldots, x_m)$ and $\mathbf{a} = (a_1, \ldots, a_m)$, then $x_1 \to a_1, \ldots, x_m \to a_m$ or

$$\lim_{\mathbf{x} \to \mathbf{a}} x_i = a_i \tag{2.8}$$

for every $i = 1, \ldots, m$.

A point $\mathbf{a}$ in U is called an *interior point* of U if there is an open ball centered at $\mathbf{a}$ that is completely contained in U. If every open ball centered at $\mathbf{a}$ (this time, $\mathbf{a}$ does not have to be in U) contains not only points in U but also points not in U, then $\mathbf{a}$ is called a *boundary point* of U. The dashed curves in Figure 2.29 denote points that do not belong to the set U. The points on the "unbroken" curves belong to U. An interior point always belongs to the set. However, a boundary point of U may or may not belong to U, as shown in Figure 2.29(b).

The definition of the limit applies to both interior and boundary points. In approaching a boundary point, we have to make sure that in the process of picking $\mathbf{x}$ from shrinking balls, we always pick only those $\mathbf{x}$ that belong to the domain U of the function.

Figure 2.29   Interior and boundary points of a set.
(a) $\mathbf{a}$ is an interior point.   (b) Each $\mathbf{a}$ is a boundary point.

Example 2.24   Show that the limit of $2xy/(x^2 + y^2)$ as $(x, y) \to (0, 0)$ does not exist.

Solution   The idea of our proof lies in the discussion preceding the definition of the limit — all we have to do is to show that different ways of approaching $(0, 0)$ give different results. Let us approach $(0, 0)$ along the x-axis: then $y = 0$ and hence

$$\lim_{(x,y)\to(0,0)} \frac{2xy}{x^2 + y^2} = \lim_{x\to 0} \frac{0}{x^2} = \lim_{x\to 0} 0 = 0.$$

Now let us walk along the y-axis towards $(0, 0)$: in this case $x = 0$ and

$$\lim_{(x,y)\to(0,0)} \frac{2xy}{x^2 + y^2} = \lim_{y\to 0} \frac{0}{y^2} = \lim_{x\to 0} 0 = 0.$$

No luck ! Moreover, we have not shown that the limit is zero, since there are infinitely many ways of approaching the origin and we would have to check each one of them. Now look at the approach along the line $y = x$:

$$\lim_{(x,y)\to(0,0)} \frac{2xy}{x^2 + y^2} = \lim_{x\to 0} \frac{2x^2}{x^2 + x^2} = \lim_{x\to 0} 1 = 1.$$

Consequently, the limit of $f(x, y)$ as $(x, y) \to (0, 0)$ does not exist.   ◀

The next definition says that the limit of a vector-valued function is computed as the limit of its components. Let $\mathbf{F}: U \subseteq \mathbb{R}^m \to \mathbb{R}^n$ be a vector-valued function of m variables defined on a set $U \subseteq \mathbb{R}^m$. $\mathbf{F}$ can be written as

$$\mathbf{F}(x_1, \ldots, x_m) = (F_1(x_1, \ldots, x_m), F_2(x_1, \ldots, x_m), \ldots, F_n(x_1, \ldots, x_m)), \qquad (2.9)$$

where $F_i: \mathbb{R}^m \to \mathbb{R}$ is the *i-th component of* $\mathbf{F}$, $i = 1, \ldots, n$. Let us emphasize that the components F_i are real-valued functions. In order to keep notation as simple as possible, we will use $\mathbf{x}$ instead of listing all variables $x_1, \ldots, x_m$; i.e., $\mathbf{x} = (x_1, \ldots, x_m)$. In particular, we will write $\mathbf{F}(\mathbf{x})$ instead of $\mathbf{F}(x_1, \ldots, x_m)$, and $\mathbf{F}(\mathbf{x}) = (F_1(\mathbf{x}), \ldots, F_n(\mathbf{x}))$ instead of (2.9).

■ **Definition 2.8**   Limit of a Vector-Valued Function.

Let $\mathbf{F}(\mathbf{x}) = (F_1(\mathbf{x}), \ldots, F_n(\mathbf{x}))$ be a vector-valued function of m variables, and let $\mathbf{a} = (a_1, \ldots, a_m)$ and $\mathbf{L} = (L_1, \ldots, L_n)$. We say that the function $\mathbf{F}(\mathbf{x})$ has limit $\mathbf{L}$ as $\mathbf{x}$ approaches $\mathbf{a}$, and write

$$\lim_{\mathbf{x} \to \mathbf{a}} \mathbf{F}(\mathbf{x}) = \mathbf{L},$$

if and only if

$$\lim_{\mathbf{x} \to \mathbf{a}} F_1(\mathbf{x}) = L_1, \ldots, \lim_{\mathbf{x} \to \mathbf{a}} F_n(\mathbf{x}) = L_n.$$

In other words, the limit of a vector-valued function is computed componentwise:

$$\lim_{\mathbf{x} \to \mathbf{a}} \mathbf{F}(\mathbf{x}) = (\lim_{\mathbf{x} \to \mathbf{a}} F_1(\mathbf{x}), \ldots, \lim_{\mathbf{x} \to \mathbf{a}} F_n(\mathbf{x})),$$

provided that all limits on the right side (and those are the limits of real-valued functions) exist. The computation of a limit can be simplified by the use of the limit laws and by the use of continuity — that will be discussed later in this section.

■ **Theorem 2.1**   Limit Laws.

Let $\mathbf{F}, \mathbf{G}: \mathbb{R}^m \to \mathbb{R}^n$, $f, g: \mathbb{R}^m \to \mathbb{R}$ and assume that $\lim_{\mathbf{x} \to \mathbf{a}} \mathbf{F}(\mathbf{x})$, $\lim_{\mathbf{x} \to \mathbf{a}} \mathbf{G}(\mathbf{x})$, $\lim_{\mathbf{x} \to \mathbf{a}} f(\mathbf{x})$ and $\lim_{\mathbf{x} \to \mathbf{a}} g(\mathbf{x})$ exist. Then

(a) $\lim_{\mathbf{x} \to \mathbf{a}} (\mathbf{F}(\mathbf{x}) + \mathbf{G}(\mathbf{x}))$ and $\lim_{\mathbf{x} \to \mathbf{a}} (\mathbf{F}(\mathbf{x}) - \mathbf{G}(\mathbf{x}))$ exist and

$$\lim_{\mathbf{x} \to \mathbf{a}} (\mathbf{F}(\mathbf{x}) + \mathbf{G}(\mathbf{x})) = \lim_{\mathbf{x} \to \mathbf{a}} \mathbf{F}(\mathbf{x}) + \lim_{\mathbf{x} \to \mathbf{a}} \mathbf{G}(\mathbf{x}),$$

and

$$\lim_{\mathbf{x} \to \mathbf{a}} (\mathbf{F}(\mathbf{x}) - \mathbf{G}(\mathbf{x})) = \lim_{\mathbf{x} \to \mathbf{a}} \mathbf{F}(\mathbf{x}) - \lim_{\mathbf{x} \to \mathbf{a}} \mathbf{G}(\mathbf{x}).$$

(b) $\lim_{\mathbf{x} \to \mathbf{a}} f(\mathbf{x}) g(\mathbf{x})$ and $\lim_{\mathbf{x} \to \mathbf{a}} c \mathbf{F}(\mathbf{x})$ (for any constant c) exist and

$$\lim_{\mathbf{x} \to \mathbf{a}} (f(\mathbf{x}) g(\mathbf{x})) = \left(\lim_{\mathbf{x} \to \mathbf{a}} f(\mathbf{x})\right) \left(\lim_{\mathbf{x} \to \mathbf{a}} g(\mathbf{x})\right),$$

and

$$\lim_{\mathbf{x} \to \mathbf{a}} (c \mathbf{F}(\mathbf{x})) = c \lim_{\mathbf{x} \to \mathbf{a}} \mathbf{F}(\mathbf{x}).$$

(c) If $\lim_{x \to a} g(x) \neq 0$ then $\lim_{x \to a} f(x)/g(x)$ exists and

$$\lim_{x \to a} \frac{f(x)}{g(x)} = \frac{\lim_{x \to a} f(x)}{\lim_{x \to a} g(x)}.$$

(d) For any $a \in \mathbb{R}^m$ and any constant $c \in \mathbb{R}^n$

$$\lim_{x \to a} x = a, \qquad \lim_{x \to a} c = c. \qquad \blacksquare$$

In part (d) the symbol c denotes the function $F: \mathbb{R}^m \to \mathbb{R}^n$ given by $F(x) = c$ for all $x \in \mathbb{R}^m$.

Proof

Rather than getting involved in arguments involving epsilons and deltas, we will provide more intuitive reasoning. Let $\lim_{x \to a} f(x) = L$ and $\lim_{x \to a} g(x) = M$, and consider part (a). We have to show that $f(x) + g(x)$ can be made as close as needed to $L + M$ by selecting an x close enough to a, $x \neq a$. Since $\lim_{x \to a} f(x) = L$, it is possible to force $f(x)$ to be as close as needed to L by requiring that x ($x \neq a$) belong to a ball of a small enough radius δ. Similarly, $\lim_{x \to a} g(x) = M$ means that $g(x)$ can be made as close as needed to M by taking x ($x \neq a$) from the inside of a ball of some small radius δ' centered at a. Taking the smaller of the two balls, we can force both $f(x)$ and $g(x)$ to be as close as needed to L and M, thus making their sum $f(x) + g(x)$ as close to $L + M$ as needed. Other properties are verified analogously. $\blacksquare$

Example 2.25 Compute $\lim_{(x,y) \to (3,2)} (x^2 - 2 + xy^2)$.

Solution By the limit laws,

$$\lim_{(x,y) \to (3,2)} (x^2 - 2 + xy^2) = \lim_{(x,y) \to (3,2)} x^2 + \lim_{(x,y) \to (3,2)} (-2) + \lim_{(x,y) \to (3,2)} xy^2$$

$$= \left(\lim_{(x,y) \to (3,2)} x \right) \cdot \left(\lim_{(x,y) \to (3,2)} x \right) + \lim_{(x,y) \to (3,2)} (-2)$$

$$+ \left(\lim_{(x,y) \to (3,2)} x \right) \cdot \left(\lim_{(x,y) \to (3,2)} y \right) \cdot \left(\lim_{(x,y) \to (3,2)} y \right) = 9 - 2 + 12 = 19. \qquad \triangleleft$$

Although we need limits to define and understand continuity and derivatives, we do not need to master (fortunately) technical intricacies involved in their computation (as we have seen in the calculus of functions of one variable, we rarely go all the way back to the limit definition of the derivative; instead, we use various formulas and properties, such as the quotient and the chain rules). Some technical issues involving limits are discussed in the exercises.

Example 2.26   Show that

$$\lim_{(x,y)\to(0,0)} \frac{x^2 y}{x^4 + y^2}$$

does not exist.

Solution   Choose the approach $x = 0$ (i.e., along the y-axis):

$$\lim_{(x,y)\to(0,0)} \frac{x^2 y}{x^4 + y^2} = \lim_{y\to0} \frac{0}{y^2} = \lim_{y\to0} 0 = 0.$$

Choose the approach $y = x$:

$$\lim_{(x,y)\to(0,0)} \frac{x^2 y}{x^4 + y^2} = \lim_{x\to0} \frac{x^3}{x^4 + x^2} = \lim_{x\to0} \frac{x}{x^2 + 1} = 0.$$

Take a (general) line through the origin, $y = mx$ (by varying the values of m we get all lines through the origin except the y-axis). Then

$$\lim_{(x,y)\to(0,0)} \frac{x^2 y}{x^4 + y^2} = \lim_{x\to0} \frac{mx^3}{x^4 + m^2 x^2} = \lim_{x\to0} \frac{mx}{x^2 + m^2} = 0.$$

But we have not exhausted all possible approaches ! (We have only exhausted all possible lines.) If we approach the origin along the parabola $y = x^2$ we get

$$\lim_{(x,y)\to(0,0)} \frac{x^2 y}{x^4 + y^2} = \lim_{x\to0} \frac{x^4}{x^4 + x^4} = \lim_{x\to0} \frac{x^4}{2x^4} = \frac{1}{2},$$

and the proof is completed.

◀

Intuitively speaking, a function is continuous if its graph has no breaks. For a function of one variable this means that the curve (which is its graph) can be drawn on a piece of paper without lifting a pen. A bird flying describes a continuous function: it cannot happen that the bird "disappears" somewhere and "reappears" at some other location a moment later. One of the properties of continuous functions states that it is possible to predict their "short-term behavior." For example, assume that the air temperature at this moment is 18^oC; a second later it could be 18.5^oC or 17^oC or 19^oC; but it will not be -100^oC. On the other hand, having a glance at a traffic light (suppose that it is red) will not help us predict whether a second later it will still be red or will change to green. A traffic light's color is a discontinuous function. A hemisphere or a plane or the graphs given in Figures 2.18, 2.19 and 2.20 are graphs of continuous functions of two variables. On the other hand, the graph of $z = \arctan(0.2y/x)$ is "broken"; that is, f is not continuous at points where $x = 0$; see Figure 2.30.

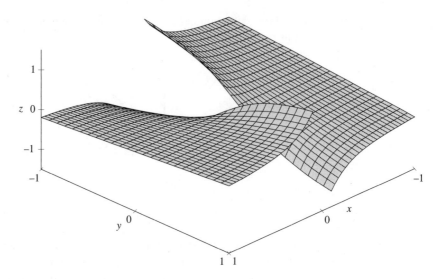

Figure 2.30   Graph of $z = \arctan(0.2y/x)$.

Recall that a function $f: \mathbb{R} \to \mathbb{R}$ is *continuous* at $x = a \in \mathbb{R}$ (see Figure 2.31) if and only if

(a) $\lim_{x \to a} f(x)$ exists,

(b) f is defined at a, and

(c) $\lim_{x \to a} f(x) = f(a)$.

We say that a function f is *continuous on an interval* (c, d) if it is continuous at every point a in (c, d). A function f is *continuous on a closed interval* $[c, d]$ if it is continuous on (c, d) and $\lim_{x \to c^+} f(x) = f(c)$ and $\lim_{x \to d^-} f(x) = f(d)$. We are *in* the interval $[c, d]$ and therefore can approach its endpoint c from the right only. Similarly, we can reach d from the left only. Any other point in $[c, d]$ can be reached from both sides; see Figure 2.32.

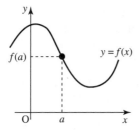

Figure 2.31   The function $y = f(x)$ is continuous at $x = a$.

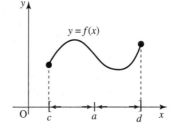

Figure 2.32   The function $y = f(x)$ is continuous on a closed interval $[c, d]$.

To understand this definition better, let us consider examples of functions that are not continuous at $x = a$.

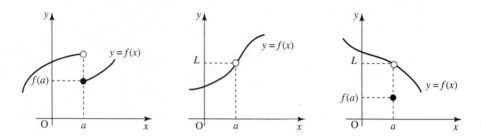

Figure 2.33   All three functions are not continuous at $x = a$.

The first function in Figure 2.33 does not have a limit as $x \to a$, hence the condition (a) fails to hold (and (c) does not make sense). For the second function, $\lim_{x \to a} f(x) = L$, but $f(a)$ is not defined; hence (b) fails to hold (and again, (c) does not make sense). Finally for the last graph in Figure 2.33, $\lim_{x \to a} f(x) = L$ and $f(a)$ is defined, but the two numbers are not equal. Condition (c) is not satisfied.

The following functions of one variable are continuous *at all points where they are defined:* $f(x) = c$, where c is a constant; $f(x) = x^n$, where n denotes any real number; polynomials and rational functions; $f(x) = e^x$, $f(x) = a^x$, for $a > 0$; $f(x) = \ln x$, $f(x) = \log x$; trigonometric and hyperbolic functions and their inverses, the absolute value function $|x|$, etc.

■ **Definition 2.9**   Continuity of Functions of Several Variables.

A function $f: U \subseteq \mathbb{R}^m \to \mathbb{R}$ is *continuous at* $\mathbf{x} = \mathbf{a}$ if and only if

(a) $\lim\limits_{\mathbf{x} \to \mathbf{a}} f(\mathbf{x})$ exists,

(b) f is defined at $\mathbf{a}$, and

(c) $\lim\limits_{\mathbf{x} \to \mathbf{a}} f(\mathbf{x}) = f(\mathbf{a})$.

We say that f is *continuous on a set U* (or just f is *continuous*) if and only if it is continuous at all points in U. A vector-valued function $\mathbf{F}: U \subseteq \mathbb{R}^m \to \mathbb{R}^n$ is *continuous* if and only if its components F_i, $i = 1, \ldots, n$, are continuous.   ■

In light of our definition of the limit of a vector-valued function, a function $\mathbf{F}$ is continuous at $\mathbf{a}$ if and only if $\lim\limits_{\mathbf{x} \to \mathbf{a}} \mathbf{F}(\mathbf{x})$ exists, $\mathbf{F}(\mathbf{a})$ is defined and

$$\lim_{\mathbf{x} \to \mathbf{a}} \mathbf{F}(\mathbf{x}) = \mathbf{F}(\mathbf{a}).$$

Let us emphasize that, when testing continuity at boundary points of U (if U has any) by computing the limit as $\mathbf{x} \to \mathbf{a}$, we must approach $\mathbf{a}$ from *within* U: that is, $\mathbf{x} \to \mathbf{a}$ assumes that $\mathbf{x} \in U$ (in the case of one variable, we had to use one-sided limits at c and d for that reason).

■ **Theorem 2.2**   Properties of Continuous Functions.

Let $\mathbf{F}, \mathbf{G}: U \subseteq \mathbb{R}^m \to \mathbb{R}^n$ ($n \geq 1$) and $f, g: U \subseteq \mathbb{R}^m \to \mathbb{R}$ be continuous at $\mathbf{a} \in U$. Then

(a) the functions $\mathbf{F} \pm \mathbf{G}$ defined by $(\mathbf{F} \pm \mathbf{G})(\mathbf{x}) = \mathbf{F}(\mathbf{x}) \pm \mathbf{G}(\mathbf{x})$ are continuous at $\mathbf{a}$.

(b) the function $c\mathbf{F}$ defined by $(c\mathbf{F})(\mathbf{x}) = c\mathbf{F}(\mathbf{x})$ is continuous at $\mathbf{a}$.

(c) the function fg defined by $(fg)(\mathbf{x}) = f(\mathbf{x})g(\mathbf{x})$ is continuous at $\mathbf{a}$.

(d) the function f/g defined by $(f/g)(\mathbf{x}) = f(\mathbf{x})/g(\mathbf{x})$ is continuous at $\mathbf{a}$, if $g(\mathbf{a}) \neq 0$.

Proof

To prove any of the above statements, all we have to do is to rewrite the corresponding limit statement. For example, let us prove part (c). Start with the definition of the product, use the "limit of the product law" (cf. (b), Theorem 2.1) and the assumption that f and g are continuous, thus getting

$$\lim_{\mathbf{x} \to \mathbf{a}} (fg)(\mathbf{x}) = \lim_{\mathbf{x} \to \mathbf{a}} f(\mathbf{x})g(\mathbf{x}) = \left(\lim_{\mathbf{x} \to \mathbf{a}} f(\mathbf{x})\right)\left(\lim_{\mathbf{x} \to \mathbf{a}} g(\mathbf{x})\right) = f(\mathbf{a})g(\mathbf{a}).$$

By the definition of the product (read in the opposite direction), $f(\mathbf{a})g(\mathbf{a}) = (fg)(\mathbf{a})$, and we are done.

∎

Consider the function $pr_i: \mathbb{R}^m \to \mathbb{R}$, defined by $pr_i(x_1, \ldots, x_m) = x_i$; it extracts the i-th component x_i from the list $(x_1, \ldots, x_m)$ of variables, and is called a *projection*. For example, $pr_2(x, y) = y$, $pr_1(x, y, z) = x$, $pr_2(x, y, z) = y$, etc. Now $\lim_{\mathbf{x} \to \mathbf{a}} pr_i(\mathbf{x}) = \lim_{\mathbf{x} \to \mathbf{a}} x_i$ by the definition of the projection, $\lim_{\mathbf{x} \to \mathbf{a}} x_i = a_i$ by (2.8) and $a_i = pr_i(\mathbf{a})$ again by the definition of projection read from right to left. In other words, $\lim_{\mathbf{x} \to \mathbf{a}} pr_i(\mathbf{x}) = pr_i(\mathbf{a})$, and the projection function is continuous. This means that, for example, functions like $f(x, y) = x$, $f(x, y, z) = z$, etc., are continuous, viewed as functions of *several* variables.

■ **Theorem 2.3**   Continuity of Composition of Functions.

Let $\mathbf{F}: U \subseteq \mathbb{R}^m \to \mathbb{R}^n$ and $\mathbf{G}: V \subseteq \mathbb{R}^n \to \mathbb{R}^p$ be such that the range $\mathbf{F}(U)$ of $\mathbf{F}$ is contained in the domain V of $\mathbf{G}$ (so that the composition $\mathbf{G} \circ \mathbf{F}$ is defined; see Figure 2.34). If $\mathbf{F}$ is continuous at $\mathbf{a}$ and $\mathbf{G}$ is continuous at $\mathbf{b} = \mathbf{F}(\mathbf{a})$, then their composition $\mathbf{G} \circ \mathbf{F}$ is continuous at $\mathbf{a}$.

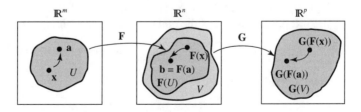

Figure 2.34   Composition of functions $\mathbf{G} \circ \mathbf{F}: U \subseteq \mathbb{R}^m \to \mathbb{R}^p$.

Proof

We give an intuitive argument: as $\mathbf{x}$ gets closer and closer to $\mathbf{a}$, the values $\mathbf{F}(\mathbf{x})$ get closer and closer to $\mathbf{F}(\mathbf{a})$, since $\mathbf{F}$ is continuous at $\mathbf{a}$. But now $\mathbf{G}$ is continuous at $\mathbf{b} = \mathbf{F}(\mathbf{a})$, and since $\mathbf{F}(\mathbf{x})$ gets closer and closer to $\mathbf{b} = \mathbf{F}(\mathbf{a})$, the values of $\mathbf{G}$, that is, $\mathbf{G}(\mathbf{F}(\mathbf{x}))$, get closer and closer to $\mathbf{G}(\mathbf{F}(\mathbf{a}))$. ∎

The following functions of two variables are continuous *at all points where they are defined*: $f(x, y) = c$, where c is a constant; $f(x, y) = x$, $f(x, y) = y$ (these are the projections); $f(x, y) = x^n$, $f(x, y) = y^n$, where n denotes any real number. Therefore polynomials and rational functions are continuous (whenever the denominator is not equal to zero), as is a composition involving any of the functions listed here with any function from the one-variable list. A list analogous to this one could be made for functions of m variables.

Example 2.27   Show that the function $\mathbf{F}(x, y, z) = (\sin x, x^2 + y^2, e^{xyz})$ is continuous for all $(x, y, z) \in \mathbb{R}^3$.

Solution   We have to analyze the components of $\mathbf{F}$. The first component $F_1(x, y, z) = \sin x$ is the composition of the projection $(x, y, z) \mapsto x$ and the trigonometric function $x \mapsto \sin x$, both of which are continuous. Hence F_1 is continuous. The component F_2 is a polynomial and hence continuous. The function F_3 is continuous as it is the composition of the polynomial $(x, y, z) \mapsto xyz$ and the exponential function. ◀

Example 2.28   Show that the function

$$f(x, y) = \begin{cases} \dfrac{\cos(x^2 + y^2) - 1}{x^2 + y^2} & \text{if } (x, y) \neq (0, 0) \\ 0 & \text{if } (x, y) = (0, 0) \end{cases}$$

is continuous on $\mathbb{R}^2$.

Solution   The function $(x, y) \mapsto x^2 + y^2$ is a polynomial, and hence its composition with the cosine function is continuous. The numerator is continuous as it is the difference of continuous functions (the function $(x, y) \mapsto 1$ is a constant function, and hence continuous). Since the denominator is continuous and nonzero except when $(x, y) = (0, 0)$, it follows that $f(x, y)$ is continuous at all points $(x, y) \neq (0, 0)$.

It remains to check the point $(0, 0)$: by Definition 2.9, it suffices to show that

$$\lim_{(x,y) \to (0,0)} f(x, y) = f(0, 0) = 0.$$

We proceed as follows:

$$\lim_{(x,y) \to (0,0)} \frac{\cos(x^2 + y^2) - 1}{x^2 + y^2}$$

(substitute $u = x^2 + y^2$; then $u \to 0$ since both $x \to 0$ and $y \to 0$)

$$= \lim_{u \to 0} \frac{\cos u - 1}{u} = \lim_{u \to 0} \frac{-\sin u}{1} = 0,$$

by L'Hôpital's rule. Hence f is also continuous at $(0, 0)$. ◀

Example 2.29   Find all points of discontinuity of the function

$$f(x, y) = \begin{cases} \dfrac{x^2 y}{x^4 + y^2} & \text{if } (x, y) \neq (0, 0) \\[2mm] 0 & \text{if } (x, y) = (0, 0) \end{cases}$$

Solution   The function $f(x, y) = x^2 y/(x^4 + y^2)$ is continuous at all points except possibly at the origin (namely, it is a quotient of continuous functions with a nonzero denominator). It was shown in Example 2.26 that $\lim_{(x,y) \to (0,0)} f(x, y)$ does not exist, and consequently $f(x, y)$ is not continuous at $(0, 0)$. ◀

EXERCISES 2.3

1. Consider the function $f \colon \mathbb{R}^2 \to \mathbb{R}$ defined by $f(x, y) = e^{-(x^2 + y^2)}$. Find an open ball $B((0, 0), r)$ (i.e., find its radius) such that, whenever $(x, y) \in B((0, 0), r)$, f satisfies $|f(x, y) - 1| < 0.01$.

2. Consider the function $f \colon \mathbb{R}^2 \to \mathbb{R}$ defined by $f(x, y) = x^2 y^3$. Find the radius of an open ball $B((0, 0), r)$ centered at the origin with the property that $|x^2 y^3| < 0.005$, if $(x, y) \in B((0, 0), r)$. Hint: find a and b such that $-a \leq x \leq a$ and $-b \leq y \leq b$ imply $|x^2 y^3| < 0.005$ first. (What region in the xy-plane is represented by $-a \leq x \leq a$ and $-b \leq y \leq b$?)

3. Figure 2.35 shows level curves of a function $f \colon \mathbb{R}^2 \to \mathbb{R}$ whose limit at $(0, 0)$ is 3. Draw a ball $B((0, 0), r_1)$ such that $|f(x, y) - 3| < 0.04$ for every $(x, y) \in B((0, 0), r_1)$. Find another ball $B((0, 0), r_2)$ such that for every $(x, y) \in B((0, 0), r_2)$, $|f(x, y) - 3| < 0.01$. Assume that the values of f in the region between two level curves are between the values of f on those level curves. For example, the value of f at a point in the region between level curves of values 2.92 and 2.96 cannot be 4 or -2, but has to be between 2.92 and 2.96.

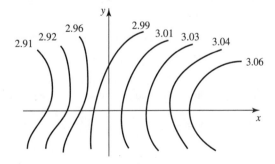

Figure 2.35   Level curves of the function f of Exercise 3.

Exercises 4 to 9: Find the limit of $f(x, y)$ as $(x, y) \to (0, 0)$ if it exists.

4. $f(x, y) = (x^3y - xy^3 - x)/(1 - xy)$ (Hint: use the limit laws.)

5. $f(x, y) = 1 - y - e^{-x^2-y^2} \cos x$

6. $f(x, y) = \sin(3x-2y+xy)/(3x-2y+xy)$ (Hint: introduce a new variable $u = 3x-2y+xy$ and reduce the limit to the one-variable case.)

7. $f(x, y) = (x + y)e^{-1/(x+y)}$

8. $f(x, y) = xy(x^2 + y^2)^{-1/2}$ (Hint: switch to polar coordinates.)

9. $f(x, y) = x^2y/(x^2 + y^2)$

Exercises 10 to 16: Show that the limit of $f(x, y)$ as $(x, y) \to (0, 0)$ does not exist.

10. $f(x, y) = \dfrac{xy}{(x^2 + y^2)^{3/2}}$ 11. $f(x, y) = \dfrac{2x^2 - y^2}{x^2 + 2y^2}$

12. $f(x, y) = \dfrac{3x^2y + 6xy + 19y^2}{x^2 + 4y^2}$ 13. $f(x, y) = \dfrac{2xy}{2x^2 + y^2}$

14. $f(x, y) = \dfrac{x^2y}{x^4 + y^2}$ (Hint: check the approach along $y = x^2$.)

15. $f(x, y) = \dfrac{x^3y}{x^6 + y^2}$ (Hint: check the approach along $y = x^3$.)

16. $f(x, y) = \dfrac{xy}{x^3 + y^3}$ (Hint: use polar coordinates, simplify and let $r \to 0$.)

17. Evaluate $\displaystyle\lim_{(x,y,z)\to(0,0,0)} \dfrac{xyz}{x^3 + y^3 + z^3}$ if it exists.

18. Give reasons why the function $\sin x \cos y(x^2+y^2+1)^{-1}$ is continuous for every $(x, y) \in \mathbb{R}^2$.

19. Find all points where the function $\mathbf{F}(x, y, z) = (x/(x^2 + y^2 + z^2), y/(x^2 + y^2 + z^2))$ is not continuous.

20. Identify the domain of the function $f(x, y) = (\ln x)^2 + \ln y^2$. Explain why f is continuous at all points in its domain.

21. Find all points of discontinuity of the function $f(x, y) = (1 + \cos^2 x)(3 - \sin x \cos x)^{-1}$.

22. Show that the function $f: \mathbb{R}^m \to \mathbb{R}$ defined by $f(\mathbf{x}) = \|\mathbf{x}\|$ is continuous for all $\mathbf{x} \in \mathbb{R}^m$. Find $\lim_{\mathbf{x}\to\mathbf{a}} \|\mathbf{x}\|$.

23. Find all points of discontinuity of the function $f: \mathbb{R}^m \to \mathbb{R}$ defined by $f(\mathbf{x}) = (\mathbf{x}-\mathbf{x}_0)/\|\mathbf{x}-\mathbf{x}_0\|$, where $\mathbf{x}_0 \in \mathbb{R}^m$.

Exercises 24 to 28: Determine whether or not the limit of f as $(x, y) \to (0, 0)$ exists. If possible, define $f(0, 0)$ so as to make f continuous at $(0, 0)$.

24. $f(x, y) = \dfrac{\sin(3x^2 + y^2)}{x^2 + 2y^2}$ 25. $f(x, y) = \dfrac{xy^3}{x^2 + y^6}$

26. $f(x, y) = \dfrac{3|x| + |y|}{|x| - 2|y|}$ 27. $f(x, y) = \dfrac{y^2 + 3|y|}{|x| + 3|y|}$

28. $f(x, y) = \dfrac{\cos(x^2 + y^2) - 1}{x^2 + y^2}$

29. Find all interior and boundary points of the set $U = \{(x, y) \mid xy \neq 0\}$.

30. Find all interior and boundary points of the set $U = \{(x, y) \mid 1 < x^2 + y^2 \leq 2\}$. What boundary points belong to U?

31. Let **a** be a fixed vector in $\mathbb{R}^m$ and let $f : \mathbb{R}^m \to \mathbb{R}$ be a function defined by ($\cdot$ denotes the dot product) $f(\mathbf{x}) = \mathbf{x} \cdot \mathbf{a}$. Show that f is continuous at all **x** in $\mathbb{R}^m$.

32. Define a vector-valued function $\mathbf{F} : \mathbb{R}^3 \to \mathbb{R}^3$ by $\mathbf{F}(\mathbf{x}) = \mathbf{x} \times \mathbf{a}$, where **a** is a fixed vector in $\mathbb{R}^3$. Find all points where **F** is continuous. Find all points where $\mathbf{G}(\mathbf{x}) = \mathbf{x} \times \mathbf{a}/\|\mathbf{x} \times \mathbf{a}\|$ is continuous.

Exercises 33 to 35: Compute the limit, if it exists, of the function $\mathbf{F}(x, y)$ as (x, y) approaches (x_0, y_0). If possible, define $\mathbf{F}(x_0, y_0)$ so as to make it continuous at (x_0, y_0).

33. $\mathbf{F}(x, y) = \left(\dfrac{y \sin x}{x}, y e^x \right)$, $(x_0, y_0) = (0, 2)$

34. $\mathbf{F}(x, y) = \left(\dfrac{x}{\sqrt{x^2 + y^2}}, \dfrac{y}{\sqrt{x^2 + y^2}} \right)$, $(x_0, y_0) = (0, 0)$

35. $\mathbf{F}(x, y) = \left(\sin(x + y), \dfrac{\cos y - 1}{xy}, e^{xy} \right)$, $(x_0, y_0) = (1, 0)$

2.4 DERIVATIVES

Using limits and continuity we can detect only some important properties of a function. To obtain more information, we make use of another powerful concept: the derivative. For example, the graph of the function $f(x) = e^{-x^2}$ has no breaks (continuity information) and the line $y = 0$ is its horizontal asymptote (limit information). With the help of the derivative ($f'(x) = -2xe^{-x^2}$) we can say much more: $f(x)$ is increasing for $x \leq 0$ and decreasing for $x \geq 0$; it has a maximum at $x = 0$, etc. Moreover, we can examine *how* $f(x)$ changes (recall that the derivative represents the rate of change): since $f'(-2) = 4e^{-4} \approx 0.0732$ and $f'(-1/2) = e^{-1/4} \approx 0.7788$, it follows that $f(x)$ increases (since the derivative is positive) much faster near $-1/2$ than near -2. Similarly, $f'(1) = -2e^{-1} \approx -0.7358$ and $f'(3) = -6e^{-9} \approx -0.0007$ imply that the function f decreases much faster (i.e., "loses more" per unit change in x) near 1 than near 3.

The derivative $f'(x)$ represents the slope of the line tangent to the graph of $f(x)$ at the point $(x, f(x))$. It is defined on open intervals (a, b) contained in the domain of $f(x)$. We say that the derivative (and hence the tangent) does not exist at "ends" $x = a$ and $x = b$ of a graph. Similarly, the derivative of a function of several variables will be defined on special subsets in the domain: they are called open sets.

■ **Definition 2.10**   Open Sets in $\mathbb{R}^m$.

A set U contained in $\mathbb{R}^m$ is *open in* $\mathbb{R}^m$ if and only if all of its points are interior points.

■

In other words, a set $U \subseteq \mathbb{R}^m$ is open in $\mathbb{R}^m$ if and only if for any point $\mathbf{a} \in U$ there is an open ball centered at $\mathbf{a}$ that is completely contained in U. For example, the inside I of a square (boundary segments not included) is open in $\mathbb{R}^2$: no matter what point in I is chosen, there is always a small open ball that contains it and is contained in I. Clearly, the balls must get smaller and smaller as we approach the edges; see Figure 2.36. The inside of a circle is an open set in $\mathbb{R}^2$; therefore, the use of the adjective "open" in the definition of the open ball has been justified. All of $\mathbb{R}^2$ or the upper half-plane $\{(x, y) \mid y > 0\}$ are open in $\mathbb{R}^2$.

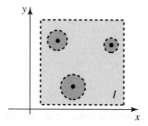

Figure 2.36   The inside of a square is an open set in $\mathbb{R}^2$.

The first octant without the coordinate planes or the inside of a cube are examples of open sets in $\mathbb{R}^3$. The interval $(1, 2)$ is open in $\mathbb{R}$ (hence the name open interval). Consider the following two cases as an illustration: pick any number in $(1, 2)$, say 1.8; the open ball $(1.7, 1.9)$ contains it, and is contained in $(1, 2)$. Pick another, say, 1.9995; for example, the ball $(1.9992, 1.9998)$ satisfies the requirement of the definition: $1.9995 \in (1.9992, 1.9998) \subseteq (1, 2)$.

On the other hand, if a set U contains any of its boundary points, then it cannot be open: any ball centered at a boundary point, no matter how small, will always contain points outside of U, as shown in Figure 2.37. For example, the interval $(1, 2]$ is not open in $\mathbb{R}$. The set $\{(x, y) \mid x^2 + y^2 \le 1\}$ (that contains the circle $x^2 + y^2 = 1$ and the region inside it) is not open in $\mathbb{R}^2$.

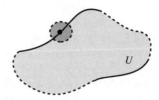

Figure 2.37   A set that contains a boundary point cannot be open.

We will start our presentation of the derivative by defining a partial derivative of a real-valued function. Throughout this section U denotes an open set.

Definition 2.11 **Partial Derivative.**

Let $f: U \subseteq \mathbb{R}^m \to \mathbb{R}$ be a real-valued function of m variables $x_1, \ldots, x_m$ defined on an open set U in $\mathbb{R}^m$. The *partial derivative* of f with respect to x_i (or with respect to the i-th variable, $i = 1, \ldots, m$) is a real-valued function $\partial f / \partial x_i$ of m variables defined by

$$\frac{\partial f}{\partial x_i}(x_1, \ldots, x_m) = \lim_{h \to 0} \frac{f(x_1, \ldots, x_i + h, \ldots, x_m) - f(x_1, \ldots, x_i, \ldots, x_m)}{h},$$

provided that the limit exists.

In other words, $\partial f / \partial x_i$ can be obtained by regarding all variables except x_i as constants and applying standard rules for computing derivatives of functions of one variable (in this case, the variable is x_i). If that is not possible, Definition 2.11 has to be used, as in Example 2.31.

Other commonly used symbols for partial derivatives $\partial f / \partial x_i$ are f_{x_i}, f_i, $D_{x_i} f$ and $D_i f$. If a function has a low number of variables, we use $\partial f / \partial x$, f_x, $D_1 f$ or $D_x f$ for the partial derivative of f with respect to x; similarly, the symbols $\partial f / \partial y$, f_y, $D_2 f$ or $D_y f$ denote the partial derivative of f with respect to y, etc.

Example 2.30 Let $f(x, y, z) = e^{xy} \sin(y^2 + z^2)$. Compute $\partial f / \partial x$, $\partial f / \partial y$ and $\partial f / \partial z$.

Solution Regarding y and z as constants, we obtain

$$\frac{\partial f}{\partial x} = e^{xy} y \cdot \sin(y^2 + z^2) = y e^{xy} \sin(y^2 + z^2).$$

Similarly,

$$\frac{\partial f}{\partial y} = e^{xy} x \cdot \sin(y^2 + z^2) + e^{xy} \cos(y^2 + z^2) \cdot 2y$$

$$= e^{xy}(x \sin(y^2 + z^2) + 2y \cos(y^2 + z^2))$$

and

$$\frac{\partial f}{\partial z} = e^{xy} \cdot \cos(y^2 + z^2) \cdot 2z.$$

Example 2.31 Compute $(\partial f / \partial x)(x, y)$ for $f(x, y) = (x^4 + y^4)^{1/3}$.

Solution The partial derivative

$$\frac{\partial f}{\partial x}(x, y) = \frac{1}{3}\left(x^4 + y^4\right)^{-2/3} \cdot 4x^3 = \frac{4x^3}{3\left(x^4 + y^4\right)^{2/3}} \tag{2.10}$$

is defined at all points (x, y) except at the origin. In order to compute $\partial f / \partial x(0, 0)$ we use Definition 2.11:

$$\frac{\partial f}{\partial x}(0,0) = \lim_{h \to 0} \frac{f(h,0) - f(0,0)}{h} = \lim_{h \to 0} \frac{\left(h^4\right)^{1/3} - 0}{h} = \lim_{h \to 0} h^{1/3} = 0.$$

Therefore $(\partial f/\partial x)(x, y)$ is given by (2.10) if $(x, y) \neq (0, 0)$, and $(\partial f/\partial x)(0, 0) = 0$.

◄

To get a better feel for partial derivatives we will investigate some functions $z = f(x, y)$ of two variables. The partial derivative $(\partial f/\partial x)(x, y)$ represents the rate of change of f at the point (x, y) with respect to x when the variable y is held fixed. A similar interpretation can be given to $(\partial f/\partial y)(x, y)$ (and for that matter, to any partial derivative of a function of any number of variables). Here is an example.

Example 2.32   The function $T(x, y) = 33e^{-x^2-2y^2}$ describes the air temperature at a location (x, y). Suppose that we start walking away from the origin along the x-axis in the positive direction. What rate of change in temperature do we experience at the moment when we reach the point $(1, 0)$? Compute $T_y(1, 2)$ and give a physical interpretation.

Solution   To answer the first question we have to compute $(\partial T/\partial x)(1, 0)$ (we walk along the x-axis, so that $y = 0$ and it does not change). Using the chain rule, we get

$$\frac{\partial T}{\partial x} = 33e^{-x^2-2y^2}(-2x) = -66xe^{-x^2-2y^2},$$

and $\partial T/\partial x(1, 0) = -66e^{-1} \approx -24.3$. Therefore we feel that the air is cooling down (the derivative is negative) as we pass through $(1, 0)$. Similarly (the vertical bar is read "evaluated at"),

$$\frac{\partial T}{\partial y}(1, 2) = -132ye^{-x^2-2y^2}\Big|_{(1,2)} = -264e^{-9} \approx -0.03.$$

In other words, at the moment we reach the point $(1, 2)$ on our walk along the vertical line $x = 1$ in the direction of the positive y-axis, we feel a very small decrease in air temperature.

◄

The derivative $f'(x)$ of a function $f(x)$ represents the slope of the line tangent to the graph of $y = f(x)$ at the point (x, y). A similar interpretation can be given to partial derivatives: consider a function $z = f(x, y)$ and pick a point (a, b) in its domain. The intersection of the graph of f and the vertical plane $y = b$ is the curve **c** that contains the point $(a, b, f(a, b))$ on the surface. Its equation is $z = f(x, b)$ (z is now a function of one variable) and the partial derivative $(\partial f/\partial x)(a, b)$ is equal to the slope of the tangent to that curve at $(a, b, f(a, b))$; see Figure 2.38.

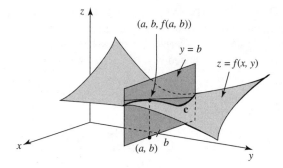

Figure 2.38 Partial derivative is the slope of a tangent.

Example 2.33 Compute $(\partial f/\partial x)(2, 1)$ for the function $f(x, y) = 2x^2 + 3xy - y^2$. Then find the curve that is the intersection of the graph of $z = f(x, y)$ and the plane $y = 1$ and compute the slope of the curve's tangent at $x = 2$. Give a geometric interpretation of $(\partial f/\partial x)(2, 1)$.

Solution The partial derivative is

$$\frac{\partial f}{\partial x}(2, 1) = (4x + 3y)\Big|_{(2,1)} = 11.$$

Substitute $y = 1$ into $z = 2x^2 + 3xy - y^2$ to get the curve $z = 2x^2 + 3x - 1$ in the plane $y = 1$. The slope of its tangent line at $x = 2$ is $z'(2) = (4x + 3)|_{x=2} = 11$. The partial derivative of f with respect to x at the point $(2, 1)$ equals the slope of the tangent line at $x = 2$ to the curve that is the intersection of the surface $z = 2x^2 + 3xy - y^2$ and the plane $y = 1$.

Let $\mathbf{F}$ be a vector-valued function $\mathbf{F} \colon U \subseteq \mathbb{R}^m \to \mathbb{R}^n$. Recall that $\mathbf{F}$ can be written in terms of its components as

$$\mathbf{F}(x_1, \ldots, x_m) = (F_1(x_1, \ldots, x_m), F_2(x_1, \ldots, x_m), \ldots, F_n(x_1, \ldots, x_m)),$$

or as $\mathbf{F}(\mathbf{x}) = (F_1(\mathbf{x}), F_2(\mathbf{x}), \ldots, F_n(\mathbf{x}))$, where $\mathbf{x} = (x_1, \ldots, x_m)$. In other words, a vector-valued function $\mathbf{F}$ can be described using n real-valued functions of m variables.

By $D\mathbf{F}(\mathbf{x})$ we denote the $n \times m$ matrix of partial derivatives of the components of $\mathbf{F}$ evaluated at $\mathbf{x}$:

$$D\mathbf{F}(\mathbf{x}) = \begin{bmatrix} \dfrac{\partial F_1}{\partial x_1}(\mathbf{x}) & \dfrac{\partial F_1}{\partial x_2}(\mathbf{x}) & \cdots & \dfrac{\partial F_1}{\partial x_m}(\mathbf{x}) \\[2ex] \dfrac{\partial F_2}{\partial x_1}(\mathbf{x}) & \dfrac{\partial F_2}{\partial x_2}(\mathbf{x}) & \cdots & \dfrac{\partial F_2}{\partial x_m}(\mathbf{x}) \\[2ex] \vdots & \vdots & & \vdots \\[2ex] \dfrac{\partial F_n}{\partial x_1}(\mathbf{x}) & \dfrac{\partial F_n}{\partial x_2}(\mathbf{x}) & \cdots & \dfrac{\partial F_n}{\partial x_m}(\mathbf{x}) \end{bmatrix}, \qquad (2.11)$$

provided that all partial derivatives exist at $\mathbf{x}$.

The matrix $D\mathbf{F}(\mathbf{x})$ has n rows and m columns (the number of rows is the dimension of the range and the number of columns equals the number of variables). The i-th row consists of partial derivatives of the i-th component F_i of $\mathbf{F}$ with respect to all variables $x_1, \ldots, x_m$, evaluated at $\mathbf{x}$. The i-th column is the matrix

$$\frac{\partial \mathbf{F}}{\partial x_i}(\mathbf{x}) = \mathbf{F}_{x_i}(\mathbf{x}) = \begin{bmatrix} \dfrac{\partial F_1}{\partial x_i}(\mathbf{x}) \\[2mm] \dfrac{\partial F_2}{\partial x_i}(\mathbf{x}) \\[2mm] \vdots \\[2mm] \dfrac{\partial F_n}{\partial x_i}(\mathbf{x}) \end{bmatrix}$$

that consists of partial derivatives of the component functions $F_1, \ldots, F_n$ with respect to the same variable x_i, evaluated at $\mathbf{x}$.

Example 2.34   Let $\mathbf{F}: \mathbb{R}^3 \to \mathbb{R}^4$ be given by $\mathbf{F}(x, y, z) = (e^{x+yz}, x^2 + 1, \sin(y + z), 4y)$. Written in components,

$$\mathbf{F}(x, y, z) = (F_1(x, y, z), F_2(x, y, z), F_3(x, y, z), F_4(x, y, z)),$$

where $F_1(x, y, z) = e^{x+yz}$, $F_2(x, y, z) = x^2 + 1$, $F_3(x, y, z) = \sin(y + z)$ and $F_4(x, y, z) = 4y$. The matrix $D\mathbf{F}(x, y, z)$ is given by

$$D\mathbf{F}(x, y, z) = \begin{bmatrix} e^{x+yz} & ze^{x+yz} & ye^{x+yz} \\ 2x & 0 & 0 \\ 0 & \cos(y + z) & \cos(y + z) \\ 0 & 4 & 0 \end{bmatrix}.$$

The second column of $D\mathbf{F}(x, y, z)$ is equal to

$$\frac{\partial \mathbf{F}}{\partial y}(x, y, z) = \begin{bmatrix} ze^{x+yz} \\ 0 \\ \cos(y + z) \\ 4 \end{bmatrix},$$

which is a matrix of derivatives of component functions with respect to y. ◀

Let us consider some special cases. If $f(x): \mathbb{R} \to \mathbb{R}$, then $Df(x)$ is a 1×1 matrix whose entry is the derivative of (the only component) f with respect to (the only variable) x. Hence $Df(x)$ is the usual derivative $f'(x)$.

Assume that $f(\mathbf{x}): U \subseteq \mathbb{R}^m \to \mathbb{R}$ is a real-valued function of m variables. Then $Df(\mathbf{x})$ is the $1 \times m$ matrix

$$Df(\mathbf{x}) = \begin{bmatrix} \dfrac{\partial f}{\partial x_1}(\mathbf{x}) & \dfrac{\partial f}{\partial x_2}(\mathbf{x}) & \cdots & \dfrac{\partial f}{\partial x_m}(\mathbf{x}) \end{bmatrix},$$

whose only row consists of partial derivatives of f with respect to all variables $x_1, \ldots, x_m$, evaluated at $\mathbf{x} = (x_1, \ldots, x_m)$. Interpreted as a vector, $Df(\mathbf{x})$ is called the *gradient* of f at $\mathbf{x}$ and is denoted by *grad* $f(\mathbf{x})$ or $\nabla f(\mathbf{x})$, where $\mathbf{x} = (x_1, \ldots, x_m)$.

Now let $\mathbf{c}: [a, b] \to \mathbb{R}^n$ be a vector-valued function of one variable (also called a path in $\mathbb{R}^n$, see Example 2.13). We use t rather than x or x_1 to denote the independent variable. In this case, $D\mathbf{c}(t)$ is the $n \times 1$ matrix

$$D\mathbf{c}(t) = \begin{bmatrix} \dfrac{dx_1}{dt}(t) \\[2mm] \dfrac{dx_2}{dt}(t) \\[2mm] \vdots \\[2mm] \dfrac{dx_n}{dt}(t) \end{bmatrix}$$

whose column consists of the derivatives of the components $x_1, \ldots, x_m$ of $\mathbf{c}$ with respect to t (since x_i are functions of one variable, we use dx_i/dt instead of $\partial x_i/\partial t$ to denote the derivative). Interpreted as a vector, $D\mathbf{c}(t)$ is called the *tangent vector* or the *velocity vector* of $\mathbf{c}(t)$, and is denoted by $\mathbf{c}'(t)$.

Example 2.35

Gradient of the Gravitational Potential.

Consider the gravitational potential function

$$V(x, y, z) = -\frac{GMm}{\sqrt{x^2 + y^2 + z^2}}$$

discussed in Example 2.4. Compute its gradient $\nabla V(x, y, z)$.

Solution By the chain rule,

$$\frac{\partial V}{\partial x} = \frac{1}{2} GMm(x^2 + y^2 + z^2)^{-3/2} \cdot 2x.$$

Similarly,

$$\frac{\partial V}{\partial y} = \frac{1}{2} GMm(x^2+y^2+z^2)^{-3/2} \cdot 2y \qquad \text{and} \qquad \frac{\partial V}{\partial z} = \frac{1}{2} GMm(x^2+y^2+z^2)^{-3/2} \cdot 2z.$$

Hence

$$\nabla V(x, y, z) = DV(x, y, z)$$

$$= \begin{bmatrix} \dfrac{\partial V}{\partial x} & \dfrac{\partial V}{\partial y} & \dfrac{\partial V}{\partial z} \end{bmatrix}$$

$$= \begin{bmatrix} \dfrac{GMm}{(x^2 + y^2 + z^2)^{3/2}}x & \dfrac{GMm}{(x^2 + y^2 + z^2)^{3/2}}y & \dfrac{GMm}{(x^2 + y^2 + z^2)^{3/2}}z \end{bmatrix}.$$

Rewriting ∇V as a vector, we get

$$\nabla V(x, y, z) = \frac{GMm}{(x^2 + y^2 + z^2)^{3/2}}x\mathbf{i} + \frac{GMm}{(x^2 + y^2 + z^2)^{3/2}}y\mathbf{j} + \frac{GMm}{(x^2 + y^2 + z^2)^{3/2}}z\mathbf{k}$$

$$= \frac{GMm}{(x^2 + y^2 + z^2)^{3/2}}(x\mathbf{i} + y\mathbf{j} + z\mathbf{k})$$

$$= \frac{GMm}{\|\mathbf{r}\|^3}\mathbf{r},$$

where $\mathbf{r} = x\mathbf{i} + y\mathbf{j} + z\mathbf{k}$. The expression in the last line is the negative of the gravitational force field.

◀

Example 2.35 shows that

$$\mathbf{F} = -\nabla V,$$

where $\mathbf{F}$ is the gravitational force field. In general, a force field $\mathbf{F}$ satisfying this formula is called *conservative*, and the scalar function V is the *potential function*. We will study properties of conservative fields and potential functions in Section 5.4.

The motion of a particle in $\mathbb{R}^3$ can be described by a vector function

$$\mathbf{c}(t) = (x(t), y(t), z(t)),$$

where t represents time and $(x(t), y(t), z(t))$ are coordinates of the position vector $\mathbf{c}(t)$ of the particle. To each point $\mathbf{c}(t)$ (recall that we agreed to identify points with the tips of vectors) on the curve we associate two vectors: the *velocity* $\mathbf{v}(t) = \mathbf{c}'(t)$ at time t and the *acceleration* $\mathbf{a}(t) = \mathbf{v}'(t) = \mathbf{c}''(t)$ at time t. Usually, velocity and acceleration are visualized as vectors whose tails are located at the point $\mathbf{c}(t)$ on the curve. The next example will serve as an illustration.

Example 2.36   The function $\mathbf{c}(t) = (t \sin t, t \cos t, t)$, $1 \le t \le 2$, represents the motion of a particle in $\mathbb{R}^3$. The matrix

$$D\mathbf{c}(t) = \mathbf{c}'(t) = \begin{bmatrix} \sin t + t \cos t \\ \cos t - t \sin t \\ 1 \end{bmatrix}$$

(thought of as a vector) gives the velocity of the particle. For example, when $t = \pi/2$, the particle is located at the point $\mathbf{c}(\pi/2) = (\pi/2, 0, \pi/2)$. Its velocity vector at that moment is computed to be

$$D\mathbf{c}(\pi/2) = \mathbf{c}'(\pi/2) = \begin{bmatrix} 1 \\ -\pi/2 \\ 1 \end{bmatrix},$$

and the acceleration is

$$\mathbf{c}''(\pi/2) = \begin{bmatrix} 2\cos t - t \sin t \\ -2\sin t - t \cos t \\ 0 \end{bmatrix}_{at\ t=\pi/2} = \begin{bmatrix} -\pi/2 \\ -2 \\ 0 \end{bmatrix}.$$

We visualize the velocity $\mathbf{c}'(\pi/2)$ and the acceleration $\mathbf{c}''(\pi/2)$ as vectors whose tails are located at the point $\mathbf{c}(\pi/2)$ on the curve; see Figure 2.39.

◀

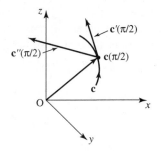

Figure 2.39   The position, velocity and acceleration vectors for the moving particle of Example 2.36.

Definition 2.12   Differentiability of a Vector-Valued Function.

A vector-valued function $\mathbf{F} = (F_1, \ldots, F_n): U \subseteq \mathbb{R}^m \to \mathbb{R}^n$, defined on an open set $U \subseteq \mathbb{R}^m$ is *differentiable at* $\mathbf{a} \in U$ if

(a) all partial derivatives of the components $F_1, \ldots, F_n$ of $\mathbf{F}$ exist at $\mathbf{a}$, and

(b) the matrix of partial derivatives $D\mathbf{F}(\mathbf{a})$ of $\mathbf{F}$ at $\mathbf{a}$ satisfies

$$\lim_{\mathbf{x} \to \mathbf{a}} \frac{\|\mathbf{F}(\mathbf{x}) - \mathbf{F}(\mathbf{a}) - D\mathbf{F}(\mathbf{a})(\mathbf{x} - \mathbf{a})\|}{\|\mathbf{x} - \mathbf{a}\|} = 0, \tag{2.12}$$

where $\|.\|$ in the numerator denotes the length in $\mathbb{R}^n$, and $\|.\|$ in the denominator is the length in $\mathbb{R}^m$.

Definition 2.13   Derivative of a Vector-Valued Function.

If a vector-valued function $\mathbf{F}$ satisfies the conditions (a) and (b) of Definition 2.12, then the matrix $D\mathbf{F}(\mathbf{a})$ of partial derivatives introduced in (2.11) is called the *derivative of* $\mathbf{F}$ *at* $\mathbf{a}$.

The subtractions in the numerator of (2.12) take place in $\mathbb{R}^n$: clearly, $\mathbf{F}(\mathbf{x})$ and $\mathbf{F}(\mathbf{a})$ are in $\mathbb{R}^n$; the third term is the product of the $n \times m$ matrix $D\mathbf{F}(\mathbf{a})$ and the vector (viewed as an $m \times 1$ matrix) $\mathbf{x} - \mathbf{a}$, and is therefore an $n \times 1$ matrix, i.e., an element of $\mathbb{R}^n$.

Let us look more closely at condition (b) in Definition 2.12. Assume that $m = n = 1$; i.e., consider the function $f: \mathbb{R} \to \mathbb{R}$ (a real-valued function of one variable can be considered as a special case of a general vector-valued function if n is allowed to be equal to 1). Then $Df(x) = f'(x)$ and the statement (b) reads (the symbol $\|.\|$ is replaced by the absolute value, since all terms involved are real numbers)

$$\lim_{x \to a} \frac{|f(x) - [f(a) + f'(a)(x - a)]|}{|x - a|} = 0. \tag{2.13}$$

The expression

$$L_a(x) = f(a) + f'(a)(x - a)$$

appearing in the numerator of (2.13) is called the *linear approximation* or the *lineariza-tion* of f at a. Geometrically, it represents the equation of the line tangent to the graph of f at a (it is written in point-slope form: the point is $(a, f(a))$, and $f'(a)$ is the slope).

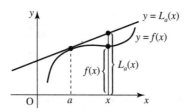

Figure 2.40   The tangent as a linear approximation.

Since the limit in (2.13) is zero and the denominator goes to zero it follows that the numerator $|f(x) - L_a(x)|$ has to approach zero as well. Consequently, (2.13) states that $L_a(x)$ approaches $f(x)$ as x approaches a; i.e., *near a* the functions $f(x)$ and $L_a(x)$ have approximately the same value. This is not important: as a matter of fact, *any* line that goes through $(a, f(a))$ satisfies this property. However, equation (2.13) says a lot more than that: if we rewrite it as

$$\lim_{x \to a} \left| \frac{f(x) - f(a) - f'(a)(x - a)}{x - a} \right| = \lim_{x \to a} \left| \frac{f(x) - f(a)}{x - a} - f'(a) \right| = 0,$$

we see that the *slopes* of $f(x)$ and $L_a(x)$ (recall that the slope of $L_a(x)$ is $f'(a)$) must approach each other. And that is true *only* for the tangent line.

In other words, $L_a(x)$ is a "*good approximation*" to $f(x)$ near a; i.e., the tangent line is a "*good approximation*" to the curve $y = f(x)$ near a; see Figure 2.40.

For example, let $f(x) = xe^{2x}$. Its linearization at $a = 1$ is computed to be ($f'(x) = e^{2x} + 2xe^{2x}$)

$$L_1(x) = f(1) + f'(1)(x - 1) = e^2 + 3e^2(x - 1).$$

Take a point near $a = 1$, say $x = 1.0001$. Then $L_1(1.0001) = 7.3912728$ approximates the value of the function $f(1.0001) = 7.3912731$. Clearly, the closer the number x is to 1, the better the approximation. For values of x that are "far" from 1, the linear approximation does not make any sense. For example, $L_1(0) = -2e^2 = -14.778112$, whereas $f(0) = 0$.

Let us discuss another special case, that of a function $f: \mathbb{R}^2 \to \mathbb{R}$ (i.e., $m = 2$ and $n = 1$). Then (with the notation $\mathbf{x} = (x, y)$ and $\mathbf{a} = (a, b)$)

$$Df(\mathbf{a})(\mathbf{x} - \mathbf{a}) = \left[\frac{\partial f}{\partial x}(a, b) \quad \frac{\partial f}{\partial y}(a, b) \right] \cdot \left[\begin{matrix} x - a \\ y - b \end{matrix} \right]$$

$$= \frac{\partial f}{\partial x}(a, b) \cdot (x - a) + \frac{\partial f}{\partial y}(a, b) \cdot (y - b),$$

and hence (2.12) reads

$$\lim_{(x,y) \to (a,b)} \frac{|f(x, y) - L_{(a,b)}(x, y)|}{\sqrt{(x - a)^2 + (y - b)^2}} = 0, \tag{2.14}$$

where

$$L_{(a,b)}(x, y) = f(a, b) + \frac{\partial f}{\partial x}(a, b) \cdot (x - a) + \frac{\partial f}{\partial y}(a, b) \cdot (y - b) \qquad (2.15)$$

is the *linear approximation* or the *linearization* of F at (a, b). It is a *"good approximation"* of f near (a, b) in the sense that the values of f and $L_{(a,b)}$ for points *near* (a, b) are almost the same; see Figure 2.41.

As an example, consider the function $f(x, y) = 1 + 4x - ye^{-x^2}$. Its linearization at $\mathbf{a} = (0, 0)$ is given by ($\partial f / \partial x = 4 + 2xye^{-x^2}$ and $\partial f / \partial y = -e^{-x^2}$)

$$L_{(0,0)}(x, y) = f(0, 0) + (4 + 2xye^{-x^2})\Big|_{(0,0)} \cdot (x - 0) - e^{-x^2}\Big|_{(0,0)} \cdot (y - 0)$$

$$= 1 + 4x - y.$$

Take a point near $(0, 0)$, for example $\mathbf{x} = (0.05, -0.1)$. The value of the function $f(\mathbf{x}) = f(0.05, -0.1) = 1 + 4 \cdot 0.05 + 0.1e^{-0.05^2} = 1.2997503$ is approximated by the value of its linearization $L_{(0,0)}(\mathbf{x}) = L_{(0,0)}(0.05, -0.1) = 1.3$.

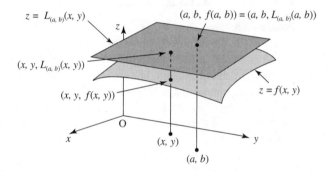

Figure 2.41 Linear approximation $L_{(a,b)}(x, y)$ of a function $f(x, y)$ at (a, b).

Geometrically, this linear approximation represents the equation of a plane in $\mathbb{R}^3$ (in the previous example, $z = L_{(0,0)}(x, y) = 1 + 4x - y$). This plane has the point $(a, b, f(a, b)) = (a, b, L_{(a,b)}(a, b))$ in common with the graph of f, and for points near (a, b), it is close to the graph of f. A plane with these properties is called a *tangent plane* and is defined by the equation

$$z = L_{(a,b)}(x, y) = f(a, b) + \frac{\partial f}{\partial x}(a, b) \cdot (x - a) + \frac{\partial f}{\partial y}(a, b) \cdot (y - b).$$

Based on the two examples we have considered, we say in general that the *linear approximation* $L_{\mathbf{a}}(\mathbf{x})$ of $\mathbf{F}(\mathbf{x})$ at $\mathbf{a}$ or the *linearization* of $\mathbf{F}(\mathbf{x})$ at $\mathbf{a}$, given by

$$L_{\mathbf{a}}(\mathbf{x}) = \mathbf{F}(\mathbf{a}) + D\mathbf{F}(\mathbf{a})(\mathbf{x} - \mathbf{a}) \qquad (2.16)$$

is a *"good approximation"* of $\mathbf{F}$ for points $\mathbf{x}$ near $\mathbf{a}$. Hence, according to Definition 2.12, a vector-valued function $\mathbf{F}$ is differentiable at $\mathbf{a}$ if and only if all partial derivatives of its components exist at $\mathbf{a}$ and its linearization at $\mathbf{a}$ is a "good approximation" in the sense just explained. Another special case, that of a function $\mathbf{F} \colon \mathbb{R}^2 \to \mathbb{R}^2$ will be studied in Section 6.4.

Example 2.37   Compute the equation of the plane tangent to the graph of the function $f(x, y) = \arctan(xy)$ at the point $(1, 1)$.

Solution   From

$$\frac{\partial f}{\partial x} = \frac{y}{1 + x^2 y^2} \quad \text{and} \quad \frac{\partial f}{\partial y} = \frac{x}{1 + x^2 y^2}$$

we get $(\partial f / \partial x)(1, 1) = 1/2$ and $(\partial f / \partial y)(1, 1) = 1/2$. Since $f(1, 1) = \arctan 1 = \pi/4$, the equation of the tangent plane is

$$z = \tfrac{\pi}{4} + \tfrac{1}{2}(x - 1) + \tfrac{1}{2}(y - 1),$$

i.e., $2x + 2y - 4z + \pi - 4 = 0$.   ◄

Example 2.38   Let $f(x, y) = 13 - x^2 - y^2$. Suppose that you use the linear approximation $L_{(1,2)}(x, y)$ of $f(x, y)$ at $(1, 2)$ to approximate the value of f at a point (x, y) near $(1, 2)$. Is this an overestimate or an underestimate of $f(x, y)$?

Solution   The level curves $f(x, y) = 13 - x^2 - y^2 = C$ are circles of radius $\sqrt{13 - C}$ for $C < 13$. The intersections of the graph of f with the xz-plane and the yz-plane are the parabolas $z = 13 - x^2$ and $z = 13 - y^2$, both of which are concave down. In other words, the graph of f is a surface built of circles, smaller ones placed on top of the larger ones in such a way that the vertical cross-sections are parabolas. The surface is concave down, so the tangent plane must lie above it. Hence the value of the linear approximation at a point near $(1, 2)$ is larger than the value of the function. The estimate is an overestimate.   ◄

We will discuss another interpretation of the linear approximation formula. Choose a point (a, b) in the domain of a differentiable function $f : \mathbb{R}^2 \to \mathbb{R}$. Measure the value of f at (a, b) and then move to a nearby point $(x, y) = (a + \Delta x, b + \Delta y)$ ("nearby" means that Δx and Δy are small). We would like to compare the value of f at this point with its initial value $f(a, b)$ at (a, b). In other words, we would like to compute or estimate the change (sometimes called the error) Δf in f, defined by $\Delta f = f(x, y) - f(a, b) = f(a + \Delta x, b + \Delta y) - f(a, b)$.

Since $f(x, y) \approx L_{(a,b)}(x, y)$, where $L_{(a,b)}(x, y)$ is the linear approximation of f at (a, b), it follows that

$$f(x, y) \approx f(a, b) + f_x(a, b)(x - a) + f_y(a, b)(y - b),$$

and

$$f(x, y) - f(a, b) \approx f_x(a, b)(x - a) + f_y(a, b)(y - b).$$

The right side of this approximate equality is equal to $f_x(a, b)\Delta x + f_y(a, b)\Delta y$ and is denoted by df (and called the *differential* of f). The left side is the change (or the error) Δf, and hence $\Delta f \approx df$; i.e.,

$$\Delta f \approx f_x(a, b)\Delta x + f_y(a, b)\Delta y.$$

This formula says that we can estimate the change in the function Δf in terms of the change (or the error) Δx in the variable x and the change (or the error) Δy in the variable y. Analogous expressions can be obtained for a function of any number of variables.

In the theory of functions of one variable one proves that if a function f has a derivative then it is continuous. The analogous statement ("differentiability implies continuity") also holds for functions of more than one variable; see Theorem 2.4. However, a function whose partial derivatives exist might not be continuous, as the following example shows.

Example 2.39   Define $f: \mathbb{R}^2 \to \mathbb{R}$ by

$$f(x, y) = \begin{cases} \dfrac{xy}{x^2 + y^2} & \text{if } (x, y) \neq (0, 0) \\[2ex] 0 & \text{if } (x, y) = (0, 0) \end{cases}.$$

By definition,

$$\frac{\partial f}{\partial x}(0, 0) = \lim_{h \to 0} \frac{f(h, 0) - f(0, 0)}{h} = \lim_{h \to 0} \frac{0 - 0}{h} = 0$$

and

$$\frac{\partial f}{\partial y}(0, 0) = \lim_{h \to 0} \frac{f(0, h) - f(0, 0)}{h} = \lim_{h \to 0} \frac{0 - 0}{h} = 0,$$

hence both partial derivatives exist at $(0, 0)$. On the other hand, the limit of f as (x, y) approaches $(0, 0)$ does not exist. To prove this, we will show that two different ways of reaching $(0, 0)$ yield two different results. Walking along the y-axis (i.e., setting $x = 0$) towards $(0, 0)$, we get

$$\lim_{x=0, y \to 0} \frac{xy}{x^2 + y^2} = \lim_{y \to 0} \frac{0}{y^2} = \lim_{y \to 0} 0 = 0.$$

Approaching $(0, 0)$ along the line $y = x$ we get

$$\lim_{(x, y) \to (0, 0)} \frac{xy}{x^2 + y^2} = \lim_{x \to 0} \frac{x^2}{x^2 + x^2} = \lim_{x \to 0} \frac{1}{2} = \frac{1}{2},$$

and therefore the limit of $f(x, y)$ as (x, y) approaches $(0, 0)$ does not exist. Consequently, f cannot be continuous at $(0, 0)$.   ◀

Therefore, the mere existence of partial derivatives does not imply the continuity of a function. However, an extra assumption fixes this problem.

■ Theorem 2.4   Differentiable Functions Are Continuous.

Let $\mathbf{F}: U \subseteq \mathbb{R}^m \to \mathbb{R}^n$ be a vector-valued function and let $\mathbf{a} \in U$. If $\mathbf{F}$ is differentiable at $\mathbf{a}$ then it is continuous at $\mathbf{a}$.   ■

This theorem is the correct generalization of the one-variable case: namely, if the components of **F** have partial derivatives *and* the derivative $D\mathbf{F}$ is a good approximation of **F**, then **F** is continuous. The proof of the theorem will be presented in Appendix A.

Example 2.39 says that a function whose partial derivatives exist might not be differentiable (if it were differentiable, it would have been continuous by Theorem 2.4). In other words, the existence of partial derivatives does not imply differentiability. However, if all partial derivatives are continuous, the implication is valid, as the following theorem shows.

■ **Theorem 2.5**   Continuity of Partial Derivatives Implies Differentiability.

Let $\mathbf{F}: U \subseteq \mathbb{R}^m \to \mathbb{R}^n$ be a vector-valued function with components $F_1, \dots, F_n: U \subseteq \mathbb{R}^m \to \mathbb{R}$. If all partial derivatives $\partial F_i / \partial x_j$ $(i = 1, \dots, n, \ j = 1 \dots, m)$ are continuous at **a**, then **F** is differentiable at **a**.   ■

Proving the differentiablity of a function using Definition 2.12 is usually fairly complicated. This theorem gives a more convenient alternative: all we have to do is to check that all partial derivatives exist and are continuous at the point(s) in question. The proof will appear in Appendix A.

■ **Definition 2.14**   Function of Class C^1.

A function whose partial derivatives exist and are continuous is said to be *continuously differentiable,* or *of class C^1.*   ▣

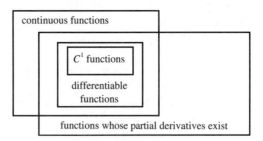

Figure 2.42   Continuity, differentiability and partial derivatives.

The definitions and theorems we have stated could be visually represented on a diagram; see Figure 2.42 (containment means implication; i.e., functions contained in one "box" have properties defining any other "box" that contains it). Let us read out a few facts from the diagram. Functions of class C^1 (those are in the smallest "box") are differentiable (those functions are in the larger box) — that is the statement of Theorem 2.5. Differentiable functions are continuous (Theorem 2.4). If a function has partial derivatives, it might not be differentiable (that was the conclusion of Example 2.39). Not every differentiable function is of class C^1, etc.

EXERCISES 2.4   **Exercises 1 to 6:** Determine which of the following sets are open.

1. $U = \{(x, y) \mid 2 < x^2 + y^2 < 3\} \subseteq \mathbb{R}^2$ 2. $U = \{(x, y, z) \mid x \geq 0\} \subseteq \mathbb{R}^3$

3. $U = \{(x, y) \mid x + y = 2\} \subseteq \mathbb{R}^2$ 4. $U = \{(x, y) \mid x + y < 2\} \subseteq \mathbb{R}^2$

5. $U = \{(x, y, z) \mid xyz > 0\} \subseteq \mathbb{R}^3$ 6. $U = \{(x, y, z) \mid x \neq 0, y > 0\} \subseteq \mathbb{R}^3$

Exercises 7 to 18: Find the indicated partial derivatives.

7. $f(x, y) = x^y + y \ln x$; f_x, f_y 8. $f(x, y, z) = xe^{yz^2}$; f_x, f_y, f_z

9. $f(x, y, z) = \ln(x + y + z^2)$; f_x, f_z 10. $f(x, y) = \arctan(x/y)$; f_x, f_y

11. $f(x, y) = (x^3 + y^3)/(x^2 - y^2)$; f_x, f_y 12. $f(x, y) = \sin(e^{xy})$; f_x, f_y

13. $f(x, y) = e^{xy} \cos x \sin y$; f_x, f_y 14. $f(x, y, z) = x\sqrt{y\sqrt{z}}$; f_x, f_y, f_z

15. $f(x_1, \ldots, x_m) = \sqrt{x_1^2 + \ldots + x_m^2}$; $\partial f/\partial x_i$, $i = 1, \ldots, m$

16. $f(x_1, \ldots, x_m) = e^{x_1 \cdots x_m}$; $\partial f/\partial x_i$, $i = 1, \ldots, m$

17. $f(x, y) = \int_0^x te^{-t^2}\, dt$; f_x, f_y 18. $f(x, y) = \int_{\ln y}^0 (t + 1)^2\, dt$; f_x, f_y

Exercises 19 to 22: The function $z(x, y)$ is defined in terms of two differentiable real-valued functions f and g of one variable. Compute z_x and z_y.

19. $z = f(x) + g(y)$ 20. $z = f(x)g(y)$

21. $z = f(x)/g(y)$ 22. $z = f(x)^{g(y)}$

23. A hiker is standing at the point $(2, 1, 11)$ on a hill whose shape is given by the graph of the function $z = 14 - (x - 3)^2 - 2(y - 2)^4$. Assume that the x-axis points east and the y-axis points north. In which of the two directions (east or north) is the hill steeper?

24. The volume of a certain amount of gas is determined by $V = 0.12TP^{-1}$, where T is the temperature and P is the pressure. Compute and interpret $\partial V/\partial P$ and $\partial V/\partial T$ when $P = 10$ and $T = 370$.

25. Consider the function $f(x, y) = -xe^{-x^2 - 2y^2}$.

   (a) Compute $f_y(2, 3)$.

   (b) Find the curve that is the intersection of the graph of f and the vertical plane $x = 2$ and compute the slope of its tangent at $y = 3$.

   (c) Using (a) and (b), give a geometric interpretation of $f_y(2, 3)$.

26. Let $u(x, y, t) = e^{-2t} \sin(3x) \cos(2y)$ denote the vertical displacement of a vibrating membrane from the point (x, y) in the xy-plane at the time t. Compute $u_x(x, y, t)$, $u_y(x, y, t)$, and $u_t(x, y, t)$ and give physical interpretations of your results.

Exercises 27 to 31: Compute the derivative of the function $\mathbf{F}$ at the point $\mathbf{a}$.

27. $\mathbf{F}(x, y) = (y, x, 11)$, $\mathbf{a} = (0, 0)$ 28. $\mathbf{F}(x, y) = (e^{xy}, x^2 + y^2)$, $\mathbf{a} = (a_1, a_2)$

29. $\mathbf{F}(x, y, z) = (\ln(x^2 + y^2 + z^2), 2xy + z)$, $\mathbf{a} = (1, 1, 0)$

30. $\mathbf{F}(x, y) = (x/\sqrt{x^2 + y^2}, y/\sqrt{x^2 + y^2})$, $\mathbf{a} = (a_1, a_2) \neq (0, 0)$

31. $f(x, y, z) = \|x\mathbf{i} + y\mathbf{j} + z\mathbf{k}\|^2$, $\mathbf{a} = (a_1, a_2, a_3)$

32. Compute $\nabla f(2, 1, -1)$ if $f(x, y, z) = xy \ln(z^2 + xy)$.

33. Find the gradient of $f(x, y) = (x - y) \cos(x^2 + y^2)$ at $(0, 0)$.

34. Let $f(x, y, z) = xyz(x^2 + y^2 + z^2)^{-2}$. Compute $\nabla f(x, y, z)$ for $(x, y, z) \neq (0, 0, 0)$.

35. Define $f : \mathbb{R}^3 \to \mathbb{R}$ by $f(\mathbf{x}) = \|\mathbf{x}\|$. Find $\nabla f(\mathbf{x})$ and state its domain.

Exercises 36 to 42: Find the linear approximation of the function f at the point $\mathbf{a}$.

36. $f(x, y) = e^{-x^2 - y^2}$, $\mathbf{a} = (0, 0)$

37. $f(x, y) = \ln(3x + 2y)$, $\mathbf{a} = (2, -1)$

38. $f(x, y) = xy(x^2 + y^2)^{-1}$, $\mathbf{a} = (0, 1)$

39. $f(x, y) = x^2 - xy + y^2/2 + 3$, $\mathbf{a} = (3, 2)$

40. $f(x, y, z) = \ln(x^2 - y^2 + z)$, $\mathbf{a} = (3, 3, 1)$

41. $f(x, y, z) = \sqrt{x^2 + y^2 + z^2}$, $\mathbf{a} = (0, 1, 1)$

42. $f(x, y) = \int_x^y e^{-t^2}\, dt$, $\mathbf{a} = (1, 1)$

43. Verify the approximation $xy(x + y)^{-1} \approx \frac{6}{5} + \frac{9}{25}(x - 2) + \frac{4}{25}(y - 3)$, for (x, y) sufficiently close to $(2, 3)$.

44. Prove that $\ln(2x^2 + 3y - 4) \approx 4x + 3y - 7$, for (x, y) sufficiently close to $(1, 1)$.

Exercises 45 to 49: Approximate the value of the given expression and compare (except in Exercise 49) with the calculator value.

45. $\sqrt{0.99^3 + 2.02^3}$

46. $-0.09\sqrt{4.11^3 - 14.98}$

47. $7.95 \ln 1.02$

48. $\sin(\pi/50) \cos(49\pi/50)$

49. $\displaystyle\int_{0.995}^{1.02} e^{-t^2}\, dt$

Exercises 50 to 53: Compare the values of Δf and df.

50. $f(x, y) = x^2 - xy + 2y^2 + 1$, $(a, b) = (0, 1)$, $\Delta x = 0.01$, $\Delta y = 0.2$

51. $f(x, y) = e^x - ye^y$, $(a, b) = (0, 1)$, $\Delta x = 0.3$, $\Delta y = 0.01$

52. $f(x, y) = x^3 + xy + y^3$, $(a, b) = (-2, 1)$, $(x, y) = (-2.05, 0.9)$

53. $f(x, y, z) = x^2 y - xyz + z^3$, $(a, b, c) = (1, 2, -1)$, $\Delta x = -0.02$, $\Delta y = 0.01$ and $\Delta z = 0.02$

54. Estimate the maximum possible error in computing $f(x, y) = x \cos y$ where $x = 2$ and $y = \pi/3$, with maximum possible errors $\Delta x = 0.2$ and $\Delta y = 0.1$.

55. About how accurately can the volume of a cylinder be calculated from the measurements of its height and radius that are in error by 1.5%?

56. The dimensions of a closed rectangular box are measured as 20 cm, 50 cm and 120 cm respectively, with a possible error of 0.4 cm in each dimension. Estimate the maximum error in computing the volume and the surface area of the box.

57. The length and the width of a rectangle are measured with a possible error of 2% in length and 3% in width. Approximate the error in computing the area of the rectangle.

58. Let $f(x, y) = 2x^2 y^3$. Estimate the change in the function f if x increases by 3% and y

increases by 2%.

59. The total resistance R of three resistors R_1, R_2 and R_3 connected in parallel is given by $R = (1/R_1 + 1/R_2 + 1/R_3)^{-1}$. Assume that $R_1 = 10 \; \Omega$, $R_2 = 10 \; \Omega$ and $R_3 = 20 \; \Omega$. Approximate the change in R when R_1 is increased by $1 \; \Omega$, R_2 is increased by $2 \; \Omega$ and R_3 is decreased by $1 \; \Omega$. Compare with the calculator value.

60. Let $\mathbf{c}(t) = (te^t, (1-t)e^t, e^t)$, $t \in [0, 1]$ describe the position of a particle. Find its velocity and acceleration.

61. The curve $\mathbf{c}(t) = (t^2, 1/t)$, $t > 0$, represents the position of a particle in the xy-plane. Find its velocity and acceleration at $t = 2$, $t = 1$ and $t = 1/10$. Describe what happens (in terms of magnitudes of the velocity and the acceleration) as t approaches 0.

62. A particle moves along the surface of the paraboloid $z = 10 - x^2 - 2y^2$ from the point $(-2, 3, -12)$ in such a way that the projection of its trajectory onto the xy-plane is a line parallel to the x-axis. Find the highest position of the particle.

63. Find the equation of the tangent plane to the graph of the function $z = 6 - x^2 - y^2$ at the point $(1, 2, 1)$.

64. Find the equation of the tangent plane to the surface $z = 3xy/(x - 2y)$ at the point $(3, 1, 9)$. Check whether the tangent plane contains the origin.

65. Define the function $f: \mathbb{R}^2 \to \mathbb{R}$ by

$$f(x, y) = \begin{cases} y \ln(x^2 + y^2) & \text{if } (x, y) \neq (0, 0) \\ 0 & \text{if } (x, y) = (0, 0) \end{cases}.$$

Show that f_x is defined for all (x, y), but that f_x is not continuous at $(0, 0)$.

66. Define the function $f: \mathbb{R}^2 \to \mathbb{R}$ by

$$f(x, y) = \begin{cases} \dfrac{xy^2}{x^2 + y^4} & \text{if } (x, y) \neq (0, 0) \\ 0 & \text{if } (x, y) = (0, 0) \end{cases}.$$

(a) Is f continuous at $(0, 0)$?

(b) Compute the linear approximation (if it exists) at $(0, 0)$.

(c) Is f_x continuous at $(0, 0)$?

(d) Is f differentiable?

67. Show that the function $\mathbf{F}(x, y) = (x + y^2, 2xy)$ is differentiable at $(0, 0)$.

2.5 PROPERTIES OF DERIVATIVES

After presenting the definition of a derivative, the calculus of functions of one variable proceeds by proving theorems that relate the derivatives of combinations of two functions (such as the sum, the product, or the composition) to the derivatives of the functions themselves. For example, the product rule formula $(fg)' = f'g + fg'$ expresses the derivative of the product of f and g in terms of f and g and their derivatives f' and g'. Although it is always possible to use the definition to find the derivative of a function, the computation is usually (technically) hard and quite lengthy. The differentiation rules provide a significantly easier alternative. We start by generalizing these rules to functions of several variables.

■ Theorem 2.6   Properties of Derivatives.

(a) Assume that the functions $\mathbf{F}, \mathbf{G}: U \subseteq \mathbb{R}^m \to \mathbb{R}^n$ are differentiable at $\mathbf{a} \in U$. Then the sum $\mathbf{F} + \mathbf{G}$ and the difference $\mathbf{F} - \mathbf{G}$ are differentiable at $\mathbf{a}$ and

$$D(\mathbf{F}+\mathbf{G})(\mathbf{a}) = D\mathbf{F}(\mathbf{a}) + D\mathbf{G}(\mathbf{a}) \quad \text{and} \quad D(\mathbf{F}-\mathbf{G})(\mathbf{a}) = D\mathbf{F}(\mathbf{a}) - D\mathbf{G}(\mathbf{a}).$$

(b) If the function $\mathbf{F}: U \subseteq \mathbb{R}^m \to \mathbb{R}^n$ is differentiable at $\mathbf{a} \in U$ and $c \in \mathbb{R}$ is a constant, then the product $c\mathbf{F}$ is differentiable at $\mathbf{a}$ and

$$D(c\mathbf{F})(\mathbf{a}) = c\, D\mathbf{F}(\mathbf{a}).$$

(c) If the real-valued functions $f, g: U \subseteq \mathbb{R}^m \to \mathbb{R}$ are differentiable at $\mathbf{a} \in U$ then their product fg is differentiable at $\mathbf{a}$ and

$$D(fg)(\mathbf{a}) = g(\mathbf{a})Df(\mathbf{a}) + f(\mathbf{a})Dg(\mathbf{a}).$$

(d) If the real-valued functions $f, g: U \subseteq \mathbb{R}^m \to \mathbb{R}$ are differentiable at $\mathbf{a} \in U$ then their quotient f/g is differentiable at $\mathbf{a}$ and

$$D\left(\frac{f}{g}\right)(\mathbf{a}) = \frac{g(\mathbf{a})Df(\mathbf{a}) - f(\mathbf{a})Dg(\mathbf{a})}{g(\mathbf{a})^2},$$

if $g(\mathbf{a}) \neq 0$.

(e) If the vector-valued functions $\mathbf{v}, \mathbf{w}: U \subseteq \mathbb{R} \to \mathbb{R}^n$ are differentiable at $a \in U$, then their dot (scalar) product $\mathbf{v} \cdot \mathbf{w}$ is differentiable at a and

$$(\mathbf{v} \cdot \mathbf{w})'(a) = \mathbf{v}'(a) \cdot \mathbf{w}(a) + \mathbf{v}(a) \cdot \mathbf{w}'(a).$$

(f) If the vector-valued functions $\mathbf{v}, \mathbf{w}: U \subseteq \mathbb{R} \to \mathbb{R}^3$ are differentiable at $a \in U$, their cross (vector) product $\mathbf{v} \times \mathbf{w}$ is differentiable at a and

$$(\mathbf{v} \times \mathbf{w})'(a) = \mathbf{v}'(a) \times \mathbf{w}(a) + \mathbf{v}(a) \times \mathbf{w}'(a).$$

■

The algebraic operations on the right sides of formulas (a) – (d) are matrix operations. The sum and the difference of two matrices appear in (a), (c) and (d) (the matrices are of type $n \times m$ in (a), and of type $1 \times m$ in (c) and (d)). The product of a scalar and a matrix appears in (b), (c) and (d) (the fraction in (d) is the product of the scalar $1/g(\mathbf{a})^2$ and the matrix $g(\mathbf{a})Df(\mathbf{a}) - f(\mathbf{a})Dg(\mathbf{a})$). Using the symbol ∇ to denote the gradient, we can rewrite (c) and (d) as

$$\nabla(fg)(\mathbf{a}) = g(\mathbf{a})\nabla f(\mathbf{a}) + f(\mathbf{a})\nabla g(\mathbf{a})$$

and

$$\nabla\left(\frac{f}{g}\right)(\mathbf{a}) = \frac{g(\mathbf{a})\nabla f(\mathbf{a}) - f(\mathbf{a})\nabla g(\mathbf{a})}{g(\mathbf{a})^2}.$$

If $\mathbf{v}$ and $\mathbf{w}$ are vector-valued functions of one variable (that is usually denoted by t) then their dot (or scalar) product is a real-valued function that assigns to every t the real number $\mathbf{v}(t) \cdot \mathbf{w}(t)$. Therefore, the derivative on the left side of (e) is the derivative of a real-valued function of one variable (hence the notation $()'$ instead of D). Each term on the right side is a dot product of two vectors in $\mathbb{R}^n$. This time, $()'$ denotes the derivative of a vector-valued function of one variable (also called the velocity). All derivatives in (f) are derivatives of vector-valued functions of one variable. The left side is the derivative of the function that assigns a cross product of vectors $\mathbf{v}(t)$ and $\mathbf{w}(t)$ to every t. Since the cross product is defined only in $\mathbb{R}^3$, both $\mathbf{v}$ and $\mathbf{w}$ must have values in $\mathbb{R}^3$.

The proofs of statements (a) – (d) are analogous to the proofs of corresponding statements in the one-variable case. If we write vectors $\mathbf{v}$ and $\mathbf{w}$ in terms of their components, we can reduce the proofs of (e) and (f) again to the one-variable case. For completeness, the proofs are given in Appendix A.

Example 2.40 Let $f(x, y, z) = xy + e^z$ and $g(x, y, z) = 5 + y^2 \sin z$. Compute $D(fg)(0, 1, \pi)$.

Solution By the product rule (the vertical bar is read "evaluated at"),

$$D(fg)(0, 1, \pi) = g(0, 1, \pi)D(f)(0, 1, \pi) + f(0, 1, \pi)D(g)(0, 1, \pi)$$

$$= (5 + y^2 \sin z)\Big|_{(0,1,\pi)} [\, y \quad x \quad e^z \,]\Big|_{(0,1,\pi)}$$

$$+ (xy + e^z)\Big|_{(0,1,\pi)} [\, 0 \quad 2y \sin z \quad y^2 \cos z \,]\Big|_{(0,1,\pi)}$$

$$= 5\,[\,1 \quad 0 \quad e^\pi\,] + e^\pi\,[\,0 \quad 0 \quad -1\,]$$

$$= [\,5 \quad 0 \quad 4e^\pi\,].$$

Example 2.41 Compute $\nabla(f/g)(x, y, z)$ if $f(x, y, z) = -x^2y^2$ and $g(x, y, z) = 2yz$.

Solution Using the quotient rule we get

$$\nabla(f/g)(x, y, z) = \frac{g(x, y, z)\nabla f(x, y, z) - f(x, y, z)\nabla g(x, y, z)}{g(x, y, z)^2}$$

$$= \frac{2yz\,[\,-2xy^2 \quad -2x^2y \quad 0\,] + x^2y^2\,[\,0 \quad 2z \quad 2y\,]}{4y^2z^2}$$

$$= \frac{[\,-4xy^3z \quad -2x^2y^2z \quad 2x^2y^3\,]}{4y^2z^2}$$

$$= \left[\,\frac{-xy}{z} \quad -\frac{x^2}{2z} \quad \frac{x^2y}{2z^2}\,\right].$$

In the last step, the matrix appearing in the numerator was multiplied by the real-valued function $1/4y^2z^2$.

Example 2.42   Let $\mathbf{v}(t) = t\mathbf{i} + \sin t\mathbf{j} + \cos t\mathbf{k}$ and $\mathbf{w} = 3t\mathbf{i} + 2\mathbf{k}$. Compute $(\mathbf{v} \cdot \mathbf{w})'(t)$ directly (i.e., by first computing the dot product and then differentiating) and check your result by using the product rule (e) from Theorem 2.6.

Solution   The dot product of $\mathbf{v}$ and $\mathbf{w}$ is computed to be

$$(\mathbf{v} \cdot \mathbf{w})(t) = \mathbf{v}(t) \cdot \mathbf{w}(t) = (t\mathbf{i} + \sin t\mathbf{j} + \cos t\mathbf{k}) \cdot (3t\mathbf{i} + 2\mathbf{k}) = 3t^2 + 2\cos t,$$

and consequently,

$$(\mathbf{v} \cdot \mathbf{w})'(t) = 6t - 2\sin t.$$

Since $\mathbf{v}'(t) = \mathbf{i} + \cos t\mathbf{j} - \sin t\mathbf{k}$ and $\mathbf{w}'(t) = 3\mathbf{i}$, it follows that

$$\mathbf{v}'(t) \cdot \mathbf{w}(t) + \mathbf{v}(t) \cdot \mathbf{w}'(t)$$
$$= (\mathbf{i} + \cos t\mathbf{j} - \sin t\mathbf{k}) \cdot (3t\mathbf{i} + 2\mathbf{k}) + (t\mathbf{i} + \sin t\mathbf{j} + \cos t\mathbf{k}) \cdot (3\mathbf{i})$$
$$= 6t - 2\sin t,$$

as expected.

◀

Example 2.43   Motion of a Particle on the Surface of a Sphere.

Assume that a particle moves in space so that its distance from the origin O remains constant; i.e., $\|\mathbf{r}(t)\| = c$, where $\mathbf{r}(t)$ is the position vector of the particle and $c > 0$. In other words, the particle moves along the surface of the sphere with radius c centered at the origin. Now $\|\mathbf{r}(t)\|^2 = c^2$ is also constant and hence $(d/dt)\|\mathbf{r}(t)\|^2 = 0$ and (by the product rule)

$$0 = \frac{d}{dt}\|\mathbf{r}(t)\|^2 = \frac{d}{dt}(\mathbf{r}(t) \cdot \mathbf{r}(t)) = \left(\frac{d}{dt}\mathbf{r}(t)\right) \cdot \mathbf{r}(t) + \mathbf{r}(t) \cdot \left(\frac{d}{dt}\mathbf{r}(t)\right) = 2\mathbf{r}(t) \cdot \mathbf{v}(t),$$

where $\mathbf{v}(t) = d\mathbf{r}(t)/dt$ is the velocity of the particle at time t. Hence $\mathbf{r}(t) \cdot \mathbf{v}(t) = 0$, so that either $\mathbf{v}(t) = 0$ (which means that the particle is at rest), or the velocity vector is always orthogonal to the position vector $\mathbf{r}(t)$; see Figure 2.43.

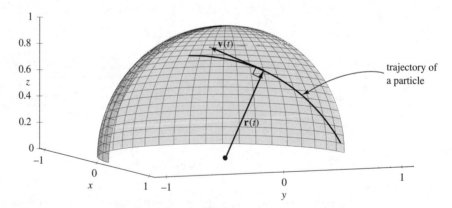

Figure 2.43   For motion on a sphere centered at the origin, the velocity vector is always perpendicular to the position vector.

The converse of the above statement is true as well: if the particle moves so that $\mathbf{r}(t) \cdot \mathbf{v}(t) = 0$, then the computation above (read from right to left) shows that $d\|\mathbf{r}(t)\|^2/dt = 0$; i.e., $\|\mathbf{r}(t)\| = $ constant. Consequently, the particle moves on the surface of a sphere.

◄

Example 2.44

Kinetic Energy of a Charged Particle in a Magnetic Field.

Consider the motion of a particle (described by the vector function $\mathbf{r}(t)$) of mass m and charge q in a constant magnetic field $\mathbf{B}$, with no electric field present. The electromagnetic force (see equation (2.5), with $\mathbf{E} = \mathbf{0}$)

$$\mathbf{F}(\mathbf{r}(t)) = q(\mathbf{v}(t) \times \mathbf{B}),$$

and Newton's Second Law

$$\mathbf{F}(\mathbf{r}(t)) = m\mathbf{a}(t) = m\mathbf{v}'(t)$$

imply that

$$m\mathbf{v}'(t) = q(\mathbf{v}(t) \times \mathbf{B}).$$

Show that the kinetic energy $K(t) = (1/2)m\|\mathbf{v}(t)\|^2$ is constant in time.

Solution   We will show that the derivative of $K(t)$ is zero:

$$\left(\frac{1}{2}m\|\mathbf{v}(t)\|^2\right)' = \frac{1}{2}m\left(\mathbf{v}(t)\cdot\mathbf{v}(t)\right)' = \frac{1}{2}m(\mathbf{v}(t)\cdot\mathbf{v}'(t) + \mathbf{v}'(t)\cdot\mathbf{v}(t))$$

$$= m\mathbf{v}(t)\cdot\mathbf{v}'(t) = m\left(\mathbf{v}(t)\cdot\frac{q}{m}(\mathbf{v}(t)\times\mathbf{B})\right)$$

$$= q\left(\mathbf{v}(t)\cdot(\mathbf{v}(t)\times\mathbf{B})\right)$$

(the product rule was used in the first line, and Newton's Second Law was used in the second line). By definition of the vector product the vector $\mathbf{v}(t) \times \mathbf{B}$ is perpendicular to $\mathbf{v}(t)$ and hence their scalar product $\mathbf{v}(t) \cdot (\mathbf{v}(t) \times \mathbf{B})$ is zero.

◄

The statement of our next theorem is a generalization of the one-variable chain rule.

■ **Theorem 2.7**   **Chain Rule.**

Suppose that $\mathbf{F}: U \subseteq \mathbb{R}^m \to \mathbb{R}^n$ is differentiable at $\mathbf{a} \in U$, U is open in $\mathbb{R}^m$, $\mathbf{G}: V \subseteq \mathbb{R}^n \to \mathbb{R}^p$ is differentiable at $\mathbf{F}(\mathbf{a}) \in V$, V is open in $\mathbb{R}^n$, and $\mathbf{F}(U) \subseteq V$ (so that the composition $\mathbf{G} \circ \mathbf{F}$ is defined). Then $\mathbf{G} \circ \mathbf{F}$ is differentiable at $\mathbf{a}$ and

$$D(\mathbf{G} \circ \mathbf{F})(\mathbf{a}) = D\mathbf{G}(\mathbf{F}(\mathbf{a})) \cdot D\mathbf{F}(\mathbf{a}),$$

where $\cdot$ denotes matrix multiplication.

■

The theorem states that the derivative of the composition $\mathbf{G} \circ \mathbf{F}$ at a point $\mathbf{a}$ in U can be computed as a matrix product of the derivative of $\mathbf{G}$ (evaluated at $\mathbf{F}(\mathbf{a})$) and the derivative of $\mathbf{F}$ (evaluated at $\mathbf{a}$). One easily checks that the matrices on both sides of the chain rule formula are of the same type: since $\mathbf{G} \circ \mathbf{F}: U \subseteq \mathbb{R}^m \to \mathbb{R}^p$, $D(\mathbf{G} \circ \mathbf{F})$ is a $p \times m$ matrix. The right side is a product of the $p \times n$ matrix $D\mathbf{G}(\mathbf{F}(\mathbf{a}))$ and the $n \times m$ matrix $D\mathbf{F}(\mathbf{a})$, and is hence a $p \times m$ matrix. The proof of the theorem is given in Appendix A. We will now compute several examples in order to become more familiar with the chain rule.

Example 2.45

Let $\mathbf{F}: \mathbb{R}^2 \to \mathbb{R}^3$ be given by $\mathbf{F}(x, y) = (x^3 + y, e^{xy}, 2 + xy)$ and let $\mathbf{G}: \mathbb{R}^3 \to \mathbb{R}^2$ be given by $\mathbf{G}(u, v, w) = (u^2 + v, uv + w^3)$. Compute $D(\mathbf{G} \circ \mathbf{F})(0, 1)$.

Solution   By the chain rule,
$$D(\mathbf{G} \circ \mathbf{F})(0, 1) = D\mathbf{G}(\mathbf{F}(0, 1)) \cdot D\mathbf{F}(0, 1) = D\mathbf{G}(1, 1, 2) \cdot D\mathbf{F}(0, 1).$$
The derivatives of F and G are computed to be
$$D\mathbf{F}(0, 1) = \begin{bmatrix} 3x^2 & 1 \\ ye^{xy} & xe^{xy} \\ y & x \end{bmatrix}_{at\ (0,1)} = \begin{bmatrix} 0 & 1 \\ 1 & 0 \\ 1 & 0 \end{bmatrix}$$
and
$$D\mathbf{G}(1, 1, 2) = \begin{bmatrix} 2u & 1 & 0 \\ v & u & 3w^2 \end{bmatrix}_{at\ (1,1,2)} = \begin{bmatrix} 2 & 1 & 0 \\ 1 & 1 & 12 \end{bmatrix},$$
so that
$$D(\mathbf{G} \circ \mathbf{F})(0, 1) = \begin{bmatrix} 2 & 1 & 0 \\ 1 & 1 & 12 \end{bmatrix} \cdot \begin{bmatrix} 0 & 1 \\ 1 & 0 \\ 1 & 0 \end{bmatrix} = \begin{bmatrix} 1 & 2 \\ 13 & 1 \end{bmatrix}.$$

To check the result, compute the composition
$$\begin{aligned} (\mathbf{G} \circ \mathbf{F})(x, y) &= \mathbf{G}(\mathbf{F}(x, y)) \\ &= \mathbf{G}(x^3 + y, e^{xy}, 2 + xy) \\ &= ((x^3 + y)^2 + e^{xy}, (x^3 + y)e^{xy} + (2 + xy)^3), \end{aligned}$$

to obtain the function $\mathbf{G} \circ \mathbf{F}: \mathbb{R}^2 \to \mathbb{R}^2$. Its derivative $D(\mathbf{G} \circ \mathbf{F})$ is a 2×2 matrix
$$\begin{bmatrix} 6(x^3 + y)x^2 + ye^{xy} & 2(x^3 + y)^2 + xe^{xy} \\ 3x^2e^{xy} + (x^3 + y)ye^{xy} + 3(2 + xy)^2y & e^{xy} + xye^{xy} + 3(2 + xy)^2x \end{bmatrix},$$
which gives
$$D(\mathbf{G} \circ \mathbf{F})(0, 1) = \begin{bmatrix} 1 & 2 \\ 13 & 1 \end{bmatrix}$$
when evaluated at $(0, 1)$.

Example 2.46

The composition $(f \circ \mathbf{c})(t)$ of $f: \mathbb{R}^2 \to \mathbb{R}$, $f(x, y) = x^2 + 2y^2$ and $\mathbf{c}: \mathbb{R} \to \mathbb{R}^2$, $\mathbf{c}(t) = (e^t, te^t)$ is a real-valued function of one variable. Compute $(f \circ \mathbf{c})'(0)$.

Solution   By the chain rule,
$$(f \circ \mathbf{c})'(0) = D(f \circ \mathbf{c})(0) = Df(\mathbf{c}(0)) \cdot D\mathbf{c}(0) = Df(1, 0) \cdot D\mathbf{c}(0).$$

The function f is a real-valued function of two variables, so its derivative (also called the gradient) is a 1×2 matrix $Df(x, y) = [\,2x \quad 4y\,]$. Hence $Df(1, 0) = [\,2 \quad 0\,]$. The function $\mathbf{c}$ (also called a path in $\mathbb{R}^2$) is a function of one variable, and its derivative $D\mathbf{c}(t) = \mathbf{c}'(t)$ is a 2×1 matrix

$$D\mathbf{c}(t) = \begin{bmatrix} e^t \\ e^t + te^t \end{bmatrix}.$$

Consequently,

$$D\mathbf{c}(0) = \begin{bmatrix} 1 \\ 1 \end{bmatrix}$$

and

$$(f \circ \mathbf{c})'(0) = [\,2 \quad 0\,] \cdot \begin{bmatrix} 1 \\ 1 \end{bmatrix} = 2.$$

The result can be checked by direct computation: Since

$$(f \circ \mathbf{c})(t) = f(\mathbf{c}(t)) = f(e^t, te^t) = e^{2t} + 2t^2 e^{2t},$$

it follows that

$$(f \circ \mathbf{c})'(t) = 2e^{2t} + 4te^{2t} + 4t^2 e^{2t},$$

and, consequently, $(f \circ \mathbf{c})'(0) = 2.$

◀

Example 2.47 Consider the composition $f \circ \mathbf{c}$, where $f = f(x, y, z): \mathbb{R}^3 \to \mathbb{R}$ and $\mathbf{c}: \mathbb{R} \to \mathbb{R}^3$ is given by $\mathbf{c}(t) = (x(t), y(t), z(t))$. Assume that both f and $\mathbf{c}$ are differentiable. Then
$$(f \circ \mathbf{c})(t) = f(\mathbf{c}(t)) = f(x(t), y(t), z(t)),$$
and, by the chain rule,

$$D(f \circ \mathbf{c})(t) = Df(\mathbf{c}(t)) \cdot D\mathbf{c}(t) = \begin{bmatrix} \dfrac{\partial f}{\partial x} & \dfrac{\partial f}{\partial y} & \dfrac{\partial f}{\partial z} \end{bmatrix}_{at\ \mathbf{c}(t)} \cdot \begin{bmatrix} \dfrac{\partial x}{\partial t} \\[6pt] \dfrac{\partial y}{\partial t} \\[6pt] \dfrac{\partial z}{\partial t} \end{bmatrix}_{at\ t} , \quad (2.17)$$

so that

$$D(f \circ \mathbf{c})(t) = \frac{\partial f}{\partial x}(\mathbf{c}(t))\frac{\partial x}{\partial t}(t) + \frac{\partial f}{\partial y}(\mathbf{c}(t))\frac{\partial y}{\partial t}(t) + \frac{\partial f}{\partial z}(\mathbf{c}(t))\frac{\partial z}{\partial t}(t),$$

or (dropping the notation for the dependence on a point)

$$D(f \circ \mathbf{c})(t) = \frac{\partial f}{\partial x}\frac{dx}{dt} + \frac{\partial f}{\partial y}\frac{dy}{dt} + \frac{\partial f}{\partial z}\frac{dz}{dt}. \quad (2.18)$$

We have replaced the partial derivative notation $\partial x/\partial t$, $\partial y/\partial t$ and $\partial z/\partial t$ by dx/dt, dy/dt and dz/dt, since x, y and z are functions of one variable (we could have used x', y' and z' instead). The 1×3 matrix in (2.17) is the gradient of f evaluated at $\mathbf{c}(t)$, and the 3×1 matrix is the derivative $\mathbf{c}'(t)$. Hence (2.18) can be written as

$$D(f \circ \mathbf{c})(t) = \nabla f(\mathbf{c}(t)) \cdot \mathbf{c}'(t), \quad (2.19)$$

where the multiplication on the right side is interpreted either as a matrix multiplication, or as a dot product if both matrices $\nabla f(\mathbf{c}(t))$ and $\mathbf{c}'(t)$ are viewed as vectors in $\mathbb{R}^3$.

Example 2.48   Let $f \colon \mathbb{R}^3 \to \mathbb{R}$ and let $\mathbf{G} \colon \mathbb{R}^3 \to \mathbb{R}^3$ be given by

$$\mathbf{G}(x, y, z) = (u(x, y, z), v(x, y, z), w(x, y, z)).$$

Assume that f and $\mathbf{G}$ are differentiable and define the function $h \colon \mathbb{R}^3 \to \mathbb{R}$ as the composition $h = f \circ \mathbf{G}$,

$$h(x, y, z) = (f \circ \mathbf{G})(x, y, z) = f(\mathbf{G}(x, y, z)) = f(u(x, y, z), v(x, y, z), w(x, y, z)).$$

Compute $\partial h/\partial x$, $\partial h/\partial y$ and $\partial h/\partial z$ using the chain rule.

Solution   The derivative of h is given by the 1×3 matrix

$$Dh = \left[\frac{\partial h}{\partial x} \quad \frac{\partial h}{\partial y} \quad \frac{\partial h}{\partial z} \right].$$

Using the symbols $D_1 f$, $D_2 f$ and $D_3 f$ to denote the partial derivatives of f with respect to its variables, we write

$$Df = [\, D_1 f \quad D_2 f \quad D_3 f \,].$$

By the chain rule,

$$Dh = Df \cdot D\mathbf{G} = [\, D_1 f \quad D_2 f \quad D_3 f \,] \cdot \begin{bmatrix} \dfrac{\partial u}{\partial x} & \dfrac{\partial u}{\partial y} & \dfrac{\partial u}{\partial z} \\[2mm] \dfrac{\partial v}{\partial x} & \dfrac{\partial v}{\partial y} & \dfrac{\partial v}{\partial z} \\[2mm] \dfrac{\partial w}{\partial x} & \dfrac{\partial w}{\partial y} & \dfrac{\partial w}{\partial z} \end{bmatrix},$$

and therefore

$$\frac{\partial h}{\partial x} = D_1 f \frac{\partial u}{\partial x} + D_2 f \frac{\partial v}{\partial x} + D_3 f \frac{\partial w}{\partial x},$$

$$\frac{\partial h}{\partial y} = D_1 f \frac{\partial u}{\partial y} + D_2 f \frac{\partial v}{\partial y} + D_3 f \frac{\partial w}{\partial y},$$

and

$$\frac{\partial h}{\partial z} = D_1 f \frac{\partial u}{\partial z} + D_2 f \frac{\partial v}{\partial z} + D_3 f \frac{\partial w}{\partial z}. \tag{2.20}$$

Using u, v and w for the variables of f, we write $D_1 f = \partial f/\partial u$, $D_2 f = \partial f/\partial v$ and $D_3 f = \partial f/\partial w$ and hence

$$\frac{\partial h}{\partial x} = \frac{\partial f}{\partial u} \frac{\partial u}{\partial x} + \frac{\partial f}{\partial v} \frac{\partial v}{\partial x} + \frac{\partial f}{\partial w} \frac{\partial w}{\partial x}, \tag{2.21}$$

with similar expressions for $\partial h/\partial y$ and $\partial h/\partial z$.

Example 2.48 shows how to write partial derivatives of f in two different ways. As another exercise in notation let us compute $\partial h/\partial x$ if $h(x, y) = f(x^2 + y^2, yz, e^x + y)$. We want the partial derivatives of f with respect to its variables, but cannot use expressions like $\partial f / \partial(x^2 + y^2)$ or $\partial f / \partial(yz)$. One approach to solving this notational difficulty is to introduce new variables $u = x^2 + y^2$, $v = yz$, $w = e^x + y$, write $h = f(u, v, w)$, and then use $\partial f / \partial u$, $\partial f / \partial v$ and $\partial f / \partial w$ for partial derivatives. Thus

$$\frac{\partial h}{\partial x} = \frac{\partial f}{\partial u} \cdot 2x + \frac{\partial f}{\partial v} \cdot 0 + \frac{\partial f}{\partial w} \cdot e^x.$$

Alternatively, using the "D_i" notation for partial derivatives, we write

$$\frac{\partial h}{\partial x} = D_1 f \cdot 2x + D_2 f \cdot 0 + D_3 f \cdot e^x,$$

without explicitly mentioning the names of variables.

Let us make note of a notational convention commonly used in expressions involving the chain rule. Assume that $f = f(x, y)$ is a real-valued function of two variables x and y — take, for example, $f(x, y) = x^2 - 2y^2$ and let $x = u^2 + v^2$ and $y = uv$. Then

$$f(x, y) = f(u^2 + v^2, uv) = (u^2 + v^2)^2 - 2(uv)^2 = u^4 + v^4,$$

so f becomes a function of (new) variables u and v. This process is called *change of variables* and will be discussed in more detail later (for example as a technique in integration). It can be described precisely as a composition of functions $h = f \circ \mathbf{P}$, where $\mathbf{P}: \mathbb{R}^2 \to \mathbb{R}^2$ is defined by

$$\mathbf{P}(u, v) = (u^2 + v^2, uv).$$

Let us check this:

$$h(u, v) = (f \circ \mathbf{P})(u, v) = f(\mathbf{P}(u, v)) = f(u^2 + v^2, uv) = u^4 + v^4.$$

Although, strictly speaking, f and h are two different functions (they depend on different variables and, in general, might have different domains), it is a standard practice (especially in applied mathematics) to use the same notation for both. In this context, $f(u, v)$ denotes the function $h(u, v)$, i.e., the function f expressed in terms of variables u and v, and $f(x, y)$ denotes, as usual, the function f as a function of x and y. For example, from $f(x, y) = x^2 - 2y^2$ we get $\partial f / \partial x = 2x$; but $\partial f / \partial u$ is not zero, since it does not refer to $f(x, y) = x^2 - 2y^2$ but to $f(u, v) = u^4 + v^4$. Hence $\partial f / \partial u = 4u^3$.

With this convention in mind, we write the chain rule formula (2.21) as

$$\frac{\partial f}{\partial x} = \frac{\partial f}{\partial u} \frac{\partial u}{\partial x} + \frac{\partial f}{\partial v} \frac{\partial v}{\partial x} + \frac{\partial f}{\partial w} \frac{\partial w}{\partial x}.$$

(f on the left represents f viewed as a function of x, y and z, and f on the right side is f viewed as a function of u, v and w).

Example 2.49 Let $f(u, v, w) = u^2 + v^3 e^w$, where $u = \sin(x + y + z)$, $v = x^2 e^y$ and $w = z$. Compute the partial derivatives $\partial f / \partial x$, $\partial f / \partial y$ and $\partial f / \partial z$.

Solution Using the convention just adopted and formula (2.21), we get

$$\frac{\partial f}{\partial x} = \frac{\partial f}{\partial u} \frac{\partial u}{\partial x} + \frac{\partial f}{\partial v} \frac{\partial v}{\partial x} + \frac{\partial f}{\partial w} \frac{\partial w}{\partial x}$$

(f on the left side is $f(x, y, z) = (\sin(x + y + z))^2 + (x^2 e^y)^3 e^z$, and f on the right side is $f(u, v, w) = u^2 + v^3 e^w$). Thus

$$\frac{\partial f}{\partial x} = 2u \cdot \cos(x + y + z) + 3v^2 e^w \cdot 2xe^y + v^3 e^w \cdot 0$$

$$= 2\sin(x + y + z)\cos(x + y + z) + 6x^5 e^{3y+z}.$$

The last line was obtained by substituting the expressions for u, v and w in terms of x, y and z. The derivatives $\partial f / \partial y$ and $\partial f / \partial z$ are computed analogously:

$$\frac{\partial f}{\partial y} = \frac{\partial f}{\partial u}\frac{\partial u}{\partial y} + \frac{\partial f}{\partial v}\frac{\partial v}{\partial y} + \frac{\partial f}{\partial w}\frac{\partial w}{\partial y}$$

$$= 2u \cdot \cos(x + y + z) + 3v^2 e^w \cdot x^2 e^y + v^3 e^w \cdot 0$$

$$= 2\sin(x + y + z)\cos(x + y + z) + 3x^6 e^{3y+z},$$

and

$$\frac{\partial f}{\partial z} = \frac{\partial f}{\partial u}\frac{\partial u}{\partial z} + \frac{\partial f}{\partial v}\frac{\partial v}{\partial z} + \frac{\partial f}{\partial w}\frac{\partial w}{\partial z}$$

$$= 2u \cdot \cos(x + y + z) + 3v^2 e^w \cdot 0 + v^3 e^w \cdot 1$$

$$= 2\sin(x + y + z)\cos(x + y + z) + x^6 e^{3y+z}.$$

◀

Example 2.50   **Partial Derivatives on a Surface.**

Let $f = f(x, y, z) \colon \mathbb{R}^3 \to \mathbb{R}$ and $z = g(x, y) \colon \mathbb{R}^2 \to \mathbb{R}$ be differentiable functions (recall that the graph of $z = g(x, y)$ is a surface in $\mathbb{R}^3$). The function

$$w = w(x, y) = f(x, y, g(x, y)) \colon \mathbb{R}^2 \to \mathbb{R}$$

computes the value of f at the points $(x, y, g(x, y))$, which belong to the (surface which is the) graph of $z = g(x, y)$. The function w is called the *restriction* of f to the surface $z = g(x, y)$. Compute $\partial w / \partial x$ and $\partial w / \partial y$.

Solution   We can view w as a composition $w = f \circ \mathbf{G}$, where $\mathbf{G} \colon \mathbb{R}^2 \to \mathbb{R}^3$ is defined by $\mathbf{G}(x, y) = (x, y, g(x, y))$. By the chain rule (dropping the notation for the variables),

$$D w = Df \cdot D\mathbf{G},$$

where

$$D w = \begin{bmatrix} \dfrac{\partial w}{\partial x} & \dfrac{\partial w}{\partial y} \end{bmatrix}$$

and

$$Df \cdot D\mathbf{G} = \begin{bmatrix} \dfrac{\partial f}{\partial x} & \dfrac{\partial f}{\partial y} & \dfrac{\partial f}{\partial z} \end{bmatrix} \cdot \begin{bmatrix} 1 & 0 \\ 0 & 1 \\ \dfrac{\partial g}{\partial x} & \dfrac{\partial g}{\partial y} \end{bmatrix}.$$

Computing the product $Df \cdot D\mathbf{G}$ and comparing to Dw we get

$$\frac{\partial w}{\partial x} = \frac{\partial f}{\partial x} + \frac{\partial f}{\partial z}\frac{\partial g}{\partial x},$$

and

$$\frac{\partial w}{\partial y} = \frac{\partial f}{\partial y} + \frac{\partial f}{\partial z}\frac{\partial g}{\partial y}.$$

Alternatively, we could have applied the first formula in (2.20) to $w = f(x, y, z)$, where $z = g(x, y)$ to get

$$\frac{\partial w}{\partial x} = D_1 f \frac{\partial x}{\partial x} + D_2 f \frac{\partial y}{\partial x} + D_3 f \frac{\partial z}{\partial x}.$$

Realizing that $\partial x/\partial x = 1$, $\partial y/\partial x = 0$ and $\partial z/\partial x = \partial g/\partial x$, we can rewrite it as

$$\frac{\partial w}{\partial x} = D_1 f + D_3 f \frac{\partial g}{\partial x}.$$

Finally, using x, y and z as the variables of f and z to replace $g(x, y)$, we write

$$\frac{\partial w}{\partial x} = \frac{\partial f}{\partial x} + \frac{\partial f}{\partial z}\frac{\partial z}{\partial x}. \qquad \blacktriangleleft$$

Example 2.51 **Polar Coordinates.**

Let $x = r\cos\theta$, $y = r\sin\theta$ and let $f = f(x, y)$ be a differentiable function. Express $\partial f/\partial r$ and $\partial f/\partial\theta$ in terms of $\partial f/\partial x$ and $\partial f/\partial y$.

Solution   We interpret the change from Cartesian coordinates to polar coordinates as the map $\mathbf{P}: \mathbb{R}^2 \to \mathbb{R}^2$ defined by $\mathbf{P}(r, \theta) = (r\cos\theta, r\sin\theta)$, and consider the composition $h = f \circ \mathbf{P}$. Then

$$h(r, \theta) = f(\mathbf{P}(r, \theta)) = f(r\cos\theta, r\sin\theta);$$

i.e., h is the function f "expressed in terms of polar coordinates." The chain rule applied to $h(r, \theta) = (f \circ \mathbf{P})(r, \theta)$ gives

$$Dh(r, \theta) = Df(\mathbf{P}(r, \theta)) \cdot D\mathbf{P}(r, \theta) = Df(x, y) \cdot D\mathbf{P}(r, \theta),$$

and in matrix notation,

$$\begin{bmatrix} \dfrac{\partial h}{\partial r} & \dfrac{\partial h}{\partial \theta} \end{bmatrix} = \begin{bmatrix} \dfrac{\partial f}{\partial x} & \dfrac{\partial f}{\partial y} \end{bmatrix} \cdot \begin{bmatrix} \cos\theta & -r\sin\theta \\ \sin\theta & r\cos\theta \end{bmatrix}.$$

Now, replacing $h(r, \theta)$ by $f(r, \theta)$, following the usual convention, we obtain

$$\frac{\partial f}{\partial r} = \frac{\partial f}{\partial x}\cos\theta + \frac{\partial f}{\partial y}\sin\theta,$$

and

$$\frac{\partial f}{\partial \theta} = \frac{\partial f}{\partial x}(-r\sin\theta) + \frac{\partial f}{\partial y}r\cos\theta. \qquad \blacktriangleleft$$

Example 2.52 Let $x = r\cos\theta$, $y = r\sin\theta$ and $f(x, y) = xe^{x^2+y^2}$. Find $\partial f/\partial r$ and $\partial f/\partial\theta$ directly, and then using the chain rule.

Solution   Since

$$f(x, y) = xe^{x^2+y^2} = r\cos\theta e^{r^2},$$

we get (notational convention!) that $f(r, \theta) = r \cos \theta e^{r^2}$, and hence

$$\frac{\partial f}{\partial r} = (e^{r^2} + 2r^2 e^{r^2}) \cos \theta$$

and

$$\frac{\partial f}{\partial \theta} = -r e^{r^2} \sin \theta.$$

Using the result of the previous example,

$$\frac{\partial f}{\partial r} = \frac{\partial f}{\partial x} \cos \theta + \frac{\partial f}{\partial y} \sin \theta$$

$$= (e^{x^2+y^2} + 2x^2 e^{x^2+y^2}) \cos \theta + 2xy e^{x^2+y^2} \sin \theta$$

$$= (e^{r^2} + 2r^2 \cos^2 \theta e^{r^2}) \cos \theta + 2r^2 e^{r^2} \sin \theta \cos \theta \sin \theta$$

$$= (e^{r^2} + 2r^2 e^{r^2}) \cos \theta.$$

The expression for $\partial f / \partial \theta$ is obtained similarly.

Notice that in this case the direct computation was faster (and easier). However, there are situations where not only does the chain rule provide a more efficient way, but the direct computation cannot be applied at all; see Exercise 19.

EXERCISES 2.5

1. Let $f(x, y) = g(x^2 y, 2x + 5y, x, y)$, where g is a differentiable function of four variables. Find f_x and f_y.

2. Let $f: \mathbb{R}^2 \to \mathbb{R}^3$ be given by $f(x, y) = (h(x), g(y), k(x, y))$, where h, g and k are differentiable functions of variables indicated. Find Df.

3. Let $F(x, y) = f(h(x), g(y), k(x, y))$, where $f: \mathbb{R}^3 \to \mathbb{R}$, and all functions involved are assumed to be differentiable. Find F_x and F_y.

4. Let $z = f(r)$, where $r = \sqrt{x^2 + y^2}$ and f is a differentiable function. Prove that $y z_x - x z_y = 0$ for all $(x, y) \neq (0, 0)$.

5. Let $f(x, y) = x^2 + xy$ and $g(x, y) = \ln x + \ln y$. Compute $\nabla(fg)(x, y)$ and $D(f/g)(2, 2)$.

6. Let $\mathbf{G}(x, y) = (2xy, y^2 - x^2)$. Compute $D\mathbf{G}(x, y)$ and $D\mathbf{G}(3, 0)$.

7. Let $f(x, y, z) = x^2 + \sin(yz) - 3$. Find $D(f/x)(1, \pi, -1)$ and $D(x^2 yf)(2, 0, 1)$.

8. Let $w = f(x, y, z)$, where $x = r \cos \theta$ and $y = r \sin \theta$. Find $\partial w / \partial r$, $\partial w / \partial \theta$ and $\partial w / \partial z$.

9. Let $w = f(x, y, z)$, where $x = \rho \sin \phi \cos \theta$, $y = \rho \sin \phi \sin \theta$ and $z = \rho \cos \phi$. Find $\partial w / \partial \rho$, $\partial w / \partial \theta$, and $\partial w / \partial \phi$.

10. Let $\mathbf{v}(t) = t\mathbf{i} + (t^2 + 1)\mathbf{j}$ and $\mathbf{w}(t) = \mathbf{i} - 2t\mathbf{j} + e^t \mathbf{k}$. Compute $(\mathbf{v} \cdot \mathbf{w})'(t)$ directly (i.e., by computing the dot product first and then differentiating) and then check your answer using the product rule.

11. Let $\mathbf{v}(t) = t^3 \mathbf{i} + t e^t \mathbf{k}$ and $\mathbf{w}(t) = -2t\mathbf{j}$. Compute $(\mathbf{v} \times \mathbf{w})'(t)$ directly (i.e., by computing the cross product first) and then check your answer using the product rule.

12. Let $\mathbf{u}(t) = \sin t \mathbf{i} + \cos t \mathbf{j} + t\mathbf{k}$, $\mathbf{v}(t) = \mathbf{i} + t\mathbf{j} + \mathbf{k}$ and $\mathbf{w}(t) = t^3(\mathbf{i} + \mathbf{j} + \mathbf{k})$. Compute $(\mathbf{u} \cdot (\mathbf{v} \times \mathbf{w}))'(t)$.

13. The function $\mathbf{F} \colon \mathbb{R}^2 \to \mathbb{R}^3$ is given by $\mathbf{F}(x, y) = (e^x, xy, e^y)$. Compute $D(g \circ \mathbf{F})(0, 0)$, where $g \colon \mathbb{R}^3 \to \mathbb{R}$ is given by $g(u, v, w) = uw + v^2$.

14. Let $f \colon \mathbb{R}^3 \to \mathbb{R}$ and $\mathbf{c} \colon \mathbb{R} \to \mathbb{R}^3$ be given by $f(x, y, z) = \sqrt{x^2 + y^2 + z^2}$ and $\mathbf{c}(t) = (\cos t, \sin t, 1)$. Compute $(f \circ \mathbf{c})'(t)$ and $(f \circ \mathbf{c})'(0)$.

15. Compute $\partial w / \partial x$ and $\partial w / \partial z$ if $w = f(x, y, z)$ and $y = g(x, z)$ are differentiable functions.

16. Let $w = \ln(r^2 + 1)$, where $r = \sqrt{x^2 + y^2}$. Find $\partial w / \partial y$.

17. Define a function $\mathbf{F} \colon \mathbb{R}^2 \to \mathbb{R}^2$ by $\mathbf{F}(\mathbf{x}) = A \cdot \mathbf{x}$, where A is a 2×2 matrix, and the dot indicates matrix multiplication. Compute $D\mathbf{F}(\mathbf{x})$. Prove that $\mathbf{F}$ is differentiable at any point $(x_0, y_0) \in \mathbb{R}^2$.

18. Let A and B be 2×2 matrices. Define $\mathbf{F}, \mathbf{G} \colon \mathbb{R}^2 \to \mathbb{R}^2$ by $\mathbf{F}(\mathbf{x}) = A \cdot \mathbf{x}$ and $\mathbf{G}(\mathbf{x}) = B \cdot \mathbf{x}$, where $\mathbf{x} \in \mathbb{R}^2$, and the dot indicates matrix multiplication. Find $D(\mathbf{G} \circ \mathbf{F})(\mathbf{x})$.

19. Let $f(x, y) = x^3 y$, where $x^3 + tx = 8$ and $ye^y = t$. Find $(df/dt)(0)$.

2.6 HIGHER ORDER PARTIAL DERIVATIVES

A real-valued function of m variables $x_1, \ldots, x_m$ is said to be of class C^1 if all of its partial derivatives $\partial f / \partial x_i$ are continuous. If, in turn, all $\partial f / \partial x_i$ have continuous partial derivatives with respect to all variables x_j, then f is called *twice continuously differentiable* or *of class C^2*. The "box" containing functions of class C^2 would be inside the smallest "box" (i.e., contained in the C^1 "box") in Figure 2.42. Similarly, we can define a function of class C^k, for any positive integer k. To introduce notation for higher-order derivatives, we assume that f is a function of three variables x, y and z. Recall that the first-order partial derivatives are denoted either by $\partial f / \partial x$, $\partial f / \partial y$, etc., or by f_x, f_y, etc., or by $D_1 f$, $D_2 f$, etc. Likewise,

$$\frac{\partial^2 f}{\partial x^2} = \frac{\partial}{\partial x}\left(\frac{\partial f}{\partial x}\right) \qquad \text{or} \qquad f_{xx} = (f_x)_x \qquad \text{or} \qquad D_{11} f = D_1(D_1 f)$$

$$\frac{\partial^2 f}{\partial x \partial y} = \frac{\partial}{\partial x}\left(\frac{\partial f}{\partial y}\right) \qquad \text{or} \qquad f_{yx} = (f_y)_x \qquad \text{or} \qquad D_{21} f = D_1(D_2 f)$$

$$\frac{\partial^2 f}{\partial z \partial y} = \frac{\partial}{\partial z}\left(\frac{\partial f}{\partial y}\right) \qquad \text{or} \qquad f_{yz} = (f_y)_z \qquad \text{or} \qquad D_{23} f = D_3(D_2 f)$$

$$\frac{\partial^2 f}{\partial y \partial z} = \frac{\partial}{\partial y}\left(\frac{\partial f}{\partial z}\right) \qquad \text{or} \qquad f_{zy} = (f_z)_y \qquad \text{or} \qquad D_{32} f = D_2(D_3 f),$$

etc. are *second-order partial derivatives* (also called *iterated partial derivatives*) of f. We can also form third-order, fourth-order, etc., partial derivatives. A function of two variables has four, and a function of three variables has nine second-order partial derivatives. However, as we will soon witness, not all of them are distinct if the function is of class C^2.

Example 2.53   Find all second-order partial derivatives of $f(x, y) = x^3y + 3y^2 - x$.

Solution   Computing the derivatives of $f_x = 3x^2y - 1$ with respect to x and y we get $f_{xx} = 6xy$ and $f_{xy} = 3x^2$. Similarly, from $f_y = x^3 + 6y$ we get $f_{yx} = 3x^2$ and $f_{yy} = 6$.

◀

Example 2.54   Compute all second-order partial derivatives of $f(x, y) = x^2e^{2y}$.

Solution   Since

$$\frac{\partial f}{\partial x} = 2xe^{2y} \quad \text{and} \quad \frac{\partial f}{\partial y} = 2x^2e^{2y},$$

it follows that

$$\frac{\partial^2 f}{\partial x^2} = \frac{\partial}{\partial x}(2xe^{2y}) = 2e^{2y},$$

$$\frac{\partial^2 f}{\partial x \partial y} = \frac{\partial}{\partial x}(2x^2e^{2y}) = 4xe^{2y},$$

$$\frac{\partial^2 f}{\partial y \partial x} = \frac{\partial}{\partial y}(2xe^{2y}) = 4xe^{2y},$$

and

$$\frac{\partial^2 f}{\partial y^2} = \frac{\partial}{\partial y}(2x^2e^{2y}) = 4x^2e^{2y}.$$

◀

Notice that, in the previous two examples, $f_{xy} = f_{yx}$ (or $\partial^2 f/\partial x \partial y = \partial^2 f/\partial y \partial x$). This is not a coincidence, but a consequence of the following theorem.

■ **Theorem 2.8**   **Equality of Mixed Partial Derivatives.**

Let f be a real-valued function of m variables $x_1, \ldots, x_m$ with continuous second-order partial derivatives (that is, of class C^2). Then

$$\frac{\partial^2 f}{\partial x_i \partial x_j} = \frac{\partial^2 f}{\partial x_j \partial x_i},$$

for all $i, j = 1, \ldots, m$.

■

This theorem states that the order of computing derivatives of a function is irrelevant, as long as the function is "smooth enough" (that is, of class C^2). This fact will be used in a number of situations, one of which is the interchanging of the gradient and the time derivative of a function. More precisely, consider a function $f(x, y, z, t)$ of four variables (where the variable t denotes time, and x, y and z are the coordinates in the space $\mathbb{R}^3$). The gradient of f, interpreted as a vector, is written as

$$\nabla f = \frac{\partial f}{\partial x}\mathbf{i} + \frac{\partial f}{\partial y}\mathbf{j} + \frac{\partial f}{\partial z}\mathbf{k}$$

(partial derivatives are taken only with respect to "space" variables x, y and z and not with respect to t). Then

$$\nabla\left(\frac{\partial f}{\partial t}\right) = \frac{\partial}{\partial x}\left(\frac{\partial f}{\partial t}\right)\mathbf{i} + \frac{\partial}{\partial y}\left(\frac{\partial f}{\partial t}\right)\mathbf{j} + \frac{\partial}{\partial z}\left(\frac{\partial f}{\partial t}\right)\mathbf{k}$$

$$= \frac{\partial^2 f}{\partial x \partial t}\mathbf{i} + \frac{\partial^2 f}{\partial y \partial t}\mathbf{j} + \frac{\partial^2 f}{\partial z \partial t}\mathbf{k}$$

$$= \frac{\partial^2 f}{\partial t \partial x}\mathbf{i} + \frac{\partial^2 f}{\partial t \partial y}\mathbf{j} + \frac{\partial^2 f}{\partial t \partial z}\mathbf{k}$$

$$= \frac{\partial}{\partial t}\left(\frac{\partial f}{\partial x}\right)\mathbf{i} + \frac{\partial}{\partial t}\left(\frac{\partial f}{\partial y}\right)\mathbf{j} + \frac{\partial}{\partial t}\left(\frac{\partial f}{\partial z}\right)\mathbf{k}$$

$$= \frac{\partial}{\partial t}\left(\frac{\partial f}{\partial x}\mathbf{i} + \frac{\partial f}{\partial y}\mathbf{j} + \frac{\partial f}{\partial z}\mathbf{k}\right) = \frac{\partial}{\partial t}(\nabla f).$$

The proof of Theorem 2.8 is presented in Appendix A.

Example 2.55

Compute f_{xzzy} if $f(x, y, z) = x^2 e^{y^2 - x^2} + x^2 y z^2 - \cos(x^2 + y^2)$.

Solution   We are asked to compute the fourth-order partial derivative of f with respect to x, z, z and y. Since f consists of sums, products and compositions of functions (polynomials, exponential function, cosine) that have as many derivatives as needed, it is certainly of class C^2 (as a matter of fact, it is of class C^k for any integer $k \geq 1$). By Theorem 2.8 we can compute the required partial derivatives in any order. Since the first and the third terms of f do not depend on z, we differentiate with respect to z first: $f_z = 2x^2 y z$. Now $f_{zz} = 2x^2 y$, $f_{zzy} = 2x^2$ and, finally, $f_{zzyx} = 4x$.   ◀

Higher order partial derivatives appear in a number of very important applications. We will examine some of them in the examples that follow.

Example 2.56

Wave Equation.

A function $u(x, t)$ of two variables x and t is said to satisfy the *wave equation* if

$$u_{tt} = c^2 u_{xx}, \tag{2.22}$$

where c is a constant. The wave equation is used in the study of the propagation of sound (in various media), propagation of electromagnetic waves and electromagnetic radiation, vibrations of strings and drums, elasticity, etc. The equation appearing in this example is a special case of a general wave equation and is called the one-dimensional wave equation: the function $u(x, t)$ describes the displacement at the location x at time t (for example, it could describe transverse vibrations of a guitar string); see Figure 2.44.

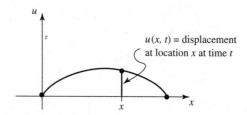

Figure 2.44   A snapshot of a vibrating string taken at a particular time t.

(a) Show that $u(x, t) = \sin x \cos(2t) + t$ satisfies the wave equation $u_{tt} - 4u_{xx} = 0$.

(b) Show that the wave equation $u_{tt} = c^2 u_{xx}$ transforms under the change of variables $v = x + ct$, $z = x - ct$ into the equation $u_{vz} = 0$.

(c) Let ϕ and ψ be differentiable functions of one variable. Show that for any constant c the function $u = \phi(x - ct) + \psi(x + ct)$ is a solution of (2.22).

Solution

(a) A straightforward computation gives

$$u_t = -2 \sin x \sin(2t) + 1, \qquad u_{tt} = -4 \sin x \cos(2t)$$

and

$$u_x = \cos x \cos(2t), \qquad u_{xx} = -\sin x \cos(2t).$$

Therefore, $u_{tt} - 4u_{xx} = 0$.

(b) Using subscripts to denote partial derivatives we get, by the chain rule,

$$u_t = u_v v_t + u_z z_t = u_v c + u_z(-c) = cu_v - cu_z$$

and

$$u_{tt} = c\Big((u_v)_v v_t + (u_v)_z z_t\Big) - c\Big((u_z)_v v_t + (u_z)_z z_t\Big)$$
$$= c\Big(u_{vv} c + u_{vz}(-c)\Big) - c\Big(u_{zv} c + u_{zz}(-c)\Big)$$
$$= c^2 u_{vv} + c^2 u_{zz} - 2c^2 u_{vz}.$$

We used the equality of mixed partials; see Theorem 2.8. Furthermore

$$u_x = u_v v_x + u_z z_x = u_v + u_z,$$

and

$$u_{xx} = (u_v)_v v_x + (u_v)_z z_x + (u_z)_v v_x + (u_z)_z z_x$$
$$= u_{vv} + 2u_{vz} + u_{zz}.$$

Substituting the expressions for u_{tt} and u_{xx} into (2.22) we get

$$0 = u_{tt} - c^2 u_{xx} = c^2 u_{vv} + c^2 u_{zz} - 2c^2 u_{vz} - c^2 (u_{vv} + 2u_{vz} + u_{zz}) = -4c^2 u_{vz},$$

i.e., $u_{vz} = 0$.

(c) Abbreviating $z = x - ct$ and $v = x + ct$ we rewrite the function u as $u = \phi(z) + \psi(v)$. The functions ϕ and ψ are functions of one variable, so "prime" notation is used to denote their derivatives: ϕ' is the derivative of ϕ with respect to its variable z, and ψ' is the derivative of ψ with respect to v. Hence

$$u_x = \phi' \cdot 1 + \psi' \cdot 1 = \phi' + \psi', \qquad u_{xx} = \phi'' \cdot 1 + \psi'' \cdot 1 = \phi'' + \psi''$$

and

$$u_t = \phi'(-c) + \psi'(c) = -c\phi' + c\psi', \qquad u_{tt} = -c\phi''(-c) + c\psi''(c) = c^2(\phi'' + \psi'').$$

Clearly, $u_{tt} - c^2 u_{xx} = 0$. ◀

Example 2.57 | **Heat Equation.**

A function $T(x, t)$ is said to satisfy the *heat equation* if

$$\frac{\partial T}{\partial t} = \sigma \frac{\partial^2 T}{\partial x^2}, \tag{2.23}$$

where $\sigma > 0$ is a constant. The heat equation can be used to describe how heat flows in some medium (the constant σ characterizes that medium). In our case, $T(x, t)$ is the temperature at the location x at time t. Only one space variable is used, and hence (2.23) describes the heat flow in one dimension (for example, along a thin metal rod). An equation of the form

$$\frac{\partial T}{\partial t} = \sigma \left(\frac{\partial^2 T}{\partial x^2} + \frac{\partial^2 T}{\partial y^2} \right)$$

could describe the heat flow in a two-dimensional medium.

Show that $T(x, t) = a + e^{-ct} \sin(kx)$ (a, c and k are constants, $c > 0$ and $k \neq 0$) satisfies the heat equation (2.23) with $\sigma = c/k^2$.

Solution A straightforward computation gives

$$\frac{\partial T}{\partial x} = ke^{-ct} \cos(kx), \qquad \frac{\partial^2 T}{\partial x^2} = -k^2 e^{-ct} \sin(kx),$$

$$\frac{\partial T}{\partial t} = -ce^{-ct} \sin(kx),$$

and therefore

$$\frac{\partial T}{\partial t} = -ce^{-ct} \sin(kx) = \frac{-c}{k^2} k^2 e^{-ct} \sin(kx) = \frac{c}{k^2} \frac{\partial^2 T}{\partial x^2}.$$

In the last line, we divided and multiplied by k^2 so that we could recognize the expression for $\partial^2 T / \partial x^2$. ◀

Example 2.58 | **Laplace's Equation and Harmonic Functions.**

A function $f(x, y)$ is said to satisfy *Laplace's equation* if

$$\Delta f(x, y) = 0, \tag{2.24}$$

where Δf is the *Laplace operator* or the *Laplacian* of f, defined by

$$\Delta f = \frac{\partial^2 f}{\partial x^2} + \frac{\partial^2 f}{\partial y^2}.$$

A function that satisfies Laplace's equation is called *harmonic*. A generalized version of Laplace's equation,

$$\Delta f(x, y) = g(x, y),$$

where $g(x, y)$ is some function is in some situations called *Poisson's equation*.

(a) Show that the function $f(x, y) = \ln(x^2 + y^2)$ is harmonic for all $(x, y) \neq (0, 0)$.

(b) Show that $u(x, y) = e^{x^2} \sin(\sqrt{2}y)$ satisfies the equation $\Delta u = 4x^2 u$.

Solution

(a) The partial derivatives are computed using the chain rule and the quotient rule:

$$f_x = \frac{2x}{x^2 + y^2},$$

$$f_{xx} = \frac{2(x^2 + y^2) - 4x^2}{(x^2 + y^2)^2} = \frac{2y^2 - 2x^2}{(x^2 + y^2)^2}.$$

The function f is symmetric in x and y (i.e., by interchanging x and y in the formula for f we get the same function). Consequently, f_{yy} can be obtained from the expression for f_{xx} by interchanging x and y:

$$f_{yy} = \frac{2x^2 - 2y^2}{(x^2 + y^2)^2}.$$

Hence $\Delta f = f_{xx} + f_{yy} = 0$, and f is harmonic at all points, except at the origin.

(b) To compute the Laplacian, we need second partials:

$$\frac{\partial u}{\partial x} = 2xe^{x^2} \sin(\sqrt{2}y), \qquad \frac{\partial^2 u}{\partial x^2} = 2e^{x^2} \sin(\sqrt{2}y) + 4x^2 e^{x^2} \sin(\sqrt{2}y)$$

and

$$\frac{\partial u}{\partial y} = \sqrt{2}e^{x^2} \cos(\sqrt{2}y), \qquad \frac{\partial^2 u}{\partial y^2} = -2e^{x^2} \sin(\sqrt{2}y).$$

Hence

$$\Delta u = \frac{\partial^2 u}{\partial x^2} + \frac{\partial^2 u}{\partial y^2} = 4x^2 e^{x^2} \sin(\sqrt{2}y) = 4x^2 u;$$

i.e., u satisfies the given Poisson's equation.   ◀

Example 2.59   **Korteweg-de Vries Equation and Soliton Waves.**

Show that the function $u(x, t) = 2k^2 \cosh^{-2}\left(k\left(x - 4k^2 t\right)\right)$, where $k \geq 0$, is a solution of the *Korteweg-de Vries equation* (sometimes abbreviated as the *KdV equation*)

$$u_t + 6uu_x + u_{xxx} = 0. \tag{2.25}$$

This equation is also called a *soliton equation* and describes, for example, the motion of a certain type of water wave in shallow water; see Figures 2.45 and 2.46. The solution $u(x, t)$ is called a *soliton wave*. No detailed knowledge of hyperbolic functions is needed here; only the derivative formulas $(\cosh x)' = \sinh x$ and $(\sinh x)' = \cosh x$ and the basic identity $\cosh^2 x - \sinh^2 x = 1$ are used.

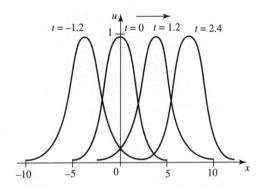

Figure 2.45   Soliton wave $u(x, t) = 2k^2 \cosh^{-2}\left(k\left(x - 4k^2 t\right)\right)$ with $k = 0.7$, for four different values of t.

Solution   Denote the expression $k\left(x - 4k^2 t\right)$ by A, so that $u(x, t) = 2k^2 \cosh^{-2} A$. Then

$$u_t = 2k^2(-2)\cosh^{-3}A \cdot \sinh A \cdot k(-4k^2) = 16k^5 \cosh^{-3}A \cdot \sinh A,$$
$$u_x = 2k^2(-2)\cosh^{-3}A \cdot \sinh A \cdot k = -4k^3 \cosh^{-3}A \cdot \sinh A,$$
$$u_{xx} = -4k^3 \left(-3\cosh^{-4}A \cdot \sinh A \cdot k \sinh A + \cosh^{-3}A \cdot \cosh A \cdot k\right)$$
$$= -4k^4 \left(-3\cosh^{-4}A \cdot \sinh^2 A + \cosh^{-2}A\right),$$

and

$$u_{xxx} = -4k^4 \left(12\cosh^{-5}A \cdot \sinh A \cdot k \sinh^2 A\right.$$
$$\left. -3\cosh^{-4}A \cdot 2\sinh A \cdot \cosh A \cdot k - 2\cosh^{-3}A \cdot \sinh A \cdot k\right)$$
$$= -4k^5 \left(12\cosh^{-5}A \cdot \sinh^3 A - 8\cosh^{-3}A \cdot \sinh A\right).$$

Therefore

$$u_t + 6uu_x + u_{xxx} = k^5 \left(16\cosh^{-3}A \cdot \sinh A - 48\cosh^{-5}A \cdot \sinh A\right.$$
$$\left. -48\cosh^{-5}A \cdot \sinh^3 A + 32\cosh^{-3}A \cdot \sinh A\right)$$
$$= 48k^5 \cosh^{-5}A \left(\cosh^2 A \cdot \sinh A - \sinh A - \sinh^3 A\right)$$
$$= 48k^5 \cosh^{-5}A \left(\sinh A(-1 + \cosh^2 A) - \sinh^3 A\right)$$
$$= 48k^5 \cosh^{-5}A \left(\sinh A(\sinh^2 A) - \sinh^3 A\right) = 0.$$

Figure 2.45 shows the soliton wave $u(x, t)$ at four different times, and the graph of the function $u(x, t)$ with all positions of the wave for $-2 \le t \le 2$ is shown in Figure 2.46.

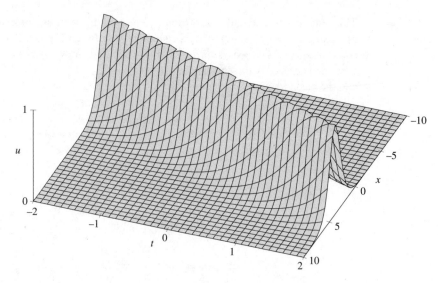

Figure 2.46 Plot of $u(x, t)$ as a function of two variables shows how the soliton wave moves for $-2 \leq t \leq 2$.

Example 2.60 Show that $u(x, t) = e^{2k(x - 4k^2 t)}$ is a solution of the *linearized Korteweg-de Vries equation*

$$u_t + u_{xxx} = 0.$$

Solution   Denoting $2k\left(x - 4k^2 t\right)$ by A we get $u(x, t) = e^A$,

$$u_t = e^A \cdot 2k(-4k^2) = -8k^3 e^A,$$

and

$$u_x = 2k e^A, \quad u_{xx} = 2k e^A \cdot 2k = 4k^2 e^A \qquad \text{and} \qquad u_{xxx} = 4k^2 e^A \cdot 2k = 8k^3 e^A.$$

Clearly, $u_t + u_{xxx} = 0$.

◀

Example 2.61 This example illustrates the use of the chain rule.

(a) Let $u(x, y) = e^x \sin y$, where $x = s^2$ and $y = st$. Compute $\partial u / \partial t$ and $\partial u / \partial s$.

(b) Let $u(x, y)$ be a twice continuously differentiable real-valued function and let $x = s^2$ and $y = st$. Compute $\partial u / \partial t$ and $\partial u / \partial s$.

(c) Compute all second partial derivatives of the function $u(x, y)$ defined in (b).

Solution

(a) One way to solve this problem is to immediately substitute expressions for x and y into $u(x, y)$ (thus getting $u(s, t) = e^{s^2} \sin(st)$) and then compute the derivatives.

We choose another approach. Using the chain rule we get

$$\frac{\partial u}{\partial t} = \frac{\partial u}{\partial x}\frac{\partial x}{\partial t} + \frac{\partial u}{\partial y}\frac{\partial y}{\partial t} = e^x \sin y \cdot 0 + e^x \cos y \cdot s = se^{s^2}\cos(st),$$

and

$$\frac{\partial u}{\partial s} = \frac{\partial u}{\partial x}\frac{\partial x}{\partial s} + \frac{\partial u}{\partial y}\frac{\partial y}{\partial s} = e^x \sin y \cdot 2s + e^x \cos y \cdot t = 2se^{s^2}\sin(st) + te^{s^2}\cos(st).$$

(b) As in (a), the chain rule gives

$$\frac{\partial u}{\partial t} = \frac{\partial u}{\partial x}\frac{\partial x}{\partial t} + \frac{\partial u}{\partial y}\frac{\partial y}{\partial t} = \frac{\partial u}{\partial x}\cdot 0 + \frac{\partial u}{\partial y}\cdot s = s\frac{\partial u}{\partial y},$$

and

$$\frac{\partial u}{\partial s} = \frac{\partial u}{\partial x}\frac{\partial x}{\partial s} + \frac{\partial u}{\partial y}\frac{\partial y}{\partial s} = \frac{\partial u}{\partial x}\cdot 2s + \frac{\partial u}{\partial y}\cdot t = 2s\frac{\partial u}{\partial x} + t\frac{\partial u}{\partial y}.$$

(c) Applying the product and the chain rules we get, from (b),

$$\frac{\partial^2 u}{\partial t^2} = \frac{\partial}{\partial t}\left(\frac{\partial u}{\partial t}\right) = \frac{\partial}{\partial t}\left(s\frac{\partial u}{\partial y}\right) = \frac{\partial}{\partial t}(s)\frac{\partial u}{\partial y} + s\frac{\partial}{\partial t}\left(\frac{\partial u}{\partial y}\right)$$

$$= 0 + s\left(\frac{\partial}{\partial x}\left(\frac{\partial u}{\partial y}\right)\frac{\partial x}{\partial t} + \frac{\partial}{\partial y}\left(\frac{\partial u}{\partial y}\right)\frac{\partial y}{\partial t}\right) = s\left(\frac{\partial^2 u}{\partial x\partial y}\cdot 0 + \frac{\partial^2 u}{\partial y^2}\cdot s\right) = s^2\frac{\partial^2 u}{\partial y^2}.$$

Similarly,

$$\frac{\partial^2 u}{\partial s^2} = \frac{\partial}{\partial s}\left(\frac{\partial u}{\partial s}\right) = \frac{\partial}{\partial s}\left(2s\frac{\partial u}{\partial x} + t\frac{\partial u}{\partial y}\right) = 2\frac{\partial u}{\partial x} + 2s\frac{\partial}{\partial s}\left(\frac{\partial u}{\partial x}\right) + 0\cdot\frac{\partial u}{\partial y} + t\frac{\partial}{\partial s}\left(\frac{\partial u}{\partial y}\right)$$

$$= 2\frac{\partial u}{\partial x} + 2s\left(\frac{\partial}{\partial x}\left(\frac{\partial u}{\partial x}\right)\cdot 2s + \frac{\partial}{\partial y}\left(\frac{\partial u}{\partial x}\right)\cdot t\right) + t\left(\frac{\partial}{\partial x}\left(\frac{\partial u}{\partial y}\right)\cdot 2s + \frac{\partial}{\partial y}\left(\frac{\partial u}{\partial y}\right)\cdot t\right)$$

$$= 2\frac{\partial u}{\partial x} + 4s^2\frac{\partial^2 u}{\partial x^2} + 4st\frac{\partial^2 u}{\partial x\partial y} + t^2\frac{\partial^2 u}{\partial y^2},$$

and

$$\frac{\partial^2 u}{\partial s\partial t} = \frac{\partial}{\partial s}\left(\frac{\partial u}{\partial t}\right) = \frac{\partial}{\partial s}\left(s\frac{\partial u}{\partial y}\right) = \frac{\partial}{\partial s}(s)\frac{\partial u}{\partial y} + s\frac{\partial}{\partial s}\left(\frac{\partial u}{\partial y}\right)$$

$$= 1\cdot\frac{\partial u}{\partial y} + s\left(\frac{\partial}{\partial x}\left(\frac{\partial u}{\partial y}\right)\cdot 2s + \frac{\partial}{\partial y}\left(\frac{\partial u}{\partial y}\right)\cdot t\right) = \frac{\partial u}{\partial y} + 2s^2\frac{\partial^2 u}{\partial x\partial y} + st\frac{\partial^2 u}{\partial y^2}.$$

The function u is twice continuously differentiable, and therefore $\partial^2 u/\partial s\partial t = \partial^2 u/\partial t\partial s$. ◀

Example 2.62 Let $u(x, y)$ be a twice differentiable function and let $x = e^s$, $y = e^t$. Show that

$$x^2 u_{xx} + y^2 u_{yy} + xu_x + yu_y = u_{ss} + u_{tt}.$$

Solution By the chain rule,

$$u_s = u_x e^s + u_y \cdot 0 = u_x e^s$$

and

$$u_{ss} = (u_x)_s \, e^s + u_x \left(e^s\right)_s = \left((u_x)_x \, e^s + (u_x)_y \, 0\right) e^s + u_x e^s$$
$$= u_{xx} e^{2s} + u_x e^s = x^2 u_{xx} + x u_x.$$

Replacing x by y and s by t (we can do this, due to symmetry) we get

$$u_{tt} = u_{yy} e^{2t} + u_y e^t = y^2 u_{yy} + y u_y.$$

The proof is now completed by adding the expressions for u_{ss} and u_{tt}. Thus a complicated differential equation can be made simpler by using new, suitably defined variables s and t.

◀

Example 2.63   Recall that the Laplace operator Δ assigns to every twice differentiable function $u = u(x, y)$ of two variables x and y a function Δu defined by

$$\Delta u = \frac{\partial^2 u}{\partial x^2} + \frac{\partial^2 u}{\partial y^2}$$

(see Example 2.58). Similar formulas can be obtained for functions of any number of variables. Now introduce polar coordinates: assume that $u = u(x, y)$, where $x = r \cos \theta$ and $y = r \sin \theta$. Show that, in polar coordinates,

$$\Delta u = \frac{\partial^2 u}{\partial r^2} + \frac{1}{r^2} \frac{\partial^2 u}{\partial \theta^2} + \frac{1}{r} \frac{\partial u}{\partial r},$$

where $u = u(r, \theta)$ denotes (according to our notational convention from Section 2.5) the function u expressed in terms of r and θ.

Solution   By the chain rule,

$$\frac{\partial u}{\partial r} = \frac{\partial u}{\partial x} \frac{\partial x}{\partial r} + \frac{\partial u}{\partial y} \frac{\partial y}{\partial r} = \cos \theta \frac{\partial u}{\partial x} + \sin \theta \frac{\partial u}{\partial y}. \tag{2.26}$$

Hence

$$\frac{\partial^2 u}{\partial r^2} = \frac{\partial}{\partial r} \left(\cos \theta \frac{\partial u}{\partial x} + \sin \theta \frac{\partial u}{\partial y} \right)$$

(apply the product rule to each summand)

$$= \frac{\partial}{\partial r} (\cos \theta) \frac{\partial u}{\partial x} + \cos \theta \frac{\partial}{\partial r} \left(\frac{\partial u}{\partial x} \right) + \frac{\partial}{\partial r} (\sin \theta) \frac{\partial u}{\partial y} + \sin \theta \frac{\partial}{\partial r} \left(\frac{\partial u}{\partial y} \right)$$

(the first and the third terms vanish; use the chain rule to compute the second and the fourth terms)

$$= \cos \theta \left(\frac{\partial}{\partial x} \left(\frac{\partial u}{\partial x} \right) \frac{\partial x}{\partial r} + \frac{\partial}{\partial y} \left(\frac{\partial u}{\partial x} \right) \frac{\partial y}{\partial r} \right)$$
$$+ \sin \theta \left(\frac{\partial}{\partial x} \left(\frac{\partial u}{\partial y} \right) \frac{\partial x}{\partial r} + \frac{\partial}{\partial y} \left(\frac{\partial u}{\partial y} \right) \frac{\partial y}{\partial r} \right)$$
$$= \cos \theta \left(\frac{\partial^2 u}{\partial x^2} \cos \theta + \frac{\partial^2 u}{\partial x \partial y} \sin \theta \right) + \sin \theta \left(\frac{\partial^2 u}{\partial x \partial y} \cos \theta + \frac{\partial^2 u}{\partial y^2} \sin \theta \right)$$
$$= \frac{\partial^2 u}{\partial x^2} \cos^2 \theta + 2 \frac{\partial^2 u}{\partial x \partial y} \cos \theta \sin \theta + \frac{\partial^2 u}{\partial y^2} \sin^2 \theta. \tag{2.27}$$

Continuing as above (but skipping some intermediate steps), we get

$$\frac{\partial u}{\partial \theta} = \frac{\partial u}{\partial x}(-r \sin \theta) + \frac{\partial u}{\partial y}(r \cos \theta),$$

and

$$\frac{\partial^2 u}{\partial \theta^2} = \frac{\partial}{\partial \theta}\left(\frac{\partial u}{\partial x}\right)(-r \sin \theta) - \frac{\partial u}{\partial x}(r \cos \theta) + \frac{\partial}{\partial \theta}\left(\frac{\partial u}{\partial y}\right)(r \cos \theta) + \frac{\partial u}{\partial y}(-r \sin \theta)$$

$$= \frac{\partial^2 u}{\partial x^2}r^2 \sin^2 \theta + \frac{\partial^2 u}{\partial x \partial y}(-r^2 \cos \theta \sin \theta) - \frac{\partial u}{\partial x}(r \cos \theta)$$

$$+ \frac{\partial^2 u}{\partial x \partial y}(-r^2 \cos \theta \sin \theta) + \frac{\partial^2 u}{\partial y^2}(r^2 \cos^2 \theta) - \frac{\partial u}{\partial y}(r \sin \theta). \qquad (2.28)$$

Dividing (2.28) by r^2 and adding to (2.27) we get (terms with $\cos \theta \sin \theta$ cancel)

$$\frac{\partial^2 u}{\partial r^2} + \frac{1}{r^2}\frac{\partial^2 u}{\partial \theta^2} = \frac{\partial^2 u}{\partial x^2} + \frac{\partial^2 u}{\partial y^2} - \frac{1}{r}\left(\frac{\partial u}{\partial x}\cos \theta + \frac{\partial u}{\partial y}\sin \theta\right),$$

and, combining with (2.26)

$$\frac{\partial^2 u}{\partial r^2} + \frac{1}{r^2}\frac{\partial^2 u}{\partial \theta^2} + \frac{1}{r}\frac{\partial u}{\partial r} = \frac{\partial^2 u}{\partial x^2} + \frac{\partial^2 u}{\partial y^2}.$$

With this form of the Laplace operator Δ, finding solutions u that depend only on r or only on θ becomes a considerably easier problem. ◀

EXERCISES 2.6 **Exercises 1 to 9:** Find the indicated second (or higher order) partial derivatives of the given function.

1. $z = e^{xy} + \ln(x^2 y^3)$; $z_{xx}, z_{xy}, z_{yx}, z_{yy}$

2. $z = x^y + (\ln y)^x$; $z_{xx}, z_{xy}, z_{yx}, z_{yy}$

3. $z = (x^2 + y^2)^{5/2}$; $z_{xx}, z_{xy}, z_{yx}, z_{yy}$

4. $z = x \arctan(y/x)$; $z_{xx}, z_{xy}, z_{yx}, z_{yy}$

5. $z = \sin^2(x + y)$; $z_{xx}, z_{xy}, z_{yx}, z_{yy}$

6. $z = f(x)g(y)$; $z_{xx}, z_{xy}, z_{yx}, z_{yy}$ (f and g are differentiable real-valued functions)

7. $z = f(ax+by)+g(ax/y)$; $z_{xx}, z_{xy}, z_{yx}, z_{yy}$ (f and g are differentiable real-valued functions of one variable and a and b are constants)

8. $z = e^{xy}$; $z_{xx}, z_{xxx}, z_{xxxx}, z_{yyyy}$

9. $w = y^3 \ln(x^2 + 3x + e^y) + x^3 y^2 z^4$; w_{xyzx}

10. A differential equation of the form $u_t = cu_{xx}$ where $u = u(x, t)$ and c is a constant is called a *diffusion equation*.

  (a) Show that $u(x, t) = e^{ax+bt}$ (a and b are constants) satisfies the diffusion equation with $c = b/a^2$.

  (b) Show that $u(x, t) = t^{-1/2}e^{-x^2/t}$ satisfies the diffusion equation with $c = 1/4$.

11. Real-valued functions $u(x, y)$ and $v(x, y)$ are said to satisfy the *Cauchy-Riemann equations* if $u_x = v_y$ and $u_y = -v_x$. Show that the following functions satisfy the Cauchy-Riemann equations:

(a) $u(x, y) = x^3 - 3xy^2$ and $v(x, y) = 3x^2y - y^3$.

(b) $u(x, y) = e^x \cos y$ and $v(x, y) = e^x \sin y$.

12. Show that if two functions $u(x, y)$ and $v(x, y)$ satisfy the Cauchy-Riemann equations (see Exercise 11) and u_{xy} and v_{xy} are continuous, then $u(x, y)$ and $v(x, y)$ satisfy Laplace's equation; i.e., $u_{xx} + u_{yy} = 0$ and $v_{xx} + v_{yy} = 0$.

13. Show that $z = xe^y + ye^x$ satisfies the equation $z_{xxx} + z_{yyy} = xz_{xyy} + yz_{yxx}$.

14. Explain why there is no C^2 function $f(x, y)$ such that $f_x(x, y) = e^x + xy$ and $f_y(x, y) = e^x + xy$.

15. How many different second-order partial derivatives does a C^2 function of 3 (and, in general, of m) variables have?

16. Show that $u(x, t) = \sin(x - ct) + \sinh(x + ct)$ (c is a constant) satisfies the wave equation $u_{tt} = c^2 u_{xx}$.

17. Assume that f and g are real-valued functions of one variable, and are of class C^2. Show that $u(x, y) = xf(x + y) + y g(x + y)$ satisfies the equation $u_{xx} - 2u_{xy} + u_{yy} = 0$.

18. Show that $z = e^{-ay} \cos(ax)$ (a is a constant) satisfies the equation $z_{xx} = az_y$.

19. Find the domain of the function $z = \ln(x^2 + y^2)$. Show that z is harmonic (i.e., it satisfies Laplace's equation $z_{xx} + z_{yy} = 0$) for all (x, y) that belong to its domain.

20. Show that $z = x^4 - 6x^2y^2 + y^4$ satisfies Laplace's equation $z_{xx} + z_{yy} = 0$.

21. When two resistors with resistances R_1 and R_2 are connected in parallel, the combined resistance is $R = (1/R_1 + 1/R_2)^{-1}$. Show that

$$\frac{\partial^2 R}{\partial R_1^2} \frac{\partial^2 R}{\partial R_2^2} = \frac{4R^2}{(R_1 + R_2)^4}.$$

22. Let $f(x, y, z): \mathbb{R}^3 \to \mathbb{R}$ and $\mathbf{c}(t): \mathbb{R} \to \mathbb{R}^3$ be C^2 functions. Using the chain rule, find $(f \circ \mathbf{c})''(t)$.

23. Show that the gravitational potential $V(x, y, z) = -GMm/\|\mathbf{r}\|$, where $\mathbf{r} = x\mathbf{i} + y\mathbf{j} + z\mathbf{k}$, satisfies Laplace's equation $V_{xx} + V_{yy} + V_{zz} = 0$, whenever $\mathbf{r} \neq \mathbf{0}$.

2.7 CYLINDRICAL AND SPHERICAL COORDINATE SYSTEMS

There are many ways of representing points in $\mathbb{R}^3$ other than using the Cartesian coordinates x, y and z. Two commonly used sets of coordinates (for example, in integration) are cylindrical and spherical coordinates.

■ **Definition 2.15**   Cylindrical Coordinates r, θ, z.

The *cylindrical coordinates* r, θ, z are related to Cartesian coordinates by

$$x = r \cos\theta, \quad y = r \sin\theta, \quad z = z, \qquad 0 \leq \theta < 2\pi, \quad r \geq 0. \quad (2.29)$$

In other words, cylindrical coordinates are a combination of polar coordinates in the xy-plane $\mathbb{R}^2$ and the z-axis (this is just a convention: we could have taken polar coordinates in the xz-plane and added the y-axis). They are usually used when the object involved exhibits symmetry with respect to an axis. For example, the cylinder $x^2 + y^2 = a^2$ (whose axis of symmetry is the z-axis) has a particularly simple equation in cylindrical coordinates: $r = a$.

Next, we give relations inverse to (2.29), expressing r, θ and z in terms of the Cartesian coordinates x, y and z (in order to understand the formula for θ keep in mind that the range of $\arctan(y/x)$ is between $-\pi/2$ and $\pi/2$, whereas the requirement in (2.29) is that the angle be between 0 and 2π). Solving (2.29) for r, θ and z we get

$$r = \sqrt{x^2 + y^2}$$

$$\theta = \begin{cases} \arctan(y/x) & \text{if } x > 0 \text{ and } y \geq 0 \\ \arctan(y/x) + \pi & \text{if } x < 0 \\ \arctan(y/x) + 2\pi & \text{if } x > 0 \text{ and } y < 0 \end{cases}$$

$$z = z. \tag{2.30}$$

Furthermore, $\theta = \pi/2$ if $x = 0$ and $y > 0$ and $\theta = 3\pi/2$ if $x = 0$ and $y < 0$.

Example 2.64   This example illustrates the conversion between Cartesian and cylindrical coordinate systems.

(a) Find cylindrical coordinates of the points with Cartesian coordinates $A_1(2, 5, -2)$, $A_2(-1, 1, 3)$, and $A_3(0, -4, 2)$.

(b) The points B_1 and B_2 have cylindrical coordinates $B_1(2, \pi/4, 1)$ and $B_2(1, 3\pi/2, -4)$. Find their Cartesian coordinates.

(c) Express the equation of the double cone $4x^2 + 4y^2 = z^2$ in cylindrical coordinates.

(d) A surface has the equation $r^2 + z^2 = z$ in cylindrical coordinates. Convert the equation to Cartesian coordinates and identify the surface.

Solution   All we need are the conversion formulas (2.29) and (2.30).

(a) Let us find the cylindrical coordinates of A_1. Since $x = 2$ and $y = 5$ it follows that $r = \sqrt{2^2 + 5^2} = \sqrt{29}$ and $\arctan(y/x) = \arctan 2.5 \approx 1.19$ rad. Therefore $\theta \approx 1.19$ and $(\sqrt{29}, 1.19, -2)$ are the cylindrical coordinates of A_1. For A_2, we get $r = \sqrt{2}$ and $\arctan(y/x) = \arctan(-1) = -\pi/4$. Therefore, $\theta = -\pi/4 + \pi = 3\pi/4$ and the cylindrical coordinates of A_2 are $(\sqrt{2}, 3\pi/4, 3)$. For A_3, we get $r = \sqrt{16} = 4$ and (since $x = 0$ and $y = -4 < 0$) $\theta = 3\pi/2$. Hence A_3 has cylindrical coordinates $A_3(4, 3\pi/2, 2)$.

(b) The Cartesian coordinates of B_1 are $x = r\cos\theta = 2\cos(\pi/4) = \sqrt{2}$, $y = r\sin\theta = 2\sin(\pi/4) = \sqrt{2}$ and $z = 1$. For the point B_2, we get $x = 2\cos(3\pi/2) = 0$, $y = 2\sin(3\pi/2) = -1$ and $z = -4$.

(c) Since $x^2 + y^2 = r^2$, the equation of the double cone $4x^2 + 4y^2 = z^2$ in cylindrical coordinates is $4r^2 = z^2$.

(d) From $r^2 = x^2 + y^2$ we get $x^2 + y^2 + z^2 = z$ and (after completing the square) $x^2 + y^2 + (z - 1/2)^2 = 1/4$. The surface in question is the sphere centered at

$(0, 0, 1/2)$ of radius $1/2$.   ◀

Let us describe the unit vectors $\mathbf{e}_r$, $\mathbf{e}_\theta$ and $\mathbf{e}_z$ for the cylindrical coordinates r, θ and z; see Figure 2.47. In general, a unit vector that corresponds to a coordinate function has a direction in which that coordinate increases while the remaining one(s) is (are) kept constant.

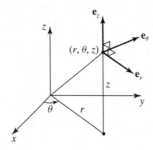

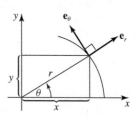

Figure 2.47   Cylindrical coordinate system with unit vectors $\mathbf{e}_r$, $\mathbf{e}_\theta$ and $\mathbf{e}_z$.

Figure 2.48   Unit vectors that correspond to the polar coordinates r and θ.

Since we took the z-axis from the Cartesian coordinate system, $\mathbf{e}_z = \mathbf{k}$. To find $\mathbf{e}_r$ and $\mathbf{e}_\theta$ we consider the polar coordinate system in the xy-plane. The vector $\mathbf{e}_r$ is the unit vector whose direction at a point (r, θ) is the direction in which r increases and θ remains constant; see Figure 2.48. It follows that

$$\mathbf{e}_r = \frac{\mathbf{r}}{\|\mathbf{r}\|} = \frac{x\mathbf{i} + y\mathbf{j}}{\sqrt{x^2 + y^2}} = \frac{x}{\sqrt{x^2 + y^2}}\mathbf{i} + \frac{y}{\sqrt{x^2 + y^2}}\mathbf{j} = \cos\theta\mathbf{i} + \sin\theta\mathbf{j}.$$

The unit vector $\mathbf{e}_\theta$ has to be perpendicular to $\mathbf{e}_r$ (take any vector in the xy-plane whose dot product with $\mathbf{e}_r$ is zero and divide your choice by its norm) and therefore $\mathbf{e}_\theta = \pm(\sin\theta\mathbf{i} - \cos\theta\mathbf{j})$. From Figure 2.48 it follows that, in the first quadrant, the direction of increasing values of θ corresponds to the negative $\mathbf{i}$ and the positive $\mathbf{j}$ components. Therefore we must choose $\mathbf{e}_\theta = (-\sin\theta\mathbf{i} + \cos\theta\mathbf{j})$, which you may verify is valid for all θ. Hence,

$$\mathbf{e}_r = \cos\theta\mathbf{i} + \sin\theta\mathbf{j}$$
$$\mathbf{e}_\theta = -\sin\theta\mathbf{i} + \cos\theta\mathbf{j}$$
$$\mathbf{e}_z = \mathbf{k}. \tag{2.31}$$

Vectors $\mathbf{e}_r$, $\mathbf{e}_\theta$ and $\mathbf{e}_z$ are called *orthonormal* (= orthogonal + normal), since they are perpendicular to each other and of unit length. The set $\{\mathbf{e}_r, \mathbf{e}_\theta, \mathbf{e}_z\}$ is called an *orthonormal basis of $\mathbb{R}^3$*. A vector $\mathbf{F}$ can be represented as $\mathbf{F} = F_r\mathbf{e}_r + F_\theta\mathbf{e}_\theta + F_z\mathbf{e}_z$, where

$$F_r = \mathbf{F} \cdot \mathbf{e}_r, \qquad F_\theta = \mathbf{F} \cdot \mathbf{e}_\theta \qquad \text{and} \qquad F_z = \mathbf{F} \cdot \mathbf{e}_z. \tag{2.32}$$

To verify this fact, compute the dot product of $\mathbf{F}$ with $\mathbf{e}_r$

$$\mathbf{F} \cdot \mathbf{e}_r = F_r\mathbf{e}_r \cdot \mathbf{e}_r + F_\theta\mathbf{e}_\theta \cdot \mathbf{e}_r + F_z\mathbf{e}_z \cdot \mathbf{e}_r,$$

and use orthonormality ($\mathbf{e}_r \cdot \mathbf{e}_r = \|\mathbf{e}_r\|^2 = 1$, $\mathbf{e}_\theta \cdot \mathbf{e}_r = 0$ and $\mathbf{e}_z \cdot \mathbf{e}_r = 0$) to get $F_r = \mathbf{F} \cdot \mathbf{e}_r$. The expressions for F_θ and F_z are checked analogously.

Example 2.65 Represent the vector field $\mathbf{F}(x, y, z) = xy\mathbf{i} + x^2 z\mathbf{k}$ in cylindrical coordinates.

Solution The components of $\mathbf{F}$ in cylindrical coordinates are computed from (2.32) by substituting (2.29) and (2.31):

$$F_r = \mathbf{F} \cdot \mathbf{e}_r = (r^2 \cos\theta \sin\theta \mathbf{i} + r^2 z \cos^2\theta \mathbf{k}) \cdot (\cos\theta \mathbf{i} + \sin\theta \mathbf{j}) = r^2 \cos^2\theta \sin\theta,$$
$$F_\theta = \mathbf{F} \cdot \mathbf{e}_\theta = (r^2 \cos\theta \sin\theta \mathbf{i} + r^2 z \cos^2\theta \mathbf{k}) \cdot (-\sin\theta \mathbf{i} + \cos\theta \mathbf{j}) = -r^2 \cos\theta \sin^2\theta,$$
$$F_z = \mathbf{F} \cdot \mathbf{e}_z = (r^2 \cos\theta \sin\theta \mathbf{i} + r^2 z \cos^2\theta \mathbf{k}) \cdot \mathbf{k} = r^2 z \cos^2\theta.$$

Therefore,
$$\mathbf{F}(r, \theta, z) = r^2 \cos^2\theta \sin\theta \mathbf{e}_r - r^2 \cos\theta \sin^2\theta \mathbf{e}_\theta + r^2 z \cos^2\theta \mathbf{e}_z.$$

◀

Solving equations (2.31) for unit vectors $\mathbf{i}$, $\mathbf{j}$ and $\mathbf{k}$ we get

$$\mathbf{i} = \cos\theta \mathbf{e}_r - \sin\theta \mathbf{e}_\theta$$
$$\mathbf{j} = \sin\theta \mathbf{e}_r + \cos\theta \mathbf{e}_\theta$$
$$\mathbf{k} = \mathbf{e}_z. \tag{2.33}$$

These formulas, combined with (2.29), provide an alternative way of expressing a vector in cylindrical coordinates: the vector field $\mathbf{F}$ of Example 2.65 can be written as

$$\mathbf{F} = xy\mathbf{i} + x^2 z\mathbf{k} = r^2 \cos\theta \sin\theta (\cos\theta \mathbf{e}_r - \sin\theta \mathbf{e}_\theta) + r^2 z \cos^2\theta \mathbf{e}_z$$
$$= r^2 \cos^2\theta \sin\theta \mathbf{e}_r - r^2 \cos\theta \sin^2\theta \mathbf{e}_\theta + r^2 z \cos^2\theta \mathbf{e}_z.$$

Example 2.66 Let $\mathbf{c}(t) = x(t)\mathbf{i} + y(t)\mathbf{j} + z(t)\mathbf{k}$ be a position vector of a particle (in Cartesian coordinates). Recall that $\mathbf{v}(t) = \mathbf{c}'(t)$ is the velocity and $\mathbf{a}(t) = \mathbf{v}'(t)$ the acceleration of the particle. Compute the expressions for the velocity and acceleration in cylindrical coordinates

$$x = r \cos\theta, \quad y = r \sin\theta, \quad z = z$$

(coordinate functions are viewed as functions of time: $r = r(t)$, $\theta = \theta(t)$ and $z = z(t)$).

Solution We first express the position vector $\mathbf{c}(t)$ in cylindrical coordinates (drop t to keep notation simple):

$$\mathbf{c}(t) = x\mathbf{i} + y\mathbf{j} + z\mathbf{k}$$
$$= r \cos\theta (\cos\theta \mathbf{e}_r - \sin\theta \mathbf{e}_\theta) + r \sin\theta (\sin\theta \mathbf{e}_r + \cos\theta \mathbf{e}_\theta) + z\mathbf{e}_z$$
$$= r \cos^2\theta \mathbf{e}_r - r \cos\theta \sin\theta \mathbf{e}_\theta + r \sin^2\theta \mathbf{e}_r + r \cos\theta \sin\theta \mathbf{e}_\theta + z\mathbf{e}_z$$
$$= r\mathbf{e}_r + z\mathbf{e}_z.$$

The velocity is computed from $\mathbf{c}(t)$ using the product rule:

$$\mathbf{v}(t) = \frac{d}{dt}(\mathbf{c}(t)) = \frac{dr}{dt}\mathbf{e}_r + r\frac{d\mathbf{e}_r}{dt} + \frac{dz}{dt}\mathbf{e}_z + z\frac{d\mathbf{e}_z}{dt}.$$

The derivatives of unit vectors are computed from (2.31) using the chain rule (keep in mind that θ is a function of t):

$$\frac{d\mathbf{e}_r}{dt} = \frac{d}{dt}\left(\cos\theta\mathbf{i} + \sin\theta\mathbf{j}\right)$$

$$= -\sin\theta\frac{d\theta}{dt}\mathbf{i} + \cos\theta\frac{d\theta}{dt}\mathbf{j} = \left(-\sin\theta\mathbf{i} + \cos\theta\mathbf{j}\right)\frac{d\theta}{dt} = \frac{d\theta}{dt}\mathbf{e}_\theta,$$

$$\frac{d\mathbf{e}_\theta}{dt} = \frac{d}{dt}\left(-\sin\theta\mathbf{i} + \cos\theta\mathbf{j}\right)$$

$$= -\cos\theta\frac{d\theta}{dt}\mathbf{i} - \sin\theta\frac{d\theta}{dt}\mathbf{j} = -\left(\cos\theta\mathbf{i} + \sin\theta\mathbf{j}\right)\frac{d\theta}{dt} = -\frac{d\theta}{dt}\mathbf{e}_r,$$

and

$$\frac{d\mathbf{e}_z}{dt} = \frac{d}{dt}(\mathbf{k}) = 0.$$

Substituting $d\mathbf{e}_r/dt$ and $d\mathbf{e}_z/dt$ into the expression for $\mathbf{v}(t)$ we get

$$\mathbf{v}(t) = \frac{dr}{dt}\mathbf{e}_r + r\frac{d\theta}{dt}\mathbf{e}_\theta + \frac{dz}{dt}\mathbf{e}_z.$$

The acceleration $\mathbf{a}(t) = \mathbf{v}'(t)$ is computed similarly: apply the product rule to $\mathbf{v}(t)$,

$$\mathbf{a}(t) = \frac{d^2r}{dt^2}\mathbf{e}_r + \frac{dr}{dt}\frac{d\mathbf{e}_r}{dt} + \frac{dr}{dt}\frac{d\theta}{dt}\mathbf{e}_\theta + r\frac{d^2\theta}{dt^2}\mathbf{e}_\theta + r\frac{d\theta}{dt}\frac{d\mathbf{e}_\theta}{dt} + \frac{d^2z}{dt^2}\mathbf{e}_z + \frac{dz}{dt}\frac{d\mathbf{e}_z}{dt}$$

and use the expressions for the derivatives of unit vectors to get

$$= \frac{d^2r}{dt^2}\mathbf{e}_r + \frac{dr}{dt}\frac{d\theta}{dt}\mathbf{e}_\theta + \frac{dr}{dt}\frac{d\theta}{dt}\mathbf{e}_\theta + r\frac{d^2\theta}{dt^2}\mathbf{e}_\theta + r\frac{d\theta}{dt}\left(-\frac{d\theta}{dt}\right)\mathbf{e}_r + \frac{d^2z}{dt^2}\mathbf{e}_z$$

$$= \left(\frac{d^2r}{dt^2} - r\left(\frac{d\theta}{dt}\right)^2\right)\mathbf{e}_r + \left(r\frac{d^2\theta}{dt^2} + 2\frac{dr}{dt}\frac{d\theta}{dt}\right)\mathbf{e}_\theta + \left(\frac{d^2z}{dt^2}\right)\mathbf{e}_z.$$

Notice that $d\mathbf{e}_r/dt = (d\theta/dt)\mathbf{e}_\theta \neq \mathbf{0}$ and $d\mathbf{e}_\theta/dt = -(d\theta/dt)\mathbf{e}_r \neq \mathbf{0}$, whereas in Cartesian coordinates $d\mathbf{i}/dt = d\mathbf{j}/dt = d\mathbf{k}/dt = \mathbf{0}$.

■ **Definition 2.16** Spherical Coordinates ρ, θ, ϕ.

The point $(x, y, z) \in \mathbb{R}^3$ is represented in *spherical coordinates* using the following data ($\mathbf{r} = x\mathbf{i} + y\mathbf{j} + z\mathbf{k}$ denotes the position vector of (x, y, z); see Figure 2.49):

(a) distance $\rho = \|\mathbf{r}\| = \sqrt{x^2 + y^2 + z^2} \geq 0$ from the origin.

(b) angle θ ($0 \leq \theta < 2\pi$) in the xy-plane (measured counterclockwise) between the x-axis and the projection $\mathbf{r}_p$ of the position vector $\mathbf{r} = x\mathbf{i} + y\mathbf{j} + z\mathbf{k}$ onto the xy-plane.

(c) angle ϕ (in the plane containing the z-axis and the position vector $\mathbf{r}$, measured from the positive direction of the z-axis), $0 \leq \phi \leq \pi$. If a point lies on the z-axis, then $\phi = 0$ if $z \geq 0$ and $\phi = \pi$ if $z < 0$.

Since $\sin\phi = \|\mathbf{r}_p\|/\rho$ — i.e., $\|\mathbf{r}_p\| = \rho\sin\phi$ — it follows that

$$x = \|\mathbf{r}_p\|\cos\theta = \rho\sin\phi\cos\theta$$
$$y = \|\mathbf{r}_p\|\sin\theta = \rho\sin\phi\sin\theta$$
$$z = \rho\cos\phi. \tag{2.34}$$

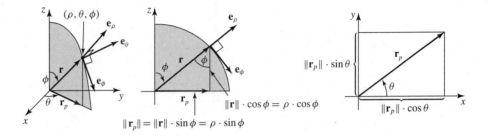

Figure 2.49 Spherical coordinate system and the corresponding unit vectors; view in the plane containing $\mathbf{r}_p$ and the z-axis; view in the xy-plane.

The coordinates ρ, θ and ϕ are called *spherical coordinates* in $\mathbb{R}^3$. They are usually used in dealing with spherically symmetric objects (that is, objects that are symmetric with respect to a point). For example (remember that $x^2 + y^2 + z^2 = \|\mathbf{r}\|^2 = \rho^2$) the equation of the sphere $x^2 + y^2 + z^2 = a^2$ in Cartesian coordinates is $\rho = a$ in spherical coordinates.

The inverse relations, expressing ρ, θ and ϕ in terms of x, y and z are

$$\rho = \sqrt{x^2 + y^2 + z^2}$$
$$\theta = \begin{cases} \arctan(y/x) & \text{if } x > 0 \text{ and } y \geq 0 \\ \arctan(y/x) + \pi & \text{if } x < 0 \\ \arctan(y/x) + 2\pi & \text{if } x > 0 \text{ and } y < 0 \end{cases}$$
$$\phi = \arccos(z/\rho). \tag{2.35}$$

Example 2.67 This example illustrates the use of conversion formulas between Cartesian and spherical coordinate systems.

(a) Compute the spherical coordinates of the points whose Cartesian coordinates are $A_1(2, -2, 3)$ and $A_2(1, 1, -1)$.

(b) In spherical coordinates the point B is represented by $(2, \pi/4, 2\pi/3)$. Find its Cartesian coordinates.

(c) Express the equation of the sphere $x^2 + y^2 + (z-1)^2 = 1$ in spherical coordinates.

Solution We make use of (2.34) and (2.35).

(a) The Cartesian coordinates of A_1 are $x = 2$, $y = -2$ and $z = 3$. Therefore $\rho = \sqrt{x^2 + y^2 + z^2} = \sqrt{2^2 + (-2)^2 + 3^2} = \sqrt{17}$, $\arctan(y/x) = \arctan(-1) = -\pi/4$ so that $\theta = -\pi/4 + 2\pi = 7\pi/4$, and $\phi = \arccos(3/\sqrt{17}) \approx 0.76$ rad. It follows that, in spherical coordinates, $A_1(\sqrt{17}, 7\pi/4, 0.76)$. Similarly, the spherical coordinates of A_2 are $\rho = \sqrt{3}$, $\arctan(y/x) = \pi/4$ so that $\theta = \pi/4$, and $\phi = \arccos(-1/\sqrt{3}) \approx 2.19$ rad.

(b) The Cartesian coordinates of the point $(2, \pi/4, 2\pi/3)$ are $x = 2\sin(2\pi/3)\cos(\pi/4) = 2(\sqrt{3}/2)(\sqrt{2}/2) = \sqrt{6}/2$, $y = 2\sin(2\pi/3)\sin(\pi/4) = 2(\sqrt{3}/2)(\sqrt{2}/2) = \sqrt{6}/2$ and $z = 2\cos(2\pi/3) = 2(-1/2) = -1$.

(c) Recall that $x^2+y^2+z^2 = \rho^2$. From $x^2+y^2+(z-1)^2 = 1$ we get $x^2+y^2+z^2-2z = 0$ and hence $\rho^2 - 2\rho\cos\theta = 0$; i.e., $\rho = 2\cos\theta$.

◀

Let us compute the unit vectors $\mathbf{e}_\rho$, $\mathbf{e}_\theta$ and $\mathbf{e}_\phi$ for spherical coordinates. Vector $\mathbf{e}_\rho$ is the unit vector in the radial direction, hence

$$\mathbf{e}_\rho = \frac{x\mathbf{i} + y\mathbf{j} + z\mathbf{k}}{\sqrt{x^2 + y^2 + z^2}} = \frac{\rho\sin\phi\cos\theta\mathbf{i} + \rho\sin\phi\sin\theta\mathbf{j} + \rho\cos\phi\mathbf{k}}{\rho}$$

$$= \sin\phi\cos\theta\mathbf{i} + \sin\phi\sin\theta\mathbf{j} + \cos\phi\mathbf{k}.$$

In order to find $\mathbf{e}_\theta$ we fix ρ and ϕ and consider the increase in θ in the (fixed) horizontal plane $z = \rho\cos\phi$. But this is just like θ in cylindrical coordinates (with r replaced by $\rho\sin\phi$; see Figure 2.49) and therefore $\mathbf{e}_\theta = -\sin\theta\mathbf{i} + \cos\theta\mathbf{j}$. From the definition, it follows that the increase in ϕ occurs in the direction perpendicular to $\mathbf{e}_\rho$ and $\mathbf{e}_\theta$. Hence

$$\mathbf{e}_\phi = \pm\mathbf{e}_\rho \times \mathbf{e}_\theta = \pm \begin{vmatrix} \mathbf{i} & \mathbf{j} & \mathbf{k} \\ \sin\phi\cos\theta & \sin\phi\sin\theta & \cos\phi \\ -\sin\theta & \cos\theta & 0 \end{vmatrix}$$

$$= \pm(-\cos\phi\cos\theta\mathbf{i} - \sin\theta\cos\phi\mathbf{j} + \sin\phi\mathbf{k}).$$

In the first octant, the $\mathbf{k}$ component of $\mathbf{e}_\phi$ has to be negative (see Figure 2.49). Since in that case $\sin\phi > 0$, we have to choose the "$-$" sign above, therefore getting $\mathbf{e}_\phi = \cos\phi\cos\theta\mathbf{i} + \cos\phi\sin\theta\mathbf{j} - \sin\phi\mathbf{k}$. You may wish to verify that this relation is valid for all θ and ϕ. Consequently, the orthonormal set of basis vectors for spherical coordinates is

$$\mathbf{e}_\rho = \sin\phi\cos\theta\mathbf{i} + \sin\phi\sin\theta\mathbf{j} + \cos\phi\mathbf{k}$$

$$\mathbf{e}_\theta = -\sin\theta\mathbf{i} + \cos\theta\mathbf{j}$$

$$\mathbf{e}_\phi = \cos\phi\cos\theta\mathbf{i} + \cos\phi\sin\theta\mathbf{j} - \sin\phi\mathbf{k}. \tag{2.36}$$

Repeating the argument presented in obtaining (2.32) in the case of cylindrical coordinates, we get that a vector $\mathbf{F}$ can be represented in spherical coordinates as $\mathbf{F} = F_\rho\mathbf{e}_\rho + F_\theta\mathbf{e}_\theta + F_\phi\mathbf{e}_\phi$, where

$$F_\rho = \mathbf{F}\cdot\mathbf{e}_\rho, \qquad F_\theta = \mathbf{F}\cdot\mathbf{e}_\theta \qquad \text{and} \qquad F_\phi = \mathbf{F}\cdot\mathbf{e}_\phi.$$

This method of decomposition works in $\mathbb{R}^2$ ($\mathbb{R}^3$) for any set of two (three) orthonormal vectors.

Example 2.68   Represent the vector field $\mathbf{F}(x, y, z) = z\mathbf{i} - x\mathbf{k}$ in spherical coordinates.

Solution   In spherical coordinates, $\mathbf{F}(\rho, \theta, \phi) = F_\rho \mathbf{e}_\rho + F_\theta \mathbf{e}_\theta + F_\phi \mathbf{e}_\phi$, where

$$F_\rho = \mathbf{F} \cdot \mathbf{e}_\rho = (z\mathbf{i} - x\mathbf{k}) \cdot (\sin\phi \cos\theta \mathbf{i} + \sin\phi \sin\theta \mathbf{j} + \cos\phi \mathbf{k})$$
$$= (\rho \cos\phi \mathbf{i} - \rho \sin\phi \cos\theta \mathbf{k}) \cdot (\sin\phi \cos\theta \mathbf{i} + \sin\phi \sin\theta \mathbf{j} + \cos\phi \mathbf{k})$$
$$= \rho \cos\phi \sin\phi \cos\theta - \rho \sin\phi \cos\theta \cos\phi = 0,$$
$$F_\theta = \mathbf{F} \cdot \mathbf{e}_\theta = (\rho \cos\phi \mathbf{i} - \rho \sin\phi \cos\theta \mathbf{k}) \cdot (-\sin\theta \mathbf{i} + \cos\theta \mathbf{j}) = -\rho \cos\phi \sin\theta,$$

and

$$F_\phi = \mathbf{F} \cdot \mathbf{e}_\phi = (\rho \cos\phi \mathbf{i} - \rho \sin\phi \cos\theta \mathbf{k}) \cdot (\cos\phi \cos\theta \mathbf{i} + \cos\phi \sin\theta \mathbf{j} - \sin\phi \mathbf{k})$$
$$= \rho \cos^2\phi \cos\theta + \rho \sin^2\phi \cos\theta = \rho \cos\theta.$$

It follows that $\mathbf{F}(\rho, \theta, \phi) = -\rho \cos\phi \sin\theta \mathbf{e}_\theta + \rho \cos\theta \mathbf{e}_\phi$.   ◀

Example 2.69   Consider unit vectors in spherical coordinates and assume that $\rho = \rho(t)$, $\theta = \theta(t)$ and $\phi = \phi(t)$. Compute $d\mathbf{e}_\rho / dt$.

Solution   Using (2.36) and applying the product rule and the chain rule, we get

$$\frac{d\mathbf{e}_\rho}{dt} = \frac{d}{dt}(\sin\phi \cos\theta \mathbf{i} + \sin\phi \sin\theta \mathbf{j} + \cos\phi \mathbf{k})$$
$$= \cos\phi \frac{d\phi}{dt} \cos\theta \mathbf{i} - \sin\phi \sin\theta \frac{d\theta}{dt} \mathbf{i} + \cos\phi \frac{d\phi}{dt} \sin\theta \mathbf{j} + \sin\phi \cos\theta \frac{d\theta}{dt} \mathbf{j} - \sin\phi \frac{d\phi}{dt} \mathbf{k}$$
$$= \frac{d\phi}{dt}(\cos\phi \cos\theta \mathbf{i} + \cos\phi \sin\theta \mathbf{j} - \sin\phi \mathbf{k}) + \frac{d\theta}{dt}(-\sin\phi \sin\theta \mathbf{i} + \sin\phi \cos\theta \mathbf{j})$$
$$= \frac{d\phi}{dt}\mathbf{e}_\phi + \sin\phi \frac{d\theta}{dt}\mathbf{e}_\theta.$$ ◀

Notice that the derivative $d\mathbf{e}_\rho / dt$ of the unit vector $\mathbf{e}_\rho$ is a non-zero vector. We have observed the same phenomenon in the case of cylindrical coordinates. On the contrary, in Cartesian coordinates the derivatives of unit coordinate vectors are always zero.

The representatives of unit vectors $\mathbf{e}_r$ and $\mathbf{e}_\theta$ in cylindrical coordinates and $\mathbf{e}_\rho$, $\mathbf{e}_\theta$ and $\mathbf{e}_\phi$ in spherical coordinates starting at different points in $\mathbb{R}^3$ are *not* parallel translates of each other. The property that all representatives of a vector are parallel translates of each other holds only in Cartesian coordinate systems.

EXERCISES 2.7

1. Find cylindrical coordinates of the points whose Cartesian coordinates are $(-4, 0, 0)$, $(0, 0, 3)$, $(0, 2, 4)$ and $(2, -3, -1)$.

2. Find spherical coordinates of the points whose Cartesian coordinates are $(-2, 0, 0)$, $(0, 4, 0)$, $(0, 0, 6)$ and $(4, 2, -3)$.

3. Describe geometrically the image of a cube of side a in the first octant whose faces are parallel to the coordinate planes under the mapping $T : \mathbb{R}^3 \to \mathbb{R}^3$ given in cylindrical coordinates by $T(r, \theta, z) = (2r, \theta + \pi, z)$.

4. Describe geometrically the image of an object in the first octant under the mapping $T : \mathbb{R}^3 \to$

$\mathbb{R}^3$ given in spherical coordinates by $T(\rho, \theta, \phi) = (\rho, \theta, \phi + \pi/2)$. Repeat for the mappings $T(\rho, \theta, \phi) = (2\rho, \theta, \phi)$ and $T(\rho, \theta, \phi) = (\rho, \theta + \pi, \phi)$.

5. Express the equation of the paraboloid $z = 4 - x^2 - y^2$ and the equation of the plane $x + 2y - z = 0$ in both cylindrical coordinates and spherical coordinates.

6. Describe the surface whose equation in spherical coordinates is $\rho = 2 \sin \phi$.

7. Describe the coordinate surfaces $r = $ constant, $\theta = $ constant and $z = $ constant and coordinate curves for the cylindrical coordinate system. Coordinate curves are the intersections of coordinate surfaces.

8. Describe the coordinate surfaces $\rho = $ constant, $\theta = $ constant and $\phi = $ constant and coordinate curves (i.e., the intersections of coordinate surfaces) for the spherical coordinate system.

9. Express the vectors $\mathbf{i}$, $\mathbf{j}$ and $\mathbf{k}$ in terms of the unit orthonormal vectors $\mathbf{e}_\rho$, $\mathbf{e}_\theta$ and $\mathbf{e}_\phi$ for spherical coordinates.

Exercises 10 to 14:   Represent the vector field $\mathbf{F}(x, y, z)$ in both cylindrical and spherical coordinate systems.

10. $\mathbf{F}(x, y, z) = x\mathbf{i} - 2y\mathbf{j} + z\mathbf{k}$ 11. $\mathbf{F}(x, y, z) = \mathbf{i} + \mathbf{j}$

12. $\mathbf{F}(x, y, z) = (x^2 + y^2)\mathbf{i} - \mathbf{k}$ 13. $\mathbf{F}(x, y, z) = y\mathbf{i} - x\mathbf{j}$

14. $\mathbf{F}(x, y, z) = \mathbf{i} - x\mathbf{j} + \mathbf{k}$

15. Assume that spherical coordinates $\rho = \rho(t)$, $\theta = \theta(t)$ and $\phi = \phi(t)$ depend on time t and let $\{\mathbf{e}_\rho, \mathbf{e}_\theta, \mathbf{e}_\phi\}$ be the corresponding orthonormal vectors. Compute $d\mathbf{e}_\theta/dt$ and $d\mathbf{e}_\phi/dt$ ($d\mathbf{e}_\rho/dt$ was computed in Example 2.69).

16. Show that the position vector $\mathbf{r} = x\mathbf{i} + y\mathbf{j} + z\mathbf{k}$ is represented in spherical coordinates as $\mathbf{r} = \rho\mathbf{e}_\rho$. Find the expressions for the velocity and acceleration of a particle in spherical coordinates.

17. Let $\mathbf{r} = x\mathbf{i} + y\mathbf{j} + z\mathbf{k}$ be the position vector of a point. Define $d\mathbf{r} = dx\mathbf{i} + dy\mathbf{j} + dz\mathbf{k}$ and $ds^2 = d\mathbf{r} \cdot d\mathbf{r} = dx^2 + dy^2 + dz^2$, where dx, dy and dz are the differentials of x, y and z. The expression ds^2 is called the *square of the line element* (or the *metric*) in $\mathbb{R}^3$. Find its expression in cylindrical coordinates and spherical coordinates.

2.8   GENERAL CURVILINEAR COORDINATE SYSTEMS

Having examined some examples in the previous section, we now turn to the study of general curvilinear coordinate systems.

■ **Definition 2.17**   Curvilinear Coordinates u_1, u_2, u_3.

Let (x, y, z) denote the Cartesian coordinates of a point in $\mathbb{R}^3$. Equations

$$x = x(u_1, u_2, u_3), \quad y = y(u_1, u_2, u_3), \quad z = z(u_1, u_2, u_3) \qquad (2.37)$$

and

$$u_1 = u_1(x, y, z), \quad u_2 = u_2(x, y, z), \quad u_3 = u_3(x, y, z) \qquad (2.38)$$

where $u_i \in I_i \subseteq \mathbb{R}$, for $i = 1, 2, 3$, define the *transformation of coordinates* between the Cartesian coordinates (x, y, z) and the *curvilinear coordinates* (u_1, u_2, u_3).

The intervals I_1, I_2 and I_3 of real numbers represent the range of the coordinates (coordinate functions) u_1, u_2, and u_3.

Example 2.70

For cylindrical coordinates, $u_1 = r$ (with the range $r \geq 0$ or $I_1 = [0, \infty)$) $u_2 = \theta$ (with $I_2 = [0, 2\pi)$) and $u_3 = z$ (with $I_3 = \mathbb{R}$). The set of equations (2.37) is given by (2.29) and the inverse relations (2.38) were obtained in (2.30). The choices $u_1 = \rho$, $u_2 = \theta$ and $u_3 = \phi$ together with (2.34) and appropriately chosen ranges (see Definition 2.16) define spherical coordinates. Equations (2.38) are given by (2.35). The equations

$$x = uv \cos \phi, \quad y = uv \sin \phi, \quad z = \tfrac{1}{2}(u^2 - v^2)$$

with $u, v \geq 0$ and $0 \leq \phi < 2\pi$ define *paraboloidal coordinates* in $\mathbb{R}^3$. Other coordinate systems in $\mathbb{R}^3$ are discussed in the exercises at the end of this section.

The surfaces $u_1 = C_1$, $u_2 = C_2$ and $u_3 = C_3$, where C_1, C_2 and C_3 are constants, are called *coordinate surfaces*, and their intersections are *coordinate curves*: the u_1-*curve* is the intersection of $u_2 = C_2$ and $u_3 = C_3$, the u_2-*curve* is the intersection of $u_1 = C_1$ and $u_3 = C_3$, and the u_3-*curve* is the intersection of $u_1 = C_1$ and $u_2 = C_2$; see Figure 2.50. If coordinate surfaces intersect at right angles (in which case coordinate curves are orthogonal to each other), the coordinate system is called an *orthogonal curvilinear coordinate system*. For example, the coordinate surfaces of the cylindrical coordinate system are: $r = C_1$ (a cylinder of radius C_1 with the z-axis as axis of symmetry, provided that $C_1 > 0$), $\theta = C_2$ (a half-plane containing the z-axis, perpendicular to the xy-plane; its intersection with the xy-plane is the half-line through the origin of slope $\tan C_2$) and $z = C_3$ (a plane parallel to the xy-plane, going through the point $(0, 0, C_3)$).

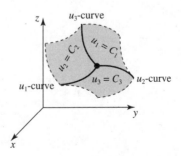

Figure 2.50 A curvilinear coordinate system in $\mathbb{R}^3$ with coordinate surfaces and coordinate curves.

Let P be a point in $\mathbb{R}^3$ and let $\mathbf{r}(x, y, z) = x\mathbf{i} + y\mathbf{j} + z\mathbf{k}$ be its position vector. In light of the transformation formulas (2.37) we can view $\mathbf{r}$ as a function of u_1, u_2 and u_3:

$$\mathbf{r}(u_1, u_2, u_3) = (x(u_1, u_2, u_3), \, y(u_1, u_2, u_3), \, z(u_1, u_2, u_3)).$$

A tangent vector to the u_1-curve (u_2 and u_3 are constant!) is given by $\partial\mathbf{r}/\partial u_1$, and hence the corresponding unit vector is

$$\mathbf{e}_1 = \frac{\partial\mathbf{r}(u_1, u_2, u_3)}{\partial u_1} \Big/ \left\| \frac{\partial\mathbf{r}(u_1, u_2, u_3)}{\partial u_1} \right\|.$$

Denoting $\|\partial\mathbf{r}(u_1, u_2, u_3)/\partial u_1\|$ by h_1, we get $\partial\mathbf{r}/\partial u_1 = h_1\mathbf{e}_1$. The tangents to the u_2-curve and the u_3-curve are computed similarly. Hence the set of unit tangent vectors $\{\mathbf{e}_1, \mathbf{e}_2, \mathbf{e}_3\}$ for the new coordinates (u_1, u_2, u_3) is determined by

$$\frac{\partial\mathbf{r}}{\partial u_1} = h_1\mathbf{e}_1, \qquad \text{where} \qquad h_1 = \left\| \frac{\partial\mathbf{r}(u_1, u_2, u_3)}{\partial u_1} \right\|,$$

$$\frac{\partial\mathbf{r}}{\partial u_2} = h_2\mathbf{e}_2, \qquad \text{where} \qquad h_2 = \left\| \frac{\partial\mathbf{r}(u_1, u_2, u_3)}{\partial u_2} \right\|,$$

$$\frac{\partial\mathbf{r}}{\partial u_3} = h_3\mathbf{e}_3, \qquad \text{where} \qquad h_3 = \left\| \frac{\partial\mathbf{r}(u_1, u_2, u_3)}{\partial u_3} \right\|.$$

The quantities h_1, h_2 and h_3 are called the *scale factors*.

Example 2.71   As an illustration, let us recompute the unit vectors for spherical coordinates $\{\rho, \theta, \phi\}$ (see equations (2.36)). The position vector is

$$\mathbf{r} = \rho \sin\phi \cos\theta \mathbf{i} + \rho \sin\phi \sin\theta \mathbf{j} + \rho \cos\phi \mathbf{k}.$$

It follows that

$$\frac{\partial\mathbf{r}}{\partial u_1} = \frac{\partial\mathbf{r}}{\partial\rho} = \sin\phi \cos\theta \mathbf{i} + \sin\phi \sin\theta \mathbf{j} + \cos\phi \mathbf{k}, \qquad h_1 = h_\rho = \left\| \frac{\partial\mathbf{r}}{\partial\rho} \right\| = 1$$

and hence

$$\mathbf{e}_1 = \mathbf{e}_\rho = \frac{\partial\mathbf{r}}{\partial\rho} \Big/ \left\| \frac{\partial\mathbf{r}}{\partial\rho} \right\| = \sin\phi \cos\theta \mathbf{i} + \sin\phi \sin\theta \mathbf{j} + \cos\phi \mathbf{k}.$$

Similarly,

$$\frac{\partial\mathbf{r}}{\partial u_2} = \frac{\partial\mathbf{r}}{\partial\theta} = -\rho \sin\phi \sin\theta \mathbf{i} + \rho \sin\phi \cos\theta \mathbf{j}, \qquad h_2 = h_\theta = \left\| \frac{\partial\mathbf{r}}{\partial\theta} \right\| = \rho \sin\phi$$

and

$$\mathbf{e}_2 = \mathbf{e}_\theta = \frac{\partial\mathbf{r}}{\partial\theta} \Big/ \left\| \frac{\partial\mathbf{r}}{\partial\theta} \right\| = -\sin\theta \mathbf{i} + \cos\theta \mathbf{j}.$$

From

$$\frac{\partial\mathbf{r}}{\partial u_3} = \frac{\partial\mathbf{r}}{\partial\phi} = \rho \cos\phi \cos\theta \mathbf{i} + \rho \cos\phi \sin\theta \mathbf{j} - \rho \sin\phi \mathbf{k}, \qquad h_3 = h_\phi = \left\| \frac{\partial\mathbf{r}}{\partial\phi} \right\| = \rho$$

we get

$$\mathbf{e}_3 = \mathbf{e}_\phi = \frac{\partial\mathbf{r}}{\partial\phi} \Big/ \left\| \frac{\partial\mathbf{r}}{\partial\phi} \right\| = \cos\phi \cos\theta \mathbf{i} + \cos\phi \sin\theta \mathbf{j} - \sin\phi \mathbf{k}.$$

From now on assume that the curvilinear coordinate system (u_1, u_2, u_3) is *orthonormal*; i.e., assume that the corresponding unit vectors $\mathbf{e}_1$, $\mathbf{e}_2$ and $\mathbf{e}_3$ are mutually orthogonal ($\mathbf{e}_1 \cdot \mathbf{e}_2 = 0$, $\mathbf{e}_1 \cdot \mathbf{e}_3 = 0$ and $\mathbf{e}_2 \cdot \mathbf{e}_3 = 0$) and of length 1. The components of a vector $\mathbf{F}$ in the coordinate system (u_1, u_2, u_3) are F_1, F_2 and F_3, where

$$\mathbf{F} = F_1\mathbf{e}_1 + F_2\mathbf{e}_2 + F_3\mathbf{e}_3,$$

and

$$F_1 = \mathbf{F} \cdot \mathbf{e}_1, \quad F_2 = \mathbf{F} \cdot \mathbf{e}_2 \quad \text{and} \quad F_3 = \mathbf{F} \cdot \mathbf{e}_3.$$

To verify these formulas, compute the dot product of $\mathbf{F}$ with $\mathbf{e}_1$

$$\mathbf{F} \cdot \mathbf{e}_1 = F_1\, \mathbf{e}_1 \cdot \mathbf{e}_1 + F_2\, \mathbf{e}_2 \cdot \mathbf{e}_1 + F_3\, \mathbf{e}_3 \cdot \mathbf{e}_1.$$

Due to the orthonormality assumptions, the second and third terms on the right side vanish, and $\mathbf{e}_1 \cdot \mathbf{e}_1 = \|\mathbf{e}_1\|^2 = 1$. Hence $\mathbf{F} \cdot \mathbf{e}_1 = F_1$. The remaining two components are computed analogously.

Example 2.72

Let u, v, ϕ describe paraboloidal coordinates

$$x = uv \cos\phi, \quad y = uv \sin\phi, \quad z = \frac{1}{2}(u^2 - v^2) \quad u, v \geq 0, \quad 0 \leq \phi < 2\pi.$$

Express the vector field $\mathbf{F} = 2x\mathbf{i} + (y/x)\mathbf{j} - \mathbf{k}$ in the new coordinate system $\{u, v, \phi\}$.

Solution We need unit vectors coresponding to the newly introduced coordinates first. The position vector is

$$\mathbf{r}(u, v, \phi) = uv \cos\phi\, \mathbf{i} + uv \sin\phi\, \mathbf{j} + \frac{1}{2}(u^2 - v^2)\mathbf{k}.$$

It follows that

$$\frac{\partial \mathbf{r}}{\partial u} = v \cos\phi\, \mathbf{i} + v \sin\phi\, \mathbf{j} + u\mathbf{k}, \qquad h_u = \left\| \frac{\partial \mathbf{r}}{\partial u} \right\| = \sqrt{u^2 + v^2}$$

and

$$\mathbf{e}_u = \frac{\partial \mathbf{r}}{\partial u} \bigg/ \left\| \frac{\partial \mathbf{r}}{\partial u} \right\| = \frac{v \cos\phi}{\sqrt{u^2 + v^2}}\mathbf{i} + \frac{v \sin\phi}{\sqrt{u^2 + v^2}}\mathbf{j} + \frac{u}{\sqrt{u^2 + v^2}}\mathbf{k}.$$

Similarly,

$$\frac{\partial \mathbf{r}}{\partial v} = u \cos\phi\, \mathbf{i} + u \sin\phi\, \mathbf{j} - v\mathbf{k}, \qquad h_v = \left\| \frac{\partial \mathbf{r}}{\partial v} \right\| = \sqrt{u^2 + v^2}$$

and

$$\mathbf{e}_v = \frac{\partial \mathbf{r}}{\partial v} \bigg/ \left\| \frac{\partial \mathbf{r}}{\partial v} \right\| = \frac{u \cos\phi}{\sqrt{u^2 + v^2}}\mathbf{i} + \frac{u \sin\phi}{\sqrt{u^2 + v^2}}\mathbf{j} - \frac{v}{\sqrt{u^2 + v^2}}\mathbf{k}.$$

From

$$\frac{\partial \mathbf{r}}{\partial \phi} = -uv \sin\phi\, \mathbf{i} + uv \cos\phi\, \mathbf{j}, \qquad h_\phi = \left\| \frac{\partial \mathbf{r}}{\partial \phi} \right\| = uv$$

it follows that

$$\mathbf{e}_\phi = \frac{\partial \mathbf{r}}{\partial \phi} \bigg/ \left\| \frac{\partial \mathbf{r}}{\partial \phi} \right\| = -\sin\phi\, \mathbf{i} + \cos\phi\, \mathbf{j}.$$

Computing the dot products, we can easily check that the vectors $\mathbf{e}_u$, $\mathbf{e}_v$ and $\mathbf{e}_\phi$ are mutually orthogonal (that is, they form an orthonormal set in $\mathbb{R}^3$). From the argument preceeding this example, we get

$$\mathbf{F} = F_u \mathbf{e}_u + F_v \mathbf{e}_v + F_\phi \mathbf{e}_\phi,$$

where

$$F_u = \mathbf{F} \cdot \mathbf{e}_u = \left(2uv \cos \phi \mathbf{i} + \tan \phi \mathbf{j} - \mathbf{k}\right) \cdot \left(\frac{v \cos \phi}{\sqrt{u^2 + v^2}} \mathbf{i} + \frac{v \sin \phi}{\sqrt{u^2 + v^2}} \mathbf{j} + \frac{u}{\sqrt{u^2 + v^2}} \mathbf{k}\right)$$

$$= \frac{2uv^2 \cos^2 \phi + v \sin \phi \tan \phi - u}{\sqrt{u^2 + v^2}},$$

$$F_v = \mathbf{F} \cdot \mathbf{e}_v = \left(2uv \cos \phi \mathbf{i} + \tan \phi \mathbf{j} - \mathbf{k}\right) \cdot \left(\frac{u \cos \phi}{\sqrt{u^2 + v^2}} + \frac{u \sin \phi}{\sqrt{u^2 + v^2}} \mathbf{j} - \frac{v}{\sqrt{u^2 + v^2}} \mathbf{k}\right)$$

$$= \frac{2u^2 v \cos^2 \phi + u \sin \phi \tan \phi + v}{\sqrt{u^2 + v^2}},$$

and

$$F_\phi = \mathbf{F} \cdot \mathbf{e}_\phi = \left(2uv \cos \phi \mathbf{i} + \tan \phi \mathbf{j} - \mathbf{k}\right) \cdot \left(-\sin \phi \mathbf{i} + \cos \phi \mathbf{j}\right)$$

$$= -2uv \cos \phi \sin \phi + \cos \phi \tan \phi.$$

◄

EXERCISES 2.8

1. Parabolic cylindrical coordinates (u, v, z) are given by

$$x = \tfrac{1}{2}(u^2 - v^2), \quad y = uv, \quad z = z,$$

where $-\infty < u < \infty$, $v \geq 0$ and $-\infty < z < \infty$.

   (a) Find unit coordinate vectors and corresponding scale factors.

   (b) Show that the coordinate system (u, v, z) is orthogonal.

   (c) Express the vector field $\mathbf{F} = x\mathbf{i} + y^2 \mathbf{j} - 2y\mathbf{k}$ in the coordinate system (u, v, z).

   (d) Describe coordinate surfaces.

   (e) Describe coordinate curves (that is, the intersections of coordinate surfaces).

2. Elliptic cylindrical cordinates (u, v, z) are given by

$$x = a \cosh u \cos v, \quad y = a \sinh u \sin v, \quad z = z,$$

where $u \geq 0$, $0 \leq v < 2\pi$, $-\infty < z < \infty$ and a is any positive constant.

   (a) Find unit coordinate vectors and corresponding scale factors.

   (b) Show that the coordinate system (u, v, z) is orthogonal.

   (c) Let $a = 1$. Express the vector field $\mathbf{F} = \mathbf{i} + xz\mathbf{j} - y^2 \mathbf{k}$ in the coordinate system (u, v, z).

   (d) Describe coordinate surfaces.

3. Prolate spheroidal coordinates (ξ, η, ϕ) are given by

$$x = a \sinh \xi \sin \eta \cos \phi, \quad y = a \sinh \xi \sin \eta \sin \phi, \quad z = a \cosh \xi \cos \eta,$$

where $\xi \geq 0$, $0 \leq \eta \leq \pi$, $0 \leq \phi < 2\pi$ and a is any positive constant.

(a) Find unit coordinate vectors and corresponding scale factors.

(b) Show that this coordinate system is orthogonal.

(c) Let $a = 1$. Express the vector field $\mathbf{F} = \sqrt{x^2 + y^2}\mathbf{k}$ in the coordinate system (ξ, η, ϕ).

(d) Describe coordinate surfaces.

4. Oblate spheroidal coordinates (ξ, η, ϕ) are given by

$$x = a \cosh \xi \cos \eta \cos \phi, \quad y = a \cosh \xi \cos \eta \sin \phi, \quad z = a \sinh \xi \sin \eta,$$

where $\xi \geq 0$, $-\frac{\pi}{2} \leq \eta \leq \frac{\pi}{2}$, $0 \leq \phi < 2\pi$ and a is any positive constant.

(a) Find unit coordinate vectors and corresponding scale factors.

(b) Show that this system is orthogonal.

(c) Describe coordinate surfaces.

5. Bipolar coordinates (u, v, z) are given by

$$x = \frac{a \sinh v}{\cosh v - \cos u}, \quad y = \frac{a \sin u}{\cosh v - \cos u}, \quad z = z,$$

where $0 \leq u < 2\pi$, $-\infty < v, z < \infty$, and a is any positive constant.

(a) Find unit coordinate vectors and corresponding scale factors.

(b) Show that the coordinate system (u, v, z) is orthogonal.

(c) Express the vector field $\mathbf{F} = z\mathbf{i}$ in the bipolar coordinate system.

CHAPTER REVIEW

Review Questions

Answer/discuss the following questions:

1. Define the domain and the range of a function. What assumption(s) on the domain and range of vector-valued functions $\mathbf{F}$ and $\mathbf{G}$ guarantee that the composition $\mathbf{G} \circ \mathbf{F}$ is defined?

2. Is it true that the composition of continuous functions is continuous? State the chain rule and all assumptions needed for the formula to hold. Write down the chain rule formula in the case of the composition $f \circ \mathbf{c}$ of a path $\mathbf{c}$ in $\mathbb{R}^3$ and a real-valued function f of three variables.

3. Show that the cross-sections (parallel to the xy-plane) of any plane $ax + by + cz + d = 0$ (at least one of a or b is not zero) are parallel lines. Why is the condition on a and b needed? Is it possible that a surface, other than a plane, has parallel lines as its cross-sections? If possible, sketch or describe in words such a surface.

4. Explain why it is impossible that the two level curves of $f(x, y)$ of values c_1 and c_2 (with $c_1 \neq c_2$) intersect each other.

5. Suppose that the limit of a function $f(x, y)$ as (x, y) approaches $(0, 0)$ along any straight line segment is 3. Is it true that the limit of the function is 3? Explain what is meant by the statement "$\mathbf{x} = (x, y)$ approaches $\mathbf{a} = (a, b)$".

6. Sketch the graph of a function $y = f(x)$, defined on an interval $[a, b]$, that is continuous

except at the boundary points $x = a$ and $x = b$. Let $D = \{(x, y) \mid -1 \le x \le 1, 0 \le y \le 2\}$. What is the boundary of D? Sketch the graph of a function $f(x, y): D \to \mathbb{R}^3$ that is continuous at all points inside D but discontinuous at all boundary points.

7. Define the derivative $D\mathbf{F}$ of a function $\mathbf{F}: \mathbb{R}^m \to \mathbb{R}^n$. When is $\mathbf{F}$ differentiable? What is the size of the matrix $D\mathbf{F}$? Write down the definition in the special cases when $m = n = 1$, $m = 1, n > 1$ and $m > 1, n = 1$.

8. Define the linear approximation of a function $f: \mathbb{R}^2 \to \mathbb{R}$. What assumptions on f guarantee its existence? Is it possible that $z = 2x - y - x^2$ is a linear approximation of a function $f(x, y)$?

9. We have seen in Section 1.4 that the product of two non-zero matrices can be a zero matrix. Suppose that $f(\mathbf{x}): \mathbb{R}^3 \to \mathbb{R}$ and $\mathbf{c}(t): \mathbb{R} \to \mathbb{R}^3$ are differentiable functions, their derivatives Df and $D\mathbf{c}$ are non-zero but the product $Df(\mathbf{c}(t)) \cdot D\mathbf{c}(t)$ is zero for all t. Find an example of such f and $\mathbf{c}$. Give a geometric explanation of the fact that the product of the two derivatives is zero. Find an example of two functions $\mathbf{F}, \mathbf{G}: \mathbb{R}^2 \to \mathbb{R}^2$ such that $D\mathbf{F}$ and $D\mathbf{G}$ are non-zero 2×2 matrices but their product $D\mathbf{G} \cdot D\mathbf{F}$ is the zero matirx. What is (in your case) the composition $\mathbf{G} \circ \mathbf{F}$?

10. What is meant by saying that the vectors $\{\mathbf{e}_1, \mathbf{e}_2, \mathbf{e}_3\}$ form an orthonormal set in $\mathbb{R}^3$? Let $\mathbf{F}$ be any vector in $\mathbb{R}^3$. Express $\mathbf{F}$ in terms of $\mathbf{e}_1$, $\mathbf{e}_2$ and $\mathbf{e}_3$.

11. In cylindrical coordinates, a cylinder (whose axis of symmetry is the z-axis) has a particularly simple equation: $r = a$ $(a > 0)$. In spherical coordinates, the equation $\rho = a$ $(a > 0)$ represents a sphere. What surface is represented by $u = a$ in paraboloidal coordinates, defined in Example 2.70? Same question for $v = a$.

12. We have already seen that computer-generated plots of surfaces can be misleading (see the end of Section 2.2). The next example shows that it can get even worse (and serves as a warning that computers should not be fully trusted; they are certainly of great help, but we have to remain in control). A fairly sophisticated software package produced a plot of the function $|\sqrt{x}|$ on $[-1, 1]$, as shown in Figure 2.51. The plot is incorrect, since the function is not defined for $x < 0$! Draw the correct plot of $|\sqrt{x}|$. What is wrong with the plot of the function $f(x, y) = |\sqrt{x + y}|$ in Figure 2.52?

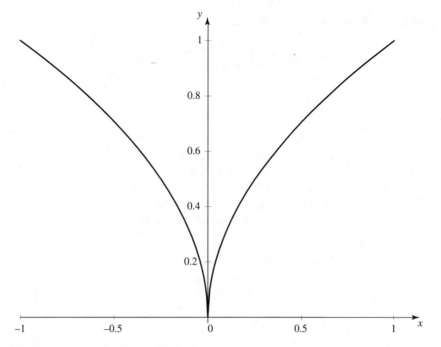

Figure 2.51   Incorrect plot of $y = |\sqrt{x}|$.

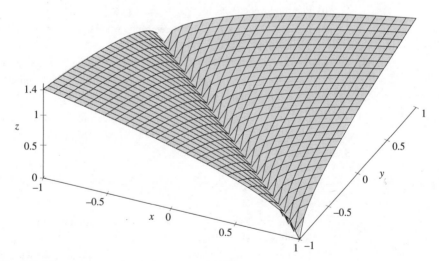

Figure 2.52   Incorrect plot of $f(x, y) = |\sqrt{x + y}|$.

Computer Projects

1. **Limit of a Function of Two Variables.**

   Consider the function

   $$f(x, y) = \frac{x \sin y + x^3 + 2y}{\sqrt{x^2 + y^2}}.$$

   (a) Find the domain of f.

   (b) Consider the values of f along the path $y = x$. Plot the graph of the function $g_1(x) = f(x, x)$, and read off the value of $\lim_{x \to 0} g_1(x)$.

   (c) Plot the graph of the function $g_2(x) = f(x, x^2)$; i.e., consider the values of f along the path $y = x^2$. Read off the value of $\lim_{x \to 0} g_2(x)$.

   (d) Plot the graph of the function $g_3(x) = f(x, 0)$; i.e., consider the values of f along the path $y = 0$. Read off the value of $\lim_{x \to 0} g_3(x)$.

   (e) Explain why $\lim_{(x,y) \to (0,0)} f(x, y)$ does not exist.

   (f) Plot the graph of $f(x, y)$ near $(0, 0)$.

2. **Level Curves and Partial Derivatives.**

   Consider the function

   $$f(x, y) = \frac{x^2 y + xy^3 + 2}{x^2 + y^2}.$$

   (a) Find the equations of the level curves of f that go through the points $(1, 0)$, $(0.9, 0)$, $(0.95, 0)$, $(1.05, 0)$, and $(1.1, 0)$. Hint: find the value of c for each level curve first; each point lies on a different level curve.

   (b) Plot the level curves in (a) in the same coordinate system.

   (c) Looking at your sketch in (b) determine whether the partial derivative $\partial f / \partial x$ at $(1, 0)$ is positive or negative. Estimate its value.

   (d) Using rules for derivatives, find $(\partial f / \partial x)(1, 0)$ (thus checking your results for (c)).

   (e) Consider the function $g(x) = f(x, 0)$ of one variable and compute the slope at $x = 1$.

   (f) What is the relation between the results of (d) and (e)?

   (g) Looking at the plot of the level curves, determine which of the partial derivatives $(\partial f / \partial y)(1/2, 1)$ or $(\partial f / \partial x)(1/2, 1)$ is larger.

3. **Level Curves.**

   Consider the function

   $$f(x, y) = \frac{xy}{x^2 + y^2}.$$

   (a) Use the facts that $(x - y)^2 \geq 0$ and $(x + y)^2 \geq 0$ to show that $-1/2 \leq f(x, y) \leq 1/2$ for all $(x, y) \neq (0, 0)$.

   (b) Plot the graph of $f(x, y)$ for $-1 \leq x, y \leq 1$, and on a smaller domain containing the origin, such as $-0.1 \leq x, y \leq 0.1$. In any case, it is difficult to clearly see what is going on around $(0, 0)$.

   (c) Let us examine level curves. Plot the level curves of f of value 0.1, 0.3, 0.4, 0.49, 0.499, -0.3, -0.4 and -0.499 for $-1 \leq x, y \leq 1$.

   (d) Let us compute level curves manually. Show that $f(x, y) = c$ can be simplified as $(x - y/2c)^2 + (1 - 1/4c^2)y^2 = 0$. Conclude that the level curve of value c consists of two lines that intersect at the origin. Compare with the plots you obtained in (c). Describe in words the surface $z = f(x, y)$ near $(0, 0)$. Explain why $\lim\limits_{(x,y) \to (0,0)} f(x, y)$ does not exist.

This example serves as another warning that what you see on your computer screen might be misleading or wrong.

Further Explorations

1. Determine whether or not the limit of $f(x, y) = xy^4/(x^2 + y^6)$ exists as $(x, y) \to (0, 0)$. If possible, define $f(0, 0)$ so as to make f continuous at $(0, 0)$. Hint: switch to polar coordinates.

2. We plan to calculate the area of a rectangular piece of land that has one side much larger than the other. Which dimension should we measure more carefully? Explain your answer.

3. Assume that $y = f(x)$ is a continuous function defined on an interval (a, b) and that $f(c) \neq 0$ for some $c \in (a, b)$. Show that there exists an interval $(a', b') \subseteq (a, b)$ such that $f(x) \neq 0$ for all $x \in (a', b')$ (in other words, a continuous function cannot have a non-zero value only at a single point). Formulate an analogous statement for a continuous function $f : U \subseteq \mathbb{R}^m \to \mathbb{R}$.

4. The period of a simple pendulum is given by $T = 2\pi \sqrt{\ell/g}$, where ℓ is its length and g is a constant. If ℓ is measured to be 1.2 m with an error of 0.03 m, g is taken to be 9.8 m/s^2 (thus an error of no more than 0.02 m/s^2 is made), and π is taken to be 3.14 (an error of no more than 0.002), find an approximate value of T (your result should be in the form (value of T) $\pm$ error).

5. Describe the level curves of the function $f(x, y) = 1 - (x^2 + y^2 - 9)^2$.

6. Assume that a C^2 function $f(x, y)$ satisfies the equation $f(tx, ty) = tf(x, y)$ for all t. Show that (drop the argument (x, y) for simplicity) $xf_x + yf_y = f$ and $x^2 f_{xx} + 2xy f_{xy} + y^2 f_{yy} = 0$.

7. The temperature of a metal rod of length 4 at position x (where $0 \leq x \leq 4$) and at time t (with $t \geq 0$) is $T(x, t) = 30e^{-2t} \sin(\pi x/2)$.

   (a) Find the rate of change of temperature with respect to position when $x = 3/2$ and $t = 2$. Sketch the cross-section for $t = 2$ and interpret your result.

   (b) Find the rate of change of temperature with respect to time when $x = 3/2$ and $t = 2$. Sketch the cross-section for $x = 3/2$ and interpret your result.

8. The function $T(x, t) = a + e^{-ct} \sin(2x)$ (a and c are constants and $c > 0$) describes the temperature at time t and at the point x on a metal rod of length π, placed along the positive x-axis with one end at the origin.

   (a) What is the initial temperature at the left end? At the right end?

   (b) At time $t = t_0 \geq 0$, what is the warmest (coolest) point of the rod?

   (c) Fix the point x_0 on the rod, $0 \leq x_0 \leq \pi/2$. When is the temperature going to reach its maximum value at that point? What happens when $t \to \infty$? Answer the same questions for the point x_0 with $\pi/2 \leq x_0 \leq \pi$.

   (d) Locate the points on the rod where the temperature does not change.

9. Prove that if $|f(x, y)| \leq x^2 + y^2$ for all $(x, y) \in \mathbb{R}^2$, then f is differentiable at $(0, 0)$.

10. Let

$$f(x, y) = \begin{cases} \dfrac{x^3y - xy^3}{x^2 + y^2} & \text{if } (x, y) \neq (0, 0) \\ 0 & \text{if } (x, y) = (0, 0) \end{cases}$$

Show that $f_{xy}(0, 0) \neq f_{yx}(0, 0)$.

Exercises 11 to 14: Answer questions (a) – (d) for the function f.

   (a) Is f differentiable at $(0, 0)$?

   (b) Is it possible to conclude from (a) that f is continuous at $(0, 0)$?

   (c) Is f continuous at $(0, 0)$?

   (d) Is f_x continuous at $(0, 0)$?

11. $f(x, y) = (xy)^{4/5}$ **12.** $f(x, y) = (xy)^{1/3}$

13.

$$f(x, y) = \begin{cases} \dfrac{x^2 + y^3}{x^2 + y^2} & \text{if } (x, y) \neq (0, 0) \\ 0 & \text{if } (x, y) = (0, 0) \end{cases}$$

14.

$$f(x, y) = \begin{cases} \ln(x^2 + y^2) & \text{if } (x, y) \neq (0, 0) \\ 0 & \text{if } (x, y) = (0, 0) \end{cases}$$

15. The force of gravity of a planet on an object of mass m at a distance r from the surface of the planet has magnitude $F(m, r) = mgR^2(R + r)^{-2}$, where g and R are constants. Find an expression for the time rate of change of F acting on a comet (whose mass m is changing) approaching the planet.

16. Let $f(x, y) = (x^3 + 3x^2y + e^y)\cos(x^4y^3)e^{yx^2\cos(1-x-y)}$. Find $(\partial f/\partial y)(0, 1)$. Hint: the computation of $(\partial f/\partial y)(x, y)$ with the use of the product rule and the chain rule is fairly messy. Find a way to simplify your task.

Chapter 3

VECTOR-VALUED FUNCTIONS OF ONE VARIABLE

A vector-valued function of one variable is called a path, and its image, visualized as a geometric object, is a curve. We will concentrate on paths in a plane and in three-dimensional space (although almost all statements and formulas — except those involving cross products — hold in any dimension), and will investigate a number of geometric properties of curves. The study of vector fields, the other important class of vector-valued functions, begins in the next chapter.

A path contains a lot more information than the representation of a curve as a graph of $y = f(x)$. In the introductory section we discuss the ways of constructing a path (also called a parametrization) for a given curve. Next, we learn how to extract information (such as velocity, acceleration or length) from such descriptions, and how to apply it to a number of physical situations, like Coriolis acceleration or a motion of a projectile. We study the close relationship between the acceleration and geometric properties of a curve, such as its curvature. This investigation leads us to the basic equations (the so-called Serret-Frenet formulas) of the differential geometry of curves in space.

A useful way of visualizing a vector field (borrowed from fluid mechanics and electromagnetism) consists of drawing flow lines. If we think of a vector field as a velocity field of a fluid, then a flow line describes how a fluid particle moves under the influence of the field.

3.1 CURVES IN $\mathbb{R}^2$ AND $\mathbb{R}^3$

A trajectory of a moving particle, a sound wave, a current in an electric circuit, the conversion between ^{o}F and ^{o}C or the dependence of air pressure on altitude can be visually represented as curves in a plane or in three-dimensional space. Various measurement instruments such as oscilloscopes, heart-beat monitors, computers and other devices display their data in the form of curves, which are more convenient and easier to interpret than a listing of thousands of numbers.

The graph of a real-valued function $y = f(x)$ is a curve. The equation $f(x, y) = 0$ represents a curve described in a slightly different way (it is given "implicitly"). In this section we introduce a new way of defining a curve and study some of its properties. Other concepts, relevant to integration along curves, are discussed in Chapter 5.

We are going to restrict our study to three-dimensional space $\mathbb{R}^3$ (and sometimes to $\mathbb{R}^2$), although all statements (except those involving cross products) hold in any dimension.

■ **Definition 3.1**   Path and Curve.

A *path* in $\mathbb{R}^3$ (or $\mathbb{R}^2$) is a function $\mathbf{c}: [a, b] \to \mathbb{R}^3$ (or $\mathbb{R}^2$), whose domain is a subset $[a, b] \subseteq \mathbb{R}$. The image of $\mathbf{c}$ is called a *curve* in $\mathbb{R}^3$ (or $\mathbb{R}^2$). The function $\mathbf{c}$ is also called a *parametrization* (or *parametric representation* or *parametric equation*) of the curve.

■

According to the definition, a path is a function, whereas a geometric object in $\mathbb{R}^3$ (or $\mathbb{R}^2$) that is the image of that function is called a curve. In other words, a path or a parametrization (the two are synonyms) represents an analytic way of describing a curve. We will soon witness that a single curve can have infinitely many parametrizations, not all of them characterized by the same properties. The reasons why the distinction between a path and a curve is needed will surface later in this chapter and in sections on integration along paths. On some occasions we will use the term "curve" to refer to both notions since the context will keep the meaning clear. For example, if we talk about composition of curves or velocity, we think of a function; on the other hand, the statement "curves are orthogonal to each other" refers to a curve as a geometric object. Likewise, we will use the same notation for both the path and the corresponding curve.

Sometimes it is useful to extend the domain $[a, b]$ in the definition of a path $\mathbf{c}$ so that $a = -\infty$ or $b = \infty$, or both (i.e., intervals $(-\infty, b], [a, \infty)$ or $(-\infty, \infty) = \mathbb{R}$ are allowed as the domain of $\mathbf{c}$). This will enable us to describe, for example, lines (such as the tangent to a curve) as paths in a plane or in space. The variable of $\mathbf{c}$ is denoted by t and is often referred to as time. In components, a curve in $\mathbb{R}^2$ can be represented as

$$\mathbf{c}(t) = (x(t), y(t)), \qquad t \in [a, b],$$

and a curve in $\mathbb{R}^3$ as

$$\mathbf{c}(t) = (x(t), y(t), z(t)), \qquad t \in [a, b],$$

where the components $x(t)$, $y(t)$ and $z(t)$ are real-valued functions of t.

Example 3.1   The curve $\mathbf{c}_1$ parametrized by $\mathbf{c}_1(t) = (t \cos t, t \sin t), t \in [0, 3\pi]$ in $\mathbb{R}^2$ is shown in Figure 3.1. Figure 3.2 represents the curve $\mathbf{c}_2$ in space given by $\mathbf{c}_2(t) = (\cos t, \sin t, \cos 4t)$, $t \in [0, 2\pi]$.

◀

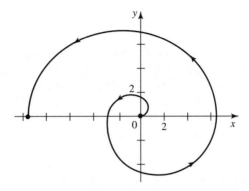

Figure 3.1 Curve c_1 parametrized by $c_1(t) = (t \cos t, t \sin t)$, $t \in [0, 3\pi]$.

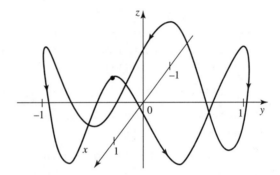

Figure 3.2 Curve c_2 parametrized by $c_2(t) = (\cos t, \sin t, \cos 4t)$, $t \in [0, 2\pi]$.

A parametric representation of a curve gives a sense of orientation, as explained in the following definition.

■ **Definition 3.2** Orientation.

Let $c(t): [a, b] \to \mathbb{R}^3$ (or $\mathbb{R}^2$) be a path. The point $c(a)$ is called the *initial point*, and $c(b)$ is called the *terminal point* of c. The initial and the terminal points are called the *endpoints* of c. The direction corresponding to increasing values of t gives the *positive orientation*, whereas the opposite direction defines the *negative orientation* of c. ■

If the domain of c includes $-\infty$ or ∞ (or both), one (or both) endpoints are not defined. The orientation is indicated on the graph by an arrow; see Figures 3.1 and 3.2. According to the definition, the positive orientation is the direction from the initial point towards the terminal point (if defined).

Example 3.2

For the path $c_1(t)$ in Figure 3.1, the initial point is $c(0) = (0, 0)$, and the terminal point is $c(3\pi) = (-3\pi, 0)$. The arrow indicates the positive orientation (that can also be described as the counterclockwise orientation). The path $c_2(t)$ of Figure 3.2 has the same point $c(0) = c(2\pi) = (1, 0, 1)$ as its initial and terminal points. To determine the orientation, compute the values of c at increasing values of t; for example, $c(\pi/6) = (\sqrt{3}/2, 1/2, -1/2)$, $c(\pi/4) = (\sqrt{2}/2, \sqrt{2}/2, -1)$, etc. The positive orientation is given by the direction from $(1, 0, 1)$ to $(\sqrt{3}/2, 1/2, -1/2)$, then to $(\sqrt{2}/2, \sqrt{2}/2, -1)$, etc., as indicated on the graph.

◄

Example 3.3

Parametric Representation of a Line and a Line Segment.

A parametric representation of the line segment joining the points $A = (a_1, a_2, a_3)$ and $B = (b_1, b_2, b_3)$ in $\mathbb{R}^3$ is given by

$$c(t) = a + tv, \qquad t \in [0, 1],$$

where $a = (a_1, a_2, a_3)$ and $v = (b_1 - a_1, b_2 - a_2, b_3 - a_3)$. This parametrization was discussed at the beginning of Section 1.2. The initial point is $A = c(0)$ and the terminal point is $B = c(1)$. In coordinates,

$$c(t) = (a_1 + t(b_1 - a_1), a_2 + t(b_2 - a_2), a_3 + t(b_3 - a_3)), \qquad t \in [0, 1].$$

A parametric representation of the line going through the point $A = (a_1, a_2, a_3)$ in the direction $v = (v_1, v_2, v_3)$ is

$$c(t) = a + tv = (a_1 + tv_1, a_2 + tv_2, a_3 + tv_3), \qquad t \in \mathbb{R}.$$

As "time" t increases (positive orientation), the point $c(t)$ moves along the line, away from A, in the direction of v. The direction of movement corresponding to decreasing time (negative orientation) corresponds to movement in the direction opposite to v.

◄

Example 3.4

Parametrization of a Circle and an Ellipse.

The curve represented parametrically as

$$c(t) = (a \cos t, a \sin t), \qquad t \in [0, 2\pi]$$

(where $a > 0$) is the circle in $\mathbb{R}^2$ of radius a centered at the origin ($x(t) = a \cos t$, $y(t) = a \sin t$ and hence $x(t)^2 + y(t)^2 = a^2$); see Figure 3.3. The parameter t represents the angle between the x-axis and the position vector $c(t)$. The initial point is $c(0) = (a, 0)$ and the terminal point is $c(2\pi) = (a, 0) = c(0)$. Thinking of c as a trajectory of a moving particle, we see that it takes a particle 2π units of time to complete one full revolution and come back to its initial position. The positive orientation (i.e., direction of increasing t) corresponds to counterclockwise motion along the circle. The path

$$c(t) = (o_1 + a \cos t, o_2 + a \sin t) = (o_1, o_2) + (a \cos t, a \sin t), \qquad t \in [0, 2\pi]$$

represents the circle centered at $O = (o_1, o_2)$ of radius a. The ellipse $x^2/a^2 + y^2/b^2 = 1$ (with semiaxes $a > 0$ and $b > 0$) can be parametrized as

$$\mathbf{c}(t) = (a\cos t, b\sin t), \qquad t \in [0, 2\pi].$$

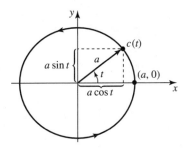

Figure 3.3 The circle $\mathbf{c}(t) = (a\cos t, a\sin t)$, $t \in [0, 2\pi]$.

Example 3.5

Parametrization of the Graph of $y = f(x)$.

The graph of a real-valued function $f: [a, b] \to \mathbb{R}$ of one variable defined on an interval $[a, b] \subseteq \mathbb{R}$ is a curve, that can be parametrized as

$$\mathbf{c}(t) = (t, f(t)), \qquad t \in [a, b].$$

For example, a parametric representation of the graph of $y = x^2$ on $[0, 2]$ is $\mathbf{c}(t) = (t, t^2)$, $t \in [0, 2]$. Similarly, a parametric representation of $y = xe^{-x}$ for $x \geq 0$ is $\mathbf{c}(t) = (t, te^{-t})$, $t \in [0, \infty)$.

Let us for a moment go back to the previous example and compare the two ways of describing the parabola in question. Although both descriptions $y = x^2$, $x \in [0, 2]$ and $\mathbf{c}(t) = (t, t^2)$, $t \in [0, 2]$ do produce (geometrically) the same curve, there are differences. To understand them better suppose that the curve $\mathbf{c}$ represents the motion of a particle. The parametric representation conveys a lot more information than just the geometric curve: for example, the initial point of the motion is $\mathbf{c}(0) = (0, 0)$, and the terminal point is $\mathbf{c}(2) = (2, 4)$; hence the particle moves along the parabola *from* $(0, 0)$ *to* $(2, 4)$. From $\mathbf{c}(t) = (t, t^2)$ we can read off the location of the particle at *any* time t, $0 \leq t \leq 2$. On the other hand, the graph of $y = x^2$ produces the path of the particle without showing any details of the motion. In the next section we will learn how to extract a lot more information from a parametric representation. For example, we will be able to find how fast the particle is moving along the curve.

It is important to notice that the values of the parameter t are not built into the graph. In other words, if we select a point on the curve, we cannot read off the value of t that produced it. To somewhat remedy this deficiency, besides plotting a point on the curve we also indicate the corresponding value of t, as shown in Figure 3.4.

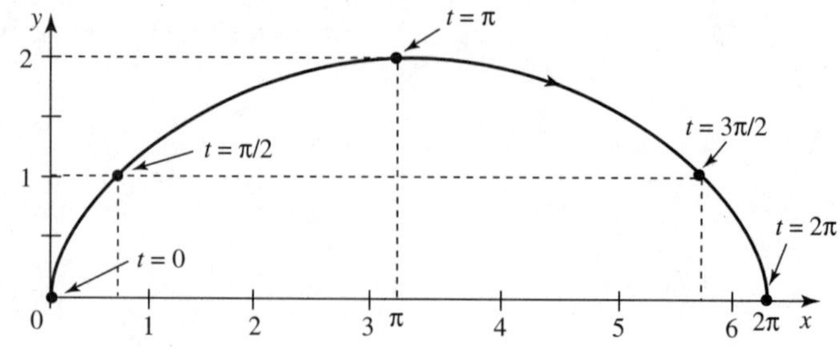

Figure 3.4 Curve $\mathbf{c}(t) = (t - \sin t, 1 - \cos t)$, $t \in [0, 2\pi]$.

Example 3.6

We have seen in Example 3.4 that the path $\mathbf{c}(t) = (\cos t, \sin t)$, $t \in [0, 2\pi]$ represents the circle $x^2 + y^2 = 1$. There are other parametrizations: for example,

$$\mathbf{c}_1(t) = (\cos 2t, \sin 2t), \qquad t \in [0, \pi]$$

satisfies $x(t)^2 + y(t)^2 = 1$ and, since $\mathbf{c}_1(0) = \mathbf{c}_1(\pi) = (1, 0)$, it describes the whole circle. Similarly, we can check that

$$\mathbf{c}_2(t) = (\sin(t + 3), \cos(t + 3)), \qquad t \in [0, 2\pi]$$

or

$$\mathbf{c}_3(t) = (-\cos(t/4), \sin(t/4)), \qquad t \in [0, 8\pi]$$

represent the same circle. As a matter of fact, a curve can have infinitely many parametrizations (in terms of Definition 3.1, we say that there are infinitely many *paths* that have the same image; i.e., that parametrize the same curve). That is the reason why we made a distinction between a path and a curve. It is worth repeating that a curve is a geometric object and a path is a way of describing it algebraically in terms of a parameter. Parametrizations need not "look alike": for example,

$$\mathbf{c}_4(t) = ((4\cos t + \sin t)/\sqrt{17}, (4\sin t - \cos t)/\sqrt{17}), \qquad t \in [0, 2\pi]$$

is another representation of the circle $x^2 + y^2 = 1$.

◀

Example 3.7

Let $\mathbf{c}$ be the part of the curve $y = 2x^4$ between $(-1, 2)$ and $(1, 2)$. Write down several parametrizations of $\mathbf{c}$.

Solution   As in Example 3.5 we can take $x = t$. Then $y = 2x^4 = 2t^4$, and we obtain

$$\mathbf{c}_1(t) = (t, 2t^4), \qquad t \in [-1, 1]$$

as a possible parametrization. There is no reason why we have to choose $x = t$. Try $x = mt$, $(m \neq 0)$; then $y = 2x^4 = 2m^4 t^4$ and

$$\mathbf{c}_2(t) = (mt, 2m^4 t^4), \qquad t \in [-1/|m|, 1/|m|].$$

(In defining an interval $[a, b]$, we have to make sure that $a \leq b$; i.e., we used the absolute value.) We already have infinitely many parametrizations, one for each non-zero value of m.

Let us list a few more parametrizations (of course, in every case $x(t)$ and $y(t)$ have to satisfy $y(t) = 2x(t)^4$, and the endpoints of the interval for the parameter must give $(-1, 2)$ and $(1, 2)$):

$$\mathbf{c}_3(t) = (mt + 1, 2(mt + 1)^4), \qquad t \in [-2/m, 0]$$

(works for $m > 0$),

$$\mathbf{c}_4(t) = (t^{1/3}, 2t^{4/3}), \qquad t \in [-1, 1],$$

or

$$\mathbf{c}_5(t) = (\tan t, 2\tan^4 t), \qquad t \in [-\pi/4, \pi/4],$$

etc. On the other hand,

$$\mathbf{c}_6(t) = (t^2, 2t^8), \qquad t \in [-1, 1]$$

parametrizes the part of the parabola in the first quadrant only: for example, no value of t gives $(-1, 2)$.

We will soon learn that there are significant differences between parametrizations. Not every parametrization of a curve can be used to compute its length. Some parametrizations will be more suitable as trajectories of the motion than others. A path integral will be defined for a special class of parametrizations, etc.

Example 3.8   The parametrizations (paths)

(a) $\mathbf{c}_1(t) = (2\cos t, 2\sin t)$, $t \in [0, \pi]$,

(b) $\mathbf{c}_2(t) = (-2\cos t, 2\sin t)$, $t \in [0, \pi]$,

(c) $\mathbf{c}_3(t) = (2\cos(3t), 2\sin(3t))$, $t \in [0, \pi/3]$,

(d) $\mathbf{c}_4(t) = (-2\cos(t/4), 2\sin(t/4))$, $t \in [0, 4\pi]$,

represent the same curve. Identify the curve and describe the differences between the parametrizations.

Solution   In all four cases, $x(t)^2 + y(t)^2 = 4$ and $y(t) \geq 0$. Next, we compute the endpoints for all paths: $\mathbf{c}_1(0) = (2, 0)$, $\mathbf{c}_1(\pi) = (-2, 0)$, $\mathbf{c}_2(0) = (-2, 0)$, $\mathbf{c}_2(\pi) = (2, 0)$, $\mathbf{c}_3(0) = (2, 0)$, $\mathbf{c}_3(\pi/3) = (-2, 0)$, $\mathbf{c}_4(0) = (-2, 0)$ and $\mathbf{c}_4(4\pi) = (2, 0)$. Consequently, the curve in question is the semi-circle of radius 2 (centered at the origin) in the upper half-plane with the endpoints $(2, 0)$ and $(-2, 0)$. Paths $\mathbf{c}_1$ and $\mathbf{c}_3$ are oriented counterclockwise, whereas $\mathbf{c}_2$ and $\mathbf{c}_4$ (having initial points at $(-2, 0)$ and terminal points at $(2, 0)$) are oriented clockwise. Now view t as time and interpret the interval for t as total time needed to complete the motion along the curve. The motion along $\mathbf{c}_3$ is the fastest, and along $\mathbf{c}_4$ the slowest. Motions along $\mathbf{c}_1$ and $\mathbf{c}_2$ are completed in π units of time.

Example 3.9   Let $\mathbf{c}$ be the ellipse that is the intersection of the cylinder $x^2 + y^2 = 13$ and the plane $z = 2y$, see Figure 3.5. Find several parametrizations of $\mathbf{c}$.

Solution   We are looking for functions $\mathbf{c}(t) = (x(t), y(t), z(t)): [a, b] \to \mathbb{R}^3$ such that $x(t)^2 + y(t)^2 = 13$ and $z(t) = 2y(t)$.

Take, for example $x(t) = \sqrt{13} \cos t$ and $y(t) = \sqrt{13} \sin t$; then $z(t) = 2\sqrt{13} \sin t$ and

$$\mathbf{c}_1(t) = (\sqrt{13} \cos t, \sqrt{13} \sin t, 2\sqrt{13} \sin t), \qquad t \in [0, 2\pi]$$

is one possible parametrization. We can now replace t by mt, $m \neq 0$ (and, of course, adjust the interval for t) to get infinitely many parametrizations.

Apart from those, there are others, such as

$$x(t) = 2 \cos t - 3 \sin t, \quad y(t) = 3 \cos t + 2 \sin t, \quad z(t) = 6 \cos t + 4 \sin t,$$

where $t \in [0, 2\pi]$.

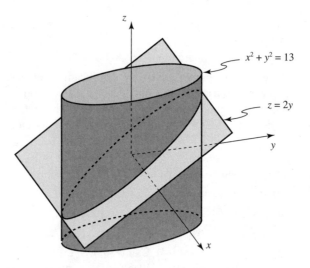

Figure 3.5   Intersection of $x^2 + y^2 = 13$ and $z = 2y$.

Example 3.10   Sketch the curve

$$\mathbf{c}(t) = (3 \cos t, 3 \sin t, t), \qquad t \in [0, 2\pi].$$

Solution   Since $x = 3 \cos t$ and $y = 3 \sin t$ it follows that $x^2 + y^2 = 9$, which means that the curve lies on the surface of the cylinder of radius 3 whose axis is the z-axis. Its projection onto the xy-plane (take $z = 0$) is the circle of radius 3 (centered at the origin) oriented counterclockwise. As time t increases, the z-coordinates of points on c increase from 0 to 2π. The initial point is $\mathbf{c}(0) = (3, 0, 0)$ and the terminal point is $(3, 0, 2\pi)$. The curve is obtained in the following way: as we move the point along the circle of radius 3 counterclockwise, we simultaneously increase its height (at a constant rate) from 0 to 2π. The curve thus obtained is called a helix; see Figure 3.6.

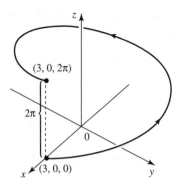

Figure 3.6   The graph of $\mathbf{c}(t) = (3\cos t, 3\sin t, t)$, $t \in [0, 2\pi]$ is a circular helix of "pitch" 2π.

■ Definition 3.3   Continuous, Differentiable and C^1 Paths and Curves.

A path (or a parametrization) $\mathbf{c}: [a, b] \rightarrow \mathbb{R}^3(\mathbb{R}^2)$ is *continuous* if and only if its components $x(t)$, $y(t)$ and $z(t)$ are continuous functions on $[a, b]$. If the components of $\mathbf{c}(t)$ are differentiable (respectively C^1) on (a, b), then the path (parametrization) is called *differentiable* (respectively C^1).

A curve is called *continuous* (*differentiable*, C^1) if among all of its parametrizations there is at least one that is continuous (differentiable, C^1).   ■

Recall that a real-valued function of one variable is called C^1 if its derivative is continuous. All curves that have appeared in this section are continuous and differentiable. When we say "a curve $\mathbf{c}$ is differentiable" we mean to say that some parametric representation of that curve (usually also denoted by $\mathbf{c}$) is differentiable.

The parametrization $\mathbf{c}_4(t) = (t^{1/3}, 2t^{4/3})$, $t \in [-1, 1]$ of Example 3.7 is not differentiable at 0 (the derivative of $x(t)$ is $x'(t) = t^{-2/3}/3$, and hence not defined at 0). Nevertheless, the parametrizations $\mathbf{c}_1$ (and $\mathbf{c}_2$, $\mathbf{c}_3$ and $\mathbf{c}_5$) are differentiable and C^1, and hence the curve $y = x^4$ is differentiable and C^1. The curve $y = |x|$, $x \in [-1, 1]$ is an example of a continuous, non-differentiable curve: $|x|$ has a "corner" at $x = 0$, and consequently, does not have a tangent (i.e., the derivative) there. As a matter of fact, to prove non-differentiability we would have to show that no parametrization of $|x|$ is differentiable. We prefer to rely on our intuitive reasoning at this moment.

Let us mention an inconsistency in notation that is a common practice. Consider the parametrizations

$$\mathbf{c}_1(t) = (t, 2t^4), \qquad t \in [-1, 1]$$

and

$$\mathbf{c}_5(t) = (\tan t, 2\tan^4 t), \qquad t \in [-\pi/4, \pi/4]$$

of Example 3.7. Strictly speaking, we should have used different symbols for the parameters, since t in $\mathbf{c}_1$ and $\mathbf{c}_5$ is not the same. For example, $\mathbf{c}_1(\pi/4) = (\pi/4, \pi^4/128)$, but $\mathbf{c}_5(\pi/4) = (1, 2)$. However, as t in $\mathbf{c}_1$ changes from -1 to 1, $\mathbf{c}_1$ describes the same curve as $\mathbf{c}_5$ (when its t changes from $-\pi/4$ to $\pi/4$). Beware of this common practice so that it will not be a cause of confusion.

EXERCISES 3.1   **Exercises 1 to 12:** Find a parametric equation of the given curve.

1. the line segment in $\mathbb{R}^3$ joining the points $(3, 1, -2)$ and $(0, 5, 0)$

2. the line in $\mathbb{R}^2$ going through the point $(3, 2)$ in the direction of the vector $(-1, 1)$

3. the circle in $\mathbb{R}^2$ centered at the origin, of radius $\sqrt{5}$

4. the circle in the plane $z = 4$ centered at the point $(0, 0, 4)$, of radius 4

5. the ellipse in $\mathbb{R}^2$ with semi-axes of length 3 (in the x-direction) and 1 (in the y-direction) whose center is located at the point $(-2, -1)$

6. the graph of $f(x) = 3x^2 - 2$ in $\mathbb{R}^2$ for $-3 \leq x \leq 2$

7. the graph of $x - y^2 = 1$ in $\mathbb{R}^2$ for $0 \leq y \leq 1$

8. the intersection of the cylinder $x^2 + y^2 = 1$ and the plane $x + z = 1$ in $\mathbb{R}^3$

9. the graph of $x^{2/3} + y^{2/3} = 1$ in $\mathbb{R}^2$

10. the intersection of the planes $x + y - z = 2$ and $2x - 5y + z = 3$ in $\mathbb{R}^3$

11. the intersection of the cylinder $y^2 + z^2 = 4$ and the surface $x = yz$ in $\mathbb{R}^3$

12. the intersection of the cylinder $(x + 2)^2 + (z - 2)^2 = 4$ and the plane $y = 3$ in $\mathbb{R}^3$

13. Find parametric representations of both curves that are the intersection of the cylinders $x^2 + z^2 = 2$ and $y^2 + z^2 = 2$ in $\mathbb{R}^3$.

14. What curve is represented by $\mathbf{c}(t) = (\cos t, \cos^2 t)$, $t \in \mathbb{R}$?

Exercises 15 to 19: Find an equation of the curve $\mathbf{c}(t)$ in a Cartesian coordinate system and sketch it, indicating its endpoints (if any) and orientation.

15. $\mathbf{c}(t) = (t - 3)\mathbf{i} + t^2\mathbf{j}$, $t \in [0, 2]$ 16. $\mathbf{c}(t) = 3 \sin 2t\, \mathbf{i} + 3 \cos 2t\, \mathbf{j}$, $t \in [0, \pi/2]$

17. $\mathbf{c}(t) = (2 \cosh t, 2 \sinh t)$, $t \in \mathbb{R}$ (hint: $\cosh^2 t - \sinh^2 t = 1$)

18. $\mathbf{c}(t) = (t^3, t^9)$, $t \in [0, 3]$ 19. $\mathbf{c}(t) = (t, e^{3t})$, $t \in [0, \ln 2]$

20. Identify the curve parametrized by $\mathbf{c}(t) = (2 - t, 1 + t, t)$, $t \in \mathbb{R}$. If t is replaced by

   (a) $-t$ **(b)** t^2 **(c)** t^3 **(d)** e^t

   what does the resulting parametrization represent?

Exercises 21 to 29: Sketch (or describe in words) the curve $\mathbf{c}(t)$, indicating its endpoints and orientation.

21. $\mathbf{c}(t) = (\cos t, \sin t, 3)$, $t \in [0, 2\pi]$ 22. $\mathbf{c}(t) = (\cos t, \sin t, t)$, $t \in [0, 3\pi]$

23. $\mathbf{c}(t) = (\cos t, \sin t, t^3)$, $t \in [0, \pi]$ 24. $\mathbf{c}(t) = (t, \cos t, \sin t)$, $t \in [0, 10\pi]$

25. $\mathbf{c}(t) = (t, \arctan t)$, $t \in [-1, 1]$ 26. $\mathbf{c}(t) = \left(1 + t^{-1}\right)\mathbf{i} + \left(1 - t^{-1}\right)\mathbf{j}$, $t \in [1, 2]$

27. $\mathbf{c}(t) = \left(t + t^{-1}\right)\mathbf{i} + \left(t - t^{-1}\right)\mathbf{j}$, $t \in [1, 2]$

28. $\mathbf{c}(t) = 4\mathbf{i} + (5 + 2\cos t)\mathbf{j} + (1 + 2\sin t)\mathbf{k}$, $t \in [0, 6\pi]$

29. $\mathbf{c}(t) = (e^{t/4} \sin t, e^{t/4} \cos t)$, $t \in [0, 2\pi]$

30. Consider the curves $\mathbf{c}(t) = (\sin(at), \cos(bt))$, $t \geq 0$, where a and b are positive integers. Investigate how the curves vary when a and b vary.

31. Check that the following parametrizations have the same image; i.e., that they represent the

same curve. Discuss their differences in terms of their speeds and orientations. Find two more parametrizations with the same image as the curves in (a) – (d).

(a) $c_1(t) = (2 \sin t, 2 \cos t)$, $t \in [0, 2\pi]$ (b) $c_2(t) = (2 \cos t, 2 \sin t)$, $t \in [0, 2\pi]$

(c) $c_3(t) = (2 \sin 3t, 2 \cos 3t)$, $t \in [0, 2\pi]$ (d) $c_4(t) = (-2 \cos(t/2), 2 \sin(t/2))$, $t \in [0, 4\pi]$

32. The following parametrizations have the same image. Describe their differences.

(a) $c_1(t) = (t, t^2)$, $t \in [-1, 1]$ (b) $c_2(t) = (\sin t, \sin^2 t)$, $t \in [-\pi/2, \pi/2]$

(c) $c_3(t) = (\sin t, \sin^2 t)$, $t \in [-\pi/2, 3\pi/2]$

(d) $c_4(t) = (t^{1/3}, t^{2/3})$, $t \in [-1, 1]$

(e) $c_5(t) = (2t/\sqrt{1 + t^2}, 4t^2/(1 + t^2))$, $t \in [-1/\sqrt{3}, 1/\sqrt{3}]$

33. Write down a parametrization of the line $y = 2x$ in $\mathbb{R}^2$ that is not differentiable.

34. Show that the path $c(t) = (t^{1/3}, 2t^{2/3})$, $t \in [-1, 1]$, is not differentiable. Identify the curve that is the image of c and prove that it is differentiable.

Exercises 35 to 38: Consider the parametrization $c(t)$ of the curve $y = x^3$, $-1 \le x \le 1$. Determine whether the parametrization is continuous, differentiable or C^1.

35. $c(t) = (t^{1/3}, t)$, $t \in [-1, 1]$ 36. $c(t) = (2 \tan t, 8 \tan^3 t)$, $t \in [-\pi/4, \pi/4]$

37. $c(t) = (t|t|, t^3|t|^3)$, $t \in [-1, 1]$ 38. $c(t) = (e^t - 2, (e^t - 2)^3)$, $t \in [0, \ln 3]$

3.2   TANGENTS, VELOCITY AND ACCELERATION

We continue our investigation of curves by studying concepts that are defined in terms of derivatives: velocity and acceleration.

Let $c(t) = (x(t), y(t), z(t))$ be a differentiable path in $\mathbb{R}^3$. The derivative $c'(t_0) = Dc(t_0)$ of c at t_0 is the 3×1 matrix

$$
\begin{bmatrix} dx/dt \\ dy/dt \\ dz/dt \end{bmatrix}_{at\ t=t_0} = \begin{bmatrix} x'(t_0) \\ y'(t_0) \\ z'(t_0) \end{bmatrix}
$$

that can be interpreted as the vector $c'(t_0) = x'(t_0)\mathbf{i} + y'(t_0)\mathbf{j} + z'(t_0)\mathbf{k}$ in $\mathbb{R}^3$. We visualize $c'(t_0)$ as a vector whose initial point is at $c(t_0)$, as shown in Figure 3.7 (we have done so already in Example 2.36 of Section 2.4). To further explore this geometric interpretation, we rewrite $c'(t_0)$ in the limit form:

$$
\begin{aligned}
c'(t_0) &= x'(t_0)\mathbf{i} + y'(t_0)\mathbf{j} + z'(t_0)\mathbf{k} \\
&= \lim_{h \to 0} \frac{x(t_0 + h) - x(t_0)}{h}\mathbf{i} + \lim_{h \to 0} \frac{y(t_0 + h) - y(t_0)}{h}\mathbf{j} + \lim_{h \to 0} \frac{z(t_0 + h) - z(t_0)}{h}\mathbf{k} \\
&= \lim_{h \to 0} \frac{(x(t_0 + h)\mathbf{i} + y(t_0 + h)\mathbf{j} + z(t_0 + h)\mathbf{k}) - (x(t_0)\mathbf{i} + y(t_0)\mathbf{j} + z(t_0)\mathbf{k})}{h} \\
&= \lim_{h \to 0} \frac{c(t_0 + h) - c(t_0)}{h}.
\end{aligned}
$$

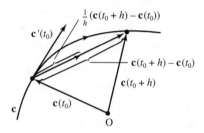

Figure 3.7 $\mathbf{c}'(t_0)$ is in the direction of the tangent line to $\mathbf{c}$ at a point $\mathbf{c}(t_0)$.

The vector $(\mathbf{c}(t_0 + h) - \mathbf{c}(t_0))/h$, being parallel to $\mathbf{c}(t_0 + h) - \mathbf{c}(t_0)$, is in the direction of the secant line joining $\mathbf{c}(t_0 + h)$ and $\mathbf{c}(t_0)$; see Figure 3.7. As $h \to 0$, the point $\mathbf{c}(t_0 + h)$ slides along the curve towards $\mathbf{c}(t_0)$ and the secant line approaches its limit position, the tangent line at $\mathbf{c}(t_0)$. Hence $\mathbf{c}'(t_0)$ (if $\mathbf{c}'(t_0) \neq \mathbf{0}$) represents the direction of the line tangent to $\mathbf{c}$ at $\mathbf{c}(t_0)$. A parametric equation for the tangent line is given by (recall that "line = point + parameter · vector")

$$\ell(u) = \mathbf{c}(t_0) + u\mathbf{c}'(t_0), \qquad u \in \mathbb{R}.$$

This argument justifies the terminology introduced in our next definition.

■ **Definition 3.4**   Tangent Vector and Tangent Line.

Let $\mathbf{c}$ be a differentiable path in $\mathbb{R}^2$ or $\mathbb{R}^3$. The vector $\mathbf{c}'(t_0)$ is called a *tangent vector* to $\mathbf{c}$ at $\mathbf{c}(t_0)$. The line tangent to a curve $\mathbf{c}$ (that is represented by a path $\mathbf{c}(t)$) at $\mathbf{c}(t_0)$ is given by

$$\ell(u) = \mathbf{c}(t_0) + u\mathbf{c}'(t_0), \qquad u \in \mathbb{R},$$

provided that $\mathbf{c}'(t_0) \neq \mathbf{0}$.

■

In order to avoid possible confusion, we use u as the parameter for the tangent line, since t has already been employed as the parameter for the curve.

Now suppose that a path $\mathbf{c}(t)$ describes the trajectory of a moving particle (and the variable t represents time). Since

$$\mathbf{c}(t_0 + h) - \mathbf{c}(t_0) = (\text{position at time } t_0 + h) - (\text{position at time } t_0);$$

i.e.,

$$\frac{\mathbf{c}(t_0 + h) - \mathbf{c}(t_0)}{h} = \frac{\text{displacement vector}}{\text{time}},$$

the limit (as time h approaches 0) gives the *instantaneous velocity vector*.

■ **Definition 3.5**   Velocity, Speed and Acceleration.

Let $\mathbf{c}(t) = (x(t), y(t), z(t))$ be a differentiable path in $\mathbb{R}^3$. The *velocity* $\mathbf{v}(t)$ at time t is given by the vector-valued function

$$\mathbf{v}(t) = \mathbf{c}'(t) = (x'(t), y'(t), z'(t)).$$

The *speed* is the real-valued function

$$\|\mathbf{v}(t)\| = \sqrt{(x'(t))^2 + (y'(t))^2 + (z'(t))^2},$$

which is the length of the velocity vector. The *acceleration* $\mathbf{a}(t)$ at time t is given by

$$\mathbf{a}(t) = \mathbf{v}'(t) = \mathbf{c}''(t) = (x''(t), y''(t), z''(t)),$$

provided that $\mathbf{c}$ is twice differentiable.

Example 3.11

Let $\mathbf{c}(t)$ be a differentiable path such that $\mathbf{c}(t) \neq \mathbf{0}$ and $\mathbf{c}'(t) \neq \mathbf{0}$ for every t. Show that
(a) $\left(\|\mathbf{c}(t)\|^2\right)' = 2\mathbf{c}(t) \cdot \mathbf{c}'(t)$.
(b) $\left(\|\mathbf{c}(t)\|\right)' = \mathbf{c}(t) \cdot \mathbf{c}'(t)/\|\mathbf{c}(t)\|$.
(c) $\left(\|\mathbf{c}(t)\|^{-1}\right)' = -\mathbf{c}(t) \cdot \mathbf{c}'(t)/\|\mathbf{c}(t)\|^3$.
(d) $(\mathbf{c}(t)/\|\mathbf{c}(t)\|)' = \left(- (\mathbf{c}(t) \cdot \mathbf{c}'(t)) \mathbf{c}(t) + (\mathbf{c}(t) \cdot \mathbf{c}(t)) \mathbf{c}'(t)\right)/\|\mathbf{c}(t)\|^3$.

Solution   We drop t to keep notation as simple as possible.

(a) Using the product rule and the fact that $\|\mathbf{c}\|^2 = \mathbf{c} \cdot \mathbf{c}$ we get

$$\left(\|\mathbf{c}\|^2\right)' = (\mathbf{c} \cdot \mathbf{c})' = \mathbf{c} \cdot \mathbf{c}' + \mathbf{c}' \cdot \mathbf{c} = 2\mathbf{c} \cdot \mathbf{c}'.$$

(b) Combining $\left(\|\mathbf{c}\|^2\right)' = 2\|\mathbf{c}\|\,\|\mathbf{c}\|'$ (which is obtained from the chain rule) and (a) we get $2\mathbf{c} \cdot \mathbf{c}' = 2\|\mathbf{c}\|\,\|\mathbf{c}\|'$, and hence $\|\mathbf{c}\|' = \mathbf{c} \cdot \mathbf{c}'/\|\mathbf{c}\|$.

(c) From the chain rule and (b) it follows that

$$\left(\|\mathbf{c}\|^{-1}\right)' = -\|\mathbf{c}\|^{-2}\|\mathbf{c}\|' = -\frac{1}{\|\mathbf{c}\|^2}\frac{\mathbf{c} \cdot \mathbf{c}'}{\|\mathbf{c}\|} = -\frac{\mathbf{c} \cdot \mathbf{c}'}{\|\mathbf{c}\|^3}.$$

(d) Using the product rule and (c) we get

$$\left(\frac{\mathbf{c}}{\|\mathbf{c}\|}\right)' = \left(\|\mathbf{c}\|^{-1}\mathbf{c}\right)' = \left(\|\mathbf{c}\|^{-1}\right)'\mathbf{c} + \|\mathbf{c}\|^{-1}\mathbf{c}'$$

$$= -\frac{\mathbf{c} \cdot \mathbf{c}'}{\|\mathbf{c}\|^3}\mathbf{c} + \frac{1}{\|\mathbf{c}\|}\mathbf{c}' = \frac{-(\mathbf{c} \cdot \mathbf{c}')\mathbf{c} + \|\mathbf{c}\|^2 \mathbf{c}'}{\|\mathbf{c}\|^3}.$$

Example 3.12

Suppose that a particle, subjected to a force field, moves away from the origin along the path $\mathbf{c}(t) = (t, 2t^2, t^3)$, where t is the time in seconds. At time $t = 1$ the source of the force field is shut off, and the particle flies off along a tangent line, as shown in Figure 3.8. Find its position at $t = 3$.

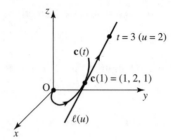

Figure 3.8 Path of the particle in Example 3.12.

Solution At $t = 1$ the particle is located at $\mathbf{c}(1) = (1, 2, 1)$ and is moving with velocity

$$\mathbf{v}(1) = \mathbf{c}'(1) = (1, 4t, 3t^2)\Big|_{t=1} = (1, 4, 3).$$

The tangent line $\ell(u)$ is now uniquely determined: it goes through the point $(1, 2, 1)$ and is parallel to the velocity vector $(1, 4, 3)$:

$$\ell(u) = (1, 2, 1) + u(1, 4, 3), \qquad u \in \mathbb{R}.$$

The position of the particle at $t = 3$ is given by $\ell(2)$ (i.e., when $u = 2$), since the particle already used one second to reach the point where it flew off its initial trajectory. Hence the position of the particle three seconds after it started moving is $\ell(2) = (3, 10, 7)$. ◀

Example 3.13 The position of a projectile fired from the origin at an angle of θ radians with respect to the positive x-axis and with the initial speed v_0 is given by

$$\mathbf{c}(t) = (v_0 \cos \theta)t\mathbf{i} + ((v_0 \sin \theta)t - gt^2/2)\mathbf{j}$$

(see Figure 3.9), where t is time and g is the acceleration due to gravity. Find

(a) the coordinates of the highest point on the trajectory, the time when the projectile reaches that point and its velocity at that moment;

(b) the time when the projectile hits the ground (that is represented by the x-axis) and the velocity at that moment.

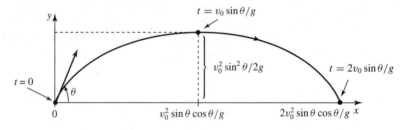

Figure 3.9 Path of a projectile in Example 3.13.

Solution

(a) The height is given by the y-coordinate $y(t) = (v_0 \sin\theta)t - gt^2/2$ of $\mathbf{c}(t)$. The critical point of $y(t)$ is (set $y'(t) = v_0 \sin\theta - gt = 0$ and solve for t) $t = v_0 \sin\theta/g$. Since $y''(t) = -g < 0$, $y(t)$ has a maximum at $t = v_0 \sin\theta/g$. Hence the projectile reaches its highest point when $t = v_0 \sin\theta/g$. The coordinates of the highest point are

$$\mathbf{c}(v_0 \sin\theta/g) = v_0 \cos\theta \frac{v_0 \sin\theta}{g}\mathbf{i} + \left(v_0 \sin\theta \frac{v_0 \sin\theta}{g} - \frac{g}{2}\frac{v_0^2 \sin^2\theta}{g^2}\right)\mathbf{j}$$

$$= \frac{v_0^2 \sin\theta \cos\theta}{g}\mathbf{i} + \frac{v_0^2 \sin^2\theta}{2g}\mathbf{j}.$$

Since $\mathbf{v}(t) = \mathbf{c}'(t) = v_0 \cos\theta\mathbf{i} + ((v_0 \sin\theta) - gt)\mathbf{j}$, it follows that $\mathbf{v}(v_0 \sin\theta/g) = v_0 \cos\theta\mathbf{i}$ is the velocity of the projectile at the moment it reaches the highest point of its trajectory.

(b) At the moment the projectile hits the ground, $y(t) = (v_0 \sin\theta)t - gt^2/2 = 0$ and $t > 0$ ($t = 0$ is the moment when the projectile is fired). Consequently, $t = 2v_0 \sin\theta/g$ is the moment when it hits the ground. Notice that this time is twice the time the projectile needs to reach its highest position. The velocity at the moment it hits the ground is $\mathbf{c}'(2v_0 \sin\theta/g) = v_0 \cos\theta\mathbf{i} - v_0 \sin\theta\mathbf{j}$.
◀

Example 3.14   Using the notion of speed, we can now confirm our somewhat intuitive reasoning in Example 3.8. Since $\|\mathbf{c}_1'(t)\| = \|\mathbf{c}_2'(t)\| = 2$, $\|\mathbf{c}_3'(t)\| = 6$ and $\|\mathbf{c}_4'(t)\| = 1/2$, it follows that (since all parametrizations have constant speed) the parametrization $\mathbf{c}_3$ is the fastest, $\mathbf{c}_4$ is the slowest, and $\mathbf{c}_1$ and $\mathbf{c}_2$ have the same speed.
◀

This example illustrates that speed can be used as a way of describing the differences between parametrizations of the same curve.

Example 3.15   A particle moves around the circle centered at the origin of radius R with constant speed s in the counterclockwise direction. Find a parametric representation of its trajectory.

Solution   By analyzing the previous example and Example 3.8 we notice that the arguments of sine and cosine are involved in determining the speed. Therefore, we start with

$$\mathbf{c}_1(t) = (R \cos\omega t, R \sin\omega t), \qquad t \geq 0$$

and determine the value of ω from the requirement that the speed be equal to s. From $\mathbf{c}_1'(t) = (-R\omega \sin\omega t, R\omega \cos\omega t)$ it follows that $\|\mathbf{c}_1'(t)\| = R\omega$, and therefore $s = R\omega$ and $\omega = s/R$. Consequently, the parametrization

$$\mathbf{c}(t) = (R \cos(st/R), R \sin(st/R)), \qquad t \geq 0$$

has the required speed (see Figure 3.10). When $t = 0$, $\mathbf{c}(0) = (R, 0)$; for small positive values of t both components of $\mathbf{c}(t)$ are positive; i.e., $\mathbf{c}(t)$ is in the first quadrant. It follows that the curve **c** is oriented counterclockwise.

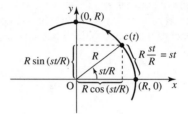

Figure 3.10 Motion around the circle with constant speed s.

From arc $= R \cdot$ angle (R is the radius) we get that speed $s =$ arc/time $= R \cdot$ angle/time. Since $s = R\omega$, it follows that $\omega =$ angle/time. In other words, the scalar ω in Example 3.15 represents the angular speed.

Denote the angle measured counterclockwise from the positive x-axis by θ. From $\theta = \omega t$ it follows that $d\theta/dt = \omega$. Consequently, the sign of ω determines the orientation: if $\omega > 0$, then $d\theta/dt > 0$; i.e., θ is increasing, and the curve is oriented counterclockwise. If $\omega < 0$, then $d\theta/dt < 0$ and the curve is oriented clockwise.

Example 3.16   **Centripetal Acceleration and Centripetal Force.**

Compute the acceleration of a particle of mass m that moves along the circle of radius R with constant speed s.

Solution   Assuming that the center of the circular path is at the origin, we get (see Example 3.15) that

$$\mathbf{c}(t) = (R\cos(s/R)t, \, R\sin(s/R)t)$$

describes the position of the particle at time t. Hence

$$\mathbf{v}(t) = (-s\sin(s/R)t, \, s\cos(s/R)t)$$

and

$$\mathbf{a}(t) = (-(s^2/R)\cos(s/R)t, \, -(s^2/R)\sin(s/R)t).$$

Since

$$\mathbf{a}(t) = -(s^2/R^2)(R\cos(s/R)t, \, R\sin(s/R)t) = -(s^2/R^2)\mathbf{c}(t),$$

it follows that the acceleration vector points in the direction opposite to the position vector $\mathbf{c}(t)$; i.e., points towards the center of rotation. For this reason, $\mathbf{a}(t)$ is called a *centripetal acceleration,* and the corresponding force $\mathbf{F} = m\mathbf{a}(t)$ is called a *centripetal force.*

It is important to notice that although the speed s (scalar!) in this example is constant, the velocity $\mathbf{v}(t)$ (vector!) is not (the velocity vector changes its direction continuously), and therefore the acceleration is not zero.

Example 3.17 Coriolis Acceleration in $\mathbf{R}^2$.

A plate in the shape of a disk of radius 1 rotates in the xy-plane with constant angular speed ω so that its center (located at the origin) coincides with the center of rotation. A particle starts moving from the center towards the edge, with the trajectory

$$\mathbf{r}(t) = t\,\mathbf{c}(t) = t\,(\cos(\omega t), \sin(\omega t)),$$

where $\mathbf{c}(t) = (\cos(\omega t), \sin(\omega t))$ describes the rotation of the boundary circle of the disk; see Figure 3.11. The function $\mathbf{r}(t)$ describes the motion relative to the x-axis and the y-axis that have their origin at the center of the disk and are fixed; i.e., do not participate in the rotation (such a coordinate system is called an *inertial system*). In a coordinate system that rotates with the disk (imagine its axes painted on the disk) the motion of the particle is along a radial line ℓ.

Another way to describe the trajectory $\mathbf{r}(t)$ is as follows: suppose that the disk is at rest and imagine a bug crawling on the surface of the disk from its center radially towards the edge. Now start rotating the disk and assume that the bug does not react to a sudden change, but continues crawling along (its planned straight) line. To the observer standing away from the rotating disk the bug will appear as crawling along $\mathbf{r}(t)$.

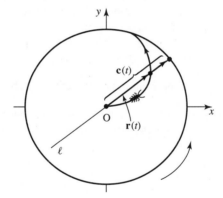

Figure 3.11   Trajectory of a particle in Example 3.17.

The velocity is computed to be

$$\mathbf{v}(t) = \mathbf{r}'(t) = \mathbf{c}(t) + t\,\mathbf{c}'(t),$$

and the acceleration is

$$\mathbf{a}(t) = \mathbf{v}'(t) = 2\mathbf{c}'(t) + t\mathbf{c}''(t) = 2\mathbf{c}'(t) - \omega^2 t\mathbf{c}(t).$$

The term $-\omega^2\mathbf{c}(t)$ has already appeared in Example 3.16 — it is the *centripetal acceleration*. The contribution $2\mathbf{c}'(t)$ to the acceleration is due to the interaction of the rotation of the disk and the movement of the particle. It is called the *Coriolis acceleration*, and it points in the direction of the velocity, as shown in Figure 3.12.

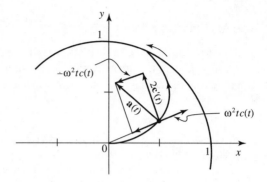

Figure 3.12   Acceleration $\mathbf{a}(t)$ is the sum of the Coriolis acceleration $2\mathbf{c}'(t)$ and the centripetal acceleration $-\omega^2\mathbf{c}(t)$.

Example 3.18   Coriolis Acceleration in $\mathbf{R}^3$.

Assume that the earth is a sphere (of radius R) rotating with constant angular speed ω. We are going to compute the acceleration of a water particle W in a river somewhere in the northern hemisphere that flows north-south or south-north with angular speed ρ. All computations will be done with respect to the *fixed* coordinate axes x, y and z (imagine, for example, that each axis points to a "fixed" distant star).

Assume that the z-axis is the axis of rotation and let $\mathbf{r}(t)$ denote the position of W at time t. Since $\mathbf{r}(t)$ always belongs to the sphere, $\|\mathbf{r}(t)\| = R$. Then (see Figure 3.13)

$$\mathbf{r}(t) = \text{component in } \mathbf{c}(t) \text{ direction} + \text{component in } \mathbf{k} \text{ direction} = \mathbf{r_c}(t) + \mathbf{r_k}(t),$$

where $\mathbf{c}(t) = (\cos(\omega t), \sin(\omega t), 0)$ describes a circle in the plane of the earth's equator (this is $\mathbf{c}(t)$ from the previous example, now viewed as a vector in three dimensions).

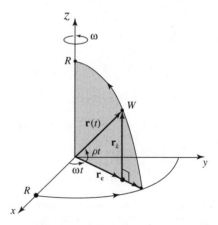

Figure 3.13   Motion of a water particle W.

Since $\mathbf{c}(t)$ and $\mathbf{k}$ are unit vectors, we can write

$$\mathbf{r}(t) = R\cos(\rho t)\mathbf{c}(t) + R\sin(\rho t)\mathbf{k}$$

and

$$\mathbf{v}(t) = \mathbf{r}'(t) = -R\rho\sin(\rho t)\mathbf{c}(t) + R\cos(\rho t)\mathbf{c}'(t) + R\rho\cos(\rho t)\mathbf{k}.$$

The acceleration is computed to be

$$\mathbf{a}(t) = -R\rho^2\cos(\rho t)\mathbf{c}(t) - 2R\rho\sin(\rho t)\mathbf{c}'(t) + R\cos(\rho t)\mathbf{c}''(t) - R\rho^2\sin(\rho t)\mathbf{k},$$

where

$$\mathbf{c}'(t) = (-\omega\sin(\omega t), \omega\cos(\omega t), 0)$$

and

$$\mathbf{c}''(t) = (-\omega^2\cos(\omega t), -\omega^2\sin(\omega t), 0) = -\omega^2\mathbf{c}(t).$$

Notice that (this fact will be needed a bit later)

$$\mathbf{c}'(t)\cdot\mathbf{r}(t) = \mathbf{c}'(t)\cdot(R\cos(\rho t)\mathbf{c}(t) + R\sin(\rho t)\mathbf{k})$$
$$= R\cos(\rho t)\mathbf{c}'(t)\cdot\mathbf{c}(t) + R\sin(\rho t)\mathbf{c}'(t)\cdot\mathbf{k} = 0,$$

since both dot products are zero.

The first and the fourth terms in $\mathbf{a}(t)$

$$-\rho^2 R(\cos(\rho t)\mathbf{c}(t) + \sin(\rho t)\mathbf{k}) = -\rho^2\mathbf{r}(t)$$

give the centripetal acceleration due to the motion of W. The third term

$$R\cos(\rho t)\mathbf{c}''(t) = -R\omega^2\cos(\rho t)\mathbf{c}(t)$$

is the centripetal acceleration due to the rotation of the earth. Finally, the second term

$$-2R\rho\sin(\rho t)\mathbf{c}'(t)$$

is called the *Coriolis acceleration* $\mathbf{a}_C(t)$. The direction of $\mathbf{a}_C(t)$ for a river in, say, Europe is opposite to $\mathbf{c}'(t)$ (since $\rho t > 0$ in the northern hemisphere, $\sin(\rho t) > 0$). In other words, $\mathbf{a}_C(t)$ is a vector tangent to the surface of the river, perpendicular to its motion (since $\mathbf{a}_C(t)\cdot\mathbf{r}(t) = -2R\rho\sin(\rho t)\mathbf{c}'(t)\cdot\mathbf{r}(t) = 0$, as shown above) and opposite to the rotation of the earth, see Figure 3.14. The force $-m\mathbf{a}_C(t)$ (m = mass of W) tends to push the particle W to the right, as viewed from above. This explains the known phenomenon that rivers in the northern hemisphere, flowing from south to north have their right banks washed off more than the left banks, whereas those (in the northern hemisphere) flowing north to south wash off their left banks more. This same type of phenomenon has been observed in motions of the atmosphere around planets; in the northern hemisphere, winds from the north or south tend to be deflected east by the earth's rotation.

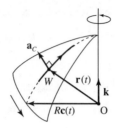

Figure 3.14   Coriolis acceleration.

For inhabitants of the earth it is convenient to use coordinate systems that are fixed to the surface of the earth. However, Newton's Second Law holds only for inertial systems and has to be modified for rotating ones. The considerations of this example appear in such modifications. However, in many applications, the earth is a sufficiently good approximation for an inertial system.

◀

Example 3.19   Geometric Interpretation of Derivatives.

Let $\mathbf{F}: \mathbb{R}^2 \to \mathbb{R}^2$ be a differentiable function and let $\mathbf{c} = \mathbf{c}(t): [a, b] \to \mathbb{R}^2$ be a differentiable curve. The derivative $\mathbf{c}'(t)$ can be interpreted as a vector tangent to $\mathbf{c}$ at the point $\mathbf{c}(t)$. The composition

$$\mathbf{d}(t) = \mathbf{F} \circ \mathbf{c}(t): [a, b] \to \mathbb{R}^2$$

is again a differentiable curve in the plane, and $\mathbf{d}'(t)$ is its tangent vector at $\mathbf{d}(t)$; see Figure 3.15. By the chain rule,

$$\mathbf{d}'(t) = D\mathbf{F}(\mathbf{c}(t)) \cdot \mathbf{c}'(t);$$

i.e., the tangent vector $\mathbf{d}'(t)$ is the image of the tangent vector $\mathbf{c}'(t)$ under the function $D\mathbf{F}$, which is the derivative of $\mathbf{F}$. Functions like $D\mathbf{F}$ that assign vectors to vectors have already been discussed in Section 1.4 (see Example 1.28 and the text preceeding it).

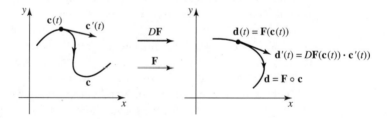

Figure 3.15   Function $\mathbf{F}$ maps points to points, and its derivative $D\mathbf{F}$ maps tangent vectors to tangent vectors.

To illustrate these ideas, consider this example: let $\mathbf{F}(x, y) = (\cos x, y)$ and take the curve $\mathbf{c}(t) = (t, \sin t)$, $t \in [0, 2\pi]$. The composition $\mathbf{d} = \mathbf{F} \circ \mathbf{c}$ is a curve

$$\mathbf{d}(t) = \mathbf{F}(\mathbf{c}(t)) = \mathbf{F}(t, \sin t) = (\cos t, \sin t), \qquad t \in [0, 2\pi].$$

Tangents to **c** and **d** are given by

$$\mathbf{c}'(t) = \begin{bmatrix} 1 \\ \cos t \end{bmatrix} \quad \text{and} \quad \mathbf{d}'(t) = \begin{bmatrix} -\sin t \\ \cos t \end{bmatrix}.$$

Our conclusion states that the tangent vector $\mathbf{d}'(t)$ is the image of $\mathbf{c}'(t)$ under DF. To check this, we compute the derivative

$$DF(x, y) = \begin{bmatrix} -\sin x & 0 \\ 0 & 1 \end{bmatrix}$$

and the image of $\mathbf{c}'(t)$ under DF:

$$DF(\mathbf{c}(t)) \cdot \mathbf{c}'(t) = DF(t, \sin t) \cdot \mathbf{c}'(t) = \begin{bmatrix} -\sin t & 0 \\ 0 & 1 \end{bmatrix} \cdot \begin{bmatrix} 1 \\ \cos t \end{bmatrix} = \begin{bmatrix} -\sin t \\ \cos t \end{bmatrix}.$$

As an example, take $t = \pi$. Then the point $\mathbf{c}(\pi) = (\pi, 0)$ on the curve **c** gets mapped to the point $\mathbf{F}(\pi, 0) = (\cos \pi, 0) = (-1, 0)$, which belongs to **d** (since $\mathbf{d}(\pi) = (\cos \pi, \sin \pi) = (-1, 0)$). Now

$$\mathbf{c}'(\pi) = \begin{bmatrix} 1 \\ \cos \pi \end{bmatrix} = \begin{bmatrix} 1 \\ -1 \end{bmatrix}$$

is the tangent vector to **c** at $\mathbf{c}(\pi) = (\pi, 0)$. The derivative of **F** at $\mathbf{c}(\pi)$ is

$$DF(\mathbf{c}(\pi)) = DF(\pi, 0) = \begin{bmatrix} 0 & 0 \\ 0 & 1 \end{bmatrix}.$$

The image of the tangent vector $\mathbf{c}'(\pi)$ under $DF(\mathbf{c}(\pi))$ is

$$DF(\mathbf{c}(\pi)) \cdot \mathbf{c}'(\pi) = \begin{bmatrix} 0 & 0 \\ 0 & 1 \end{bmatrix} \cdot \begin{bmatrix} 1 \\ -1 \end{bmatrix} = \begin{bmatrix} 0 \\ -1 \end{bmatrix}.$$

To check, we compute directly that $\mathbf{d}'(\pi) = (-\sin \pi, \cos \pi) = (0, -1)$. Hence **F** mapped the point $(\pi, 0)$ to the point $(-1, 0)$, and its derivative $DF(\pi, 0)$ at $(\pi, 0)$ mapped the tangent vector $\mathbf{c}'(\pi)$ to **c** at $(\pi, 0)$ to the tangent vector $\mathbf{d}'(\pi)$ of **d** at $(-1, 0)$.

◀

Let us repeat the conclusion of the previous example: we interpret $\mathbf{F} \colon \mathbb{R}^2 \to \mathbb{R}^2$ (or $\mathbf{F} \colon \mathbb{R}^3 \to \mathbb{R}^3$) as a function that maps points on one curve to points on the image curve. In that case, the derivative DF maps the tangent vector at a point on the first curve to the tangent vector at the corresponding point on the image curve.

Example 3.20   **Torque Equals the Rate of Change of Angular Momentum.**

Let $\mathbf{r}(t)$ be the position vector of a particle moving in $\mathbb{R}^3$. The *angular momentum* is defined as the vector

$$\mathbf{L}(t) = \mathbf{r}(t) \times \mathbf{p}(t),$$

where $\mathbf{p}(t) = m\mathbf{v}(t)$ is the momentum vector (m is the mass of the particle and $\mathbf{v}(t)$ is its velocity). The *torque* of a force $\mathbf{F}(t) = m\mathbf{a}(t)$ exerted at the point $\mathbf{r}(t)$ is

$$\mathbf{T}(t) = \mathbf{r}(t) \times \mathbf{F}(t).$$

Since (with the use of the product rule for the cross product of vector functions)

$$\frac{d\mathbf{L}(t)}{dt} = \frac{d}{dt}(\mathbf{r}(t) \times \mathbf{p}(t)) = \frac{d\mathbf{r}(t)}{dt} \times (m\mathbf{v}(t)) + \mathbf{r}(t) \times \frac{d(m\mathbf{v}(t))}{dt}$$

$$= m\mathbf{v}(t) \times \mathbf{v}(t) + \mathbf{r}(t) \times m\frac{d\mathbf{v}(t)}{dt}$$

$$= \mathbf{r}(t) \times m\mathbf{a}(t) = \mathbf{r}(t) \times \mathbf{F}(t) = \mathbf{T}(t),$$

(since $\mathbf{v} \times \mathbf{v} = \mathbf{0}$ for any vector $\mathbf{v}$ and $\mathbf{v}'(t) = \mathbf{a}(t)$) it follows that the torque $\mathbf{T}(t)$ on a particle equals the rate of change of the particle's angular momentum.

◀

Let $\mathbf{b}(t)$ and $\mathbf{c}(t)$ be two vector-valued functions of one variable. If $\mathbf{b}'(t) = \mathbf{c}(t)$, then the function $\mathbf{b}(t)$ is called an *antiderivative* (or an *indefinite integral*) of $\mathbf{c}(t)$, and is denoted by

$$\mathbf{b}(t) = \int \mathbf{c}(t)\,dt.$$

If $\mathbf{c}(t) = c_1(t)\mathbf{i} + c_2(t)\mathbf{j} + c_3(t)\mathbf{k}$, then

$$\mathbf{b}(t) = \int \mathbf{c}(t)\,dt = \left(\int c_1(t)\,dt\right)\mathbf{i} + \left(\int c_2(t)\,dt\right)\mathbf{j} + \left(\int c_3(t)\,dt\right)\mathbf{k}.$$

Example 3.21   Suppose that a projectile is launched from the origin with initial speed v_0 at an angle of θ radians with respect to the positive x-axis. Assuming no forces or effects other than gravity are present (hence the acceleration is $\mathbf{a}(t) = -g\mathbf{j}$, $g \approx 9.80$ m/s^2), find the trajectory of the projectile.

Solution   Since the acceleration is $\mathbf{a}(t) = -g\mathbf{j}$, it follows that the velocity is

$$\mathbf{v}(t) = \int \mathbf{a}(t)\,dt = \int -g\mathbf{j}\,dt = C_1\mathbf{i} + (-gt + C_2)\mathbf{j},$$

where C_1 and C_2 are constants. The initial condition (the data for $\mathbf{v}(0)$ is given in polar form) $\mathbf{v}(0) = v_0 \cos\theta\,\mathbf{i} + v_0 \sin\theta\,\mathbf{j}$ implies that $v_0 \cos\theta\,\mathbf{i} + v_0 \sin\theta\,\mathbf{j} = C_1\mathbf{i} + C_2\mathbf{j}$, i.e., $C_1 = v_0 \cos\theta$, $C_2 = v_0 \sin\theta$, and hence

$$\mathbf{v}(t) = v_0 \cos\theta\,\mathbf{i} + (-gt + v_0 \sin\theta)\mathbf{j}.$$

Another integration gives the position vector

$$\mathbf{c}(t) = ((v_0 \cos\theta)t + D_1)\mathbf{i} + (-gt^2/2 + (v_0 \sin\theta)t + D_2)\mathbf{j}$$

up to the additive constants D_1 and D_2. Using $\mathbf{c}(0) = (0, 0)$, we get $D_1 = 0$, $D_2 = 0$ and thus

$$\mathbf{c}(t) = (v_0 \cos\theta)t\,\mathbf{i} + (-gt^2/2 + (v_0 \sin\theta)t)\mathbf{j}.$$

This is precisely the formula that was used in Example 3.13.

◀

EXERCISES 3.2   **Exercises 1 to 7:**   The vector function $\mathbf{c}(t)$ represents the trajectory of a moving particle in $\mathbb{R}^2$ or in $\mathbb{R}^3$. Compute the velocity, speed and acceleration.

1. $\mathbf{c}(t) = (1 + t^3, t^{-1}, 2)$

2. $\mathbf{c}(t) = e^t \cos t \mathbf{i} + e^t \sin t \mathbf{j} + t \mathbf{k}$

3. $\mathbf{c}(t) = \ln(\cos t)\mathbf{i} + \ln(\sin t)\mathbf{j}$

4. $\mathbf{c}(t) = \tan t \mathbf{i} + \sec t \mathbf{j}$

5. $\mathbf{c}(t) = e^{2t} \sin(2t)\,\mathbf{i} + e^{2t} \cos(2t)\,\mathbf{j}$

6. $\mathbf{c}(t) = (\cosh t, \sinh t, t)$

7. $\mathbf{c}(t) = (t^{1/2}, t, t^{3/2})$

8. Find the maximum speed of the projectile in Example 3.13 and the time when it is reached.

Exercises 9 to 13:   Find the velocity $\mathbf{v}(t)$ and the position $\mathbf{c}(t)$ of a particle, given its acceleration $\mathbf{a}(t)$, initial velocity and initial position.

9. $\mathbf{a}(t) = (-1, 1, 0)$, $\mathbf{v}(0) = (1, 2, 0)$, $\mathbf{c}(0) = (0, 2, 0)$

10. $\mathbf{a}(t) = -9.8\mathbf{k}$, $\mathbf{v}(0) = \mathbf{i} + \mathbf{j}$, $\mathbf{c}(0) = \mathbf{i} + 2\mathbf{j} - \mathbf{k}$

11. $\mathbf{a}(t) = (t, 1, 1)$, $\mathbf{v}(0) = (0, 1, 0)$, $\mathbf{c}(0) = (-2, 0, 3)$

12. $\mathbf{a}(t) = e^t(1, 0, 1)$, $\mathbf{v}(0) = (1, 0, -2)$, $\mathbf{c}(0) = (0, 1, 0)$

13. $\mathbf{a}(t) = t\mathbf{i} + t^2\mathbf{j} + t\mathbf{k}$, $\mathbf{v}(0) = 2\mathbf{j} - 3\mathbf{k}$, $\mathbf{c}(0) = 4\mathbf{i} + 2\mathbf{j} - 6\mathbf{k}$

14. Find a parametrization of the circle $x^2 + y^2 = 1$ of non-constant speed. Find another parametrization $\mathbf{c}(t)$ such that $\|\mathbf{c}''(t)\|$ is non-constant and $\|\mathbf{c}''(t)\| \neq 0$ for all t.

15. The position of a particle is given by $\mathbf{c}(t) = (t^{-1}, 1, t^2)$, where $t \in [1, 4]$. When and where does the particle reach its maximum speed?

16. The position of a particle is given by $\mathbf{c}(t) = (3e^{-t} \cos t, 3e^{-t} \sin t)$, where $t \in [1, 3]$. When and where does the particle reach its maximum speed?

17. A particle moves with acceleration $\mathbf{a}(t) = (3, 0, 1)$, where $0 \leq t \leq 12$. Assuming that the particle is initially located at the origin and its initial velocity is $(1, 3, 2)$, find the time needed for the particle to reach its highest position.

18. Prove that if a particle moves with constant speed, then its velocity and acceleration vectors are always perpendicular.

19. A projectile is fired from the origin with an initial speed of 700 m/s at an angle of elevation of 60°. Find the range of the projectile, the maximum height reached, the time needed to reach it and the speed and the time of impact. Assume that no forces other than gravity act on the projectile.

20. An object is thrown upward from a point 10 m above the ground at an angle of 30° and with an initial speed of 100 m/s. Find a parametric equation of the path of the object. When does it reach its highest point? Where and when does it hit the ground? Assume that no forces other than gravity act on the object.

21. Find a parametrization of the line tangent to the ellipse $x^2 + 4y^2 = 3$ at the point where $x = \sqrt{3}$.

Exercises 22 to 25:   Find a parametrization of the line tangent to the given curve $\mathbf{c}(t)$ at the point indicated.

22. $\mathbf{c}(t) = (2t, t^3, 0)$, at the point $(4, 8, 0)$

23. $\mathbf{c}(t) = (3 \cos t, 3 \sin t, 4t)$, at the point $(0, 3, 2\pi)$

24. $\mathbf{c}(t) = (t, t^2, t^3)$, at the point $(1, 1, 1)$

25. $\mathbf{c}(t) = (-\cosh t, 1 + \sinh t)$ at the point $(-1, 1)$

26. Let $\mathbf{c}(t) = (x(t), y(t))$ be a curve in $\mathbb{R}^2$ and let $\mathbf{c}(t_0) = (x_0, y_0)$. Find an equation and the slope of the tangent line at (x_0, y_0).

27. Let $\mathbf{c}(t) = (r(t)\cos\theta(t), r(t)\sin\theta(t))$ be the trajectory of a particle moving in $\mathbb{R}^2$. Show that its velocity and acceleration are given by the expressions (drop the notation for the dependence on t)

$$\mathbf{v} = r'(\cos\theta, \sin\theta) + r\theta'(-\sin\theta, \cos\theta)$$

and

$$\mathbf{a} = (r'' - r(\theta')^2)(\cos\theta, \sin\theta) + (2r'\theta' + r\theta'')(-\sin\theta, \cos\theta).$$

28. Show that if a particle moves along the spiral $(2e^t \cos t, 2e^t \sin t)$, then the angle between its position and velocity vectors is constant.

29. The curve $\mathbf{c}(t) = (e^{-t}\cos t, e^{-t}\sin t)$, $0 \le t \le 3\pi$ represents the trajectory of a particle moving in $\mathbb{R}^2$. Compute its velocity and find all points at which the velocity is horizontal or vertical.

30. Let $\mathbf{F}(x, y) = (-y, x)$. Compute the curve that is the image under $\mathbf{F}$ of $\mathbf{c}(t) = (\sin t, \cos t)$, $t \in [0, \pi]$. Describe in words the map $D\mathbf{F}$.

31. Define the map $\mathbf{F}: \mathbb{R}^2 \to \mathbb{R}^2$ by $\mathbf{F}(x, y) = (x^2 y - x^3, ye^x - 2)$. Find the tangent vector to the image of the curve $\mathbf{c}(t) = (\sin t, t^2 - t)$ under $\mathbf{F}$ at $t = 0$.

32. Let $\mathbf{c}(t)$ be a curve such that $\mathbf{c}(0) = (1, 1)$ and $\mathbf{c}'(0) = (2, -1)$. Find the tangent vector to the image of $\mathbf{c}$ under the map $\mathbf{F} = (-y/\sqrt{x^2 + y^2}, x/\sqrt{x^2 + y^2})$ at $t = 0$.

33. Define the map $\mathbf{F}: \mathbb{R}^2 \to \mathbb{R}^2$ by $\mathbf{F}(\mathbf{x}) = A \cdot \mathbf{x}$, where A is a non-zero 2×2 matrix and the dot denotes matrix multiplication. Find the tangent vector to the image under $\mathbf{F}$ of the curve $\mathbf{c}(t)$ at $t = 0$ such that $\mathbf{c}(0) = (0, 0)$ and $\mathbf{c}'(0) = (c_1, c_2)$.

3.3   LENGTH OF A CURVE

Our next goal is to find a way of calculating the length of a curve. We will first define the length of a path (that is, of a description of the curve using a parametrization). The length of a curve is defined to be equal to the length of a special class of paths, called smooth paths. The definition is independent of the choice of a smooth path (parametrization). This sounds reasonable: no matter how fast or how slow (or in what direction) we walk along the same curve, we always cover the same distance.

Let $\mathbf{c}(t) = (x(t), y(t)): [a, b] \to \mathbb{R}^2$ be a path in the xy-plane. Divide the interval $[a, b]$ into n subintervals $[a = t_1, t_2], [t_2, t_3], \ldots, [t_n, t_{n+1} = b]$ and join the corresponding points on the curve $\mathbf{c}(t_1), \mathbf{c}(t_2), \ldots, \mathbf{c}(t_{n+1})$ on $\mathbf{c}$ with straight line segments $c_1, c_2, \ldots, c_n$ (see Figure 3.16), thus forming a polygonal path p_n.

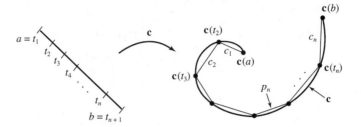

Figure 3.16 Polygonal path p_n approximates the path **c**.

The lengths of $c_1, \ldots, c_n$ are $\ell(c_1) = \|\mathbf{c}(t_2) - \mathbf{c}(t_1)\|, \ldots, \ell(c_n) = \|\mathbf{c}(t_{n+1}) - \mathbf{c}(t_n)\|$, and the total length of p_n is $\ell(p_n) = \ell(c_1) + \ldots + \ell(c_n)$. As we keep increasing n, we obtain polygonal paths p_n that approximate the path **c** better and better. The length $\ell(\mathbf{c})$ of **c** is defined as the limit of lengths of those polygonal paths as $n \to \infty$. Now, for every $i = 1, \ldots, n$ (the symbol $\approx$ means "approximately equal")

$$\mathbf{c}'(t_i) = x'(t_i)\mathbf{i} + y'(t_i)\mathbf{j}$$
$$\approx \frac{x(t_{i+1}) - x(t_i)}{t_{i+1} - t_i}\mathbf{i} + \frac{y(t_{i+1}) - y(t_i)}{t_{i+1} - t_i}\mathbf{j}$$
$$= \frac{(x(t_{i+1}) + y(t_{i+1}))\mathbf{i} - (x(t_i) + y(t_i))\mathbf{j}}{t_{i+1} - t_i} = \frac{\mathbf{c}(t_{i+1}) - \mathbf{c}(t_i)}{t_{i+1} - t_i}$$

(we viewed $x(t)$ and $y(t)$ as real-valued functions of one variable and used the fact that $x'(t_i)$ and $y'(t_i)$, interpreted as the slope of a tangent, can be approximated by the slopes of secant lines). Therefore

$$\mathbf{c}'(t_i) \approx \frac{\mathbf{c}(t_{i+1}) - \mathbf{c}(t_i)}{t_{i+1} - t_i}$$

and hence the length of the i-th segment c_i is approximately equal to

$$\ell(c_i) = \|\mathbf{c}(t_{i+1}) - \mathbf{c}(t_i)\| \approx \|\mathbf{c}'(t_i)\|(t_{i+1} - t_i) = \|\mathbf{c}'(t_i)\|\Delta t_i, \qquad (3.1)$$

where $\Delta t_i = t_{i+1} - t_i$. Consequently, the length of the polygonal path p_n

$$\ell(p_n) = \sum_{i=1}^{n} \ell(c_i) \approx \sum_{i=1}^{n} \|\mathbf{c}'(t_i)\|\Delta t_i \qquad (3.2)$$

approximates the length of the curve. Now compute the limit as $n \to \infty$. By definition, the limit $\lim_{n\to\infty} \ell(p_n)$ on the left side is equal to the length $\ell(\mathbf{c})$ of the path **c**. Since $n \to \infty$, $\Delta t_i \to 0$ and we recognize the limit on the right side as the definition of the definite integral of the function $\|\mathbf{c}'(t)\|$ over the interval $[a, b]$. This somewhat intuitive argument justifies the following definition. Recall that a function is called C^1 if its derivative is continuous.

■ **Definition 3.6**   Length of a Path.

Let $\mathbf{c}: [a, b] \to \mathbb{R}^2$ (or $\mathbb{R}^3$) be a C^1 path. The *length* $\ell(\mathbf{c})$ of $\mathbf{c}$ is given by

$$\ell(\mathbf{c}) = \int_a^b \|\mathbf{c}'(t)\| \, dt.$$

■

Before proceeding, let us consider an example.

Example 3.22   Compute the length of the paths $\mathbf{c}_1(t) = (\cos t, \sin t)$, $t \in [0, 2\pi]$ and $\mathbf{c}_2(t) = (\cos 3t, \sin 3t)$, $t \in [0, 2\pi]$ in $\mathbb{R}^2$.

Solution   By definition,

$$\ell(\mathbf{c}_1) = \int_0^{2\pi} \sqrt{(-\sin t)^2 + (\cos t)^2} \, dt = \int_0^{2\pi} dt = 2\pi$$

and

$$\ell(\mathbf{c}_2) = \int_0^{2\pi} \sqrt{(-3 \sin 3t)^2 + (3 \cos 3t)^2} \, dt = \int_0^{2\pi} 3 \, dt = 6\pi.$$

◀

Both $\mathbf{c}_1$ and $\mathbf{c}_2$ represent the same curve, the circle of radius 1. However, only the first parametrization gives its length. The path $\mathbf{c}_2$ traverses the circle three times (and hence its length is three times the length of the circle). Therefore, if we want to measure the length of a curve, we have to exclude some parametrizations, such as $\mathbf{c}_2$ in the previous example. This is one of the reasons why we made a fuss about the distinction between a path and a curve.

■ **Definition 3.7**   Smooth Path (Smooth Parametrization).

A C^1 path (or a C^1 parametrization) $\mathbf{c}: [a, b] \to \mathbb{R}^2$ (or $\mathbb{R}^3$) is called *smooth* if $\mathbf{c}'(t) \neq \mathbf{0}$ for all $t \in (a, b)$, and if distinct points in (a, b) map to distinct points on the curve.   ■

According to the definition, a smooth path can be closed (i.e., $\mathbf{c}(a) = \mathbf{c}(b)$ is allowed) but cannot intersect itself, be tangent to itself or (partly or completely) retrace itself (like the path $\mathbf{c}_2$ of Example 3.22). The paths $\mathbf{c}_1$, $\mathbf{c}_2$ (for $m \neq 0$), $\mathbf{c}_3$ and $\mathbf{c}_5$ of Example 3.7 in Section 3.1 are smooth.

Notice that a smooth path has a non-zero velocity at every point.

■ **Definition 3.8**   Smooth Curve and its Length.

A curve $\mathbf{c}$ is called *smooth* if it has a smooth parametrization. The length $\ell(\mathbf{c})$ of $\mathbf{c}$ (also called the *arc-length*) is defined as the length of that smooth parametrization.   ■

In order to show that a curve $\mathbf{c}$ is smooth, all we have to do is to find *one* smooth parametrization of **c**. Its length is then equal to the length of the curve. As a consequence of the Change of Variables Theorem (in an integral), we show in Section 5.2 that the length of a curve is independent of the smooth parametrization that is used in the computation.

Example 3.23 Figure 3.17 shows the path $\mathbf{c}(t) = (\cos^3 t, \sin^3 t)$, $t \in [-\pi/2, \pi/2]$. It is C^1 and has no self-intersections. However, it is not smooth (and, looking at the point $(1, 0)$, we expect it not to be smooth) since $\mathbf{c}'(t) = (-3\cos^2 t \sin t, 3\sin^2 t \cos t)$ is zero when $t = 0$.

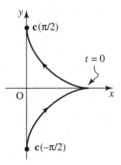

Figure 3.17 The path $\mathbf{c}(t) = (\cos^3 t, \sin^3 t)$, $t \in [-\pi/2, \pi/2]$ is not smooth.

Thinking of **c** as a trajectory of a motion, we translate the smoothness condition as the requirement that the *speed* be non-zero. At points where the speed is zero the particle can make sharp turns (thus describing a non-smooth trajectory), as in the previous example.

Example 3.24 Compute the length of the helix $\mathbf{c}(t) = (\cos t, \sin t, t)$ between $\mathbf{c}(0) = (1, 0, 0)$ and $\mathbf{c}(2\pi) = (1, 0, 2\pi)$ (that corresponds to one full revolution of its projection onto the xy-plane).

Solution The given parametrization is smooth since it is C^1 (components are C^1 by inspection), $\|\mathbf{c}'(t)\| = \sqrt{(-\sin t)^2 + (\cos t)^2 + 1} = \sqrt{2} \neq 0$, and if $t_1 \neq t_2$ then $\mathbf{c}(t_1) \neq \mathbf{c}(t_2)$ (since, for example, the z-coordinates are different). Consequently, the length (or the arc-length) of the helix in question is

$$\ell(\mathbf{c}) = \int_0^{2\pi} \sqrt{2}\, dt = 2\sqrt{2}\pi.$$

In this case, there is an alternative, more visual way to compute this. Cut the cylinder along the vertical line joining $(1, 0, 0)$ and $(1, 0, 2\pi)$ and unfold it, as shown on Figure 3.18. Then $\ell(\mathbf{c})$ is the length of the hypotenuse of the triangle with sides 2π (one side is the circumference of the circle which is the projection of the helix onto the xy-plane and the other side is the "pitch"; i.e., total increase in the z-coordinate from $t = 0$ to $t = 2\pi$).

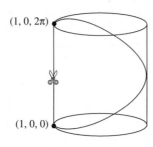
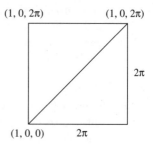

Figure 3.18   "Unfolding" the helix of Example 3.24.

Example 3.25   Length of the Graph of $y = f(x)$.

The graph of a C^1 function $f(x)$: $[a, b] \to \mathbb{R}$ can be parametrized as $\mathbf{c}(t) = (t, f(t))$, $t \in [a, b]$. The path $\mathbf{c}$ is C^1 (since f is C^1 by assumption), $\|\mathbf{c}'(t)\| = \sqrt{1 + (f'(t))^2} \neq 0$ for all t, and if $t_1 \neq t_2$, then $\mathbf{c}(t_1) = (t_1, f(t_1)) \neq (t_2, f(t_2)) = \mathbf{c}(t_2)$. Consequently, the path $\mathbf{c}(t)$ is smooth and its length (and hence the length of the graph of $y = f(x)$ on $[a, b]$) is

$$\ell(\mathbf{c}) = \int_a^b \sqrt{1 + (f'(t))^2} \, dt = \int_a^b \sqrt{1 + (f'(x))^2} \, dx.$$

In other words, we have shown that our definition agrees with the formula from the calculus of functions of one variable.

◀

■ **Theorem 3.1**   The Shortest Distance Between Two Points.

The shortest smooth curve connecting two given points in a plane is a straight line.   ■

Proof

Take two points, A and B, and choose the coordinate system so that they both lie on the x-axis, having the coordinates $A = (a, 0)$ and $B = (b, 0)$. Choose any smooth curve $\mathbf{c}$ (think of it as of a graph of some continuously differentiable function $y = f(x)$) other than the straight line segment $\mathbf{s}$ joining A and B (see Figure 3.19). Parametrizing $\mathbf{c}$ by $\mathbf{c}(t) = (t, f(t))$, we get

$$\ell(\mathbf{c}) = \int_a^b \sqrt{1 + (f'(t))^2} \, dt.$$

We have to show that $\ell(\mathbf{c}) > \ell(\mathbf{s}) = b - a$. First of all, there exists t such that $f'(t) \neq 0$ (otherwise, if $f'(t) = 0$ for all t then $f(t) = $ constant; i.e., the graph of f is the straight line). But f' is continuous, so there exists a whole interval (a', b') containing t where $f' \neq 0$; see Figure 3.20 (in other words, a continuous function f' cannot have a nonzero value at a single point in its domain; this is a consequence of the definition of continuity). It follows that the strict inequality $\sqrt{1 + (f'(t))^2} > 1$ holds on (a', b')

(and clearly, $\sqrt{1 + (f'(t))^2} \geq 1$ everywhere else), and therefore

$$\ell(\mathbf{c}) = \int_a^b \sqrt{1 + (f'(t))^2}\, dt$$

$$= \int_a^{a'} \sqrt{1 + (f'(t))^2}\, dt + \int_{a'}^{b'} \sqrt{1 + (f'(t))^2}\, dt + \int_{b'}^b \sqrt{1 + (f'(t))^2}\, dt$$

$$> \int_a^{a'} 1\, dt + \int_{a'}^{b'} 1\, dt + \int_{b'}^b 1\, dt = \int_a^b 1\, dt = b - a = \ell(\mathbf{s});$$

i.e., $\ell(\mathbf{c}) > \ell(\mathbf{s})$.

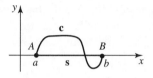

Figure 3.19   The length of $\mathbf{c}$ is larger than the length $b - a$ of $\mathbf{s}$.

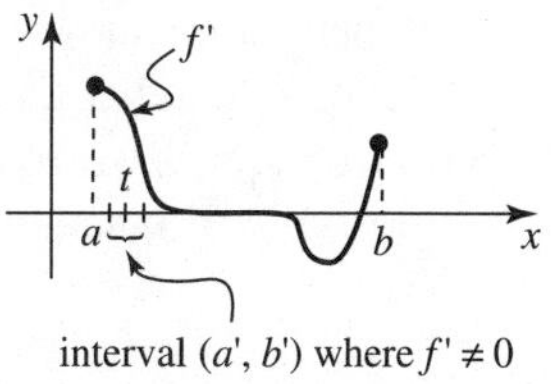

Figure 3.20   Possible graph of $f'(t)$.

> **Definition 3.9**   Arc-length Function.
>
> Let $\mathbf{c}: [a, b] \to \mathbb{R}^2$ (or $\mathbb{R}^3$) be a C^1 path. The *arc-length function* $s(t)$ of $\mathbf{c}(t)$ is given by
>
> $$s(t) = \int_a^t \|\mathbf{c}'(\tau)\|\, d\tau.$$

Geometrically, the arc-length function $s(t)$ measures the length of $\mathbf{c}$ from $\mathbf{c}(a)$ to the point $\mathbf{c}(t)$; i.e., the distance traversed in time t. Clearly, $s(a) = \int_a^a \|\mathbf{c}'(\tau)\|\, d\tau = 0$ and $s(b) = \int_b^a \|\mathbf{c}'(\tau)\|\, d\tau = \ell(\mathbf{c})$. By the Fundamental Theorem of Calculus,

$$\frac{d}{dt} s(t) = \frac{d}{dt} \left(\int_a^t \|\mathbf{c}'(\tau)\|\, d\tau \right) = \|\mathbf{c}'(t)\|. \tag{3.3}$$

This makes sense: $ds(t)/dt$ is the rate of change of the arc-length (i.e., the distance) with respect to time, which is the speed $\|\mathbf{c}'(t)\|$.

The arc-length function can be used as a new parameter for $\mathbf{c}$; i.e., a parametrization $\mathbf{c}(t)$ can be replaced by the parametrization $\mathbf{c}(s)$ (read the next two examples to see how this is done). Strictly speaking, we should use different symbols for the two parametrizations (although they represent the same curve, they are not equal as functions). However, this sloppiness has become a common practice. We say that the parametrization $\mathbf{c}(s)$ is the *parametrization by arc-length*.

Example 3.26   Parametrization by Arc-length.

Compute the arc-length function of the circle $\mathbf{c}(t) = (3\cos t, 3\sin t)$, where $t \in [0, 2\pi]$ and parametrize the circle by its arc-length.

Solution   Since $\|\mathbf{c}'(t)\| = 3$, it follows that $s(t) = \int_0^t 3\,dt = 3t$ is the arc-length function. To express $\mathbf{c}$ in terms of s, solve $s = 3t$ for t and substitute into the given parametrization, thus getting the parametrization by arc-length

$$\mathbf{c}(s) = (3\cos(s/3), 3\sin(s/3)), \qquad s \in [0, 6\pi].$$

Since $0 \le t \le 2\pi$, it follows that $0 \le s = 3t \le 6\pi$.

The curve that corresponds to values of t from $t = 0$ to $t = \pi/2$ in the original parametrization $\mathbf{c}(t)$ is the part of the circle of radius 3 in the first quadrant; its length is $3\pi/2$. On the other hand, it takes $s = 3\pi/2$ units of "s-time" for the point on the path $\mathbf{c}(s)$ to reach $(0, 3)$ from $(3, 0)$. So in this case, the "s-time" needed is (numerically) the same as the distance traveled.   ◀

Example 3.27   Parametrization by Arc-length.

Consider the circular helix in $\mathbb{R}^3$ given by

$$\mathbf{c}(t) = (a\cos t, a\sin t, bt), \qquad t \in [0, 2\pi]$$

$(a, b > 0)$. Compute its arc-length function and parametrize it by arc-length.

Solution   Since $\mathbf{c}'(t) = (-a\sin t, a\cos t, b)$ it follows that

$$s(t) = \int_0^t \sqrt{a^2 + b^2}\,dt = \sqrt{a^2 + b^2}\,t.$$

Consequently, $t = s/\sqrt{a^2 + b^2}$ and the required parametrization is given by

$$\mathbf{c}(s) = (a\cos\frac{s}{\sqrt{a^2+b^2}}, a\sin\frac{s}{\sqrt{a^2+b^2}}, \frac{bs}{\sqrt{a^2+b^2}}), \qquad s \in [0, 2\pi\sqrt{a^2+b^2}].$$

Notice that we adjusted the interval (domain) of $\mathbf{c}(s)$.

The length of the helix is

$$\ell(c) = \int_0^{2\pi} \|\mathbf{c}'(t)\|\,dt = \int_0^{2\pi} \sqrt{a^2 + b^2}\,dt = 2\pi\sqrt{a^2 + b^2},$$

which is exactly how much "s-time" is needed to trace the reparametrized curve $\mathbf{c}(s)$.   ◀

The previous two examples have something in common: the time spent walking along a curve parametrized by arc-length is numerically equal to the distance covered. We will now demonstrate that this property is always true.

Take a C^1 path $\mathbf{c}(t)$, $t \in [a, b]$, and parametrize it by the arc-length function; i.e., consider the parametrization $\mathbf{c}(s)$, $s \in [a', b']$. By definition,

$$\ell(\mathbf{c}(s)) = \int_{a'}^{b'} \|\mathbf{c}'(s)\| ds.$$

From the chain rule and (3.3) it follows that

$$\mathbf{c}'(t) = \frac{d\mathbf{c}(t)}{dt} = \frac{d\mathbf{c}(s)}{ds}\frac{ds}{dt} = \mathbf{c}'(s)\|\mathbf{c}'(t)\|.$$

Therefore, $\mathbf{c}'(s) = \mathbf{c}'(t)/\|\mathbf{c}'(t)\|$ (consequently, $\|\mathbf{c}'(s)\| = 1$) and

$$\ell(\mathbf{c}(s)) = \int_{a'}^{b'} 1 ds = b' - a'.$$

In words, the length $b' - a'$ of a curve parametrized by its arc-length function is numerically equal to the time needed to trace it (which is equal to the length of the interval $[a', b']$). This should come as no surprise since $\|\mathbf{c}'(s)\| = 1$ (i.e., a curve parametrized by arc-length is traversed with a constant speed of 1).

The vector

$$\mathbf{T}(t) = \frac{\mathbf{c}'(t)}{\|\mathbf{c}'(t)\|}$$

is called the *unit tangent vector* to $\mathbf{c}$ at $\mathbf{c}(t)$. It is worth repeating that $\mathbf{T}(t) = \mathbf{c}'(s)$.

No matter what smooth parametrization of a curve we use, we always arrive at the same parametrization by arc-length. The fact that the unit tangent vector for any parametrization is equal to $\mathbf{c}'(s)$ means that although tangent vectors differ from parametrization to parametrization the tangent *direction* is the same for all of them.

Example 3.28   Let $\mathbf{c}(t) = (t^2/2, t^3/3)$, $t \in [0, 2]$.

(a) Find the arc-length function s and parametrize $\mathbf{c}$ by the new parameter s.

(b) Check that $ds/dt = \|\mathbf{c}'(t)\|$.

(c) Verify that $\mathbf{T}(t) = \mathbf{c}'(s)$.

Solution

(a) From $\mathbf{c}'(t) = (t, t^2)$, it follows that $\|\mathbf{c}'(t)\| = \sqrt{t^2 + t^4} = |t|\sqrt{1 + t^2} = t\sqrt{1 + t^2}$ (since $t \geq 0$) and

$$s = \int_0^t \|\mathbf{c}'(\tau)\| d\tau = \int_0^t \tau\sqrt{1 + \tau^2} d\tau$$

(using the substitution $u = 1 + \tau^2$)

$$= \tfrac{1}{3}(1 + \tau^2)^{3/2}\big|_0^t = \tfrac{1}{3}(1 + t^2)^{3/2} - \tfrac{1}{3}.$$

This computation gives us the arc-length parameter $s = (1+t^2)^{3/2}/3 - 1/3$. Solving for t we get $3s + 1 = (1+t^2)^{3/2}$ and $t = \left((3s + 1)^{2/3} - 1\right)^{1/2}$ (we take the positive value of the square root since t is positive by definition of the domain of $\mathbf{c}(t)$).

Finally, the parametrization of $\mathbf{c}$ by the arc-length function s is

$$\mathbf{c}(s) = \left(\tfrac{1}{2} \left((3s+1)^{2/3} - 1 \right), \tfrac{1}{3} \left((3s+1)^{2/3} - 1 \right)^{3/2} \right).$$

(b) From $s = (1+t^2)^{3/2}/3 - 1/3$ it follows that

$$\frac{ds}{dt} = \tfrac{1}{3} \cdot \tfrac{3}{2}(1+t^2)^{1/2} \cdot 2t = t(1+t^2)^{1/2} = \|\mathbf{c}'(t)\|.$$

(c) The unit tangent vector is computed to be

$$\mathbf{T}(t) = \frac{\mathbf{c}'(t)}{\|\mathbf{c}'(t)\|} = \frac{(t, t^2)}{t\sqrt{1+t^2}} = \left(\frac{1}{\sqrt{1+t^2}}, \frac{t}{\sqrt{1+t^2}} \right).$$

The velocity of $\mathbf{c}(s)$ is

$$\begin{aligned}
\mathbf{c}'(s) &= \left(\tfrac{1}{2} \cdot \tfrac{2}{3}(3s+1)^{-1/3} \cdot 3, \tfrac{1}{3} \cdot \tfrac{3}{2} \left((3s+1)^{2/3} - 1 \right)^{1/2} \cdot \tfrac{2}{3}(3s+1)^{-1/3} \cdot 3 \right) \\
&= (3s+1)^{-1/3} \left(1, \left((3s+1)^{2/3} - 1 \right)^{1/2} \right) \\
&= (1+t^2)^{-1/2}(1, t) = \mathbf{T}(t),
\end{aligned}$$

since $3s+1 = (1+t^2)^{3/2}$ (that was computed in (a)).   ◀

Example 3.29   Let $\mathbf{c}(t) = (t, \cosh t)$, $t \in [0, 1]$. The arc-length function is

$$s(t) = \int_0^t \sqrt{1 + (\sinh \tau)^2} d\tau = \int_0^t \cosh \tau \, d\tau = \sinh t.$$

Hence $t = \sinh^{-1} s$, so that the parametrization by arc-length is given by

$$\mathbf{c}(s) = (\sinh^{-1} s, \cosh(\sinh^{-1} s)), \qquad s \in [0, \sinh 1].$$

The tangent is computed to be (the derivative of $\sinh^{-1} x$ is $(1+x^2)^{-1/2}$)

$$\mathbf{c}'(s) = \left(\frac{1}{\sqrt{1+s^2}}, s \frac{1}{\sqrt{1+s^2}} \right),$$

which is a unit vector:

$$\|\mathbf{c}'(s)\| = \sqrt{ \frac{1}{1+s^2} + \frac{s^2}{1+s^2} } = 1.$$

As shown earlier, the length of the curve from $\mathbf{c}(0)$ to $\mathbf{c}(s)$ equals s. For example, the length of the part of the curve between $\mathbf{c}(s = 0) = (0, 1)$ and $\mathbf{c}(s = 1) = (\sinh^{-1} 1, \cosh(\sinh^{-1} 1))$ is 1.   ◀

EXERCISES 3.3   1. Consider the curve parametrized by $\mathbf{c}(t) = (t, 1/t)$, $t \in [1, 2]$. Divide $[1, 2]$ into 5 subintervals of equal length, sketch the curve $\mathbf{c}$ and the polygonal path p_5 that approximates it. Approximate the length of p_5 using formula (3.2).

2. Consider the curve parametrized by $c(t) = (t, e^{2t})$, $t \in [0, 1]$. Divide $[0, 1]$ into 4 subintervals of equal length, sketch the curve c and the polygonal path p_4 that approximates it. Approximate the length of p_4 using formula (3.2). Compare your approximation with the length of p_4 computed using the formula for the distance between two points.

Exercises 3 to 12: Find the length of the curve $c(t)$.

3. $c(t) = (\sin 2t, \cos 2t)$, $t \in [0, \frac{\pi}{2}]$

4. $c(t) = (2t^{3/2}, 2t)$, from $(0, 0)$ to $(2, 2)$

5. $c(t) = e^t \cos t\, \mathbf{i} + e^t \sin t\, \mathbf{j}$, $0 \leq t \leq \pi$

6. $c(t) = t^3 \mathbf{i} + t^2 \mathbf{j}$, $-2 \leq t \leq 1$

7. $c(t) = ((1 + t), (1 + t)^{3/2})$, $t \in [0, 1]$

8. $c(t) = (e^{2t}, e^{-2t}, \sqrt{8}t)$, $t \in [0, 1]$

9. (catenary) $c(t) = (t, \cosh t)$, $t \in [0, 1]$

10. (four-cusped hypocycloid) $c(t) = (a \cos^3 t, a \sin^3 t)$, $a > 0$, $t \in [0, 2\pi]$

11. $c(t) = (2t - t^2)\mathbf{i} + \frac{8}{3}t^{3/2}\mathbf{j} + \mathbf{k}$, from $t = 1$ to $t = 3$

12. $c(t) = \cos^2 t\, \mathbf{i} + \sin^2 t\, \mathbf{j}$, from $t = 0$ to $t = 2\pi$

13. Is it true that the curve $y = 2 \sin x$, $x \in [0, 2\pi]$ is twice as long as $y = \sin x$, $x \in [0, 2\pi]$?

14. Let $r = f(\theta)$, $\theta \in [\alpha, \beta]$ be a representation of a path in polar coordinates. Show that its length is

$$\ell = \int_\alpha^\beta \sqrt{r^2 + (dr/d\theta)^2}\, d\theta.$$

Exercises 15 to 20: Using Exercise 14 compute the length of the given curve.

15. $r = a \cos \theta$, $a > 0$, $0 \leq \theta \leq \pi/4$

16. $r = a \cos 2\theta$, $a > 0$, $0 \leq \theta \leq \pi/4$

17. $r = 3\theta^2$, $1 \leq \theta \leq 2$

18. $r = e^{2\theta}$, $0 \leq \theta \leq \ln 6$

19. $r = 1 + \sin \theta$, $-\pi/2 \leq \theta \leq \pi/2$

20. (cardioid) $r = 1 - \cos \theta$, $0 \leq \theta \leq \pi$

21. Find the arc-length function of $c(t) = (t \sin 2t, t \cos 2t, 4t^{3/2}/3)$, $0 \leq t \leq 2\pi$.

Exercises 22 to 26: Consider the path $c(t)$. Find its arc-length function $s(t)$ and reparametrize it by its arc-length.

22. $c(t) = \sin 2t\, \mathbf{i} + \cos 2t\, \mathbf{j} + \frac{2}{3}t^{3/2}\mathbf{k}$, $t \in [-4, 4]$

23. $c(t) = 5 \cos t\, \mathbf{i} + 5 \sin t\, \mathbf{j} + 12t\mathbf{k}$, $t \in [0, \pi/4]$

24. $c(t) = (3 + 4t)\mathbf{i} + (5t - 1)\mathbf{j} + 11\mathbf{k}$, $t \in [-2, 1]$

25. $c(t) = e^t \cos t\, \mathbf{i} + e^t \sin t\, \mathbf{j}$, $t \in [0, 1]$

26. $c(t) = 2 \cos^3 t\, \mathbf{i} + \cos 2t\mathbf{j} + 2 \sin^3 t\mathbf{k}$, $t \in [\pi/4, \pi/2]$

27. Consider the following parametrizations:

   (a) $c_1(t) = (\cos 2t, \sin 2t, t)$, $t \in [0, \pi]$ (b) $c_2(t) = (\cos t, \sin t, t/2)$, $t \in [0, 2\pi]$

   (c) $c_3(t) = (\cos 2t, -\sin 2t, -t)$, $t \in [-\pi, 0]$

   Check that they all represent the same curve. Compute the length in each case and compare your results.

28. Find the unit tangent vector to the curve $c(t) = (e^{-t} \sin t, e^{-t} \cos t)$.

29. Find the unit tangent vector to the curve $c(t) = (t^{-1} - t, t^{-1} + t, -1)$ at $t = 1$.

30. Consider the curve $\mathbf{c}$ parametrized by $\mathbf{c}(t) = (t^3, 3t^6 + 1)$, $t \in [-1, 1]$. This parametrization is not smooth (where?), and hence cannot be used to compute the length of $\mathbf{c}$. Find a smooth parametrization of $\mathbf{c}$ and compute its length.

31. Is the curve $\mathbf{c}(t) = (\sin t, 2\sin 2t)$, $t \in [0, 2\pi]$, smooth?

32. Compute the length of the curve $\mathbf{c}(t) = (\cos^3 t, \sin^3 t)$, $t \in [-\pi/2, \pi/2]$, of Example 3.23.

3.4   ACCELERATION AND CURVATURE

The acceleration of a particle moving in $\mathbb{R}^2$ or $\mathbb{R}^3$ can be written as a sum of two components: one is parallel to the motion, and the other orthogonal to it. We now study this decomposition and relate it to geometric features of a path, namely its curvature. We start with an example.

Example 3.30   Consider the motion $\mathbf{c}_1(t) = (1 + t^3, 2t^3 - 3)$ along a straight line and the motion $\mathbf{c}_2(t) = (a\cos(bt), a\sin(bt))$ around a circle of radius $a > 0$ (assume that $b \neq 0$). Compute the acceleration in both cases and describe its direction.

Solution   The path $\mathbf{c}_1(t)$ is indeed a line: we can rewrite it in a more recognizable form as $\mathbf{c}_1(t) = (1, -3) + t^3(1, 2)$. It follows that its initial point is $(1, -3)$ and the direction is given by the vector $(1, 2) = \mathbf{i} + 2\mathbf{j}$. The velocity $\mathbf{v}_1(t) = \mathbf{c}_1'(t) = 3t^2(1, 2)$ is not constant (it *does* have a constant direction), and therefore the acceleration $\mathbf{a}_1(t) = \mathbf{c}_1''(t) = 6t(1, 2)$ is a non-zero vector. The direction of $\mathbf{a}_1(t)$ is parallel to the motion; see Figure 3.21(a).

The velocity of $\mathbf{c}_2(t)$ is $\mathbf{v}_2(t) = \mathbf{c}_2'(t) = (-ab\sin(bt), ab\cos(bt))$, and its acceleration is $\mathbf{a}_2(t) = \mathbf{v}_2'(t) = (-ab^2\cos(bt), -ab^2\sin(bt))$. Since $\mathbf{a}_2(t) = -ab^2\mathbf{c}_2(t)$ (and $\mathbf{a}_2(t) \cdot \mathbf{v}_2(t) = 0$) it follows that the acceleration is perpendicular to the motion and points towards the center of the circle, as shown in Figure 3.21(b).

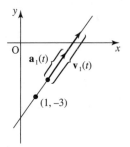

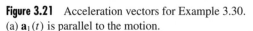

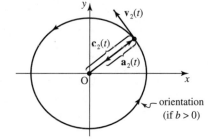

Figure 3.21   Acceleration vectors for Example 3.30.
(a) $\mathbf{a}_1(t)$ is parallel to the motion.   (b) $\mathbf{a}_2(t)$ is perpendicular to the motion.

The acceleration vectors for both $\mathbf{c}_1$ and $\mathbf{c}_2$ in the previous example are non-zero. The path $\mathbf{c}_1$ represents motion along a straight line with non-constant speed (the speed increases as t increases), which corresponds to non-zero acceleration (whose direction coincides with the direction of motion). The path $\mathbf{c}_2$ has a constant speed of a (units). However, the *velocity* changes its direction all the time, and hence in this case also the acceleration (which is now orthogonal to the motion) is non-zero.

These two cases are the "extreme" cases. In general, an acceleration vector has a component in the direction of motion, and a component in the direction perpendicular to it. Our goal is to find this decomposition of an acceleration vector.

Let $\mathbf{c}(t)$ be a smooth C^2 path (we are going to compute the acceleration, and hence need two derivatives) describing the trajectory of a motion and let $s(t)$ be its arc-length function. Maybe the best way to think about $s(t)$ at this moment is to visualize it with the aid of

$ds/dt =$ rate of change of arc-length with respect to time $=$ speed $= \|\mathbf{c}'(t)\|$.

The velocity of $\mathbf{c}(t)$ is computed to be

$$\mathbf{v}(t) = \mathbf{c}'(t) = \|\mathbf{c}'(t)\| \frac{\mathbf{c}'(t)}{\|\mathbf{c}'(t)\|} = \frac{ds}{dt} \mathbf{T}(t),$$

where $\mathbf{T}(t)$ is the unit tangent vector (we need the smoothness assumption to guarantee that the denominator is non-zero).

Applying the product rule we compute the acceleration vector to be

$$
\begin{aligned}
\mathbf{a}(t) = \frac{d\mathbf{v}(t)}{dt} &= \frac{d}{dt}\left(\frac{ds}{dt}\mathbf{T}(t)\right) \\
&= \frac{d}{dt}\left(\frac{ds}{dt}\right)\mathbf{T}(t) + \frac{ds}{dt}\left(\frac{d}{dt}\mathbf{T}(t)\right) \\
&= \frac{d^2 s}{dt^2}\mathbf{T}(t) + \|\mathbf{c}'(t)\|\,\mathbf{T}'(t).
\end{aligned}
\tag{3.4}
$$

The vector $\mathbf{T}(t)$ is of unit length, hence $\|\mathbf{T}(t)\|^2 = \mathbf{T}(t) \cdot \mathbf{T}(t) = 1$. Differentiating $\mathbf{T}(t) \cdot \mathbf{T}(t) = 1$ with respect to t we get

$$\mathbf{T}'(t) \cdot \mathbf{T}(t) + \mathbf{T}(t) \cdot \mathbf{T}'(t) = 2\mathbf{T}(t) \cdot \mathbf{T}'(t) = 0;$$

i.e., $\mathbf{T}'(t)$ is always perpendicular to $\mathbf{T}(t)$. Consequently, formula (3.4) gives the decomposition of the acceleration vector into the tangential component

$$\mathbf{a}_T = \frac{d^2 s}{dt^2}\mathbf{T}(t)$$

(called the *tangential acceleration*) and the normal (i.e., perpendicular to tangent) component

$$\mathbf{a}_N = \|\mathbf{c}'(t)\|\,\mathbf{T}'(t)$$

(called the *normal acceleration*). With the help of the chain rule we obtain the expression for the normal component in terms of the arc-length parameter: since

$$\mathbf{T}'(t) = \frac{d}{dt}\mathbf{T}(t) = \left(\frac{d}{ds}\mathbf{T}(s)\right)\frac{ds}{dt} = \|\mathbf{c}'(t)\|\frac{d\mathbf{T}(s)}{ds}$$

it follows that

$$\mathbf{a}_N(s) = \|\mathbf{c}'(t)\| \, \mathbf{T}'(t) = \|\mathbf{c}'(t)\|^2 \frac{d\mathbf{T}(s)}{ds}.$$

Example 3.31   Express the acceleration of the motion $\mathbf{c}(t) = 2\cos t\mathbf{i} + \sin t\mathbf{j}$, $t \in [0, 2\pi]$ as the sum of its normal and tangential components.

Solution   The velocity and the acceleration of $\mathbf{c}$ are given by $\mathbf{c}'(t) = -2\sin t\mathbf{i} + \cos t\mathbf{j}$ and $\mathbf{a}(t) = \mathbf{c}''(t) = -2\cos t\mathbf{i} - \sin t\mathbf{j}$. The arc-length function of $\mathbf{c}(t)$ is

$$s(t) = \int_0^t \|\mathbf{c}'(\tau)\| \, d\tau = \int_0^t \sqrt{4\sin^2 \tau + \cos^2 \tau} \, d\tau.$$

and the unit tangent vector is computed to be

$$\mathbf{T}(t) = \frac{\mathbf{c}'(t)}{\|\mathbf{c}'(t)\|} = \frac{-2\sin t}{\sqrt{4\sin^2 t + \cos^2 t}}\mathbf{i} + \frac{\cos t}{\sqrt{4\sin^2 t + \cos^2 t}}\mathbf{j}.$$

Since $ds(t)/dt = \|\mathbf{c}'(t)\| = \sqrt{4\sin^2 t + \cos^2 t}$ it follows that

$$\frac{d^2 s}{dt^2} = \tfrac{1}{2}\left(4\sin^2 t + \cos^2 t\right)^{-1/2}(8\sin t\cos t - 2\cos t\sin t) = \frac{3\sin t\cos t}{\sqrt{4\sin^2 t + \cos^2 t}},$$

and consequently, the tangential component of the acceleration is

$$\mathbf{a}_T = \frac{d^2 s}{dt^2}\mathbf{T}(t) = \frac{3\sin t\cos t}{4\sin^2 t + \cos^2 t}(-2\sin t\mathbf{i} + \cos t\mathbf{j}).$$

The normal component $\mathbf{a}_N$ can be computed from either of the formulas we derived or directly from $\mathbf{a} = \mathbf{a}_T + \mathbf{a}_N$ since $\mathbf{a}$ and $\mathbf{a}_T$ are known. To avoid somewhat messy computation of the derivatives, we choose the second approach:

$$\mathbf{a}_N = \mathbf{a} - \mathbf{a}_T = -2\cos t\mathbf{i} - \sin t\mathbf{j} - \frac{3\sin t\cos t}{4\sin^2 t + \cos^2 t}(-2\sin t\mathbf{i} + \cos t\mathbf{j})$$

$$= \frac{(-8\sin^2 t\cos t - 2\cos^3 t + 6\cos t\sin^2 t)\mathbf{i} + (-4\sin^3 t - \sin t\cos^2 t - 3\cos^2 t\sin t)\mathbf{j}}{4\sin^2 t + \cos^2 t}$$

$$= \frac{-2\cos t(\cos^2 t + \sin^2 t)\mathbf{i} - 4\sin t(\sin^2 t + \cos^2 t)\mathbf{j}}{4\sin^2 t + \cos^2 t}$$

$$= \frac{-2}{4\sin^2 t + \cos^2 t}(\cos t\mathbf{i} + 2\sin t\mathbf{j}). \qquad \blacktriangleleft$$

Example 3.32   The path $\mathbf{c}(t) = (\cos t + t\sin t, -\sin t + t\cos t, t^2/2)$, $t \geq 0$ describes a motion in $\mathbb{R}^3$. Find the normal and the tangential components of the acceleration.

Solution   The velocity, speed, unit tangent vector and acceleration of $\mathbf{c}(t)$ are given by

$$\mathbf{v}(t) = \mathbf{c}'(t) = (t\cos t, -t\sin t, t),$$

$$\|\mathbf{c}'(t)\| = \sqrt{t^2 \cos^2 t + t^2 \sin^2 t + t^2} = \sqrt{2}\,t,$$
$$\mathbf{T}(t) = \mathbf{c}'(t)/\|\mathbf{c}'(t)\| = (\cos t, -\sin t, 1)/\sqrt{2}$$

and

$$\mathbf{a}(t) = \mathbf{c}''(t) = (\cos t - t \sin t, -\sin t - t \cos t, 1).$$

We do not need to compute the arc-length function, but only its derivatives: $ds/dt = \|\mathbf{c}'(t)\| = \sqrt{2}\,t$, and $d^2s/dt^2 = \sqrt{2}$. The acceleration can be written as $\mathbf{a}(t) = \mathbf{a}_T(t) + \mathbf{a}_N(t)$, where

$$\mathbf{a}_T(t) = \frac{d^2 s}{dt^2} \mathbf{T}(t) = (\cos t, -\sin t, 1)$$

and

$$\mathbf{a}_N(t) = \|\mathbf{c}'(t)\| \, \mathbf{T}'(t) = \sqrt{2}\,t \, \frac{(-\sin t, -\cos t, 0)}{\sqrt{2}} = (-t \sin t, -t \cos t, 0). \quad \blacktriangleleft$$

Let us repeat what we have done so far: we have decomposed the acceleration vector $\mathbf{a}(t)$ as the sum $\mathbf{a}(t) = \mathbf{a}_T(t) + \mathbf{a}_N(t)$ of the component $\mathbf{a}_T(t) = (d^2s/dt^2)\mathbf{T}(t)$ in the direction of the motion (the term $d^2s/dt^2 = (d/dt)(ds/dt) = d\|\mathbf{c}'(t)\|/dt$ is the rate of change of the speed) and the component $\mathbf{a}_N(t) = \|\mathbf{c}'(t)\| \, \mathbf{T}'(t)$ perpendicular to the motion ($\mathbf{T}'(t)$ is the rate of change of the unit tangent vector). In words, the tangential component of acceleration corresponds to changes in *speed*. The normal component of acceleration corresponds to changes in the *direction* of motion. We can now fully explain the results of Example 3.30: for motion along the line there is no change in direction and hence the normal component of acceleration is zero. Motion along the circle has constant speed and, consequently, the tangential component of acceleration is zero.

These observations suggest that there is a connection between the acceleration of a moving particle and geometric properties (i.e., the "shape") of the curve representing the particle's trajectory. Our next goal is to investigate this connection.

Since the normal component of acceleration $\mathbf{a}_N$ is related to motion around a circle in Example 3.30, our idea is to find the circle that best approximates a motion at a given point on a curve. To solve this problem, we need the concept of curvature that will enable us to measure how fast a curve changes its direction. It will be defined to be independent of a particular parametrization, in terms of the unit tangent vector $\mathbf{T}$ and the arc-length function s.

■ **Definition 3.10** Curvature.

Let $\mathbf{c}$ be a curve that is the image of a smooth C^2 path in $\mathbb{R}^2$ (or $\mathbb{R}^3$) parametrized by its arc-length s. The *curvature* $\kappa(s)$ of $\mathbf{c}$ at a point $\mathbf{c}(s)$ is given by

$$\kappa(s) = \left\| \frac{d\mathbf{T}(s)}{ds} \right\|,$$

where $\mathbf{T}(s)$ is the unit tangent vector.

In words, $\kappa(s)$ is the magnitude of the rate of change of the unit tangent vector $\mathbf{T}(s)$ (that is, the unit tangent expressed in terms of s) with respect to the arc-length. By definition, $\kappa(s) \geq 0$. The application of the chain rule

$$\frac{d\mathbf{T}(s)}{ds} = \frac{d\mathbf{T}(t)}{dt}\frac{dt}{ds} = \mathbf{T}'(t)\frac{1}{\|\mathbf{c}'(t)\|} = \frac{\mathbf{T}'(t)}{\|\mathbf{c}'(t)\|}$$

gives the formula for the curvature

$$\kappa(t) = \left\|\frac{d\mathbf{T}(s)}{ds}\right\| = \frac{\|\mathbf{T}'(t)\|}{\|\mathbf{c}'(t)\|},$$

in terms of the parameter t instead of s (that is usually easier to use). Looking at this expression, we notice that the assumption about the smoothness of $\mathbf{c}$ is needed to guarantee that the denominator of $\kappa(t)$ is not zero.

Example 3.33   Curvature of a Line.

Compute the curvature of the line $\mathbf{c}(t) = (at, bt)$, where $t \in \mathbb{R}$ and at least one of a or b is non-zero.

Solution   The unit tangent vector is

$$\mathbf{T}(t) = \frac{\mathbf{c}'(t)}{\|\mathbf{c}'(t)\|} = \frac{(a, b)}{\sqrt{a^2 + b^2}}.$$

Since $\mathbf{T}'(t) = \mathbf{0}$, it follows that the curvature of the line is $\kappa(t) = \|\mathbf{T}'(t)\|/\|\mathbf{c}'(t)\| = 0$. This certainly coincides with our intuitive understanding of curvature: as we move along the line, we do not change our direction.   ◄

Example 3.34   Curvature of a Circle.

Compute the curvature of the circle $\mathbf{c}(t) = (a\cos t, a\sin t)$ of radius $a > 0$.

Solution   From $\mathbf{c}'(t) = (-a\sin t, a\cos t)$ we get the speed $\|\mathbf{c}'(t)\| = a$ and the unit tangent vector $\mathbf{T}(t) = \mathbf{c}'(t)/\|\mathbf{c}'(t)\| = (-\sin t, \cos t)$. The arc-length function of the circle is

$$s(t) = \int_0^t \|\mathbf{c}'(\tau)\|\, d\tau = \int_0^t a\, d\tau = at.$$

Hence $t = s/a$, $\mathbf{T}(s) = (-\sin(s/a), \cos(s/a))$, and

$$\kappa(s) = \left\|\frac{d\mathbf{T}(s)}{ds}\right\| = \left\|\left(-\frac{\cos(s/a)}{a}, -\frac{\sin(s/a)}{a}\right)\right\|$$

$$= \left(\frac{1}{a^2}\cos^2(s/a) + \frac{1}{a^2}\sin^2(s/a)\right)^{1/2} = \frac{1}{a}.$$

Alternatively, $\mathbf{T}'(t) = (-\cos t, -\sin t)$ and

$$\kappa(t) = \frac{\|\mathbf{T}'(t)\|}{\|\mathbf{c}'(t)\|} = 1/a.$$

From our computation it follows that the circle has the same curvature at all points (certainly not a surprise), equal to the reciprocal of its radius. Circles of smaller radii are "curved more"; i.e., have larger curvature than big circles (that are "curved less"). Once again, the results correspond to our intuitive understanding of curvature.

◀

Example 3.35 Compute the curvature of the helix

$$\mathbf{c}(t) = a\cos t\mathbf{i} + a\sin t\mathbf{j} + bt\mathbf{k}, \qquad t \geq 0,$$

where $a, b > 0$.

Solution Since $\mathbf{c}'(t) = -a\sin t\mathbf{i} + a\cos t\mathbf{j} + b\mathbf{k}$, it follows that $\|\mathbf{c}'(t)\| = \sqrt{a^2 + b^2}$ and the unit tangent vector is

$$\mathbf{T}(t) = -\frac{a\sin t}{\sqrt{a^2 + b^2}}\mathbf{i} + \frac{a\cos t}{\sqrt{a^2 + b^2}}\mathbf{j} + \frac{b}{\sqrt{a^2 + b^2}}\mathbf{k}.$$

Consequently,

$$\mathbf{T}'(t) = -\frac{a\cos t}{\sqrt{a^2 + b^2}}\mathbf{i} - \frac{a\sin t}{\sqrt{a^2 + b^2}}\mathbf{j},$$

$$\|\mathbf{T}'(t)\| = \sqrt{\frac{a^2\cos^2 t + a^2\sin^2 t}{a^2 + b^2}} = \frac{|a|}{\sqrt{a^2 + b^2}} = \frac{a}{\sqrt{a^2 + b^2}}$$

(since $a > 0$) and the curvature $\kappa(t)$ at the point $\mathbf{c}(t)$ on the helix is

$$\kappa(t) = \frac{\|\mathbf{T}'(t)\|}{\|\mathbf{c}'(t)\|} = \frac{a/\sqrt{a^2 + b^2}}{\sqrt{a^2 + b^2}} = \frac{a}{a^2 + b^2}.$$

It turns out that a helix, like a line or a circle, has constant curvature.

◀

Example 3.36 Compute the curvature of the parabola $y = x^2$.

Solution Parametrize $y = x^2$ as $\mathbf{c}(t) = t\mathbf{i} + t^2\mathbf{j}$. Then $\mathbf{c}'(t) = \mathbf{i} + 2t\mathbf{j}$, $\|\mathbf{c}'(t)\| = \sqrt{1 + 4t^2}$ and the unit tangent vector is

$$\mathbf{T}(t) = \frac{\mathbf{c}'(t)}{\|\mathbf{c}'(t)\|} = \frac{1}{\sqrt{1 + 4t^2}}\mathbf{i} + \frac{2t}{\sqrt{1 + 4t^2}}\mathbf{j}.$$

Its derivative is computed to be

$$\mathbf{T}'(t) = -\frac{4t}{(1 + 4t^2)^{3/2}}\mathbf{i} + \frac{2}{(1 + 4t^2)^{3/2}}\mathbf{j}.$$

Consequently,

$$\|\mathbf{T}'(t)\| = \sqrt{\frac{16t^2 + 4}{(1 + 4t^2)^3}} = \sqrt{\frac{4}{(1 + 4t^2)^2}} = \frac{2}{1 + 4t^2}$$

and

$$\kappa(t) = \frac{\|\mathbf{T}'(t)\|}{\|\mathbf{c}'(t)\|} = \frac{2}{(1 + 4t^2)^{3/2}}.$$

Figure 3.22 shows the graph of the parabola $y = x^2$ and its curvature. Our intuition works again: the parabola is curved most at the vertex $\mathbf{c}(0) = (0, 0)$ (the curvature there is $\kappa(0) = 2$). As we move away from the vertex in either of the two directions, we notice that the parabola becomes curved less and less, so the graph of κ comes closer and closer to the x-axis. As t (or x) approaches $\pm\infty$, the curvature approaches zero. ◄

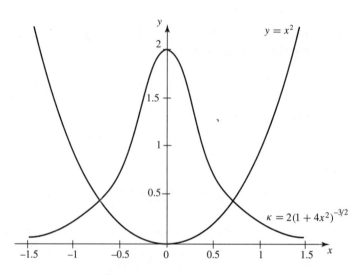

Figure 3.22   The parabola $y = x^2$ and its curvature function.

Let $\mathbf{c}(t)$ be a smooth C^2 path in $\mathbb{R}^2$ (or $\mathbb{R}^3$) and let $\mathbf{T}(t) = \mathbf{c}'(t)/\|\mathbf{c}'(t)\|$ be its unit tangent vector at $\mathbf{c}(t)$. Since $\|\mathbf{T}(t)\| = 1$ it follows that $\mathbf{T}'(t)$ is perpendicular to $\mathbf{T}(t)$ (see the computation immediately following (3.4)). However, $\mathbf{T}'(t)$ might not be of unit length. But if $\mathbf{T}'(t) \neq \mathbf{0}$, we can define the *principal unit normal* (or just *unit normal*) *vector* $\mathbf{N}(t)$ by

$$\mathbf{N}(t) = \frac{\mathbf{T}'(t)}{\|\mathbf{T}'(t)\|}.$$

Example 3.37   Compute the principal unit normal vectors for the circle of Example 3.34 and the helix of Example 3.35.

Solution   In the case of the circle, $\mathbf{T}'(t) = (-\cos t, -\sin t)$ is a unit vector, and hence $\mathbf{N}(t) = \mathbf{T}'(t) = (-\cos t, -\sin t)$. The vector $\mathbf{N}(t)$ is orthogonal to $\mathbf{T}(t)$ and points towards the center of the circle (the origin); see Figure 3.23(a). For the helix, the unit normal $\mathbf{N}(t) = \mathbf{T}'(t)/\|\mathbf{T}'(t)\| = -\cos t\mathbf{i} - \sin t\mathbf{j}$ is the vector pointing towards the z-axis, as shown on Figure 3.23(b). ◄

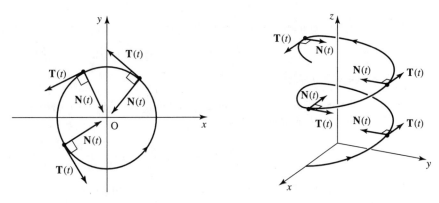

Figure 3.23 Principal unit normal vectors.
(a) to the circle of Example 3.34.

(b) to the helix of Example 3.35.

■ Definition 3.11 Osculating Plane and Osculating Circle.

Let $\mathbf{c}(t)$ be a smooth C^2 path such that $\mathbf{c}''(t) \neq \mathbf{0}$ (recall that smoothness guarantees that $\mathbf{c}'(t) \neq \mathbf{0}$). The plane through $\mathbf{c}(t)$ spanned by the vectors $\mathbf{T}(t)$ and $\mathbf{N}(t)$ is called the *osculating plane* of $\mathbf{c}$ at $\mathbf{c}(t)$. The circle that lies in the osculating plane of $\mathbf{c}$ at $\mathbf{c}(t)$ on the side of $\mathbf{c}(t)$ toward which $\mathbf{N}(t)$ points, that has the point $\mathbf{c}(t)$ in common with the curve, whose tangent at $\mathbf{c}(t)$ is parallel to $\mathbf{c}'(t)$ and whose radius is $1/\kappa(t)$ (where $\kappa(t)$ is the curvature of $\mathbf{c}$ at $\mathbf{c}(t)$) is called the *osculating circle* (or the *circle of curvature*) of $\mathbf{c}$ at $\mathbf{c}(t)$; see Figure 3.24.   ▪

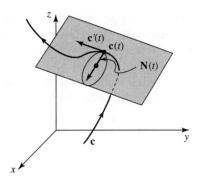

Figure 3.24 Osculating plane and osculating circle.

The osculating plane of a curve in $\mathbb{R}^2$ is $\mathbb{R}^2$. The osculating circle (osculum means "kiss" in Latin), having the same tangent, normal and curvature as the given curve, is the best approximation by a circle to the curve at a point $\mathbf{c}(t)$.

Example 3.38 Find the equation of the osculating plane at the point $\mathbf{c}(\pi) = (-a, 0, b\pi)$ for the helix

$$\mathbf{c}(t) = a \cos t \mathbf{i} + a \sin t \mathbf{j} + bt\mathbf{k}, \qquad t \geq 0,$$

where $a, b > 0$.

Solution   The osculating plane goes through $\mathbf{c}(\pi) = (-a, 0, b\pi)$ and is spanned by the vectors (cf. Examples 3.35 and 3.37)

$$\mathbf{T}(\pi) = -\frac{a}{\sqrt{a^2 + b^2}}\mathbf{j} + \frac{b}{\sqrt{a^2 + b^2}}\mathbf{k}$$

and $\mathbf{N}(\pi) = \mathbf{i}$. The normal vector to the osculating plane is

$$\mathbf{T}(\pi) \times \mathbf{N}(\pi) = \begin{vmatrix} \mathbf{i} & \mathbf{j} & \mathbf{k} \\ 0 & -a/\sqrt{a^2 + b^2} & b/\sqrt{a^2 + b^2} \\ 1 & 0 & 0 \end{vmatrix} = \frac{b}{\sqrt{a^2 + b^2}}\mathbf{j} + \frac{a}{\sqrt{a^2 + b^2}}\mathbf{k},$$

and hence its equation is (recall the equation of the plane defined by a normal vector and a point discussed at the end of Section 1.3)

$$0(x + a) + \frac{b}{\sqrt{a^2 + b^2}}(y - 0) + \frac{a}{\sqrt{a^2 + b^2}}(z - b\pi) = 0,$$

i.e., $by + az - ab\pi = 0$.

◀

Example 3.39 Find the curvature and the osculating circle of the parabola $y = x^2$ at $(0, 0)$.

Solution   All computations that are needed here have been already done in Example 3.36. The osculating circle has radius of $1/\kappa = 1/2$, since the curvature of $y = x^2$ at the origin is $\kappa = 2$. It has to lie above (i.e., "inside") the parabola, since the normal $\mathbf{N}(0) = \mathbf{T}'(0)/\|\mathbf{T}'(0)\| = (0, 1) = \mathbf{j}$ points that way; see Figure 3.25. The center of the osculating circle has to lie on the line normal to the tangent at $(0, 0)$; i.e., on the y-axis. It follows that the equation $x^2 + (y - 1/2)^2 = 1/4$ represents the desired osculating circle.

◀

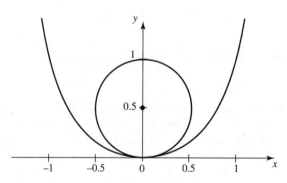

Figure 3.25   The parabola $y = x^2$ and its osculating circle at the origin.

We are now ready to give a geometric interpretation of the normal acceleration $\mathbf{a}_N$. Start with $\mathbf{a}_N = \|\mathbf{c}'(t)\| \, \mathbf{T}'(t)$, and divide and multiply the right side by $\|\mathbf{c}'(t)\| \, \|\mathbf{T}'(t)\|$ to get

$$\mathbf{a}_N = \|\mathbf{c}'(t)\|^2 \frac{\|\mathbf{T}'(t)\|}{\|\mathbf{c}'(t)\|} \frac{\mathbf{T}'(t)}{\|\mathbf{T}'(t)\|}.$$

We recognize the first factor as the square of the speed $\|\mathbf{c}'(t)\| = ds/dt$. The second factor is the curvature $\kappa(t)$, and the third is the principal normal vector. Hence

$$\mathbf{a}_N = \left(\frac{ds}{dt}\right)^2 \kappa(t)\mathbf{N}(t);$$

i.e., the magnitude of the normal component of acceleration is the product of the square of the speed and the curvature.

EXERCISES 3.4

Exercises 1 to 6: Find the tangential and normal components of acceleration for the motion of a particle described by its position vector $\mathbf{c}(t)$.

1. $\mathbf{c}(t) = (t^2, t, t^2)$ **2.** $\mathbf{c}(t) = (e^t, \sqrt{2}t, e^{-t})$

3. $\mathbf{c}(t) = 5t\mathbf{i} + 12\sin t\mathbf{j} + 12\cos t\mathbf{k}$ **4.** $\mathbf{c}(t) = 2t\mathbf{i} + 2\sin^2 t\mathbf{j} - 2\cos^2 t\mathbf{k}$

5. $\mathbf{c}(t) = (t - \sin t)\mathbf{i} + (1 - \cos t)\mathbf{j}$ **6.** $\mathbf{c}(t) = (\cos 3t, \sin 3t, 4t)$

7. Let $\mathbf{c}(t) = (x(t), y(t))$ be a smooth C^2 parametrization of a curve $\mathbf{c}$ in $\mathbb{R}^2$. Show that its curvature can be computed from

$$\kappa(t) = \frac{|x'(t)y''(t) - x''(t)y'(t)|}{((x'(t))^2 + (y'(t))^2)^{3/2}}.$$

8. Using the formula from Exercise 7 find the curvature of the plane curves $\mathbf{c}_1(t) = (t \sin t, t \cos t)$ and $\mathbf{c}_2(t) = (t, t^2)$.

9. Compute the curvature of $\mathbf{c}(t) = (2 - 2t^3, t^3 + 1)$, $t \in \mathbb{R}$. Identify the curve, thus checking your answer.

10. Compute the curvature of $\mathbf{c}(t) = (t, \sin t)$, $t \in \mathbb{R}$, and plot the curve and its curvature function using the same coordinate system. Identify the points (if any) where the curvature is zero and where it is largest.

11. Find the curvature of the plane curve $\mathbf{c}(t) = (t^2, 3 - t)$. Identify the point(s) where the curvature is largest. What happens as $t \to \infty$?

Exercises 12 to 17: For each parametrization, find the unit tangent and the unit normal vector, the curvature and the normal component of acceleration.

12. $\mathbf{c}(t) = (\sin 2t, \cos 2t, 5t)$ **13.** $\mathbf{c}(t) = (e^t \sin t, 0, e^t \cos t)$

14. $\mathbf{c}(t) = (3 + 2t, -t, t - 3)$ **15.** $\mathbf{c}(t) = (t, \cos t, 1 - \sin t)$

16. $\mathbf{c}(t) = (1, 0, t^2/2)$ **17.** $\mathbf{c}(t) = (e^{-t} \cos t, e^{-t} \sin t, e^{-t})$

18. Find equations of the lines tangent and normal to the curve $\mathbf{c}(t) = (t^3/3 - t)\mathbf{i} + t^2\mathbf{j}$ at the point $(0, 3)$.

19. Find an equation of the osculating circle of $\mathbf{c}(t) = t^3\mathbf{i} + t\mathbf{j}$ at the point $(8, 2)$.

20. Find an equation of the osculating plane of the curve $\mathbf{c}(t) = (1/t + 1, 1/t - 1, t)$ at a point $\mathbf{c}(t_0)$, $t_0 \neq 0$.

21. Find an equation of the osculating plane of the helix $\mathbf{c}(t) = (2\cos t, 2\sin t, t)$ at the point $\mathbf{c}(\pi/2)$.

22. Prove that the curvature of the graph of a C^2 function $y = f(x)$ is given by

$$\kappa(x) = \frac{|f''(x)|}{(1 + (f'(x))^2)^{3/2}}.$$

Show that this formula is a special case of formulas in Exercises 7 and 28.

Exercises 23 to 26:   Use the result of Exercise 22 to solve the following problems.

23. Find the curvature of $y = x^2$ at a point (x_0, y_0).

24. Find the curvature of $y = x + \ln x$ at $(1, 1)$. What happens to the curvature as $x \to \infty$?

25. Where does the graph of $y = \ln x$ have maximum curvature?

26. Find the curvature of the graph of $y = \sin x$ at $(\pi/2, 1)$ and at $(\pi, 0)$.

27. Find the equation of the osculating plane of the curve $\mathbf{c}(t) = (t, 1 - t^2, 2t^2)$ at the point $\mathbf{c}(1)$.

28. Prove that the curvature of a smooth C^2 curve $\mathbf{c}(t)$ in $\mathbb{R}^3$ can be computed from

$$\kappa(t) = \frac{\|\mathbf{c}'(t) \times \mathbf{c}''(t)\|}{\|\mathbf{c}'(t)\|^3}.$$

Show that the equation of Exercise 7 is a special case of this formula.

29. Find the equation of the osculating circle of the graph of $y = \sin x$ at $(\pi/2, 1)$.

30. Find the equation of the osculating circle of the graph of $y = e^x$ at $(1, e)$.

3.5   INTRODUCTION TO DIFFERENTIAL GEOMETRY OF CURVES

The material we have covered so far in this chapter shows that a large amount of information can be represented visually as a curve (or algebraically as its parametric representation). This is certainly a good reason to study curves in more depth. In this section we only indicate one possible approach, the so-called differential geometry of curves. In the next section we will relate curves and vector fields by defining a flow line of a vector field, and the concepts relevant to integration along paths will be discussed at the beginning of Chapter 5.

Consider a path $\mathbf{c}$ in $\mathbb{R}^3$. We will construct a coordinate system that "travels along $\mathbf{c}$"; i.e., we will find continuous, mutually orthogonal unit vector fields defined at the points of $\mathbf{c}$. The motion along the curve can then be studied in terms of the changes of those three vectors as the point $\mathbf{c}(t)$ (that is their common initial point) slides along the curve.

Let us clarify one technical point first. We use $\mathbf{c}(t)$ to denote a representation of a curve in terms of a general parameter t and $\mathbf{c}(s)$ to denote the parametrization of $\mathbf{c}$ by its arc-length parameter s (strictly speaking, we should have used two different symbols).

Recall that s is defined in terms of t by

$$s = \int_0^t \|\mathbf{c}'(\tau)\| \, d\tau. \tag{3.5}$$

However, we usually use the equivalent form

$$\frac{ds}{dt} = \|\mathbf{c}'(t)\|;$$

the equivalence is a consequence of the Fundamental Theorem of Calculus. The "prime" ($'$) notation denotes the derivative with respect to the corresponding variable. For example, $\mathbf{c}'(t) = d\mathbf{c}(t)/dt$ and $\mathbf{c}'(s) = d\mathbf{c}(s)/ds$ or $\mathbf{T}'(t) = d\mathbf{T}(t)/dt$ and $\mathbf{T}'(s) = d\mathbf{T}(s)/ds$, etc. To find the formula that relates the two derivatives, we use the chain rule. For example,

$$\mathbf{c}'(t) = \frac{d\mathbf{c}(t)}{dt} = \frac{d\mathbf{c}(s)}{ds}\frac{ds}{dt} = \mathbf{c}'(s) \, \|\mathbf{c}'(t)\|.$$

The part $d\mathbf{c}(t)/dt = (d\mathbf{c}(s)/ds)(ds/dt)$ is a case of the general chain rule sloppiness (as discussed in Section 2.5): the left side is the derivative of $\mathbf{c}(t)$ with respect to t and the first factor on the right side is the derivative of $\mathbf{c}$, now viewed as a function of s, with respect to s.

The above computation shows that the velocity $\mathbf{c}'(s)$ of a path parametrized by its arc-length is always equal to the unit tangent vector (provided that, of course, $\mathbf{c}'(t) \neq \mathbf{0}$); i.e., $\mathbf{c}'(s) = \mathbf{c}'(t)/\|\mathbf{c}'(t)\| = \mathbf{T}(t)$ (the equation $\mathbf{c}'(s) = \mathbf{T}(t)$ actually means that, after replacing s by t (according to the defining identity (3.5)) on the left, or t by s on the right side, the two vectors are the same). One more consequence of our computation: Since $\mathbf{T}(t)$ is of unit length, it follows that $\|\mathbf{c}'(s)\| = 1$; i.e., the speed of a path parametrized by its arc-length parameter is always constant and equal to 1.

Now let us return to our task of finding the three mutually orthogonal unit vectors. Part of the work has been done already: we found the unit tangent vector $\mathbf{T}(t) = \mathbf{c}'(t)/\|\mathbf{c}'(t)\|$ and the principal unit normal vector $\mathbf{N}(t) = \mathbf{T}'(t)/\|\mathbf{T}'(t)\|$. These formulas make sense only if $\mathbf{c}(t)$ is C^2 (to get $\mathbf{T}'$ we need two derivatives of $\mathbf{c}$), smooth (meaning that $\|\mathbf{c}'(t)\| \neq \mathbf{0}$, which implies that $\mathbf{T}(t)$ is defined) and such that $\mathbf{T}'(t) \neq \mathbf{0}$ (so that $\mathbf{N}(t)$ is defined).

Recall that we defined the curvature by $\kappa(s) = \|d\mathbf{T}(s)/ds\|$. It follows that

$$\frac{d\mathbf{T}(s)}{ds} = \|d\mathbf{T}(s)/ds\| \frac{d\mathbf{T}(s)/ds}{\|d\mathbf{T}(s)/ds\|} = \kappa(s)\mathbf{N}(s).$$

The vectors $\mathbf{T}(t)$ and $\mathbf{N}(t)$ define the osculating plane of $\mathbf{c}$ at $\mathbf{c}(t)$. In a neighborhood of $\mathbf{c}(t)$, the curve $\mathbf{c}$ looks like part of the circle (called the osculating circle) of radius equal to the reciprocal of the curvature centered along the line normal to $\mathbf{c}$ at $\mathbf{c}(t)$. The points on the curve that are near $\mathbf{c}(t)$ either lie in the osculating plane or are very close to it.

The properties of the cross product imply that the vector $\mathbf{B}(t) = \mathbf{T}(t) \times \mathbf{N}(t)$ is orthogonal to both the unit tangent vector and the principal unit normal vector and is of unit length. It is called the *binormal vector* to $\mathbf{c}$ at $\mathbf{c}(t)$. The vectors $\mathbf{T}(t)$, $\mathbf{N}(t)$ and $\mathbf{B}(t)$ form the right coordinate system at $\mathbf{c}(t)$ ("right" means that the third unit orthogonal vector is determined by the right-hand rule) that is called the *TNB frame at* $\mathbf{c}(t)$. It is useful to think of a TNB frame as a set of three unit, mutually orthogonal vectors that are locked in their positions. No matter how the frame changes along a curve, their mutual position remains the same; see Figure 3.26.

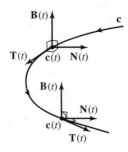

Figure 3.26   TNB frame moving along a curve.

If a curve lies in a plane, its tangent and normal vectors lie in it as well — consequently, the binormal is a *constant* vector: it is a unit vector perpendicular to that plane.

Example 3.40   Find the TNB frame for the helix

$$\mathbf{c}(t) = a\cos t\mathbf{i} + a\sin t\mathbf{j} + bt\mathbf{k}, \qquad t \geq 0,$$

where $a, b > 0$.

Solution   In Example 3.35 we computed the unit tangent vector to be

$$\mathbf{T}(t) = -\frac{a\sin t}{\sqrt{a^2 + b^2}}\mathbf{i} + \frac{a\cos t}{\sqrt{a^2 + b^2}}\mathbf{j} + \frac{b}{\sqrt{a^2 + b^2}}\mathbf{k}.$$

Since

$$\mathbf{T}'(t) = -\frac{a\cos t}{\sqrt{a^2 + b^2}}\mathbf{i} - \frac{a\sin t}{\sqrt{a^2 + b^2}}\mathbf{j}$$

and $\|\mathbf{T}'(t)\| = a/\sqrt{a^2 + b^2}$, it follows that the principal unit normal vector is

$$\mathbf{N}(t) = \frac{\mathbf{T}'(t)}{\|\mathbf{T}'(t)\|} = -\cos t\mathbf{i} - \sin t\mathbf{j}.$$

(see Example 3.37). The binormal vector is the cross product of **T** and **N**:

$$\mathbf{B} = \mathbf{T} \times \mathbf{N} = \begin{vmatrix} \mathbf{i} & \mathbf{j} & \mathbf{k} \\ -a\sin t/\sqrt{a^2+b^2} & a\cos t/\sqrt{a^2+b^2} & b/\sqrt{a^2+b^2} \\ -\cos t & -\sin t & 0 \end{vmatrix}$$

$$= \frac{b\sin t}{\sqrt{a^2+b^2}}\mathbf{i} - \frac{b\cos t}{\sqrt{a^2+b^2}}\mathbf{j} + \frac{a}{\sqrt{a^2+b^2}}\mathbf{k}.$$

The vectors $\mathbf{T}(t)$, $\mathbf{N}(t)$ and $\mathbf{B}(t)$ form the TNB frame at the point $\mathbf{c}(t)$ on the helix.

Now let us investigate how the TNB frame changes along the curve. We already know that

$$\frac{d\mathbf{T}(s)}{ds} = \kappa(s)\mathbf{N}(s), \tag{3.6}$$

where $\kappa(s)$ is the curvature. Geometrically, (3.6) states that the tangent $\mathbf{T}(s)$ turns towards the normal $\mathbf{N}(s)$ at a rate $\kappa(s)$ (since there is no $\mathbf{B}$ component in (3.6), $\mathbf{T}(s)$ changes *only* in the $\mathbf{N}(s)$ direction). Since the mutual position of the three vectors is fixed, if $\mathbf{T}(s)$ turns towards $\mathbf{N}(s)$ at a rate $\kappa(s)$, then $\mathbf{N}(s)$ must turn towards $-\mathbf{T}(s)$ at the same rate.

But $\mathbf{N}(s)$ could also turn towards $\mathbf{B}(s)$ (for example, $\mathbf{N}(s)$ could rotate about the direction of $\mathbf{T}(s)$); see Figure 3.27. Therefore,

$$\frac{d\mathbf{N}(s)}{ds} = -\kappa(s)\mathbf{T}(s) + \tau(s)\mathbf{B}(s), \tag{3.7}$$

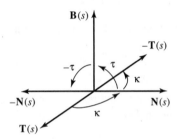

Figure 3.27 Changes of vectors in the TNB frame.

where the scalar $\tau(s)$ is called the *torsion* of the curve. Since $\mathbf{N}(s)$ turns towards $\mathbf{B}(s)$ at a rate $\tau(s)$, $\mathbf{B}(s)$ has to turn at the same rate towards $-\mathbf{N}(s)$. $\mathbf{B}(s)$ cannot turn towards $\mathbf{T}(s)$, since then $\mathbf{T}(s)$ would have to turn towards $-\mathbf{B}(s)$ (but $d\mathbf{T}(s)/ds = \kappa(s)\mathbf{N}(s)$ means that $\mathbf{T}(s)$ turns *only* towards $\mathbf{N}(s)$). It follows that

$$\frac{d\mathbf{B}(s)}{ds} = -\tau(s)\mathbf{N}(s). \tag{3.8}$$

The formulas (3.6), (3.7) and (3.8) are called the *Serret-Frenet formulas* and describe the way the TNB frame changes along a curve.

Computing the dot product of (3.8) with $\mathbf{N}(s)$ (remember that $\mathbf{N}$ is of unit length) we get a formula

$$\tau(s) = -\mathbf{N}(s) \cdot \frac{d\mathbf{B}(s)}{ds}$$

for the torsion. Computing the norms of both sides in (3.8) we get

$$\left\| \frac{d\mathbf{B}(s)}{ds} \right\| = |-\tau(s)| \, \|\mathbf{N}(s)\| = |\tau(s)|,$$

i.e., $\tau(s) = \pm\|d\mathbf{B}(s)/ds\|$.

Example 3.41   Compute the torsion of a plane curve.

Solution   By construction, both $\mathbf{T}$ and $\mathbf{N}$ belong to the plane of the curve. Consequently, the binormal $\mathbf{B}$ is a constant vector (always unit and perpendicular to the plane) and therefore $\tau(s) = \pm \|d\mathbf{B}(s)/ds\| = 0$.

◄

If the binormal vector starts changing, it will force the curve out of the plane; in other words, the torsion (that is, the rate of change of the binormal) measures how fast the curve moves away from its osculating plane.

Example 3.42   Compute the curvature and the torsion of the helix

$$\mathbf{c}(t) = a\cos t\,\mathbf{i} + a\sin t\,\mathbf{j} + bt\,\mathbf{k}, \qquad t \geq 0,$$

$a, b > 0$, from the Serret-Frenet formulas (3.6) and (3.8). Using the results obtained, check the second Serret-Frenet formula (3.7).

Solution   The arc-length parameter of the helix is computed to be

$$s(t) = \int_0^t \|\mathbf{c}'(\tau)\|d\tau = \int_0^t \sqrt{(-a\sin\tau)^2 + (a\cos\tau)^2 + b^2}\, d\tau = \sqrt{a^2 + b^2}\, t.$$

Using $t = s/\sqrt{a^2 + b^2}$, we now express the unit tangent vector, the principal unit normal vector and the binormal vector from Example 3.40 as

$$\mathbf{T}(s) = -\frac{a}{\sqrt{a^2 + b^2}}\sin(s/\sqrt{a^2 + b^2})\mathbf{i} + \frac{a}{\sqrt{a^2 + b^2}}\cos(s/\sqrt{a^2 + b^2})\mathbf{j} + \frac{b}{\sqrt{a^2 + b^2}}\mathbf{k},$$

$$\mathbf{N}(s) = -\cos(s/\sqrt{a^2 + b^2})\mathbf{i} - \sin(s/\sqrt{a^2 + b^2})\mathbf{j},$$

and

$$\mathbf{B}(s) = \frac{b}{\sqrt{a^2 + b^2}}\sin(s/\sqrt{a^2 + b^2})\mathbf{i} - \frac{b}{\sqrt{a^2 + b^2}}\cos(s/\sqrt{a^2 + b^2})\mathbf{j} + \frac{a}{\sqrt{a^2 + b^2}}\mathbf{k}.$$

According to the first Serret-Frenet formula (3.6), the rate of change of the unit tangent vector

$$\frac{d\mathbf{T}(s)}{ds} = -\frac{a}{\sqrt{a^2 + b^2}}\frac{1}{\sqrt{a^2 + b^2}}\cos(s/\sqrt{a^2 + b^2})\mathbf{i}$$

$$-\frac{a}{\sqrt{a^2 + b^2}}\frac{1}{\sqrt{a^2 + b^2}}\sin(s/\sqrt{a^2 + b^2})\mathbf{j}$$

is equal to $\kappa(s)\mathbf{N}(s)$, where $\kappa(s)$ is the curvature. Since

$$\frac{d\mathbf{T}(s)}{ds} = \frac{a}{a^2 + b^2}(-\cos(s/\sqrt{a^2 + b^2})\mathbf{i} - \sin(s/\sqrt{a^2 + b^2})\mathbf{j}) = \frac{a}{a^2 + b^2}\mathbf{N}(s),$$

it follows that $\kappa(s) = a/(a^2 + b^2)$ (in Example 3.35 in the previous section we obtained the same result using the definition of curvature). The third Serret-Frenet formula (3.8) states that the rate of change of the binormal

$$\frac{d\mathbf{B}(s)}{ds} = \frac{b}{\sqrt{a^2 + b^2}} \frac{1}{\sqrt{a^2 + b^2}} \cos(s/\sqrt{a^2 + b^2})\mathbf{i}$$

$$+ \frac{b}{\sqrt{a^2 + b^2}} \frac{1}{\sqrt{a^2 + b^2}} \sin(s/\sqrt{a^2 + b^2})\mathbf{j}$$

is equal to $-\tau(s)\mathbf{N}(s)$, where $\tau(s)$ is the torsion. Since

$$\frac{d\mathbf{B}(s)}{ds} = -\frac{b}{a^2 + b^2}(-\cos(s/\sqrt{a^2 + b^2})\mathbf{i} - \sin(s/\sqrt{a^2 + b^2})\mathbf{j})$$

it follows that $\tau(s) = b/(a^2 + b^2)$.

The left side in (3.7) is computed to be

$$\frac{d\mathbf{N}(s)}{ds} = \frac{1}{\sqrt{a^2 + b^2}} \sin(s/\sqrt{a^2 + b^2})\mathbf{i} - \frac{1}{\sqrt{a^2 + b^2}} \cos(s/\sqrt{a^2 + b^2})\mathbf{j}.$$

The right side

$$-\kappa(s)\mathbf{T}(s) + \tau(s)\mathbf{B}(s) = -\frac{a}{a^2 + b^2}\left(-\frac{a}{\sqrt{a^2 + b^2}} \sin(s/\sqrt{a^2 + b^2})\mathbf{i}\right.$$

$$\left. + \frac{a}{\sqrt{a^2 + b^2}} \cos(s/\sqrt{a^2 + b^2})\mathbf{j} + \frac{b}{\sqrt{a^2 + b^2}}\mathbf{k}\right)$$

$$+ \frac{b}{a^2 + b^2}\left(\frac{b}{\sqrt{a^2 + b^2}} \sin(s/\sqrt{a^2 + b^2})\mathbf{i}\right.$$

$$\left. - \frac{b}{\sqrt{a^2 + b^2}} \cos(s/\sqrt{a^2 + b^2})\mathbf{j} + \frac{a}{\sqrt{a^2 + b^2}}\mathbf{k}\right)$$

$$= \left(\frac{a^2}{(a^2 + b^2)^{3/2}} + \frac{b^2}{(a^2 + b^2)^{3/2}}\right) \sin(s/\sqrt{a^2 + b^2})\mathbf{i}$$

$$- \left(\frac{a^2}{(a^2 + b^2)^{3/2}} + \frac{b^2}{(a^2 + b^2)^{3/2}}\right) \cos(s/\sqrt{a^2 + b^2})\mathbf{j}$$

$$= \frac{1}{\sqrt{a^2 + b^2}} \sin(s/\sqrt{a^2 + b^2})\mathbf{i} - \frac{1}{\sqrt{a^2 + b^2}} \cos(s/\sqrt{a^2 + b^2})\mathbf{j}$$

is equal to $d\mathbf{N}(s)/ds$, as predicted by the Serret-Frenet formula (3.7). ◀

XERCISES 3.5

1. Find formulas for the following quantities: $d(\mathbf{T}(s)\cdot\mathbf{T}(s))/ds$, $(d\mathbf{c}(t)/dt)\cdot\mathbf{T}(t)$ and $d\mathbf{N}(s)/ds\cdot$ $\mathbf{B}(s)$.

2. Show that the curve $\mathbf{c}(t) = (a\cos t, a\sin t, \sin t + \cos t + b)$, where a and b are any constants, is a plane curve.

3. Is it true that the acceleration of a particle moving along a path in $\mathbb{R}^3$ is always perpendicular to the binormal vector? Explain.

Exercises 4 to 7: Find the TNB frame.

4. $\mathbf{c}(t) = (e^t, 2e^t, 0)$, at $t = 1$

5. $\mathbf{c}(t) = e^t \cos t\mathbf{i} + e^t \sin t\mathbf{k}$, at $t = \pi/2$

6. $\mathbf{c}(t) = (t \sin t, t \cos t, t)$, for any t

7. $\mathbf{c}(t) = (\sin t, \sin t, \sqrt{2} \cos t)$, for any t

8. Using the fact that the binormal vector $\mathbf{B}$ is of unit length and orthogonal to $\mathbf{T}$, show that $d\mathbf{B}/ds$ is parallel to $\mathbf{N}$ (s, as usual, denotes the arc-length parameter).

9. Show that $d\mathbf{N}/ds + \kappa\mathbf{T}$ is perpendicular to both $\mathbf{T}$ and $\mathbf{N}$, without using formula (3.7). Explain how one can use this fact to define the torsion of a curve.

10. By differentiating $\mathbf{B} = \mathbf{T} \times \mathbf{N}$ prove the third Serret-Frenet formula (3.8).

Exercises 11 to 14: Let $\mathbf{c}$ be a smooth C^2 curve (C^3 for Exercise 14) in $\mathbb{R}^3$. Use the Serret-Frenet formulas to prove the following results.

11. $\mathbf{c}''(t) = \dfrac{d^2s}{dt^2}\mathbf{T}(t) + \kappa(t)\left(\dfrac{ds}{dt}\right)^2 \mathbf{N}(t)$

12. Show that if $\|\mathbf{c}(t)\| = 1$, then $\mathbf{c}(t) = -\dfrac{1}{\kappa}\mathbf{N} - \dfrac{1}{\tau}\left(\dfrac{d\kappa^{-1}}{ds}\right)\mathbf{B}$. (Hint: start by differentiating $\mathbf{c}(t) \cdot \mathbf{c}(t) = 1$.)

13. $\mathbf{c}'(t) \times \mathbf{c}''(t) = \kappa(t)\left(\dfrac{ds}{dt}\right)^3 \mathbf{B}(t)$

14. $\tau(t) = \dfrac{(\mathbf{c}'(t) \times \mathbf{c}''(t)) \cdot \mathbf{c}'''(t)}{\|\mathbf{c}'(t) \times \mathbf{c}''(t)\|^2}$

15. Using Exercise 14 find the torsion of the helix $\mathbf{c}(t) = a \cos t\mathbf{i} + a \sin t\mathbf{j} + bt\mathbf{k}$, $t \geq 0$, $a, b > 0$.

16. Show that the curve $\mathbf{c}(t) = (1 + 1/t, -t + 1/t, t)$, $t > 0$, lies in a plane.

17. Find the curvature and torsion of $\mathbf{c}(t) = at^2\mathbf{i} + 2at\mathbf{j}$, where $a > 0$ and $t \in \mathbb{R}$. At what point(s) on $\mathbf{c}(t)$ does the curvature attain its maximum?

18. Find the TNB frame for the curve $\mathbf{c}(t) = (3t - t^3)\mathbf{i} + 3t^2\mathbf{j} + (3t + t^3)\mathbf{k}$ at the point $\mathbf{c}(0)$.

19. Compute the curvature and the torsion of the curve $\mathbf{c}(t) = (t + \cos t, t - \sin t, t)$ in $\mathbb{R}^3$.

3.6   FLOW LINES

Assume that the motion of a fluid is described by a vector field $\mathbf{F}$ (i.e., the value of $\mathbf{F}$ at a point gives the velocity of the fluid at that point). One way of visualizing $\mathbf{F}$ is to isolate a point in the fluid and follow its trajectory under the influence of the field. The path thus obtained is called a flow line.

A familiarity with basic concepts in the theory of ordinary differential equations is needed in this section.

■ **Definition 3.12**   Flow Lines of a Vector Field.

Let $\mathbf{F}(x, y)$ (respectively, $\mathbf{F}(x, y, z)$) be a continuous vector field defined on a subset U

of $\mathbb{R}^2$ (respectively, $\mathbb{R}^3$). A *flow line* of **F** is a path **c**(t) in $\mathbb{R}^2$ (respectively, $\mathbb{R}^3$) such that

$$\mathbf{c}'(t) = \mathbf{F}(\mathbf{c}(t)).$$

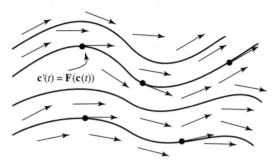

Figure 3.28 Flow lines of a vector field.

Let us emphasize that the definition requires that the vector field be independent of time. (Vector fields that also depend on time are dealt with in more advanced texts.) Of course, values of **F** may change from point to point, but the value of **F** at a particular point is the same for all times. For example, a vector field that describes the motion of the wind depends on time: at this moment, a vector **v** at a particular location P might point north, indicating a northerly wind. A moment later, the wind could change its intensity or direction at P, and can no longer be described by **v**.

A flow line is also called an *integral curve,* a *streamline* or a *line of force.* By definition, **c**(t) is a flow line of a vector field **F** if its velocity vector **c**$'(t)$ at **c**(t) coincides with the value $\mathbf{F}(\mathbf{c}(t))$ of the field **F** at the point **c**(t) on the curve; see Figure 3.28. Now pick a point P in the domain of a vector field **F**. Let us trace a flow line of **F** that goes through P. The only way to leave P is in the direction of the vector $\mathbf{F}(P)$ (that is the value of the field **F** at P); see Figure 3.29. Once we move to a nearby point, say Q, we find another vector, $\mathbf{F}(Q)$, that tells us how to proceed. A moment later, arriving at a nearby point R, we proceed in the direction of $\mathbf{F}(R)$, etc. It follows that once we choose a starting point, our walk is completely determined by **F**.

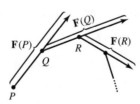

Figure 3.29 Tracing a flow line from P.

This intuitive argument shows that a flow line is uniquely determined by a vector field and one point. In other words, distinct flow lines cannot intersect or touch each other. Here is the outline of a proof: suppose that two flow lines have a point P in common. By uniqueness, from P "onward" (i.e., in the direction of the vector field $\mathbf{F}$) the two flow lines have to agree. Since the flow lines of $-\mathbf{F}$ are the flow lines of $\mathbf{F}$ with reversed orientation (see Exercise 11), by uniqueness again, the remaining parts of the flow lines have to overlap.

Imagine that a vector field $\mathbf{F}$ describes the motion of a fluid. The flow line through a given point $\mathbf{x}_0$ describes the trajectory of a particle (located initially at $\mathbf{x}_0$) participating in the motion of the fluid. Figure 3.30 shows several flow lines of the vector field $\mathbf{F} = (x, 2y)$ in $\mathbb{R}^2$.

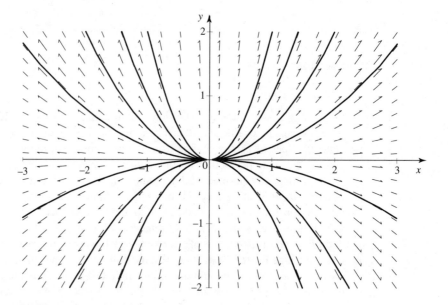

Figure 3.30   Several flow lines of $\mathbf{F} = (x, 2y)$.

Let $\mathbf{c}(t) = (x(t), y(t), z(t))$ be a differentiable curve in $\mathbb{R}^3$ and let

$$\mathbf{F}(x, y, z) = (F_1(x, y, z), F_2(x, y, z), F_3(x, y, z))$$

be a vector field in $\mathbb{R}^3$. The equation $\mathbf{c}'(t) = \mathbf{F}(\mathbf{c}(t))$ or

$$(x'(t), y'(t), z'(t)) = (F_1(x(t), y(t), z(t)), F_2(x(t), y(t), z(t)), F_3(x(t), y(t), z(t)))$$

of the flow line $\mathbf{F}$ going through the point (x_0, y_0, z_0) can be written as the system of ordinary differential equations

$$x'(t) = F_1(x(t), y(t), z(t))$$
$$y'(t) = F_2(x(t), y(t), z(t))$$
$$z'(t) = F_3(x(t), y(t), z(t)),$$

with the initial condition

$$\mathbf{c}(0) = (x(0), y(0), z(0)) = (x_0, y_0, z_0).$$

From the theory of ordinary differential equations (more precisely, from the Existence and Uniqueness Theorem for systems of equations) it follows that continuous vector fields always have flow lines, and they are uniquely determined once a particular point has been specified (this argument formalizes our intuitive argument presented earlier).

Example 3.43 Find the flow lines of the vector field $\mathbf{F}(x, y) = (y, -x)$ on $\mathbb{R}^2$ going through points $(1, 0)$ and $(3, -1)$.

Solution Let $\mathbf{c}(t) = (x(t), y(t))$ be a flow line. By definition,

$$(x'(t), y'(t)) = (y(t), -x(t))$$

and hence (dropping t for simplicity)

$$x' = y \quad \text{and} \quad y' = -x.$$

Differentiating the first equation and substituting y' from the second we get $x'' + x = 0$. The characteristic equation is $\lambda^2 + 1 = 0$; thus $\lambda = \pm i$, and the solution is

$$x(t) = C_1 \cos t + C_2 \sin t,$$

where C_1 and C_2 are constants. Now use $y = x'$ to obtain

$$y(t) = -C_1 \sin t + C_2 \cos t.$$

Substituting $t = 0$, $x(0) = 1$ and $y(0) = 0$ we get $C_1 = 1$ and $C_2 = 0$, so that the equation of the flow line through $(1, 0)$ is

$$\mathbf{c}_1(t) = (\cos t, -\sin t),$$

which is a circle of unit radius traced clockwise.

Similarly, we obtain

$$\mathbf{c}_2(t) = (3 \cos t - \sin t, -3 \sin t - \cos t),$$

as the flow line of $\mathbf{F}$ through $(3, -1)$. It is a circle (in Cartesian coordinates $x^2 + y^2 = 10$) of radius $\sqrt{10}$. The two flow lines are shown in Figure 3.31.

◀

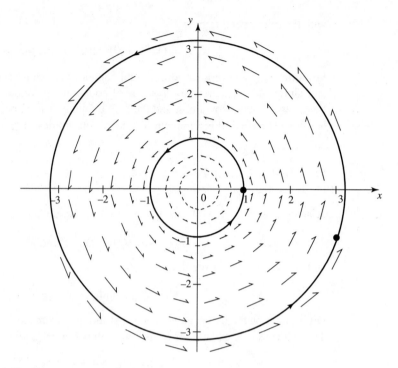

Figure 3.31   Flow lines of $\mathbf{F}(x, y) = (y, -x)$ from Example 3.43.

Example 3.44   Show that the curves

$$\mathbf{c}(t) = \left(\frac{C_1 \cos t + C_2 \sin t}{\sqrt{C_1^2 + C_2^2}}, \frac{-C_1 \sin t + C_2 \cos t}{\sqrt{C_1^2 + C_2^2}} \right)$$

(where C_1 and C_2 are constants) are flow lines of the vector field

$$\mathbf{F} = \left(\frac{y}{\sqrt{x^2 + y^2}}, -\frac{x}{\sqrt{x^2 + y^2}} \right).$$

Solution   We have to show that $\mathbf{c}'(t) = \mathbf{F}(\mathbf{c}(t))$. Since

$$x^2 + y^2 = \frac{(C_1 \cos t + C_2 \sin t)^2}{C_1^2 + C_2^2} + \frac{(-C_1 \sin t + C_2 \cos t)^2}{C_1^2 + C_2^2} = 1$$

it follows that

$$\mathbf{F}(\mathbf{c}(t)) = \left(\frac{-C_1 \sin t + C_2 \cos t}{\sqrt{C_1^2 + C_2^2}}, \frac{-C_1 \cos t - C_2 \sin t}{\sqrt{C_1^2 + C_2^2}} \right).$$

On the other hand, the tangent vector is computed to be

$$\mathbf{c}'(t) = \left(\frac{-C_1 \sin t + C_2 \cos t}{\sqrt{C_1^2 + C_2^2}}, \frac{-C_1 \cos t - C_2 \sin t}{\sqrt{C_1^2 + C_2^2}} \right).$$

Examples 3.43 and 3.44 show that different vector fields can have the same flow lines. In both cases the flow lines are circles (with one difference: the flow line in Example 3.43 going through the origin consists of a single point (origin), but there is no flow line of the vector field in Example 3.44 that contains the origin).

Example 3.45   **Flow Lines of an Electrostatic Field.**

Consider the electrostatic field $\mathbf{F}$ on $\mathbb{R}^2 - \{(0, 0)\}$ given by

$$\mathbf{F}(x, y) = \frac{1}{4\pi \epsilon_0} \frac{Qq}{\|\mathbf{r}\|^3} \mathbf{r} = \left(\frac{1}{4\pi \epsilon_0} \frac{Qq}{\|\mathbf{r}\|^3} x, \frac{1}{4\pi \epsilon_0} \frac{Qq}{\|\mathbf{r}\|^3} y \right)$$

(see Section 2.1), where $\mathbf{r} = x\mathbf{i} + y\mathbf{j}$. To find the flow lines of $\mathbf{F}$ we have to solve the system $(x', y') = \mathbf{F}(x, y)$, i.e.,

$$x' = \frac{K}{\|\mathbf{r}\|^3} x,$$

$$y' = \frac{K}{\|\mathbf{r}\|^3} y,$$

where $K = Qq/4\pi \epsilon_0$. Dividing the second equation by the first and simplifying we get (keep in mind that $y' = dy/dt$ and $x' = dx/dt$)

$$\frac{y'}{y} = \frac{x'}{x},$$

and $(\ln y)' = (\ln x)'$. Integration gives $C_1 y = C_2 x$, where C_1 and C_2 are constants, which is the equation of a line through the origin (where the charge Q has been placed). Hence the flow lines of this electrostatic field in the plane are straight lines through the origin.

EXERCISES 3.6

1. Find the flow lines of the vector field $\mathbf{F}(x, y) = (x, 2y)$. Compare with the flow lines of the vector fields $\mathbf{F}_1(x, y) = (3x, 6y)$ and $\mathbf{F}_2(x, y) = (-2x, -4y)$.

2. Show that the curve $\mathbf{c}(t) = \left(\frac{3}{5} \cos t + \frac{4}{5} \sin t \right)\mathbf{i} + \left(-\frac{3}{5} \sin t + \frac{4}{5} \cos t \right)\mathbf{j}$ is the flow line of the vector field $\mathbf{F}(x, y) = y\mathbf{i}/\sqrt{x^2 + y^2} - x\mathbf{j}/\sqrt{x^2 + y^2}$ going through the point $(4/5, -3/5)$.

3. Find the flow line of the vector field $\mathbf{F}(x, y) = 2\|\mathbf{r}\|^{-1}\mathbf{r}$ (where $\mathbf{r} = x\mathbf{i} + y\mathbf{j}$) going through the point $(3, 2)$.

Exercises 4 to 8:   Sketch the vector field $\mathbf{F}$ and several of its flow lines.

4. $\mathbf{F}(x, y) = y\mathbf{i} - 2x\mathbf{j}$ 5. $\mathbf{F}(x, y) = (x, x^2)$

6. $\mathbf{F}(x, y) = x\mathbf{i} + \mathbf{j}$ 7. $\mathbf{F}(x, y) = (-2x, y)$

8. $\mathbf{F}(x, y) = \sin x\,\mathbf{i} + \mathbf{j}$

9. Find a vector field for which the curve $\mathbf{c}(t) = (t^2, 2t, t)$, $t \in \mathbb{R}$ is a flow line.

10. Show that the curve $\mathbf{c}(t) = (e^t, 2\ln t, t^{-1})$, $t > 0$ is a flow line of the vector field $\mathbf{F}(x, y, z) = (x, 2z, -z^2)$.

11. Assume that $\mathbf{c}(t)$, $t \in [a, b]$, is a flow line of $\mathbf{F}$. Show that $\boldsymbol{\gamma}(t) = \mathbf{c}(a + b - t)$, $t \in [a, b]$, is a flow line of $-\mathbf{F}$. Interpret this fact geometrically.

CHAPTER REVIEW

Review Questions

Answer/discuss the following questions:

1. Define a path and a curve and describe the difference. Define a continuous path and a continuous curve. Is it possible for a continuous curve to have a discontinuous parametrization? Define a differentiable path and a differentiable curve. Write down a parametric representation of the line $y = 0$ that is not differentiable.

2. Describe the relationship between the position, velocity and acceleration vectors of a motion along a circle with constant speed. Write down a parametrization of the circle $x^2 + y^2 = 1$ with non-constant speed. Is the relation between the position, velocity and acceleration vectors the same as in the constant-speed case?

3. Describe the geometric meaning of the derivative $D\mathbf{F}$ of a function $\mathbf{F}: \mathbb{R}^2 \to \mathbb{R}^2$. If two curves $\mathbf{c}_1(t)$ and $\mathbf{c}_2(t)$ intersect at the angle θ, is it true that their images under $\mathbf{F}$ intersect at the same angle? (If false, provide a counterexample.)

4. Let $\mathbf{c}(t)$ be a continuous path. Define the arc-length parameter s and consider the parametrization $\mathbf{c}(s)$ of $\mathbf{c}$ by its arc-length parameter. Explain the geometric/physical meaning of $ds/dt = \|\mathbf{c}'(t)\|$. Using the chain rule show that $\|\mathbf{c}'(s)\| = 1$ and give a physical interpretation.

5. Define the unit tangent vector, the principal unit normal vector and the binormal vector. Define the curvature and the torsion of a curve. Explain the relationship between curvature and acceleration. Why do we use the arc-length parameter instead of a general parameter t in *defining* the curvature and torsion?

Computer Projects

1. **Curvature and Torsion.**
   Consider the ellipse $x^2 + y^2/4 = 1$ in the xy-plane.

   (a) Compute its curvature and torsion.

   (b) Plot the curvature function. Where is it largest? smallest?

   (c) Find the equation of the osculating circle at $(1, 0)$.

2. The Brachistochrone Problem.

The *Brachistochrone* problem can be stated as follows: given two points, A, and a lower point B (that is not directly below A), find the curve joining A and B along which a particle will slide in the shortest time, under the influence of gravity only. We will not attempt to solve the problem, but will rather compute times along different curves and compare them.

Given a parametrization $\mathbf{c}(t)$, $t \in [a, b]$ of a curve (such that $\mathbf{c}(a) = A$ and $\mathbf{c}(b) = B$) the time needed for the particle to slide from A to B is given by

$$T = \frac{1}{\sqrt{2g}} \int_a^b \sqrt{\frac{(x'(t))^2 + (y'(t))^2}{y}}\, dt.$$

Use a coordinate system in which the y-axis points downward, and let $A(0, 0)$ and $B(1, 1)$. Consider the following paths.

(a) $\mathbf{c}_1(t) = (t, t)$, $t \in [0, 1]$

(b) $\mathbf{c}_2(t) = ((t - \sin t)/\pi, (1 - \cos t)/2)$, $t \in [0, \pi]$

(c) $\mathbf{c}_3(t) = (\sin t + 1, \cos t)$, $t \in [3\pi/2, 2\pi]$

(d) $\mathbf{c}_4(t) = (t, \sin(\pi t/2))$, $t \in [0, 1]$.

Check that all parametrizations give curves with initial point $A(0, 0)$ and terminal point $B(1, 1)$. Compute the lengths of the paths in (a) – (d). Plot all curves and compute T for each of them. Which one is the "fastest"?

3. "Smooth" Flight.

Suppose that an airplane flies along a straight line at a constant speed and then, at the point P, starts turning, continuing its motion along a circle of radius a towards Q and R, as shown in Figure 3.32. Due to the sudden change in curvature (and hence the acceleration) at P (from 0 to $1/a$), the passengers will experience a "jerk" at the point P. We are going to fix this problem, by suggesting a possible trajectory that will connect P and Q, and then continue along the circle towards R, but with the property that the curvature changes continuously from 0 at P to $1/a$ at Q.

(a) Assume that $\mathbf{c}(t) = (a_1 t^3 + b_1 t^2 + c_1 t + d_1, a_2 t^3 + b_2 t^2 + c_2 t + d_2)$ is such a curve. Find the 8 unknown coefficients from the following requirements: $\mathbf{c}(t)$ has to go through P and Q, has to have the slope 0 at P and a vertical tangent line at Q, and has to satisfy the curvature requirements.

(b) Plot both the initial trajectory and your suggestion.

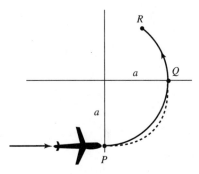

Figure 3.32   The path of the airplane in Project 3.

Further Explorations

1. Find a vector $\mathbf{W}$ such that the Serret-Frenet formulas can be written as $d\mathbf{T}/ds = \mathbf{W} \times \mathbf{T}$, $d\mathbf{N}/ds = \mathbf{W} \times \mathbf{N}$ and $d\mathbf{B}/ds = \mathbf{W} \times \mathbf{B}$.

2. Sometimes the parameter t can be eliminated from the parametric equation $\mathbf{c}(t) = (x(t), y(t))$ and an equation of the form $f(x, y) = 0$ is obtained (for example, $\mathbf{c}(t) = (\cos t, \sin t)$ gives $x^2 + y^2 = 1$ after the elimination of t). Express dy/dx and d^2y/dx^2 in terms of the derivatives of x and y with respect to t.

3. Let $\mathbf{c}$ be a plane curve and let θ be the angle between the tangent to $\mathbf{c}$ at $\mathbf{c}(t)$ and the positive x-axis. Show that the curvature of $\mathbf{c}$ is equal to $|d\theta/ds|$, where s is the arc-length parameter of $\mathbf{c}$.

4. Fix a point P on the circumference of a circle of radius r that is placed so that it touches the x-axis. The curve traced out by P as the circle rolls along the x-axis is called a *cycloid*. Find its parametric representation (use the angle of rotation of the circle as a parameter).

5. Show that if a particle is acted on by the radial force $\mathbf{F} = (f(r)\cos\theta, f(r)\sin\theta)$, where $r = r(t)$ and $\theta = \theta(t)$, then $r^2(d\theta/dt)$ is constant in time.

6. Assume that a curve $\mathbf{c}(s)$ is parametrized by its arc-length.

   (a) Show that $\mathbf{c}'''(s) = -\kappa^2(s)\mathbf{T}(s) + \kappa'(s)\mathbf{N}(s) + \tau(s)\kappa(s)\mathbf{B}(s)$.

   (b) Prove that the scalar triple product $\mathbf{c}'(s) \cdot (\mathbf{c}''(s) \times \mathbf{c}'''(s))$ is equal to $\kappa^2(s)\tau(s)$.

7. Where does the graph of $y = e^{2x}$ have maximum curvature?

8. A particle moves along the trajectory $\mathbf{r}(t) = (\sin 3t, \cos 3t, 2t^{3/2})$, where $0 \le t \le \pi$.

   (a) Show that $\mathbf{r}(t)$ lies on the surface of a cylinder of radius 1.

   (b) Sketch the curve $\mathbf{r}(t)$.

   (c) Find the velocity and speed of the particle.

   (d) Find the distance travelled by the particle from $t = 0$ to $t = \pi$.

   (e) Suppose that the particle flies off the given trajectory at $t = \pi$ and continues its motion, subject only to a constant gravitational force directed along the (negative) z-axis. Find its position π (units of time) later.

9. A particle moves in $\mathbb{R}^3$ along the path $\mathbf{c}(t) = (e^t \cos t, e^t \sin t, e^t)$. Compute its velocity. Does the particle travel with constant speed? Is the magnitude of its acceleration constant?

Chapter 4

SCALAR AND VECTOR FIELDS

A vector field is a function that assigns a vector to a point in a plane or in space. In the spirit of this interpretation, a scalar field can be described as an assignment of a scalar to a point in a plane or in space (we have been calling such assignments real-valued functions).

With the help of partial derivatives we will develop tools (so-called vector differential operators) that are instrumental in investigating properties of scalar and vector fields.

The gradient operator is used to describe rates of change of scalar functions, and the divergence and curl operators are employed in the investigation of rates of change of vector fields. We will discuss the properties of these operators and give various interpretations and applications in a number of physical situations.

The last section introduces differential forms, the importance of which will be understood best in the context of vector integral theorems in the last chapter.

4.1 GRADIENTS AND DIRECTIONAL DERIVATIVES

In this section we use gradient vector fields to investigate rates of change of real-valued functions of several variables. We will be able to obtain valuable information that will give us a deeper understanding of the behavior and properties of real-valued functions.

The derivative Df of a differentiable real-valued function f of m variables $x_1, \ldots x_m$ is a $1 \times m$ matrix

$$Df(\mathbf{x}) = \left[\frac{\partial f}{\partial x_1}(\mathbf{x}) \quad \frac{\partial f}{\partial x_2}(\mathbf{x}) \quad \ldots \quad \frac{\partial f}{\partial x_m}(\mathbf{x}) \right].$$

This matrix, interpreted as a vector in $\mathbb{R}^m$, is called the gradient of f at $\mathbf{x}$.

Definition 4.1   Gradient of a Function.

Let $f: U \subseteq \mathbb{R}^2 \to \mathbb{R}$ be a differentiable function. The *gradient* of f is the vector field ∇f (also denoted by *grad f*) whose value at a point (x, y) in U is

$$\nabla f(x, y) = \left(\frac{\partial f}{\partial x}(x, y), \frac{\partial f}{\partial y}(x, y) \right).$$

The gradient of a function $f: U \subseteq \mathbb{R}^3 \to \mathbb{R}$ is the vector field

$$\nabla f(x, y, z) = \left(\frac{\partial f}{\partial x}(x, y, z), \frac{\partial f}{\partial y}(x, y, z), \frac{\partial f}{\partial z}(x, y, z) \right),$$

defined on a subset U of $\mathbb{R}^3$.

Example 4.1   Compute $\nabla f(2, 1)$ if $f(x, y) = x^2 + x \ln y$.

Solution   By definition,

$$\nabla f(2, 1) = \left(\frac{\partial f}{\partial x}(2, 1), \frac{\partial f}{\partial y}(2, 1) \right) = \left(2x + \ln y, \frac{x}{y} \right) \bigg|_{(2,1)} = (4, 2).$$ ◀

Example 4.2   Let $f(x, y, z) = \sqrt{x^2 + y^2 + z^2}$; i.e., the function f measures the distance from the origin. Its gradient is computed to be

$$\nabla f(x, y, z) = \left(x(x^2 + y^2 + z^2)^{-1/2}, y(x^2 + y^2 + z^2)^{-1/2}, z(x^2 + y^2 + z^2)^{-1/2} \right)$$

$$= (x^2 + y^2 + z^2)^{-1/2} \cdot (x, y, z) = \frac{1}{\|\mathbf{r}\|} \mathbf{r},$$

where $\mathbf{r} = x\mathbf{i} + y\mathbf{j} + z\mathbf{k}$ is the position vector of the point (x, y, z). In words, the gradient of the distance from a point to the origin is the unit vector in the direction of that point.

◀

Definition 4.2   Directional Derivative.

Let $f: U \subseteq \mathbb{R}^2 \to \mathbb{R}$ be a real-valued differentiable function. The *directional derivative* of f at the point $\mathbf{p} = (x_0, y_0)$ in the direction of the *unit* vector $\mathbf{u} = (u, v)$ is given by

$$D_{\mathbf{u}} f(x_0, y_0) = \frac{d}{dt} f(\mathbf{p} + t\mathbf{u}) \bigg|_{t=0}.$$

Example 4.3   Compute the directional derivative of $f(x, y) = x^2 + 3xy$ in the direction of the vector $3\mathbf{i} + 4\mathbf{j}$ at the point $\mathbf{p} = (2, -1)$.

Solution   First of all, we need a unit vector in the given direction: $\mathbf{u} = (3\mathbf{i} + 4\mathbf{j})/\|3\mathbf{i} + 4\mathbf{j}\| = (3/5)\mathbf{i} + (4/5)\mathbf{j}$. By definition, $D_{\mathbf{u}} f(2, -1)$ is the derivative of the function

$$f(\mathbf{p} + t\mathbf{u}) = f\left((2, -1) + t(\tfrac{3}{5}, \tfrac{4}{5}) \right) = f\left(2 + \tfrac{3}{5}t, -1 + \tfrac{4}{5}t \right)$$

$$= \left(2 + \tfrac{3}{5}t\right)^2 + 3\left(2 + \tfrac{3}{5}t\right)\left(-1 + \tfrac{4}{5}t\right) = \tfrac{9}{5}t^2 + \tfrac{27}{5}t - 2$$

of *one* variable, evaluated at zero. Therefore,

$$D_{\mathbf{u}}f(2, -1) = \left.\frac{d}{dt}f(\mathbf{p} + t\mathbf{u})\right|_{t=0} = \left.\left(\tfrac{18}{5}t + \tfrac{27}{5}\right)\right|_{t=0} = \tfrac{27}{5}.$$

Now we will give a geometric meaning to the directional derivative.

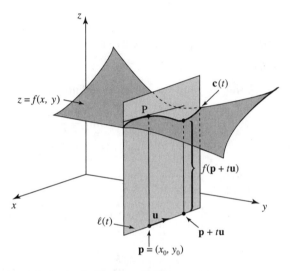

Figure 4.1 Directional derivative is the slope of the tangent.

The expression $\mathbf{p} + t\mathbf{u} = (x_0 + tu, y_0 + tv)$ represents the line $\ell(t)$ in $\mathbb{R}^2$ that goes through the point $\mathbf{p} = \ell(0)$ and whose direction is given by the direction of $\mathbf{u} = (u, v)$. Compute the value $f(\mathbf{p} + t\mathbf{u})$ of the function f for each point $\mathbf{p} + t\mathbf{u}$ on $\ell(t)$ that is in U. The collection of all those values forms a curve $\mathbf{c}(t) = (x_0 + tu, y_0 + tv, f(\mathbf{p} + t\mathbf{u}))$ on the surface (that is the graph of f). Notice that $\mathbf{c}(t)$ belongs to the plane perpendicular to the xy-plane that crosses it along the line $\ell(t)$; see Figure 4.1. Denote the point $\mathbf{c}(0) = (x_0, y_0, f(x_0, y_0))$ by P. The directional derivative $D_{\mathbf{u}}f$ is the slope of the tangent to $\mathbf{c}(t)$ at P, and hence describes how f changes in the direction specified by the unit vector $\mathbf{u}$.

In other words, what we are interested in are not the values of f everywhere in its domain, but only at the points of ℓ (i.e., we consider the so-called *restriction* of f to ℓ). The directional derivative $D_{\mathbf{u}}f(x_0, y_0)$ gives the rate of change of that restriction at (x_0, y_0). Let us emphasize that, since in the definition the parameter t represents the distance along ℓ ($\mathbf{u}$ is a unit vector, and consequently, $\mathbf{p} + t\mathbf{u}$ is t units away from $\mathbf{p}$), the directional derivative gives the rate of change with respect to *distance*.

From the limit definition of the derivative it follows that

$$D_{\mathbf{u}}f(x_0, y_0) = \lim_{t \to 0} \frac{f(\mathbf{p} + t\mathbf{u}) - f(\mathbf{p})}{t} = \lim_{t \to 0} \frac{f((x_0, y_0) + t(u, v)) - f(x_0, y_0)}{t}.$$

The directional derivative of a function $f: U \subseteq \mathbb{R}^3 \to \mathbb{R}$ of three variables is defined and interpreted analogously.

Example 4.4 Let $f: \mathbb{R}^2 \to \mathbb{R}$ be given by

$$f(x, y) = \begin{cases} \dfrac{xy^2}{x^2 + y^4} & \text{if } (x, y) \neq (0, 0) \\ 0 & \text{if } (x, y) = (0, 0) \end{cases}$$

(a) Compute $D_{(0,1)} f(0, 0)$.

(b) Compute $D_{\mathbf{u}} f(0, 0)$, where $\mathbf{u} = (u, v)$ is a unit vector.

Solution

(a) Using the limit version of the definition,

$$D_{(0,1)} f(0, 0) = \lim_{t \to 0} \frac{f((0, 0) + t(0, 1)) - f(0, 0)}{t}$$
$$= \lim_{t \to 0} \frac{f(0, t) - f(0, 0)}{t} = \lim_{t \to 0} \frac{0 - 0}{t} = 0.$$

(b) Similarly,

$$D_{\mathbf{u}} f(0, 0) = \lim_{t \to 0} \frac{f((0, 0) + t(u, v)) - f(0, 0)}{t} = \lim_{t \to 0} \frac{f(tu, tv) - f(0, 0)}{t}$$
$$= \lim_{t \to 0} \frac{1}{t} \frac{t^3 u v^2}{t^2 u^2 + t^4 v^4} = \lim_{t \to 0} \frac{u v^2}{u^2 + t^2 v^4} = \frac{v^2}{u}.$$

It follows that $D_{(u,v)} f(0, 0) = v^2/u$, provided that $u \neq 0$. If $u = 0$, then v must be 1 (**u** has to be unit!); i.e., $(u, v) = (0, 1)$ and the directional derivative $D_{(0,1)} f(0, 0)$ is given by (a). ◀

The previous example shows how "pathological" a function of several variables can be. We showed that f has a derivative at the origin *in all directions,* but f is *not continuous* there. Namely, the limit of $xy^2/(x^2+y^4)$ as $(x, y) \to (0, 0)$ does not exist (the approach $y = 0$ gives 0, whereas the approach $x = y^2$ gives $1/2$).

Consider a differentiable function $f: U \subseteq \mathbb{R}^3 \to \mathbb{R}$, take a point $\mathbf{p} = (x_0, y_0, z_0)$ in its domain and let $\mathbf{u} = \mathbf{i} = (1, 0, 0)$. It follows that $\mathbf{p} + t\mathbf{u} = (x_0 + t, y_0, z_0)$, and the directional derivative

$$D_{\mathbf{i}} f(x_0, y_0, z_0) = \lim_{t \to 0} \frac{f(x_0 + t, y_0, z_0) - f(x_0, y_0, z_0)}{t}$$

is just the partial derivative $\partial f/\partial x$ computed at (x_0, y_0, z_0)! Similarly,

$$D_{\mathbf{j}} f(x_0, y_0, z_0) = \frac{\partial f}{\partial y}(x_0, y_0, z_0), \quad \text{and} \quad D_{\mathbf{k}} f(x_0, y_0, z_0) = \frac{\partial f}{\partial z}(x_0, y_0, z_0).$$

The partial derivatives $\partial f/\partial x$, $\partial f/\partial y$ and $\partial f/\partial z$ at (x_0, y_0, z_0) describe the rates of change of f in the directions of the coordinate axes at the point in question. The directional derivative is a generalization: it enables us to investigate the rate of change of f in *any* direction that is defined by a unit vector $\mathbf{u}$ in $\mathbb{R}^3$.

Similarly, if $f: U \subseteq \mathbb{R}^2 \to \mathbb{R}$, is a differentiable function, then

$$D_{\mathbf{i}} f(x_0, y_0) = \frac{\partial f}{\partial x}(x_0, y_0) \qquad \text{and} \qquad D_{\mathbf{j}} f(x_0, y_0) = \frac{\partial f}{\partial y}(x_0, y_0)$$

at any point (x_0, y_0) in U.

Our next goal is to obtain a "workable" description of the directional derivative. As we have already witnessed, having only the limit definition of the derivative could lead to technically involved and very long computations.

■ **Theorem 4.1**   **Coordinate Description of the Directional Derivative.**

Let $f: U \subseteq \mathbb{R}^3 \to \mathbb{R}$ be a differentiable function. Then

$$D_{\mathbf{u}} f(x_0, y_0, z_0) = \nabla f(x_0, y_0, z_0) \cdot \mathbf{u},$$

where $\mathbf{u} = (u, v, w)$ is a unit vector in $\mathbb{R}^3$.   ■

Proof

Let $\ell(t) = \mathbf{p} + t\mathbf{u}$, where $\mathbf{p} = (x_0, y_0, z_0)$; then $\ell(0) = \mathbf{p} = (x_0, y_0, z_0)$ and $\ell'(0) = \mathbf{u} = (u, v, w)$. Consider the composition $f(\ell(t)) = f(\mathbf{p} + t\mathbf{u})$ of ℓ and f. By the chain rule (see (2.19) in Section 2.5)

$$\frac{d}{dt} f(\mathbf{p} + t\mathbf{u}) = \frac{d}{dt} f(\ell(t)) = \nabla f(\ell(t)) \cdot \ell'(t).$$

Consequently,

$$D_{\mathbf{u}} f(x_0, y_0, z_0) = \left. \frac{d}{dt} f(\mathbf{p} + t\mathbf{u}) \right|_{t=0} = \nabla f(\ell(0)) \cdot \ell'(0) = \nabla f(x_0, y_0, z_0) \cdot \mathbf{u}. \quad ■$$

This theorem actually states two facts: a differentiable function has a directional derivative in every direction, and it is computed as the dot product of the gradient of the function at the point in question and the unit vector in the desired direction. If f is a function of two variables, then

$$D_{\mathbf{u}} f(x_0, y_0) = \nabla f(x_0, y_0) \cdot \mathbf{u}, \tag{4.1}$$

where $\mathbf{u}$ is a unit vector in $\mathbb{R}^2$.

Example 4.5   Compute the rate of change of the function $f(x, y, z) = x^2 + y^2 + z^2$ in the direction of the vector $\mathbf{u} = (1, 1, 1)$ at the point $(1, -2, 0)$.

Solution   The requested rate of change is given by the directional derivative

$$D_{\mathbf{u}}f(1,-2,0) = \nabla f(1,-2,0) \cdot \frac{\mathbf{u}}{\|\mathbf{u}\|} = (2x,2y,2z)\Big|_{(1,-2,0)} \cdot \frac{1}{\sqrt{3}}(1,1,1)$$

$$= (2,-4,0) \cdot (1/\sqrt{3}, 1/\sqrt{3}, 1/\sqrt{3}) = -2/\sqrt{3}.$$

◀

Example 4.6   Suppose that the function $T(x,y) = 30e^{-x^2-y^2}$ gives the temperature at a location (x,y) in the plane. Compute $D_{\mathbf{u}}T(0,1)$ if $\mathbf{u} = (\mathbf{i}-\mathbf{j})/\sqrt{2}$ and interpret your result.

Solution   Using (4.1) we get

$$D_{\mathbf{u}}T(0,1) = \nabla T(0,1) \cdot (1/\sqrt{2}, -1/\sqrt{2})$$

$$= (-60xe^{-x^2-y^2}, -60ye^{-x^2-y^2})\Big|_{(0,1)} \cdot (1/\sqrt{2}, -1/\sqrt{2})$$

$$= (0, -60e^{-1}) \cdot (1/\sqrt{2}, -1/\sqrt{2}) = 60e^{-1}/\sqrt{2} \approx 15.6.$$

Therefore, if we walk away from $(0,1)$ in the direction of $(\mathbf{i}-\mathbf{j})/\sqrt{2}$, we will experience an increase in temperature, at a rate of approximately 15.6 degrees per unit distance.

◀

Example 4.7   Directional Derivative of a Gravitational Potential.

Consider the gravitational potential function $V(x,y,z) = -GMm/\|\mathbf{r}\|$ defined in $\mathbb{R}^3 - \{(0,0,0)\}$, where $\mathbf{r} = (x,y,z) = x\mathbf{i} + y\mathbf{j} + z\mathbf{k}$. The gradient of V is given by $\nabla V(x,y,z) = GMm\mathbf{r}/\|\mathbf{r}\|^3$ (see Example 2.35 in Section 2.4), and the directional derivative in the unit direction $\mathbf{u}$ is computed to be

$$D_{\mathbf{u}}V(x,y,z) = \nabla V(x,y,z) \cdot \mathbf{u} = \frac{GMm}{\|\mathbf{r}\|^3}\mathbf{r} \cdot \mathbf{u}.$$

Choose the point $(1,0,0)$; i.e., let $\mathbf{r} = \mathbf{i}$. Then, for example, $D_{\mathbf{i}}V(1,0,0) = GMm\mathbf{i} \cdot \mathbf{i} = GMm$, $D_{-\mathbf{i}}V(1,0,0) = GMm\mathbf{i} \cdot (-\mathbf{i}) = -GMm$, $D_{\mathbf{j}}V(1,0,0) = GMm\mathbf{i} \cdot \mathbf{j} = 0$ and $D_{\mathbf{k}}V(1,0,0) = GMm\mathbf{i} \cdot \mathbf{k} = 0$.

◀

■ **Theorem 4.2**   Maximum Rate of Change of a Function

Let f be a differentiable function on $U \subseteq \mathbb{R}^2$ (or $\mathbb{R}^3$) and assume that $\nabla f(\mathbf{x}) \neq \mathbf{0}$ for $\mathbf{x} \in U$. The direction of the largest rate of increase in f at $\mathbf{x}$ is the direction of the vector $\nabla f(\mathbf{x})$.

■

Proof

Let $\mathbf{u}$ be a unit vector. By Theorem 4.1

$$D_{\mathbf{u}}f(\mathbf{x}) = \nabla f(\mathbf{x}) \cdot \mathbf{u} = \|\nabla f(\mathbf{x})\| \|\mathbf{u}\| \cos\theta = \|\nabla f(\mathbf{x})\| \cos\theta$$

(since $\|\mathbf{u}\| = 1$), where θ denotes the angle between $\nabla f(\mathbf{x})$ and $\mathbf{u}$. Since $-1 \leq \cos\theta \leq 1$, $D_{\mathbf{u}}f(\mathbf{x})$ attains its largest value when $\cos\theta = 1$; i.e., when $\theta = 0$. Consequently, maximum directional derivative $D_{\mathbf{u}} f(\mathbf{x})$ at $\mathbf{x}$ occurs in the direction parallel to the vector $\nabla f(\mathbf{x})$.

■

When $\theta = 0$, $D_{\mathbf{u}} f(\mathbf{x}) = \|\nabla f(\mathbf{x})\|$; i.e., the magnitude of the largest rate of increase at $\mathbf{x}$ equals $\|\nabla f(\mathbf{x})\|$ per unit distance.

An argument similar to the one given in Theorem 4.2 shows that the function f decreases most rapidly in the direction opposite to the gradient (i.e., when $\cos \theta = -1$). The magnitude of that decrease equals $\|\nabla f(\mathbf{x})\|$ per unit length. The rate of change in f in directions perpendicular to $\nabla f(\mathbf{x})$ is zero. If $\nabla f(\mathbf{x}) = \mathbf{0}$, then $D_{\mathbf{u}} f(\mathbf{x}) = 0$ in all directions.

Example 4.8

We are now ready to interpret the results obtained in Example 4.7. Suppose that the mass m is located at the point $(1, 0, 0)$. The gradient of the potential is $\nabla V(1, 0, 0) = GMm\mathbf{i}$. The potential decreases most rapidly (at the rate GMm per unit distance) in the radial direction of $-\mathbf{i}$; i.e., towards the mass M, located at the origin. The largest increase in the gravitational potential occurs in the (radial) direction away from the origin, at the rate GMm per unit distance. The rate of change of the potential in the $\mathbf{j}$ and $\mathbf{k}$ directions at $(1, 0, 0)$ is zero. These directions belong to the plane tangent to the level surface (so-called equipotential surface) through $(1, 0, 0)$; see Figure 4.2.

◄

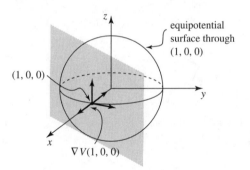

Figure 4.2 The gravitational potential at $(1, 0, 0)$ increases fastest in the direction away from the origin, perpendicular to the equipotential surface through $(1, 0, 0)$.

Example 4.9

Let $f(x, y, z) = x^2 + y^2 + z^2$; i.e., f is the distance squared from the origin. The function f increases most rapidly in the direction of its gradient $\nabla f(x, y, z) = (2x, 2y, 2z) = 2(x, y, z)$, i.e., radially away from the origin. The maximum rate of change at a point (x, y, z) is $\|\nabla f(x, y, z)\| = 2\sqrt{x^2 + y^2 + z^2}$.

◄

Consider a C^1 function $f = f(x, y): U \subseteq \mathbb{R}^2 \to \mathbb{R}$ and one if its level curves $\mathbf{c}$ given by $f(x, y) = C$, where C is a constant. This means that at all points on the level curve the value of f is the same (and equal C), i.e., $f(\mathbf{c}(t)) = C$ for all t, where $\mathbf{c}(t)$ is a parametrization of $\mathbf{c}$. Consequently, $(f(\mathbf{c}(t)))' = 0$ and since (by the chain rule)

$(f(\mathbf{c}(t)))' = \nabla f(\mathbf{c}(t)) \cdot \mathbf{c}'(t)$, it follows that $\nabla f(\mathbf{c}(t)) \cdot \mathbf{c}'(t) = 0$. The conclusion of this argument is contained in our next theorem.

■ **Theorem 4.3**   Gradient Vector in $\mathbf{R}^2$ is Perpendicular to Level Curves.

Let $f: U \subseteq \mathbf{R}^2 \rightarrow \mathbf{R}$ be a differentiable function and let $\mathbf{c}(t)$ be a parametrization of one of its level curves. If $\nabla f(\mathbf{c}(t)) \neq \mathbf{0}$, then $\nabla f(\mathbf{c}(t))$ is perpendicular to the tangent vector $\mathbf{c}'(t)$.   ■

In other words, the gradient vector (if non-zero) is always perpendicular to the level curves; see Figure 4.3.

Now assume that $f: U \subseteq \mathbf{R}^3 \rightarrow \mathbf{R}$ is differentiable and consider one of its level surfaces S defined by $f(x, y, z) = C$. Pick a point P in S and consider any curve $\mathbf{c}$ in S that passes through P (i.e., $\mathbf{c}(t_0) = P$ for some t_0). Since the curve $\mathbf{c}$ belongs to the level surface S, it follows that $f(\mathbf{c}(t)) = C$ for all t. Continuing as before, we get that ∇f is perpendicular to $\mathbf{c}'$ at P for *any* curve $\mathbf{c}$ in S that contains P. In other words, $\nabla f(P)$ (if non-zero) is perpendicular to all tangent vectors (at P) belonging to curves in S; consequently, it is perpendicular to the tangent plane to S at P; see Figure 4.4.

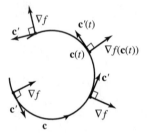

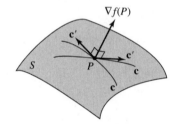

Figure 4.3   Gradient in $\mathbf{R}^2$ is perpendicular to a level curve.

Figure 4.4   Gradient in $\mathbf{R}^3$ is perpendicular to a level surface.

■ **Theorem 4.4**   Gradient Vector in $\mathbf{R}^3$ is Perpendicular to Level Surfaces.

Let $f: U \subseteq \mathbf{R}^3 \rightarrow \mathbf{R}$ be a differentiable function and let S be one of its level surfaces. If $\nabla f(x_0, y_0, z_0) \neq \mathbf{0}$, where (x_0, y_0, z_0) is a point on S, then $\nabla f(x_0, y_0, z_0)$ is perpendicular (normal) to S at (x_0, y_0, z_0).   ■

Example 4.10   Compute the equation of the line tangent to $y = xe^x + 1$ at $(0, 1)$.

Solution   Rewrite the equation $y = xe^x + 1$ as $y - xe^x = 1$ and interpret it geometrically as the level curve of the function $f(x, y) = y - xe^x$ of value 1. By Theorem 4.3 the gradient

$$\nabla f(0, 1) = (-e^x - xe^x, 1)\Big|_{(0,1)} = -\mathbf{i} + \mathbf{j}$$

is perpendicular to the level curve in question. Consequently, the direction of the tangent is any vector perpendicular to $-\mathbf{i}+\mathbf{j}$; for example $\mathbf{i}+\mathbf{j} = (1, 1)$. The parametric equation of the tangent line is

$$\mathbf{c}(t) = (0, 1) + t(1, 1) = (t, 1 + t), \qquad t \in \mathbb{R}.$$

We could have interpreted the equation $y = xe^x + 1$ of the previous example as $y - xe^x - 1 = 0$, (i.e., as the level curve of $y - xe^x - 1$ of value 0), or as $y - xe^x + 6 = 7$, (i.e., as the level curve of $y - xe^x + 6$ of value 7), or in many other ways. However, the results would have been the same (and the reader is encouraged to check this).

Let us compute the equation of the plane tangent to the surface (which is the graph of) $z = f(x, y)$ at the point (x_0, y_0). Interpret the surface $z = f(x, y)$ as the level surface $F(x, y, z) = 0$ of the function $F(x, y, z) = z - f(x, y)$ of value 0. By Theorem 4.4 the normal vector to the level surface (hence also the normal to the tangent plane) is given by the vector $\nabla F(x_0, y_0, z_0)$, where $z_0 = f(x_0, y_0)$. If $\mathbf{x} = (x, y, z)$ is a point in the tangent plane, other than $\mathbf{x}_0$, then $\nabla F(x_0, y_0, z_0)$ is perpendicular to $\mathbf{x} - \mathbf{x}_0$, where $\mathbf{x}_0 = (x_0, y_0, z_0)$, and hence both

$$\nabla F(x_0, y_0, z_0) \cdot (\mathbf{x} - \mathbf{x}_0) = 0$$

and

$$\frac{\partial F}{\partial x}(x_0, y_0, z_0)(x - x_0) + \frac{\partial F}{\partial y}(x_0, y_0, z_0)(y - y_0) + \frac{\partial F}{\partial z}(x_0, y_0, z_0)(z - z_0) = 0.$$

are equations of the plane tangent to the surface $z = f(x, y)$ (or $F(x, y, z) = 0$).

Since $F(x, y, z) = z - f(x, y)$, it follows that $\partial F/\partial x = -\partial f/\partial x$, $\partial F/\partial y = -\partial f/\partial y$ and $\partial F/\partial z = 1$, and we can rewrite the tangent plane equation as

$$z = z_0 + \frac{\partial f}{\partial x}(x_0, y_0)(x - x_0) + \frac{\partial f}{\partial y}(x_0, y_0)(y - y_0).$$

This is precisely the equation we discussed in Section 2.4 in the context of the linear approximation of a function of several variables.

Example 4.11 Compute the equation of the plane tangent to the surface $z = x^2 + y^2 - 1$ at the point $(1, 0, 0)$.

Solution Think of the given surface as the level surface of $F(x, y, z) = z - x^2 - y^2 + 1$ of value 0. The normal to the surface is

$$\nabla F(1, 0, 0) = (-2x, -2y, 1)\Big|_{(1,0,0)} = (-2, 0, 1),$$

so the tangent plane has the equation

$$-2(x - 1) + 0(y - 0) + 1(z - 0) = 0;$$

i.e., $-2x + z + 2 = 0$.

Example 4.12

Let $f(x, y) = e^{x^2+y^2}$. The level curves of value $C > 1$ are given by $e^{x^2+y^2} = C$; i.e., they are the circles $x^2 + y^2 = \ln C$ of radius $\ln C$ centered at the origin (the level curve of value $C = 1$ reduces to a point (origin); there are no level curves of value $C < 1$). The normal vectors to the level curves are given by $\nabla f(x, y) = e^{x^2+y^2}(2x, 2y)$. In particular, a normal vector to the circle given by $C = e$ (that is, the circle of radius 1) is $\nabla f(x, y) = 2e(x, y)$. For example, $\nabla f(1, 0) = 2e(1, 0)$ is normal to $x^2 + y^2 = 1$ at $(1, 0)$. Moreover, $2e(1, 0) = 2e\mathbf{i}$ is the direction of the largest increase of $e^{x^2+y^2}$ at that point.

◄

Example 4.13

Conservative Field and its Potential Function.

We have already seen that the gravitational force field can be obtained as the negative of the gradient of a scalar function V; i.e., $\mathbf{F} = -\nabla V$ (cf. Example 2.35 in Section 2.4). In general, a vector field $\mathbf{F}$ with that property is called *conservative* and the corresponding scalar function V is the *potential function*. Examples of such fields are gravitational and electrostatic fields (see Section 2.1). Their properties with respect to integration (for example, work) will be discussed in Chapter 5.

The gradient vector is perpendicular to level surfaces. Translated into the language of physics, this sentence says that the conservative force field $\mathbf{F} = -\nabla V$ is perpendicular to its *equipotential surfaces*. For example, the equipotential surfaces for the gravitational potential are spheres centered at the origin (see Example 2.20 in Section 2.2). The direction of the gradient vector field (that is, the direction of the force) is radial (i.e., along lines through the origin), and clearly perpendicular to the spheres.

◄

Example 4.14

Heat Flux Vector Field.

We know from experience that heat flows from regions of higher temperature towards regions of lower temperature. This process is described by the *heat flux vector field*

$$\mathbf{J} = -k\nabla T,$$

where $T = T(x, y, z)$ gives the temperature at a point (x, y, z) and $k > 0$ is a constant (called the *conductivity*). The direction of the gradient ∇T is the direction of the largest increase in temperature; the heat flows in the opposite direction; i.e., in the direction $-\nabla T$ of the largest decrease in temperature.

◄

Example 4.15

Conservation of Energy.

Assume that a particle of mass m moves along a curve $\mathbf{c}(t)$ in a conservative force field $\mathbf{F}$ (with potential energy function V). The quantity

$$E(t) = \tfrac{1}{2}m\|\mathbf{c}'(t)\|^2 + V(\mathbf{c}(t))$$

is called the *total energy*. It is the sum of the *potential energy* of the particle $V(\mathbf{c}(t))$ and its *kinetic energy* $m\|\mathbf{c}'(t)\|^2/2$. We are going to check the *Law of Conservation of Energy*, which states that the total energy is constant (i.e., energy only transforms from one form to another, but can neither be destroyed nor created). In the computation Newton's Second Law $\mathbf{F}(\mathbf{c}(t)) = m\mathbf{c}''(t)$ will be used.

Solution We will show that the derivative of the energy is zero. Using the product rule and the chain rule and writing $\|\mathbf{c}'(t)\|^2$ as $\mathbf{c}'(t) \cdot \mathbf{c}'(t)$ we get

$$\frac{d}{dt}E(t) = \frac{1}{2}m\big(\mathbf{c}'(t) \cdot \mathbf{c}'(t)\big)' + \big(V(\mathbf{c}(t))\big)' = m\mathbf{c}'(t) \cdot \mathbf{c}''(t) + \nabla V(\mathbf{c}(t)) \cdot \mathbf{c}'(t),$$

and hence

$$\frac{d}{dt}E(t) = \big(m\mathbf{c}''(t) + \nabla V(\mathbf{c}(t))\big) \cdot \mathbf{c}'(t).$$

The force $\mathbf{F}$ is conservative, so that $\mathbf{F}(\mathbf{c}(t)) = -\nabla V(\mathbf{c}(t))$. Combining with Newton's Second Law we get $m\mathbf{c}''(t) = -\nabla V(\mathbf{c}(t))$; i.e., the first factor in the scalar product on the right side in $dE(t)/dt$ is zero. Hence $dE(t)/dt = 0$, which implies that $E(t)$ is constant.

◀

Example 4.16

Potential Due to a Point Charge.

The potential due to a point charge q located at $\mathbf{r}_0 = (x_0, y_0, z_0)$ in $\mathbb{R}^3$ is given by the formula

$$\Phi = \frac{1}{4\pi\epsilon_0} \frac{q}{\|\mathbf{r} - \mathbf{r}_0\|},$$

where ϵ_0 is a constant. The corresponding electrostatic field $\mathbf{E}$ at the point $\mathbf{r} = (x, y, z)$ is given by $\mathbf{E} = -\nabla\Phi$; i.e.

$$\begin{aligned}
\mathbf{E} &= -\frac{q}{4\pi\epsilon_0}\nabla\left(\frac{1}{\|\mathbf{r} - \mathbf{r}_0\|}\right) \\
&= -\frac{q}{4\pi\epsilon_0}\nabla\left(\big((x - x_0)^2 + (y - y_0)^2 + (z - z_0)^2\big)^{-1/2}\right) \\
&= \frac{q}{4\pi\epsilon_0}\big((x - x_0)^2 + (y - y_0)^2 + (z - z_0)^2\big)^{-3/2}\big(x - x_0, y - y_0, z - z_0\big) \\
&= \frac{q}{4\pi\epsilon_0}\frac{\mathbf{r} - \mathbf{r}_0}{\|\mathbf{r} - \mathbf{r}_0\|^3}.
\end{aligned}$$

◀

Let us clarify the use of the word "potential." In physics, one distinguishes between *potential* and *potential energy*. In general, potential = potential energy per unit "source." For example, electrostatic potential = electrostatic potential energy per unit charge; gravitational potential = gravitational potential energy per unit mass, and so on. So if $\mathbf{F} = q\mathbf{E}$, ($\mathbf{F}$ is an electrostatic force and $\mathbf{E}$ the corresponding electrostatic field) then $\mathbf{F} = -\nabla V$, but $\mathbf{E} = -\nabla\Phi$, where $\Phi = V/q$. The function V is the electrostatic potential energy and Φ is the electrostatic potential. In math literature this distinction is somewhat blurred, and both the potential and the potential energy are referred to as "potential."

The next example explains how to find a potential function for a given conservative vector field. (Not every vector field has a potential function. Necessary and sufficient conditions for the existence of potential functions will be discussed in Chapter 5.)

Example 4.17

The function $\mathbf{F}(x, y, z) = yz\mathbf{i} + (xz - 1)\mathbf{j} + xy\mathbf{k}$ defines a conservative vector field. Find its potential function $V(x, y, z)$.

Solution From $\nabla V = -\mathbf{F} = -(yz, xz - 1, xy)$ it follows that $\partial V/\partial x = -yz$, $\partial V/\partial y = -xz + 1$ and $\partial V/\partial z = -xy$. Integrating the first equation with respect to x we get

$$V(x, y, z) = -xyz + C(y, z),$$

where the "constant" $C(y, z)$ of integration might depend on y and z, since these two variables were viewed as constants. We managed to partially recover V. To compute $C(y, z)$ substitute the expression for $V(x, y, z)$ into $\partial V/\partial y$, thus getting

$$-xz + \frac{\partial C(y, z)}{\partial y} = -xz + 1,$$

which implies that $\partial C(y, z)/\partial y = 1$ and $C(y, z) = y + C(z)$, by integration with respect to y (the variable z was kept fixed, so the integration "constant" might still depend on z). Hence

$$V(x, y, z) = -xyz + y + C(z).$$

Finally, substituting this expression into the equation for $\partial V/\partial z$, we get

$$-xy + C'(z) = -xy,$$

so that $C(z) = C$ after integrating with respect to z. (C is a real number, not a function any longer). It follows that any function of the form

$$V(x, y, z) = -xyz + y + C$$

(where C is a real number) is a potential function for the given vector field.

◀

Example 4.18   Infinite Parallel Straight Wires.

Two infinite straight wires uniformly charged with electricity are orthogonal to the xy-plane and pass through the points $(1, 0)$ and $(-1, 0)$ respectively. Assume that the wires are charged so that the charge of one is opposite to the charge of the other, but both charges have the same magnitude. The corresponding electrostatic field at a point (x, y) in the xy-plane is proportional to (we drop all physical constants for simplicity)

$$\mathbf{E}(x, y) = \frac{2(x^2 - y^2 - 1)}{((x + 1)^2 + y^2)((x - 1)^2 + y^2)}\mathbf{i} + \frac{4xy}{((x + 1)^2 + y^2)((x - 1)^2 + y^2)}\mathbf{j}.$$

Show that the field $\mathbf{E}$ is conservative by checking that

$$V(x, y) = -\frac{1}{2}\ln\frac{(x - 1)^2 + y^2}{(x + 1)^2 + y^2}$$

is its potential.

Solution   Using the chain rule and quotient rule we get

$$\frac{\partial V}{\partial x} = -\frac{1}{2} \frac{(x+1)^2 + y^2}{(x-1)^2 + y^2} \frac{2(x-1)((x+1)^2 + y^2) - ((x-1)^2 + y^2)2(x+1)}{((x+1)^2 + y^2)^2}$$

$$= -\frac{(x-1)((x+1)^2 + y^2) - ((x-1)^2 + y^2)(x+1)}{((x-1)^2 + y^2)((x+1)^2 + y^2)}$$

$$= -\frac{2(x^2 - y^2 - 1)}{((x+1)^2 + y^2)((x-1)^2 + y^2)}.$$

Hence $\partial V/\partial x$ equals the negative of the **i** component of **E**. The partial derivative $\partial V/\partial y$ is computed similarly.   ◀

Example 4.19   Find the equipotential curves in the xy-plane for $\mathbf{E}(x, y)$ given in the previous example.

Solution   Setting

$$V(x, y) = -\frac{1}{2} \ln \frac{(x-1)^2 + y^2}{(x+1)^2 + y^2} = C_1,$$

where C_1 is a constant, we get

$$\frac{(x-1)^2 + y^2}{(x+1)^2 + y^2} = C,$$

with $C = e^{-2C_1} > 0$. Hence

$$(x-1)^2 + y^2 = C((x+1)^2 + y^2)$$

and

$$x^2(1 - C) - 2x(1 + C) + 1 - C + y^2(1 - C) = 0.$$

Divide by $1 - C$ (assuming, of course, that $C \neq 1$)

$$x^2 - 2x\frac{1 + C}{1 - C} + 1 + y^2 = 0,$$

and complete the square

$$\left(x - \frac{1 + C}{1 - C}\right)^2 - \left(\frac{1 + C}{1 - C}\right)^2 + 1 + y^2 = 0$$

to get

$$\left(x - \frac{1 + C}{1 - C}\right)^2 + y^2 = \left(\frac{1 + C}{1 - C}\right)^2 - 1.$$

Hence, for $C \neq 1$, the level curves are circles centered on the x-axis at $(1+C)/(1-C)$ of radius $\sqrt{(1 + C)^2/(1 - C)^2 - 1}$ (the constant C is positive, which implies that $1 + C >$

$1 - C$ and hence $(1+C)/(1-C) > 1$, so the expression under the square root is always positive); see Figure 4.5. If $C = 1$ then

$$\frac{(x - 1)^2 + y^2}{(x + 1)^2 + y^2} = 1$$

implies that $x = 0$, i.e., the level curve corresponding to $C = 1$ (i.e., $V = 0$) is the y-axis (which can be viewed as the limiting case as the circles (computed above) increase in size).

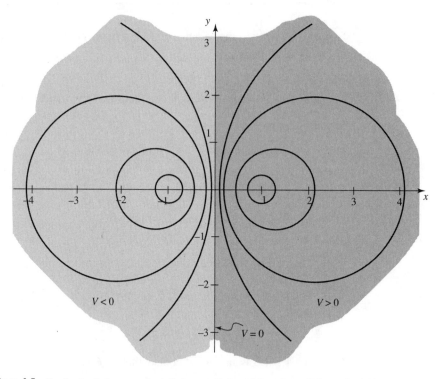

Figure 4.5   Equipotential curves for infinite parallel straight wires of Example 4.19.

EXERCISES 4.1   **Exercises 1 to 3:** Find the directional derivative of the function f at the point $\mathbf{p}$ in the direction of the vector $\mathbf{v}$.

  1. $f(x, y) = e^{xy}(\cos x + \sin y)$, $\mathbf{p} = (\pi/2, 0)$, $\mathbf{v} = 2\mathbf{i} - \mathbf{j}$

  2. $f(x, y, z) = x^2 - y^2 z^3$, $\mathbf{p} = (0, 2, -1)$, $\mathbf{v} = (1, 2, -4)$

  3. $f(x, y) = x \ln y^2 + 2y - 3$, $\mathbf{p} = (1, 2)$, $\mathbf{v} = 3\mathbf{i} + 4\mathbf{j}$

Exercises 4 to 6: Find the directional derivative of the function f at the point $\mathbf{p}$ in the direction given by the angle θ, measured from the positive direction of the x-axis in the counterclockwise direction.

4. $f(x, y) = xy^4 + x^2y^2 - 2$, $\mathbf{p} = (0, -1)$, $\theta = \pi/4$

5. $f(x, y) = e^{xy}$, $\mathbf{p} = (0, 1)$, $\theta = \pi/2$

6. $f(x, y) = \cos(2x + y)$, $\mathbf{p} = (2, -3)$, $\theta = -\pi/3$

Exercises 7 to 11: Compute the gradient of the function f at the point $\mathbf{p}$ and find the rate of change of f at $\mathbf{p}$ in the direction of the vector $\mathbf{v}$.

7. $f(x, y) = x^3y + 2x^2y^2 - xy^3$, $\mathbf{p} = (2, 3)$, $\mathbf{v} = (1, -1)$

8. $f(x, y, z) = x^2yz^2$, $\mathbf{p} = (1, 0, -3)$, $\mathbf{v} = (3, 0, 0)$

9. $f(x, y) = e^x \cos y$, $\mathbf{p} = (0, \pi)$, $\mathbf{v} = (-1, -\pi)$

10. $f(x, y) = \arctan(y/x)$, $\mathbf{p} = (1, 1)$, $\mathbf{v} = \mathbf{i} - 4\mathbf{j}$

11. $f(x, y, z) = e^{-x^2-y^2-z^2}$, $\mathbf{p} = (0, -1, 2)$, $\mathbf{v} = \mathbf{i} + \mathbf{j} + \mathbf{k}$

12. Show that the function $f(x, y) = x^{1/3}y^{1/3}$ is continuous at $(0, 0)$ and has partial derivatives f_x and f_y at $(0, 0)$, but the directional derivative of f in any other direction does not exist.

Exercises 13 to 17: Determine the maximum rate of change of the function f at the point $\mathbf{p}$, and the direction in which it occurs.

13. $f(x, y) = \sec x \tan y$, $\mathbf{p} = (\pi/4, \pi/4)$ **14.** $f(x, y) = 2ye^x + e^{-y}$, $\mathbf{p} = (0, 0)$

15. $f(x, y, z) = xy^{-1} + yz^{-1} + zx^{-1}$, $\mathbf{p} = (1, 2, -1)$

16. $f(x, y, z) = \sqrt{xyz}$, $\mathbf{p} = (3, 3, 2)$ **17.** $f(x, y) = |xy|$, $\mathbf{p} = (3, -2)$

18. The temperature inside an object is given by $T(x, y, z) = 30(x^2 + y^2 + z^2)^{-1}$, at all points $(x, y, z) \neq (0, 0, 0)$.

   (a) Find the rate of change of the temperature at the point $(1, 2, 0)$ inside the object in the direction toward the point $(2, -1, -1)$.

   (b) Find the direction of the largest rate of increase in temperature at the point $(0, 0, 1)$.

   (c) Find the direction of the most rapid decrease in temperature at a point (x, y, z) inside the object, if $(x, y, z) \neq (0, 0, 0)$.

19. The pressure $P(x, y)$ at a point $(x, y) \in \mathbb{R}^2$ on a metal membrane is given by the function $P(x, y) = 100e^{-x^2-2y^2}$.

   (a) Find the rate of change of the pressure at the point $\mathbf{p} = (0, 1)$ in the direction $\mathbf{i} + \mathbf{j}$.

   (b) In what direction away from the point $\mathbf{p}$ does the pressure increase most rapidly? Decrease most rapidly?

   (c) Find the maximum rate of increase of pressure at $\mathbf{p}$.

   (d) Locate the direction(s) at $\mathbf{p}$ in which the rate of change of pressure is zero.

20. Let $f(x, y) = e^x \cos(2x - y)$. Find the directional derivative of f at the point $(0, 1)$ in the direction of the line $y = 3x + 1$, for increasing values of x.

21. Consider the function $f(x, y) = 2xy$. In what directions at the point $(1, 2)$ is the directional derivative of f equal to 4?

22. The temperature produced by a source located at the origin is given by the formula $T(x, y, z) = e^{-(x^2+y^2+z^2)}$.

   (a) Find the isothermal surfaces; i.e., the surfaces on which the temperature is constant.

   (b) What point is the warmest?

   (c) What is the direction of the most rapid decrease in temperature at the point $(1, 2, -4)$?

(d) Describe the direction(s) at the point $(1, 2, -4)$ in which the rate of change of the temperature is no larger than $0.4e^{-21}$.

23. Assume that the function $f = f(x, y)$ has continuous partial derivatives. The directional derivative of f at $(0, 2)$ in the direction $\mathbf{i} + 2\mathbf{j}$ is 4 and the directional derivative of f at $(0, 2)$ in the direction $2\mathbf{i} - \mathbf{j}$ is 12. Find the directional derivative of f at $(0, 2)$ in the direction of the vector $3\mathbf{i} + 3\mathbf{j}$.

24. Consider the function $f(x, y) = 3x^2 - y^2 - 2$.

   (a) Find the directional derivative of f in the direction of the tangent vector to the curve $\mathbf{c}(t) = (\cos t, t \sin t)$ at the point where $t = \pi/2$.

   (b) Let $F(t) = f(\mathbf{c}(t))$. Compute $F'(\pi/2)$.

   (c) What is the relation between the directional derivative in (a) and the rate of change $F'(\pi/2)$ in (b)?

Exercises 25 to 28: Let f and g be differentiable functions and let a, b and n be constants. Prove the following identities.

25. $\nabla(af \pm bg) = a\nabla f \pm b\nabla g$ 26. $\nabla(fg) = g\nabla f + f\nabla g$

27. $\nabla(f/g) = (g\nabla f - f\nabla g)/g^2$, at all points where g is not zero

28. $\nabla f^n = nf^{n-1}\nabla f$

29. Find the acute angle between the surfaces $x^3y^3 - 3yz = 8$ and $x + 3z^2 = y^2 - 3$ at the point $(1, 2, 0)$.

Exercises 30 to 33: Find an equation of the tangent plane to the graph of the function $z = f(x, y)$ at the point $\mathbf{p}$.

30. $x^2 - y^2 + z^2 = 2$, $\mathbf{p} = (0, 0, \sqrt{2})$

31. $\sin(xy) - 2\cos(yz) = 0$, $\mathbf{p} = (\pi/2, 1, \pi/3)$

32. $2e^{xyz} = 3$, $\mathbf{p} = (1, 1, \ln 1.5)$ 33. $z^2 = \dfrac{4x - y}{x + y + 1}$, $\mathbf{p} = (1, 0, \sqrt{2})$

Exercises 34 to 38: Find equations of both the line normal to the given surface at the point $\mathbf{p}$, and the plane tangent to the given surface at the same point.

34. $2x - 6y - z = -4$, $\mathbf{p} = (1, 2, -6)$

35. $(x - 2)^2 + (y - 3)^2 + z^2 - 4 = 0$, $\mathbf{p} = (2, 4, \sqrt{3})$

36. $xyz - 16 = 0$, $\mathbf{p} = (-2, 2, -4)$ 37. $\ln(x^2 + y^2) - 2 = 0$, $\mathbf{p} = (0, e, 1)$

38. $e^x \cos y - e^x \cos z = 0$, $\mathbf{p} = (1, \pi/4, \pi/4)$

Exercises 39 to 42: Find equations of the tangent line and the normal line to the given curve at the point $\mathbf{p}$.

39. $3x - 2y - 4 = 0$, $\mathbf{p} = (0, -2)$ 40. $x^{3/2} + y^{3/2} = 1$, $\mathbf{p} = (0, 1)$

41. $e^x \sin y = 2$, $\mathbf{p} = (\ln 2, \pi/2)$ 42. $y = x^{-2}$, $\mathbf{p} = (1/2, 4)$

43. Locate all points on the paraboloid $z = x^2 + y^2 - 5$ where the tangent plane is parallel to the plane $x + 3y - z = 0$.

44. Find an equation of the plane tangent to the sphere centered at $(2, 0, -1)$ at the point $(1, 3, 3)$.

45. Find unit normal vectors to the surface $\cos(xy) = e^z - 1$ at the point $(1, \pi/2, 0)$.

46. A particle is ejected from the surface $2x^2 + 4y^2 + z^2 = 16$ at the point $(2, 1, 2)$ in the direction perpendicular to the surface. Assuming that its trajectory is a straight line, and that it moves at a constant speed of 3 units/s, find its position 10 s later.

47. Show that a line normal to a sphere goes through its center.

48. Let $g(s, t) = f(s^2 t, s^2 - t^2)$, where f is a differentiable function. If $\nabla f(4, 3) = (3, -1)$, find $\nabla g(2, 1)$.

49. Check that the families of curves $xy = k$ and $x^2 - y^2 = m$ (k and m are constants) intersect orthogonally. Such families are sometimes called *orthogonal trajectories*.

50. Check that the families of curves $(x - k)^2 + y^2 = k^2$ and $x^2 + (y - m)^2 = m^2$ (k and m are constants) intersect orthogonally.

51. Show that the spheres $x^2 + y^2 + z^2 = 16$ and $(x - 5)^2 + y^2 + z^2 = 9$ are orthogonal (that is, corresponding normals at the points of intersection are orthogonal).

52. Show that $\nabla \|\mathbf{r}\|^{-1} = -\|\mathbf{r}\|^{-3}\mathbf{r}$, where $\mathbf{r} = x\mathbf{i} + y\mathbf{j} + z\mathbf{k}$.

Exercises 53 to 57: The vector field $\mathbf{F}$ is conservative. Find its potential function (i.e., find V such that $\mathbf{F} = -\nabla V$).

53. $\mathbf{F}(x, y) = e^{xy}(1 + xy)\mathbf{i} + x^2 e^{xy}\mathbf{j}$ 54. $\mathbf{F}(x, y) = (3x^2 - 3y^2)\mathbf{i} - 6xy\mathbf{j}$

55. $\mathbf{F}(x, y, z) = -(2xy^2 + 3x^2 z, 2x^2 y - z^3, x^3 - 3yz^2)$

56. $\mathbf{F}(x, y) = -y\cos(xy)\mathbf{i} - x\cos(xy)\mathbf{j}$ 57. $\mathbf{F}(x, y) = (xy^2 + 3x^2 y)\mathbf{i} + (x^3 + yx^2)\mathbf{j}$

58. Let $f: \mathbb{R}^2 \to \mathbb{R}$ be given by

$$f(x, y) = \begin{cases} \dfrac{2xy}{x^2 + y^2} & \text{if } (x, y) \neq (0, 0) \\ 0 & \text{if } (x, y) = (0, 0) \end{cases}.$$

Compute $D_{\mathbf{u}} f(0, 0)$, where $\mathbf{u} = (u, v)$ is a unit vector in $\mathbb{R}^2$.

4.2 DIVERGENCE AND CURL OF A VECTOR FIELD

In this section we introduce and discuss two operations involving partial derivatives and use them to investigate the rate of change of a vector field.

Recall that a vector field $\mathbf{F}$ on $U \subseteq \mathbb{R}^3$ can be expressed as

$$\mathbf{F}(x, y, z) = (F_1(x, y, z), F_2(x, y, z), F_3(x, y, z)),$$

where the components F_1, F_2 and F_3 of $\mathbf{F}$ are real-valued functions. Sometimes we express the variables x, y and z as a vector $\mathbf{x} = (x, y, z)$ and write $\mathbf{F}(\mathbf{x}) = (F_1(\mathbf{x}), F_2(\mathbf{x}), F_3(\mathbf{x}))$. More often, we completely drop the variables and write $\mathbf{F} = (F_1, F_2, F_3)$.

■ **Definition 4.3**   Divergence and Curl of a Vector Field.

Let $\mathbf{F} = (F_1, F_2, F_3): U \subseteq \mathbb{R}^3 \to \mathbb{R}^3$ be a differentiable vector field. The *divergence* of $\mathbf{F}$ is the real-valued function

$$div\,\mathbf{F} = \frac{\partial F_1}{\partial x} + \frac{\partial F_2}{\partial y} + \frac{\partial F_3}{\partial z}.$$

The *curl* of $\mathbf{F}$ is the vector field

$$curl\,\mathbf{F} = \left(\frac{\partial F_3}{\partial y} - \frac{\partial F_2}{\partial z}\right)\mathbf{i} + \left(\frac{\partial F_1}{\partial z} - \frac{\partial F_3}{\partial x}\right)\mathbf{j} + \left(\frac{\partial F_2}{\partial x} - \frac{\partial F_1}{\partial y}\right)\mathbf{k}.$$ ■

The definition of the divergence generalizes in a straightforward way to a vector field $\mathbf{F}: U \subseteq \mathbb{R}^m \to \mathbb{R}^m$, $m \geq 2$. For example, $div\,\mathbf{F} = \partial F_1/\partial x + \partial F_2/\partial y$ if $\mathbf{F}(x, y) = (F_1(x, y), F_2(x, y))$ is a vector field on $U \subseteq \mathbb{R}^2$. The curl is defined for vector fields in $\mathbb{R}^3$ only. To find the curl of a vector field $\mathbf{F}(x, y) = (F_1(x, y), F_2(x, y))$ we have to express it as the vector field $(F_1(x, y), F_2(x, y), 0)$ in $\mathbb{R}^3$ and then use Definition 4.3 (see Examples 4.26 and 4.28).

Example 4.20   Let $\mathbf{F}(x, y, z) = (x^3, xy, e^{xyz})$. Compute $div\,\mathbf{F}$ and $curl\,\mathbf{F}$.

Solution   By definition,

$$div\,\mathbf{F} = \frac{\partial}{\partial x}\left(x^3\right) + \frac{\partial}{\partial y}\left(xy\right) + \frac{\partial}{\partial z}\left(e^{xyz}\right) = 3x^2 + x + xye^{xyz}$$

and

$$curl\,\mathbf{F} = \left(\frac{\partial}{\partial y}\left(e^{xyz}\right) - \frac{\partial}{\partial z}\left(xy\right)\right)\mathbf{i} + \left(\frac{\partial}{\partial z}\left(x^3\right) - \frac{\partial}{\partial x}\left(e^{xyz}\right)\right)\mathbf{j}$$
$$+ \left(\frac{\partial}{\partial x}\left(xy\right) - \frac{\partial}{\partial y}\left(x^3\right)\right)\mathbf{k}$$
$$= xze^{xyz}\mathbf{i} - yze^{xyz}\mathbf{j} + y\mathbf{k}.$$ ◀

We are going to introduce a formalism that is often used in computations involving gradient, divergence and curl.

In general, an *operator* acts on a function by assigning some other function to it. For example, the operator $A(y) = y''$ assigns the second derivative y'' to a twice differentiable function y; for example, $A(\sin x) = -\sin x$, $A(x^3 + 3) = 6x$, and so on.

Define the operator ∇ (pronounced "del") by

$$\nabla = \frac{\partial}{\partial x}\mathbf{i} + \frac{\partial}{\partial y}\mathbf{j} + \frac{\partial}{\partial z}\mathbf{k} = \left(\frac{\partial}{\partial x}, \frac{\partial}{\partial y}, \frac{\partial}{\partial z}\right).$$

Its action on a differentiable real-valued function $f: \mathbb{R}^3 \to \mathbb{R}$ is defined by

$$\nabla f = \frac{\partial f}{\partial x}\mathbf{i} + \frac{\partial f}{\partial y}\mathbf{j} + \frac{\partial f}{\partial z}\mathbf{k} = \left(\frac{\partial f}{\partial x}, \frac{\partial f}{\partial y}, \frac{\partial f}{\partial z}\right),$$

i.e., the ∇ operator assigns to f its gradient vector field $\nabla f = grad\ f$ (this justifies the notation ∇f that we have used already).

Now think of ∇ as a "vector" (it is not really a vector; for convenience, we will borrow two words from the vector vocabulary) and let $\mathbf{F} \colon \mathbb{R}^3 \to \mathbb{R}^3$ be a vector field. Define the action of ∇ on $\mathbf{F}$ by the scalar product as follows:

$$\nabla \cdot \mathbf{F} = \left(\frac{\partial}{\partial x}, \frac{\partial}{\partial y}, \frac{\partial}{\partial z} \right) \cdot (F_1, F_2, F_3) = \frac{\partial F_1}{\partial x} + \frac{\partial F_2}{\partial y} + \frac{\partial F_3}{\partial z}.$$

The expression on the right side is the divergence of F, and hence

$$div\ \mathbf{F} = \nabla \cdot \mathbf{F}.$$

If we consider the action of ∇ on $\mathbf{F}$ by the cross product,

$$\nabla \times \mathbf{F} = \begin{vmatrix} \mathbf{i} & \mathbf{j} & \mathbf{k} \\ \partial/\partial x & \partial/\partial y & \partial/\partial z \\ F_1 & F_2 & F_3 \end{vmatrix}$$

$$= \left(\frac{\partial F_3}{\partial y} - \frac{\partial F_2}{\partial z} \right) \mathbf{i} + \left(\frac{\partial F_1}{\partial z} - \frac{\partial F_3}{\partial x} \right) \mathbf{j} + \left(\frac{\partial F_2}{\partial x} - \frac{\partial F_1}{\partial y} \right) \mathbf{k},$$

we get that the resulting vector field is the curl of $\mathbf{F}$. Therefore

$$curl\ \mathbf{F} = \nabla \times \mathbf{F}.$$

Example 4.21   **Curl of an Electrostatic Field.**

Compute the curl of the electrostatic field $\mathbf{E}(\mathbf{r}) = Q\mathbf{r}/4\pi\epsilon_0 \|\mathbf{r}\|^3$, where $\mathbf{r} = x\mathbf{i} + y\mathbf{j} + z\mathbf{k}$.

Solution   All terms in the expression for the curl involve derivatives, and therefore we can factor out the constant $Q/4\pi\epsilon_0$ (see the comment following the example). We proceed as follows:

$$curl\ \mathbf{E} = \frac{Q}{4\pi\epsilon_0} \begin{vmatrix} \mathbf{i} & \mathbf{j} & \mathbf{k} \\ \partial/\partial x & \partial/\partial y & \partial/\partial z \\ x\left(x^2 + y^2 + z^2\right)^{-3/2} & y\left(x^2 + y^2 + z^2\right)^{-3/2} & z\left(x^2 + y^2 + z^2\right)^{-3/2} \end{vmatrix}$$

$$= \left(-\frac{3}{2}z\left(x^2 + y^2 + z^2\right)^{-5/2} 2y + \frac{3}{2}y\left(x^2 + y^2 + z^2\right)^{-5/2} 2z \right) \mathbf{i}$$

$$+ \left(-\frac{3}{2}z\left(x^2 + y^2 + z^2\right)^{-5/2} 2x + \frac{3}{2}x\left(x^2 + y^2 + z^2\right)^{-5/2} 2z \right) \mathbf{j}$$

$$+ \left(-\frac{3}{2}y\left(x^2 + y^2 + z^2\right)^{-5/2} 2x + \frac{3}{2}x\left(x^2 + y^2 + z^2\right)^{-5/2} 2y \right) \mathbf{k} = \mathbf{0},$$

in $\mathbb{R}^3 - \{(0, 0, 0)\}$.

Since the gradient, divergence and curl are built of (partial) derivatives, it is reasonable to expect that they satisfy properties of derivatives, namely linearity and the product rule — and indeed they do. Precise formulation of these properties can be found in Section

4.3. In this section we need only the fact that a constant C can be "factored out" of divergence and curl; i.e., $div\,(C\mathbf{F}) = C\,div\,\mathbf{F}$ and $curl\,(C\mathbf{F}) = C\,curl\,\mathbf{F}$ (the proofs are one-liners: just write out the left and right sides using the definitions and use the fact that the constant can be "factored out" of partial derivatives of real-valued functions).

■ **Theorem 4.5**   "Curl of Gradient and Divergence of Curl are Zero."

   (a) Let f be a twice continuously differentiable real-valued function. Then

$$curl(grad\ f) = \mathbf{0}.$$

   (b) Let $\mathbf{F}$ be a twice continuously differentiable vector field on $U \subseteq \mathbb{R}^3$. Then

$$div(curl\ \mathbf{F}) = 0. \qquad\qquad ■$$

Using the "∇ formalism" just introduced, the identities (a) and (b) can be written as $\nabla \times \nabla f = \mathbf{0}$ and $\nabla \cdot (\nabla \times \mathbf{F}) = 0$. A twice continuously differentiable function (vector field) is also called a C^2 function (vector field).

Proof

Both statements are proven by a straightforward computation with the use of appropriate definitions. To prove (a) we proceed as follows:

$$curl(grad\ f) = curl\left(\frac{\partial f}{\partial x}\mathbf{i} + \frac{\partial f}{\partial y}\mathbf{j} + \frac{\partial f}{\partial z}\mathbf{k}\right)$$

$$= \begin{vmatrix} \mathbf{i} & \mathbf{j} & \mathbf{k} \\ \partial/\partial x & \partial/\partial y & \partial/\partial z \\ \partial f/\partial x & \partial f/\partial y & \partial f/\partial z \end{vmatrix}$$

$$= \left(\frac{\partial^2 f}{\partial y \partial z} - \frac{\partial^2 f}{\partial z \partial y}\right)\mathbf{i} + \left(\frac{\partial^2 f}{\partial z \partial x} - \frac{\partial^2 f}{\partial x \partial z}\right)\mathbf{j} + \left(\frac{\partial^2 f}{\partial x \partial y} - \frac{\partial^2 f}{\partial y \partial x}\right)\mathbf{k} = \mathbf{0},$$

due to the equality of mixed partial derivatives (see Theorem 2.8 in Section 2.6); this is where the assumption on f is needed. The statement (b) is proven analogously. ■

Part (a) of the theorem serves as a useful test for checking whether a given vector field $\mathbf{F}$ is conservative or not. If $\mathbf{F}$ is a conservative field, then $\mathbf{F} = -\nabla V$ for some real-valued function and

$$curl\ \mathbf{F} = curl\,(-\nabla f) = -curl\,(\nabla f) = \mathbf{0}.$$

Equivalently, a vector field $\mathbf{F}$ with $curl\ \mathbf{F} \neq \mathbf{0}$ *cannot* be conservative. In Section 5.4 we will show that under certain conditions on the domain U of $\mathbf{F}$ (i.e., that it be simply connected) the implication goes both ways: $\mathbf{F}$ is conservative in U if and only if $curl\ \mathbf{F} = \mathbf{0}$ in U.

▨ **Definition 4.4**   The Laplace Operator.

The action of the *Laplace operator* (also called the *Laplacian* or the *Laplacian operator*)

Δ on a twice differentiable real-valued function f is defined by

$$\Delta f = div(grad\ f) = \nabla \cdot \nabla f.$$

The gradient of f is a vector field and therefore it makes sense to apply the divergence to it. Consequently, Δf is a real-valued function. The expression $\nabla \cdot \nabla f$ is sometimes abbreviated as $\nabla^2 f$. In Cartesian coordinates,

$$\Delta f = div\left(\frac{\partial f}{\partial x}\mathbf{i} + \frac{\partial f}{\partial y}\mathbf{j} + \frac{\partial f}{\partial z}\mathbf{k}\right) = \frac{\partial^2 f}{\partial x^2} + \frac{\partial^2 f}{\partial y^2} + \frac{\partial^2 f}{\partial z^2}.$$

The equation $\Delta f = 0$ is called *Laplace's equation*, and its solutions are called *harmonic functions*. The nonhomogeneous version of Laplace's equation $\Delta f = g$, where g is a continuous function, is (in some cases) called *Poisson's equation*.

Let $\mathbf{F} = (F_1, F_2, F_3)$ be a twice differentiable vector field. The action of the *Laplace operator* on $\mathbf{F}$ is defined by

$$\Delta \mathbf{F} = (\Delta F_1, \Delta F_2, \Delta F_3),$$

if the rectangular coordinates x, y and z are used.

Example 4.22 Gravitational Potential Satisfies Laplace's Equation.

Show that the gravitational potential $V(x, y, z) = -GMm/\|\mathbf{r}\|$, $\mathbf{r} = x\mathbf{i} + y\mathbf{j} + z\mathbf{k}$, satisfies Laplace's equation, $\Delta V = 0$.

Solution In Example 2.35 in Section 2.4 it was shown that

$$\nabla V(x, y, z) = \frac{GMm}{\|\mathbf{r}\|^3}\mathbf{r} = -\mathbf{F},$$

where $\mathbf{F} = (F_1, F_2, F_3)$ denotes the gravitational force field. Therefore

$$\Delta V = div(\nabla V) = -div\,\mathbf{F},$$

and it remains to show that $div\,\mathbf{F} = 0$. Since

$$\mathbf{F} = -GMm\left(\frac{x}{(x^2 + y^2 + z^2)^{3/2}}, \frac{y}{(x^2 + y^2 + z^2)^{3/2}}, \frac{z}{(x^2 + y^2 + z^2)^{3/2}}\right),$$

it follows that

$$\frac{\partial F_1}{\partial x} = -GMm\frac{(x^2 + y^2 + z^2)^{3/2} - 3x^2(x^2 + y^2 + z^2)^{1/2}}{(x^2 + y^2 + z^2)^3}$$

$$= -GMm\frac{(x^2 + y^2 + z^2)^{1/2}(x^2 + y^2 + z^2 - 3x^2)}{(x^2 + y^2 + z^2)^3}$$

$$= -GMm\frac{y^2 + z^2 - 2x^2}{(x^2 + y^2 + z^2)^{5/2}},$$

and similarly,

$$\frac{\partial F_2}{\partial y} = -GMm\frac{x^2 + z^2 - 2y^2}{(x^2 + y^2 + z^2)^{5/2}},$$

$$\frac{\partial F_3}{\partial z} = -GMm\frac{x^2 + y^2 - 2z^2}{(x^2 + y^2 + z^2)^{5/2}}.$$

Adding up the three partials, we get $div\, \mathbf{F} = 0$, in $\mathbb{R}^3 - \{(0,0,0)\}$. Consequently, the gravitational potential is a harmonic function.

◄

Example 4.23   Divergence of an Electrostatic Field.

We have just seen that the divergence of a gravitational force field equals zero. Changing constants G, m and M into $1/4\pi\epsilon_0$, q and Q we get that $div\, \mathbf{F} = 0$, where $\mathbf{F}$ now denotes an electrostatic force field. Since $\mathbf{E} = \mathbf{F}/q$, it follows that

$$div\, \mathbf{E} = (div\, \mathbf{F})/q = 0;$$

i.e., the divergence of an electrostatic field vanishes in $\mathbb{R}^3 - \{(0,0,0)\}$.

◄

Example 4.24   Show that $f(x,y) = \ln(x^2 + y^2)$ is a harmonic function whenever $(x,y) \neq (0,0)$.

Solution   By the chain rule and quotient rule

$$\frac{\partial^2 f}{\partial x^2} = \frac{\partial}{\partial x}\left(\frac{\partial f}{\partial x}\right) = \frac{\partial}{\partial x}\left(\frac{2x}{x^2 + y^2}\right) = \frac{2(x^2 + y^2) - 2x \cdot 2x}{(x^2 + y^2)^2} = \frac{-2x^2 + 2y^2}{(x^2 + y^2)^2}.$$

The function f is symmetric in x and y: exchanging x and y does not change f. Consequently, just exchange x and y in the expression for $\partial^2 f/\partial x^2$ to get

$$\frac{\partial^2 f}{\partial y^2} = \frac{-2y^2 + 2x^2}{(x^2 + y^2)^2}.$$

Therefore

$$\Delta f = \frac{\partial^2 f}{\partial x^2} + \frac{\partial^2 f}{\partial y^2} = 0,$$

which means that f is harmonic for $(x,y) \neq (0,0)$.

◄

The examples that follow give you an opportunity to improve your understanding of the curl and the divergence, and provide interpretations in physical situations connected with fluid flow.

Example 4.25   To illustrate the definition of the curl, let us compute the curl of a rotational vector field $\mathbf{F}$ pictured in Figure 4.6 at the point A. Assume that the z-component F_3 of $\mathbf{F}$ is zero (therefore $\partial F_3/\partial x = 0$ and $\partial F_3/\partial y = 0$), and that there is no variation of $\mathbf{F}$ in the z-direction, that is, $\partial F_1/\partial z = 0$ and $\partial F_2/\partial z = 0$. Looking at points on the x-axis that are close to A (i.e., going from A' to A'') we see that the y-component F_2 increases, and hence

$$\frac{\partial F_2}{\partial x} > 0$$

at A. Let us determine the rate of change of F_1 with respect to y. Below the x-axis (say, at B') F_1 is positive, it is 0 at A and negative above the x-axis (say, at B''). So F_1 changes from positive to negative values (i.e., it decreases) as we go through A in the y-direction, and consequently

$$\frac{\partial F_1}{\partial y} < 0$$

at A. The derivatives $\partial F_2/\partial x$ and $\partial F_1/\partial y$ are the only nonzero terms in the expression for the curl (see Definition 4.3): it follows that, at A, $curl\ \mathbf{F} = C\mathbf{k}$, where C is positive. ◀

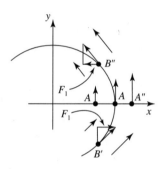

Figure 4.6 Rotational vector field $\mathbf{F}$ of Example 4.25.

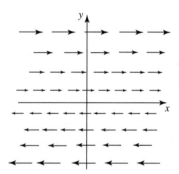

Figure 4.7 Vector field $\mathbf{F}(x, y) = g(y)\mathbf{i}$ of Example 4.26.

Example 4.26   Determine the curl of the vector field in Figure 4.7. Assume that $\mathbf{F} = \mathbf{0}$ on the x-axis.

Solution   Let us try to find a formula for $\mathbf{F}$. Clearly, both $\mathbf{j}$ and $\mathbf{k}$ components are zero. The $\mathbf{i}$ component increases as we move up along the y-axis (increases from negative values below the x-axis towards positive values above it). Hence $\mathbf{F} = g(y)\mathbf{i}$, where $g(0) = 0$ (so that $\mathbf{F} = \mathbf{0}$ on the x-axis) and g is increasing. By definition,

$$curl\ \mathbf{F} = \begin{vmatrix} \mathbf{i} & \mathbf{j} & \mathbf{k} \\ \partial/\partial x & \partial/\partial y & \partial/\partial z \\ g(y) & 0 & 0 \end{vmatrix} = -\frac{\partial g(y)}{\partial y}\mathbf{k},$$

with $\partial g(y)/\partial y > 0$ (since g is increasing). Therefore the vector $curl\ \mathbf{F}$ points into the page. ◀

Example 4.27

Rotation of a Rigid Body.

The velocity vector field of the rotation of a rigid body is given by (see Example 1.34 in Section 1.5):

$$\mathbf{v} = \mathbf{w} \times \mathbf{r},$$

where $\mathbf{r}$ denotes the position vector, $\mathbf{w} = (w_1, w_2, w_3)$ is the angular velocity vector (assumed to be constant) and $\mathbf{v}$ is the tangential velocity. Then

$$\mathbf{v} = \mathbf{w} \times \mathbf{r} = \begin{vmatrix} \mathbf{i} & \mathbf{j} & \mathbf{k} \\ w_1 & w_2 & w_3 \\ x & y & z \end{vmatrix} = (w_2 z - w_3 y)\mathbf{i} + (w_3 x - w_1 z)\mathbf{j} + (w_1 y - w_2 x)\mathbf{k}$$

and

$$curl\ \mathbf{v} = \begin{vmatrix} \mathbf{i} & \mathbf{j} & \mathbf{k} \\ \partial/\partial x & \partial/\partial y & \partial/\partial z \\ w_2 z - w_3 y & w_3 x - w_1 z & w_1 y - w_2 x \end{vmatrix} = 2(w_1 \mathbf{i} + w_2 \mathbf{j} + w_3 \mathbf{k}),$$

i.e., $curl\ \mathbf{v} = 2\mathbf{w}$. Therefore, the curl of the velocity vector of the rotation of a rigid body is parallel to the axis of rotation (given by the direction of $\mathbf{w}$) and its magnitude is twice the angular speed of rotation.

◀

In the previous example we gave an interpretation of the curl in the context of the rotation of a rigid body. Here is another interpretation connected with fluid flow. We present it at this moment although we will not be able to justify our statements until we introduce Stokes' Theorem in the last chapter.

Suppose that a vector field $\mathbf{F}$ describes the flow of a fluid. If $curl\ \mathbf{F} = \mathbf{0}$ at some point P then there are no rotations (whirlpools) in the flow at that point (the flow itself could be circular, but *within* the flow there are no rotations). More precisely, imagine that we place a coordinate system on a small floating device. "No rotations" means that the coordinate system does not rotate around its origin as our object moves along with the flow; see Figure 4.8(a).

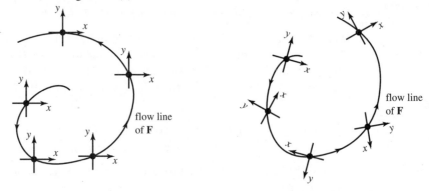

Figure 4.8 Vector fields in $\mathbb{R}^2$ (visualized through flow lines).

(a) irrotational; i.e., zero curl   (b) not irrotational; i.e., non-zero curl

curl $\mathbf{F} \neq \mathbf{0}$ allows rotations of a small coordinate system; see Figure 4.8(b). In other words, *curl* $\mathbf{F}$ is a measurement of the tendency of a fluid to swirl around an axis. We will explain this in more detail in Section 8.3. A field $\mathbf{F}$ with *curl* $\mathbf{F} = \mathbf{0}$ at a point P is called *irrotational at P*.

Example 4.28   Check that the vector field $\mathbf{F}_1 = \mathbf{i}y/(x^2 + y^2) - \mathbf{j}x/(x^2 + y^2)$ is irrotational whenever $(x, y) \neq (0, 0)$, but the vector field $\mathbf{F}_2 = y\mathbf{i} - x\mathbf{j}$ is not irrotational at any point.

Solution   By definition,

$$curl\, \mathbf{F}_1 = \begin{vmatrix} \mathbf{i} & \mathbf{j} & \mathbf{k} \\ \partial/\partial x & \partial/\partial y & \partial/\partial z \\ y/(x^2 + y^2) & -x/(x^2 + y^2) & 0 \end{vmatrix}$$

$$= 0\mathbf{i} + 0\mathbf{j} + \left(\frac{\partial}{\partial x} \left(\frac{-x}{x^2 + y^2} \right) - \frac{\partial}{\partial y} \left(\frac{y}{x^2 + y^2} \right) \right) \mathbf{k}$$

$$= \left(\frac{-(x^2 + y^2) + x \cdot 2x}{(x^2 + y^2)^2} - \frac{(x^2 + y^2) - y \cdot 2y}{(x^2 + y^2)^2} \right) \mathbf{k} = \mathbf{0}.$$

However,

$$curl\, \mathbf{F}_2 = \begin{vmatrix} \mathbf{i} & \mathbf{j} & \mathbf{k} \\ \partial/\partial x & \partial/\partial y & \partial/\partial z \\ y & -x & 0 \end{vmatrix} = \left(\frac{\partial}{\partial x}(-x) - \frac{\partial}{\partial y}(y) \right) \mathbf{k} = -2\mathbf{k}.$$

The vector fields $\mathbf{F}_1$ and $\mathbf{F}_2$ of the previous example have the same flow lines (they are concentric circles; that was shown in Examples 3.43 and 3.44 in Section 3.6). However, $\mathbf{F}_1$ is irrotational and $\mathbf{F}_2$ is not. That means that we cannot determine whether a vector field is irrotational or not just by looking at its flow lines.

Now let us turn to a physical interpretation of the divergence. Consider the motion of a compressible fluid (such as a vapor or a gas) in $\mathbb{R}^2$, with no sources or sinks (i.e., there are no points where extra amounts of fluid are produced or where fluid disappears). We choose $\mathbb{R}^2$ rather than $\mathbb{R}^3$ to simplify the computations.

Let $\mathbf{F}(x, y, t)$ be a vector field describing the flow of the fluid and let $\rho(x, y, t)$ be its density. Assume that both $\mathbf{F}$ and ρ are differentiable functions of their variables (the variable t denotes time and the variables (x, y) give the location of a point in the flow). Consider a small rectangle R with sides Δx and Δy; see Figure 4.9. We are going to approximate the flux across the boundary of R; i.e., the change of mass of fluid in R due to the flow.

By the conservation of mass principle,

$$\text{loss of mass in } R = \text{outflowing mass} - \text{inflowing mass}. \qquad (4.2)$$

Furthermore,

$$\text{loss of mass in } R = \text{time rate change of mass} \cdot \text{time}.$$

Since mass = density $\cdot$ area, and the area of R is fixed,

$$\text{loss of mass in } R = \text{time rate change of density} \cdot \text{area} \cdot \text{time}$$

$$= -\frac{\partial \rho}{\partial t} \Delta x \, \Delta y \, \Delta t.$$

Let us clarify the appearance of the minus sign in the formula. If the derivative of the density $\partial \rho / \partial t$ is positive at some point in R, then the density increases at that point; i.e., more mass is coming in than is flowing out. Hence the *gain* in mass is $(\partial \rho / \partial t) \Delta x \, \Delta y \, \Delta t$ (which is positive), and the *loss* is $-(\partial \rho / \partial t) \Delta x \, \Delta y \, \Delta t$. If $\partial \rho / \partial t < 0$ then the density is decreasing, and more mass is flowing out than is coming in. Hence the *gain* in the mass is $(\partial \rho / \partial t) \Delta x \, \Delta y \, \Delta t$ (which is now negative), i.e., the *loss* is $-(\partial \rho / \partial t) \Delta x \, \Delta y \, \Delta t$. (A little dictionary for translating into everyday language: positive gain means gain, negative gain means loss, positive loss means loss, and negative loss means gain.)

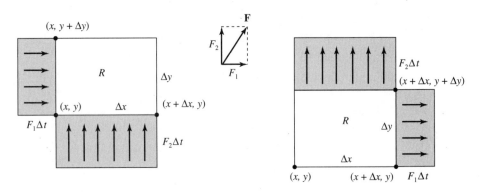

Figure 4.9   Mass inflow into R.   **Figure 4.10**   Mass outflow from R.

Now let us compute the inflowing mass. Only the x-component F_1 of $\mathbf{F}$ contributes to the flow through the left side of R, and hence (approximately)

$$\text{mass inflow (left side)} = \text{density} \cdot \text{"area,"}$$

(where "area" = area occupied by particles that flow into R in time Δt)

$$= \text{density} \cdot \text{base} \cdot \text{height}$$

(since base = velocity · time)

$$= \rho(x, y, t) F_1(x, y, t) \Delta t \, \Delta y.$$

We have assumed that the left side (of length Δy) is so small that ρ and F_1 have approximately the same values (equal to $\rho(x, y, t)$ and $F_1(x, y, t)$ respectively) at points near that side. With a similar assumption for the lower side

$$\text{mass inflow (lower side)} = \rho(x, y, t) F_2(x, y, t) \Delta t \, \Delta x,$$

since only the y-component F_2 of $\mathbf{F}$ contributes to the inflow. The total inflow into R is

$$\rho(x, y, t) F_1(x, y, t) \Delta t \, \Delta y + \rho(x, y, t) F_2(x, y, t) \Delta t \, \Delta x$$
$$= \Delta t \big(\rho(x, y, t) F_1(x, y, t) \Delta y + \rho(x, y, t) F_2(x, y, t) \Delta x \big)$$

(multiply and divide by $\Delta x \, \Delta y$)

$$= \Delta t \Delta x \Delta y \left(\rho(x, y, t) \frac{F_1(x, y, t)}{\Delta x} + \rho(x, y, t) \frac{F_2(x, y, t)}{\Delta y} \right).$$

Analogous computations give (see Figure 4.10)

$$\text{mass outflow (right side)} = \rho(x + \Delta x, y, t) F_1(x + \Delta x, y, t) \Delta t \Delta y$$

(we assume that Δy is so small that the density ρ and the component F_1 have approximately the same values (equal to $\rho(x + \Delta x, y, t)$ and $F_1(x + \Delta x, y, t)$ respectively) at points near the right edge of R). With a similar assumption for the upper side,

$$\text{mass outflow (upper side)} = \rho(x, y + \Delta y, t) F_2(x, y + \Delta y, t) \Delta t \Delta x.$$

The total outflow from R equals

$$\rho(x + \Delta x, y, t) F_1(x + \Delta x, y, t) \Delta t \Delta y + \rho(x, y + \Delta y, t) F_2(x, y + \Delta y, t) \Delta t \Delta x$$

$$= \Delta t \big(\rho(x + \Delta x, y, t) F_1(x + \Delta x, y, t) \Delta y + \rho(x, y + \Delta y, t) F_2(x, y + \Delta y, t) \Delta x \big)$$

$$= \Delta t \Delta x \Delta y \left(\rho(x + \Delta x, y, t) \frac{F_1(x + \Delta x, y, t)}{\Delta x} + \rho(x, y + \Delta y, t) \frac{F_2(x, y + \Delta y, t)}{\Delta y} \right).$$

Now substitute the expressions for the loss of mass, total inflow and total outflow into the conservation of mass formula (4.2):

$$-\frac{\partial \rho}{\partial t} \Delta x \Delta y \Delta t = \Delta x \Delta y \Delta t \left(\frac{\rho(x + \Delta x, y, t) F_1(x + \Delta x, y, t) - \rho(x, y, t) F_1(x, y, t)}{\Delta x} \right.$$

$$\left. + \frac{\rho(x, y + \Delta y, t) F_2(x, y + \Delta y, t) - \rho(x, y, t) F_2(x, y, t)}{\Delta y} \right),$$

divide by $\Delta x \Delta y \Delta t$ and let $\Delta x \to 0$ and $\Delta y \to 0$, thus getting

$$-\frac{\partial \rho}{\partial t} = \frac{\partial}{\partial x} \big(\rho(x, y, t) F_1(x, y, t) \big) + \frac{\partial}{\partial y} \big(\rho(x, y, t) F_2(x, y, t) \big),$$

(by using the definition of the partial derivatives of ρF_1 with respect to x and ρF_2 with respect to y) i.e.,

$$\frac{\partial \rho}{\partial t} + div(\rho \mathbf{F}) = 0.$$

This equation is called the *continuity equation* for compressible fluid flow.

The density $\rho = \rho(x, y, t)$ is in general a function of position and time. If $\partial \rho / \partial t = 0$ (i.e., the density is not explicitly dependent on time) then the continuity equation implies that

$$div(\rho \mathbf{F}) = 0.$$

If the density of the fluid is constant (i.e., $\partial \rho / \partial x = 0$ and $\partial \rho / \partial y = 0$) then $div(\rho \mathbf{F}) = \rho\, div\, \mathbf{F} = 0$, hence $div\, \mathbf{F} = 0$. In this case the total outflow from R equals the total inflow to R. Keeping this in mind we say that the vector field $\mathbf{F}$ is *incompressible* if $div\, \mathbf{F} = 0$.

An interpretation of the divergence that involves integral theorems will be given in the last chapter (see Section 8.2).

In light of our discussion we interpret intuitively the divergence of a vector field as a total outflow (or total outflux) per unit area. Let us consider a few examples.

Example 4.29   Argue geometrically that the divergence of $\mathbf{F}(x, y) = x\mathbf{i}$ shown in Figure 4.11 is positive.

Solution   In this case, there is no flow in the y-direction, and the flow in the x-direction increases as x increases. The flow out of the rectangle R of small area is larger than the inflow, and consequently, the divergence is positive. The definition gives that $div\,\mathbf{F} = 1$, which confirms our conclusion.   ◀

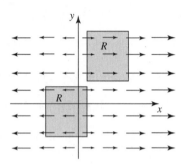

Figure 4.11   Vector field $\mathbf{F}(x, y) = x\mathbf{i}$.   **Figure 4.12**   Vector field $\mathbf{F}$ of Example 4.30.

Example 4.30   Determine the divergence of the vector field $\mathbf{F}$ in Figure 4.12.

Solution   There is no flow in the direction of the y-axis, and the flow in the x-direction is constant along horizontal lines. Therefore the inflow along any horizontal line is the same as the outflow, and the divergence is zero (at every point). One can use the definition $div\,\mathbf{F} = \partial F_1/\partial x + \partial F_2/\partial y$ and argue as follows: clearly, $F_2 = 0$, and hence $\partial F_2/\partial y = 0$. The derivative $\partial F_1/\partial x$ represents the rate of change of the component F_1 in the x-direction; but F_1 does not change in the horizontal directions, and therefore $\partial F_1/\partial x = 0$.   ◀

Example 4.31   Explain why the divergence of the rotational vector field $\mathbf{F}(x, y) = (-y, x)$ is equal to zero.

Solution   Pick a point A on the x-axis (see Figure 4.13). The x-component F_1 of $\mathbf{F}$ is zero along the x-axis, and hence $\partial F_1/\partial x = 0$. Consider the y-components F_2 of vectors on the flow line which goes through A. As we move from A' towards A, we realize that F_2 increases, reaches its maximal value at A, and then starts decreasing. Hence $\partial F_2/\partial y = 0$ at A (since it is a critical point) and $div\,\mathbf{F} = 0$. From the rotational symmetry it follows that $div\,\mathbf{F} = 0$ everywhere.   ◀

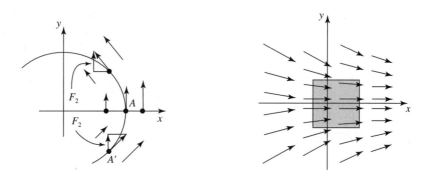

Figure 4.13 Vector field $\mathbf{F}(x, y) = (-y, x)$.   **Figure 4.14** Vector field $\mathbf{F}$ of Example 4.32.

Example 4.32 Determine the sign of the divergence of the vector field $\mathbf{F}$ in Figure 4.14.

Solution Place a rectangular "window" of small area in the flow as shown: the mass (or fluid particles, or stream of sand particles in a sand storm, or electrons) flows in through three sides; and the inflow is stronger ($\|\mathbf{F}\|$ is larger) than the outflow through the right side. Consequently, the divergence (i.e., the difference between the ouflow and inflow) of this field is negative.

◀

Example 4.33 Laplace Operator Describes Diffusion.

The concentration of a liquid changes ("diffuses") when some chemical is dissolved in it. The heat of a solid "diffuses," "flowing" from warmer regions towards cooler ones. Such processes of "transport" (or "transfer") are described by a *flux density vector field* $\mathbf{F}$. In the case of heat transfer, $\mathbf{F} = -k\nabla T$, where T is the temperature (see Example 4.14). Heat transfer is a special case of *Fick's Law,* which states that the flux vector $\mathbf{F}$ is always parallel (and of the opposite direction) to the gradient of the "species" concentration:

$$\mathbf{F}(x, y, z) = -k\nabla f(x, y, z);$$

see Figure 4.15. For example, $f(x, y, z)$ could be the concentration of bacteria in air or the concentration of acid in a water solution. The symbol k ($k > 0$) denotes a constant, whose name (*conductivity, diffusivity*) depends on the process considered. The minus sign in Fick's Law indicates that the direction of the flow is always *away* from regions of higher concentration.

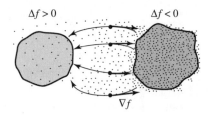

Figure 4.15 The Laplace operator describes a diffusion process.

The divergence of **F** is

$$div\,\mathbf{F}(x, y, z) = -k\,div\,(\nabla f(x, y, z)) = -k\Delta f(x, y, z).$$

We have seen that the divergence measures the net outflow of the "species" (that is, "species that go out" − "species that go in"). At a point where the Laplacian Δ is negative, the outflow is positive, and the "species" must "go away" from that point; i.e., the concentration decreases. Similarly, if $\Delta f(x, y, z) > 0$ then $div\,\mathbf{F} < 0$ and therefore the inflow is larger than the outflow, and the concentration increases. (It is assumed, of course, that there are no outside "sources" or "sinks.") The equilibrium for a diffusion process is attained when the concentration "evens out" or "averages out" — in that case the flow "stops" and the Laplacian of f is zero.

◀

EXERCISES 4.2

Exercises 1 to 8: Let f be a scalar function and let **F** and **G** be vector fields in $\mathbb{R}^3$. State whether each expression is a scalar function, a vector field or meaningless.

  1. $grad\,(grad\,f)$ **2.** $curl\,(grad\,f) - \mathbf{G}$

  3. $curl\,(curl\,\mathbf{F}) - \mathbf{G}$ **4.** $(curl\,\mathbf{F}) \cdot \mathbf{G}$

  5. $curl\,(\mathbf{F} - \mathbf{G}) \times grad\,(div\,\mathbf{F})$ **6.** $div\,(div\,\mathbf{F})$

  7. $div\,(curl\,(grad\,f))$ **8.** $grad\,f^2 \times grad\,(\mathbf{F} \cdot \mathbf{G})$

Exercises 9 to 14: Find the curl and the divergence of the vector field **F**.

  9. $\mathbf{F}(x, y, z) = y^2 z\mathbf{i} - xz\mathbf{j} + xyz\mathbf{k}$ **10.** $\mathbf{F}(x, y, z) = \sin^2 x\mathbf{i} + \cos^2 x\mathbf{j} + 3\mathbf{k}$

11. $\mathbf{F}(x, y, z) = -ze^{-y}\mathbf{i} + xe^y\mathbf{j}$ **12.** $\mathbf{F}(x, y, z) = (\ln z + xy)\mathbf{k}$

13. $\mathbf{F}(x, y, z) = (x^2 + y^2 + z^2)(3\mathbf{i} + \mathbf{j} - \mathbf{k})$ **14.** $\mathbf{F}(x, y, z) = e^{xy}\mathbf{i} + e^{yz}\mathbf{j} + e^{xz}\mathbf{k}$

Exercises 15 to 19: It will be shown in the next chapter that a vector field **F** defined on all of $\mathbb{R}^3$ (or all of $\mathbb{R}^2$) is conservative if and only if $curl\,\mathbf{F} = \mathbf{0}$. Determine whether the vector field **F** is conservative or not. If it is, find its potential function (i.e., find a real-valued function V such that $\mathbf{F} = -grad\,V$).

15. $\mathbf{F}(x, y, z) = \cos y\mathbf{i} + \sin x\mathbf{j} + \tan z\mathbf{k}$

16. $\mathbf{F}(x, y, z) = -y^2 z\mathbf{i} + (3y^2/2 - 2xyz)\mathbf{j} - xy^2\mathbf{k}$

17. $\mathbf{F}(x, y) = 3x^2 y\mathbf{i} + (x^3 + y^3)\mathbf{j}$ **18.** $\mathbf{F}(x, y, z) = x\mathbf{i} + y^2\mathbf{j} + z\mathbf{k}$

19. $\mathbf{F}(x, y, z) = -y\mathbf{i} - x\mathbf{j} - 3\mathbf{k}$

20. Check whether the vector field $\mathbf{F}(x, y) = \mathbf{i}/(x \ln xy) + \mathbf{j}/(y \ln xy)$ is conservative for $x, y > 0$, and if so, find all functions f such that $\mathbf{F} = grad\, f$.

21. Verify that $curl\,(grad\, f) = \mathbf{0}$ for the function $f(x, y, z) = (x^2 + y^2 + z^2)^{-1}$.

22. Verify that $\partial(curl\,\mathbf{F})_1/\partial x + \partial(curl\,\mathbf{F})_2/\partial y + \partial(curl\,\mathbf{F})_3/\partial z = 0$ for the vector field $\mathbf{F}(x, y, z) = 3x^3y^2\mathbf{i} + yx^2\mathbf{j} - x^3z^3\mathbf{k}$, where $(curl\,\mathbf{F})_1$, $(curl\,\mathbf{F})_2$ and $(curl\,\mathbf{F})_3$ are the components of $curl\,\mathbf{F}$.

23. Is there a C^2 vector field $\mathbf{F}$ such that $curl\,\mathbf{F} = xy^2\mathbf{i} + yz^2\mathbf{j} + zx^2\mathbf{k}$? Explain.

24. Is there a C^2 vector field $\mathbf{F}$ such that $curl\,\mathbf{F} = 2\mathbf{i} + \mathbf{j} + 3\mathbf{k}$? If so, find it.

25. A vector field $\mathbf{F}$ is irrotational if $curl\,\mathbf{F} = \mathbf{0}$. Show that any vector field of the form $\mathbf{F}(x, y, z) = f(x)\mathbf{i} + g(y)\mathbf{j} + h(z)\mathbf{k}$, where f, g and h are differentiable real-valued functions of one variable, is irrotational.

26. A vector field $\mathbf{F}$ is incompressible if $div\,\mathbf{F} = 0$. Show that any vector field of the form $\mathbf{F}(x, y, z) = f(y, z)\mathbf{i} + g(x, z)\mathbf{j} + h(x, y)\mathbf{k}$, where f, g and h are differentiable real-valued functions of two variables, is incompressible.

27. (For those familiar with complex numbers.) Show that the real and imaginary parts of the complex-valued function $z = (x - iy)^3$ (taken as the $\mathbf{i}$ and $\mathbf{j}$ components of a vector field whose $\mathbf{k}$ component is equal to 0) define an incompressible and irrotational vector field.

Exercises 28 to 31: Decompose the vector field $\mathbf{F}$ as a sum of an irrotational and an incompressible vector field. Is such a decomposition unique?

28. $\mathbf{F} = (x^2 + e^{yz})\mathbf{i} + x^2z^2\mathbf{j} + \sin z\mathbf{k}$ 29. $\mathbf{F} = z\mathbf{i} + 2\mathbf{j} - z\mathbf{k}$

30. $\mathbf{F} = (x + y + z)\mathbf{i} + (y^2 + 1)\mathbf{j} + \ln(xyz)\mathbf{k}$ 31. $\mathbf{F} = -4\mathbf{i} + e^{2y}\mathbf{j} + \arctan z\mathbf{k}$

32. Find constants a, b and c so that the vector field $\mathbf{F} = (3x - y + az)\mathbf{i} + (bx - z)\mathbf{j} + (4x + cy)\mathbf{k}$ is irrotational. Find the scalar function f so that $\mathbf{F} = grad\, f$.

33. Show that if the function $f(x, y, z)$ is harmonic (i.e., if it satisfies Laplace's equation $\Delta f = 0$) then $grad\, f$ is not only an irrotational vector field but also an incompressible vector field.

34. Find the most general differentiable function $f(\|\mathbf{r}\|)$ defined on $\mathbb{R}^2$ such that the vector field $f(\|\mathbf{r}\|)\mathbf{r}$ is incompressible.

35. Show that the vector field $\mathbf{F} = (2x^2 + 8xy^2z)\mathbf{i} + (3x^3y - 3xy)\mathbf{j} - (4y^2z^2 + 2x^3z)\mathbf{k}$ is not incompressible but the vector field $\mathbf{G} = xyz^2\mathbf{F}$ is incompressible.

36. Prove that $\mathbf{F} \times \mathbf{G}$ is incompressible if the vector fields $\mathbf{F}$ and $\mathbf{G}$ are irrotational.

37. If f is a differentiable function of one variable, show that $f(\|\mathbf{r}\|)\mathbf{r}$ is an irrotational vector field.

Exercises 38 to 46: Prove the following identities, assuming that the functions and vector fields involved are differentiable as many times as needed. State those assumptions in each case. The vector $\mathbf{r}$ is the position vector $\mathbf{r} = x\mathbf{i} + y\mathbf{j} + z\mathbf{k}$.

38. $div\,(f\mathbf{F}) = f\,div\,\mathbf{F} + \mathbf{F} \cdot grad\, f$ 39. $curl\,(f\mathbf{F}) = f\,curl\,\mathbf{F} + (grad\, f) \times \mathbf{F}$

40. $curl\,\mathbf{r} = \mathbf{0}$ 41. $div\,\mathbf{r} = 3$

42. $grad\,\|\mathbf{r}\| = \dfrac{\mathbf{r}}{\|\mathbf{r}\|}$ 43. $div\,(\|\mathbf{r}\|\mathbf{r}) = 4\|\mathbf{r}\|$

44. $div\,(\mathbf{F} \times \mathbf{G}) = \mathbf{G} \cdot curl\,\mathbf{F} - \mathbf{F} \cdot curl\,\mathbf{G}$

45. $div\,(grad\, f \times grad\, g) = 0$ 46. $\Delta\|\mathbf{r}\|^3 = 12\|\mathbf{r}\|$

47. Evaluate the expression $div\,(\mathbf{F} \times \mathbf{r})$ if $curl\,\mathbf{F} = \mathbf{0}$, and $\mathbf{r} = x\mathbf{i} + y\mathbf{j} + z\mathbf{k}$.

48. Evaluate the expression $curl\,(f(\|\mathbf{r}\|)\mathbf{r})$, where f is a differentiable scalar function and $\mathbf{r} = x\mathbf{i} + y\mathbf{j} + z\mathbf{k}$.

49. It can be easily checked that $curl\,\mathbf{r} = \mathbf{0}$, where $\mathbf{r} = x\mathbf{i} + y\mathbf{j} + z\mathbf{k}$. Interpret this result physically, by visualizing $\mathbf{r}$ as the velocity vector field of a fluid.

50. Consider the following vector fields.

  (a) $\mathbf{F} = -y\mathbf{i} + x\mathbf{j}$ **(b)** $\mathbf{G} = \mathbf{F}/\sqrt{x^2 + y^2}$ **(c)** $\mathbf{H} = \mathbf{F}/(x^2 + y^2)$

Compare their divergences and curls. Show that circles centered at the origin are the flow lines for all three vector fields. Describe their differences in physical terms.

51. Find $grad\,(div\,\mathbf{F})$ if $\mathbf{F} = \dfrac{\mathbf{r}}{\|\mathbf{r}\|}$ and $\mathbf{r} = x\mathbf{i} + y\mathbf{j} + z\mathbf{k}$.

4.3   SOME IDENTITIES OF VECTOR ANALYSIS

In this section we give some identities illustrating relationships among the differential operators $grad$, div, $curl$ and Δ and their properties with respect to algebraic operations on functions and vector fields, and with respect to vector operations. After listing the identities we will prove some of them (the proofs are all computational and use relevant definitions and rules for differentiation).

Assume that f and g are differentiable (once or twice, as needed) real-valued functions and $\mathbf{F}$ and $\mathbf{G}$ are differentiable (once or twice, as needed) vector fields. If a statement involves a cross product, then f and g are assumed to be functions of three variables and $\mathbf{F}$ and $\mathbf{G}$ are assumed to be defined on a subset of $\mathbb{R}^3$. Let C denote any constant.

Linearity properties.

$$grad\,(f + g) = grad\,f + grad\,g, \qquad grad\,(Cf) = C\,grad\,f$$
$$div\,(\mathbf{F} + \mathbf{G}) = div\,\mathbf{F} + div\,\mathbf{G}, \qquad div\,(C\mathbf{F}) = C\,div\,\mathbf{F}$$
$$curl\,(\mathbf{F} + \mathbf{G}) = curl\,\mathbf{F} + curl\,\mathbf{G}, \qquad curl\,(C\mathbf{F}) = C\,curl\,\mathbf{F}$$
$$\Delta(f + g) = \Delta f + \Delta g, \qquad \Delta(Cf) = C\Delta f$$
$$\Delta(\mathbf{F} + \mathbf{G}) = \Delta\mathbf{F} + \Delta\mathbf{G}, \qquad \Delta(C\mathbf{F}) = C\Delta\mathbf{F}$$

Recall that, in Cartesian coordinates, the action of the Laplace operator on a twice differentiable vector field $\mathbf{F}$ is defined componentwise; i.e., $\Delta\mathbf{F} = (\Delta F_1, \Delta F_2, \Delta F_3)$.

Product rules.

$$grad\,(fg)(\mathbf{x}) = g(\mathbf{x})\,grad\,f(\mathbf{x}) + f(\mathbf{x})\,grad\,g(\mathbf{x})$$
$$grad\left(\frac{f}{g}\right)(\mathbf{x}) = \frac{g(\mathbf{x})\,grad\,f(\mathbf{x}) - f(\mathbf{x})\,grad\,g(\mathbf{x})}{g(\mathbf{x})^2}, \qquad \text{if } g(\mathbf{x}) \neq 0$$

Before moving to the next identity we have to introduce a piece of notation appearing there and in some other formulas. Given vector fields $\mathbf{F} = (F_1, F_2, F_3)$ and $\mathbf{G} =$

(G_1, G_2, G_3), the expression $(\mathbf{F} \cdot \nabla)\mathbf{G}$ denotes the vector field whose components are $(\mathbf{F} \cdot (grad\, G_1), \mathbf{F} \cdot (grad\, G_2), \mathbf{F} \cdot (grad\, G_3))$. In words, the components of $(\mathbf{F} \cdot \nabla)\mathbf{G}$ are dot products of the vector field $\mathbf{F}$ and the vector field that is the gradient of the corresponding component of $\mathbf{G}$.

$$grad\,(\mathbf{F} \cdot \mathbf{G}) = (\mathbf{F} \cdot \nabla)\mathbf{G} + (\mathbf{G} \cdot \nabla)\mathbf{F} + \mathbf{F} \times curl\,\mathbf{G} + \mathbf{G} \times curl\,\mathbf{F}$$

$$div\,(f\mathbf{F}) = f\,div\,\mathbf{F} + \mathbf{F} \cdot grad\,f$$

$$div\,(\mathbf{F} \times \mathbf{G}) = \mathbf{G} \cdot curl\,\mathbf{F} - \mathbf{F} \cdot curl\,\mathbf{G} \qquad (4.3)$$

$$curl\,(f\mathbf{F}) = f\,curl\,\mathbf{F} + grad\,f \times \mathbf{F}$$

$$curl\,(\mathbf{F} \times \mathbf{G}) = \mathbf{F}\,div\,\mathbf{G} - \mathbf{G}\,div\,\mathbf{F} + (\mathbf{G} \cdot \nabla)\mathbf{F} - (\mathbf{F} \cdot \nabla)\mathbf{G}$$

$$\Delta(fg) = g\Delta f + f\Delta g + 2\,grad\,f \cdot grad\,g$$

$$\Delta(\mathbf{F} \cdot \mathbf{G}) = \mathbf{G} \cdot \Delta\mathbf{F} + \mathbf{F} \cdot \Delta\mathbf{G} + 2\,grad\,\mathbf{F} \cdot grad\,\mathbf{G}, \qquad (4.4)$$

where $grad\,\mathbf{F} \cdot grad\,\mathbf{G}$ denotes the scalar field

$$grad\,\mathbf{F} \cdot grad\,\mathbf{G} = (grad\,F_1) \cdot (grad\,G_1) + (grad\,F_2) \cdot (grad\,G_2)$$
$$+ (grad\,F_3) \cdot (grad\,G_3).$$

Combinations of two operators.

$$div\,(grad\,f) = \Delta f \qquad (4.5)$$

$$div\,(curl\,\mathbf{F}) = 0 \qquad (4.6)$$

$$curl\,(grad\,f) = \mathbf{0} \qquad (4.7)$$

$$curl\,(curl\,\mathbf{F}) = grad\,(div\,\mathbf{F}) - \Delta\mathbf{F} \qquad (4.8)$$

$$div\,(grad\,f \times grad\,g) = 0$$

$$div\,(g\,grad\,f \times f\,grad\,g) = 0$$

$$div\,(f\,grad\,g) = f\Delta g + grad\,f \cdot grad\,g$$

$$div\,(f\,grad\,g - g\,grad\,f) = f\Delta g - g\Delta f$$

Miscellanea. Let $\mathbf{r} = x\mathbf{i} + y\mathbf{j} + z\mathbf{k}$ and $\|\mathbf{r}\| = \sqrt{x^2 + y^2 + z^2}$. Assume that f is a differentiable real-valued function and let n be a real number. If there is a fraction involved (for example, the exponent n could be negative) it is assumed that its denominator is not zero.

$$grad\,\left(\|\mathbf{r}\|^n\right) = n\|\mathbf{r}\|^{n-2}\,\mathbf{r} \qquad (4.9)$$

$$grad\,\left(f^n\right) = nf^{n-1}\,grad\,f$$

$$grad\,\left(\frac{1}{\|\mathbf{r}\|}\right) = -\frac{\mathbf{r}}{\|\mathbf{r}\|^3} \qquad (4.10)$$

$$div\,\frac{\mathbf{r}}{\|\mathbf{r}\|^3} = 0 \qquad (4.11)$$

$$curl\,\mathbf{r} = \mathbf{0}$$

$$curl\,(\|\mathbf{r}\|^n\mathbf{r}) = \mathbf{0} \qquad (4.12)$$

$$\Delta\left(\frac{1}{\|\mathbf{r}\|}\right) = 0 \qquad (4.13)$$

$$\Delta\left(\|\mathbf{r}\|^n\right) = n(n+1)\|\mathbf{r}\|^{n-2}$$

Chain rule. If $f = f(u, v, w)$ and $u = u(x, y, z)$, $v = v(x, y, z)$ and $w = w(x, y, z)$, then

$$grad\, f(u, v, w) = \frac{\partial f}{\partial u}\, grad\, u + \frac{\partial f}{\partial v}\, grad\, v + \frac{\partial f}{\partial w}\, grad\, w. \qquad (4.14) \quad \blacksquare$$

Formula (4.5) is the definition of the Laplace operator, and (4.6) and (4.7) were proven in Theorem 4.5. Identity (4.10) was proven in Example 2.35 in Section 2.4 and (4.11) was proven in Example 4.22. Equation (4.13) follows from (4.5), (4.10) and (4.11), since

$$\Delta\left(\frac{1}{\|\mathbf{r}\|}\right) = div\left(grad\,\frac{1}{\|\mathbf{r}\|}\right) = -div\left(\frac{\mathbf{r}}{\|\mathbf{r}\|^3}\right) = 0.$$

Next, we give proofs of (4.3), (4.4), (4.8), (4.12), and (4.14).

Proof of (4.3): The left side is computed to be

$$div(\mathbf{F} \times \mathbf{G}) = div \begin{vmatrix} \mathbf{i} & \mathbf{j} & \mathbf{k} \\ F_1 & F_2 & F_3 \\ G_1 & G_2 & G_3 \end{vmatrix}$$

$$= div\left((F_2 G_3 - F_3 G_2)\mathbf{i} - (F_1 G_3 - F_3 G_1)\mathbf{j} + (F_1 G_2 - F_2 G_1)\mathbf{k}\right)$$

$$= \frac{\partial}{\partial x}(F_2 G_3 - F_3 G_2) - \frac{\partial}{\partial y}(F_1 G_3 - F_3 G_1) + \frac{\partial}{\partial z}(F_1 G_2 - F_2 G_1)$$

$$= \frac{\partial F_2}{\partial x}G_3 + F_2\frac{\partial G_3}{\partial x} - \frac{\partial G_2}{\partial x}F_3 - G_2\frac{\partial F_3}{\partial x} - \frac{\partial F_1}{\partial y}G_3 - F_1\frac{\partial G_3}{\partial y}$$

$$+ \frac{\partial G_1}{\partial y}F_3 + G_1\frac{\partial F_3}{\partial y} + \frac{\partial F_1}{\partial z}G_2 + F_1\frac{\partial G_2}{\partial z} - \frac{\partial F_2}{\partial z}G_1 - F_2\frac{\partial G_1}{\partial z}$$

$$= G_1\left(\frac{\partial F_3}{\partial y} - \frac{\partial F_2}{\partial z}\right) + G_2\left(\frac{\partial F_1}{\partial z} - \frac{\partial F_3}{\partial x}\right) + G_3\left(\frac{\partial F_2}{\partial x} - \frac{\partial F_1}{\partial y}\right)$$

$$- F_1\left(\frac{\partial G_3}{\partial y} - \frac{\partial G_2}{\partial z}\right) - F_2\left(\frac{\partial G_1}{\partial z} - \frac{\partial G_3}{\partial x}\right) - F_3\left(\frac{\partial G_2}{\partial x} - \frac{\partial G_1}{\partial y}\right).$$

On the other hand,

$$\mathbf{G} \cdot curl\, \mathbf{F} - \mathbf{F} \cdot curl\, \mathbf{G} = \mathbf{G} \cdot \begin{vmatrix} \mathbf{i} & \mathbf{j} & \mathbf{k} \\ \partial/\partial x & \partial/\partial y & \partial/\partial z \\ F_1 & F_2 & F_3 \end{vmatrix} - \mathbf{F} \cdot \begin{vmatrix} \mathbf{i} & \mathbf{j} & \mathbf{k} \\ \partial/\partial x & \partial/\partial y & \partial/\partial z \\ G_1 & G_2 & G_3 \end{vmatrix}$$

$$= (G_1, G_2, G_3) \cdot \left(\frac{\partial F_3}{\partial y} - \frac{\partial F_2}{\partial z}, \frac{\partial F_1}{\partial z} - \frac{\partial F_3}{\partial x}, \frac{\partial F_2}{\partial x} - \frac{\partial F_1}{\partial y}\right)$$

$$- (F_1, F_2, F_3) \cdot \left(\frac{\partial G_3}{\partial y} - \frac{\partial G_2}{\partial z}, \frac{\partial G_1}{\partial z} - \frac{\partial G_3}{\partial x}, \frac{\partial G_2}{\partial x} - \frac{\partial G_1}{\partial y}\right),$$

and we are done. ■

Proof of (4.4):

$$\Delta(\mathbf{F} \cdot \mathbf{G}) = \Delta(F_1 G_1 + F_2 G_2 + F_3 G_3)$$

$$= \frac{\partial}{\partial x}\left(\frac{\partial F_1}{\partial x}G_1 + F_1\frac{\partial G_1}{\partial x} + \frac{\partial F_2}{\partial x}G_2 + F_2\frac{\partial G_2}{\partial x} + \frac{\partial F_3}{\partial x}G_3 + F_3\frac{\partial G_3}{\partial x}\right)$$

$$+ \frac{\partial}{\partial y}(A) + \frac{\partial}{\partial z}(B),$$

where A and B denote expressions similar to the one inside the parentheses (i.e., the one acted upon by $\partial/\partial x$), with all partial derivatives with respect to x replaced with partial derivatives with respect to y (for A) and all partial derivatives with respect to x replaced with partial derivatives with respect to z (for B). We continue by using the product rule

$$= \frac{\partial^2 F_1}{\partial x^2}G_1 + 2\frac{\partial F_1}{\partial x}\frac{\partial G_1}{\partial x} + F_1\frac{\partial^2 G_1}{\partial x^2} + \frac{\partial^2 F_2}{\partial x^2}G_2 + 2\frac{\partial F_2}{\partial x}\frac{\partial G_2}{\partial x} + F_2\frac{\partial^2 G_2}{\partial x^2}$$

$$+ \frac{\partial^2 F_3}{\partial x^2}G_3 + 2\frac{\partial F_3}{\partial x}\frac{\partial G_3}{\partial x} + F_3\frac{\partial^2 G_3}{\partial x^2} + C + D;$$

C and D consist of nine terms each; to get C we have to replace all partial derivatives with respect to x with partial derivatives with respect to y, and to get D we have to replace all partial derivatives with respect to x with partial derivatives with respect to z. Rearranging terms, we obtain

$$= G_1 \cdot \Delta F_1 + G_2 \cdot \Delta F_2 + G_3 \cdot \Delta F_3 + F_1 \cdot \Delta G_1 + F_2 \cdot \Delta G_2 + F_3 \cdot \Delta G_3$$

$$+ 2\Big((grad\ F_1) \cdot (grad\ G_1) + (grad\ F_2) \cdot (grad\ G_2) + (grad\ F_3) \cdot (grad\ G_3)\Big).$$

■

Proof of (4.8):

$$curl\,(curl\,\mathbf{F}) = curl \begin{vmatrix} \mathbf{i} & \mathbf{j} & \mathbf{k} \\ \partial/\partial x & \partial/\partial y & \partial/\partial z \\ F_1 & F_2 & F_3 \end{vmatrix} = \begin{vmatrix} \mathbf{i} & \mathbf{j} & \mathbf{k} \\ \partial/\partial x & \partial/\partial y & \partial/\partial z \\ \frac{\partial F_3}{\partial y} - \frac{\partial F_2}{\partial z} & \frac{\partial F_1}{\partial z} - \frac{\partial F_3}{\partial x} & \frac{\partial F_2}{\partial x} - \frac{\partial F_1}{\partial y} \end{vmatrix}$$

$$= \left(\frac{\partial^2 F_2}{\partial y\partial x} - \frac{\partial^2 F_1}{\partial y^2} - \frac{\partial^2 F_1}{\partial z^2} + \frac{\partial^2 F_3}{\partial x\partial z}\right)\mathbf{i} - \left(\frac{\partial^2 F_2}{\partial x^2} - \frac{\partial^2 F_1}{\partial x\partial y} - \frac{\partial^2 F_3}{\partial z\partial y} + \frac{\partial^2 F_2}{\partial z^2}\right)\mathbf{j}$$

$$+ \left(\frac{\partial^2 F_1}{\partial x\partial z} - \frac{\partial^2 F_3}{\partial x^2} - \frac{\partial^2 F_3}{\partial y^2} + \frac{\partial^2 F_2}{\partial y\partial z}\right)\mathbf{k}.$$

The right side of (4.8) is computed to be

$$grad\,(div\,\mathbf{F}) - \Delta\mathbf{F} = grad\left(\frac{\partial F_1}{\partial x} + \frac{\partial F_2}{\partial y} + \frac{\partial F_3}{\partial z}\right) - (\Delta F_1, \Delta F_2, \Delta F_3)$$

$$= \left(\frac{\partial^2 F_1}{\partial x^2} + \frac{\partial^2 F_2}{\partial x\partial y} + \frac{\partial^2 F_3}{\partial x\partial z}\right)\mathbf{i} + \left(\frac{\partial^2 F_1}{\partial y\partial x} + \frac{\partial^2 F_2}{\partial y^2} + \frac{\partial^2 F_3}{\partial y\partial z}\right)\mathbf{j}$$

$$+ \left(\frac{\partial^2 F_1}{\partial z\partial x} + \frac{\partial^2 F_2}{\partial z\partial y} + \frac{\partial^2 F_3}{\partial z^2}\right)\mathbf{k} - \left(\frac{\partial^2 F_1}{\partial x^2} + \frac{\partial^2 F_1}{\partial y^2} + \frac{\partial^2 F_1}{\partial z^2}\right)\mathbf{i}$$

$$-\left(\frac{\partial^2 F_2}{\partial x^2} + \frac{\partial^2 F_2}{\partial y^2} + \frac{\partial^2 F_2}{\partial z^2}\right)\mathbf{j} - \left(\frac{\partial^2 F_3}{\partial x^2} + \frac{\partial^2 F_3}{\partial y^2} + \frac{\partial^2 F_3}{\partial z^2}\right)\mathbf{k}.$$

The two sides are equal due to the equality of mixed second partial derivatives (cf. Section 2.6). ∎

Proof of (4.12): From (4.9) we get $(\partial/\partial x)(\|\mathbf{r}\|^n) = n\|\mathbf{r}\|^{n-2}x$, $(\partial/\partial y)(\|\mathbf{r}\|^n) = n\|\mathbf{r}\|^{n-2}y$ and $(\partial/\partial z)(\|\mathbf{r}\|^n) = n\|\mathbf{r}\|^{n-2}z$. Therefore

$$curl\,(\|\mathbf{r}\|^n\mathbf{r}) = \begin{vmatrix} \mathbf{i} & \mathbf{j} & \mathbf{k} \\ \partial/\partial x & \partial/\partial y & \partial/\partial z \\ \|\mathbf{r}\|^n x & \|\mathbf{r}\|^n y & \|\mathbf{r}\|^n z \end{vmatrix}$$

$$= \left(n\|\mathbf{r}\|^{n-2}y \cdot z - n\|\mathbf{r}\|^{n-2}z \cdot y\right)\mathbf{i} - \left(n\|\mathbf{r}\|^{n-2}x \cdot z - n\|\mathbf{r}\|^{n-2}z \cdot x\right)\mathbf{j}$$
$$+ \left(n\|\mathbf{r}\|^{n-2}x \cdot y - n\|\mathbf{r}\|^{n-2}y \cdot x\right)\mathbf{k} = \mathbf{0}.$$ ∎

Proof of (4.14): From the definition of the gradient and the chain rule we get

$$grad\,f(u, v, w) = \frac{\partial}{\partial x}f(u, v, w)\mathbf{i} + \frac{\partial}{\partial y}f(u, v, w)\mathbf{j} + \frac{\partial}{\partial z}f(u, v, w)\mathbf{k}$$

$$= \left(\frac{\partial f}{\partial u}\frac{\partial u}{\partial x} + \frac{\partial f}{\partial v}\frac{\partial v}{\partial x} + \frac{\partial f}{\partial w}\frac{\partial w}{\partial x}\right)\mathbf{i} + \left(\frac{\partial f}{\partial u}\frac{\partial u}{\partial y} + \frac{\partial f}{\partial v}\frac{\partial v}{\partial y} + \frac{\partial f}{\partial w}\frac{\partial w}{\partial y}\right)\mathbf{j}$$

$$+ \left(\frac{\partial f}{\partial u}\frac{\partial u}{\partial z} + \frac{\partial f}{\partial v}\frac{\partial v}{\partial z} + \frac{\partial f}{\partial w}\frac{\partial w}{\partial z}\right)\mathbf{k}.$$

To complete the proof, we rearrange terms by factoring out $\partial f/\partial u$, $\partial f/\partial v$ and $\partial f/\partial w$:

$$grad\,f(u, v, w) = \frac{\partial f}{\partial u}\left(\frac{\partial u}{\partial x}\mathbf{i} + \frac{\partial u}{\partial y}\mathbf{j} + \frac{\partial u}{\partial z}\mathbf{k}\right) + \frac{\partial f}{\partial v}\left(\frac{\partial v}{\partial x}\mathbf{i} + \frac{\partial v}{\partial y}\mathbf{j} + \frac{\partial v}{\partial z}\mathbf{k}\right)$$

$$+ \frac{\partial f}{\partial w}\left(\frac{\partial w}{\partial x}\mathbf{i} + \frac{\partial w}{\partial y}\mathbf{j} + \frac{\partial w}{\partial z}\mathbf{k}\right)$$

$$= \frac{\partial f}{\partial u}grad\,u + \frac{\partial f}{\partial v}grad\,v + \frac{\partial f}{\partial w}grad\,w.$$ ∎

Differential operators in curvilinear coordinate systems. Let (u_1, u_2, u_3) be an orthogonal curvilinear coordinate system and let $\{\mathbf{e}_1, \mathbf{e}_2, \mathbf{e}_3\}$ be the corresponding orthonormal basis (see Section 2.8), let f be a differentiable scalar field and let $\mathbf{F} = F_1\mathbf{e}_1 + F_2\mathbf{e}_2 + F_3\mathbf{e}_3$ be a differentiable vector field. The differential operators $grad$, div, $curl$ and Δ can be expressed as

$$grad\,f = \frac{1}{h_1}\frac{\partial f}{\partial u_1}\mathbf{e}_1 + \frac{1}{h_2}\frac{\partial f}{\partial u_2}\mathbf{e}_2 + \frac{1}{h_3}\frac{\partial f}{\partial u_3}\mathbf{e}_3$$

$$div\,\mathbf{F} = \frac{1}{h_1 h_2 h_3}\left(\frac{\partial}{\partial u_1}(h_2 h_3 F_1) + \frac{\partial}{\partial u_2}(h_1 h_3 F_2) + \frac{\partial}{\partial u_3}(h_1 h_2 F_3)\right)$$

$$curl\,\mathbf{F} = \frac{1}{h_1 h_2 h_3}\begin{vmatrix} h_1\mathbf{e}_1 & h_2\mathbf{e}_2 & h_3\mathbf{e}_3 \\ \frac{\partial}{\partial u_1} & \frac{\partial}{\partial u_2} & \frac{\partial}{\partial u_3} \\ h_1 F_1 & h_2 F_2 & h_3 F_3 \end{vmatrix}$$

$$\Delta f = \frac{1}{h_1 h_2 h_3} \left(\frac{\partial}{\partial u_1} \left(\frac{h_2 h_3}{h_1} \frac{\partial f}{\partial u_1} \right) + \frac{\partial}{\partial u_2} \left(\frac{h_1 h_3}{h_2} \frac{\partial f}{\partial u_2} \right) + \frac{\partial}{\partial u_3} \left(\frac{h_1 h_2}{h_3} \frac{\partial f}{\partial u_3} \right) \right),$$

where h_i are the scale factors (they were defined in Section 2.8). In the Cartesian coordinate system in $\mathbb{R}^3$, $u_1 = x$, $u_2 = y$ and $u_3 = z$, $h_1 = h_2 = h_3 = 1$ and above formulas reduce to the usual expressions given in Sections 4.1 and 4.2.

For cylindrical coordinates $u_1 = r$, $u_2 = \theta$ and $u_3 = z$, the position vector field is $\mathbf{r} = r \cos \theta \mathbf{i} + r \sin \theta \mathbf{j} + z \mathbf{k}$, and the scale factors are

$$\frac{\partial \mathbf{r}}{\partial u_1} = \frac{\partial \mathbf{r}}{\partial r} = \cos \theta \mathbf{i} + \sin \theta \mathbf{j}, \qquad h_1 = \left\| \frac{\partial \mathbf{r}}{\partial r} \right\| = 1,$$

$$\frac{\partial \mathbf{r}}{\partial u_2} = \frac{\partial \mathbf{r}}{\partial \theta} = -r \sin \theta \mathbf{i} + r \cos \theta \mathbf{j}, \qquad h_2 = \left\| \frac{\partial \mathbf{r}}{\partial \theta} \right\| = r,$$

$$\frac{\partial \mathbf{r}}{\partial u_3} = \frac{\partial \mathbf{r}}{\partial z} = 1, \qquad h_3 = \left\| \frac{\partial \mathbf{r}}{\partial z} \right\| = 1.$$

Therefore, in cylindrical coordinates, (with $\mathbf{F} = F_r \mathbf{e}_r + F_\theta \mathbf{e}_\theta + F_z \mathbf{e}_z$)

$$grad \, f = \frac{\partial f}{\partial r} \mathbf{e}_r + \frac{1}{r} \frac{\partial f}{\partial \theta} \mathbf{e}_\theta + \frac{\partial f}{\partial z} \mathbf{e}_z$$

$$div \, \mathbf{F} = \frac{1}{r} \frac{\partial (r F_r)}{\partial r} + \frac{1}{r} \frac{\partial F_\theta}{\partial \theta} + \frac{\partial F_z}{\partial z}$$

$$curl \, \mathbf{F} = \frac{1}{r} \begin{vmatrix} \mathbf{e}_r & r\mathbf{e}_\theta & \mathbf{e}_z \\ \frac{\partial}{\partial r} & \frac{\partial}{\partial \theta} & \frac{\partial}{\partial z} \\ F_r & r F_\theta & F_z \end{vmatrix}$$

$$\Delta f = \frac{1}{r} \left(\frac{\partial}{\partial r} \left(r \frac{\partial f}{\partial r} \right) + \frac{\partial}{\partial \theta} \left(\frac{1}{r} \frac{\partial f}{\partial \theta} \right) + \frac{\partial}{\partial z} \left(r \frac{\partial f}{\partial z} \right) \right)$$

$$= \frac{\partial^2 f}{\partial r^2} + \frac{1}{r} \frac{\partial f}{\partial r} + \frac{1}{r^2} \frac{\partial^2 f}{\partial \theta^2} + \frac{\partial^2 f}{\partial z^2}.$$

For spherical coordinates $h_1 = 1$, $h_2 = \rho \sin \phi$ and $h_3 = \rho$ (cf. Example 2.71 in Section 2.8), and the expressions for the differential operators are (with $\mathbf{F} = F_\rho \mathbf{e}_\rho + F_\theta \mathbf{e}_\theta + F_\phi \mathbf{e}_\phi$):

$$grad \, f = \frac{\partial f}{\partial \rho} \mathbf{e}_\rho + \frac{1}{\rho \sin \phi} \frac{\partial f}{\partial \theta} \mathbf{e}_\theta + \frac{1}{\rho} \frac{\partial f}{\partial \phi} \mathbf{e}_\phi$$

$$div \, \mathbf{F} = \frac{1}{\rho^2 \sin \phi} \left(\frac{\partial}{\partial \rho} \left(\rho^2 \sin \phi F_\rho \right) + \frac{\partial}{\partial \theta} \left(\rho F_\theta \right) + \frac{\partial}{\partial \phi} \left(\rho \sin \phi F_\phi \right) \right)$$

$$= \frac{1}{\rho^2} \frac{\partial}{\partial \rho} \left(\rho^2 F_\rho \right) + \frac{1}{\rho \sin \phi} \frac{\partial}{\partial \theta} \left(F_\theta \right) + \frac{1}{\rho \sin \phi} \frac{\partial}{\partial \phi} \left(\sin \phi F_\phi \right)$$

$$curl \, \mathbf{F} = \frac{1}{\rho^2 \sin \phi} \begin{vmatrix} \mathbf{e}_\rho & \rho \mathbf{e}_\phi & \rho \sin \phi \mathbf{e}_\theta \\ \frac{\partial}{\partial \rho} & \frac{\partial}{\partial \phi} & \frac{\partial}{\partial \theta} \\ F_\rho & \rho F_\phi & \rho \sin \phi F_\theta \end{vmatrix}$$

$$\Delta f = \frac{1}{\rho^2 \sin \phi} \left(\frac{\partial}{\partial \rho} \left(\rho^2 \sin \phi \frac{\partial f}{\partial \rho} \right) + \frac{\partial}{\partial \theta} \left(\frac{1}{\sin \phi} \frac{\partial f}{\partial \theta} \right) + \frac{\partial}{\partial \phi} \left(\sin \phi \frac{\partial f}{\partial \phi} \right) \right)$$

$$= \frac{\partial^2 f}{\partial \rho^2} + \frac{2}{\rho} \frac{\partial f}{\partial \rho} + \frac{1}{\rho^2 \sin^2 \phi} \frac{\partial^2 f}{\partial \theta^2} + \frac{1}{\rho^2} \frac{\partial^2 f}{\partial \phi^2} + \frac{\cot \phi}{\rho^2} \frac{\partial f}{\partial \phi}.$$

Example 4.34   Find an expression for the gradient in parabolic cylindrical coordinates

$$x = \frac{1}{2}(u^2 - v^2), \quad y = uv, \quad z = z, \quad -\infty < u, z < \infty, \quad v \geq 0.$$

Solution   The position vector is $\mathbf{r} = \frac{1}{2}(u^2 - v^2)\mathbf{i} + uv\mathbf{j} + z\mathbf{k}$, and

$$\frac{\partial \mathbf{r}}{\partial u} = u\mathbf{i} + v\mathbf{j}, \quad h_1 = h_u = \left\| \frac{\partial \mathbf{r}}{\partial u} \right\| = \sqrt{u^2 + v^2}, \quad \text{and} \quad \mathbf{e}_u = \frac{u\mathbf{i} + v\mathbf{j}}{\sqrt{u^2 + v^2}}$$

$$\frac{\partial \mathbf{r}}{\partial v} = -v\mathbf{i} + u\mathbf{j}, \quad h_2 = h_v = \left\| \frac{\partial \mathbf{r}}{\partial v} \right\| = \sqrt{u^2 + v^2}, \quad \text{and} \quad \mathbf{e}_v = \frac{-v\mathbf{i} + u\mathbf{j}}{\sqrt{u^2 + v^2}}$$

$$\frac{\partial \mathbf{r}}{\partial z} = \mathbf{k}, \quad h_3 = h_z = \left\| \frac{\partial \mathbf{r}}{\partial z} \right\| = 1, \quad \text{and} \quad \mathbf{e}_z = \mathbf{k}.$$

Therefore

$$grad \; f = \frac{1}{\sqrt{u^2 + v^2}} \frac{\partial f}{\partial u} \mathbf{e}_u + \frac{1}{\sqrt{u^2 + v^2}} \frac{\partial f}{\partial v} \mathbf{e}_v + \frac{\partial f}{\partial z} \mathbf{e}_z.$$

In particular, take $f(x, y, z) = 4x^2 + 2y^2 + z^2$. Then $f(u, v, z) = 4\frac{1}{4}(u^2 - v^2)^2 + 2(uv)^2 + z^2 = u^4 + v^4 + z^2$ and

$$grad \; f = \frac{1}{\sqrt{u^2 + v^2}} 4u^3 \mathbf{e}_u + \frac{1}{\sqrt{u^2 + v^2}} 4v^3 \mathbf{e}_v + 2z\mathbf{e}_z.$$

To check this, we substitute the expressions for $\mathbf{e}_u$, $\mathbf{e}_v$ and $\mathbf{e}_z$ and use the definition of parabolic coordinates:

$$grad \; f = \frac{1}{\sqrt{u^2 + v^2}} 4u^3 \frac{u\mathbf{i} + v\mathbf{j}}{\sqrt{u^2 + v^2}} + \frac{1}{\sqrt{u^2 + v^2}} 4v^3 \frac{-v\mathbf{i} + u\mathbf{j}}{\sqrt{u^2 + v^2}} + 2z\mathbf{k}$$

$$= \frac{4u^4 - 4v^4}{u^2 + v^2} \mathbf{i} + \frac{4u^3 v + 4uv^3}{u^2 + v^2} \mathbf{j} + 2z\mathbf{k}$$

$$= 4(u^2 - v^2)\mathbf{i} + 4uv\mathbf{j} + 2z\mathbf{k} = 8x\mathbf{i} + 4y\mathbf{j} + 2z\mathbf{k},$$

which is the gradient of f in Cartesian coordinates.   ◄

EXERCISES 4.3   **Exercises 1 to 9:** Prove the following identities.

1. $grad \; (\mathbf{F} \cdot \mathbf{G}) = (\mathbf{F} \cdot \nabla)\mathbf{G} + (\mathbf{G} \cdot \nabla)\mathbf{F} + \mathbf{F} \times curl \; \mathbf{G} + \mathbf{G} \times curl \; \mathbf{F}$, where $\mathbf{F} = (F_1, F_2, F_3)$, $\mathbf{G} = (G_1, G_2, G_3)$ and $(\mathbf{F} \cdot \nabla)\mathbf{G}$ denotes the vector field $(\mathbf{F} \cdot (grad \; G_1), \mathbf{F} \cdot (grad \; G_2), \mathbf{F} \cdot (grad \; G_3))$ (each component is a dot product)

2. $div \; (f\mathbf{F}) = f \, div \, \mathbf{F} + \mathbf{F} \cdot grad \; f$ 3. $curl \; (f\mathbf{F}) = f \, curl \, \mathbf{F} + grad \; f \times \mathbf{F}$

4. $curl \; (\mathbf{F} \times \mathbf{G}) = \mathbf{F} div \, \mathbf{G} - \mathbf{G} div \, \mathbf{F} + (\mathbf{G} \cdot \nabla)\mathbf{F} - (\mathbf{F} \cdot \nabla)\mathbf{G}$ (see problem 1 for the definition of the vector field $(\mathbf{F} \cdot \nabla)\mathbf{G}$)

5. $\Delta(fg) = g\Delta f + f\Delta g + 2\,grad\,f \cdot grad\,g$

6. $div\,(grad\,f \times grad\,g) = 0$ $\qquad\qquad$ **7.** $div\,(g\,grad\,f \times f\,grad\,g) = 0$

8. $div\,(f\,grad\,g) = f\Delta g + grad\,f \cdot grad\,g$

9. $div\,(f\,grad\,g - g\,grad\,f) = f\Delta g - g\Delta f$

Exercises 10 to 12: Let $\mathbf{r} = x\mathbf{i} + y\mathbf{j} + z\mathbf{k}$. Prove the following identities and state the domain where each is valid.

10. $grad\,\|\mathbf{r}\|^{-1} = -\|\mathbf{r}\|^{-3}\mathbf{r}$ $\qquad\qquad$ **11.** $div\,\|\mathbf{r}\|^{-3}\mathbf{r} = 0$

12. $\Delta\|\mathbf{r}\|^n = n(n+1)\|\mathbf{r}\|^{n-2}$

13. Find the gradient of f, if $f(x, y) = g(u(x, y), v(x, y), x, y)$, g is a differentiable function of four variables and u and v are differentiable functions of x and y.

14. Compute $grad\,f$, if $f(x, y) = g(x^2y, x^3 - y, y^4)$ and g is differentiable.

Exercises 15 to 17: Let $\mathbf{r} = x\mathbf{i} + y\mathbf{j} + z\mathbf{k}$. Compute each expression.

15. $grad\,(\ln\|\mathbf{r}\|)$ $\qquad$ **16.** $curl\,(\mathbf{r}/\|\mathbf{r}\|^2)$ $\qquad$ **17.** $\Delta(\ln\|\mathbf{r}\|)$

18. Let $f(r, \theta, z) = z\arctan\theta/r^2$ be the expression for the function f in cylindrical coordinates. Compute $grad\,f$ and Δf.

19. Let $\mathbf{F}(r, \theta, z) = r^2\mathbf{e}_r + rz\mathbf{e}_\theta + \sin\theta\mathbf{e}_z$ be the expression for the vector field $\mathbf{F}$ in cylindrical coordinates. Compute $div\,\mathbf{F}$ and $curl\,\mathbf{F}$.

20. Compute $grad\,f$ and Δf for the function $f(\rho, \theta, \phi) = \rho^2\sin\phi$ in spherical coordinates.

21. Compute $div\,\mathbf{F}$ and $curl\,\mathbf{F}$ for the vector field $\mathbf{F}(\rho, \theta, \phi) = \theta\mathbf{e}_\rho + \cos\theta\cos\phi\mathbf{e}_\theta - \rho\mathbf{e}_\phi$ in spherical coordinates.

22. Find the expression for the gradient and the divergence in parabolic cylindrical coordinates (see Exercise 1 in Section 2.8).

23. Compute the divergence of the vector field $\mathbf{F} = uv\mathbf{i} - \mathbf{j}$ in elliptic cylindrical coordinates (see Exercise 2 in Section 2.8; take $a = 1$).

24. Compute the gradient and the Laplacian of the function $f(u, v, z) = u^2 - v^2z$ in elliptic cylindrical coordinates (see Exercise 2 in Section 2.8; take $a = 1$).

25. Find the expression for the curl in bipolar coordinates (see Exercise 5 in Section 2.8).

26. Write Laplace's equation in parabolic cylindrical coordinates (see Exercise 1 in Section 2.8).

27. Express the heat equation $\partial\phi/\partial t = c\Delta\phi$, where $\phi = \phi(u, v, z, t)$, in elliptic cylindrical coordinates (see Exercise 2 in Section 2.8; take $a = 1$).

28. Let (u_1, u_2, u_3) be an orthogonal curvilinear coordinate system and let $\{\mathbf{e}_1, \mathbf{e}_2, \mathbf{e}_3\}$ be the corresponding orthonormal basis. Show that

(a) $\|grad\,u_i\| = h_i^{-1}$, $i = 1, 2, 3$.

(b) $\mathbf{e}_1 = h_2h_3(grad\,u_2 \times grad\,u_3)$ (with similar expressions for $\mathbf{e}_2$ and $\mathbf{e}_3$).

(c) $div\,(f\mathbf{e}_1) = \dfrac{1}{h_1h_2h_3}\dfrac{\partial}{\partial u_1}(fh_2h_3)$.

(d) $curl\,(f\mathbf{e}_1) = \dfrac{1}{h_1h_3}\dfrac{\partial}{\partial u_3}(fh_1)\mathbf{e}_2 - \dfrac{1}{h_1h_2}\dfrac{\partial}{\partial u_2}(fh_1)\mathbf{e}_3$.

29. Express the heat equation $\partial U/\partial t = c\Delta U$ in spherical coordinates if the function U is independent of the following variables.

(a) θ (b) θ and ϕ (c) θ, ϕ and t (d) ρ and t

4.4   DIFFERENTIAL FORMS

Throughout this section U will denote an open set in $\mathbb{R}^3$. All functions are assumed to be differentiable as many times as needed (for example, $\partial^2 f/\partial x^2$ means that f is assumed to be twice differentiable).

■ **Definition 4.5**   Zero-forms.

A *(differential) 0-form* on U (or a *(differential) form of degree 0*) is a real-valued (differentiable) function $f: U \subseteq \mathbb{R}^3 \to \mathbb{R}$. Two 0-forms f_1 and f_2 on U can be added or multiplied, thus giving 0-forms $f_1 + f_2$ and $f_1 \cdot f_2$ (these operations are, of course, just the usual addition and multiplication of real-valued functions). A *zero 0-form* is a constant function $f(x, y, z) = 0$.

■

■ **Definition 4.6**   One-forms.

Formal expressions dx, dy and dz are called *basic 1-forms*. A *(differential) 1-form* on a set U (or a *(differential) form of degree 1*) is a combination

$$\alpha = f(x, y, z)dx + g(x, y, z)dy + h(x, y, z)dz,$$

where the components (or coefficients) $f(x, y, z)$, $g(x, y, z)$ and $h(x, y, z)$ are (differentiable) real-valued functions defined on U.

■

For the moment we do not attach any meaning to dx, dy and dz. We can think of them as forming a basis of some (three-dimensional) vector space, where the rôle of the scalars is played by the real-valued functions. Such a structure, strictly speaking, is not a vector space (it is called a vector bundle). Nevertheless, it helps to use vector space terminology. For example, we say that a 1-form is a linear combination of basic 1-forms dx, dy and dz. The order of dx, dy and dz in a 1-form is not relevant. The *zero 1-form* is the 1-form $0 = 0dx + 0dy + 0dz$, with components $f(x, y, z) = 0$, $g(x, y, z) = 0$ and $h(x, y, z) = 0$.

Example 4.35   In this example we just list several 1-forms. $\alpha = (2x^2 + y^2)dx + e^{xy}dy + 3yz^3dz$ is a 1-form whose components are $f(x, y, z) = 2x^2 + y^2$, $g(x, y, z) = e^{xy}$ and $h(x, y, z) = 3yz^3$. The form $dx + 2xdy$ has components $f(x, y, z) = 1$, $g(x, y, z) = 2x$ and $h(x, y, z) = 0$. The components of the 1-form dz are $f(x, y, z) = 0$, $g(x, y, z) = 0$ and $h(x, y, z) = 1$. Let $\alpha = (x^2 + y)dz - dx - 3dy$. The components of α are

$$f(x, y, z) = -1, \ g(x, y, z) = -3 \text{ and } h(x, y, z) = x^2 + y.$$

◀

As in the case of a vector space, we can define the operations of addition and multiplication by scalars (which are here replaced by functions). Let $\alpha = f_1 dx + g_1 dy + h_1 dz$ and $\beta = f_2 dx + g_2 dy + h_2 dz$ be 1-forms and let p be a function $p: U \to \mathbb{R}$. Then

$$\alpha + \beta = (f_1 + f_2)dx + (g_1 + g_2)dy + (h_1 + h_2)dz$$

and

$$p\alpha = pf_1 dx + pg_1 dy + ph_1 dz.$$

In words, 1-forms are added by adding up their respective components. Multiplying a 1-form by a function amounts to multiplying each component by that function.

Definition 4.7 Two-forms.

Expressions $dxdy$, $dydz$ and $dzdx$ are called *basic 2-forms*. A *(differential) 2-form* on a set U (or a *(differential) form of degree 2*) is a combination

$$\alpha = f(x, y, z)dxdy + g(x, y, z)dydz + h(x, y, z)dzdx,$$

where the components $f(x, y, z)$, $g(x, y, z)$ and $h(x, y, z)$ are (differentiable) real-valued functions on U.

Basic two-forms are "built" of 1-forms (we will clarify this later) that appear in cyclic order (dx, dy, dz, dx, etc.). Think of basic 2-forms as a basis of some three dimensional vector space. A 2-form is then a linear combination of basic two-forms. The order of $dxdy$, $dydz$ and $dzdx$ in a 2-form does not play any role.

The addition of 2-forms and the product of a 2-form and a function are defined "componentwise," as for 1-forms: let $\alpha = f_1 dxdy + g_1 dydz + h_1 dzdx$ and $\beta = f_2 dxdy + g_2 dydz + h_2 dzdx$ be 2-forms and let p be a function $p: U \to \mathbb{R}$. Then

$$\alpha + \beta = (f_1 + f_2)dxdy + (g_1 + g_2)dydz + (h_1 + h_2)dzdx$$

and

$$p\alpha = pf_1 dxdy + pg_1 dydz + ph_1 dzdx.$$

The *zero 2-form* is the 2-form $0 = 0dxdy + 0dydz + 0dzdx$.

Example 4.36 The expressions $\alpha = 3yzdxdy + (x^2 + y^2)dydz + dzdx$ and $\beta = z^3 dxdy - x^2 dydz$ are 2-forms defined on $U = \mathbb{R}^3$. Their sum is

$$\alpha + \beta = (3yz + z^3)dxdy + y^2 dydz + dzdx,$$

and the product of α and e^{xy} is

$$e^{xy}\alpha = 3yze^{xy}dxdy + (x^2 + y^2)e^{xy}dydz + e^{xy}dzdx.$$

The sum of 1-forms $\alpha = -dx + xdy + (xy + e^z)dz$ and $\beta = dx - e^zdz$ is the 1-form

$$\alpha + \beta = xdy + xydz.$$

The product of the 1-form α by the function $p(x, y, z) = y$ is

$$y\alpha = -ydx + xydy + (xy^2 + ye^z)dz.$$

◀

There will be no need to add forms of different degrees, such as 1-forms and 2-forms.

■ **Definition 4.8**   Three-forms.

The *basic 3-form* is the expression $dxdydz$. A *(differential) 3-form* on U (or a *(differential) form of degree 3*) is an expression

$$\alpha = f(x, y, z)dxdydz,$$

where $f(x, y, z)$ is a real-valued function on U.

■

This time, $dxdydz$ is the only "basis" element, so the vector space considered here is one-dimensional. If $\alpha = f_1 dxdydz$ and $\beta = f_2 dxdydz$ are 3-forms and p is a function, then the sum $\alpha + \beta$ is a 3-form

$$\alpha + \beta = (f_1 + f_2)dxdydz$$

and the product of p and α is a 3-form

$$p\alpha = pf_1 dxdydz.$$

The *zero 3-form* is the 3-form $0 = 0dxdydz$.

■ **Definition 4.9**   Wedge Product.

The *wedge product* is an operation on forms that satisfies the following properties.

(a) If α is a k-form and β is an l-form, $0 \le k, l \le 3$, then their wedge product is a $(k + l)$-form $\alpha \wedge \beta$.

(b) Anticommutativity: $\alpha \wedge \beta = (-1)^{kl} \beta \wedge \alpha$, where α is a k-form and β is an l-form.

(c) Associativity: $(\alpha \wedge \beta) \wedge \gamma = \alpha \wedge (\beta \wedge \gamma)$, for any forms α, β and γ.

(d) If 0 is a zero form of any degree, then $\alpha \wedge 0 = 0$ for any α.

(e) If f is a real-valued function (also called a 0-form) then the wedge product $f \wedge \alpha$ is just the product $f \cdot \alpha$ of a form and a function; i.e., $f \wedge \alpha = f \cdot \alpha$.

(f) Distributivity: if α and β are of the same degree, and γ is any form, then $(\alpha + \beta) \wedge \gamma = \alpha \wedge \gamma + \beta \wedge \gamma$

(g) Homogeneity with respect to functions: if f is a real-valued function, then $f(\alpha \wedge \beta) = (f\alpha) \wedge \beta = \alpha \wedge (f\beta)$.

(h) The wedge products of basic 1-forms are basic 2-forms:

$$dx \wedge dy = dxdy, \qquad dy \wedge dz = dydz \qquad \text{and} \qquad dz \wedge dx = dzdx;$$

moreover,

$$dy \wedge dx = dydx, \qquad dz \wedge dy = dzdy \qquad \text{and} \qquad dx \wedge dz = dxdz.$$

The basic 3-form is the wedge product of basic 1-forms in their cyclic order, i.e.,
$$dx \wedge dy \wedge dz = (dx \wedge dy) \wedge dz = dx \wedge (dy \wedge dz) = dxdydz. \qquad \blacksquare$$

From the anticommutativity and (h) it follows that

$$dydx \overset{(h)}{=} dy \wedge dx \overset{(b)}{=} -dx \wedge dy \overset{(h)}{=} -dxdy.$$

Moreover, the equality

$$dx \wedge dx = -dx \wedge dx,$$

which was obtained by switching dx and dx using (b) with $k = l = 1$, implies that

$$2\,dx \wedge dx = 0, \qquad \text{i.e.,} \qquad dx \wedge dx = 0.$$

Analogous computations can be performed for other combinations of basic 1-forms. Hence:

$$dydx = dy \wedge dx = -dx \wedge dy = -dxdy,$$
$$dzdy = dz \wedge dy = -dy \wedge dz = -dydz,$$
$$dzdx = dx \wedge dz = -dz \wedge dx = -dzdx,$$

and

$$dx \wedge dx = 0, \qquad dy \wedge dy = 0, \qquad dz \wedge dz = 0.$$

A triple product in which a basic 1-form occurs more than once is zero. For example,

$$dxdy \wedge dx \overset{(h)}{=} (dx \wedge dy) \wedge dx \overset{(b)}{=} (-dy \wedge dx) \wedge dx$$
$$\overset{(c)}{=} -dy \wedge (dx \wedge dx) = -dy \wedge 0 \overset{(d)}{=} 0,$$

since $dx \wedge dx = 0$.

Similar computations lead us to the following conclusion: since there are only three basic 1-forms in $\mathbb{R}^3$, every 4-form (written as the wedge product of 1-forms) has at least one of dx, dy or dz repeated — and therefore is equal to zero. In other words, all 4-forms, 5-forms and, in general, all forms of degree greater than three in $\mathbb{R}^3$ are zero. That is the reason why we say that there are no (non-trivial) forms of degree greater than three in $\mathbb{R}^3$.

The basic 3-form can be written in different ways as a product of 1-forms and 2-forms; for example

$$dxdydz \overset{(h)}{=} dx \wedge (dy \wedge dz) \overset{(b)}{=} dx \wedge (-dz \wedge dy) \overset{(g)}{=} -dx \wedge (dz \wedge dy)$$
$$\overset{(h)}{=} -dxdzdy \overset{(h)}{=} (-dx \wedge dz) \wedge dy \overset{(h)}{=} -dxdz \wedge dy = \text{etc.}$$

Example 4.37   Let $\alpha = x^2 dx + y dy$. Compute $\alpha \wedge \alpha$.

Solution   By definition,

$$\alpha \wedge \alpha = (x^2 dx + y dy) \wedge (x^2 dx + y dy)$$

$$\overset{(f)}{=} x^2 dx \wedge x^2 dx + y dy \wedge x^2 dx + x^2 dx \wedge y dy + y dy \wedge y dy$$

$$\overset{(g)}{=} x^4 dx \wedge dx + x^2 y dy \wedge dx + x^2 y dx \wedge dy + y^2 dy \wedge dy = 0.$$

The first and last terms are zero since $dx \wedge dx = 0$ and $dy \wedge dy = 0$. The middle two terms cancel due to the anticommutativity (b).

◀

Examine the computation in the previous example. As an alternative, by imitating the way we proved that $dx \wedge dx = 0$ we realize that $\alpha \wedge \alpha = 0$ for any 1-form α. This identity also holds for 2-forms and 3-forms in $\mathbb{R}^3$ (that could be checked by direct computation; actually, it is enough to notice that the wedge product of a 2-form (or 3-form) with itself is a 4-form (or 6-form), and all such forms are zero in $\mathbb{R}^3$). However, $\alpha \wedge \alpha \neq 0$, in general, for forms in $\mathbb{R}^m$.

Example 4.38   Let $\alpha = y dx dy + xz dy dz$ and let $\beta = dx + y dy + z^2 dz$. Compute $\alpha \wedge \beta$.

Solution   Using distributivity property (f) and homogeneity (g), we get

$$\alpha \wedge \beta = (y dx dy + xz dy dz) \wedge (dx + y dy + z^2 dz)$$

$$= y dx dy \wedge dx + xz dy dz \wedge dx + y^2 dx dy \wedge dy$$

$$+ xyz dy dz \wedge dy + z^2 y dx dy \wedge dz + xz^3 dy dz \wedge dz.$$

All triple products with a repeated basic 1-form are zero. Hence

$$\alpha \wedge \beta = xz dy dz \wedge dx + z^2 y dx dy \wedge dz$$

and since (no parentheses needed, due to associativity)

$$dy dz \wedge dx = dy \wedge dz \wedge dx = -dy \wedge dx \wedge dz = dx \wedge dy \wedge dz = dx dy dz$$

(anticommutativity has been used twice) it follows that

$$\alpha \wedge \beta = (xz + z^2 y) dx dy dz.$$

◀

■ **Definition 4.10**   Differential of a Form.

The *differential* is an operation that assigns a $(k+1)$-form $d\alpha$ to a k-form α ($0 \leq k \leq 3$) according to the following rules.

(a) If $f : U \to \mathbb{R}$ is a 0-form, then df is the 1-form

$$df = \frac{\partial f}{\partial x} dx + \frac{\partial f}{\partial y} dy + \frac{\partial f}{\partial z} dz.$$

(b) If $\alpha = f\,dx + g\,dy + h\,dz$ is a 1-form, then $d\alpha$ is the 2-form

$$d\alpha = df \wedge dx + dg \wedge dy + dh \wedge dz,$$

where df, dg and dh are computed by (a), since f, g and h are functions (or 0-forms).

(c) If $\alpha = f\,dx\,dy + g\,dy\,dz + h\,dz\,dx$ is a 2-form, then $d\alpha$ is the 3-form

$$d\alpha = df \wedge dx\,dy + dg \wedge dy\,dz + dh \wedge dz\,dx,$$

where df, dg and dh are computed by (a).

(d) If $\alpha = f\,dx\,dy\,dz$ is a 3-form then
$$d\alpha = 0.$$

■

Example 4.39

Compute the differential $d\alpha$ of the following forms.

(a) the 0-form $\alpha = xy + e^{yz}$

(b) the 1-form $\alpha = (x^2 + y^2)dx + \sin z\,dz$

(c) the 1-form $\alpha = y\,dx$

(d) the 2-form $\alpha = x^3 dx\,dy - x\cos z\,dy\,dz$

(e) the 2-form $\alpha = dz\,dx$

Solution

(a) Using part (a) of Definition 4.10, we get

$$d\alpha = \frac{\partial}{\partial x}(xy + e^{yz})dx + \frac{\partial}{\partial y}(xy + e^{yz})dy + \frac{\partial}{\partial z}(xy + e^{yz})dz$$
$$= y\,dx + (x + z e^{yz})dy + y e^{yz} dz.$$

(b) The differential of a 1-form is computed according to Definiton 4.10 (b):

$$d\alpha = d(x^2 + y^2) \wedge dx + d(\sin z) \wedge dz$$
$$= \left(\frac{\partial}{\partial x}(x^2 + y^2)dx + \frac{\partial}{\partial y}(x^2 + y^2)dy + \frac{\partial}{\partial z}(x^2 + y^2)dz \right) \wedge dx$$
$$+ \left(\frac{\partial}{\partial x}(\sin z)dx + \frac{\partial}{\partial y}(\sin z)dy + \frac{\partial}{\partial z}(\sin z)dz \right) \wedge dz$$
$$= (2x\,dx + 2y\,dy) \wedge dx + \cos z\,dz \wedge dz$$
$$= 2y\,dy \wedge dx = -2y\,dx\,dy.$$

(c) The form α has only one non-zero component. By (b) of Definition 4.10,

$$d\alpha = d(y) \wedge dx = \left(\frac{\partial}{\partial x}(y)dx + \frac{\partial}{\partial y}(y)dy + \frac{\partial}{\partial z}(y)dz \right) \wedge dx$$
$$= dy \wedge dx = -dx \wedge dy = -dx\,dy.$$

(d) By definition,

$$d\alpha = d(x^3) \wedge dx\,dy + d(-x\cos z) \wedge dy\,dz$$

$$= \left(\frac{\partial}{\partial x}(x^3)dx + \frac{\partial}{\partial y}(x^3)dy + \frac{\partial}{\partial z}(x^3)dz \right) \wedge dxdy$$

$$- \left(\frac{\partial}{\partial x}(x\cos z)dx + \frac{\partial}{\partial y}(x\cos z)dy + \frac{\partial}{\partial z}(x\cos z)dz \right) \wedge dydz$$

$$= 3x^2 dx \wedge dxdy - (\cos z dx - x\sin z dz) \wedge dydz$$

$$= -\cos z dx \wedge dydz = -\cos z dxdydz.$$

(e) $\alpha = 1 \cdot dzdx$ and hence

$$d\alpha = \left(\frac{\partial}{\partial x}(1)dx + \frac{\partial}{\partial y}(1)dy + \frac{\partial}{\partial z}(1)dz \right) \wedge dzdx = 0 \wedge dzdx = 0. \qquad \blacktriangleleft$$

We will now see how the vector differential operators (gradient, divergence and curl) can be interpreted as differentials on forms.

By definition, the differential of the 0-form f (which is a function) is given by

$$df = \frac{\partial f}{\partial x}dx + \frac{\partial f}{\partial y}dy + \frac{\partial f}{\partial z}dz = \nabla f \cdot d\mathbf{s},$$

where $d\mathbf{s} = dx\mathbf{i} + dy\mathbf{j} + dz\mathbf{k}$ is a formal expression called the *line element*, and ∇f is the gradient of f.

Take a 1-form $\alpha = F_1 dx + F_2 dy + F_3 dz$ and a vector field $\mathbf{F} = (F_1, F_2, F_3)$. The differential of α is computed to be

$$d\alpha = dF_1 \wedge dx + dF_2 \wedge dy + dF_3 \wedge dz$$

$$= \left(\frac{\partial F_1}{\partial x}dx + \frac{\partial F_1}{\partial y}dy + \frac{\partial F_1}{\partial z}dz \right) \wedge dx + \left(\frac{\partial F_2}{\partial x}dx + \frac{\partial F_2}{\partial y}dy + \frac{\partial F_2}{\partial z}dz \right) \wedge dy$$

$$+ \left(\frac{\partial F_3}{\partial x}dx + \frac{\partial F_3}{\partial y}dy + \frac{\partial F_3}{\partial z}dz \right) \wedge dz$$

$$= \frac{\partial F_1}{\partial y}dy \wedge dx + \frac{\partial F_1}{\partial z}dz \wedge dx + \frac{\partial F_2}{\partial x}dx \wedge dy + \frac{\partial F_2}{\partial z}dz \wedge dy$$

$$+ \frac{\partial F_3}{\partial x}dx \wedge dz + \frac{\partial F_3}{\partial y}dy \wedge dz$$

$$= \left(\frac{\partial F_2}{\partial x} - \frac{\partial F_1}{\partial y} \right) dx \wedge dy + \left(\frac{\partial F_3}{\partial y} - \frac{\partial F_2}{\partial z} \right) dy \wedge dz + \left(\frac{\partial F_1}{\partial z} - \frac{\partial F_3}{\partial x} \right) dz \wedge dx.$$

The coefficients of $d\alpha$ coincide with the components of *curl* $\mathbf{F}$; cf. Definition 4.3: the coefficient of $dy \wedge dz$ equals the $\mathbf{i}$ component of *curl* $\mathbf{F}$, the coefficient of $dz \wedge dx$ equals the $\mathbf{j}$ component of *curl* $\mathbf{F}$ and the coefficient of $dx \wedge dy$ equals the $\mathbf{k}$ component of *curl* $\mathbf{F}$.

Finally, let $\alpha = F_1 dydz + F_2 dzdx + F_3 dxdy$ be a 2-form. Then

$$d\alpha = dF_1 \wedge dydz + dF_2 \wedge dzdx + dF_3 \wedge dxdy$$

$$= \left(\frac{\partial F_1}{\partial x}dx + \frac{\partial F_1}{\partial y}dy + \frac{\partial F_1}{\partial z}dz \right) \wedge dydz + \left(\frac{\partial F_2}{\partial x}dx + \frac{\partial F_2}{\partial y}dy + \frac{\partial F_2}{\partial z}dz \right) \wedge dzdx$$

$$+ \left(\frac{\partial F_3}{\partial x} dx + \frac{\partial F_3}{\partial y} dy + \frac{\partial F_3}{\partial z} dz \right) \wedge dxdy$$

$$= \frac{\partial F_1}{\partial x} dx \wedge dydz + \frac{\partial F_2}{\partial y} dy \wedge dzdx + \frac{\partial F_3}{\partial z} dz \wedge dxdy$$

$$= \left(\frac{\partial F_1}{\partial x} + \frac{\partial F_2}{\partial y} + \frac{\partial F_3}{\partial z} \right) dxdydz.$$

The coefficient in the expression in the last line is the divergence of the vector field $\mathbf{F} = (F_1, F_2, F_3)$. Let us summarize: the differential of a 0-form corresponds to the gradient, the differential of a 1-form corresponds to the curl and the differential of a 2-form corresponds to the divergence. In other words, the "classical" vector calculus operations can be considered as special cases of the differential d acting on differential forms.

■ **Theorem 4.6** **Properties of the Differential.**

For k-forms α_1, α_2 and α and l-form β the following identities hold:

(a) $d(\alpha_1 + \alpha_2) = d\alpha_1 + d\alpha_2$,

(b) $d(d\alpha) = 0$,

(c) $d(\alpha \wedge \beta) = d\alpha \wedge \beta + (-1)^k \alpha \wedge d\beta$.

Proof

(a) If α_1 and α_2 are 3-forms, then $d\alpha_1 = 0$ and $d\alpha_2 = 0$ by definition. Their sum $\alpha_1 + \alpha_2$ is again a 3-form and hence $d(\alpha_1 + \alpha_2) = 0$. Therefore (a) holds for 3-forms.

Now let $\alpha_1 = f_1$ and $\alpha_2 = f_2$ be 0-forms. Then

$$d(f_1 + f_2) = \frac{\partial}{\partial x}(f_1 + f_2)dx + \frac{\partial}{\partial y}(f_1 + f_2)dy + \frac{\partial}{\partial z}(f_1 + f_2)dz$$

$$= \frac{\partial f_1}{\partial x}dx + \frac{\partial f_1}{\partial y}dy + \frac{\partial f_1}{\partial z}dz + \frac{\partial f_2}{\partial x}dx + \frac{\partial f_2}{\partial y}dy + \frac{\partial f_2}{\partial z}dz$$

$$= df_1 + df_2,$$

so (a) is true for 0-forms. This identity is now used to prove the statement for 1-forms and 2-forms. Let $\alpha_1 = f_1 dx + g_1 dy + h_1 dz$ and $\alpha_2 = f_2 dx + g_2 dy + h_2 dz$ be 1-forms. By definition of the differential and the distributivity of the wedge product it follows that

$$d(\alpha_1 + \alpha_2)$$
$$= d(f_1 dx + g_1 dy + h_1 dz + f_2 dx + g_2 dy + h_2 dz)$$
$$= d((f_1 + f_2)dx + (g_1 + g_2)dy + (h_1 + h_2)dz)$$
$$= d(f_1 + f_2) \wedge dx + d(g_1 + g_2) \wedge dy + d(h_1 + h_2) \wedge dz$$
$$= (df_1 + df_2) \wedge dx + (dg_1 + dg_2) \wedge dy + (dh_1 + dh_2) \wedge dz$$
$$= df_1 \wedge dx + df_2 \wedge dx + dg_1 \wedge dy + dg_2 \wedge dy + dh_1 \wedge dz + dh_2 \wedge dz$$
$$= (df_1 \wedge dx + dg_1 \wedge dy + dh_1 \wedge dz) + (df_2 \wedge dx + dg_2 \wedge dy + dh_2 \wedge dz)$$

$$= d\alpha_1 + d\alpha_2.$$

An analogous computation gives the proof of (a) for 2-forms.

(b) There are two trivial cases: if α is a 3-form, then $d\alpha = 0$, and so $d(d\alpha) = d(0) = 0$. If α is a 2-form, then $d\alpha$ is a 3-form, and $d(d\alpha) = 0$ (we have used the fact that, by definition, the differential of any 3-form is zero).

We have actually proved the remaining parts of (b) before: if $\alpha = f$ is a 0-form, then $d(d\alpha) = d(df)$ can be interpreted as $curl(grad\ f)$, which was proven to be zero in Theorem 4.5. And if α is a 1-form, then $d(d\alpha)$ corresponds to the div of the $curl$, which is again zero, by the same theorem.

Comment: we can use (a) to simplify the computations in the proof. More precisely: if statement (b) or (c) holds for expressions of the form (function · basic form), such as $f_1 dx$, $f_2 dy$ or $f_1 dx dy$, then, by (a), it must hold for their sum (for example, for $f_1 dx + g_1 dy + h_1 dz$, which is a general 1-form).

Another proof of (b): in light of the previous comment, take $\alpha = f dx$. Then (whenever differentiating, we immediately drop terms where some basic form appears more than once)

$$d\left(d(f dx)\right) = d(df \wedge dx) = d\left(\left(\frac{\partial f}{\partial x}dx + \frac{\partial f}{\partial y}dy + \frac{\partial f}{\partial z}dz\right) \wedge dx\right)$$

$$= d\left(\frac{\partial f}{\partial y}dy \wedge dx + \frac{\partial f}{\partial z}dz \wedge dx\right)$$

$$= \frac{\partial^2 f}{\partial z \partial y}dz \wedge dy \wedge dx + \frac{\partial^2 f}{\partial y \partial z}dy \wedge dz \wedge dx$$

$$= \left(-\frac{\partial^2 f}{\partial z \partial y} + \frac{\partial^2 f}{\partial y \partial z}\right)dxdydz = 0,$$

by the equality of mixed second partial derivatives. The remaining cases in (b) are verified analogously.

(c) This statement is proved in a similar way, by considering forms of different degrees. To illustrate the proof, take for example 1-forms $\alpha = f dx$ and $\beta = g dy$. Then

$$d(\alpha \wedge \beta) = d(f dx \wedge g dy) = d(fg) \wedge dx \wedge dy = \left(\frac{\partial}{\partial z}(fg)dz\right) \wedge dx \wedge dy$$

$$= \left(\frac{\partial f}{\partial z}g + f\frac{\partial g}{\partial z}\right)dz \wedge dx \wedge dy = \left(\frac{\partial f}{\partial z}g + f\frac{\partial g}{\partial z}\right)dx \wedge dy \wedge dz,$$

by the product rule. The right side of (c) is

$$d\alpha \wedge \beta + (-1)^1 \alpha \wedge d\beta = d(f dx) \wedge g dy - (f dx) \wedge d(g dy)$$

$$= \left(\frac{\partial f}{\partial y}dy \wedge dx + \frac{\partial f}{\partial z}dz \wedge dx\right) \wedge g dy - f dx \wedge \left(\frac{\partial g}{\partial x}dx \wedge dy + \frac{\partial g}{\partial z}dz \wedge dy\right)$$

$$= \frac{\partial f}{\partial z}g dz \wedge dx \wedge dy - f\frac{\partial g}{\partial z}dx \wedge dz \wedge dy$$

$$= \left(\frac{\partial f}{\partial z}g + f\frac{\partial g}{\partial z}\right)dxdydz.$$

∎

EXERCISES 4.4

Exercises 1 to 12: Let $f = e^{x+y}$, $\alpha = 3x\,dx + yz\,dy$, $\beta = (x^2 + y^2)dz$, $\gamma = 2dx\,dy - x\cos y\,dy\,dz$, $\mu = e^{-x}dx\,dz + e^{-y}dz\,dy$ and $\nu = \sin x\,dx\,dy\,dz$ be differential forms defined on $\mathbb{R}^3$. Determine whether the following expressions are defined, and if so, evaluate them.

1. $f\beta$

2. $f\mu - \alpha \wedge \alpha$

3. $\alpha \wedge \beta$

4. $x\alpha + 2yz\beta$

5. $\beta - \mu$

6. $f\nu - (\alpha \wedge \beta) \wedge \beta$

7. $\alpha \wedge \alpha$

8. $\nu - (\alpha \wedge \nu)$

9. $(\beta \wedge \gamma) - \nu$

10. $-\mu + (\alpha \wedge \beta)$

11. $\nu \wedge \alpha$

12. $\beta - f\alpha$

13. Let $\alpha = x^2 dx$, $\beta = 2dx - e^z dy$ and $\gamma = dy + dz - z\,dx$ be 1-forms defined on $\mathbb{R}^3$. Verify each identity.

   (a) $\alpha \wedge (\beta \wedge \gamma) = (\alpha \wedge \beta) \wedge \gamma$

   (b) $\alpha \wedge \gamma = -\gamma \wedge \alpha$

14. Let $\alpha = x^2 y\,dx - y^3 dy + y^2 dz$ and let $\beta = y\,dx\,dy + z\,dy\,dz + x\,dz\,dx$. Verify each identity.

   (a) $\alpha \wedge \beta = \beta \wedge \alpha$

   (b) $\alpha \wedge \alpha = 0$

   (c) $\beta \wedge \beta = 0$

Exercises 15 to 26: Find $d\alpha$ for the form α.

15. $\alpha = e^{xyz}$, on $\mathbb{R}^3$

16. $\alpha = (x^2 + y^2)dx\,dz$, on $\mathbb{R}^3$

17. $\alpha = x^2(dx\,dy + dy\,dz)$, on $\mathbb{R}^3$

18. $\alpha = \sin x \cos y\,dx\,dy\,dz$, on $\mathbb{R}^3$

19. $\alpha = \sinh x\,dx + \sinh^2 x\,dy - dz$, on $\mathbb{R}^3$

20. $\alpha = (x^2 + y^2 + z^2)dy$, on $\mathbb{R}^3$

21. $\alpha = z\,dx\,dy + y\,dy\,dz + xy\,dz\,dx$, on $\mathbb{R}^3$

22. $\alpha = x\,dy$, on $\mathbb{R}^2$

23. $\alpha = \arctan x$, on $\mathbb{R}^2$

24. $\alpha = x\,dx/(x^2 + y^2) - y\,dy/(x^2 + y^2)$, on $\mathbb{R}^2 - \{(0, 0)\}$

25. $\alpha = dy\,dz - dx\,dy$, on $\mathbb{R}^3$

26. $\alpha = dy\,dz\,dx$, on $\mathbb{R}^3$

27. Let $\alpha = x^3 dy - 2y\,dx + z\,dz$. Check that $d(d\alpha) = 0$.

28. Let $\alpha = xy\,dz - 2dx + y\,dy$ and $\beta = dx\,dz$. Verify each identity.

   (a) $d(\alpha \wedge \beta) = d\alpha \wedge \beta - \alpha \wedge d\beta$

   (b) $d(\beta \wedge \alpha) = d\beta \wedge \alpha + \beta \wedge d\alpha$

29. Verify that $d(fg) = df \wedge g + f \wedge dg$ for $f = xye^z$ and $g = 2x - y^2 - xz$.

30. In defining differential forms in $\mathbb{R}^3$, we defined forms of degree zero, one, two and three. Why didn't we define 4-forms, 5-forms, etc.?

31. Let $\alpha = f(x, y)dx\,dy + g(y, z)dy\,dz + h(x, z)dz\,dx$ be a 2-form in $\mathbb{R}^3$, and let f, g and h be differentiable functions of the variables indicated. Compute $d\alpha$.

32. Let $\alpha = f(x, y)dx + g(y, z)dy + h(x, z)dz$ be a 1-form in $\mathbb{R}^3$, and let f, g and h be differentiable functions of the variables indicated. Compute $d\alpha$ and check that $d(d\alpha) = 0$. What assumption on the functions f, g and h is needed for this identity to hold?

33. Consider the vector field $\mathbf{F}(x, y, z) = x^2 yz\mathbf{i} - (x^2 + y^2)\mathbf{j} + yz\mathbf{k}$ and the 2-form $\alpha = yz\,dx\,dy - (x^2 + y^2)dz\,dx + x^2 yz\,dy\,dz$. (Compare their coefficients!) Compute $div\,\mathbf{F}$ and show that it is equal to the component of $dx\,dy\,dz$ in the expression for $d\alpha$.

34. Consider the vector field $\mathbf{F}(x, y, z) = yz\mathbf{i} + \mathbf{j} + xy\mathbf{k}$ and the 1-form $\alpha = yz\,dx + dy + xy\,dz$. (Compare their coefficients!) Show that the components of $d\alpha$ coincide with the components of $curl\,\mathbf{F}$. What vector identity is represented by $d(d\alpha) = 0$?

35. Consider the 0-form (i.e., a real-valued function) $f = \ln(x^2 + y^2 + z^2 + 1)$. Show that the components of df coincide with the components of $grad\ f$. What vector identity is represented by $d(df) = 0$?

CHAPTER REVIEW

Review Questions

Answer/discuss the following questions:

1. State the relationship between the gradient and level curves or level surfaces. Give several examples that illustrate this relationship. Explain how to use a topographical map (i.e., a map of level curves of the height function) to climb to the top of a hill fastest.

2. Define a conservative vector field and a corresponding potential function. How many potential functions does a conservative vector field have?

3. Give physical interpretations of the divergence and the curl. Sketch examples of vector fields $\mathbf{F}_1$, $\mathbf{F}_2$ and $\mathbf{F}_3$ such that $div\ \mathbf{F}_1 = 0$ and $curl\ \mathbf{F}_1 = \mathbf{0}$, $div\ \mathbf{F}_2 > 0$ and $curl\ \mathbf{F}_2 = \mathbf{0}$, $div\ \mathbf{F}_3 < 0$ and $curl\ \mathbf{F}_3 \neq \mathbf{0}$.

4. Is there a C^2 vector field $\mathbf{F}$ such that $curl\ \mathbf{F} = xy^2\mathbf{i} + z\mathbf{k}$? such that $curl\ \mathbf{F} = y\mathbf{i} + \mathbf{k}$? Explain your answers.

5. Define the differential of a form and explain how gradient, divergence and curl can be interpreted as special cases. Suppose that there are 4 basic one-forms, say dx, dy, dz and dt (we will encounter this situation in the last chapter, during our investigation of the electromagnetic tensor). How many basic two-forms and three-forms are there? Are there any non-trivial four-forms, five-forms, etc.?

Computer Projects

1. **Rate of Change of a Function.**
   Consider the function $f(x, y) = 4y^2e^{-x/2} - 3\pi \cos x$.

   (a) Find the maximum rate of change of f at $(1, 2)$ and the direction in which it occurs.

   (b) Describe (in terms of the angle with respect to the gradient) all directions at $(1, 2)$ where the rate of change of f is smaller than 3.26.

   (c) Define the function $g(\theta)$ as the rate of change of f at $(1, 2)$ in the direction of the (unit) vector that forms the angle θ with respect to the positive x-axis. Write down the formula for $g(\theta)$. Find its extreme values on $[0, 2\pi]$.

   (d) Plot $g(\theta)$ on $[0, 2\pi]$ and read off the answer for (c).

2. **Flow Lines and Level Curves.**
   Consider the vector field $\mathbf{F}(x, y) = (3\sin(6x)\cos^2(4y) + 1, -4\sin^2(3x)\sin(8y) + 1)$.

   (a) Check that $curl\ \mathbf{F} = \mathbf{0}$.

   (b) Find a function $f(x, y)$ such that $\mathbf{F} = \nabla f$ and $f(0, 0) = 2$.

   (c) Plot $\mathbf{F}$ for $-1 \leq x, y \leq 1$. Based on that plot, draw several flow lines of $\mathbf{F}$.

   (d) Plot several level curves of f for $-1 \leq x, y \leq 1$.

(e) Explain the connection between the curves in (c) and (d).

Further Explorations

1. Show that $\Delta(div\,(\|\mathbf{r}\|^{-2}\mathbf{r})) = 2\|\mathbf{r}\|^{-4}$, where $\mathbf{r} = x\mathbf{i} + y\mathbf{j} + z\mathbf{k} \neq \mathbf{0}$.

2. Prove that the equation of the tangent plane to the ellipsoid $x^2/a^2 + y^2/b^2 + z^2/c^2 = 1$ at the point (x_0, y_0, z_0) is $xx_0/a^2 + yy_0/b^2 + zz_0/c^2 = 1$.

3. Let $f: \mathbb{R}^3 \to \mathbb{R}$ be a differentiable function satisfying $f(t\mathbf{x}) = t^p f(\mathbf{x})$, where p is a constant and $t \in \mathbb{R}$. Prove that $\mathbf{x} \cdot \nabla f(\mathbf{x}) = pf(\mathbf{x})$ for every $\mathbf{x} \in \mathbb{R}^3$.

4. The electrostatic potential over a certain region in $\mathbb{R}^3$ is given by the function $V(x, y, z) = 0.5\|\mathbf{r}\|^{1/3}$, where $\mathbf{r} = x\mathbf{i} + y\mathbf{j} + z\mathbf{k}$.

   (a) Find the rate of change of V at $(1, 2, -1)$ in the direction toward $(5, -3, -2)$.

   (b) Find the maximum rate of change of V at $(1, 2, -1)$ and the direction in which it occurs.

5. The shape of a hill corresponds to the graph of the function $z = 440 - 0.1x^2 - 0.4y^2$. A climber is located at the point $(10, 10, 390)$ on the hill.

   (a) In which direction should the climber proceed in order to descend most rapidly?

   (b) In which direction should the climber proceed in order to reach the top of the hill fastest? At what angle with respect to the horizontal is the climber climbing in that case?

   (c) In which direction should the climber proceed in order to gain height at the rate of 10% (i.e., 1 meter up for 10 meters horizontal distance)?

6. Assume that $D_{\mathbf{i}+\mathbf{j}}f(\mathbf{a}) = 2$ and $D_{\mathbf{i}-\mathbf{j}}f(\mathbf{a}) = 5$, where $f: \mathbb{R}^2 \to \mathbb{R}$ is a differentiable function and $\mathbf{a}$ is a point in $\mathbb{R}^2$.

   (a) Find $\dfrac{\partial f}{\partial x}(\mathbf{a})$ and $\dfrac{\partial f}{\partial y}(\mathbf{a})$.

   (b) Find the largest rate of change of f at $\mathbf{a}$ and the direction in which it occurs.

7. Let $\mathbf{c}(t)$ be a flow line of the vector field $\mathbf{F} = -grad\,f$ (i.e., $\mathbf{F}$ is a conservative field and f its potential function). Show that $f(\mathbf{c}(t))$ is a decreasing function (that is, potential decreases as one moves along its flow lines).

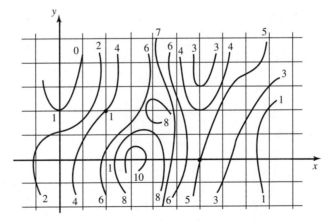

Figure 4.16 Level curves of Exercise 8.

8. Figure 4.16 shows several level curves of a function $f(x, y)$. Estimate $(\partial f/\partial x)(1, 1)$ and $(\partial f/\partial y)(3, 0)$. Draw the gradient vector field along the level curve of value 6.

9. The voltage (potential) at a point (x, y, z) is given by $V(x, y, z) = (1 + \|\mathbf{r}\|)^{-1}$, where $\mathbf{r} = x\mathbf{i} + y\mathbf{j} + z\mathbf{k}$.

   (a) What is the direction of the largest increase in the voltage at the point $(1, 1, -3)$?

   (b) In which direction(s) (answer in terms of the angle with respect to the direction of the largest increase) at the point $(1, 1, -3)$ is there no change in V?

10. Let the curve c be the intersection of the paraboloid $z = 3 + 2x^2 + 4y^2$ and the sphere $x^2 + y^2 + z^2 = 50$. Find the equation of the line tangent to c at the point $(0, 1, 7)$.

Chapter 5

INTEGRATION ALONG PATHS

The next three chapters are devoted to the development of generalizations of the definite integral to various regions. We will learn how to integrate real-valued functions of several variables and vector fields along curves, over surfaces and (in case of real-valued functions only) over three-dimensional regions. In all cases, the constructions follow the same theme: an integral will be the limit of approximating sums, that are called Riemann sums.

We start this chapter by studying paths (or parametrizations) as an analytic way of describing a curve in a plane or in space. Concepts relevant to integration are introduced and illustrated in a number of examples. We proceed by constructing path integrals of real-valued functions and vector fields (the latter are also known as line integrals). The work done by a force and the circulation of a vector field are presented as main applications of these concepts. As a consequence of the fact that the path integral of a real-valued function does not depend on the way a curve is traversed, we obtain the fact that the length of a curve does not depend on its parametrization.

A vector field is called a gradient vector field if it is the gradient of some real-valued function (probably the most important example is a conservative force field). It turns out that such vector fields possess remarkable properties when integrated along closed curves. Due to their importance in mathematics and in applications, a whole section is devoted to the investigation of gradient vector fields.

5.1   PATHS AND PARAMETRIZATIONS

In Chapter 3 we studied a number of concepts and properties related to paths in a plane or in space. Now we turn our attention to those properties that are needed for integration along paths.

A path $\mathbf{c}$ in $\mathbb{R}^2$ (or $\mathbb{R}^3$) is a function $\mathbf{c}(t) \colon [a, b] \to \mathbb{R}^2$ (or $\mathbb{R}^3$) defined on an interval $[a, b] \subseteq \mathbb{R}$, where a and b are real numbers (for the purposes of integration we normally do not allow $a = -\infty$ or $b = \infty$; see Exercise 3 at the end of Section 5.2 for a case when $b = \infty$). The image of $\mathbf{c}$ is called a curve in $\mathbb{R}^2$ (or $\mathbb{R}^3$), and the function $\mathbf{c}(t)$ is said to parametrize the curve (or, we say that $\mathbf{c}(t)$ is a parametrization of the curve $\mathbf{c}$). A path $\mathbf{c}$ in $\mathbb{R}^2$ (or $\mathbb{R}^3$) can be expressed in terms of its components as $\mathbf{c}(t) = (x(t), y(t))$ (or $\mathbf{c}(t) = (x(t), y(t), z(t))$ in $\mathbb{R}^3$), where $x(t)$, $y(t)$ and $z(t)$ are real-valued functions of one variable, defined on $[a, b]$.

Before proceeding, let us clarify the meaning of the statements "$f(t)$ is continuous on $[a, b]$" and "$f(t)$ is differentiable on $[a, b]$." Continuity and differentiability are defined in terms of a limit: a function $f(t)$ is continuous at $t_0 \in (a, b)$ if and only if $\lim_{t \to t_0} f(t)$ exists and equals $f(t_0)$; it is differentiable at $t_0 \in (a, b)$ if and only if $\lim_{h \to 0} (f(t_0 + h) - f(t_0))/h$ exists. These definitions apply to any t_0 that lies inside the interval (a, b). To define continuity and differentiability at the endpoints a and b, all we have to do is to replace the (two-sided) limits with the appropriate one-sided limits in such a way that the endpoints are always approached from within the interval. For example, the function $f(t)$ is continuous at $t = b$ if and only if $\lim_{t \to b^-} f(t)$ exists and equals $f(b)$; it is differentiable at $t = a$ if and only if $\lim_{h \to 0^+} (f(a + h) - f(a))/h$ exists.

With this in mind, we say that the path $\mathbf{c}(t)$ defined on the interval $[a, b]$ is continuous (differentiable) if and only if all of its component functions are continuous (differentiable) on $[a, b]$.

Our next definition introduces paths that will be used in integration of scalar-valued and vector-valued functions.

■ **Definition 5.1** C^1 Path and Piecewise C^1 Path.

A path $\mathbf{c}(t) \colon [a, b] \to \mathbb{R}^2$ (or $\mathbb{R}^3$) is called a C^1 *path* if and only if its component functions have continuous derivatives (i.e., are C^1) on $[a, b]$.

A path $\mathbf{c}$ is a *piecewise* C^1 path if its domain $[a, b]$ can be broken into subintervals $[a = t_1, t_2], [t_2, t_3], \dots, [t_{n-1}, t_n = b]$ so that the restriction of $\mathbf{c}$ to each subinterval $[t_i, t_{i+1}]$, $i = 1, \dots, n - 1$, is a C^1 path. ■

In other words, a piecewise C^1 path is obtained by glueing together C^1 paths so that the terminal point of one path becomes the initial point of the following one. By definition, a C^1 path is also a piecewise C^1 path.

Example 5.1   Consider the path $\mathbf{c}(t) = (t, |t^2 - 1|)$, $t \in [-2, 3]$, shown in Figure 5.1. It is continuous, but not differentiable (and hence not C^1), since the component $y(t) = |t^2 - 1|$ does not have a derivative at $t = \pm 1$.

Now break up the interval $[-2, 3]$ into three subintervals $[-2, -1]$, $[-1, 1]$ and $[1, 3]$, and consider the restrictions $\mathbf{c}(t)|_{[-2,-1]} = (t, t^2 - 1)$ (when $-2 < t < -1$, $t^2 - 1 > 0$, and therefore $|t^2 - 1| = t^2 - 1$), $\mathbf{c}(t)|_{[-1,1]} = (t, -t^2 + 1)$ (when $-1 < t < 1$, $t^2 - 1 < 0$, and therefore $|t^2 - 1| = -(t^2 - 1)$) and $\mathbf{c}(t)|_{[1,3]} = (t, t^2 - 1)$ (when $t > 1$, $t^2 - 1 > 0$). All components of all restrictions are polynomials, and hence continuously differentiable on the given intervals. It follows that the path $\mathbf{c}$ is built of three C^1 paths. We say that $\mathbf{c}$ is piecewise continuously differentiable, or piecewise C^1.   ◀

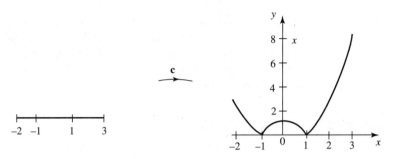

Figure 5.1 Piecewise C^1 path $\mathbf{c}(t) = (t, |t^2 - 1|)$, $t \in [-2, 3]$.

Example 5.2

The path $\mathbf{c}(t) = (\cos^3 t, \sin^3 t)$, $t \in [0, 2\pi]$, shown in Figure 5.2 is C^1, since both components of $\mathbf{c}'(t) = (-3 \cos^2 t \sin t, 3 \sin^2 t \cos t)$ are continuous on the interval $[0, 2\pi]$.

The path $\mathbf{c}(t) = (t^{1/3}, 2t^{1/3})$, $t \in [-1, 1]$, represents the straight line segment joining $(-1, -2)$ and $(1, 2)$. It is not C^1 (not even piecewise C^1), since its derivative $\mathbf{c}'(t) = (t^{-2/3}/3, 2t^{-2/3}/3)$ does not exist when $t = 0$. ◀

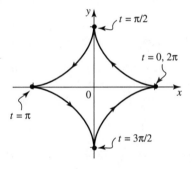

Figure 5.2 The path $\mathbf{c}(t) = (\cos^3 t, \sin^3 t)$, $t \in [0, 2\pi]$, is C^1.

Examples 5.1 and 5.2 show that it is not possible to determine whether a path is C^1 or not just by looking at its image. In particular, the existence of a cusp does not mean that a path is not C^1. And a path that "looks like" it is C^1 (e.g., a line) is not necessarily C^1.

Definition 5.2   Bijective Function.

A function $\phi \colon [\alpha, \beta] \to [a, b]$, where $[\alpha, \beta]$ and $[a, b]$ are closed intervals in $\mathbb{R}$, is called *bijective* if it has an inverse $\phi^{-1} \colon [a, b] \to [\alpha, \beta]$. ■

The function $\phi \colon [0, 1] \to [1, 4]$ given by $\phi(t) = 1 + 3t$ is bijective (its inverse is $\phi^{-1}(t) = (t - 1)/3$), as is the map $\phi \colon [0, 1] \to [0, 1]$, $\phi(t) = t^3$ (the inverse map is $\phi^{-1}(t) = t^{1/3}$). On the other hand, $\phi \colon [-1, 1] \to [0, 1]$ defined by $\phi(t) = t^2$ does not have an inverse (what would $\phi^{-1}(1)$ be, 1 or -1?), so it is not bijective.

In Section 3.1 we noticed that it is possible that infinitely many paths represent the same curve. However, they are not all unrelated to each other: among all paths that represent a curve we can always find so-called reparametrizations of a path. Let us make this concept precise.

Definition 5.3   Reparametrization of a Path.

Let $\mathbf{c}: [a, b] \to \mathbb{R}^2$ (or $\mathbb{R}^3$) be a C^1 path. The composition

$$\boldsymbol{\gamma} = \mathbf{c} \circ \phi: [\alpha, \beta] \to \mathbb{R}^2 \text{ (or } \mathbb{R}^3),$$

where $\phi: [\alpha, \beta] \to [a, b]$ is C^1 and bijective, is called a *reparametrization* of $\mathbf{c}$.

Example 5.3   Consider the helix

$$\mathbf{c}(t) = (\cos t, \sin t, t), \qquad t \in [0, 2\pi]$$

in $\mathbb{R}^3$. The initial point is $(1, 0, 0)$ and the terminal point is $(1, 0, 2\pi)$. The speed is computed to be $\|\mathbf{c}'(t)\| = \sqrt{2}$. Use $\phi_1: [0, \pi/2] \to [0, 2\pi]$, defined by $\phi_1(t) = 4t$ (ϕ_1 is clearly C^1 and a bijection: the inverse function is $\phi_1^{-1}(t) = t/4$), to reparametrize $\mathbf{c}(t)$; set

$$\boldsymbol{\gamma}(t) = \mathbf{c}(\phi_1(t)) = \mathbf{c}(4t) = (\cos 4t, \sin 4t, 4t), \qquad t \in [0, \pi/2].$$

Curves $\boldsymbol{\gamma}$ and $\mathbf{c}$ have the same endpoints, but the speed of $\boldsymbol{\gamma}$ is $\|\boldsymbol{\gamma}'(t)\| = \sqrt{32} = 4\sqrt{2}$, i.e., it is four times the speed of $\mathbf{c}$. Now define a new parametrization; let $\phi_2: [0, 2\pi] \to [0, 2\pi]$ be defined by $\phi_2(t) = 2\pi - t$ (ϕ_2 is bijective, since $\phi_2^{-1}(t) = 2\pi - t$). Then

$$\boldsymbol{\gamma}(t) = \mathbf{c}(2\pi - t) = (\cos(2\pi - t), \sin(2\pi - t), 2\pi - t), \qquad t \in [0, 2\pi].$$

This time $\boldsymbol{\gamma}(0) = (1, 0, 2\pi)$ and $\boldsymbol{\gamma}(2\pi) = (1, 0, 0)$; i.e., $\boldsymbol{\gamma}$ is traced in the direction opposite to $\mathbf{c}$. The speed of $\boldsymbol{\gamma}$ is $\sqrt{2}$.

The chain rule applied to the composition $\boldsymbol{\gamma}(t) = \mathbf{c}(\phi(t))$ implies that

$$\boldsymbol{\gamma}'(t) = \mathbf{c}'(\phi(t)) \, \phi'(t).$$

In words, the velocity vector $\boldsymbol{\gamma}'(t)$ of the reparametrization $\boldsymbol{\gamma}$ at the point $\boldsymbol{\gamma}(t)$ is equal to the product of the scalar $\phi'(t)$ and the velocity vector $\mathbf{c}'(\phi(t))$ of $\mathbf{c}$ at the point $\mathbf{c}(\phi(t)) = \boldsymbol{\gamma}(t)$; i.e., $\mathbf{c}'(\phi(t))$ and $\boldsymbol{\gamma}'(t)$ are parallel (of the same or opposite orientations, depending on the sign of $\phi'(t)$). Moreover, (using $\|\alpha \mathbf{v}\| = |\alpha| \cdot \|\mathbf{v}\|$, where α is a scalar and $\mathbf{v}$ a vector) we get the formula

$$\|\boldsymbol{\gamma}'(t)\| = |\phi'(t)| \, \|\mathbf{c}'(\phi(t))\|$$

stating the relationship between the speeds of $\boldsymbol{\gamma}$ and $\mathbf{c}$. In light of these observations, we interpret a reparametrization as a change of speed (as we have done already in Example 5.3).

From Definition 5.3 it follows that a reparametrization $\phi\colon [\alpha, \beta] \to [a, b]$ maps the endpoints of the interval $[\alpha, \beta]$ to the endpoints of the interval $[a, b]$. There are two cases: either $\phi(\alpha) = a$ and $\phi(\beta) = b$, or $\phi(\alpha) = b$ and $\phi(\beta) = a$. In the former case, $\boldsymbol{\gamma}(\alpha) = \mathbf{c}(\phi(\alpha)) = \mathbf{c}(a)$ and $\boldsymbol{\gamma}(\beta) = \mathbf{c}(\phi(\beta)) = \mathbf{c}(b)$; i.e., $\boldsymbol{\gamma}$ and $\mathbf{c}$ have the same initial point and the same terminal point. In this case we say that ϕ is *orientation-preserving*. In the latter case, $\boldsymbol{\gamma}(\alpha) = \mathbf{c}(\phi(\alpha)) = \mathbf{c}(b)$ and $\boldsymbol{\gamma}(\beta) = \mathbf{c}(\phi(\beta)) = \mathbf{c}(a)$, and ϕ is *orientation-reversing*. This time, the initial point of $\mathbf{c}$ is the terminal point of $\boldsymbol{\gamma}$, and vice versa.

The reparametrization $\phi_1(t) = 4t$ in Example 5.3 is orientation-preserving and the reparametrization $\phi_2(t) = 2\pi - t$ in the same example is orientation-reversing.

■ **Theorem 5.1**   Orientation-preserving and Orientation-reversing Reparametrizations.

A reparametrization ϕ is orientation-preserving if and only if $\phi' \geq 0$ (i.e., if and only if ϕ is an increasing function), and orientation-reversing if and only if $\phi' \leq 0$ (i.e., if and only if ϕ is a decreasing function).   ■

Proof

We present an intuitive version of the proof. Assume that ϕ is an orientation-preserving reparametrization and try to imagine what its graph would look like. By assumption, $\phi(\alpha) = a$ and $\phi(\beta) = b$, and consequently the graph has to connect the points (α, a) and (β, b); see Figure 5.3. Since ϕ maps $[\alpha, \beta]$ into $[a, b]$, the graph has to be contained in the rectangle with vertices (α, a), (β, a), (β, b) and (α, b).

Now suppose that the graph of ϕ starts decreasing at some point. Since it has to reach (β, b) it will have to start increasing again, so its shape will be something like the one shown in Figure 5.3. But then there are more points (in our case those are t_1, t_2 and t_3) that get mapped into the same point T, and that implies that the inverse ϕ^{-1} is not defined at T. (Where would ϕ^{-1} map T?) Evidently the assumption that ϕ decreases somewhere leads to a contradiction, so ϕ is always increasing.

Now assume that $\phi\colon [\alpha, \beta] \to [a, b]$ is increasing (i.e., $t_1 < t_2$ implies that $\phi(t_1) < \phi(t_2)$). In that case, $\phi(\alpha) < \phi(\beta)$ and therefore $\phi(\alpha) = a$ ($\phi(\alpha)$ can be equal to a or b only!) and $\phi(\beta) = b$, so that ϕ is orientation-preserving.

Similar argument can be applied in the orientation-reversing case.   ■

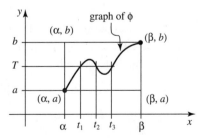

Figure 5.3   Graph of the function ϕ from the proof of Theorem 5.1.

Example 5.4 Let $\mathbf{c}: [a, b] \to \mathbb{R}^3$ be a curve in $\mathbb{R}^3$.

(a) Assume that the speed of $\mathbf{c}$ is constant, i.e., $\|\mathbf{c}'(t)\| = C > 0$, for all t. Find an orientation-preserving reparametrization of $\mathbf{c}$ whose speed equals $S > 0$.

(b) Reparametrize $\mathbf{c}$ so that it takes T units of time to trace it.

(c) Reparametrize $\mathbf{c}$ so that it is traced in the opposite direction with the same speed C.

Solution

(a) The speed of $\mathbf{c}(t)$ and its reparametrization $\boldsymbol{\gamma}(t) = \mathbf{c}(\phi(t))$ are related by

$$\|\boldsymbol{\gamma}'(t)\| = |\phi'(t)| \, \|\mathbf{c}'(\phi(t))\|.$$

By assumption, the speed of $\mathbf{c}$ is equal to C everywhere; therefore, $\|\mathbf{c}'(\phi(t))\| = C$ and the above equation implies that $|\phi'(t)| = S/C$; i.e., $\phi'(t) = \pm S/C$. We have to choose the plus sign in order to preserve orientation (cf. Theorem 5.1). Therefore, $\phi'(t) = S/C$ and $\phi(t) = St/C + D$, where D is a real number (as a matter of fact, we have found infinitely many desired reparametrizations). We need the domain $[\alpha, \beta]$ of ϕ. Since ϕ is orientation-preserving, it maps the initial (terminal) point to the initial (terminal) point. It follows that $\phi(\alpha) = S\alpha/C + D = a$ (and hence $\alpha = (a - D)C/S$) and $\phi(\beta) = S\beta/C + D = b$ (and hence $\beta = (b - D)C/S$). We are done: the reparametrization of $\mathbf{c}(t)$, $t \in [a, b]$, is given by the composition

$$\boldsymbol{\gamma}(t) = \mathbf{c}(\phi(t)) = \mathbf{c}(St/C + D), \qquad t \in [(a - D)C/S, (b - D)C/S].$$

Let us check our result: The function ϕ is bijective, its inverse being $\phi^{-1}(t) = C(t - D)/S$. Since $\phi(t) = St/C + D$ is a polynomial (of degree one), it is of class C^1, and therefore ϕ is a reparametrization. From

$$\boldsymbol{\gamma}\left(\frac{(a - D)C}{S}\right) = \mathbf{c}\left(\frac{S}{C}\frac{(a - D)C}{S} + D\right) = \mathbf{c}(a)$$

and

$$\boldsymbol{\gamma}\left(\frac{(b - D)C}{S}\right) = \mathbf{c}\left(\frac{S}{C}\frac{(b - D)C}{S} + D\right) = \mathbf{c}(b)$$

it follows that ϕ preserves orientation. Its speed is

$$\|\boldsymbol{\gamma}'(t)\| = \left\|\mathbf{c}'\left(\frac{St}{C} + D\right)\frac{S}{C}\right\| = \left\|\mathbf{c}'\left(\frac{St}{C} + D\right)\right\| \left|\frac{S}{C}\right| = C\frac{S}{C} = S,$$

since, by asumption, the speed of $\mathbf{c}$ is constant (equal to C).

(b) One needs $b - a$ units of time to trace $\mathbf{c}$. We have to find a C^1 bijective map ϕ whose domain has length T; for example

$$\phi: [0, T] \to [a, b].$$

It follows that we need a function ϕ satisfying $\phi(0) = a$ and $\phi(T) = b$. One way to find it is to compute the equation of the line joining $(0, a)$ and (T, b) (its point-slope equation is $y - a = (b - a)x/T$) so that (set $x = t$, $y = \phi(t)$)

$$\phi(t) = \frac{b - a}{T}t + a, \qquad t \in [0, T].$$

ϕ is a polynomial (of degree one), and hence continuously differentiable. Its inverse is given by $\phi^{-1}(t) = (t - a)T/(b - a)$. The composition

$$\gamma(t) = \mathbf{c}(\phi(t)) = \mathbf{c}\left(\frac{b - a}{T}t + a\right), \qquad t \in [0, T]$$

is a desired parametrization.

(c) We need a map ϕ such that $\phi(a) = b$ and $\phi(b) = a$. Proceeding as in (b), we compute the equation of the line through (a, b) and (b, a): $y - b = (a - b)(x - a)/(b - a)$; i.e., $y - b = -x + a$, and hence (replace y by $\phi(t)$ and x by t) $\phi(t) = a + b - t$. The function $\phi(t)$ is continuously differentiable and its inverse is $\phi^{-1}(t) = a + b - t$. It follows that the reparametrized curve

$$\gamma(t) = \mathbf{c}(\phi(t)) = \mathbf{c}(a + b - t), \qquad t \in [a, b]$$

describes the curve $\mathbf{c}$ traced backwards. Since $\phi'(t) = -1 < 0$, the reparametrization is orientation-reversing. (Alternatively, we could have computed the endpoints of γ: $\gamma(a) = \mathbf{c}(a - b - a) = \mathbf{c}(b)$, and $\gamma(b) = \mathbf{c}(a - b - b) = \mathbf{c}(a)$.) ◀

Example 5.5   Let $\mathbf{c}$ be the path in $\mathbb{R}^2$ given by $\mathbf{c}(t) = (t, t^2)$, $t \in [-1, 1]$. The image of $\mathbf{c}$ is the part of the parabola $y = x^2$ between the points $\mathbf{c}(-1) = (-1, 1)$ (the initial point of $\mathbf{c}$) and $\mathbf{c}(1) = (1, 1)$ (the terminal point of $\mathbf{c}$).

Define $\phi: [0, 1] \to [-1, 1]$ by $\phi(t) = -1 + 2t$. Clearly $\phi(0) = -1$ and $\phi(1) = 1$ so ϕ is orientation-preserving (alternatively, we can apply Theorem 5.1 to $\phi'(t) = 2 > 0$). The reparametrized curve $\mathbf{c}_1: [0, 1] \to \mathbb{R}^2$ has the equation

$$\begin{aligned}\mathbf{c}_1(t) = \mathbf{c}(\phi(t)) &= \big(x(\phi(t)), y(\phi(t))\big) \\ &= \big(-1 + 2t, (-1 + 2t)^2\big) = (-1 + 2t, 1 - 4t + 4t^2).\end{aligned}$$

The endpoints of the curve $\mathbf{c}_1$ are $\mathbf{c}_1(0) = (-1, 1)$ and $\mathbf{c}_1(1) = (1, 1)$, which confirms that the reparametrization is orientation-preserving.

On the other hand, the reparametrization $\phi: [-1, 1] \to [-1, 1]$ defined by $\phi(t) = -t$ gives the path

$$\mathbf{c}_2(t) = \mathbf{c}(\phi(t)) = \mathbf{c}(-t) = \big(-t, (-t)^2\big) = (-t, t^2),$$

which has orientation opposite to $\mathbf{c}$. To verify this, all we have to do is to compute the endpoints: $\mathbf{c}_2(-1) = (1, 1)$ and $\mathbf{c}_2(1) = (-1, 1)$, or check the derivative: $\phi'(t) = -1 < 0$. ◀

Example 5.6   Consider a reparametrization of the helix (cf. Example 5.3)

$$\mathbf{c}(t) = (\cos t, \sin t, t), \qquad t \in [0, 2\pi]$$

defined by $\phi: [0, \sqrt{2\pi}] \to [0, 2\pi]$, $\phi(t) = t^2$. (Notice that ϕ does have an inverse $\phi^{-1}: [0, 2\pi] \to [0, \sqrt{2\pi}]$, given by $\phi^{-1}(t) = +\sqrt{t}$; there is no ambiguity about the sign of the square root.) The curve

$$\gamma(t) = \mathbf{c}(\phi(t)) = (\cos t^2, \sin t^2, t^2), \qquad t \in [0, \sqrt{2\pi}]$$

has the speed (this time non-constant) $\|\mathbf{c}'(t)\| = \sqrt{8t^2} = 2\sqrt{2}t$. Curves $\boldsymbol{\gamma}$ and $\mathbf{c}$ have the same orientation; that is, ϕ is orientation-preserving.

◀

Recall that a function $f(t)$ is called *one-to-one* if $t_1 \neq t_2$ implies $f(t_1) \neq f(t_2)$ for all t_1, t_2 in its domain. In other words, a one-to-one function maps distinct points to distinct points. The equivalent statement, that $f(t)$ is one-to-one if and only if $f(t_1) = f(t_2)$ implies $t_1 = t_2$, provides a more "workable" version of the definition (it merely restates it in the follwing sense: if two points t_1 and t_2 map to the same point, then they must have been the same point to start with).

For example, the path $\mathbf{c}(t) = (2t, t^3 - t)$ is one-to-one, since $\mathbf{c}(t_1) = \mathbf{c}(t_2)$ implies $(2t_1, t_1^3 - t_1) = (2t_2, t_2^3 - t_2)$ and therefore $t_1 = t_2$. However, $\mathbf{c}(t) = (t^2, \sin t)$, $t \in [-2\pi, 2\pi]$ is not one-to-one: both $t_1 = -\pi$ and $t_2 = \pi$ map to the same point, $\mathbf{c}(t_1) = \mathbf{c}(t_2) = (\pi^2, 0)$.

▨ **Definition 5.4**   Simple Curve.

The image of a one-to-one, piecewise C^1 mapping $\mathbf{c} \colon [a, b] \to \mathbb{R}^2$ (or $\mathbb{R}^3$) is called a *simple curve*.

▪

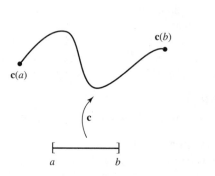

Figure 5.4   A simple curve.   **Figure 5.5**   A curve that is not simple.

In other words (since "one-to-one" means that no two points of the interval $[a, b]$ are mapped onto the same point on the curve) a simple curve cannot intersect itself.

▨ **Definition 5.5**   Simple Closed Curve.

The image of a piecewise C^1 mapping $\mathbf{c} \colon [a, b] \to \mathbb{R}^2$ (or $\mathbb{R}^3$) that is one-to-one on $[a, b)$ and is such that $\mathbf{c}(a) = \mathbf{c}(b)$ is called a *simple closed curve*.

▪

In other words, no points other than the endpoints a and b of $[a, b]$ are mapped onto the same point. It follows that a simple closed curve cannnot intersect or retrace (partly or fully) itself.

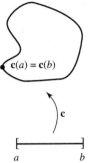

Figure 5.6 A simple closed curve.

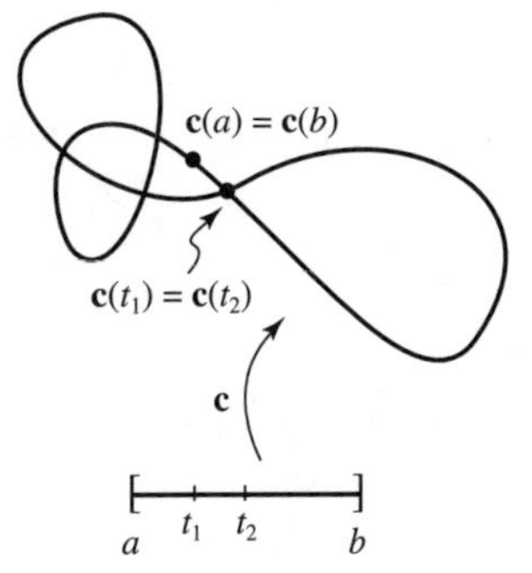

Figure 5.7 A closed curve that is not a simple closed curve.

Example 5.7

The circle $\mathbf{c}(t) = (\cos t, \sin t), t \in [0, 2\pi]$ is a simple closed curve. The image of the map $\boldsymbol{\gamma} = (\cos t, \sin t), t \in [0, 6\pi]$ is the same circle, but $\boldsymbol{\gamma}$ is not simple: for example, $\boldsymbol{\gamma}(\pi) = \boldsymbol{\gamma}(3\pi) = \boldsymbol{\gamma}(5\pi) = (-1, 0)$. In fact, $\boldsymbol{\gamma}$ wraps around the circle $x^2 + y^2 = 1$ three times.

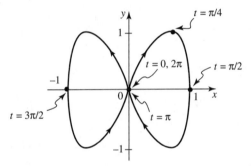

Figure 5.8 The image of $\mathbf{c}(t) = (\sin t, \sin 2t), t \in [0, 2\pi]$ is a "figure-8" curve.

The image of the path $\mathbf{c}(t) = (\sin t, \sin 2t), t \in [0, 2\pi]$ is a closed curve ($\mathbf{c}(0) = \mathbf{c}(2\pi) = (0, 0)$); however, it is not a simple closed curve, since it intersects itself: $\mathbf{c}(\pi) = (0, 0)$. It is an example of a so-called *"figure-8" curve,* and is shown in Figure 5.8.

■ **Definition 5.6** Oriented Simple Curve and Oriented Simple Closed Curve.

Let $\mathbf{c}$ be a simple curve and let A and B be its endpoints. There are two orientations associated with $\mathbf{c}$, defined by the choice of the initial and the terminal points (see Figure 5.9). If $\mathbf{c}$ is a simple closed curve, then the orientation is specified by one of the two possible ways of moving around $\mathbf{c}$. In $\mathbb{R}^2$, these two ways are usually referred to as the "clockwise" and the "counterclockwise" orientation; see Figure 5.10. A simple closed curve together with the choice of an orientation is called an *oriented simple closed curve.*

Figure 5.9 Possible orientations of a simple curve.

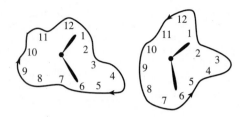

Figure 5.10 Clockwise and counterclockwise orientations of a simple closed curve in $\mathbb{R}^2$.

EXERCISES 5.1

Exercises 1 to 7: State whether it is possible for the map ϕ to be a reparametrization of a path.

1. $\phi: [0, 1] \to [0, \ln 2]$, $\phi(t) = \ln(t + 1)$ **2.** $\phi: [-1, 1] \to [0, 1]$, $\phi(t) = t^2$

3. $\phi: [-8, 1] \to [-2, 1]$, $\phi(t) = t^{1/3}$ **4.** $\phi: [1, 2] \to [0, 3]$, $\phi(t) = t^2 - 1$

5. $\phi: [0, 1] \to [1, e]$, $\phi(t) = e^t$ **6.** $\phi: [-1, 1] \to [-\pi/4, \pi/4]$, $\phi(t) = \arctan t$

7. $\phi: [-2, 1] \to [0, 2]$, $\phi(t) = |t|$

8. Let $\mathbf{c}(t) = (t - 2, 3 - t - t^2)$, $t \in [0, 1]$. Is the reparametrization $\phi: [0, 3] \to [0, 1]$, given by $\phi(t) = 1 - t/3$, orientation-preserving or orientation-reversing?

Exercises 9 to 14: Check whether the curve $\mathbf{c}(t)$ is simple or not, closed or not, simple closed or not.

9. $\mathbf{c}(t) = (\sin t, \cos t, (t - 2\pi)^2)$, $t \in [-2\pi, 6\pi]$

10. $\mathbf{c}(t) = (\sin t, \cos t, (t - 2\pi)^2)$, $t \in [-2\pi, 4\pi]$

11. $\mathbf{c}(t) = (t \sin t, t \cos t)$, $t \in [0, 2\pi]$ **12.** $\mathbf{c}(t) = (\sin 2t, t \cos t)$, $t \in [0, \pi/2]$

13. $\mathbf{c}(t) = (t - t^{-1}, t + t^{-1})$, $t \in [1, 2]$ **14.** $\mathbf{c}(t) = (t^2 - t, 3 - \sqrt{t^2 - t})$, $t \in [0, 1]$

15. Find a parametrization of the part of the curve $y = \sqrt{x^2 + 1}$ from $(-1, \sqrt{2})$ to $(1, \sqrt{2})$. Is your parametrization continuous? Differentiable? Piecewise C^1? C^1?

16. Find a parametrization of the curve $x^{2/3} + y^{2/3} = 1$. Is your parametrization continuous? Differentiable? Piecewise C^1? C^1?

17. Consider the following parametrizations of the straight line segment from $(-1, 1)$ to $(1, 1)$. State which parametrizations are continuous, piecewise C^1 and C^1.

(a) $\mathbf{c}_1(t) = (t, 1)$, $-1 \le t \le 1$

(b) $\mathbf{c}_2(t) = \begin{cases} (-t^2, 1) & \text{if } -1 \le t \le 0 \\ (t^2, 1) & \text{if } 0 \le t \le 1 \end{cases}$

(c) $\mathbf{c}_3(t) = (t^{1/3}, 1)$, $-1 \le t \le 1$

(d) $\mathbf{c}_4(t) = (t^3, 1)$, $-1 \le t \le 1$

(e) $\mathbf{c}_5(t) = \begin{cases} (t, 1) & \text{if } -1 \le t \le 0 \\ (1 - t, 1) & \text{if } 0 \le t \le 1 \end{cases}$

18. Consider the curve $\mathbf{c}$ in $\mathbb{R}^2$ given by $\mathbf{c}(t) = (t, t^2)$, $t \in [-1, 2]$. State which of the following maps ϕ are reparametrizations of $\mathbf{c}$. Describe the curve $\mathbf{c}(\phi(t))$ for those ϕ that are reparametrizations:

(a) $\phi : [-1, \sqrt{3}] \to [-1, 2]$, $\phi(t) = t^2 - 1$ (b) $\phi : [-1/2, 1] \to [-1, 2]$, $\phi(t) = 2t$

(c) $\phi : [-1, 8] \to [-1, 2]$, $\phi(t) = t^{1/3}$ (d) $\phi : [-2/3, 1/3] \to [-1, 2]$, $\phi(t) = -3t$

19. Let $\mathbf{c}(t) = (t^2, 2 - t^2)$, $t \in [1, 3]$. Reparametrize $\mathbf{c}$ so that its speed is constant.

20. Let $\mathbf{c}(t) = (\cos 2\pi t, \sin 2\pi t, t)$, $0 \le t \le 1$.

(a) Reparametrize $\mathbf{c}$ so that its speed equals 1.

(b) Reparametrize $\mathbf{c}$ so that it takes 3 units of time to trace it.

(c) Reparametrize $\mathbf{c}$ so that it is traced in the opposite direction.

21. Let $\mathbf{c}$ be the circle $x^2 + y^2 = a^2$, $a > 0$, oriented clockwise. Find an orientation-preserving parametrization of $\mathbf{c}$ of constant speed S. Find an orientation-reversing parametrization of $\mathbf{c}$ of constant speed 1.

5.2 PATH INTEGRALS OF REAL-VALUED FUNCTIONS

To motivate the definition of a path integral, let us first recall the construction of the definite integral of a real-valued function of one variable.

Assume that $y = f(x)$ is a continuous, positive function defined on an interval $[a, b]$. The graph of f, the vertical lines $x = a$ and $x = b$ and the x-axis define a region R in the xy-plane (called the *region below f over $[a, b]$*). We would like to find a way to compute the area of R.

Subdivide the interval $[a, b]$ into n subintervals $[a = t_1, t_2], [t_2, t_3], \ldots, [t_n, t_{n+1} = b]$ and construct rectangles $R_1, \ldots, R_n$ in the following way: the base of R_i, $i = 1, \ldots, n$, is the i-th subinterval $[t_i, t_{i+1}]$ and its height is the value $f(t_i^*)$ of f at some point t_i^* in $[t_i, t_{i+1}]$; see Figure 5.11.

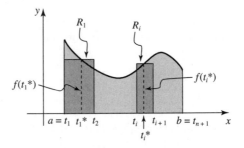

Figure 5.11 Approximating rectangles for the region R.

The area of R_i is $f(t_i^*)(t_{i+1} - t_i) = f(t_i^*)\Delta t_i$, where $\Delta t_i = t_{i+1} - t_i$. The rectangles

$R_1, \ldots, R_n$ approximate the region R, and the sum of their areas

$$A_n = \sum_{i=1}^{n} f(t_i^*) \Delta t_i$$

approximates the area of R. The more rectangles we use, the better approximation we get; consequently, as $n \to \infty$, the sequence A_n of approximations of the area of R by the areas of rectangles will approach the area of R; i.e.,

$$\text{area}(R) = \lim_{n \to \infty} A_n = \lim_{n \to \infty} \sum_{i=1}^{n} f(t_i^*) \Delta t_i.$$

We *define* the definite integral of f on $[a, b]$ as

$$\int_a^b f(x)\,dx = \text{area}(R) = \lim_{n \to \infty} \sum_{i=1}^{n} f(t_i^*) \Delta t_i,$$

provided that the limit exists.

Now assume that f is any function defined on $[a, b]$, not necessarily positive. It can be shown that the above construction works (i.e., the limit in question exists) whenever f is continuous, or, more generally, when it is piecewise continuous and bounded ("piecewise continuous" means that f is not continuous only at finitely many points; "bounded" means that there exists a number $M > 0$ such that $|f(x)| \le M$ for all x in $[a, b]$). In other words, all discontinuities of f (if any) are "jumps" from one finite value to another finite value. Discontinuities like that of the function $y = 1/x$ at $x = 0$ are not allowed. For example, all continuous functions defined on a closed interval $[a, b]$ are bounded. Of course, in this general case, a definite integral does not necessarily represent an area. It can be demonstrated that the limit in the definition is independent of the choices made in the construction (recall that we chose the subintervals and then selected a point in each). To repeat:

Definition 5.7   Definite Integral of a Function $y = f(x)$.

The definite integral of a piecewise continuous and bounded function $y = f(x)$ defined on an interval $[a, b]$ is the real number

$$\int_a^b f(x)\,dx = \lim_{n \to \infty} \sum_{i=1}^{n} f(t_i^*) \Delta t_i.$$

The sum on the right side is called a *Riemann sum*. The definition clarifies the reference to the definite integral as a "limit of (Riemann) sums."

With the help of parametrizations, path integrals of scalar-valued functions and vector-valued functions will be reduced to definite integrals of real-valued functions of one variable.

We will now generalize this important concept. So far, we have considered a function $y = f(x)$ defined on an interval $[a, b]$. To rephrase: we have considered a function defined at the points belonging to the straight line segment from a to b on the

x-axis. Now assume that a function f is defined at the points on a curve in a plane or in space (for example, f could be the temperature at points on a piece of metal wire bent in the shape of a helix). Is it possible to define (in a meaningful way) the definite integral of f along that curve?

The answer is yes—and all we have to do is to adjust the construction we described in the introduction.

Let $f = f(x, y): \mathbb{R}^2 \to \mathbb{R}$ be a continuous function and let $\mathbf{c}(t) = (x(t), y(t))$: $[a, b] \to \mathbb{R}^2$ be a path in $\mathbb{R}^2$ (the construction for $\mathbb{R}^3$ and, in general, for $\mathbb{R}^n$, $n \geq 3$ is identical). The composition $f(\mathbf{c}(t))$ represents the values of f along the points on the curve $\mathbf{c}$ (for example, if f is the electrostatic potential and $\mathbf{c}(t)$ is the trajectory of a charged particle then $f(\mathbf{c}(t))$ describes the potential along the points on the trajectory).

Break up the interval $[a, b]$ into n subintervals $[a = t_1, t_2], [t_2, t_3], \ldots, [t_n, t_{n+1} = b]$ and approximate the curve $\mathbf{c}$ by the polygonal path p_n, whose vertices are $\mathbf{c}(a) = \mathbf{c}(t_1), \mathbf{c}(t_2), \ldots, \mathbf{c}(t_n), \mathbf{c}(t_{n+1}) = \mathbf{c}(b)$ (this is the same type of polygonal path that we considered in deriving the formula for arc-length in Section 3.3). The length of the segment c_i connecting the points $\mathbf{c}(t_i)$ and $\mathbf{c}(t_{i+1})$ was approximated in (3.1) as

$$\ell(c_i) \approx \|\mathbf{c}'(t_i)\| \Delta t_i,$$

where $\Delta t_i = t_{i+1} - t_i$. In the spirit of the construction in the introduction, we form the sums

$$A_n = \sum_{i=1}^{n} f(\mathbf{c}(t_i)) \|\mathbf{c}'(t_i)\| \Delta t_i.$$

If f were positive then A_n would represent the approximate area of the "fence" built along $\mathbf{c}$ from $\mathbf{c}(a)$ to $\mathbf{c}(b)$ whose height is determined by f; see Figures 5.12 and 5.13.

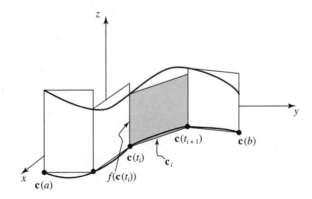

Figure 5.12 The sums A_n approximate the area of a "fence".

The integral of f along $\mathbf{c}$ is now defined as the limiting case of this construction as $n \to \infty$. With the understanding that A_n represents a Riemann sum of the *real-valued function* $f(\mathbf{c}(t)) \|\mathbf{c}'(t)\|$ of one variable over $[a, b]$, the following definition becomes fully transparent.

Definition 5.8   Path Integral of a Real-Valued Function.

Let $\mathbf{c} : [a, b] \rightarrow \mathbb{R}^2$ be a C^1 path and let $f : \mathbb{R}^2 \rightarrow \mathbb{R}$ be a function such that the composition $f(\mathbf{c}(t))$ is continuous on $[a, b]$. The *path integral* $\int_{\mathbf{c}} f \, ds$ of f along $\mathbf{c}$ is given by

$$\int_{\mathbf{c}} f \, ds = \int_a^b f(\mathbf{c}(t)) \|\mathbf{c}'(t)\| \, dt = \int_a^b f(x(t), y(t)) \sqrt{(x'(t))^2 + (y'(t))^2} \, dt.$$

If $\mathbf{c}$ is a piecewise C^1 path, consisting of C^1 paths $\mathbf{c}_j$, $j = 1, \dots, m$, then

$$\int_{\mathbf{c}} f \, ds = \sum_{j=1}^m \int_{\mathbf{c}_j} f \, ds.$$

The assumptions on f and $\mathbf{c}$ in the definition guarantee that the function $f(\mathbf{c}(t)) \|\mathbf{c}'(t)\|$ is continuous, so that the definite integral $\int_a^b f(\mathbf{c}(t)) \|\mathbf{c}'(t)\| dt$ makes sense. If $f : \mathbb{R}^3 \rightarrow \mathbb{R}$ and $\mathbf{c} : [a, b] \rightarrow \mathbb{R}^3$ is a C^1 path such that the composition $f(\mathbf{c}(t))$ is continuous on $[a, b]$, then

$$\int_{\mathbf{c}} f \, ds = \int_a^b f(\mathbf{c}(t)) \|\mathbf{c}'(t)\| \, dt$$

$$= \int_a^b f(x(t), y(t), z(t)) \sqrt{(x'(t))^2 + (y'(t))^2 + (z'(t))^2} \, dt.$$

Sometimes a more dramatic notation $\oint_{\mathbf{c}} f \, ds$ is used for a path integral along closed paths.

Let us emphasize that, if $f(x, y) \geq 0$, then the path integral $\int_{\mathbf{c}} f \, ds$ along the curve $\mathbf{c}$ in the xy-plane represents the area of the region "along $\mathbf{c}$ and below the graph of f," as shown in Figure 5.13.

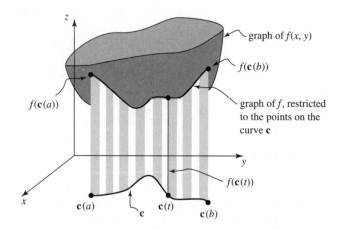

Figure 5.13   The integral $\int_{\mathbf{c}} f \, ds$ represents the area of the "fence" defined by f and $\mathbf{c}$.

Example 5.8 Compute the path integral $\int_{\mathbf{c}} f \, ds$ of the function $f(x, y, z) = xyz$ along the curve $\mathbf{c}(t) = (-\sin t, \sqrt{2}\cos t, \sin t)$, $t \in [0, \pi/2]$.

Solution The values of $f(x, y, z) = xyz$ along the curve $\mathbf{c}(t)$ are

$$f(\mathbf{c}(t)) = f(-\sin t, \sqrt{2}\cos t, \sin t) = -\sqrt{2}\sin^2 t \cos t.$$

From $\mathbf{c}'(t) = (-\cos t, -\sqrt{2}\sin t, \cos t)$ it follows that $\|\mathbf{c}'(t)\| = \sqrt{2}$ and

$$\int_{\mathbf{c}} f \, ds = -\sqrt{2}\int_0^{\pi/2} \sin^2 t \cos t \sqrt{2} \, dt$$

$$= -2\int_0^{\pi/2} \sin^2 t \cos t \, dt = -2\left.\frac{\sin^3 t}{3}\right|_0^{\pi/2} = -\frac{2}{3}$$

(the integral of $\sin^2 t \cos t$ was computed using the substitution $u = \sin t$). ◄

Example 5.9 Let $f(x, y) = 2x + y$. Consider the path integral $\int_{\mathbf{c}} f \, ds$ along the following paths in $\mathbb{R}^2$ joining the points $(1, 0)$ and $(0, 1)$:

(a) counterclockwise along the quarter circle $\mathbf{c}_1(t) = (\cos t, \sin t)$, $t \in [0, \pi/2]$.

(b) along the straight line segment $\mathbf{c}_2(t) = (1, 0) + t(-1, 1) = (1 - t, t)$, $t \in [0, 1]$, from $(1, 0)$ to $(0, 1)$.

(c) along the piecewise C^1 path $\mathbf{c}_3(t)$ that consists of the path $\mathbf{c}_4(t) = (1 - t, 0)$, $t \in [0, 1]$ (from $(1, 0)$ to $(0, 0)$), followed by the path $\mathbf{c}_5(t) = (0, t)$, $t \in [0, 1]$ (from $(0, 0)$ to $(0, 1)$).

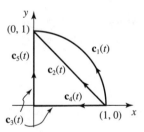

Figure 5.14 The paths of Example 5.9.

Solution

(a) The tangent vector is computed to be $\mathbf{c}_1'(t) = (-\sin t, \cos t)$, its norm is $\|\mathbf{c}_1'(t)\| = 1$ and hence

$$\int_{\mathbf{c}_1} f \, ds = \int_0^{\pi/2} (2\cos t + \sin t) \, dt = (2\sin t - \cos t)\Big|_0^{\pi/2} = 3.$$

(b) This time, $c_2'(t) = (-1, 1)$, $\|c_2'(t)\| = \sqrt{2}$ and

$$\int_{c_2} f \, ds = \int_0^1 (2 - t)\sqrt{2} \, dt = \sqrt{2}\left(2t - \frac{t^2}{2}\right)\Big|_0^1 = \tfrac{3}{2}\sqrt{2}.$$

(c) Since $\|c_4'(t)\| = 1$ and $\|c_5'(t)\| = 1$, it follows that

$$\int_{c_3} f \, ds = \int_{c_4} f \, ds + \int_{c_5} f \, ds = \int_0^1 (2 - 2t) \, dt + \int_0^1 t \, dt = \tfrac{3}{2}.$$

Example 5.10 Compute $\int_c e^{x+y} ds$, where c is the line segment from $(0, 0)$ to $(2, 1)$.

Solution In order to compute the integral, we need a parametrization of the given line segment. Consider the path

$$c_1(t) = (0, 0) + t(2, 1) = (2t, t), \qquad t \in [0, 1].$$

Then $\|c_1'(t)\| = \|(2, 1)\| = \sqrt{5}$ and

$$\int_{c_1} e^{x+y} ds = \int_0^1 e^{3t} \sqrt{5} \, dt = \frac{\sqrt{5}}{3} e^{3t}\Big|_0^1 = \frac{\sqrt{5}}{3}(e^3 - 1).$$

What will happen if we try some other parametrization?

Consider the reparametrization (take $\phi(t) = 2t$) $c_2(t) = (4t, 2t)$, $t \in [0, 1/2]$ of c_1. Then $c_2'(t) = (4, 2)$, $\|c_2'(t)\| = \sqrt{20}$ and

$$\int_{c_2} e^{x+y} ds = \int_0^{1/2} e^{6t} \sqrt{20} \, dt = \frac{\sqrt{20}}{6} e^{6t}\Big|_0^{1/2} = \frac{\sqrt{5}}{3}(e^3 - 1).$$

Now use $\phi(t) = t^2$ to reparametrize c_1, thus getting $c_3(t) = (2t^2, t^2)$, $t \in [0, 1]$. Then $c_3'(t) = (4t, 2t)$, $\|c_3'(t)\| = \sqrt{20t^2} = \sqrt{20}\,|t| = \sqrt{20}\,t$ (since $t \geq 0$) and

$$\int_{c_3} e^{x+y} ds = \int_0^1 e^{3t^2} \sqrt{20}\,t \, dt = \sqrt{20}\frac{1}{6} e^{3t^2}\Big|_0^1 = \frac{\sqrt{5}}{3}(e^3 - 1).$$

It seems that, no matter what parametrization is used, we obtain the same result.

Let us examine another example.

Example 5.11 Consider the reparametrization

$$c_1(t) = (-\sin 2t, \sqrt{2}\cos 2t, \sin 2t), \qquad t \in [0, \pi/4]$$

of the path $c(t)$ in Example 5.8, and recompute the path integral of $f(x, y, z) = xyz$. It follows that $c_1'(t) = (-2\cos 2t, -2\sqrt{2}\sin 2t, 2\cos 2t)$, $\|c_1'(t)\| = \sqrt{8}$ and

$$\int_{c_1} f \, ds = -\sqrt{2} \int_0^{\pi/4} \sin^2 2t \cos 2t \sqrt{8} \, dt$$

$$= -4 \int_0^{\pi/4} \sin^2 2t \cos 2t \, dt = -4 \left. \frac{\sin^3 2t}{6} \right|_0^{\pi/4} = -\frac{2}{3}.$$

Consider yet another parametrization,

$$\mathbf{c}_2(t) = (-\cos(t/\sqrt{2}), \sqrt{2}\sin(t/\sqrt{2}), \cos(t/\sqrt{2})), \qquad t \in [0, \pi\sqrt{2}/2].$$

Then $\mathbf{c}_2'(t) = (\sin(t/\sqrt{2})/\sqrt{2}, \cos(t/\sqrt{2}), -\sin(t/\sqrt{2})/\sqrt{2})$, $\|\mathbf{c}_2'(t)\| = 1$, and

$$\int_{\mathbf{c}_2} f \, ds = -\sqrt{2} \int_0^{\pi\sqrt{2}/2} \sin\frac{t}{\sqrt{2}} \cos^2\frac{t}{\sqrt{2}} \, 1 \, dt = 2 \left. \frac{\cos^3(t/\sqrt{2})}{3} \right|_0^{\pi\sqrt{2}/2} = -\frac{2}{3}. \qquad \triangleleft$$

As Example 5.9 shows, the path integral $\int_{\mathbf{c}} f \, ds$ *depends on the path* used: the integral of f along the circular path from $(1, 0)$ to $(0, 1)$ is equal to 3, whereas integration along the straight line segment joining the two points gives $3\sqrt{2}/2$.

On the other hand, Examples 5.8 and 5.11 suggest that $\int_{\mathbf{c}} f \, ds$ might not depend on the parametrization: the given path was traversed first with a speed of $\sqrt{2}$ then twice that fast (that path was called $\mathbf{c}_1(t)$), and finally, in the opposite direction with unit speed (reparametrization $\mathbf{c}_2(t)$). All integrations gave the same result: $-2/3$. We observed the same phenomenon occuring in Example 5.10. This is not a coincidence, but a consequence of the following theorem.

■ **Theorem 5.2**   Independence of Path Integrals on Parametrization.

Let $\mathbf{c}$ be a C^1 path in $\mathbb{R}^2$ (or $\mathbb{R}^3$), let f be a real-valued function continuous on the image of $\mathbf{c}$ and let $\boldsymbol{\gamma} = \mathbf{c} \circ \phi$ be a reparametrization of $\mathbf{c}$. Then

$$\int_{\mathbf{c}} f \, ds = \int_{\boldsymbol{\gamma}} f \, ds \qquad\qquad ■$$

Proof

Let $\mathbf{c}(t): [a, b] \to \mathbb{R}^2$ (or $\mathbb{R}^3$) be a parametrization of $\mathbf{c}$ and consider its reparametrization $\boldsymbol{\gamma}(t) = \mathbf{c}(\phi(t)): [\alpha, \beta] \to \mathbb{R}^2$ (or $\mathbb{R}^3$), where $\phi: [\alpha, \beta] \to [a, b]$. By definition,

$$\int_{\boldsymbol{\gamma}} f \, ds = \int_{\alpha}^{\beta} f(\boldsymbol{\gamma}(t)) \, \|\boldsymbol{\gamma}'(t)\| \, dt.$$

Applying the chain rule $\boldsymbol{\gamma}'(t) = \mathbf{c}'(\phi(t)) \, \phi'(t)$ and the identity $\|s\mathbf{v}\| = \|\mathbf{v}\| \, |s|$ (where $\mathbf{v}$ is a vector and s is a scalar) we get

$$\int_{\boldsymbol{\gamma}} f \, ds = \int_{\alpha}^{\beta} f(\mathbf{c}(\phi(t))) \, \|\mathbf{c}'(\phi(t)) \, \phi'(t)\| \, dt = \int_{\alpha}^{\beta} f(\mathbf{c}(\phi(t))) \, \|\mathbf{c}'(\phi(t))\| \, |\phi'(t)| \, dt.$$

Removing the absolute value signs we get

$$
\int_{\gamma} f \, ds = \begin{cases} \displaystyle\int_{\alpha}^{\beta} f(\mathbf{c}(\phi(t))) \, \|\mathbf{c}'(\phi(t))\| \, \phi'(t) \, dt & \text{if } \phi'(t) \geq 0 \\[2ex] \displaystyle -\int_{\alpha}^{\beta} f(\mathbf{c}(\phi(t))) \, \|\mathbf{c}'(\phi(t))\| \, \phi'(t) \, dt & \text{if } \phi'(t) \leq 0, \end{cases}
$$

and continue by introducing a new variable $\tau = \phi(t)$, $d\tau = \phi'(t) dt$

$$
\int_{\gamma} f \, ds = \begin{cases} \displaystyle\int_{\phi(\alpha)}^{\phi(\beta)} f(\mathbf{c}(\tau)) \, \|\mathbf{c}'(\tau)\| \, d\tau & \text{if } \phi'(t) \geq 0 \\[2ex] \displaystyle -\int_{\phi(\alpha)}^{\phi(\beta)} f(\mathbf{c}(\tau)) \, \|\mathbf{c}'(\tau)\| \, d\tau & \text{if } \phi'(t) \leq 0. \end{cases}
$$

In the first integral $\phi(\alpha) = a$ and $\phi(\beta) = b$, since $\phi' \geq 0$ implies that ϕ is an orientation-preserving reparametrization. In the latter case, $\phi(\alpha) = b$ and $\phi(\beta) = a$, since $\phi' \leq 0$ (so that ϕ is an orientation-reversing reparametrization). In any case, the integrals are equal to

$$
\int_{\gamma} f \, ds = \int_{a}^{b} f(\mathbf{c}(\tau)) \, \|\mathbf{c}'(\tau)\| \, d\tau = \int_{\mathbf{c}} f \, ds. \qquad \blacksquare
$$

In Theorem 5.2, the assumption that f is continuous on the image of $\mathbf{c}$ means that the composition $f(\mathbf{c}(t))$ is continuous (that is needed to guarantee the existence of the path integral of f).

The statement of the theorem remains valid if the assumption that $\mathbf{c}$ is C^1 is relaxed to the requirement that $\mathbf{c}$ be a piecewise C^1 path.

Substituting $f(x, y) = 1$ (or $f(x, y, z) = 1$) into the definition of the path integral, we get

$$
\int_{\mathbf{c}} f \, ds = \int_{a}^{b} \|\mathbf{c}'(t)\| \, dt = \ell(\mathbf{c}).
$$

In other words, the path integral of the constant function $f = 1$ gives the length of the path $\mathbf{c}$. Theorem 5.2 states that the above computation is independent of the paramaterization used. Therefore, in order to compute the length of a curve, we are free to choose any (C^1) parametrization we like (that is what we claimed in Section 3.3, but did not give a justification).

Generalizing the definition of the average value of a function of one variable we define the *average value of a function f along a curve* $\mathbf{c}$ ($\mathbf{c}$ is defined on an interval $[a, b]$) to be

$$
\overline{f} = \frac{1}{\ell(\mathbf{c})} \int_{\mathbf{c}} f \, ds = \frac{1}{\ell(\mathbf{c})} \int_{a}^{b} f(\mathbf{c}(t)) \, \|\mathbf{c}'(t)\| \, dt,
$$

where $\ell(\mathbf{c})$ denotes the length of $\mathbf{c}$.

Example 5.12 Compute the average temperature of a wire in the shape of the helix

$$\mathbf{c}(t) = (\cos t, t/10, \sin t), \qquad t \in [0, 10\pi],$$

if the temperature at the point (x, y, z) in $\mathbb{R}^3$ is given by $T(x, y, z) = x^2 + y + z^2$.

Solution From $\mathbf{c}(t) = (\cos t, t/10, \sin t)$ we get $\mathbf{c}'(t) = (-\sin t, 1/10, \cos t)$ and

$$\|\mathbf{c}'(t)\| = \sqrt{(-\sin t)^2 + \left(\tfrac{1}{10}\right)^2 + (\cos t)^2} = \sqrt{1 + \tfrac{1}{100}} = \frac{\sqrt{101}}{10}.$$

The average temperature along the helix is

$$\overline{T} = \frac{1}{\ell(c)} \int_0^{10\pi} \left(\cos^2 t + \tfrac{1}{10}t + \sin^2 t\right) \frac{\sqrt{101}}{10}\, dt,$$

where

$$\ell(c) = \int_0^{10\pi} \|\mathbf{c}'(t)\|\, dt = \int_0^{10\pi} \frac{\sqrt{101}}{10}\, dt = \sqrt{101}\,\pi.$$

Hence

$$\overline{T} = \frac{1}{\sqrt{101}\,\pi} \int_0^{10\pi} \left(1 + \tfrac{1}{10}t\right) \frac{\sqrt{101}}{10}\, dt = \frac{1}{10\pi} \left.\left(t + \tfrac{1}{20}t^2\right)\right|_0^{10\pi} = 1 + \frac{\pi}{2}.$$

It is worth repeating that in order to compute $\int_{\mathbf{c}} f\, ds$ it suffices to know the values of the function at the points on the curve only (that is the $f(\mathbf{c}(t))$ term in the path integral). In light of this fact, we notice that Example 5.12 contains more data than needed — the temperature function was defined at all points in $\mathbb{R}^3$.

A curve in $\mathbb{R}^2$ (or $\mathbb{R}^3$) can be defined in various ways. For example, it can be described as the image of a map $\mathbf{c}: [a, b] \to \mathbb{R}^2$ (or $\mathbb{R}^3$), or as the graph of a function $f: \mathbb{R} \to \mathbb{R}$. Alternatively, we can use geometric terms, such as "a straight line segment from A to B," or "a circle of radius 4 centered at the origin," or "the intersection of the paraboloid $z = x^2 + 3y^2$ and the plane $-2x - y + 3z = 1$," etc.

Let $\mathbf{c}$ be a curve described in any of the ways given above, or in some other way. Assume that it is either a simple curve or a simple closed curve, endowed with an orientation (see Definitions 5.4, 5.5 and 5.6 at the end of Section 5.1). We would like to define an integral of a function along $\mathbf{c}$.

In order to compute a path integral, we need a parametrization. But how do we decide which one to use? The answer is — it does not matter! We define the integral of a real-valued function f along $\mathbf{c}$ as the path integral of f with respect to *any* smooth parametrization of $\mathbf{c}$. Here is why it works: it can be proved that any two one-to-one, C^1 maps (i.e., paths that parametrize a curve as a simple or a simple closed curve) that have the same image (i.e., represent the same curve) are reparametrizations of each other. And according to Theorem 5.2, the path integral does not depend on the parametrization used. Example 5.10 serves as an illustration of this fact.

A consequence of Theorem 5.2 states that when we integrate a *scalar* function along a curve, the orientation does not play any role. This sounds reasonable: for example, the average temperature of the wire should not depend on the way (i.e., on the direction in which) we measure the temperature at the points of the wire. The analogous statement does not hold for integrals of vector-valued functions, as we will witness in the next section.

However, the path integral *does* depend on the path used, as shown in Example 5.9. There is an important class of functions whose path integrals depend only on the endpoints, and not on the curve that joins them. Section 5.4 is entirely devoted to a study of such functions.

EXERCISES 5.2

Exercises 1 to 11: Compute $\int_c f \, ds$.

1. $f(x, y) = 2x - y$, $\mathbf{c}(t) = (e^t + 1, e^t - 2)$, $0 \le t \le \ln 2$

2. $f(x, y, z) = xy$, $\mathbf{c}(t) = (2\cos t, 3\sin t, 5t)$, $0 \le t \le \pi/2$

3. $f(x, y, z) = (x^2 + y^2 + z^2)^{-1}$, $\mathbf{c}(t) = (t, t, t)$, $1 \le t < \infty$ (Hint: take $1 \le t \le b$ and then compute the limit as b approaches ∞.)

4. $f(x, y) = x^3 + y^3$, $\mathbf{c}$ is the part of the curve $x^{2/3} + y^{2/3} = 1$ in the first quadrant

5. $f(x, y, z) = y - z^2$, $\mathbf{c}(t) = t^2\mathbf{i} + \ln t\,\mathbf{j} + 2t\mathbf{k}$, $1 \le t \le 4$

6. $f(x, y) = x^2 + 3y^2 - xy$, $\mathbf{c}$ is the circular arc of radius 3 in the xy-plane, from $(0, 3)$ to $(-3, 0)$

7. $f(x, y, z) = xy + y + z$, $\mathbf{c}(t) = (2t, 3t, 1 - 4t)$, $0 \le t \le 1$

8. $f(x, y, z) = z\sqrt{x^2 + y^2 + z^2}$, $\mathbf{c}(t) = (1, 0, t)$, $-1 \le t \le 1$

9. $f(x, y, z) = xyz$, $\mathbf{c}$ is the helix given by $\mathbf{c}(t) = (2\sin t, 4t, 2\cos t)$, $0 \le t \le 6\pi$

10. $f(x, y, z) = (x + y + z)/(x^2 + y^2 + z^2)$, $\mathbf{c}$ is the straight line segment joining $(1, 1, 1)$ and (a, a, a), where $a \ne 1$

11. $f(x, y) = e^{x+3y}$, $\mathbf{c}$ is the line segment in $\mathbb{R}^2$ from $(0, 0)$ to $(3, -4)$

12. Compute $\int_c f \, ds$, where $f(x, y, z) = x + 2y - z^2$, and $\mathbf{c}$ consists of the parabolic path $t\mathbf{i} + t^2\mathbf{j}$ from $(0, 0, 0)$ to $(1, 1, 0)$, followed by the straight line to $(1, -1, 1)$.

13. Compute $\int_c f \, ds$, where $f(x, y, z) = x - 4y + z$, and $\mathbf{c}$ consists of the straight line from $(4, 2, 0)$ to $(0, 2, 0)$, followed by the circular path in the yz-plane (and above the xy-plane) with center at the origin, from $(0, 2, 0)$ to $(0, -2, 0)$.

14. Let $f(x, y, z) = x - 3y^2 + z$ and let $\mathbf{c}$ be the straight line segment from the origin to the point $(1, 1, 1)$. Consider the following parametrizations of $\mathbf{c}$

   (i) $\mathbf{c}_1(t) = (t, t, t)$, $t \in [0, 1]$

   (ii) $\mathbf{c}_2(t) = (1 - t, 1 - t, 1 - t)$, $t \in [0, 1]$

   (iii) $\mathbf{c}_3(t) = (e^t - 1, e^t - 1, e^t - 1)$, $t \in [0, \ln 2]$

   (iv) $\mathbf{c}_4(t) = (\ln t, \ln t, \ln t)$, $t \in [1, e]$

   (a) Describe their differences in terms of the orientation and speed.

   (b) Compute $\int_{c_i} f \, ds$, $i = 1, \ldots, 4$.

15. Suppose that a continuous function f is integrated along two different paths joining the points $(1, 2)$ and $(3, -5)$, and two different answers are obtained. Is that possible, or has an error been made in the evaluation of integrals?

16. Compute the integral of $f(x, y) = xy - x - y + 1$ along the following curves connecting the points $(1, 0)$ and $(0, 1)$.

    (a) c_1: circular arc $c_1(t) = (\cos t, \sin t)$, $0 \leq t \leq \pi/2$

    (b) c_2: straight line segment $c_2(t) = (1 - t, t)$, $0 \leq t \leq 1$

    (c) c_3: from $(1, 0)$ horizontally to the origin, then vertically to $(0, 1)$

    (d) c_4: from $(1, 0)$ vertically to $(1, 1)$, then horizontally to $(0, 1)$

    (e) c_5: circular arc $c_5(t) = (\cos t, -\sin t)$, $0 \leq t \leq 3\pi/2$

17. Compute the area of the part of the cylinder $x^2 + y^2 = 4$ between the xy-plane and the plane $z = y + 2$.

18. Compute the area of the part of the surface $y^2 = x$ defined by $0 \leq x \leq 2$, $0 \leq z \leq 2$.

19. Compute the area of the part of the surface $y = \sin x$, $0 \leq x \leq \pi/2$, above the xy-plane and below the surface $z = \sin x \cos x$.

20. Let c be the straight line segment joining $(1, 0, 0)$ and $(0, 2, 0)$. Use a geometric argument (i.e., do not evaluate the integral) to find $\int_c (x + 3y)ds$.

21. Use a geometric argument to find $\int_c e^{x^2+y^2} ds$ where c is the circle centered at the origin of radius 4.

22. Argue geometrically that $\int_c \sin(x^3)ds \geq 0$, where c is the graph of $y = \tan x$, $-\pi/4 \leq x \leq \pi/4$.

23. Is it possible that the average value of $f(x, y) = \sin x \cos y$ along some curve c is equal to 5?

24. Write down the version of the statement of Theorem 5.2 in the case when c is a piecewise C^1 path and prove it.

25. Find the average value of the function $f(x, y, z) = -\sqrt{x^2 + z^2}$ along the curve $c(t) = (3 \cos t)\mathbf{j} + (3 \sin t)\mathbf{k}$, $0 \leq t \leq 2\pi$.

26. Find the average value $\overline{f}$ of the function $f(x, y, z) = 2x^2 - y^2$ along the unit circle in the xy-plane. Identify all points on c where the value of f is equal to $\overline{f}$.

5.3   PATH INTEGRALS OF VECTOR FIELDS

In this section we are going to introduce one of the most important and useful concepts in vector calculus (and its applications), that of an integral of a vector field along a curve. It will be defined as the limiting case of a summation, in much the same way as the path integral in the previous section (and as the double, triple and surface integrals in the next two chapters). To motivate the definition, let us consider the problem of computing the work of a force.

The work W performed by a constant force $\mathbf{F}$ on an object that moves from the position P to the position Q along a straight line is given by the dot product $W = \mathbf{F} \cdot \mathbf{d}$, where $\mathbf{d} = \overrightarrow{PQ}$ is the displacement vector. But what if the force is non-constant and/or the path is not a straight line?

Assume that the force is described as a vector field $\mathbf{F}\colon U \subseteq \mathbb{R}^3 \to \mathbb{R}^3$ (and thus could change from point to point) and the path is parametrized by $\mathbf{c}(t)\colon [a, b] \to \mathbb{R}^3$. Subdivide the interval $[a, b]$ into n subintervals $[a = t_1, t_2], [t_2, t_3], \ldots, [t_n, t_{n+1} = b]$ and consider the vectors $\mathbf{d}_i = \overrightarrow{\mathbf{c}(t_i)\mathbf{c}(t_{i+1})}$. Using the definition of the derivative, we showed in Section 3.3 that $\mathbf{d}_i \approx \mathbf{c}'(t_i)\Delta t_i$, where $\mathbf{c}'(t_i)$ is the tangent vector at $\mathbf{c}(t_i)$ and $\Delta t_i = t_{i+1} - t_i$; see Figure 5.15.

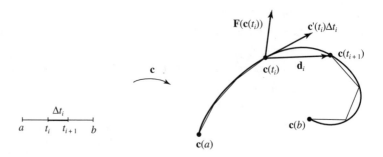

Figure 5.15   Construction of the path integral of $\mathbf{F}$.

Take the subdivision points t_i to be so close to each other (i.e., take Δt_i to be so small) that the part of the curve $\mathbf{c}$ between $\mathbf{c}(t_i)$ and $\mathbf{c}(t_{i+1})$ can be viewed as the straight line segment from $\mathbf{c}(t_i)$ to $\mathbf{c}(t_{i+1})$ and that the force $\mathbf{F}$ can be assumed constant (say, equal to $\mathbf{F}(\mathbf{c}(t_i))$) over that line segment. The work of $\mathbf{F}$ done in moving the object from $\mathbf{c}(t_i)$ to $\mathbf{c}(t_{i+1})$ is approximately equal to $\mathbf{F}(\mathbf{c}(t_i)) \cdot \mathbf{c}'(t_i)\Delta t_i$, and for the whole path, from $\mathbf{c}(a)$ to $\mathbf{c}(b)$,

$$W \approx \sum_{i=1}^{n} \mathbf{F}(\mathbf{c}(t_i)) \cdot \mathbf{c}'(t_i)\Delta t_i.$$

The exact *work* done is now computed by repeating this construction as $n \to \infty$; i.e.,

$$W = \lim_{n \to \infty} \sum_{i=1}^{n} \mathbf{F}(\mathbf{c}(t_i)) \cdot \mathbf{c}'(t_i)\Delta t_i.$$

This limit is the path integral (or the line integral) of the force $\mathbf{F}$ along the path $\mathbf{c}$.

Definition 5.9   Path Integral of a Vector Field.

Let $\mathbf{F}\colon \mathbb{R}^2 \to \mathbb{R}^2$ (or $\mathbf{F}\colon \mathbb{R}^3 \to \mathbb{R}^3$) be a continuous vector field on $\mathbb{R}^2$ (or $\mathbb{R}^3$) and let $\mathbf{c}(t)\colon [a, b] \to \mathbb{R}^2$ (or $\mathbb{R}^3$) be a C^1 path. The *path integral* (or the *line integral*) $\int_{\mathbf{c}} \mathbf{F} \cdot d\mathbf{s}$ *of* $\mathbf{F}$ *along* $\mathbf{c}$ is given by

$$\int_{\mathbf{c}} \mathbf{F} \cdot d\mathbf{s} = \int_{a}^{b} \mathbf{F}(\mathbf{c}(t)) \cdot \mathbf{c}'(t)\, dt.$$

The integrand on the right side is the dot product of the value $\mathbf{F}(\mathbf{c}(t))$ of $\mathbf{F}$ at $\mathbf{c}(t)$ with the velocity vector $\mathbf{c}'(t)$ of $\mathbf{c}$ at $\mathbf{c}(t)$. Consequently, the path integral of a vector function reduces to the definite integral of a real-valued function of one variable.

Rewriting the definition of $\int_{\mathbf{c}} \mathbf{F} \cdot d\mathbf{s}$ as (assume that $\|\mathbf{c}'(t)\| \neq 0$)

$$\int_a^b \mathbf{F}(\mathbf{c}(t)) \cdot \mathbf{c}'(t)\, dt = \int_a^b \left(\mathbf{F}(\mathbf{c}(t)) \cdot \frac{\mathbf{c}'(t)}{\|\mathbf{c}'(t)\|} \right) \|\mathbf{c}'(t)\|\, dt,$$

we interpret the path integral of a *vector field* $\mathbf{F}$ as the path integral of the *scalar function* $\mathbf{F}(\mathbf{c}(t)) \cdot \mathbf{c}'(t)/\|\mathbf{c}'(t)\|$ (which is the component of $\mathbf{F}$ in the direction of the unit tangent vector to $\mathbf{c}$ at $\mathbf{c}(t)$) along the curve $\mathbf{c}$. It is worth repeating that $\int_{\mathbf{c}} \mathbf{F} \cdot d\mathbf{s}$ depends on the values of $\mathbf{F}$ along the curve and not at other points. If $\mathbf{c}$ is a piecewise C^1 path, then

$$\int_{\mathbf{c}} \mathbf{F} \cdot d\mathbf{s} = \sum_{j=1}^m \int_{\mathbf{c}_j} \mathbf{F} \cdot d\mathbf{s},$$

where $\mathbf{c}_j$, $j = 1, \ldots, m$, are the pieces of $\mathbf{c}$ that are C^1.

Example 5.13 Compute the path integral $\int_{\mathbf{c}} \mathbf{F} \cdot d\mathbf{s}$ of the vector field $\mathbf{F}(x, y) = (-e^{x+y}, 3x)$ along the path $\mathbf{c}(t) = (t^2, 3 - 2t^2)$, $t \in [-1, 1]$.

Solution From $x(t) = t^2$ and $y(t) = 3 - 2t^2$ we get the values

$$\mathbf{F}(\mathbf{c}(t)) = \mathbf{F}(t^2, 3 - 2t^2) = (-e^{3-t^2}, 3t^2)$$

of $\mathbf{F}$ along the curve. Since $\mathbf{c}'(t) = (2t, -4t)$, it follows that

$$\int_{\mathbf{c}} \mathbf{F} \cdot d\mathbf{s} = \int_{-1}^1 \mathbf{F}(\mathbf{c}(t)) \cdot \mathbf{c}'(t)\, dt = \int_{-1}^1 (-e^{3-t^2}, 3t^2) \cdot (2t, -4t)\, dt$$

$$= \int_{-1}^1 (-2t e^{3-t^2} - 12t^3)\, dt = (e^{3-t^2} - 3t^4)\Big|_{-1}^1 = 0.$$

As a matter of fact, we did not have to evaluate the integral. The function $-2t e^{3-t^2} - 12t^3$ is odd (i.e., symmetric with respect to the origin) and hence its integral over any interval $[-a, a]$, $a > 0$, is zero. ◀

Example 5.14 Work of a Force.

Recall that the *work* done by a force $\mathbf{F}$ acting upon a particle that moves along the trajectory $\mathbf{c}(t): [a, b] \to \mathbb{R}^3$ is given by the path integral

$$W = \int_a^b \mathbf{F}(\mathbf{c}(t)) \cdot \mathbf{c}'(t)\, dt.$$

Compute the work done by $\mathbf{F} = (-y, x, 1)$ acting upon the particle that moves

(a) along the semi-circular trajectory $\mathbf{c}(t) = (\cos t, \sin t, 0)$, $t \in [0, \pi]$,

(b) radially away from the origin along $\mathbf{c}(t) = (t, t, t)$, $t \in [0, 1]$, and

(c) along the helix $\mathbf{c}(t) = (\cos t, \sin t, t)$, $t \in [0, 2\pi]$.

Solution

(a) From $x(t) = \cos t$, $y(t) = \sin t$, $z(t) = 0$ it follows that $\mathbf{F}(\mathbf{c}(t)) = (-\sin t, \cos t, 1)$. Since $\mathbf{c}'(t) = (-\sin t, \cos t, 0)$ we get

$$W = \int_0^\pi (-\sin t, \cos t, 1) \cdot (-\sin t, \cos t, 0)\, dt = \int_0^\pi 1\, dt = \pi.$$

(b) In this case, $x(t) = y(t) = z(t) = t$, $\mathbf{F}(\mathbf{c}(t)) = (-t, t, 1)$, $\mathbf{c}'(t) = (1, 1, 1)$ and

$$W = \int_0^1 (-t, t, 1) \cdot (1, 1, 1)\, dt = \int_0^1 1\, dt = 1.$$

(c) This time, $x(t) = \cos t$, $y(t) = \sin t$, $z(t) = t$, $\mathbf{F}(\mathbf{c}(t)) = (-\sin t, \cos t, 1)$, $\mathbf{c}'(t) = (-\sin t, \cos t, 1)$ and

$$W = \int_0^{2\pi} (-\sin t, \cos t, 1) \cdot (-\sin t, \cos t, 1)\, dt = \int_0^{2\pi} 2\, dt = 4\pi.$$

To obtain a geometric interpretation of the path integral we go back to the definition. If $\mathbf{F}$ is a continuous vector field and $\mathbf{c}$ is a C^1 path defined on $[a, b]$ then

$$\int_{\mathbf{c}} \mathbf{F} \cdot d\mathbf{s} = \int_a^b \mathbf{F}(\mathbf{c}(t)) \cdot \mathbf{c}'(t)\, dt = \int_a^b \|\mathbf{F}(\mathbf{c}(t))\|\, \|\mathbf{c}'(t)\| \cos \theta(t)\, dt,$$

where $\theta(t)$ is the angle between the vectors $\mathbf{F}(\mathbf{c}(t))$ and $\mathbf{c}'(t)$. The integrand is largest when $\theta(t) = 0$, equals zero if $\theta(t) = \pi/2$ and attains its minimum when $\theta(t) = \pi$. Consequently, the path integral is the largest for curves that are parallel to the vector field at all points (such curves are called flow lines, and were discussed in Section 3.6), and remains large for curves whose direction does not differ much from the direction of $\mathbf{F}$ (i.e., $\theta(t)$ is small so that $\cos \theta(t)$ is close to 1). The path integral is zero for curves running orthogonally to $\mathbf{F}$, and is the smallest if the direction of the curve is opposite to $\mathbf{F}$. With this in mind, we interpret the path integral of a vector field as a measure of how well the curve "lines up" with the vector field (see Figure 5.16).

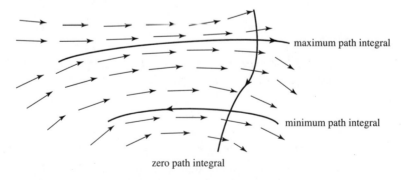

Figure 5.16   A path integral measures how well a curve "lines up" with a vector field.

Example 5.15   Consider the vector field $\mathbf{F}(x, y) = (-y/\sqrt{x^2 + y^2}, x/\sqrt{x^2 + y^2})$ in $\mathbb{R}^2$.

(a) Explain why $\int_{\mathbf{c}_1} \mathbf{F} \cdot d\mathbf{s} = 0$, if $\mathbf{c}_1(t) = (t, at)$, $t \in [1, 2]$.

(b) Determine the sign of $\int_{\mathbf{c}_2} \mathbf{F} \cdot d\mathbf{s}$ if $\mathbf{c}_2(t) = (t, 1)$, $t \in [0, 4]$.

Solution   The field $\mathbf{F}$ is a rotational vector field whose flow lines are circles (check: let $\mathbf{c}(t) = (\cos t, \sin t)$; then $\mathbf{c}'(t) = (-\sin t, \cos t)$ and $\mathbf{F}(\mathbf{c}(t)) = (-\sin t/1, \cos t/1) = \mathbf{c}'(t)$).

(a) The path $\mathbf{c}_1(t)$ represents a part of the line through the origin of slope a. It intersects the flow lines of $\mathbf{F}$ orthogonally (this is just another way of saying that the directions of $\mathbf{c}_1'(t)$ and $\mathbf{F}$ (at a point $\mathbf{c}_1(t)$) are orthogonal) and therefore the path integral is zero.

(b) At all points on the given line segment the angle $\theta(t)$ between $\mathbf{F}(\mathbf{c}_2(t))$ and $\mathbf{c}_2'(t)$ satisfies $\pi/2 < \theta(t) \le \pi$; see Figure 5.17. Therefore all contributions

$$\|\mathbf{F}(\mathbf{c}_2(t))\| \, \|\mathbf{c}_2'(t)\| \cos \theta(t)$$

to the integral are negative (or zero, at $(0, 1)$) and it follows that the integral in question is negative.   ◀

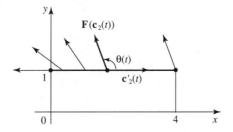

Figure 5.17   Vector field $\mathbf{F}$ along the segment from Example 5.15(b).

Example 5.16   **Work Equals Gain in Kinetic Energy.**

Let $\mathbf{F}$ be a force acting on a particle of mass m moving along the trajectory $\mathbf{c}(t)$ from $\mathbf{c}(a)$ to $\mathbf{c}(b)$. By *Newton's Second Law*, $\mathbf{F}(\mathbf{c}(t)) = m\mathbf{a}(t) = m\mathbf{v}'(t)$, where $\mathbf{v}(t) = \mathbf{c}'(t)$ is the velocity of the particle. The work done by $\mathbf{F}$ is

$$W = \int_a^b \mathbf{F}(\mathbf{c}(t)) \cdot \mathbf{c}'(t) \, dt = \int_a^b m\mathbf{v}'(t) \cdot \mathbf{v}(t) \, dt$$

(now use the product rule $(\|\mathbf{v}\|^2)' = (\mathbf{v} \cdot \mathbf{v})' = \mathbf{v}' \cdot \mathbf{v} + \mathbf{v} \cdot \mathbf{v}' = 2\mathbf{v} \cdot \mathbf{v}'$, to replace $\mathbf{v}' \cdot \mathbf{v}$ by $(\|\mathbf{v}\|^2)'/2)$

$$= m \int_a^b \tfrac{1}{2}\left(\|\mathbf{v}(t)\|^2\right)' \, dt$$

(by the Fundamental Theorem of Calculus)

$$= \tfrac{1}{2}m\|\mathbf{v}(t)\|^2 \Big|_a^b = \tfrac{1}{2}m\|\mathbf{v}(b)\|^2 - \tfrac{1}{2}m\|\mathbf{v}(a)\|^2,$$

which is the difference of the final kinetic energy and the initial kinetic energy.

Recall that the Fundamental Theorem of Calculus states that

$$\int_a^b f'(t)\,dt = f(t)\Big|_a^b = f(b) - f(a)$$

where f is a continuously differentiable function. In our case, $f(t) = (\|\mathbf{v}(t)\|^2)/2$. ◀

In the last section we proved that the path integral of a scalar function does not depend on the parametrization used. This is no longer true for integrals of vector fields: from the construction, we see that reversing the orientation of a path changes the sign of the path integral. Our next theorem states that it does not get any worse than that: the path integral actually depends on the orientation of a parametrization only (and not, for example, on its speed).

■ **Theorem 5.3**   **Path Integrals of Vector Fields and Parametrizations.**

Let $\mathbf{F}$ be a continuous vector field on $\mathbb{R}^2$ (or $\mathbb{R}^3$), let $\mathbf{c}\colon [a, b] \to \mathbb{R}^2$ (or $\mathbb{R}^3$) be a C^1 curve and let $\boldsymbol{\gamma}(t) = \mathbf{c}(\phi(t))$ be a reparametrization of $\mathbf{c}$, where $\phi\colon [\alpha, \beta] \to [a, b]$. Then

$$\int_\mathbf{c} \mathbf{F}\cdot d\mathbf{s} = \begin{cases} \displaystyle\int_{\boldsymbol{\gamma}} \mathbf{F}\cdot d\mathbf{s} & \text{if } \phi \text{ is orientation-preserving} \\[2mm] -\displaystyle\int_{\boldsymbol{\gamma}} \mathbf{F}\cdot d\mathbf{s} & \text{if } \phi \text{ is orientation-reversing.} \end{cases}$$ ■

Proof

By definition of the path integral and the chain rule $\boldsymbol{\gamma}'(t) = \mathbf{c}'(\phi(t))\phi'(t)$ we obtain (keep in mind that $\boldsymbol{\gamma}\colon [\alpha, \beta] \to \mathbb{R}^2$ (or $\mathbb{R}^3$))

$$\int_{\boldsymbol{\gamma}} \mathbf{F}\cdot d\mathbf{s} = \int_\alpha^\beta \mathbf{F}(\boldsymbol{\gamma}(t))\cdot\boldsymbol{\gamma}'(t)\,dt = \int_\alpha^\beta \mathbf{F}(\mathbf{c}(\phi(t)))\cdot\mathbf{c}'(\phi(t))\,\phi'(t)\,dt.$$

Introduce the new variable $\tau = \phi(t)$; then $d\tau = \phi'(t)dt$ and

$$\int_{\boldsymbol{\gamma}} \mathbf{F}\cdot d\mathbf{s} = \int_{\phi(\alpha)}^{\phi(\beta)} \mathbf{F}(\mathbf{c}(\tau))\cdot\mathbf{c}'(\tau)\,d\tau$$

($\phi(\alpha) = a$ and $\phi(\beta) = b$ if ϕ is an orientation-preserving parametrization; $\phi(\alpha) = b$ and $\phi(\beta) = a$ if ϕ reverses the orientation)

$$= \begin{cases} \displaystyle\int_a^b \mathbf{F}(\mathbf{c}(\tau))\cdot\mathbf{c}'(\tau)d\tau = \int_\mathbf{c} \mathbf{F}\cdot d\mathbf{s} & \text{if } \phi \text{ is orientation-preserving} \\[2mm] -\displaystyle\int_a^b \mathbf{F}(\mathbf{c}(\tau))\cdot\mathbf{c}'(\tau)d\tau = -\int_\mathbf{c} \mathbf{F}\cdot d\mathbf{s} & \text{if } \phi \text{ is orientation-reversing.} \end{cases}$$ ■

Example 5.17

Compute $\int_{\mathbf{c}} \mathbf{F} \cdot d\mathbf{s}$, where $\mathbf{F}(x, y, z) = xy\mathbf{i} + e^z\mathbf{j} + z\mathbf{k}$ and $\mathbf{c}$ is given by $\mathbf{c}(t) = (t^2, -t, t)$, $t \in [0, 1]$.

Solution   A straightforward computation gives

$$\int_{\mathbf{c}} \mathbf{F} \cdot d\mathbf{s} = \int_0^1 (-t^3, e^t, t) \cdot (2t, -1, 1)\, dt$$

$$= \int_0^1 (-2t^4 - e^t + t)\, dt = -\tfrac{2}{5}t^5 - e^t + \tfrac{1}{2}t^2 \Big|_0^1 = \tfrac{11}{10} - e.$$

Now reparametrize $\mathbf{c}$ by $\phi \colon [0, 1/2] \to [0, 1]$, $\phi(t) = 1 - 2t$. In other words, consider the curve $\mathbf{c}_1 \colon [0, 1/2] \to \mathbb{R}^3$ given by

$$\mathbf{c}_1(t) = \mathbf{c}(\phi(t)) = \mathbf{c}(1 - 2t) = ((1 - 2t)^2, -(1 - 2t), 1 - 2t).$$

Since $\mathbf{c}_1(0) = (1, -1, 1) = \mathbf{c}(1)$ and $\mathbf{c}_1(1/2) = (0, 0, 0) = \mathbf{c}(0)$, it follows that $\mathbf{c}_1$ has orientation opposite to that of $\mathbf{c}$. With the new parametrization,

$$\int_{\mathbf{c}_1} \mathbf{F} \cdot d\mathbf{s} = \int_0^{1/2} (-(1 - 2t)^3, e^{1-2t}, 1 - 2t) \cdot (-4(1 - 2t), 2, -2)\, dt$$

$$= \int_0^{1/2} \left(4(1 - 2t)^4 + 2e^{1-2t} - 2(1 - 2t) \right) dt$$

$$= -\frac{2(1 - 2t)^5}{5} - e^{1-2t} + \frac{(1 - 2t)^2}{2} \Bigg|_0^{1/2} = -\tfrac{11}{10} + e.$$

Hence the integral of $\mathbf{F}$ along $\mathbf{c}$ is the negative of the integral along $\mathbf{c}_1$, as predicted by Theorem 5.3. ◀

Let $\mathbf{c}$ be a curve equipped with an orientation, assumed to be a simple curve or a simple closed curve. Theorem 5.3 states that in order to compute the integral of a vector field $\mathbf{F}$ along $\mathbf{c}$ we can use *any* orientation-preserving parametrization of $\mathbf{c}$!

As a matter of fact, we could use an orientation-reversing parametrization as well, but we must keep in mind that we have to change the sign of the result. Let us emphasize that, in contrast to the integral of a real-valued function, the integral of a vector field is *oriented*; i.e., depends on the direction in which the curve is traversed.

Theorem 5.3 holds not only for C^1 paths, but also for piecewise C^1 paths. Our next example illustrates this point.

Example 5.18

Compute the integral of $\mathbf{F}(x, y, z) = (y + z)\mathbf{i} + x\mathbf{j} + x\mathbf{k}$ along the following path: from $(1, 0, 0)$ counterclockwise along a circular path in the xy-plane to $(0, 1, 0)$, then along the straight line to $(0, 0, 1)$, and then along the straight line to $(1, 0, 1)$, as shown in Figure 5.18.

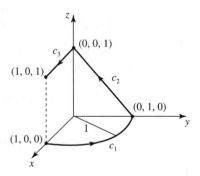

Figure 5.18   Path of Example 5.18.

Solution   Parametrize the path c_1 by $c_1(t) = (\cos t, \sin t, 0)$, $t \in [0, \pi/2]$. Then

$$\int_{c_1} \mathbf{F} \cdot d\mathbf{s} = \int_0^{\pi/2} (\sin t, \cos t, \cos t) \cdot (-\sin t, \cos t, 0) \, dt$$

$$= \int_0^{\pi/2} (\cos^2 t - \sin^2 t) \, dt = \int_0^{\pi/2} \cos 2t \, dt = \tfrac{1}{2} \sin 2t \big|_0^{\pi/2} = 0.$$

Parametrize c_2 by $c_2(t) = (0, 1, 0) + t(0, -1, 1) = (0, 1 - t, t)$, $t \in [0, 1]$. It follows that

$$\int_{c_2} \mathbf{F} \cdot d\mathbf{s} = \int_0^1 (1, 0, 0) \cdot (0, -1, 1) \, dt = \int_0^1 0 \, dt = 0.$$

Finally, parametrize c_3 by $c_3(t) = (0, 0, 1) + t(1, 0, 0) = (t, 0, 1)$, $t \in [0, 1]$. Then

$$\int_{c_3} \mathbf{F} \cdot d\mathbf{s} = \int_0^1 (1, t, t) \cdot (1, 0, 0) \, dt = \int_0^1 1 \, dt = 1.$$

Thus,

$$\int_c \mathbf{F} \cdot d\mathbf{s} = \int_{c_1} \mathbf{F} \cdot d\mathbf{s} + \int_{c_2} \mathbf{F} \cdot d\mathbf{s} + \int_{c_3} \mathbf{F} \cdot d\mathbf{s} = 0 + 0 + 1 = 1.$$

Our next definition introduces the path integral of a differential form.

Definition 5.10   Path Integral of a Differential Form.

Let $\alpha = F_1 dx + F_2 dy + F_3 dz$ be a differentiable 1-form and let $\mathbf{c} \colon [a, b] \to \mathbb{R}^3$ be a C^1 path. The *path integral of α along* $\mathbf{c}$ is defined by

$$\int_c \alpha = \int_c F_1 dx + F_2 dy + F_3 dz = \int_a^b \left(F_1 \left(\frac{dx}{dt} \right) + F_2 \left(\frac{dy}{dt} \right) + F_3 \left(\frac{dz}{dt} \right) \right) dt.$$

Example 5.19   Compute the integral of the 1-form $\alpha = x^2 dx + y dy + 2yz dz$ along the curve $\mathbf{c}(t) = (1, t, -t^2)$, $t \in [0, 1]$.

Solution By definition (of course, $dx/dt = x'$, $dy/dt = y'$ and $dz/dt = z'$),

$$\int_c x^2 dx + y dy + 2yz dz = \int_0^1 \left(x^2 \frac{dx}{dt} + y\frac{dy}{dt} + 2yz\frac{dz}{dt} \right) dt$$

$$= \int_0^1 \left(1 \cdot 0 + t \cdot 1 + 2t(-t^2)(-2t) \right) dt$$

$$= \int_0^1 (t + 4t^4) \, dt = \left(\frac{t^2}{2} + \frac{4t^5}{5} \right) \Bigg|_0^1 = \tfrac{13}{10}.$$

◀

Let $\alpha = F_1 dx + F_2 dy + F_3 dz$ be a 1-form and let $\mathbf{F} = (F_1, F_2, F_3)$ be a vector field with the same component functions. Take a C^1 curve $\mathbf{c} = (x(t), y(t), z(t))$ defined on an interval $[a, b]$. Then (dropping the independent variable from the notation)

$$\int_c \mathbf{F} \cdot d\mathbf{s} = \int_a^b \mathbf{F}(\mathbf{c}(t)) \cdot \mathbf{c}'(t) \, dt$$

$$= \int_a^b (F_1, F_2, F_3) \cdot (x', y', z') \, dt = \int_a^b (F_1 x' + F_2 y' + F_3 z') \, dt;$$

i.e., by Definition 5.10,

$$\int_c \mathbf{F} \cdot d\mathbf{s} = \int_c \alpha. \tag{5.1}$$

In words, the path integral of a vector field can be interpreted as the path integral of the corresponding 1-form. In particular, if $\mathbf{F} = (F_1, F_2)$, then $\int_c \mathbf{F} \cdot d\mathbf{s} = \int_c \alpha$, where $\alpha = F_1 dx + F_2 dy$. This is not only a useful formalism; its importance can best be understood and appreciated in the context of classical integration theorems presented in Chapter 8.

The path integral of a vector field has several important physical interpretations. We discussed the work of a force in the introduction to this section. Now we turn to the circulation of a vector field, the interpretation coming from fluid mechanics, electromagnetism and other disciplines. We start with an example, where we investigate the behavior of several vector fields as "seen" from a closed curve.

Example 5.20 Circulation of a Vector Field.

Let us compute the path integrals $\text{circ}(\mathbf{F}_i) = \int_c \mathbf{F}_i \cdot d\mathbf{s}$, $i = 1, 2, 3, 4$, around the unit circle (oriented counterclockwise) in $\mathbb{R}^2$ of the following vector fields: $\mathbf{F}_1(x, y) = (-y, x)$, $\mathbf{F}_2(x, y) = (-3y, 3x)$, $\mathbf{F}_3(x, y) = (x, y)$ and $\mathbf{F}_4(x, y) = (y, -x)$.

Parametrize the circle by $\mathbf{c}(t) = (\cos t, \sin t)$, $t \in [0, 2\pi]$. Then

$$\int_c \mathbf{F}_1 \cdot d\mathbf{s} = \int_0^{2\pi} (-\sin t, \cos t) \cdot (-\sin t, \cos t) \, dt = \int_0^{2\pi} dt = 2\pi,$$

$$\int_c \mathbf{F}_2 \cdot d\mathbf{s} = \int_0^{2\pi} (-3\sin t, 3\cos t) \cdot (-\sin t, \cos t) \, dt = \int_0^{2\pi} 3 \, dt = 6\pi,$$

$$\int_{\mathbf{c}} \mathbf{F}_3 \cdot d\mathbf{s} = \int_0^{2\pi} (\cos t, \sin t) \cdot (-\sin t, \cos t) \, dt = \int_0^{2\pi} 0 \, dt = 0$$

and

$$\int_{\mathbf{c}} \mathbf{F}_4 \cdot d\mathbf{s} = \int_0^{2\pi} (\sin t, -\cos t) \cdot (-\sin t, \cos t) \, dt = \int_0^{2\pi} -1 \, dt = -2\pi.$$

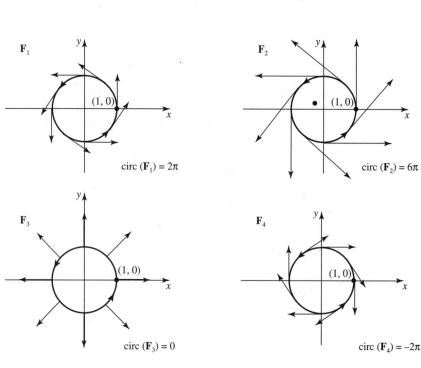

Figure 5.19   Vector fields of Example 5.20.

Think of the given vector fields as velocity vector fields of a fluid. Suppose that a particle is placed at the point $(1, 0)$; see Figure 5.19. Subjected to $\mathbf{F}_1$, it will tend to circulate counterclockwise, and subjected to $\mathbf{F}_2$ it will circulate three times faster, since $\|\mathbf{F}_2\| = 3\|\mathbf{F}_1\|$; i.e., $\mathbf{F}_2$ is three times "stronger" than $\mathbf{F}_1$. There will be no circulation in the field $\mathbf{F}_3$; in fact every particle just moves in a radial direction. Subjected to $\mathbf{F}_4$, a particle will tend to circulate clockwise. Corresponding path integrals were positive in the first two cases, zero for $\mathbf{F}_3$ and negative for $\mathbf{F}_4$. Hence, loosely speaking, $\int_{\mathbf{c}} \mathbf{F} \cdot d\mathbf{s}$ measures the "turning of the fluid" in the counterclockwise sense. For example, a particle subjected to $\mathbf{F}_2$ will turn more (integral was computed to be 6π) than if it were subjected to $\mathbf{F}_1$ (integral was 2π). In the field $\mathbf{F}_4$ the "turning of the fluid" in the counterclockwise sense is negative, i.e., the fluid turns clockwise. The comments we have just made justify calling the path integral $\int_{\mathbf{c}} \mathbf{F} \cdot d\mathbf{s}$ the *circulation of* $\mathbf{F}$ *around* $\mathbf{c}$.

Assume that **c** is a closed curve. Since

$$\int_{\mathbf{c}} \mathbf{F} \cdot d\mathbf{s} = \int_a^b \mathbf{F}(\mathbf{c}(t)) \cdot \mathbf{c}'(t)\, dt = \int_{\mathbf{c}} \left(\mathbf{F}(\mathbf{c}(t)) \cdot \frac{\mathbf{c}'(t)}{\|\mathbf{c}'(t)\|} \right) ds,$$

it follows that the path integral of a vector field is actually the path integral of the (scalar function that is the) tangential component of **F**. Since an integral is a limit of sums, this means that $\int_{\mathbf{c}} \mathbf{F} \cdot d\mathbf{s}$ represents the *total tangential component of* **F** *around* **c**. In other words, $\int_{\mathbf{c}} \mathbf{F} \cdot d\mathbf{s}$ is the total amount of counterclockwise turning of the fluid.

Example 5.21   Find the circulation of the constant vector field $\mathbf{F} = b\mathbf{i}$, $b > 0$ around a circle of radius a, oriented counterclockwise.

Solution   We will "add up" all tangential components of **F**. At A and A' (see Figure 5.20) the vector field is orthogonal to the curve, so its tangential component is zero. Now consider a pair of diametrically opposite points B and B'. The contribution at B to the total tangential component is

$$\mathbf{F} \cdot \frac{\mathbf{c}'}{\|\mathbf{c}'\|}\bigg|_{\text{at } B} = \|\mathbf{F}\| \left\| \frac{\mathbf{c}'}{\|\mathbf{c}'\|} \right\| \cos\theta = b\cos\theta$$

and that of B' is

$$\mathbf{F} \cdot \frac{\mathbf{c}'}{\|\mathbf{c}'\|}\bigg|_{\text{at } B'} = \|\mathbf{F}\| \left\| \frac{\mathbf{c}'}{\|\mathbf{c}'\|} \right\| \cos\theta' = b\cos\theta'.$$

Since $\theta = \pi - \theta'$, it follows that $\cos\theta = -\cos\theta'$ and the two contributions cancel each other. Consequently, the circulation of **F** around the circle is zero.

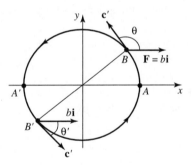

Figure 5.20   Computing circulation in Example 5.21.

Now imagine walking around the circle and measuring the field **F** of the previous example. After completing one full revolution, we notice that there has been no change in the direction of **F**. In general, "no circulation" means that, when we look under a microscope (i.e., for small circles around the point in question), we see no change in the vector field along the circle.

As an illustration, let us try to determine the circulation of the vector field in Figure 5.21 (pictured are the flow lines; i.e., the trajectories of particles subjected to the field).

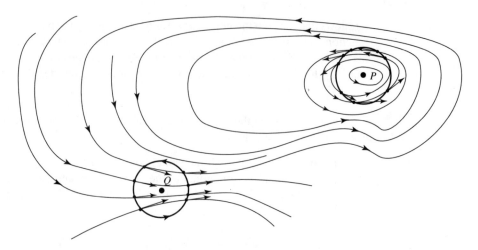

Figure 5.21   Determining the circulation of a vector field.

To determine the circulation around Q, we choose a small circle centered at Q, and as we walk around in the counterclockwise direction, we record the vector defining the motion of the fluid corresponding to the point where we are. After completing our walk (i.e., we are back at the initial point of the walk), we realize that the corresponding vector did not rotate, so there is no circulation around Q. Now take a circle around P and repeat the same experiment. This time, a vector will rotate by 360 degrees as we complete our counterclockwise walk. Therefore there is a (positive) circulation at P.

We will finish this section by introducing path integrals that appear in electromagnetism. A reader not familiar with the concepts of electric and magnetic fields may skip this part and move to the next section.

The *electric circulation* $\mathcal{E}$ of an electric field $\mathbf{E} = \mathbf{E}(x, y, z)$ (also called the *electromotive force*) is given by

$$\mathcal{E} = \int_{\mathbf{c}} \mathbf{E} \cdot d\mathbf{s},$$

where $\mathbf{c}$ is some closed curve in space. The *magnetic circulation* $\mathcal{B}$ is defined by

$$\mathcal{B} = \int_{\mathbf{c}} \mathbf{B} \cdot d\mathbf{s},$$

where $\mathbf{B}$ is the magnetic field and $\mathbf{c}$ denotes a closed curve in space.

Example 5.22   The magnetic field at a point (x, y, z) due to a single filament that carries a current I and whose direction is determined by the unit vector $\mathbf{u}$ is given by (see, for example: J.D. Jackson, *Classical Electrodynamics*, second ed., pp. 169–170)

$$\mathbf{B}(x, y, z) = \frac{\mu_0 I}{2\pi} \frac{\mathbf{u} \times \mathbf{r}}{\|\mathbf{u} \times \mathbf{r}\|^2},$$

where $\mathbf{r} = x\mathbf{i} + y\mathbf{j} + z\mathbf{k}$, and μ_0 is a constant. Let us compute the magnetic circulation $\mathcal{B}$ along a circle $\mathbf{c}$ that lies in the yz-plane and encloses the filament. Place the filament so that $\mathbf{u} = \mathbf{i}$, as shown in Figure 5.22. Then

$$\mathbf{B} = \frac{\mu_0 I}{2\pi} \frac{\mathbf{i} \times (x\mathbf{i} + y\mathbf{j} + z\mathbf{k})}{\|\mathbf{i} \times (x\mathbf{i} + y\mathbf{j} + z\mathbf{k})\|^2} = \frac{\mu_0 I}{2\pi} \frac{-z\mathbf{j} + y\mathbf{k}}{y^2 + z^2} \tag{5.2}$$

and hence ($\mathbf{c}$ lies in the yz-plane, so we parametrize it by $\mathbf{c}(t) = (0, \cos t, \sin t)$, $t \in [0, 2\pi]$) the magnetic circulation is computed to be

$$\mathcal{B} = \int_{\mathbf{c}} \mathbf{B} \cdot d\mathbf{s} = \int_0^{2\pi} \mathbf{B}(\mathbf{c}(t)) \cdot \mathbf{c}'(t)\, dt$$

$$= \frac{\mu_0 I}{2\pi} \int_0^{2\pi} \frac{-\sin t\mathbf{j} + \cos t\mathbf{k}}{1} \cdot (-\sin t\mathbf{j} + \cos t\mathbf{k})\, dt = \frac{\mu_0 I}{2\pi} \int_0^{2\pi} dt = \mu_0 I.$$

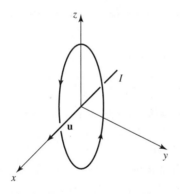

Figure 5.22 Filament of Example 5.22.

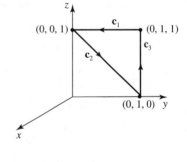

Figure 5.23 Magnetic circulation around $\mathbf{c}$

Let us check, with an example, the physical fact that the magnetic circulation $\mathcal{B}$ vanishes along any closed curve that does not enclose the current filament. Consider the piecewise C^1 curve shown in Figure 5.23.

Parametrize the curve $\mathbf{c}_1$ by $\mathbf{c}_1(t) = (0, 1, 1) + t(0, -1, 0) = (0, 1-t, 1)$, $t \in [0, 1]$. From (5.2) it follows that (use $\int 1/(x^2 + 1)\, dx = \arctan x$)

$$\int_{\mathbf{c}_1} \mathbf{B} \cdot d\mathbf{s} = \frac{\mu_0 I}{2\pi} \int_0^1 \frac{(0, -1, 1-t)}{(1-t)^2 + 1} \cdot (0, -1, 0)\, dt$$

$$= \frac{\mu_0 I}{2\pi} \int_0^1 \frac{1}{(1-t)^2 + 1}\, dt = \frac{\mu_0 I}{2\pi} \arctan(t - 1) \Big|_0^1 = \frac{\mu_0 I}{2\pi} \frac{\pi}{4} = \frac{\mu_0 I}{8}.$$

Parametrize c_2 by $c_2(t) = (0, 0, 1) + t(0, 1, -1) = (0, t, 1 - t)$, $t \in [0, 1]$. Then

$$\int_{c_2} \mathbf{B} \cdot d\mathbf{s} = \frac{\mu_0 I}{2\pi} \int_0^1 \frac{(0, -1 + t, t)}{(-1 + t)^2 + t^2} \cdot (0, 1, -1) \, dt = \frac{\mu_0 I}{2\pi} \int_0^1 \frac{-1}{2t^2 - 2t + 1} \, dt$$

$$= \frac{\mu_0 I}{2\pi} \int_0^1 \frac{-1}{\frac{1}{2}\left((2t - 1)^2 + 1\right)} \, dt$$

$$= -\frac{\mu_0 I}{2\pi} \arctan(2t - 1) \Big|_0^1 = -\frac{\mu_0 I}{2\pi} \frac{\pi}{2} = -\frac{\mu_0 I}{4}.$$

Parametrize c_3 by $c_3(t) = (0, 1, 0) + t(0, 0, 1) = (0, 1, t)$, $t \in [0, 1]$. Then

$$\int_{c_3} \mathbf{B} \cdot d\mathbf{s} = \frac{\mu_0 I}{2\pi} \int_0^1 \frac{(0, -t, 1)}{1 + t^2} \cdot (0, 0, 1) \, dt$$

$$= \frac{\mu_0 I}{2\pi} \int_0^1 \frac{1}{1 + t^2} \, dt = \frac{\mu_0 I}{2\pi} \arctan t \Big|_0^1 = \frac{\mu_0 I}{2\pi} \frac{\pi}{4} = \frac{\mu_0 I}{8}.$$

Hence

$$\mathcal{B} = \int_{c_1} \mathbf{B} \cdot d\mathbf{s} + \int_{c_2} \mathbf{B} \cdot d\mathbf{s} + \int_{c_3} \mathbf{B} \cdot d\mathbf{s} = 0.$$

EXERCISES 5.3   **Exercises 1 to 10:** Compute $\int_c \mathbf{F} \cdot d\mathbf{s}$.

1. $\mathbf{F}(x, y) = y^2 \mathbf{i} - x^2 \mathbf{j}$, c is the part of the parabola $y = x^2$ from $(-1, 1)$ to $(1, 1)$

2. $\mathbf{F}(x, y) = x^2 y \mathbf{i} + (y - 1) \mathbf{j}$, c is the triangle with vertices $(0, 0)$, $(2, 0)$ and $(1, 1)$, oriented counterclockwise

3. $\mathbf{F}(x, y) = e^{x+y} \mathbf{i} - \mathbf{j}$, c is the boundary of the square with vertices $(0, 0)$, $(1, 0)$, $(1, 1)$ and $(0, 1)$, oriented clockwise

4. $\mathbf{F}(x, y) = \ln x \mathbf{i} + \ln y \mathbf{j}$, c is parametrized by $c(t) = 2t \mathbf{i} + t^3 \mathbf{j}$, $1 \le t \le 2$

5. $\mathbf{F}(x, y, z) = (y, -x, 1)$, c is the curve $c(t) = (\sin t, \cos t, 2t)$, $t \in [0, \pi]$

6. $\mathbf{F}(x, y, z) = (yz^2, xyz, 2x^2 z)$, c consists of straight line segments from $(-1, 2, -2)$ to $(-1, -2, -2)$, then to $(-1, -2, 0)$ and then to $(0, -2, 0)$

7. $\mathbf{F}(x, y, z) = (x^2, xy, 2z^2)$, $c(t) = (\sin t, \cos t, t^2)$, $0 \le t \le \pi/2$

8. $\mathbf{F}(x, y) = e^{x+y} \mathbf{i} + e^{x-y} \mathbf{j}$, c is the triangle with vertices $(0, 0)$, $(0, 1)$ and $(1, 0)$, oriented counterclockwise

9. $\mathbf{F}(x, y) = 2xy \mathbf{i} + e^y \mathbf{j}$, $c(t) = 4t^3 \mathbf{i} + t^2 \mathbf{j}$, $t \in [0, 1]$

10. $\mathbf{F}(x, y, z) = (xy, yz, xz)$, c consists of the straight line segments from the origin to $(1, 0, 1)$, and then to $(1, 1, 0)$

11. Compute the work done when the force $\mathbf{F}(x, y) = x^3 \mathbf{i} + (x + y) \mathbf{j}$ acts on a particle that moves from $(0, 0)$ to $(1, \pi^2/4)$ along the curve $c(t) = \sin t \mathbf{i} + t^2 \mathbf{j}$.

12. Assume that $\mathbf{F}$ is a constant force field acting in $\mathbb{R}^2$. Show that $\mathbf{F}$ does zero work on a particle that moves counterclockwise once around a circle in the xy-plane with constant speed.

13. Assume that the force $\mathbf{F} = C(x\mathbf{i} + y\mathbf{j})$ (C is a constant) acts on a particle moving in $\mathbb{R}^2$. Show that $\mathbf{F}$ does zero work if the particle moves counterclockwise once around a circle with constant speed.

14. The force between two positive electric charges (one, of charge ρ, is placed at the origin, and the other, of charge one coulomb, is placed at (x, y)) is given by the formula $\mathbf{F} = \rho\mathbf{r}/\|\mathbf{r}\|^3$. How much work is needed in order to move the one-coulomb charge along the straight line from $(1, 0)$ to $(-1, 2)$ if the other charge remains at the origin?

15. Consider the force field $\mathbf{F}(x, y) = (y, 0)$. Compute the work done on a particle by the force $\mathbf{F}$ if the particle moves from $(0, 0)$ to $(1, 1)$ in each of the following ways.

(a) along the x-axis to $(1, 0)$, then vertically up to $(1, 1)$

(b) along the parabolic path $y = x^2$ (c) along the path $y = x^4$

(d) along the straight line   (e) along the path $y = \sin(\pi x/2)$

(f) along the y-axis to $(0, 1)$, then horizontally to $(1, 1)$

Interpret your results.

Exercises 16 to 24: Compute $\int_c \alpha$ for the 1-form α along the curve $\mathbf{c}$.

16. $\alpha = 3(x + y)dx$, $\mathbf{c}(t) = (e^t + 1, e^t - 2)$, $0 \le t \le 1$

17. $\alpha = xydy$, $\mathbf{c}(t) = (t, 2t^3)$, $0 \le t \le 1$

18. $\alpha = 2x^2y^2dx - y^3xdy$, $\mathbf{c}$ is the line segment from $(-1, 0)$ to $(1, 1)$, followed by the segment from $(1, 1)$ to $(0, 0)$

19. $\alpha = ydy - xyzdz$, $\mathbf{c}(t) = (\sqrt{t}, t^2, t^3)$, $0 \le t \le 1$

20. $\alpha = (x^3 + xy^2)dx - (x^2 + y^2)dy + 2zdz$, $\mathbf{c}(t) = (3\sin t, 3\cos t, 2t)$, $0 \le t \le \pi/2$

21. $\alpha = (1 + x^2)^{-1}dx + (1 + y^2)^{-1}dy$, $\mathbf{c}$ is the circle centered at the origin of radius 1, oriented clockwise

22. $\alpha = \ln(xy)dx + (e^x - e^y)dy$, $\mathbf{c}$ is the line segment from $(1, 2)$ to $(2, 1)$

23. $\alpha = (ydx + xdy)/(x^2 + y^2)$, $\mathbf{c}$ is the circle centered at the origin of radius 2, oriented counterclockwise

24. $\alpha = xydx + ye^xdy$, $\mathbf{c}$ is the rectangle with vertices $(0, 0)$, $(1, 0)$, $(1, 1)$ and $(0, 1)$, oriented counterclockwise

25. Consider $\int_{\mathbf{c}_i} xydx + 2ydy$, where $\mathbf{c}_i$ is the straight line segment joining the points $(0, 0)$ and $(1, 1)$ parametrized in the following ways.

(a) $\mathbf{c}_1(t) = (t, t)$, $t \in [0, 1]$ (b) $\mathbf{c}_2(t) = (\sin t, \sin t)$, $t \in [0, \pi/2]$

(c) $\mathbf{c}_3(t) = (\cos t, \cos t)$, $t \in [0, \pi/2]$

Are all the results the same? Explain why or why not.

26. Compute $\int_c M(x, y, z)dx$, where M is a continuous function and $\mathbf{c}$ is any curve contained in a plane parallel to the yz-plane.

27. Show that the assumption "$\mathbf{c}$ is a C^1 curve" in Theorem 5.3 can be replaced by "$\mathbf{c}$ is a piecewise C^1 curve."

Exercises 28 to 31: In $\mathbb{R}^2$, the flux (flow) of a vector field $\mathbf{F}$ across a smooth closed curve $\mathbf{c}$ is defined as $\int_c \mathbf{F} \cdot \mathbf{n}\, ds$, where $\mathbf{n}$ denotes the outward unit normal vector field along $\mathbf{c}$. The circulation of $\mathbf{F}$ is given by $\int_c \mathbf{F} \cdot d\mathbf{s}$. Compute the flux and the circulation for the vector field $\mathbf{F}$ and the curve $\mathbf{c}$.

28. $\mathbf{F}(x, y) = 4x\mathbf{i} - 2y\mathbf{j}$, $\mathbf{c}$ is a circle of radius r, oriented clockwise

29. $\mathbf{F}(x, y) = x\mathbf{i} + y\mathbf{j}$, $\mathbf{c}$ is a circle of radius r, oriented counterclockwise

30. $\mathbf{F}(x, y) = x^2\mathbf{i} + y^2\mathbf{j}$, $\mathbf{c}$ is the semi-circle of radius r from $(r, 0)$ to $(-r, 0)$, followed by the straight line segment back to $(r, 0)$, oriented counterclockwise

31. $\mathbf{F}(x, y) = x\mathbf{i} + y\mathbf{j}$, $\mathbf{c}$ is the curve from Exercise 30

32. Let $\mathbf{F}(x, y) = P(x, y)\mathbf{i} + Q(x, y)\mathbf{j}$ be a continuous vector field. Show that its outward flux is given by $\int_\mathbf{c} \mathbf{F} \cdot \mathbf{n}\, ds = \int_\mathbf{c} P(x, y)dy - Q(x, y)dx$.

5.4   PATH INTEGRALS INDEPENDENT OF PATH

In this section we investigate so-called gradient vector fields by studying their properties with respect to integration along curves. Probably the most famous examples of gradient vector fields are conservative force fields, two types of which (gravitational, electrostatic) have already appeared in this book.

One of the most important theorems of vector calculus states that the path integral of a gradient vector field does not depend on the path, but only on its endpoints. We will prove this theorem in one special case and derive very useful consequences.

We start by defining a gradient vector field and addressing the first question that comes to mind: how does one identify a gradient vector field? Is there a test that can determine whether a given vector field is a gradient vector field?

Definition 5.11   Gradient Vector Field.

A vector field $\mathbf{F}: U \subseteq \mathbb{R}^2 \to \mathbb{R}^2$ (or $\mathbf{F}: U \subseteq \mathbb{R}^3 \to \mathbb{R}^3$) is called a *gradient vector field* if and only if there is a differentiable function $f: U \to \mathbb{R}$ such that $\mathbf{F} = \nabla f$.

Example 5.23   The vector field $\mathbf{F}(x, y, z) = (2x + x^2 y)e^{xy}\mathbf{i} + x^3 e^{xy}\mathbf{j} + \mathbf{k}$ is a gradient vector field defined on $\mathbb{R}^3$; if $f(x, y, z) = x^2 e^{xy} + z$, then

$$\nabla f(x, y, z) = (2xe^{xy} + x^2 ye^{xy})\mathbf{i} + x^3 e^{xy}\mathbf{j} + \mathbf{k} = \mathbf{F}(x, y, z).$$

Example 5.24   The vector field $\mathbf{F}(x, y) = (x/\sqrt{x^2 + y^2})\mathbf{i} + (y/\sqrt{x^2 + y^2})\mathbf{j}$ is a gradient vector field defined on $\mathbb{R}^2 - \{(0, 0)\}$; if $f(x, y) = \sqrt{x^2 + y^2}$, then $\nabla f(x, y) = \mathbf{F}(x, y)$.

Reading Definition 5.11 with $f = -V$, we get

$$\mathbf{F} = -\nabla V. \tag{5.3}$$

A gradient vector field $\mathbf{F}$ satisfying (5.3) is called a *conservative vector field*, and the function V is its *potential function*. For example, the gravitational field (see Example 2.35 in Section 2.4) $\mathbf{F}(x, y, z) = -GMm\mathbf{r}/\|\mathbf{r}\|^3$, where $\mathbf{r} = x\mathbf{i} + y\mathbf{j} + z\mathbf{k}$, is conservative; its potential function is $V = -GMm/\|\mathbf{r}\|$, defined on $\mathbb{R}^3 - \{(0, 0, 0)\}$. The electrostatic field (see Example 2.8 in Section 2.1; let ϵ denote the constant $(4\pi\epsilon_0)^{-1}$) $\mathbf{F}(x, y, z) = Qq\epsilon\mathbf{r}/\|\mathbf{r}\|^3$ is also a conservative field; the function $V = Qq\epsilon/\|\mathbf{r}\|$ defined on $\mathbb{R}^3 - \{(0, 0, 0)\}$ is its potential function. (See the comment immediately following Example 4.16 in Section 4.1 for the use of the word "potential.")

Let $\mathbf{F}$ be a gradient vector field; i.e., $\mathbf{F} = \nabla f$ for some function f. Assuming that there is another function g such that $\mathbf{F} = \nabla g$, we would like to find the relation between f and g. In other words, we would like to identify all functions f that satisfy $\mathbf{F} = \nabla f$ for a given field $\mathbf{F}$. Since $\nabla f = \nabla g$, it follows that $\nabla(f - g) = \mathbf{0}$. Denoting $f - g$ by h, we get $\nabla h = \mathbf{0}$. Consequently, $\partial h/\partial x = 0$, $\partial h/\partial y = 0$ and $\partial h/\partial z = 0$; i.e., h must be a constant function. Hence, $f - g = \text{constant}$, and

$$g = f + \text{constant}.$$

It follows that there are infinitely many functions f satisfying $\mathbf{F} = \nabla f$; however, they can differ from each other by, at most, an additive constant. Consequently, there are infinitely many potential functions for a given conservative field, and they all differ by a constant. With an extra condition (like prescribing the value of a potential function at a point, or the value of a limit (as in the next example) we can compute the constant and the potential function becomes uniquely determined.

Example 5.25   Any function of the form

$$V(x, y, z) = -\frac{GMm}{\|\mathbf{r}\|} + C$$

(C is a constant) is a potential function of the gravitational force field

$$\mathbf{F} = -\frac{GMm}{\|\mathbf{r}\|^3}\mathbf{r}$$

(see Example 2.35). The condition that the potential vanishes at infinity implies that

$$0 = \lim_{\|\mathbf{r}\|\to\infty} V = -\lim_{\|\mathbf{r}\|\to\infty} \frac{GMm}{\|\mathbf{r}\|} + C = C,$$

hence $C = 0$; thus

$$V(x, y, z) = -\frac{GMm}{\|\mathbf{r}\|}$$

is the gravitational potential of $\mathbf{F}$, satisfying $\lim V = 0$ as $\|\mathbf{r}\| \to \infty$. ◄

Now we turn to the problem of determining whether a given vector field is a gradient vector field or not. First of all we have to explain the assumption on the domain U of the vector field that will appear in the statement of the theorem.

Definition 5.12   Connected and Simply-connected Sets.

We say that a set $U \subseteq \mathbb{R}^2$ (or $\mathbb{R}^3$) is *connected* if any two points in U can be joined by a continuous curve that is completely contained in U. A set U is *simply-connected* if it is connected and every simple closed curve in U can be continuously deformed (i.e., deformed without breaking) to a point without leaving U.

A set is connected if it is in "one piece". For example, $\mathbb{R}^2$, $\mathbb{R}^3$ or $\{(x, y) \mid y \geq x^2\}$ are connected. The set obtained from $\mathbb{R}^2$ by removing the x-axis is not connected. A plane in $\mathbb{R}^3$, the disk $\{(x, y)|x^2 + y^2 < 1\} \subseteq \mathbb{R}^2$ and $\mathbb{R}^3$ are examples of simply-connected sets.

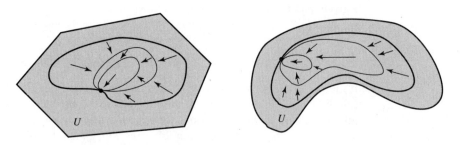

Figure 5.24   Simply-connected sets.

By definition, a set is simply-connected if every simple, closed curve can be continuously shrunk to a point without leaving the set, as shown in Figure 5.24. A plane with a "hole" (for example, the set $\mathbb{R}^2 - \{(x, y) \mid x^2 + y^2 \leq 1\}$) is not simply-connected: it is impossible to deform a loop which goes around the hole to a point without breaking the loop; see Figure 5.25. Similarly, the "punctured plane" $\mathbb{R}^2 - \{(0, 0)\}$ is not simply-connected.

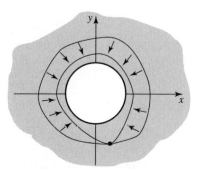

Figure 5.25   A plane with a "hole" is not a simply-connected set.

The set U obtained from $\mathbb{R}^3$ by removing finitely many points is simply-connected. In the case of the "punctured plane," we got stuck in deforming the curve when we encountered a hole. What we wanted to do was to "jump over" (or under) the hole to continue the deformation; since the curve was supposed to remain in the plane, that was not possible. In three-dimensional space, we can actually do that: since we have an extra dimension, we can easily avoid "holes" in deforming a curve to a point, as shown in Figure 5.26.

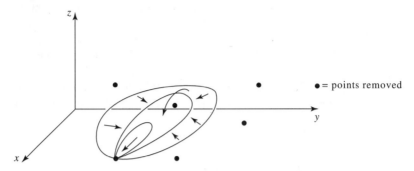

Figure 5.26 $\mathbb{R}^3$ with finitely many points removed is simply-connected.

The sphere $\{(x, y, z) | x^2 + y^2 + z^2 = 1\}$ and the sphere with a hole on its surface (take the surface of a globe and cut out the North Pole) are simply-connected; see Figure 5.27. In order to deform a loop that encloses the hole, all we have to do is to "go around" the other side of the hole.

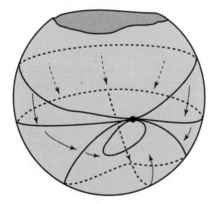

Figure 5.27   The surface of a globe with the North Pole removed is simply-connected.

Recall that, for a vector field $\mathbf{F} = (F_1, F_2, F_3)$ in $\mathbb{R}^3$,

$$curl\,\mathbf{F} = \left(\frac{\partial F_3}{\partial y} - \frac{\partial F_2}{\partial z}\right)\mathbf{i} + \left(\frac{\partial F_1}{\partial z} - \frac{\partial F_3}{\partial x}\right)\mathbf{j} + \left(\frac{\partial F_2}{\partial x} - \frac{\partial F_1}{\partial y}\right)\mathbf{k}.$$

■ **Theorem 5.4**   **Necessary and Sufficient Conditions for a Gradient Vector Field.**

Let $\mathbf{F}$ be a C^1 vector field defined on an open, simply-connected set $U \subseteq \mathbb{R}^3$. Then $\mathbf{F} = \nabla f$ for some function f (i.e., $\mathbf{F}$ is a gradient vector field) if and only if $curl\,\mathbf{F} = \mathbf{0}$.

Notice that one implication is immediate: if $\mathbf{F} = \nabla f$, then $curl\,\mathbf{F} = curl\,(\nabla f) = \mathbf{0}$ by Theorem 4.5 in Section 4.2. We are not going to present the proof of the other implication in its full generality, but in a special case when U is a star-shaped set; we will give another proof using Stokes' Theorem in the last chapter. However, that proof will have a "weak" link: it will assume one fact that we will not be able to prove in this book.

A set U is called *star-shaped* if there is a point A in U such that, for every point P in U the entire line segment $\overline{AP}$ lies in U. A plane, all of $\mathbb{R}^3$ or the sets in Figure 5.28 are examples of star-shaped sets.

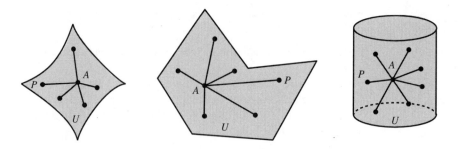

Figure 5.28   Star-shaped sets.

The set $U = \mathbb{R}^2 - \{(0,0)\}$ is not star-shaped: no matter what point A is chosen, the line segment from A to the point P symmetric to A with respect to the origin (see Figure 5.29) has to go through the origin, and is not entirely in U.

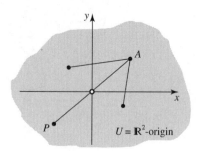

Figure 5.29 $\mathbb{R}^2 - \{(0,0)\}$ is not a star-shaped set.

A simple closed curve in a star-shaped set can always be continuously deformed to a point (this may seem reasonable, but a proof is beyond the scope of this book); therefore, a star-shaped set is always simply-connected. The converse is not true: $\mathbb{R}^3 - \{(0,0,0)\}$ is simply-connected, but not star-shaped.

In the proof of Theorem 5.4 (and later in this section) we will need the Fundamental Theorem of Calculus for functions of one variable. Roughly speaking, the Fundamental Theorem of Calculus states that the derivative and integral are operations inverse to each other: when both are applied (in any order) to a function, we get it back. More precisely, if f is a continuous function, then

$$\frac{d}{dx}\left(\int_a^x f(t)\,dt\right) = f(x),\tag{5.4}$$

where a is any constant. This formula is known as the Fundamental Theorem of Calculus, Part One. The second part of the theorem states that if f is continuously differentiable (i.e., if it is C^1), then

$$\int_a^b f'(t)\,dt = f(b) - f(a),\tag{5.5}$$

for any a and b in its domain.

We will also make use of the fact that it is possible to interchange partial derivatives and integrals of C^1 functions. For example,

$$\frac{\partial}{\partial x}\left(\int_a^b f(x, y, t)\,dt\right) = \int_a^b \frac{\partial f(x, y, t)}{\partial x}\,dt.\tag{5.6}$$

This formula is called *Leibniz's rule*. For a proof, see W. Kaplan, *Advanced Calculus*, 4th Ed., p. 266.

Proof of Theorem 5.4:

Let $\mathbf{F} = (F_1, F_2, F_3)$ be a C^1 vector field defined on a star-shaped set U, satisfying *curl* $\mathbf{F} = \mathbf{0}$. Choose a coordinate system so that U is star-shaped with respect to the origin (i.e., the point A from the definition of a star-shaped set is the origin). Define a real-valued function f by

$$f(x, y, z) = \int_0^1 (F_1(tx, ty, tz)x + F_2(tx, ty, tz)y + F_3(tx, ty, tz)z)\,dt.$$

We will show that $\nabla f = \mathbf{F}$, and that will complete the proof. First we compute $\partial f/\partial x$. Interchanging the integral and partial derivatives ($\mathbf{F}$ is C^1, and so are its components) we get (in order to avoid writing partial derivatives as $\partial F_1(tx, ty, tz)/\partial(tx)$, $\partial F_2(tx, ty, tz)/\partial(tx)$, etc. we use $D_1 F_1(tx, ty, tz)$, $D_1 F_2(tx, ty, tz)$, etc. instead)

$$\frac{\partial f}{\partial x}(x, y, z) = \int_0^1 \frac{\partial}{\partial x}(F_1(tx, ty, tz)x + F_2(tx, ty, tz)y + F_3(tx, ty, tz)z)\,dt$$

$$= \int_0^1 (D_1 F_1(tx, ty, tz)\,tx + F_1(tx, ty, tz)$$

$$+ D_1 F_2(tx, ty, tz)\,ty + D_1 F_3(tx, ty, tz)\,tz)\,dt,$$

where the first two terms in the integrand come from the product rule applied to compute the partial derivative of $F_1(tx, ty, tz)\,x$ with respect to x. Since *curl* $\mathbf{F} = \mathbf{0}$, we have $D_1 F_2 = D_2 F_1$ and $D_1 F_3 = D_3 F_1$, and the integrand is equal to

$$F_1(tx, ty, tz) + D_1 F_1(tx, ty, tz)\,tx + D_2 F_1(tx, ty, tz)\,ty + D_3 F_1(tx, ty, tz)\,tz.$$

Using the product and the chain rules we check that this expression is the derivative of $t F_1(tx, ty, tz)$ with respect to t:

$$\frac{\partial}{\partial t}(t F_1(tx, ty, tz)) = F_1(tx, ty, tz) + t\frac{\partial}{\partial t}(F_1(tx, ty, tz))$$

$$= F_1(tx, ty, tz) + t(D_1 F_1(tx, ty, tz)\, x + D_2 F_1(tx, ty, tz)\, y + D_3 F_1(tx, ty, tz)\, z).$$

Therefore, by the Fundamental Theorem (5.5) applied to the function $t F_1(tx, ty, tz)$ we get

$$\frac{\partial f}{\partial x}(x, y, z) = \int_0^1 \frac{\partial}{\partial t}(t F_1(tx, ty, tz))\, dt = t F_1(tx, ty, tz)\Big|_0^1 = F_1(x, y, z).$$

The remaining identities $\partial f/\partial y = F_2$ and $\partial f/\partial z = F_3$ are checked analogously. ∎

Theorem 5.4 states that a C^1 vector field $\mathbf{F} = (F_1, F_2, F_3)$ defined on an open, simply-connected set $U \subseteq \mathbb{R}^3$ is a gradient vector field (i.e., $\mathbf{F} = \nabla f$) if and only if $\mathrm{curl}\ \mathbf{F} = \mathbf{0}$; i.e., if and only if

$$\frac{\partial F_3}{\partial y} = \frac{\partial F_2}{\partial z}, \qquad \frac{\partial F_1}{\partial z} = \frac{\partial F_3}{\partial x} \qquad \text{and} \qquad \frac{\partial F_2}{\partial x} = \frac{\partial F_1}{\partial y}.$$

Now think of a vector field $\mathbf{F} = (F_1, F_2)$ in $\mathbb{R}^2$ as a vector field $\mathbf{F} = (F_1, F_2, 0)$ in $\mathbb{R}^3$ and apply Theorem 5.4. It follows that a C^1 vector field $\mathbf{F} = (F_1, F_2)$ defined on an open, simply-connected set $U \subseteq \mathbb{R}^2$ is a gradient vector field if and only if

$$\frac{\partial F_2}{\partial x} = \frac{\partial F_1}{\partial y}.$$

The Fundamental Theorem of Calculus (Part Two) states that, for a C^1 function f,

$$\int_a^b f'(t)dt = f(b) - f(a).$$

In other words, the definite integral of $f'(t)$ on $[a, b]$ depends on the value of f at the endpoints a and b only! Therefore, if f and g are *any* two C^1 functions that coincide at a and b (i.e., $f(a) = g(a)$ and $f(b) = g(b)$) then

$$\int_a^b f'(t)dt = \int_a^b g'(t)dt.$$

The generalization of this statement to functions of several variables is given in the following theorem.

■ **Theorem 5.5**   Generalization of the Fundamental Theorem of Calculus.

Let $f: \mathbb{R}^2$ (or $\mathbb{R}^3$) $\to \mathbb{R}$ be a C^1 function and let $\mathbf{c}: [a, b] \to \mathbb{R}^2$ (or $\mathbb{R}^3$) be a piecewise C^1 path. Then

$$\int_{\mathbf{c}} \nabla f \cdot d\mathbf{s} = f(\mathbf{c}(b)) - f(\mathbf{c}(a)).$$

■

Proof

By definition of the path integral (assuming that $\mathbf{c}$ is C^1) we get

$$\int_{\mathbf{c}} \nabla f \cdot d\mathbf{s} = \int_a^b \nabla f(\mathbf{c}(t)) \cdot \mathbf{c}'(t)\, dt.$$

The integrand is the product of the derivative of f and the derivative of $\mathbf{c}$, which "smells like" the chain rule. Indeed, as in Example 2.47 in Section 2.5 we get

$$(f(\mathbf{c}(t)))' = Df(\mathbf{c}(t)) \cdot D\mathbf{c}(t) = \nabla f(\mathbf{c}(t)) \cdot \mathbf{c}'(t)$$

and

$$\int_{\mathbf{c}} \nabla f \cdot d\mathbf{s} = \int_a^b (f(\mathbf{c}(t)))'\, dt = f(\mathbf{c}(b)) - f(\mathbf{c}(a)),$$

by the Fundamental Theorem of Calculus (5.5) applied to the function $f(\mathbf{c}(t))$ of one variable.

Now assume that $[a, b]$ consists of two subintervals $[a = t_1, t_2]$ and $[t_2, t_3 = b]$ such that the restrictions $\mathbf{c}_1 = \mathbf{c}|_{[t_1, t_2]}$ and $\mathbf{c}_2 = \mathbf{c}|_{[t_2, t_3]}$ are C^1 (this is the proof in the piecewise C^1 case; for convenience, we assumed that $\mathbf{c}$ consists of two C^1 pieces; the general case of n C^1 pieces is done in the same way).

Then

$$\int_{\mathbf{c}} \nabla f \cdot d\mathbf{s} = \int_{\mathbf{c}_1} \nabla f \cdot d\mathbf{s} + \int_{\mathbf{c}_2} \nabla f \cdot d\mathbf{s}$$

($\mathbf{c}_1$ and $\mathbf{c}_2$ are C^1, and we proved the theorem in that case)

$$= f(\mathbf{c}(t_2)) - f(\mathbf{c}(t_1)) + f(\mathbf{c}(t_3)) - f(\mathbf{c}(t_2))$$
$$= f(\mathbf{c}(t_3)) - f(\mathbf{c}(t_1)) = f(\mathbf{c}(b)) - f(\mathbf{c}(a)). \qquad \blacksquare$$

Example 5.26 Let $f(x, y, z) = e^{x^2+y^2+z^2}$ and let $\mathbf{c}(t) = (\cos t, t, \sin t)$, $t \in [0, 2\pi]$. Then

$$\int_{\mathbf{c}} \nabla f \cdot d\mathbf{s} = f(\mathbf{c}(2\pi)) - f(\mathbf{c}(0)) = f(1, 2\pi, 0) - f(1, 0, 0) = e^{1+4\pi^2} - e. \qquad \triangleleft$$

Theorem 5.5 provides a powerful tool for computing path integrals: if we know that we are integrating the gradient of a function, we do not need to parametrize the path(s) in question; all we have to do is to evaluate the function at the terminal point and at the initial point and subtract. The next three examples will serve as illustrations of this principle.

Example 5.27 Let us go back to Example 5.18 of the previous section. The vector field $\mathbf{F} = (y+z)\mathbf{i} + x\mathbf{j} + x\mathbf{k}$ is a gradient vector field since

$$\nabla(xy + xz) = (y + z)\mathbf{i} + x\mathbf{j} + x\mathbf{k}.$$

The application of Fundamental Theorem 5.5 greatly simplifies the computation of the path integral:

$$\int_c \mathbf{F} \cdot d\mathbf{s} = \int_c \nabla(xy + xz) \cdot d\mathbf{s} = (xy + xz)\Big|_{(1,0,0)}^{(1,0,1)} = 1.$$

◀

Example 5.28   Compute the work of the electrostatic force $\mathbf{F}(\mathbf{r}) = (Qq/4\pi\epsilon_0)\mathbf{r}/\|\mathbf{r}\|^3$ acting on a charge q that moves from the point A to the point B along a curve $\mathbf{c}$.

Solution   A straightforward computation gives that $\mathbf{F}(\mathbf{r}) = -\nabla V(\mathbf{r})$, where $V(\mathbf{r}) = (Qq/4\pi\epsilon_0)\|\mathbf{r}\|^{-1}$ is the electrostatic potential and $\mathbf{r} = x\mathbf{i}+y\mathbf{j}+z\mathbf{k}$. Let $\mathbf{r} = \mathbf{r}(t)\colon [a,b] \to \mathbb{R}^3$ be a parametrization of $\mathbf{c}$, $\mathbf{r}(a) = A$ and $\mathbf{r}(b) = B$. The work of $\mathbf{F}$ is computed to be

$$W = \int_c \mathbf{F} \cdot d\mathbf{s} = -\int_c \nabla V(\mathbf{r}) \cdot d\mathbf{s}$$

$$= -V(\mathbf{r})\Big|_{\mathbf{r}(a)}^{\mathbf{r}(b)} = V(\mathbf{r}(a)) - V(\mathbf{r}(b)) = \frac{Qq}{4\pi\epsilon_0}\left(\frac{1}{\|\mathbf{r}(a)\|} - \frac{1}{\|\mathbf{r}(b)\|}\right).$$

◀

Example 5.29   Compute $\int_c \mathbf{F} \cdot d\mathbf{s}$, where $\mathbf{F} = 2x\mathbf{i} + 2e^z\mathbf{j} + 2ye^z\mathbf{k}$, and $\mathbf{c}$ is the piecewise C^1 curve shown in Figure 5.30.

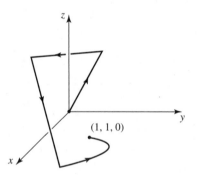

Figure 5.30   The curve of Example 5.29.

Solution   A straightforward computation shows that $curl\ \mathbf{F} = \mathbf{0}$. Therefore, $\mathbf{F} = \nabla f$ for some scalar function f, and

$$\int_c \mathbf{F} \cdot d\mathbf{s} = \int_c \nabla f\, d\mathbf{s} = f(1, 1, 0) - f(0, 0, 0). \qquad (5.7)$$

by Theorem 5.5. So all we have to do is to find f (the method was explained and illustrated in Example 4.17 in Section 4.1). The equation $\mathbf{F} = \nabla f$ implies that

$$\frac{\partial f}{\partial x} = 2x, \qquad \frac{\partial f}{\partial y} = 2e^z \qquad \text{and} \qquad \frac{\partial f}{\partial z} = 2ye^z.$$

Integrating the first equation with respect to x we get

$$f(x, y, z) = x^2 + C(y, z),$$

where $C(y, z)$ denotes a function (to be determined) of y and z only. Differentiating this expression with respect to y and substituting into the equation $\partial f/\partial y = 2e^z$ yields $\partial C(y, z)/\partial y = 2e^z$, hence $C(y, z) = 2ye^z + C(z)$, after integration with respect to y. We have recovered some parts of f; so far

$$f(x, y, z) = x^2 + 2ye^z + C(z),$$

and the function $C(z)$ is yet to be found. Differentiate this expression with respect to z and combine with the equation for $\partial f/\partial z$, thus getting

$$\frac{\partial f}{\partial z} = 2ye^z + \frac{dC(z)}{dz} = 2ye^z,$$

hence $dC(z)/dz = 0$ and $C(z) = C$ (where C is a constant). Therefore, $f(x, y, z) = x^2 + 2ye^z + C$ and (5.7) implies that

$$\int_{\mathbf{c}} \mathbf{F} \cdot d\mathbf{s} = f(1, 1, 0) - f(0, 0, 0) = 3.$$

◀

Assume that $\mathbf{F}$ is a C^1 gradient vector field, so that $\mathbf{F} = \nabla f$ for some function f. An immediate consequence of the Fundamental Theorem 5.5 is the fact that if $\mathbf{c}: [a, b] \to \mathbb{R}^2$ (or $\mathbb{R}^3$) is an oriented simple *closed* curve (i.e., $\mathbf{c}(a) = \mathbf{c}(b)$), then

$$\int_{\mathbf{c}} \mathbf{F} \cdot d\mathbf{s} = \int_{\mathbf{c}} \nabla f \cdot d\mathbf{s} = f(\mathbf{c}(b)) - f(\mathbf{c}(a)) = 0. \tag{5.8}$$

Now take a curve $\mathbf{c}$ in the domain U of $\mathbf{F}$ whose initial point is A and terminal point is B. Let $\bar{\mathbf{c}}$ be any curve in U with the same initial and terminal points as $\mathbf{c}$, see Figure 5.31.

Consider the following curve (call it Γ): along $\mathbf{c}$ from A to B and then along $\bar{\mathbf{c}}$ in the opposite direction back to A. Assume that Γ does not intersect itself (i.e., that it is a simple closed curve). Then, (5.8) implies that

$$\int_{\Gamma} \mathbf{F} \cdot d\mathbf{s} = 0.$$

On the other hand,

$$0 = \int_{\Gamma} \mathbf{F} \cdot d\mathbf{s} = \int_{\mathbf{c}} \mathbf{F} \cdot d\mathbf{s} + \int_{\bar{\mathbf{c}}^{opp}} \mathbf{F} \cdot d\mathbf{s} = \int_{\mathbf{c}} \mathbf{F} \cdot d\mathbf{s} - \int_{\bar{\mathbf{c}}} \mathbf{F} \cdot d\mathbf{s},$$

by Theorem 5.3 in Section 5.3, where $\bar{\mathbf{c}}^{opp}$ denotes the curve $\bar{\mathbf{c}}$ traversed in the opposite direction. Hence

$$\int_{\mathbf{c}} \mathbf{F} \cdot d\mathbf{s} = \int_{\bar{\mathbf{c}}} \mathbf{F} \cdot d\mathbf{s};$$

i.e., if $\mathbf{F}$ is a gradient vector field, then the path integral of $\mathbf{F}$ is the same for any curve joining A and B.

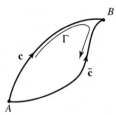

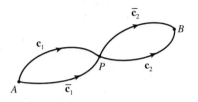

Figure 5.31   Curve Γ made of $\mathbf{c}$ and $\bar{\mathbf{c}}$.   **Figure 5.32**   A case when Γ intersects itself.

It remains to discuss the case when $\mathbf{c}$ and $\bar{\mathbf{c}}$ intersect so that Γ is not simple (assume that they intersect at one point, P; the same argument will prove the case for any number of intersections). Let $\mathbf{c}_1$ be the part of $\mathbf{c}$ from A to P and let $\mathbf{c}_2$ be the part from P to B. Similarly, $\bar{\mathbf{c}}_1$ is the part of $\bar{\mathbf{c}}$ from A to P and $\bar{\mathbf{c}}_2$ is the part from P to B; see Figure 5.32. Then, since $\mathbf{c}_1$ and $\bar{\mathbf{c}}_1$ and $\mathbf{c}_2$ and $\bar{\mathbf{c}}_2$ do not intersect,

$$\int_{\mathbf{c}_1} \mathbf{F} \cdot d\mathbf{s} = \int_{\bar{\mathbf{c}}_1} \mathbf{F} \cdot d\mathbf{s} \qquad \text{and} \qquad \int_{\mathbf{c}_2} \mathbf{F} \cdot d\mathbf{s} = \int_{\bar{\mathbf{c}}_2} \mathbf{F} \cdot d\mathbf{s}$$

and therefore

$$\int_{\mathbf{c}} \mathbf{F} \cdot d\mathbf{s} = \int_{\mathbf{c}_1} \mathbf{F} \cdot d\mathbf{s} + \int_{\mathbf{c}_2} \mathbf{F} \cdot d\mathbf{s} = \int_{\bar{\mathbf{c}}_1} \mathbf{F} \cdot d\mathbf{s} + \int_{\bar{\mathbf{c}}_2} \mathbf{F} \cdot d\mathbf{s} = \int_{\bar{\mathbf{c}}} \mathbf{F} \cdot d\mathbf{s}.$$

The conclusions of our argument are summarized in the next theorem.

■ **Theorem 5.6**   **Path Independence of Integrals of Vector Fields.**

Let $\mathbf{F}$ be a C^1 gradient vector field defined on an open, simply-connected set U. If $\mathbf{c}$ is an oriented simple closed curve in U, then

$$\int_{\mathbf{c}} \mathbf{F} \cdot d\mathbf{s} = 0.$$

If $\mathbf{c}$ and $\bar{\mathbf{c}}$ are two oriented, simple curves in U with the same initial and terminal points, then

$$\int_{\mathbf{c}} \mathbf{F} \cdot d\mathbf{s} = \int_{\bar{\mathbf{c}}} \mathbf{F} \cdot d\mathbf{s}. \qquad\qquad ■$$

In Examples 5.27 and 5.29 we computed the path integral of a gradient vector field $\mathbf{F} = \nabla f$ by finding the function f and then using the Fundamental Theorem 5.5. Theorem 5.6 suggests an alternative, that does not require that we compute the function f. The next two examples illustrate how this is done.

Example 5.30   Let us revisit Example 5.18 of the previous section once again (we have also discussed it in Example 5.27). Since

$$curl\,\mathbf{F} = \begin{vmatrix} \mathbf{i} & \mathbf{j} & \mathbf{k} \\ \partial/\partial x & \partial/\partial y & \partial/\partial z \\ y+z & x & x \end{vmatrix} = -(1-1)\mathbf{j} + (1-1)\mathbf{k} = \mathbf{0},$$

the integral $\int_c \mathbf{F} \cdot d\mathbf{s}$ does not depend on the curve, just on the endpoints. So take $\mathbf{c}$ to be the simplest possible curve: the straight line segment from $(1, 0, 0)$ to $(1, 0, 1)$. Parametrize it by

$$\mathbf{c}(t) = (1, 0, 0) + t(0, 0, 1) = (1, 0, t), \qquad t \in [0, 1].$$

Then

$$\int_{\mathbf{c}} \mathbf{F} \cdot d\mathbf{s} = \int_0^1 (t, 1, 1) \cdot (0, 0, 1)\, dt = \int_0^1 1\, dt = 1. \qquad \triangleleft$$

Example 5.31 We will recompute the path integral of Example 5.29. Since $curl\,(2x\mathbf{i}+2e^z\mathbf{j}+2ye^z\mathbf{k}) = \mathbf{0}$, the integral $\int_c \mathbf{F} \cdot d\mathbf{s}$ is independent of path. So take the straight line segment $\mathbf{c}(t) = (t, t, 0)$, $t \in [0, 1]$, joining $(0, 0, 0)$ and $(1, 1, 0)$. Then

$$\int_{\mathbf{c}} \mathbf{F} \cdot d\mathbf{s} = \int_0^1 (2t, 2, 2t) \cdot (1, 1, 0)\, dt = \int_0^1 (2t + 2)\, dt = 3. \qquad \triangleleft$$

■ **Theorem 5.7** Independence of $\int_c \mathbf{F} \cdot d\mathbf{s}$ on the Path Implies That $\mathbf{F}$ is a Gradient Vector Field

Let $\mathbf{F}$ be a C^1 vector field defined on an open, connected set $U \subseteq \mathbb{R}^2$ (or $\mathbb{R}^3$). The independence of the integral $\int_c \mathbf{F} \cdot d\mathbf{s}$ on the path chosen implies that $\mathbf{F}$ is a gradient vector field.   ■

Proof

For simplicity, we will consider the case when $\mathbf{F}$ is defined on $U \subseteq \mathbb{R}^2$ (the case $U \subseteq \mathbb{R}^3$ is discussed analogously). Assume that $\int_c \mathbf{F} \cdot d\mathbf{s}$ does not depend on the path $\mathbf{c}$. We have to find a scalar function $f : U \subseteq \mathbb{R}^2 \to \mathbb{R}$ such that $\nabla f = \mathbf{F} = (F_1, F_2)$.

Define

$$f(x, y) = \int_{\mathbf{c}} \mathbf{F} \cdot d\mathbf{s},$$

where $\mathbf{c}$ is *any* curve joining $(0, 0)$ and the point (x, y) in U. If $(0, 0)$ does not belong to U, choose any point in U as the initial point of integration. By assumption, $\int_c \mathbf{F} \cdot d\mathbf{s}$ depends only on the endpoints, and not on the curve joining them: therefore take $\mathbf{c}$ to be the following piecewise C^1 curve: along the x-axis from $(0, 0)$ to $(x, 0)$ and then along the straight line to (x, y); see Figure 5.33(a).

Parametrize $\mathbf{c}_1$ by $\mathbf{c}_1(t) = (t, 0)$, $t \in [0, x]$. Then $\mathbf{c}_1'(t) = (1, 0)$ and

$$\int_{\mathbf{c}_1} \mathbf{F} \cdot d\mathbf{s} = \int_0^x \mathbf{F}(\mathbf{c}_1(t)) \cdot \mathbf{c}_1'(t)\, dt$$

$$= \int_0^x \big(F_1(t, 0), F_2(t, 0)\big) \cdot (1, 0)\, dt = \int_0^x F_1(t, 0)\, dt.$$

Parametrize $\mathbf{c}_2$ by $\mathbf{c}_2(t) = (x, t)$, $t \in [0, y]$. Then $\mathbf{c}'_2(t) = (0, 1)$ and

$$\int_{\mathbf{c}_2} \mathbf{F} \cdot d\mathbf{s} = \int_0^y \mathbf{F}(\mathbf{c}_2(t)) \cdot \mathbf{c}'_2(t)\, dt$$
$$= \int_0^y \big(F_1(x, t), F_2(x, t)\big) \cdot (0, 1)\, dt = \int_0^y F_2(x, t)\, dt.$$

Hence

$$f(x, y) = \int_0^x F_1(t, 0)\, dt + \int_0^y F_2(x, t)\, dt.$$

We have to check that $\nabla f = \mathbf{F}$. The first integral depends on x only, and the second one depends on x and y. Therefore,

$$\frac{\partial f}{\partial y}(x, y) = 0 + \frac{\partial}{\partial y}\left(\int_0^y F_2(x, t)\, dt\right) = F_2(x, y),$$

where the right side was computed using the Fundamental Theorem of Calculus (5.5) with $f(t) = F_2(x, t)$.

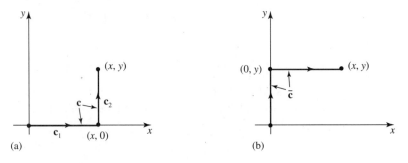

Figure 5.33 Paths of integration in the proof of Theorem 5.7.

Choosing another path $\overline{\mathbf{c}}$ joining $(0, 0)$ and (x, y) shown in Figure 5.33(b) we get

$$f(x, y) = \int_0^y F_2(0, t)\, dt + \int_0^x F_1(t, y)\, dt.$$

Differentiating with respect to x (the first integral does not depend on x) and using the Fundamental Theorem once again, we get

$$\frac{\partial f}{\partial x}(x, y) = F_1(x, y),$$

and therefore $\nabla f(x, y) = \mathbf{F}(x, y)$. ■

We omitted one technical point in the proof: what if the paths that we considered do not belong to U?

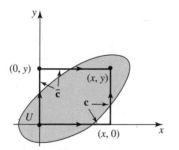 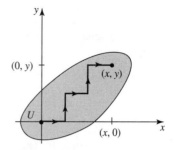

Figure 5.34   A case not considered in the proof of Theorem 5.7.
(a) Curves **c** and **c̄**.   (b) Polygonal path joining $(0, 0)$ and (x, y).

Figure 5.34(a) shows one such case: neither of the paths (call them **c** and **c̄**) belong to U. In the proof we learned how to express f in terms of integrals with respect to horizontal and vertical line segments. In the general case, all we have to do is to consider polygonal paths joining $(0, 0)$ and (x, y) with the property that all of their segments are either horizontal or vertical, as in Figure 5.34(b).

We have proven a number of useful results in this section. Let us put them all together.

■ **Theorem 5.8**   Properties of a Gradient Vector Field.

Let **F** be a C^1 vector field defined on an open, connected set $U \subseteq \mathbb{R}^2$ (or $\mathbb{R}^3$). The following statements are equivalent.

(a) **F** is a gradient field; i.e., $\mathbf{F} = \nabla f$ for some function $f: U \subseteq \mathbb{R}^2$ (or $\mathbb{R}^3$) $\to \mathbb{R}$.

(b) For any oriented simple closed curve **c**,

$$\int_{\mathbf{c}} \mathbf{F} \cdot d\mathbf{s} = 0.$$

(c) For any two oriented simple curves $\mathbf{c}_1$ and $\mathbf{c}_2$ having the same initial and terminal points,

$$\int_{\mathbf{c}_1} \mathbf{F} \cdot d\mathbf{s} = \int_{\mathbf{c}_2} \mathbf{F} \cdot d\mathbf{s}.$$

If U is also simply-connected, then any of the above is equivalent to

(d) $curl\ \mathbf{F} = \mathbf{0}$ (if $\mathbf{F}: U \subseteq \mathbb{R}^2 \to \mathbb{R}^2$ then view it as a vector field in $\mathbb{R}^3$ with z-component equal to 0).   ■

Proof

The implications (a) $\Rightarrow$ (b) and (b) $\Rightarrow$ (c) are contained in Theorem 5.6. The statement (c) $\Rightarrow$ (a) is proven in Theorem 5.7. The equivalence of (a) and (d) was shown in Theorem 5.4.   ■

Example 5.32   Compute $\int_{\mathbf{c}} \mathbf{F} \cdot d\mathbf{s}$ if $\mathbf{F} = (-y/(x^2 + y^2), x/(x^2 + y^2))$ and **c** is the unit circle $\mathbf{c}(t) =$

$(\cos t, \sin t)$, $t \in [0, 2\pi]$.

Solution Since $\mathbf{F}(\mathbf{c}(t)) = (-\sin t, \cos t)$ and $\mathbf{c}'(t) = (-\sin t, \cos t)$, it follows that

$$\int_{\mathbf{c}} \mathbf{F} \cdot d\mathbf{s} = \int_0^{2\pi} \mathbf{F}(\mathbf{c}(t)) \cdot \mathbf{c}'(t) \, dt$$

$$= \int_0^{2\pi} (-\sin t, \cos t) \cdot (-\sin t, \cos t) \, dt = \int_0^{2\pi} 1 \, dt = 2\pi.$$

According to Theorem 5.8 ($\mathbf{F}$ is defined on $U = \mathbb{R}^2 - \{(0,0)\}$, which is open and connected) $\mathbf{F}$ cannot be a gradient vector field. But notice that

$$\frac{\partial F_2}{\partial x} = \frac{y^2 - x^2}{(x^2 + y^2)^2} = \frac{\partial F_1}{\partial y},$$

i.e., *curl* $\mathbf{F} = \mathbf{0}$!

However, this is not a contradiction: the vector field $\mathbf{F}$ is C^1 on U, but U is not *simply-connected*— and therefore, the equivalence of statements (b) and (d) in Theorem 5.8 cannot be applied. ◀

Next, we restate Theorem 5.8 in the context of conservative force fields. Recall that a force field is called conservative if $\mathbf{F} = -\nabla V$ (V is a potential function), and keep in mind that the path integral of $\mathbf{F}$ represents the work done by $\mathbf{F}$.

■ **Theorem 5.9** Conservative Force Fields.

Let $\mathbf{F}$ be a C^1 force field defined on an open, connected set $U \subseteq \mathbb{R}^2$ (or $\mathbb{R}^3$). The following statements are equivalent.

(a) $\mathbf{F}$ is conservative.

(b) The work of the force $\mathbf{F}$ along any oriented simple closed curve is zero (i.e., mechanical energy is conserved).

(c) The work of $\mathbf{F}$ does not depend on the path, but only on its endpoints.
If U is also simply-connected, then any of the above is equivalent to

(d) *curl* $\mathbf{F} = \mathbf{0}$ (if $\mathbf{F}: U \subseteq \mathbb{R}^2 \to \mathbb{R}^2$ then view it as a vector field in $\mathbb{R}^3$ with z-component equal to 0). ■

Example 5.33 A particle of mass m moves in the xy-plane subject to the force field $\mathbf{F} = -C(x(1 + y^2)\mathbf{i} + x^2 y\mathbf{j})$, where C is a constant.

(a) Show that $\mathbf{F}$ is conservative.

(b) Find the potential energy $V(x, 0)$ if $V(0, 0) = 0$.

(c) Find the potential energy $V(x, y)$ at a general position (x, y).

Solution The domain $U = \mathbb{R}^2$ of $\mathbf{F}$ is simply-connected.

(a) A vector field $\mathbf{F} = F_1 \mathbf{i} + F_2 \mathbf{j}$ is conservative if and only if *curl* $\mathbf{F} = \mathbf{0}$, if and only if $\partial F_2/\partial x = \partial F_1/\partial y$. In our case, $F_1 = -Cx(1+y^2)$ and $F_2 = -Cx^2y$ and hence

$$\frac{\partial F_2}{\partial x} = -Cy \cdot 2x, \qquad \frac{\partial F_1}{\partial y} = -Cx \cdot 2y.$$

(b) Part (a) implies that there exists a potential function (that is, a scalar function V such that $\mathbf{F} = -\nabla V$) and that the integral along a curve depends only on its endpoints. Let us compute $\int_c \mathbf{F} \cdot d\mathbf{s}$ along the straight line segment (call it $\mathbf{c}$) from $(0,0)$ to $(x,0)$. Parametrize it by $\mathbf{c}(t) = (t,0)$, $t \in [0,x]$. Then

$$\int_c \mathbf{F} \cdot d\mathbf{s} = \int_0^x \mathbf{F}(\mathbf{c}(t)) \cdot \mathbf{c}'(t)\, dt = \int_0^x (-Ct)\mathbf{i} \cdot \mathbf{i}\, dt = -C\frac{t^2}{2}\Big|_0^x = -C\frac{x^2}{2}.$$

The Fundamental Theorem of Calculus (Theorem 5.5) implies that

$$\int_c \mathbf{F} \cdot d\mathbf{s} = -\int_c \nabla V(x,y) \cdot d\mathbf{s}$$

$$= -V(x,y)\Big|_{(0,0)}^{(x,0)} = -V(x,0) + V(0,0) = -V(x,0),$$

since $V(0,0) = 0$ by assumption. Combining the two expressions we get $V(x,0) = Cx^2/2$.

(c) This time we have to reach a general position (x,y) from the origin. As in (b), take a straight line segment joining $(0,0)$ and (x,y),

$$\mathbf{c}(t) = (0,0) + t(x,y) = (tx,ty), \qquad t \in [0,1].$$

Then

$$\int_c \mathbf{F} \cdot d\mathbf{s} = \int_0^1 \mathbf{F}(\mathbf{c}(t)) \cdot \mathbf{c}'(t)\, dt$$

$$= \int_0^1 \left(-Cxt(1 + y^2t^2)\mathbf{i} - Cx^2t^2yt\mathbf{j}\right) \cdot \left(x\mathbf{i} + y\mathbf{j}\right) dt$$

$$= \int_0^1 \left(-Cx^2t - Cx^2y^2t^3 - Cx^2y^2t^3\right) dt$$

$$= -Cx^2\frac{t^2}{2} - 2Cx^2y^2\frac{t^4}{4}\Big|_0^1 = -\frac{Cx^2}{2} - \frac{Cx^2y^2}{2} = -\frac{C}{2}\left(x^2 + x^2y^2\right).$$

By the Fundamental Theorem of Calculus

$$\int_c \mathbf{F} \cdot d\mathbf{s} = -\int_c \nabla V(x,y) \cdot d\mathbf{s}$$

$$= -V(x,y)\Big|_{(0,0)}^{(x,y)} = -V(x,y) + V(0,0) = -V(x,y),$$

(since $V(0,0) = 0$) and hence

$$V(x,y) = \frac{C}{2}\left(x^2 + x^2y^2\right).$$

Here is another way to compute (c). In part (b) we came to the point $(x, 0)$, so let us continue from there to (x, y), that is, walk along the curve $\mathbf{c}(t) = (x, t)$, $t \in [0, y]$. Then

$$
\int_{\mathbf{c}} \mathbf{F} \cdot d\mathbf{s} = \int_0^y \mathbf{F}(\mathbf{c}(t)) \cdot \mathbf{c}'(t)\, dt
$$

$$
= \int_0^y \left(-Cx(1 + t^2)\mathbf{i} - Cx^2 t\mathbf{j} \right) \cdot \mathbf{j}\, dt = -C \int_0^y x^2 t\, dt = -C\frac{x^2 y^2}{2}.
$$

As before, combine this result with the Fundamental Theorem of Calculus

$$
\int_{\mathbf{c}} \mathbf{F} \cdot d\mathbf{s} = -\int_{\mathbf{c}} \nabla V(x, y) \cdot d\mathbf{s} = -V(x, y)\Big|_{(x,0)}^{(x,y)} = -V(x, y) + V(x, 0)
$$

to get

$$
V(x, y) = C\frac{x^2 y^2}{2} + V(x, 0) = C\frac{x^2 y^2}{2} + C\frac{x^2}{2} = \frac{C}{2}(x^2 y^2 + x^2).
$$

Another way to solve parts (b) and (c) would be to compute V from the system of differential equations

$$
\frac{\partial V}{\partial x} = Cx(1 + y^2) \qquad \text{and} \qquad \frac{\partial V}{\partial y} = Cx^2 y
$$

with the initial condition $V(0, 0) = 0$. Integrating the first equation with respect to x we get

$$
V(x, y) = C\frac{x^2}{2}(1 + y^2) + D(y),
$$

where $D(y)$ depends (possibly) on y. Computing the derivative of $V(x, y)$ with respect to y and combining with $\partial V/\partial y$ yields

$$
C\frac{x^2}{2} 2y + \frac{dD(y)}{dy} = Cx^2 y,
$$

hence $dD(y)/dy = 0$ and $D(y) = D$ (D is a real number). Therefore $V = Cx^2(1 + y^2)/2 + D$. The condition $V(0, 0) = 0$ implies that $D = 0$, and hence

$$
V = \frac{C}{2}x^2(1 + y^2).
$$

◀

Recall that (cf. Section 4.4) there is a close relationship between functions and their derivatives and differential forms. The differential of a real-valued function f is a 1-form df whose components are the components of the gradient vector field ∇f. To a vector field $\mathbf{F} = F_1\mathbf{i} + F_2\mathbf{j} + F_3\mathbf{k}$ we can assign a 1-form $\alpha = F_1 dx + F_2 dy + F_3 dz$ or a 2-form $\beta = F_1 dy dz + F_2 dx dz + F_3 dx dy$. The components of the differential $d\alpha$ of α are the components of $curl\, \mathbf{F}$ (therefore, $d\alpha = 0$ if and only if $curl\, \mathbf{F} = \mathbf{0}$). The differential of β can be written as $d\beta = (div\, \mathbf{F})dx dy dz$.

This relationship is much deeper— we will now study one of its aspects.

■ **Definition 5.13**   Closed Differential Form.

A differential form α defined on $U \subseteq \mathbb{R}^3$ is *closed* if $d\alpha = 0$.   ▩

A constant real-valued function is a closed 0-form. The 1-form $\alpha = y^2 dx + 2xy dy + dz$ is closed since

$$d\alpha = d(y^2 dx + 2xy dy + dz) = 2y dy \wedge dx + 2y dx \wedge dy = 0.$$

The differential of the 2-form $\beta = x^2 dx dy + y e^z dy dz$ is zero, and hence β is closed. The definition of the differential implies that every 3-form defined on $U \subseteq \mathbb{R}^3$ is closed.

■ **Definition 5.14**   Exact Differential Form.

A k-form α $(1 \leq k \leq 3)$ defined on $U \subseteq \mathbb{R}^3$ is *exact* if there exists a $(k-1)$-form β such that $d\beta = \alpha$.   ▩

For example, the 3-form $\alpha = 2xy dx dy dz$ is exact since $d(x^2 y dy dz) = 2xy dx dy dz$.

The form β in Definition 5.14 is not uniquely determined by α: there are infinitely many choices, for example

$$d(x^2 y dy dz + g(x, y) dx dy + h(x, z) dz dx) = 2xy dx dy dz,$$

where g and h are any differentiable functions (of the variables listed). The fact that

$$d(e^x dy + y dz) = e^x dx dy + dy dz$$

proves that the 2-form $e^x dx dy + dy dz$ is exact, being the differential of $e^x dy + y dz$.

Let α be an exact form; that is, $\alpha = d\beta$ for some form β. Then $d\alpha = d(d\beta) = 0$ by Theorem 4.6 in Section 4.4, which proves that α is closed. In other words, we have just shown that every exact form is closed. The converse of this statement does not hold in general (i.e., for any form defined on any subset $U \subseteq \mathbb{R}^3$).

■ **Theorem 5.10**   Closed Forms Are Exact.

(a) Let α be a closed 1-form defined on an open, simply-connected set $U \subseteq \mathbb{R}^3$. Then α is exact.

(b) Let α be a closed 2-form defined on an open, star-shaped set $U \subseteq \mathbb{R}^3$. Then α is exact.   ■

Since star-shaped sets are simply-connected, the condition on U in (b) is stronger than the condition in (a). The proof of part (b) is similar to the proof of the statement that $curl \, \mathbf{F} = \mathbf{0}$ implies $\mathbf{F} = \nabla f$ for star-shaped sets. Part (a) is a consequence of Stokes' Theorem and another theorem that we will have to take for granted (although its statement is intuitively clear, its proof is beyond the scope of this book), and will be discussed in the last chapter.

Let us now translate the statements from the language of differential forms to the language of vector differential operators. Assume that U is a simply-connected set and let $\alpha = F_1 dx + F_2 dy + F_3 dz$ be a 1-form and let $\mathbf{F} = F_1\mathbf{i} + F_2\mathbf{j} + F_3\mathbf{k}$ be a vector field defined on U. Theorem 5.10(a) and the remark preceding it state that the 1-form α is exact if and only if it is closed; i.e.,

$$\alpha = df \text{ for some differentiable function } f \text{ if and only if } d\alpha = 0.$$

This equivalence can be interpreted as

$$\mathbf{F} = \nabla f \text{ for some differentiable function } f \text{ if and only if } curl\, \mathbf{F} = \mathbf{0},$$

which is precisely the statement of Theorem 5.4.

Interpreting the second part of Theorem 5.10 in terms of vector differential operators actually produces a new statement. Assume that U is a star-shaped set and consider $\mathbf{F} = F_1\mathbf{i} + F_2\mathbf{j} + F_3\mathbf{k}$ and $\beta = F_1 dydz + F_2 dxdz + F_3 dxdy$. The equivalence

$$\beta = d\gamma \text{ (i.e., } \beta \text{ is exact) if and only if } d\beta = 0 \text{ (i.e., } \beta \text{ is closed)}$$

means that

$$\mathbf{F} = curl\, \mathbf{H} \text{ if and only if } div\, \mathbf{F} = 0. \tag{5.9}$$

EXERCISES 5.4   **Exercises 1 to 10:**   State which of the following sets are connected, simply-connected and/or star-shaped.

1. $\mathbb{R}^2$, with the circle $x^2 + y^2 = 1$ removed

2. The set $\{(x, y) \mid y < |x|\}$ in $\mathbb{R}^2$

3. $\mathbb{R}^3$, with the circle $x^2 + y^2 = 1$, $z = 1$ removed

4. the set $\{(x, y, z) \mid x^2 + y^2 + z^2 \le 1 \text{ and } z \ne 1\}$ in $\mathbb{R}^3$

5. $\mathbb{R}^3$, with the sphere $x^2 + y^2 + z^2 = 1$ removed

6. $\mathbb{R}^3$, with the ball $x^2 + y^2 + z^2 \le 1$ removed

7. $\mathbb{R}^3$, with the helix $\mathbf{c}(t) = (\cos t, \sin t, t)$, $t \in [0, \pi]$ removed

8. the set $\{(x, y) \mid x^2 + y^2 < 1 \text{ or } x^2 + y^2 > 2\}$ in $\mathbb{R}^2$

9. the region inside the polygonal line joining the points $(0, 5)$, $(2, 0)$, $(2, 3)$, $(4, 3)$, $(4, 5)$ and $(0, 5)$ (in that order)

10. the set $\{(x, y) \mid x^2 - y^2 < 0\}$ in $\mathbb{R}^2$

11. Compute $\int_{\mathbf{c}} \mathbf{F} \cdot d\mathbf{s}$, where $\mathbf{F} = y^2 \cos x\mathbf{i} + 2y \sin x\mathbf{j}$, and $\mathbf{c}$ is any path starting at $(1, 1)$ and ending at $(1, 3)$.

12. Compute the path integral $\int_{\mathbf{c}} \mathbf{F} \cdot d\mathbf{s}$, where $\mathbf{F} = (\cos(xy) - xy \sin(xy))\mathbf{i} - x^2 \sin(xy)\mathbf{j}$, and $\mathbf{c}(t) = (e^t \cos t, e^t \sin t)$, $0 \le t \le \pi$.

13. Check that the vector field $\mathbf{F} = (-y/(x^2 + y^2), x/(x^2 + y^2), 1)$ satisfies $curl\, \mathbf{F} = \mathbf{0}$ in $\mathbb{R}^3 - \{(0, 0, 0)\}$, but is not conservative in $\mathbb{R}^3$. In order to show that $\mathbf{F}$ is not conservative, compute path integrals of $\mathbf{F}$ along the curves $\mathbf{c}_1(t) = (\cos t, \sin t, 0)$, $0 \le t \le \pi$ and

$c_2(t) = (\cos t, -\sin t, 0)$, $0 \leq t \leq \pi$, joining $(1, 0)$ and $(-1, 0)$. Explain why this does not contradict Theorem 5.8.

14. Let $\mathbf{F}(x, y) = y\mathbf{i} + x\mathbf{j}$.

    (a) Compute $\int_c \mathbf{F} \cdot d\mathbf{s}$ along the circular path from $(1, 0)$ counterclockwise to $(0, -1)$, then along the y-axis from $(0, -1)$ to $(0, 2)$ and then along the straight line from $(0, 2)$ to $(1, 0)$.

    (b) Show that $\mathbf{F}(x, y)$ is a gradient vector field and use this fact to check your answer in (a).

Exercises 15 to 19: Determine whether $\mathbf{F}$ is a gradient vector field, and if so, specify its domain U and find all functions f such that $\mathbf{F} = \nabla f$.

15. $\mathbf{F} = (4x^2 - 4y^2 + x)\mathbf{i} + (7xy + \ln y)\mathbf{j}$

16. $\mathbf{F} = (3x^2 \ln x + x^2)\mathbf{i} + x^3 y^{-1}\mathbf{j}$ **17.** $\mathbf{F} = 2x \ln y\mathbf{i} + (2y + x^2/y)\mathbf{j}$

18. $\mathbf{F} = (yz + e^x \sin z)\mathbf{i} + (xz + y^2 - e^y)\mathbf{j} + (xy + e^x \cos z)\mathbf{k}$

19. $\mathbf{F} = y\cos(xy)\mathbf{i} + (x\cos(xy) - z\sin y)\mathbf{j} + \cos y\mathbf{k}$

Exercises 20 to 22: Evaluate the following integrals.

20. $\displaystyle\int_{(0,1,0)}^{(3,3,1)} (4xy - 2xy^2z^2)dx + (2x^2 - 2x^2yz^2)dy - 2x^2y^2zdz$

21. $\displaystyle\int_{(0,0,0)}^{(\pi,\pi/2,\pi/3)} \cos x \tan z dx + dy + \sin x \sec^2 z dz$

22. $\displaystyle\int_{(1,2,1)}^{(2,2,2)} x^{-2}dx + z^{-1}dy + yz^{-2}dz$

23. Consider the vector field $\mathbf{F}(x, y) = -(1 + x)ye^x\mathbf{i} - xe^x\mathbf{j}$.

    (a) Show that $\mathbf{F}(x, y)$ is conservative.

    (b) Using the Fundamental Theorem of Calculus, find the potential energy $V(x, 0)$ along the x-axis, if $V(0, 0) = 0$.

    (c) Using the Fundamental Theorem of Calculus, find the potential energy $V(0, y)$ along the y-axis, if $V(0, 0) = 0$.

24. Let $\mathbf{F}(x, y, z) = x^3 y\mathbf{i} + z^2\mathbf{k}$. Does there exist a function f such that $\mathbf{F} = \nabla f$? a vector field $\mathbf{H}$ such that $\mathbf{F} = curl\,\mathbf{H}$?

25. Find $\int_c \mathbf{F} \cdot d\mathbf{s}$ if $\mathbf{F}(x, y) = 2xye^y\mathbf{i} + x^2e^y(1 + y)\mathbf{j}$ and $\mathbf{c}$ is the straight line segment from $(0, 0)$ to $(3, -2)$

    (a) using a parametrization for $\mathbf{c}$, and

    (b) using the fact that $curl\,\mathbf{F} = \mathbf{0}$.

26. Check that $\mathbf{F}(x, y, z) = 2xy^2\mathbf{i} + (2x^2y + e^z)\mathbf{j} + ye^z\mathbf{k}$ is a conservative force field in $\mathbb{R}^3$. Find the work done by $\mathbf{F}$ on an object that moves from $(0, 2, -1)$ to $(3, 2, 0)$.

27. Show that the vector field $\mathbf{F}(\mathbf{r}) = \|\mathbf{r}\|^2\mathbf{r}$ is a gradient vector field ($\mathbf{r} = x\mathbf{i} + y\mathbf{j} + z\mathbf{k}$), and find a function f such that $\nabla f = \mathbf{F}$.

28. Show that the vector field $\mathbf{F}(\mathbf{r}) = \|\mathbf{r}\|\mathbf{r}$ is a gradient vector field ($\mathbf{r} = x\mathbf{i} + y\mathbf{j} + z\mathbf{k}$), and find a function f such that $\nabla f = \mathbf{F}$.

29. Compute $\int_c \mathbf{F} \cdot d\mathbf{s}$ where $\mathbf{F} = (\ln(x + y^2) + x/(x + y^2))\mathbf{i} + (2xy/(x + y^2))\mathbf{j}$, and $\mathbf{c}$ is the part of the curve $y = x^3$ from $(1, 1)$ to $(2, 8)$. Use the fact (check it!) that $\mathbf{F}$ is a gradient vector field.

30. State which of the following forms are closed and/or exact or neither.

(a) $\alpha = ye^{xy}dx + xe^{xy}dy$ (b) $\alpha = xdx + ydy + zdz$

(c) $\alpha = -ydx + xdy + zdz$ (d) $\alpha = -2ydxdy - ydzdy + zdxdz$

(e) $\alpha = \sin x \, dxdy + (\sin y + \cos z)dydz$ (f) $\alpha = \sin(xyz^2)dxdydz$

31. Let α be an exact form (i.e., $\alpha = df$ for some differentiable function f) defined on $\mathbb{R}^3$ and let $\mathbf{c}(t)$, $t \in [a, b]$, be a smooth differentiable curve. Show that $\int_{\mathbf{c}} \alpha = f(\mathbf{c}(b)) - f(\mathbf{c}(a))$.

32. Show that the form $\alpha = ydx + xdy + 4dz$ is exact and compute $\int_{\mathbf{c}} \alpha$ along any path from $(0, 0, 0)$ to $(0, 4, 1)$.

CHAPTER REVIEW

Review Questions

Answer/discuss the following questions:

1. Define continuous, C^1 and piecewise C^1 paths. Is it possible to parametrize the same curve using a continuous path, a C^1 path and a piecewise C^1 path? If possible, find an example.

2. Define a reparametrization of a path and describe the ways of checking whether it is orientation-preserving or orientation-reversing. Explain to what extent the path integral of a vector field depends on reparametrization.

3. Define the circulation of a vector field and explain its physical significance. Draw an example of a vector field that has a non-zero circulation at more than one point.

4. What is the value of $\int_{\mathbf{c}} \mathbf{T} \cdot d\mathbf{s}$, where $\mathbf{T}$ is the unit tangent vector field to $\mathbf{c}$?

5. Let $\mathbf{F}$ be an inverse-square law force field and let $\mathbf{c}$ be any curve lying on the sphere $x^2 + y^2 + z^2 = a^2$. Explain why $\mathbf{F}$ does zero work in moving the particle along $\mathbf{c}$.

6. Suppose that the path integral of a C^1 vector field $\mathbf{F}$ is zero for *all* paths connecting two points A and B in space. Is $\mathbf{F}$ a gradient vector field?

7. Define and give examples of connected, simply-connected and star-shaped sets in $\mathbb{R}^2$ and $\mathbb{R}^3$. Find an example of a set in $\mathbb{R}^3$ that is not star-shaped. Is every star-shaped set simply-connected?

8. Give a definition of a conservative vector field. If $\mathbf{F}_1$ and $\mathbf{F}_2$ are conservative vector fields, is their sum a conservative vector field? If it is, find its potential function. Discuss the same question for the cross product $\mathbf{F}_1 \times \mathbf{F}_2$.

9. List equivalent properties of a gradient vector field. State the assumptions on the domain of the field needed for the statements to hold.

Computer Projects

1. Work.

Consider the vector field $\mathbf{F}(x, y) = ye^{xy}\mathbf{i} + y^2\mathbf{j}$.

(a) Compute the work of $\mathbf{F}$ along a straight line segment of length 1 that starts at the origin and makes an angle θ, $0 \leq \theta \leq 2\pi$ with respect to the positive x-axis.

(b) Identify the directions of minimum and maximum work, and the directions along which the work is zero. Hint: in (a) you will obtain a function of θ, defined on $[0, 2\pi]$; you can read off the result for (b) from the plot of that function.

(c) Looking at your result in (b), what can you say about the direction of the field $\mathbf{F}$?

(d) Plot the vector field $\mathbf{F}$ to confirm your result in (c).

2. Path Integral of a Scalar Function.

Consider the function $f(x, y) = x^2 + 3ye^{-2x^2 - 2y^2}$.

(a) Write down a parametric representation of a straight line segment from $(0, 0)$ to a point on the unit circle $x^2 + y^2 = 1$. Use the angle with respect to the x-axis as a parameter.

(b) Compute the path integral of f along paths in (a). (Your result will contain the parameter from (a).)

(c) Find the line segment(s) along which the path integral in (b) is largest.

(d) Find the line segments along which the path integral in (b) is smaller than 0.1.

Further Explorations

1. Let $\mathbf{c}(t) = (t^{3/2}, t)$, $t \in [0, 1]$. Find an orientation-preserving reparametrization ϕ of $\mathbf{c}$ such that $\mathbf{c}(\phi(t))$ has constant speed.

2. In this exercise we investigate an estimate for a path integral.

(a) Assume that $|f(x, y)| \leq M$ for all points on the curve $\mathbf{c}(t)$ in $\mathbb{R}^2$, $t \in [a, b]$. Show that $\left| \int_{\mathbf{c}} f\, ds \right| \leq M\ell$, where ℓ is the length of $\mathbf{c}$.

(b) Consider $f(x, y) = x^2 + y^2$ and $\mathbf{c}(t) = (\cos t, \sin t)$, $t \in [0, 4\pi]$. Show that $\int_{\mathbf{c}} f\, ds = 4\pi$. Clearly, $|f(x, y)| = |x^2 + y^2| \leq 1 = M$ for all points on $\mathbf{c}$; furthermore, $\ell = 2\pi$, being the length of the circle. Hence $M\ell = 2\pi$, and the inequality in (a) seems to be false. What is wrong with this argument?

3. Let $\mathbf{F} = \ln x \mathbf{i} + \mathbf{j}$. Compute the limit of $\int_{\mathbf{c}_\epsilon} \mathbf{F} \cdot d\mathbf{s}$ as $\epsilon \to 0$, where $\mathbf{c}_\epsilon$ is the straight line segment joining $(1, 1)$ and (ϵ, ϵ), for $\epsilon > 0$.

4. Let f be a C^1 function and let $\mathbf{c}$ be a smooth curve with endpoints (x_0, y_0) and (x_1, y_1). Show that $\int_{\mathbf{c}} (f_x dx + f_y dy) = f(x_1, y_1) - f(x_0, y_0)$.

5. A radial force acting on a particle is given by $\mathbf{F} = a \|\mathbf{r}\| \mathbf{r}$, where a is a constant and $\mathbf{r} = x\mathbf{i} + y\mathbf{j} + z\mathbf{k}$. The potential of a conservative force is defined to be the work done by the force on a particle as it moves from $(0, 0, 0)$ to (x, y, z). Assuming that its value at the origin is zero, find the potential of the radial force $\mathbf{F}$.

6. Compute $\int_{\mathbf{c}} f\, ds$ if $f(x, y, z) = (x + yz)/(x^2 + y^2 + z^2)$ and $\mathbf{c}$ is the straight line segment joining $(1, 1, 1)$ and (a, a, a), where $a \neq 1$. Describe what happens as $a \to 0$ and as $a \to \infty$.

7. Let $\mathbf{F} = -\nabla f$ (i.e., $\mathbf{F}$ is a conservative force field) and assume that a particle of mass m moves along the curve $\mathbf{c}(t)$ in this field. Show that the quantity $f(\mathbf{c}(t)) + m\|\mathbf{c}'(t)\|^2/2$ is constant in time and give a physical interpretation.

8. Consider the gravitational force field $\mathbf{F}(\mathbf{r}) = -GMR\mathbf{r}/\|\mathbf{r}\|$ (where $\mathbf{r} = x\mathbf{i}+y\mathbf{j}+z\mathbf{k}$) defined on $\mathbb{R}^3 - \{(0, 0, 0)\}$. Check that $div\,\mathbf{F} = 0$. However, prove that there is no C^1 vector field $\mathbf{H}$ such that $\mathbf{F} = curl\,\mathbf{H}$.

Chapter 6

DOUBLE AND TRIPLE INTEGRALS

In order to compute an integral along a curve **c** in $\mathbb{R}^2$ or $\mathbb{R}^3$ we have to find a suitable parametrization of **c** first. Then, with the help of that analytic description of the curve, we reduce the integral along **c** to the definite integral over an interval of real numbers.

Now we move one dimension higher: our goal is to define integrals over surfaces in space. The construction proceeds in the same way as for curves: a surface will be described in analytic terms (i.e., will be "parametrized"). A surface integral will then be defined in terms of a double integral over a region in $\mathbb{R}^2$. That will be done in the next chapter.

In this chapter we define and study double integrals over various regions in $\mathbb{R}^2$. We start by considering the simplest possible regions in the plane— rectangles. Our approach is certainly not new: the double integral is constructed as the limit of approximating Riemann sums. Next, the definition is extended to more general regions in $\mathbb{R}^2$ (called elementary regions) and the properties of double integrals are studied and illustrated by examples. Two sections are devoted to worked examples of evaluation of double integrals, with special attention given to the Change of Variables Theorem.

Taking advantage of the construction of the double integral, we define, in analogous terms, the triple integral over a region in space. Triple integrals will appear in various applications in Section 7.4 and in the Divergence Theorem in Chapter 8.

6.1 DOUBLE INTEGRALS: DEFINITION AND PROPERTIES

In this section we define the double integral in order to generalize the concept of the definite integral to functions of two variables (the extension to functions of three variables will be discussed in Section 6.5).

The definite integral of a real-valued functon of one variable is defined as a limit of approximating sums, called Riemann sums. For a non-negative function f (f is non-negative if $f \geq 0$), a Riemann sum represents a sum of areas of rectangles that approximate a region under the graph of f. In this case, a definite integral can be interpreted as the area of a region in $\mathbb{R}^2$. As a matter of fact, one could *define* the area of a region as a limit of corresponding Riemann sums; i.e., as a definite integral.

One of many reasons why definite integrals are so important is that they allow us to do more complicated integrations: in particular, integrals of real-valued functions of several variables and vector fields along curves in $\mathbb{R}^2$ and $\mathbb{R}^3$ are reduced to definite integrals over intervals on the x-axis.

By analogy with this situation, the double integral of a non-negative function of two variables over a region in $\mathbb{R}^2$ can be interpreted as a volume. Moreover, integrals over surfaces in space will be defined in terms of integration in $\mathbb{R}^2$. In the first stage of our construction we will define double integrals over special regions in $\mathbb{R}^2$ that we now introduce.

A *rectangle* (or a *closed rectangle*) $R = [a, b] \times [c, d]$ is the set of all points (x, y) in $\mathbb{R}^2$ such that $a \le x \le b$ and $c \le y \le d$. Figure 6.1 shows two rectangles, $R_1 = [2, 4] \times [1, 4]$ and $R_2 = [-3, 0] \times [-2, 2]$.

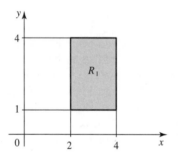
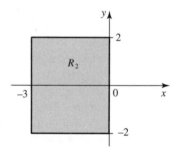

Figure 6.1   Rectangles $R_1 = [2, 4] \times [1, 4]$ and $R_2 = [-3, 0] \times [-2, 2]$ in $\mathbb{R}^2$.

Let $z = f(x, y) : U \subseteq \mathbb{R}^2 \to \mathbb{R}$ be a continuous function and let $R = [a, b] \times [c, d]$ be a rectangle contained in its domain U. Assume that $f(x, y) \ge 0$ for all $(x, y) \in R$.

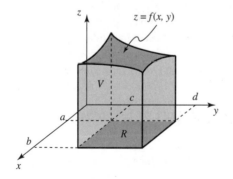

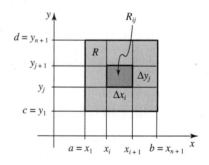

Figure 6.2   Solid under the surface $z = f(x, y)$ above the region R.

Figure 6.3   Subdivision of R into n^2 rectangles.

The graph of $z = f(x, y)$, the xy-plane and the four vertical planes $x = a$, $x = b$, $y = c$ and $y = d$ (see Figure 6.2) define a three-dimensional solid V, called the "solid under the surface $z = f(x, y)$ above R." Our aim is to find the volume of V.

Once again, we will use the method of constructing Riemann sums, also called the method of exhaustion; although formalized by B. Riemann in the 19th century, it has been known and used for over 2200 years.

Divide the intervals $[a, b]$ and $[c, d]$ into n subintervals $[a = x_1, x_2], [x_2, x_3], \ldots,$ $[x_n, x_{n+1} = b]$ and $[c = y_1, y_2], [y_2, y_3], \ldots, [y_n, y_{n+1} = d]$ and form the rectangles $R_{ij} = [x_i, x_{i+1}] \times [y_j, y_{j+1}], i, j = 1, \ldots, n$; see Figure 6.3. We have thus obtained a division of R into n^2 subrectangles R_{ij} with sides $\Delta x_i = x_{i+1} - x_i$ and $\Delta y_j = y_{j+1} - y_j$. Choose a point (x_i^*, y_j^*) in each R_{ij} and build a parallelepiped (rectangular box) over R_{ij} whose height is equal to the value $f(x_i^*, y_j^*)$ of f at (x_i^*, y_j^*). The volume of the parallelepiped, $f(x_i^*, y_j^*)\Delta A_{ij}$, where $\Delta A_{ij} = \Delta x_i \Delta y_j$ is the area of R_{ij}, approximates the volume of the three-dimensional region under the surface $z = f(x, y)$ and above R_{ij}. The sum of the volumes of all n^2 parallelepipeds thus obtained (also called the *(double) Riemann sum*)

$$\mathcal{R}_n = \sum_{i=1}^{n} \sum_{j=1}^{n} f(x_i^*, y_j^*)\Delta A_{ij}$$

approximates the volume of V; see Figure 6.4.

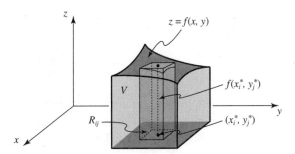

Figure 6.4 Approximating parallelepiped defined by the subrectangle R_{ij}.

It can be shown that this sequence converges as $n \to \infty$, irrespective of the choices for x_i, y_j and (x_i^*, y_j^*) made in the construction. This is intuitively clear, since as $n \to \infty$ each rectangle shrinks to a point, and there is less and less freedom to choose a point (x_i^*, y_j^*) inside it. The rigorous proof of this fact will not be given here. We have assumed that f is continuous; more general conditions will be spelled out in a moment.

We define the double integral of f (recall that $f \geq 0$) over the rectangle R to be

$$\iint_R f \, dA = \lim_{n \to \infty} \mathcal{R}_n,$$

i.e., to be equal to the volume $v(V)$ of the solid V.

Example 6.1

Approximate the value of $\iint_R (x^2 + y^2)\, dA$, where $R = [0, 1] \times [-1, 2]$, using the double Riemann sum $\mathcal{R}_3$ (take (x_i^*, y_j^*) to be the center of each subrectangle).

Solution Let $f(x, y) = x^2 + y^2$. Form the partition of R into 9 rectangles $R_{11}, R_{12}, \ldots, R_{33}$ using vertical lines $x = 0$, $x = 1/3$, $x = 2/3$ and $x = 1$ and horizontal lines $y = -1$, $y = 0$, $y = 1$ and $y = 2$ as shown in Figure 6.5. The Riemann sum $\mathcal{R}_3$ has nine terms, each in the form

(value of f at the center of the subrectangle) · (area of the subrectangle).

For example, the contribution of $R_{32} = [2/3, 1] \times [0, 1]$ to $\mathcal{R}_3$ is

$$ f\left(\tfrac{5}{6}, \tfrac{1}{2}\right) \cdot \left(\tfrac{1}{3}\right) \cdot 1 = \left(\tfrac{34}{36}\right) \cdot \left(\tfrac{1}{3}\right) = \tfrac{34}{108}, $$

etc. Therefore

$$
\begin{aligned}
\mathcal{R}_3 = & \; f\left(\tfrac{1}{6}, \tfrac{-1}{2}\right) \Delta A_{11} + f\left(\tfrac{1}{6}, \tfrac{1}{2}\right) \Delta A_{12} + f\left(\tfrac{1}{6}, \tfrac{3}{2}\right) \Delta A_{13} \\
& + f\left(\tfrac{3}{6}, \tfrac{-1}{2}\right) \Delta A_{21} + f\left(\tfrac{3}{6}, \tfrac{1}{2}\right) \Delta A_{22} + f\left(\tfrac{3}{6}, \tfrac{3}{2}\right) \Delta A_{23} \\
& + f\left(\tfrac{5}{6}, \tfrac{-1}{2}\right) \Delta A_{31} + f\left(\tfrac{5}{6}, \tfrac{1}{2}\right) \Delta A_{32} + f\left(\tfrac{5}{6}, \tfrac{3}{2}\right) \Delta A_{33},
\end{aligned}
$$

where $\Delta A_{ij} = 1/3$ (for all i and j) is the area of R_{ij}.

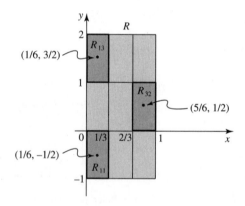

Figure 6.5 Subdivision of $R = [0, 1] \times [-1, 2]$ into 9 subrectangles.

It follows that (factor out $\Delta A_{ij} = 1/3$)

$$
\begin{aligned}
\mathcal{R}_3 = & \; \tfrac{1}{3}\left(\tfrac{1}{36} + \tfrac{1}{4} + \tfrac{1}{36} + \tfrac{1}{4} + \tfrac{1}{36} + \tfrac{9}{4} + \tfrac{9}{36} + \tfrac{1}{4} + \tfrac{9}{36} + \tfrac{1}{4} + \tfrac{9}{36} + \tfrac{9}{4}\right. \\
& \left. + \tfrac{25}{36} + \tfrac{1}{4} + \tfrac{25}{36} + \tfrac{1}{4} + \tfrac{25}{36} + \tfrac{9}{4}\right) \\
= & \; \tfrac{1}{3}\left(\tfrac{105}{36} + \tfrac{33}{4}\right) = \tfrac{402}{108} \approx 3.722.
\end{aligned}
$$

The value 3.722 for $\mathcal{R}_3$ is an approximation of the volume of the solid region V shown in Figure 6.6.

◀

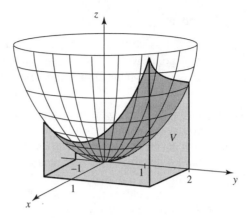

Figure 6.6 Solid V of Example 6.1.

To obtain a better approximation of the integral in Example 6.1, we have to increase the number of subrectangles and repeat the computation (for example, $\mathcal{R}_4 = 3.844$, $\mathcal{R}_5 = 3.900$, $\mathcal{R}_{10} = 3.975$, $\mathcal{R}_{20} = 3.994$, etc.). The exact volume will be computed in Example 6.10 in Section 6.2. In Example 6.1, values for f were calculated at the centers of subrectangles. From the comment preceeding this example, we notice that we could have chosen (x_i^*, y_j^*) any way we liked— we would have obtained different approximations, but their limits as $n \to \infty$ are the same.

The construction of the double integral that we have described and illustrated in this section can be carried out in general, for functions that can also be negative; in such cases, the double integral does not necessarily represent a volume.

Recall that a function $f(x, y)$ is *bounded on a set* $R \subseteq \mathbb{R}^2$ if there is a constant $M \geq 0$ such that $|f(x, y)| \leq M$ for all $(x, y) \in R$.

■ Definition 6.1   **Integrable Function and Double Integral.**

A function $f(x, y)$ defined on a rectangle $R \subseteq \mathbb{R}^2$ is called *integrable on R* if the limit of the sequence of Riemann sums

$$\mathcal{R}_n = \sum_{i=1}^{n} \sum_{j=1}^{n} f(x_i^*, y_j^*) \Delta A_{ij}$$

(where $n = 1, 2, \ldots$) exists and does not depend on the way the points (x_i^*, y_j^*) are chosen in each subrectangle R_{ij}.

If f is integrable, then the *double integral* $\iint_R f \, dA$ *of f over a rectangle R* is given by

$$\iint_R f \, dA = \lim_{n \to \infty} \mathcal{R}_n = \lim_{n \to \infty} \sum_{i=1}^{n} \sum_{j=1}^{n} f(x_i^*, y_j^*) \Delta A_{ij}.$$

The following theorem answers probably the first question that comes to mind: we know what integrable functions are, but how do we find/identify them?

■ **Theorem 6.1**   Integrable Functions.

Let $f: R \subseteq \mathbb{R}^2 \to \mathbb{R}$ be a bounded function defined on a rectangle R in $\mathbb{R}^2$. Assume that the set of points where f is not continuous consists of a finite number of continuous curves and/or a finite number of points. Then f is integrable over R.

■

The definition of a curve actually includes the case of a point (for example, the image of the path $\mathbf{c}(t) = (a_1, a_2)$, $t \in [0, 1]$ is the curve that consists of the single point (a_1, a_2)), so it was not necessary to mention "points" separately in the theorem.

It can be proved (see an advanced calculus or analysis text) that all continuous functions defined on a closed rectangle R are bounded. Consequently, all continuous functions are integrable over rectangles in $\mathbb{R}^2$. Figure 6.7 shows a discontinuous function that is still integrable on R.

The proof of the theorem is quite long and technically involved and will not be presented here.

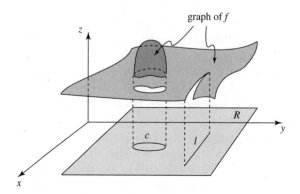

Figure 6.7   Example of an integrable function over $R \subseteq \mathbb{R}^2$.

Let us repeat that if $f \geq 0$, then the double integral $\iint_R f \, dA$ represents a volume (and hence $\iint_R f \, dA \geq 0$).

A number of symbols, such as

$$\int_R f, \qquad \int_R f \, dA, \qquad \iint_R f \, dA, \qquad \iint_R f \, dxdy$$

and some others are used to denote double integrals.

Example 6.2   Find $\iint_R 5 \, dA$, where $R = [-2, 2] \times [0, 3]$.

Solution   The graph of $f(x, y) = 5$ is the plane parallel to the xy-plane, five units above it. Hence $\iint_R 5 \, dA$ can be interpreted as the volume of the rectangular box (parallelepiped) of height 5 built over the rectangle $[-2, 2] \times [0, 3]$. Therefore, $\iint_R 5 \, dA = 4 \cdot 3 \cdot 5 = 60$.

◄

Example 6.3   Explain why $\iint_R y^3 \, dA = 0$, where $R = [0, 1] \times [-1, 1]$.

Solution   The graph of $z = y^3$ is a surface obtained by sliding the graph of $z = y^3$ in the yz-plane along the x-axis from 0 to 1; see Figure 6.8. For $y > 0$ it lies above the xy-plane, and for $y < 0$ it lies below the xy-plane, and the two parts are symmetric with respect to the x-axis.

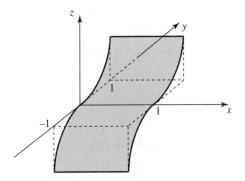

Figure 6.8   The surface $z = y^3$, $0 \le x \le 1$, $-1 \le y \le 1$.

Let us compare the contributions to the Riemann sum $\mathcal{R}_n$ that come from a subrectangle R_{ij} and its symmetric (with respect to the x-axis) counterpart. We know that we are free to choose a point in each subrectangle any way we like— all sequences of Riemann sums will give the same limit, since $z = f(x, y) = y^3$ is continuous, and hence integrable. Figure 6.9(a) shows a partition into subrectangles for $\mathcal{R}_5$, and Figure 6.9(b) for $\mathcal{R}_6$.

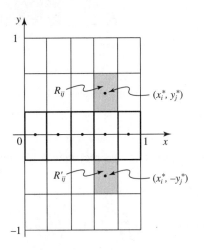
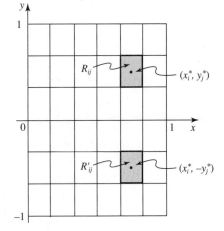

Figure 6.9   Subrectangles for Riemann sums.
(a) case $n = 5$ (b) case $n = 6$

The contribution of R_{ij} to the Riemann sum is $f(x_i^*, y_j^*)\Delta A_{ij} = (y_j^*)^3 \Delta A_{ij}$, where

ΔA_{ij} is the area of R_{ij} and (x_i^*, y_j^*) is a point in R_{ij}. If R_{ij} is halved by the x-axis (that will happen if n is odd, as in Figure 6.9(a)) then take $(x_i^*, y_j^*) = (x_i^*, 0)$, in which case the contribution to the Riemann sum will be $f(x_i^*, 0)\Delta A_{ij} = (0)^3 \Delta A_{ij} = 0$. Therefore, we can drop all such subrectangles from our consideration. To compute the contribution of the symmetric counterpart R'_{ij} of R_{ij} (that is not halved by the x-axis), select the (symmetric) point $(x_i^*, -y_j^*)$ in R'_{ij}; thus, its contribution $f(x_i^*, -y_j^*)\Delta A_{ij} = -(y_j^*)^3 \Delta A_{ij}$ cancels the contribution of R_{ij} (all subrectangles have the same area). It follows that every Riemann sum thus constructed is zero, and therefore

$$\iint_R f \, dA = \lim_{n \to \infty} \mathcal{R}_n = \lim_{n \to \infty} 0 = 0.$$

◄

Example 6.4   Find $\iint_R f \, dA$, if $f(x, y) = 1 - |x|$ and $R = [-1, 1] \times [0, 3]$.

Solution   Since $z = f(x, y) = 1 - |x| \geq 0$ for $-1 \leq x \leq 1$, the double integral in question represents the volume of the solid V defined over the rectangle $[-1, 1] \times [0, 3]$. V is the prism (triangular solid) obtained by sliding the graph of $z = 1 - |x|$ (see Figure 6.10(a)) along the y-axis from 0 to 3; see Figure 6.10(b). Its volume is $(1/2) \cdot 2 \cdot 1 \cdot 3 = 3$ and hence $\iint_R (1 - |x|) \, dA = 3$.

◄

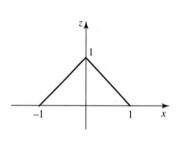

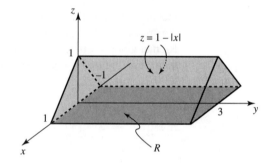

Figure 6.10   Solid V of Example 6.4.
(a) the graph of $z = 1 - |x|$, $-1 \leq x \leq 1$ (b) the surface $z = 1 - |x|$, over $[-1, 1] \times [0, 3]$

■ **Theorem 6.2**   Properties of Double Integrals

Let f and g be integrable functions defined on a rectangle R and let C be a constant. Then

(a) The function $f + g$ is integrable, and

$$\iint_R (f + g) \, dA = \iint_R f \, dA + \iint_R g \, dA.$$

(b) The function Cf is integrable, and

$$\iint_R Cf \, dA = C \iint_R f \, dA.$$

(c) If R is divided into n rectangles R_i $(i = 1, \ldots, n)$ that are mutually disjoint (i.e., their intersection may contain only the bounding line segments), then f is integrable over each R_i and

$$\iint_R f \, dA = \sum_{i=1}^{n} \iint_{R_i} f \, dA.$$

(d) If $f(x, y) \le g(x, y)$ on R then

$$\iint_R f \, dA \le \iint_R g \, dA.$$

(e) The absolute value of the double integral satisfies

$$\left| \iint_R f \, dA \right| \le \iint_R |f| \, dA. \qquad \blacksquare$$

Proof

The properties (a) – (d) can be understood by visualizing a double integral as the limit of Riemann sums. The Riemann sums for $f + g$ in (a) can be written as

$$\sum_{i=1}^{n} \sum_{j=1}^{n} (f + g)(x_i^*, y_j^*) \Delta A_{ij} = \sum_{i=1}^{n} \sum_{j=1}^{n} f(x_i^*, y_j^*) \Delta A_{ij} + \sum_{i=1}^{n} \sum_{j=1}^{n} g(x_i^*, y_j^*) \Delta A_{ij}.$$

Now take the limit of this equation as $n \to \infty$. The limits on the right side exist (since, by assumption, f and g are integrable) and therefore, the right side is equal to $\iint_R f \, dA + \iint_R g \, dA$. It follows that the limit on the left side exists as well, and is (by definition) equal to the double integral $\iint_R (f + g) \, dA$.

Statement (b) is proven analogously. To prove (d), consider Riemann sums

$$\sum_{i=1}^{n} \sum_{j=1}^{n} f(x_i^*, y_j^*) \Delta A_{ij} \qquad \text{and} \qquad \sum_{i=1}^{n} \sum_{j=1}^{n} g(x_i^*, y_j^*) \Delta A_{ij}$$

where the same points $(x_i^*, y_j^*) \in R_{ij}$ are chosen for both sums. Since $f(x_i^*, y_j^*) \le g(x_i^*, y_j^*)$, it follows that

$$\sum_{i=1}^{n} \sum_{j=1}^{n} f(x_i^*, y_j^*) \Delta A_{ij} \le \sum_{i=1}^{n} \sum_{j=1}^{n} g(x_i^*, y_j^*) \Delta A_{ij}$$

holds for all Riemann sums thus constructed. The claim of (d) is now obtained by computing the limit of both sides as $n \to \infty$.

Clearly, we can extend property (d) to the situation where $f \le g \le h$, in which case $\iint_R f \, dA \le \iint_R g \, dA \le \iint_R h \, dA$.

To prove (e), we first recall two statements about absolute values. First, for any real number a, $-|a| \le a \le |a|$. If a and A are two real numbers, $A \ge 0$ and $-A \le a \le A$, then $|a| \le A$. Applying (d) to $-|f(x, y)| \le f(x, y) \le |f(x, y)|$ (that is the first statement with $a = f(x, y)$), we get

$$-\iint_R |f(x, y)| \, dA \le \iint_R f(x, y) \, dA \le \iint_R |f(x, y)| \, dA.$$

Now apply the second statement with $a = \iint_R f(x, y)\, dA$ and $A = \iint_R |f(x, y)|\, dA$ to get

$$\left| \iint_R f(x, y)\, dA \right| \leq \iint_R |f(x, y)|\, dA.$$

Although statement (c) may be intuitively clear, its proof is quite involved and will not be discussed here. ∎

Example 6.5   Show that $\iint_R x \sin(x + y)\, dA \leq 8\pi^3$, where $R = [0, 2\pi] \times [-\pi, \pi]$.

Solution   Since $\sin(x + y) \leq 1$ and $0 \leq x \leq 2\pi$, it follows that $x \sin(x + y) \leq 2\pi$. Applying Theorem 6.2(d), we get

$$\iint_R x \sin(x + y)\, dA \leq \iint_R 2\pi\, dA.$$

The integral on the right side is the double integral of the constant positive function $f(x, y) = 2\pi$, and represents the volume of the rectangular box of height 2π whose base is the rectangle $[0, 2\pi] \times [-\pi, \pi]$. Hence $\iint_R 2\pi\, dA = 8\pi^3$, and we are done. ◀

Example 6.6   Let

$$f(x, y) = \begin{cases} 2x^2 + 1 & \text{if } x^2 + y^2 < 1 \\ \\ 0 & \text{if } x^2 + y^2 \geq 1 \end{cases}.$$

Is f integrable on the rectangle $R_1 = [0, 1/2] \times [0, 1/2]$? If it is, find an upper bound for the double integral $\iint_{R_1} f(x, y)\, dA$ (i.e., find a number M such that $\iint_{R_1} f(x, y)\, dA \leq M$). Is f integrable on $R_2 = [-1/2, 1/2] \times [-2, 2]$?

Solution   The given function f is equal to 0, except inside the circle $x^2 + y^2 < 1$, where $f(x, y) = 2x^2 + 1$. Since $|f(x, y)| = 2x^2 + 1 \leq 2(x^2 + y^2) + 1 < 3$ for (x, y) inside the circle $x^2 + y^2 < 1$, it follows that $|f(x, y)| < 3$ for *all* (x, y); i.e., the function f is bounded. The limit of $f(x, y)$ as (x, y) approaches any point on the circle $x^2 + y^2 = 1$ does not exist: an approach from inside the circle gives a number greater than or equal to 1 (since $2x^2 + 1 \geq 1$), but an approach from outside gives 0. It follows that f is not continuous at the points on the circle $x^2 + y^2 = 1$.

Since R_1 is contained inside the disk $\{x^2 + y^2 < 1\}$, $f(x, y) = 2x^2 + 1$ on R_1. Consequently, f is continuous on R_1 and therefore integrable. From $f(x, y) < 3$ it follows that

$$\iint_{R_1} f(x, y)\, dA \leq \iint_{R_1} 3\, dA = 3A(R_1) = \tfrac{3}{4},$$

where $A(R_1) = 1/4$ is the area of R_1. Notice that we can easily get a better estimate: If $(x, y) \in R_1$, then $0 \leq x \leq 1/2$, and the largest value of $f(x, y) = 2x^2 + 1$ is $2(1/2)^2 + 1 = 3/2$. Therefore,

$$\iint_{R_1} f(x, y)\, dA \leq \iint_{R_1} \tfrac{3}{2}\, dA = \tfrac{3}{2} A(R_1) = \tfrac{3}{8}.$$

The function f is continuous on R_2 except along the two curves that are the parts of the circle $x^2 + y^2 = 1$ inside R_2. By Theorem 6.1, f is integrable over R_2.

In the next section we will define double integrals over more general regions and will extend Theorem 6.2 to such integrals. We will use that opportunity to discuss more examples and illustrate various properties of double integrals.

EXERCISES 6.1

1. Compute the Riemann sum $\mathcal{R}_3$ for the function $f(x, y) = x + 4y^2 - 1$ defined on the rectangle $R = [0, 3] \times [0, 2]$. Take (x_i^*, y_j^*) to be the upper left corner of each subrectangle R_{ij}.

2. Compute the Riemann sum $\mathcal{R}_4$ for the function $f(x, y) = 2xy + 1$ defined on the rectangle $R = [0, 4] \times [0, 1]$. Take (x_i^*, y_j^*) to be the lower left corner of each subrectangle R_{ij}.

3. Compute the Riemann sum $\mathcal{R}_2$ for the function $f(x, y) = x^2 - y^2$ defined on the rectangle $R = [0, 5] \times [0, 3]$. Take (x_i^*, y_j^*) to be the upper left corner of each subrectangle R_{ij}.

4. Compute the Riemann sum $\mathcal{R}_3$ for the function $f(x, y) = xy - y^2 - x$ defined on the rectangle $R = [0, 5] \times [0, 4]$. Take (x_i^*, y_j^*) to be the center of each subrectangle R_{ij}.

5. Compute the Riemann sum $\mathcal{R}_2$ for the function $f(x, y) = (x - y)e^{xy}$ defined on the rectangle $R = [-1, 1] \times [0, 1]$. Take (x_i^*, y_j^*) to be the lower right corner of each subrectangle R_{ij}.

6. Let R be the square with vertices $(0, 0)$, $(0, 4)$, $(4, 4)$ and $(4, 0)$ and let $f(x, y)$ be the distance from the point (x, y) to the x-axis.

   (a) Estimate $\iint_R f \, dA$ by partitioning the square R into 4 squares and using the midpoint of each square.

   (b) Show that $0 \le \iint_R f \, dA \le 64$.

7. What is a geometric meaning (besides the interpretation as a volume) of $\iint_R 1 \, dA$, where R is a rectangle?

8. In Theorem 6.2 we listed some properties of double integrals.

   (a) Provide details of the proof of part (b).

   (b) If $h \ge 0$ then $\iint_R h \, dA \ge 0$ (since it represents the volume of a region). Use this fact to give another proof of part (d).

   (c) Find an example of f and R such that $\left| \iint_R f \, dA \right| \le \iint_R |f| \, dA$.

9. Evaluate the integral $\iint_R (3 - x) \, dA$, where $R = [0, 1] \times [0, 2]$, by identifying it as a volume of a solid.

10. Show that $\iint_R K \, dA = K(b - a)(d - c)$ (K is a constant) where $R = [a, b] \times [c, d]$.

11. Show that $4 \le \iint_R e^{x^2 + y^2} \, dA \le 4e^2$, where $R = [-1, 1] \times [-1, 1]$.

12. Find an upper bound and a lower bound for the integral $\iint_R e^{-x^2 - y^2} \, dA$, where R is the rectangle with vertices $(0, 0)$, $(1, 0)$, $(1, 1)$ and $(0, 1)$ (if $m \le \iint_R f \, dA \le M$, then m is a lower bound, and M is an upper bound for the integral of f over R).

13. Find an upper bound for the integral $\iint_R \sin(2x) \cos(5y) \, dA$, where R is the rectangle with vertices $(0, 0)$, $(2\pi, 0)$, $(2\pi, \pi)$ and $(0, \pi)$.

14. Find an example of a function such that $\left| \iint_R f \, dA \right| < \iint_R |f| \, dA$, where $R = [0, 1] \times [0, 1]$.

15. Let

$$f(x, y) = \begin{cases} 3 & \text{if } x \geq 0 \\ \\ x + 3 & \text{if } x < 0 \end{cases}.$$

Is f integrable over $R = [-1, 1] \times [0, 2]$? If so, find $\iint_R f \, dA$.

16. Let

$$f(x, y) = \begin{cases} \sqrt{4 - x^2} & \text{if } 0 \leq x \leq 2 \\ \\ 2 & \text{otherwise} \end{cases}.$$

Is f continuous on $R = [-2, 2] \times [0, 2]$? Integrable over R? If f is integrable, find $\iint_R f \, dA$ by interpreting it as a volume.

17. Is it true that $\iint_R (x^2 + y^2) \, dA \leq \iint_R (x^3 + y^3) \, dA$ if $R = [0, 1] \times [0, 1]$? If $R = [1, 2] \times [2, 3]$?

18. Is the function $f(x, y) = 2x(x^2 + y^2 - 10)^{-1}$ integrable over $[0, 1] \times [0, 1]$? Over $[-3, 3] \times [-3, 3]$? Over $[-10, 10] \times [-10, 10]$?

19. The function $f(x, y) = e^{1/(x^2+y^2)}$ is not continuous at $(0, 0)$. Is it integrable on $[-1, 1] \times [-1, 1]$?

20. Is the function

$$f(x, y) = \begin{cases} 3 & \text{if } (x, y) = (0, 0) \\ \\ x^2 + y^2 & \text{otherwise} \end{cases}$$

integrable on any rectangle that contains the origin?

6.2 DOUBLE INTEGRALS OVER GENERAL REGIONS

Guided by the geometric concept of the volume of a solid, we constructed the double integral of a real-valued function of two variables as a limit of approximating (Riemann) sums. In this section we will start developing methods of evaluating double integrals, not only over rectangles but also over more general regions in $\mathbb{R}^2$.

Let us once again recall the definition of the definite integral of a function f over $[a, b]$:

$$\int_a^b f(x) \, dx = \lim_{n \to \infty} \sum_{i=1}^n f(x_i^*) \Delta x_i$$

(points $a = x_1, x_2, \ldots, x_{n+1} = b$ define the subdivision of the interval $[a, b]$, $\Delta x_i = x_{i+1} - x_i$, and x_i^* is any point in $[x_i, x_{i+1}]$). Assume that $f(x) \geq 0$ (so that $\int_a^b f(x) dx$ represents the area of the region D below f; see Figure 6.11), and rephrase the definition as follows: consider the cross sections of D with respect to lines parallel to the y-axis: at a location x_i^* on the x-axis the cross section is the line segment of length $f(x_i^*)$. "Fatten it up" a bit, to obtain a thin rectangle with base length Δx_i. The area of D can be viewed as the sum of all such "fattened" cross sections of D, from a to b.

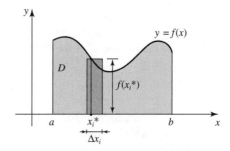

Figure 6.11 Area of D viewed as the sum of "fattened" cross sections.

Now we move one dimension higher: Let V be a solid in $\mathbb{R}^3$ placed so that the points a and b on the x-axis represent its minimum and maximum distances from the reference plane (in our case it is the yz-plane), as shown in Figure 6.12.

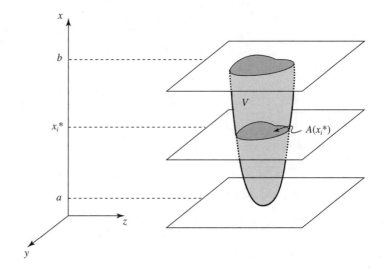

Figure 6.12 Volume of V by cross sections.

Consider the cross sections of V defined by planes parallel to the yz-plane: let $A(x_i^*)$ be the area of the cross section defined by the plane x_i^* units away from the yz-plane. The volume of a thin disk defined by that cross section is $A(x_i^*)\Delta x_i$; and the sum

$$\sum_{i=1}^n A(x_i^*)\Delta x_i$$

of all thin disks thus obtained approximates the volume $v(V)$ of V. Since

$$v(V) = \lim_{n \to \infty} \sum_{i=1}^{n} A(x_i^*) \Delta x_i,$$

it follows (by the definition of the definite integral) that

$$v(V) = \int_a^b A(x)dx. \tag{6.1}$$

In other words, the volume of V is obtained by integrating (i.e., by adding up) its cross sections with respect to planes parallel to a reference plane. Formula (6.1) is called *Cavalieri's principle*. A consequence of this principle is the fact that two solids V_1 and V_2 with the same cross-sectional areas $A_1(x) = A_2(x)$ for every x, have the same volume; see Figure 6.13.

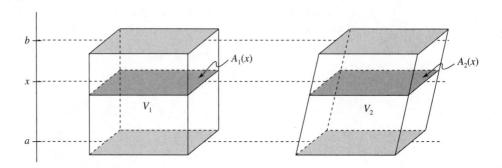

Figure 6.13   Solids V_1 and V_2 have the same volume.

Example 6.7   Volume of a Solid of Revolution.

Suppose that the graph of $y = f(x)$, $x \in [a, b]$, is rotated about the x-axis. The volume of the solid V obtained by the rotation (called the *solid of revolution*) can be computed from Cavalieri's principle:

$$v(V) = \int_a^b A(x)dx,$$

where $A(x)$ denotes the cross-sectional area. The cross section at x is the disk of radius $f(x)$; see Figure 6.14. Consequently $A(x) = \pi(f(x))^2$, and

$$v(V) = \pi \int_a^b (f(x))^2 \, dx.$$

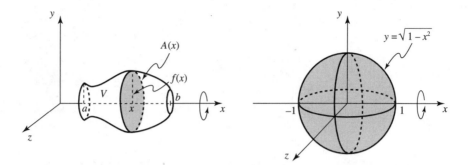

Figure 6.14 Solid of revolution.   **Figure 6.15** Sphere as a solid of revolution.

As an illustration, consider the graph of the semicircle $y = \sqrt{1 - x^2}$ (i.e., $y \geq 0$), $x \in [-1, 1]$. The solid of revolution is a sphere of radius 1, and its volume is

$$v = \pi \int_{-1}^{1} \left(1 - x^2\right) dx = \pi \left(x - \frac{x^3}{3}\right)\Bigg|_{-1}^{1} = \frac{4\pi}{3}.$$

Suppose that $z = f(x, y)$ is a continuous non-negative (i.e., $f(x, y) \geq 0$ for all (x, y)) function defined on a rectangle $[a, b] \times [c, d]$ in $\mathbb{R}^2$. We are going to compute the volume of the "solid V below f" (that is, the solid bounded by the surface $z = f(x, y)$, the xy-plane and the four planes $x = a$, $x = b$, $y = c$ and $y = d$) using Cavalieri's principle.

Consider the cross sections of V by planes parallel to the yz-plane. Fix a value of x, $a \leq x \leq b$. The cross section at x is the region $D(x)$ under $f(x, y)$ (f is now viewed as a function of one variable, y, since x is held fixed) defined on the interval $[c, d]$; see Figure 6.16(a). The area of $D(x)$ is computed as the definite integral

$$A(x) = \int_c^d f(x, y)\, dy$$

(notice that y is the variable of integration, and will therefore vanish when the integral is evaluated; what will remain is an expression involving x).

By Cavalieri's principle, the volume of V is

$$v(V) = \int_a^b \left(\text{cross-sectional area at } x\right) dx = \int_a^b A(x)\, dx = \int_a^b \left(\int_c^d f(x, y) dy\right) dx.$$

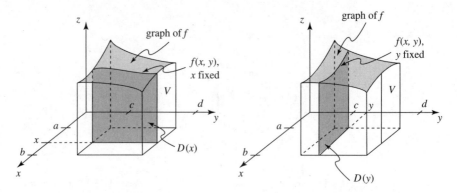

Figure 6.16   Cross sections of V.

(a) parallel to the yz-plane, at x (b) parallel to the xz-plane, at y

Now fix a value for y, $c \leq y \leq d$, and repeat this process. The cross section (this time parallel to the xz-plane) is the region $D(y)$ under $f(x, y)$ (f is now viewed as a function of x only) defined on $a \leq x \leq b$; see Figure 6.16(b). The area of $D(y)$ is

$$A(y) = \int_a^b f(x, y) \, dx,$$

and by Cavalieri's principle,

$$v(V) = \int_c^d \left(\text{cross-sectional area at } y \right) dy = \int_c^d A(y) \, dy = \int_c^d \left(\int_a^b f(x, y) dx \right) dy.$$

Our somewhat intuitive argument in the previous section leads to the interpretation of the double integral as volume. And we have just computed the volume of V in two different ways. Therefore,

$$\iint_R f \, dA = \int_a^b \left(\int_c^d f(x, y) dy \right) dx = \int_c^d \left(\int_a^b f(x, y) dx \right) dy,$$

where $R = [a, b] \times [c, d]$. This formula holds in general, and not only for non-negative functions.

■ **Theorem 6.3**   Fubini's Theorem.

If $f = f(x, y)$ is a continuous function defined on a rectangle $R = [a, b] \times [c, d]$ in $\mathbb{R}^2$, then

$$\iint_R f \, dA = \int_a^b \left(\int_c^d f(x, y) dy \right) dx = \int_c^d \left(\int_a^b f(x, y) dx \right) dy. \qquad ■$$

The theorem states that the double integral $\iint_R f \, dA$ over a rectangle is computed as an *iterated integral*: we integrate with respect to y first, and then integrate the result with respect to x, or alternatively, we do the two integrals in the reversed order. The statement of the theorem remains true in the more general case when f is bounded on R, discontinuous along finitely many curves and when the iterated integrals exist.

The proof of the theorem is omitted.

Example 6.8   Evaluate $\iint_R 6x^2 y \, dA$, where $R = [-1, 1] \times [0, 4]$.

Solution   The function $f(x, y) = 6x^2 y$ is continuous, and by Fubini's Theorem

$$\iint_R 6x^2 y \, dA = \int_{-1}^{1} \left(\int_0^4 6x^2 y \, dy \right) dx = \int_0^4 \left(\int_{-1}^{1} 6x^2 y \, dx \right) dy.$$

Let us evaluate the first iterated integral

$$\int_{-1}^{1} \left(\int_0^4 6x^2 y \, dy \right) dx.$$

To find $\int_0^4 6x^2 y \, dy$, view x as a constant and evaluate it as the definite integral of a function of one variable:

$$\int_0^4 6x^2 y \, dy = 6x^2 \int_0^4 y \, dy = 6x^2 \left(\frac{y^2}{2} \Big|_0^4 \right) = 6x^2(8 - 0) = 48x^2.$$

Therefore,

$$\int_{-1}^{1} \left(\int_0^4 6x^2 y \, dy \right) dx = \int_{-1}^{1} 48x^2 \, dx = 16x^3 \Big|_{-1}^{1} = 32.$$

The second iterated integral is computed analogously: fixing y and integrating with respect to x, we get

$$\int_{-1}^{1} 6x^2 y \, dx = 6y \int_{-1}^{1} x^2 \, dx = 6y \left(\frac{x^3}{3} \Big|_{-1}^{1} \right) = 4y.$$

Therefore,

$$\int_0^4 \left(\int_{-1}^{1} 6x^2 y \, dx \right) dy = \int_0^4 4y \, dy = 2y^2 \Big|_0^4 = 32. \qquad \blacktriangleleft$$

Example 6.9   Evaluate $\iint_R x^2 e^y \, dA$, where $R = [0, 1] \times [0, 2]$.

Solution   By Fubini's Theorem,

$$\iint_R x^2 e^y \, dA = \int_0^1 \left(\int_0^2 x^2 e^y \, dy \right) dx = \int_0^1 x^2 \left(e^y \Big|_0^2 \right) dx$$

$$= \int_0^1 (e^2 - 1) x^2 \, dx = (e^2 - 1) \frac{x^3}{3} \Big|_0^1 = \frac{e^2 - 1}{3}.$$

Reversing the order, we get

$$\iint_R x^2 e^y \, dA = \int_0^2 \left(\int_0^1 x^2 e^y dx \right) dy = \int_0^2 e^y \left(\frac{x^3}{3} \Big|_0^1 \right) dy$$

$$= \frac{1}{3} \int_0^2 e^y \, dy = \frac{1}{3} e^y \Big|_0^2 = \frac{e^2 - 1}{3}.$$

◀

We will see in the next section that a particular order of iterated integration could lead to either significantly easier or harder computations. It gets worse: sometimes only one (or possibly neither) of the iterated integrals can be evaluated exactly as compact formulas (that is, using exact methods of integration, unlike power series methods or approximate (numerical) integration).

Example 6.10
In Example 6.1 we approximated the value of $\iint_R (x^2 + y^2) \, dA$, where $R = [0, 1] \times [-1, 2]$, using Riemann sums. Let us now compute the exact value of the integral using Fubini's Theorem:

$$\iint_R (x^2 + y^2) \, dA = \int_0^1 \left(\int_{-1}^2 (x^2 + y^2) dy \right) dx = \int_0^1 \left(x^2 y + \frac{y^3}{3} \Big|_{-1}^2 \right) dx$$

$$= \int_0^1 (3x^2 + 3) \, dx = x^3 + 3x \Big|_0^1 = 4.$$

◀

Recall that the double integral $\iint_R f \, dA$, for $f \geq 0$, can be interpreted as the volume of the solid under f and above R.

Example 6.11
Find the volume of the solid V bounded by the surface $z = 5 - 2x - y^2$, the three coordinate planes and the planes $x = 1$ and $y = 1$.

Solution The solid V is the solid that lies above the rectangle $R = [0, 1] \times [0, 1]$ in the xy-plane and is bounded from above by the graph of $z = 5 - 2x - y^2$ (notice that $z > 0$ on R!). The volume of V is

$$v(V) = \iint_R (5 - 2x - y^2) \, dA,$$

and by Fubini's Theorem,

$$v(V) = \int_0^1 \left(\int_0^1 (5 - 2x - y^2) dx \right) dy$$

$$= \int_0^1 \left(5x - x^2 - xy^2 \Big|_0^1 \right) dy = \int_0^1 (4 - y^2) \, dy = 4y - \frac{y^3}{3} \Big|_0^1 = \tfrac{11}{3}.$$

◀

Having learned how to integrate over rectangles, we now move one step further, to integration over more general regions in $\mathbb{R}^2$.

■ **Definition 6.2**   **Bounded and Closed Region, Boundary of a Region.**

A region (i.e., a subset) D of $\mathbb{R}^2$ is called *bounded* if it can be enclosed in a rectangle $R = [a, b] \times [c, d] \subseteq \mathbb{R}^2$ (see Figure 6.17). The collection of boundary points (see Section 2.3 for the definition) of D forms the *boundary* ∂D of D (see Figure 6.18). A region is called *closed* if it contains all of its boundary. ■

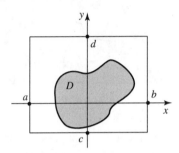

Figure 6.17   A bounded region in $\mathbb{R}^2$.   **Figure 6.18**   Boundary of a region D.

The boundary of the regions that we will meet in this book will consist of at most finitely many curves (and/or points; recall that a point is a special case of a curve). For example, the boundary of the disk $D = \{(x, y) \mid x^2 + y^2 \leq 1\}$ is the circle $\partial D = \{(x, y) \mid x^2 + y^2 = 1\}$. Since ∂D is contained in D, the disk D is closed. The boundary ∂D of the "punctured disk" $D = \{(x, y) \mid x^2 + y^2 \leq 1 \text{ and } (x, y) \neq (0, 0)\}$ consists of the circle $\{(x, y) \mid x^2 + y^2 = 1\}$ and the point $(0, 0)$. The "punctured disk" is not closed, since it does not contain $(0, 0)$. The boundary of the annulus $\{(x, y) \mid 1 \leq x^2 + y^2 \leq 4\}$ consists of two circles $\{(x, y) \mid x^2 + y^2 = 1\}$ and $\{(x, y) \mid x^2 + y^2 = 4\}$. The boundary of the rectangle $R = [a, b] \times [c, d] = \{(x, y) \mid a \leq x \leq b, c \leq y \leq d\}$ consists of four straight line segments: $\{(x, c) \mid a \leq x \leq b\}$, $\{(x, d) \mid a \leq x \leq b\}$, $\{(a, y) \mid c \leq y \leq d\}$ and $\{(b, y) \mid c \leq y \leq d\}$. Clearly, $\partial R \subseteq R$, and therefore R is closed (that justifies the term "closed rectangle" that we have used already).

The boundary ∂D of the region $D = \{(x, y) \mid x^2 + y^2 \leq 1 \text{ and } y > 0\}$ consists of the semi-circle $x^2 + y^2 = 1$, $y \geq 0$ and the line segment from $(-1, 0)$ to $(1, 0)$. D contains only a part of its boundary, and is therefore not closed.

Let $z = f(x, y)$ be a continuous function defined on a closed and bounded region D in $\mathbb{R}^2$. Since D is bounded, it is possible to choose a rectangle R such that $D \subseteq R$. Consider the function $F(x, y)$ defined on R by

$$F(x, y) = \begin{cases} f(x, y) & \text{if } (x, y) \in D \\ 0 & \text{if } (x, y) \notin D, \text{ but } (x, y) \in R \end{cases}$$

In words, $F(x, y)$ equals $f(x, y)$ on D, and is zero for points in R that do not belong to D; see Figure 6.19. We say that F is an *extension by zero* (a *trivial extension*) of f to R.

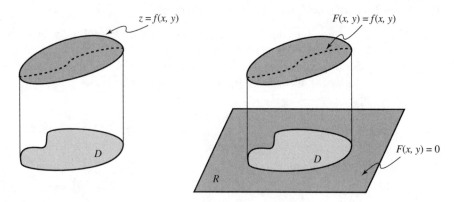

Figure 6.19   Extension of f on D to F on R.

The function F thus defined is continuous, except possibly along the curve(s) that form the boundary of D. Since f is bounded (as a continuous function defined on a closed and bounded set, see Appendix A for the precise statement), it follows that F is bounded, and Theorem 6.1 implies that F is integrable over R.

■ **Definition 6.3**   Double Integral Over a Closed and Bounded Region.

Let $f = f(x, y)$ be a continuous function defined on a closed, bounded region $D \subseteq \mathbb{R}^2$. The double integral $\iint_D f \, dA$ of f over D is given by

$$\iint_D f \, dA = \iint_R F \, dA.$$

In other words, the double integral of f over a closed and bounded region D is defined as the double integral of the extension F of f over a rectangle R that contains D. The extension is defined so that it agrees with f on D and is zero otherwise. Consequently, the points outside of D do not contribute anything to the integral $\iint_D f \, dA$. This means that it does not matter what rectangle R is taken in Definition 6.3, as long as it encloses D.

From the construction it follows that, for $f \geq 0$, $\iint_D f \, dA$ represents the volume of the solid under the graph of f and above the region D in the xy-plane.

Although we gave the definition of the double integral for any closed and bounded region, we will have to restrict our study to some special regions. They are introduced in our next definition.

Definition 6.4   Regions of Type 1, 2 and 3; Elementary Regions.

A *region of type 1* is a subset D of $\mathbb{R}^2$ of the form

$$D = \{(x, y) \mid a \le x \le b, \phi(x) \le y \le \psi(x)\},$$

where $\phi(x)$ and $\psi(x)$ are continuous functions defined on $[a, b]$ satisfying $\phi(x) \le \psi(x)$. See Figure 6.20.

A *region of type 2* is defined by

$$D = \{(x, y) \mid c \le y \le d, \phi(y) \le x \le \psi(y)\},$$

where $\phi(y)$ and $\psi(y)$ are continuous functions defined on $[c, d]$ satisfying $\phi(y) \le \psi(y)$. See Figure 6.21.

We say that D is a *region of type 3* if it is both of type 1 and type 2. See Figure 6.22.

A region of type 1, 2 or 3 is called an *elementary region*.

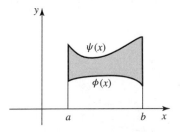 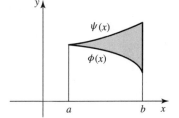

Figure 6.20   Regions of type 1.

By definition, all elementary regions are closed and bounded. A region of type 1 is also called *x-simple* or *vertically simple*, and a region of type 2 is referred to as *y-simple* or *horizontally simple*. A region of type 1 is bounded from above and below by graphs of continuous functions; see Figure 6.20 (i.e., the "top" and the "bottom" are curves, whereas the "left" and the "right sides" are either vertical lines or points).

Figure 6.21 shows two examples of regions of type 2 (the "sides" are curves, whereas the "top" and the "bottom" are horizontal lines or points).

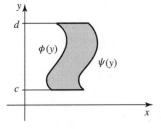 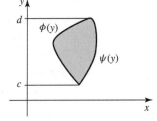

Figure 6.21   Regions of type 2.

Any rectangle, the disk $\{(x, y) \mid x^2 + y^2 \leq 1\}$ or the set (see Figure 6.22) $D = \{(x, y) \mid x^3 \leq y \leq \sqrt{x}, 0 \leq x \leq 1\}$ are regions of type 3.

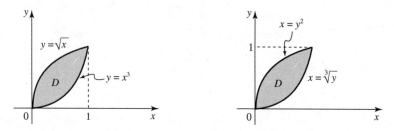

Figure 6.22   The region $D = \{(x, y) \mid x^3 \leq y \leq \sqrt{x}, 0 \leq x \leq 1\}$.
(a) as a type-1 region   (b) as a type-2 region

Now let us evaluate $\iint_D f \, dA$ if D is a region of type 1. Choose a rectangle $R = [a, b] \times [c, d]$ as shown in Figure 6.23.

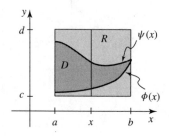

Figure 6.23   Integral over a region of type 1.

By Definition 6.3,

$$\iint_D f \, dA = \iint_R F \, dA,$$

where F is the extension by zero of f on R. From Fubini's Theorem we get that

$$\iint_R F \, dA = \int_a^b \left(\int_c^d F(x, y) dy \right) dx.$$

By construction, $F(x, y) = 0$ if $(x, y) \notin D$; i.e., when $y < \phi(x)$ and $y > \psi(x)$. Therefore (in this computation x is fixed; we are doing the inner integration)

$$\int_c^d F(x, y) \, dy = \int_c^{\phi(x)} F(x, y) \, dy + \int_{\phi(x)}^{\psi(x)} F(x, y) \, dy + \int_{\psi(x)}^d F(x, y) \, dy$$

$$= \int_{\phi(x)}^{\psi(x)} F(x, y) \, dy,$$

since the first and the third integrals in the sum are zero. Since $F = f$ on D, we get

$$\int_{\phi(x)}^{\psi(x)} F(x, y)\, dy = \int_{\phi(x)}^{\psi(x)} f(x, y)\, dy,$$

and therefore

$$\iint_R F\, dA = \int_a^b \left(\int_{\phi(x)}^{\psi(x)} f(x, y)\, dy \right) dx.$$

The double integral over a region of type 2 is computed analogously. Let us formulate these results in the statement of the next theorem.

■ Theorem 6.4 **Iterated Integrals over Elementary Regions.**

Assume that $f : D \subseteq \mathbb{R}^2 \to \mathbb{R}$ is a continuous function.

(a) If D is a region of type 1, then

$$\iint_D f\, dA = \int_a^b \left(\int_{\phi(x)}^{\psi(x)} f(x, y)\, dy \right) dx.$$

(b) If D is a region of type 2, then

$$\iint_D f\, dA = \int_c^d \left(\int_{\phi(y)}^{\psi(y)} f(x, y)\, dx \right) dy.$$

(c) If D is a region of type 3, then either (a) or (b) can be used to evaluate the double integral over D.   ■

Let us emphasize that, in (a), the limits of the inner integration are functions of x (that means that the boundary curves have to be expressed in the form $y = \phi(x)$ and $y = \psi(x)$). In (b), the limits of the inner integration are functions of y (consequently, the boundary curves have to be expressed in the form $x = \phi(y)$ and $x = \psi(y)$).

Example 6.12   Evaluate $\iint_D e^{2x+y}\, dA$, where D is the region bounded by the lines $y = 2x$, $y = x$, $x = 1$ and $x = 2$.

Solution   The region D is of type 3; see Figure 6.24(a). For convenience, we choose to view D as a type-1 region. It follows that

$$\iint_D e^{2x+y}\, dA = \int_1^2 \left(\int_x^{2x} e^{2x+y}\, dy \right) dx.$$

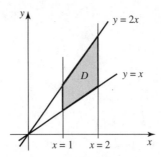 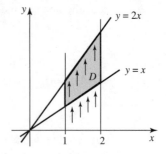

Figure 6.24 Region of Example 6.12.

(a) D is a type-3 region   (b) "arrows argument" for the inner integration

Before evaluating the integral, let us explain how the limits of integration were set. The outer integration is with respect to x, so its limits are defined by the interval on the x-axis that contains the values of x (in this case, it is $[1, 2]$). The inner integration (i.e., the first to be evaluated) is with respect to y. Think of arrows "travelling" parallel to the y-axis, starting below D and finishing above D, as shown on Figure 6.24(b). They enter D along the line $y = x$ (that is the lower limit of integration) and leave D along $y = 2x$ (that is the upper limit).

We evaluate the integral as an iterated integral

$$\iint_D e^{2x+y}\, dA = \int_1^2 \left(\int_x^{2x} e^{2x+y} dy \right) dx = \int_1^2 \left(e^{2x+y} \Big|_x^{2x} \right) dx$$

$$= \int_1^2 (e^{4x} - e^{3x})\, dx = \left(\frac{e^{4x}}{4} - \frac{e^{3x}}{3} \right) \Bigg|_1^2 = \tfrac{1}{4}(e^8 - e^4) - \tfrac{1}{3}(e^6 - e^3).$$

Example 6.13   Evaluate $\iint_D 2y\, dA$, where D is the region in the xy-plane bounded by $y = x - 6$ and $y^2 = x$.

Solution   To make an accurate sketch and to set up the limits of integration we need to find the points of intersection of the two curves. Substituting $x = y^2$ into $y = x - 6$ we get $y^2 - y - 6 = 0$ and $y = -2$ or $y = 3$. From either of the two equations we compute the corresponding x-coordinates, thus getting $(4, -2)$ and $(9, 3)$ as the points of intersection. The region D is shown in Figure 6.25.

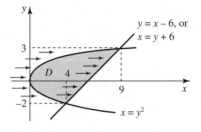

Figure 6.25   Region D of Example 6.13.

D can be viewed as a type-2 region: y-coordinates of all points in D belong to the interval $[-2, 3]$; arrows "travelling" parallel to the x-axis enter D along $x = y^2$ and leave along $y = x - 6$ (we need it in the form $x = y + 6$). Therefore,

$$\iint_D 2y \, dA = \int_{-2}^3 \left(\int_{y^2}^{y+6} 2y \, dx \right) dy = \int_{-2}^3 \left(2yx \, \Big|_{y^2}^{y+6} \right) dy$$

$$= \int_{-2}^3 2y(y + 6 - y^2) \, dy = \left(\frac{2y^3}{3} + 6y^2 - \frac{y^4}{2} \right) \Big|_{-2}^3 = \frac{125}{6}.$$

It follows from the definition given at the beginning of this section that, in the general case of a closed and bounded region D, the double integral $\iint_D f \, dA$ over D of a non-negative function f represents the volume (of the solid above D and under the graph of f).

Substituting $f(x, y) = 1$ into Theorem 6.4(a) we get that

$$\iint_D 1 \, dA = \int_a^b \left(\int_{\phi(x)}^{\psi(x)} 1 \, dy \right) dx = \int_a^b (\psi(x) - \phi(x)) \, dx,$$

which is the formula for the area of the region D (of type 1) between two curves given in standard calculus texts. Similarly, from Theorem 6.4(b) it follows that

$$\iint_D 1 \, dA = \int_c^d \left(\int_{\phi(y)}^{\psi(y)} 1 \, dx \right) dy = \int_c^d (\psi(y) - \phi(y)) \, dy.$$

In any case,

$$\iint_D dA = \text{area of } D,$$

where D is an elementary region. In the following example, we use Riemann sums to verify this.

Example 6.14 Using Riemann sums, compute $\iint_D 1 \, dA$, where D is any closed and bounded region.

Solution First of all, enclose D in a rectangle R and extend the function $f(x, y) = 1$ defined on D by zero to the function $F(x, y)$ on R; i.e., $F(x, y) = f(x, y) = 1$ for all points in D, and $F(x, y) = 0$ for points in R that are not in D. Divide R into n^2 subrectangles R_{ij} and form the Riemann sum

$$\mathcal{R}_n = \sum_{i=1}^n \sum_{j=1}^n F(x_i^*, y_j^*) \Delta A_{ij},$$

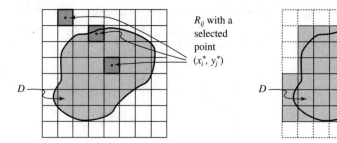

Figure 6.26 Region D of Example 6.14.

(a) possible positions of R_{ij} in D (b) rectangles R_{ij} "circumscribe" D

where ΔA_{ij} is the area of R_{ij}. If the subrectangle R_{ij} is inside D, take (x_i^*, y_j^*) to be any point in it; then $F(x_i^*, y_j^*) = 1$. If R_{ij} has no points in common with D, then $F(x_i^*, y_j^*) = 0$, no matter what point (x_i^*, y_j^*) is selected. Finally, if R_{ij} intersects D, take (x_i^*, y_j^*) to be any point in the intersection of D and R_{ij}; see Figure 6.26(a).

Therefore,

$$\mathcal{R}_n = \sum^D F(x_i^*, y_j^*)\Delta A_{ij} + \sum^{D'} F(x_i^*, y_j^*)\Delta A_{ij}$$

where Σ^D represents the sum over all rectangles that intersect D (including, of course, those that are completely contained in D) and $\Sigma^{D'}$ is the sum over those R_{ij} that have no points in common with D. By construction, $\Sigma^{D'} F(x_i^*, y_j^*)\Delta A_{ij} = 0$ and therefore

$$\mathcal{R}_n = \sum^D F(x_i^*, y_j^*)\Delta A_{ij} = \sum^D \Delta A_{ij}$$

(since $F(x_i^*, y_j^*) = 1$ for all R_{ij} included in Σ^D by construction). In words, $\mathcal{R}_n$ is the sum of areas of those R_{ij} that "circumscribe" D, as shown in Figure 6.26(b). As $n \to \infty$, the rectangles that contribute to $\mathcal{R}_n$ will "circumscribe" D better and better, and in the limit,

$$\lim_{n\to\infty} \mathcal{R}_n = \iint_D 1\, dA = \text{area of } D.$$ ◄

The properties (a), (b), (d) and (e) of Theorem 6.2 continue to hold for double integrals over general closed and bounded regions. Now we will add a few more properties to this list.

■ **Theorem 6.5**   Properties of Double Integrals.

Let D be a closed and bounded region in $\mathbb{R}^2$.

(a) Assume that f is an integrable function defined on D. If D is divided into n mutually disjoint elementary regions D_i, then f is integrable over each D_i and

$$\iint_D f\, dA = \sum_{i=1}^n \iint_{D_i} f\, dA$$

("mutually disjoint" means that the intersections of any two, three, etc., elementary regions are either empty or contain curves and/or points only).

(b) Assume that f is a continuous function defined on D. There exist real numbers m and M such that

$$m A(D) \leq \iint_D f \, dA \leq M A(D),$$

where $A(D)$ is the area of D.

(c) Assume that f is a continuous function defined on D. There exists a point (x_0, y_0) in D such that

$$\iint_D f \, dA = f(x_0, y_0) A(D),$$

where $A(D)$ is the area of D.   ∎

Part (c) of the theorem is called the *Mean Value Theorem for Integrals*. We can rephrase it as follows: there exists a point (x_0, y_0) in D such that

$$f(x_0, y_0) = \frac{1}{A(D)} \iint_D f \, dA. \tag{6.2}$$

The right side is the "total value of f over D" divided by the area of D— that is, the *average value of f over D*. Formula (6.2) states that, if f is continuous, then there must be a point in D where the average value is attained (an example will illustrate this point soon).

The real numbers $m A(D)$ and $M A(D)$ in (b) are called a lower bound and an upper bound for the double integral $\iint_D f \, dA$.

Proof

Part (a) of the theorem is intuitively clear (its special case appeared in the previous section). However, the proof is technically involved and will not be presented here.

A continuous function defined on a closed and bounded set D has a minimum (call it m) and a maximum (call it M); see Appendix A. Hence $m \leq f(x, y) \leq M$, and therefore

$$\iint_D m \, dA \leq \iint_D f \, dA \leq \iint_D M \, dA$$

(by the extension of Theorem 6.2(d) to D). The ends of the inequalities are

$$\iint_D m \, dA = m \iint_D dA = m A(D) \qquad \text{and} \qquad \iint_D M \, dA = M \iint_D dA = M A(D),$$

and the conclusion of (b) follows.

Divide the formula in (b) by $A(D)$, to get

$$m \leq \frac{1}{A(D)} \iint_D f \, dA \leq M.$$

In words, the average value of f is a number between the minimum m and the maximum M of f. By the Intermediate Value Theorem (see Appendix A for the precise statement) a continuous function assumes every value between its minimum and maximum. Therefore, there must be a point (x_0, y_0) in D where

$$f(x_0, y_0) = \frac{1}{A(D)} \iint_D f \, dA.$$

∎

Example 6.15   Let $T(x, y) = 120 + 30x^2 - 18y$ be the temperature (in °C) at a point (x, y) on a metal plate D in the shape of a triangle with vertices $(0, 0)$, $(1, 0)$ and $(1, 1)$. Compute the average temperature $\overline{T}$ on the plate.

Solution   The region D is both of type 1 and of type 2. View it as a type-1 region, bounded by the curves $y = 0$ and $y = x$ over the interval $0 \le x \le 1$. It follows that (the area of D is $1/2$— no integration needed!)

$$\overline{T} = \frac{1}{A(D)} \iint_D (120 + 30x^2 - 18y) \, dA$$
$$= 2 \int_0^1 \left(\int_0^x (120 + 30x^2 - 18y) dy \right) dx = 2 \int_0^1 \left(120y + 30x^2y - 9y^2 \Big|_0^x \right) dx$$
$$= 2 \int_0^1 (120x + 30x^3 - 9x^2) \, dx = 2(60x^2 + 7.5x^4 - 3x^3) \Big|_0^1 = 129°C.$$

The Mean Value Theorem claims that there must be a point (or points) in D where the temperature is exactly 129 °C. Let us identify such point(s). From $T = 120 + 30x^2 - 18y = 129$ we get $18y = 30x^2 - 9$, i.e., $y = 5x^2/3 - 1/2$. It follows that the temperature at all points on the parabola $y = 5x^2/3 - 1/2$ that belong to D (see Figure 6.27) is equal to the average value of 129 °C.

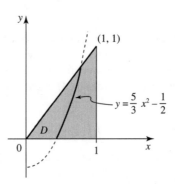

Figure 6.27   Points in D where the temperature equals its average value of 129 °C belong to the parabola $y = 5x^2/3 - 1/2$.

Example 6.16   Find an upper bound and a lower bound for $\iint_D 3 \sin^2(3x - y^4) \, dA$, where D is the circle $\{(x, y) \mid x^2 + y^2 \le 9\}$.

Solution   Since $-1 \le \sin a \le 1$ for any real number a, it follows that $0 \le \sin^2(3x - y^4) \le 1$ and $0 \le 3 \sin^2(3x - y^4) \le 3$; i.e., $m = 0$ and $M = 3$. The area of D is 9π, and therefore

$$0 = \iint_D 0 \, dA \le \iint_D 3 \sin^2(3x - y^4) \, dA \le \iint_D 3 \, dA = 27\pi.$$ ◀

Example 6.17   Find the volume of the solid V below the graph of $z = 12 + 2xy^2$ and above the triangle in the xy-plane with vertices $(-1, 0, 0)$, $(1, 0, 0)$ and $(0, 1, 0)$.

Solution   The volume of V is computed using the double integral

$$v(V) = \iint_D (12 + 2xy^2) \, dA,$$

where D is the given triangle. D is bounded by the x-axis and the lines $y = x + 1$ and $y = -x + 1$; see Figure 6.28. Viewing it as a type-2 region, we get

$$v(V) = \iint_D (12 + 2xy^2) \, dA$$

$$= \int_0^1 \left(\int_{y-1}^{-y+1} (12 + 2xy^2) dx \right) dy = \int_0^1 \left(12x + x^2 y^2 \Big|_{y-1}^{-y+1} \right) dy$$

$$= \int_0^1 \left(12(-y+1) + (-y+1)^2 y^2 - 12(y-1) - (y-1)^2 y^2 \right) dy$$

$$= 24 \int_0^1 (1 - y) \, dy = 24(y - \frac{y^2}{2}) \Big|_0^1 = 12.$$ ◀

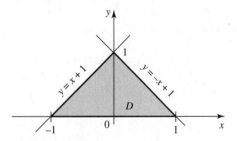

Figure 6.28   Triangle D of Example 6.17.

Now assume that $f(x, y) \ge g(x, y) \ge 0$ for all (x, y) in a region $D \subseteq \mathbb{R}^2$, and consider the solid V over D bounded from above by the graph of $z = f(x, y)$ and from below by the graph of $z = g(x, y)$; see Figure 6.29.

The double integral $\iint_D f \, dA$ represents the volume of the solid under $z = f(x, y)$ over the region D in the xy-plane. Similarly, $\iint_D g \, dA$ is the volume of the solid under $z = g(x, y)$ over D. The volume of V is their difference,

$$v(V) = \iint_D f \, dA - \iint_D g \, dA = \iint_D (f - g) \, dA.$$

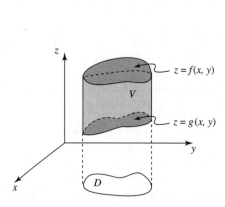

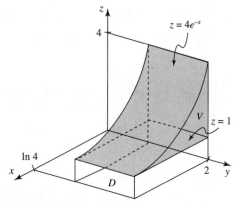

Figure 6.29 Solid V bounded by the graphs of $z = f(x, y)$ and $z = g(x, y)$.

Figure 6.30 Solid V of Example 6.18.

Example 6.18

Find the volume of the solid V bounded from above by the surface $z = 4e^{-x}$, from below by the plane $z = 1$ and from the sides by vertical planes $y = 1$, $y = 2$ and $x = 0$.

Solution   The surface $z = 4e^{-x}$ and the plane $z = 1$ intersect when $4e^{-x} = 1$, i.e., when $x = -\ln(1/4) = \ln 4$ (in words, they intersect along the line $x = \ln 4$ in the plane $z = 1$); see Figure 6.30. The region D of integration is the rectangle $0 \le x \le \ln 4$, $1 \le y \le 2$, and the volume of V is given by

$$v(V) = \iint_D (4e^{-x} - 1)\, dA,$$

since, on D, $4e^{-x} \ge 1$. Therefore

$$v(V) = \iint_D (4e^{-x} - 1)\, dA$$
$$= \int_1^2 \left(\int_0^{\ln 4} (4e^{-x} - 1)dx \right) dy = \int_1^2 \left(-4e^{-x} - x \, \Big|_0^{\ln 4} \right) dy$$
$$= \int_1^2 (3 - \ln 4)\, dy = 3 - \ln 4 \approx 1.61.$$

Additional worked examples and some techniques for computing double integrals will be presented in the following two sections.

EXERCISES 6.2

1. Suppose that $f(x, y) \le 0$ for all $(x, y) \in D \subseteq \mathbb{R}^2$. What is a geometric meaning of $\iint_D f\, dA$? If $f(x, y) \ge g(x, y)$ for all $(x, y) \in D$, what geometric interpretation could be given to $\iint_D (f - g)\, dA$?

2. Using Cavalieri's principle, find the volume of the solid V in Figure 6.31.

3. Using Cavalieri's principle, find the volume of a cone of radius r and height h.

4. Find the volume of the solid obtained by rotating the graph of $y = \ln x$, $1 \le x \le 2$, about the x-axis. Now imagine that the same graph is rotated about the y-axis. Find the volume of the solid thus obtained.

5. Using Cavalieri's Principle, find the volume of the solid V in Figure 6.32.

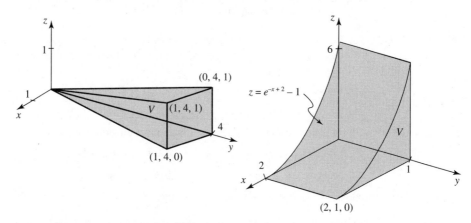

Figure 6.31   Solid V of Exercise 2.   **Figure 6.32**   Solid V of Exercise 5.

Exercises 6 to 11: Evaluate the following iterated integrals.

6. $\displaystyle\int_0^1 \left(\int_0^x \cos(x^2)dy \right) dx$

7. $\displaystyle\int_0^2 \left(\int_{2-x}^{x+1} (xe^y - 2y - 1)dy \right) dx$

8. $\displaystyle\int_{-1}^1 \left(\int_0^{3x} e^{x+3y}dy \right) dx$

9. $\displaystyle\int_0^\pi \left(\int_0^{\cos\theta} \rho^2 \sin\theta d\rho \right) d\theta$

10. $\displaystyle\int_1^2 \left(\int_0^{y/2} x\sqrt{x^2 + y^2}dx \right) dy$

11. $\displaystyle\int_0^{\pi/2} \left(\int_0^{\sin y} x \cos y dx \right) dy$

Exercises 12 to 18:   Evaluate $\iint_D f \, dA$ for the function f and the region $D \subseteq \mathbb{R}^2$.

12. $f(x, y) = e^{-x-3y}$, $D = [0, \ln 2] \times [0, \ln 3]$

13. $f(x, y) = xy^{-1} - x^2y^2$, $D = [0, 2] \times [3, 4]$

14. $f(x, y) = xye^{x^2}$, $D = [-1, 1] \times [0, 1]$

15. $f(x, y) = 2xy - y$, $D = \{(x, y) \mid 0 \le y \le 1, -y \le x \le 1 + y\}$

16. $f(x, y) = e^{x/y}$, $D = \{(x, y) \mid 0 \le x \le 3, x \le y \le 2x^2\}$

17. $f(x, y) = x^{-2/3}$, D is the region in the first quadrant bounded by the parabolas $y = x^2$ and $y = 4 - x^2$

18. $f(x, y) = \ln(xy)$, D is the triangular region bounded by the lines $y = 1$, $y = x$ and $x = 0$

19. Find an upper bound and a lower bound for $\iint_D e^{-x-y} \, dA$, where $D = [-1, 1] \times [0, 2]$.

20. Find an upper bound and a lower bound for the double integral $\iint_D x^2 \sin(x^2 - y) \, dA$, where D is the disk $x^2 + y^2 \le 1$.

Exercises 21 to 24: Find the volume of the solid in $\mathbb{R}^3$.

21. the solid under the plane $x + y/2 + z = 6$ and above the rectangle $[-1, 1] \times [0, 2]$

22. the solid in the first octant bounded by the cylindrical sheet $z = -y^2 + 9$ and the plane $z = 2$

23. the solid between the planes $x + y + z = 1$ and $x + y + 2z = 1$ in the first octant

24. the solid below $z = 9 - x^2 - y^2$ and above the triangle in the xy-plane with the vertices $(0, 0, 0)$, $(1, 0, 0)$ and $(0, 2, 0)$

25. Let $D \subseteq \mathbb{R}^2$ be an elementary region and let f and g be continuous, real-valued functions on D. Show that if $\iint_D f \, dA = \iint_D g \, dA$ then there exists a point (x_0, y_0) in D such that $f(x_0, y_0) = g(x_0, y_0)$.

Exercises 26 to 30: Find the area of the region $D \subseteq \mathbb{R}^2$.

26. bounded by $y = 2x$, $y = 5x$ and $x^2 + y^2 = 1$

27. the ellipse with the semiaxes $a > 0$ (in the x-direction) and $b > 0$ (in the y-direction)

28. below $y = x^{-1}$, between $x = a$ and $x = b$, where $a, b > 0$

29. between $y = x^2$ and $y = 4 - x^2$, to the right of the y-axis

30. inside the disk $x^2 + y^2 \leq 2$ and outside the square $[-1, 1] \times [-1, 1]$

31. Let $f(x, y) = k(x^2 + y^2)$ describe the temperature ($k > 0$ is a constant) at points on a rectangular metal plate $R = [0, 1] \times [0, 2]$. Find all points (x_0, y_0) in R that satisfy the conclusion of the Mean Value Theorem.

32. Find the point (x_0, y_0) from the Mean Value Theorem if $f(x, y) = x^2$ and D is the triangle defined by the coordinate axes and the line $x + y = 1$.

6.3   EXAMPLES AND TECHNIQUES OF EVALUATION OF DOUBLE INTEGRALS

In this section we will give several examples of computations of double integrals and will illustrate two elementary techniques. Due to its importance, the change of variables technique will be presented separately in the following section.

Example 6.19   Evaluate $\iint_R y \sin(xy) \, dA$, where R is the rectangle $R = [1, 3] \times [0, \pi/2]$.

Solution   Using Fubini's Theorem, we get

$$\iint_R y \sin(xy) \, dA = \int_0^{\pi/2} \left(\int_1^3 y \sin(xy) dx \right) dy = \int_0^{\pi/2} \left(-\cos(xy) \Big|_{x=1}^{x=3} \right) dy$$

$$= \int_0^{\pi/2} (\cos y - \cos(3y)) \, dy = \left(\sin y - \frac{1}{3} \sin(3y) \right) \Big|_0^{\pi/2} = \frac{4}{3}.$$

Now let us reverse the order of integration:

$$\iint_R y \sin(xy) \, dA = \int_1^3 \left(\int_0^{\pi/2} y \sin(xy) dy \right) dx$$

(use integration by parts with $u = y$, $du = dy$, $dv = \sin(xy)dy$ and $v = -\cos(xy)/x$)

$$= \int_1^3 \left(-\frac{y}{x} \cos(xy) \Big|_0^{\pi/2} + \int_0^{\pi/2} \frac{1}{x} \cos(xy) \, dy \right) dx$$

(use substitution $u = xy$, $du = xdy$)

$$= \int_1^3 \left(-\frac{\pi}{2x} \cos\left(\frac{\pi}{2}x\right) + \frac{1}{x^2} \sin(xy) \Big|_0^{\pi/2} \right) dx$$

$$= \int_1^3 \left(-\frac{\pi}{2x} \cos\left(\frac{\pi}{2}x\right) + \frac{1}{x^2} \sin\left(\frac{\pi}{2}x\right) \right) dx$$

(apply integration by parts (with $u = \pi/(2x)$, $du = -\pi dx/(2x^2)$, $dv = \cos(\pi x/2)dx$ and $v = (2/\pi) \sin(\pi x/2)$) to the first integrand, keep the second one)

$$= - \left(\frac{1}{x} \sin\left(\frac{\pi}{2}x\right) \Big|_1^3 + \int_1^3 \frac{1}{x^2} \sin\left(\frac{\pi}{2}x\right) \, dx \right) + \int_1^3 \frac{1}{x^2} \sin\left(\frac{\pi}{2}x\right) \, dx$$

$$= -\frac{1}{x} \sin\left(\frac{\pi}{2}x\right) \Big|_1^3 = \frac{4}{3},$$

since two integrals cancel each other.   ◄

This example shows that a specific order of integration could lead to significantly easier (or harder) computation. Sometimes it may even be impossible to evaluate exactly an iterated integral (i.e., using methods that give exact solutions in compact form— unlike, for example, numerical or power series methods).

Example 6.20   Evaluate $\iint_D e^{x/y} \, dA$, where D is the region between the curves $y = x$ and $x = y^3$ in the first quadrant.

Solution   Combining $y = x$ and $x = y^3$ we get $y^3 - y = 0$, and therefore $y = -1$, 0 or 1. The points of intersection are $(-1, -1)$, $(0, 0)$ and $(1, 1)$. The region D is shown in Figure 6.33. View it as a type-2 region. Then

$$\iint_D e^{x/y} \, dA = \int_0^1 \left(\int_{y^3}^y e^{x/y} dx \right) dy$$

$$= \int_0^1 \left(ye^{x/y} \Big|_{x=y^3}^{x=y} \right) dy = \int_0^1 ye - ye^{y^2} \, dy$$

(substitute $u = y^2$, $du = 2ydy$ in the second integral)

$$= \left(\frac{y^2}{2} e - \frac{1}{2} e^{y^2} \right) \Big|_0^1 = \frac{1}{2}.$$

If we view D as a type-1 region, we end up with the iterated integral

$$\iint_R e^{x/y} \, dA = \int_0^1 \left(\int_x^{\sqrt[3]{x}} e^{x/y} dy \right) dx,$$

that cannot be solved by exact means.

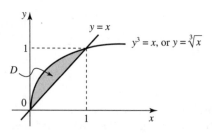

Figure 6.33   Region of Example 6.20.

Example 6.21

Find the volume of the solid V in the first octant bounded by the parabolic cylinder $x^2 + z = 9$ and the vertical plane $x + 3y = 3$.

Solution   To obtain the graph of $x^2 + z = 9$ draw the parabola $z = 9 - x^2$ in the xz-plane first. Since there is no mention of y in the equation (and hence no restriction on its values), the same graph must be repeated for every y; i.e., for every plane parallel to the xz-plane. Mechanically, the graph is obtained by moving the xz-plane that contains the parabola along the y-axis (keeping the origin on the y-axis, the plane has to remain perpendicular to the xy-plane and parallel to its initial position); see Figure 6.34(a). The region D in the xy-plane is determined from $x^2 = 9$ (set $z = 0$ in $x^2 + z = 9$), $x + 3y = 3$, and $x, y \geq 0$ (V is in the first octant). The solid V is that part of the three-dimensional region under the graph of $z = 9 - x^2$ that lies above D; see Figure 6.34(b). Its volume is (view D as a type 2 region)

$$v(V) = \iint_D (9 - x^2) \, dA = \int_0^1 \left(\int_0^{3-3y} (9 - x^2) dx \right) dy.$$

The y-coordinates of all points in D are between 0 and 1. Arrows "travelling" parallel to the x-axis enter D along the y-axis (hence $x = 0$) and exit D along the line $x + 3y = 3$ (hence $x = 3 - 3y$).

The iterated integral is equal to

$$\int_0^1 \left(9x - \frac{x^3}{3} \Big|_0^{3-3y} \right) dy = \int_0^1 (18 - 27y^2 + 9y^3) \, dy = \frac{45}{4}.$$

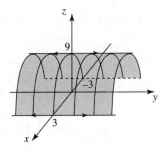 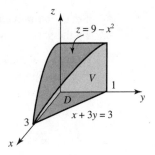

Figure 6.34 Region of Example 6.21.

(a) parabolic sheet $z = 9 - x^2$ (b) solid V above D and under $z = 9 - x^2$

Example 6.22   Find the volume of the region V in the first octant bounded by the planes $x + y + z = 1$ and $x + y + z/2 = 1$.

Solution   A good way to visualize a plane is to compute its x-intercept, y-intercept and z-intercept and join them with line segments (thus representing the part of the plane that belongs to a particular octant). This is how the sketch in Figure 6.35 was obtained (set $y = z = 0$; both equations give $x = 1$, hence $(1, 0, 0)$ is the x-intercept for both planes. Now set $x = z = 0$ to get the y-intercept, etc.) The region D in the xy-plane is determined by $x \geq 0$, $y \geq 0$ and $x + y = 1$ (substitute $z = 0$ into both equations).

The volume of V is the difference of the volumes of the solid under $z = 2 - 2x - 2y$ and the solid under $z = 1 - x - y$ (and above D). Hence (view D as a region of type 1)

$$
\begin{aligned}
v(V) &= \iint_D (2 - 2x - 2y) \, dA - \iint_D (1 - x - y) \, dA \\
&= \iint_D (1 - x - y) \, dA = \int_0^1 \left(\int_0^{1-x} (1 - x - y) dy \right) dx \\
&= \int_0^1 \left(y - xy - \tfrac{1}{2} y^2 \, \Big|_0^{1-x} \right) dx = \int_0^1 \left(\tfrac{1}{2} y - x + \tfrac{1}{2} x^2 \right) dx = \tfrac{1}{6}.
\end{aligned}
$$

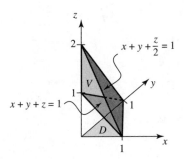

Figure 6.35   Solid V of Example 6.22.

Example 6.23   Set up iterated integrals for $\iint_D x^3 y \, dA$, where D is the region in the xy-plane bounded by the parabola $y = x^2$ and the line $y = x + 2$.

Solution   Combining $y = x^2$ and $y = x + 2$ we get $x^2 - x - 2 = 0$ and $x = -1, 2$. The points of intersection are $(-1, 1)$ and $(2, 4)$. D can be viewed as a type-1 region (defined for $-1 \leq x \leq 2$, between $y = x^2$ and $y = x + 2$); see Figure 6.36(a). Therefore,

$$\iint_D f \, dA = \int_{-1}^{2} \left(\int_{x^2}^{x+2} x^3 y \, dy \right) dx.$$

Thinking of the reversed order, consider the inner integration (that will be with respect to x). Arrows that "travel" parallel to the x-axis do not enter D along the same curve: some enter along the parabola (if $0 \leq y \leq 1$), and some along the line (if $1 \leq y \leq 4$). We break up D into two type-2 regions accordingly: D_1 is defined by $0 \leq y \leq 1$ and D_2 by $1 \leq y \leq 4$, see Figure 6.36(b). There is one more issue: we need to express x in terms of y; from $y = x^2$ we get $x = \pm\sqrt{y}$. The equation $x = \sqrt{y}$ represents the part of the parabola in the first quadrant, and $x = -\sqrt{y}$ is its symmetric part in the second quadrant. By Theorem 6.5(a),

$$\iint_D x^3 y \, dA = \iint_{D_1} x^3 y \, dA + \iint_{D_2} x^3 y \, dA,$$

where

$$\iint_{D_1} x^3 y \, dA = \int_0^1 \left(\int_{-\sqrt{y}}^{\sqrt{y}} x^3 y \, dx \right) dy$$

and

$$\iint_{D_2} x^3 y \, dA = \int_1^4 \left(\int_{y-2}^{\sqrt{y}} x^3 y \, dx \right) dy. \qquad \blacktriangleleft$$

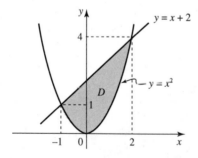

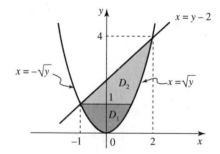

Figure 6.36   Region D of Example 6.23.
(a) as a type-1 region   (b) as a type-2 region

Example 6.24   Separation of Variables.

We are going to evaluate the integral $\iint_R f \, dA$, where $R = [a, b] \times [c, d]$ is a rectangle in

$\mathbb{R}^2$ and f is a function of the form $f(x, y) = g(x)h(y)$ (i.e., the variables are separated, as in $f(x, y) = x^2 \cos y$ or in $f(x, y) = e^{x+y} = e^x e^y$; on the other hand, the variables in $f(x, y) = (x + y)^2$ cannot be separated).

By Fubini's Theorem,

$$\iint_R f \, dA = \int_c^d \left(\int_a^b f(x, y) dx \right) dy = \int_c^d \left(\int_a^b g(x)h(y) dx \right) dy$$

($h(y)$ is constant for inner integration, so factor it out)

$$= \int_c^d h(y) \left(\int_a^b g(x) dx \right) dy = \left(\int_a^b g(x) \, dx \right) \left(\int_c^d h(y) \, dy \right).$$

The definite integral $\int_a^b g(x) dx$ is a real number, so we factored it out of the integration with respect to y in the last step. ◄

Example 6.25 Compute $\iint_D e^{x+y} \, dA$, where $D = [0, 1] \times [0, 1]$, using separation of variables.

Solution Since $e^{x+y} = e^x e^y$, it follows that

$$\iint_{[0,1] \times [0,1]} e^{x+y} dA = \int_0^1 \left(\int_0^1 e^x e^y dx \right) dy = \left(\int_0^1 e^x \, dx \right) \left(\int_0^1 e^y \, dy \right)$$

$$= \left(\int_0^1 e^x \, dx \right)^2 = \left(e^x \Big|_0^1 \right)^2 = (e - 1)^2.$$

◄

The formulas in Theorem 6.4 provide two different ways of computing double integrals over regions of type 3. This fact can be used to simplify the computation of iterated integrals. We have already witnessed that the order of integration chosen in the first part of Example 6.19 was significantly easier to handle than the reversed order. Sometimes it is even impossible to compute the iterated integral (as a compact formula) without reversing the order of integration, as examples that follow will illustrate.

The idea of this technique is simple: given an iterated integral, all we have to do is to reconstruct the double integral (i.e., find the region D) that corresponds to that iterated integral. Then we try to evaluate the double integral as an iterated integral in the reversed order of integration.

Example 6.26 Compute

$$\int_0^1 \left(\int_{\sqrt{y}}^1 (x^2 + 2y) dx \right) dy$$

by reversing the order of integration.

Solution The given integral is equal to the iterated integral of the double integral

$$\iint_D (x^2 + 2y) \, dA,$$

where D is the region (see Figure 6.37) described by $0 \leq y \leq 1$ and $\sqrt{y} \leq x \leq 1$. It is the region bounded by the graph of $y = x^2$, the x-axis and the vertical line $x = 1$. Therefore,

$$\int_D (x^2 + 2y)\, dA = \int_0^1 \left(\int_0^{x^2} (x^2 + 2y)\, dy \right) dx$$

$$= \int_0^1 \left((x^2 y + y^2) \Big|_{y=0}^{y=x^2} \right) dx = \int_0^1 (x^4 + x^4)\, dx = \frac{2x^5}{5} \Big|_0^1 = \frac{2}{5}.$$

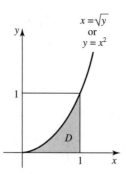

Figure 6.37 Region D of Example 6.26.

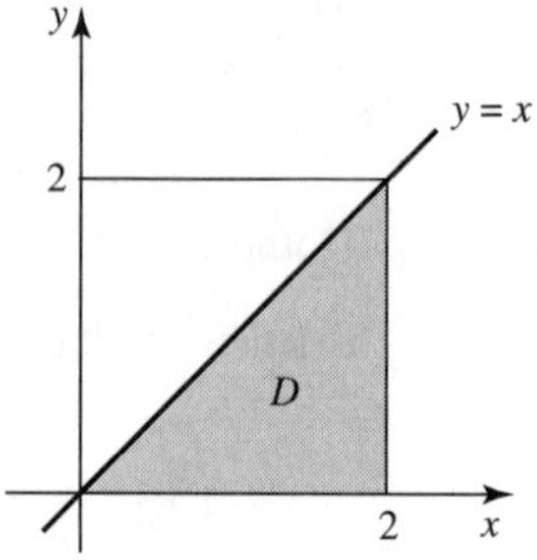

Figure 6.38 Region D of Example 6.27

Example 6.27 Compute

$$\int_0^2 \left(\int_y^2 e^{x^2}\, dx \right) dy.$$

Solution Since it is impossible to find a formula for $\int e^{x^2}\, dx$ we have to reverse the order of integration, hoping that we will get an integrand we can handle. The given integral is equal to

$$\iint_D e^{x^2}\, dA,$$

where D is the region described by $0 \leq y \leq 2$ and $y \leq x \leq 2$. In other words, D is the triangular region bounded by the graph of $y = x$, the x-axis and the vertical line $x = 2$ (see Figure 6.38). Hence

$$\int_0^2 \left(\int_y^2 e^{x^2}\, dx \right) dy = \int_0^2 \left(\int_0^x e^{x^2}\, dy \right) dx$$

$$= \int_0^2 \left(y e^{x^2} \Big|_{y=0}^{y=x} \right) dx = \int_0^2 x e^{x^2}\, dx = \frac{1}{2} e^{x^2} \Big|_0^2 = \frac{1}{2} e^4 - \frac{1}{2},$$

where the substitution $u = x^2$, $du = 2x\,dx$ was used to compute the integral of xe^{x^2}.

Example 6.28   Compute

$$\int_0^1 \left(\int_x^1 \frac{\cos y}{y} dy \right) dx.$$

Solution   The integral of $\cos y/y$ cannot be computed (exactly, as a compact formula) and we will reverse the order of integration. The region of integration, given by the inequalities $0 \le x \le 1$ and $x \le y \le 1$ is the triangle with sides $y = x$, $y = 1$ and the y-axis shown in Figure 6.39. Therefore

$$\int_0^1 \left(\int_x^1 \frac{\cos y}{y} dy \right) dx = \int_0^1 \left(\int_0^y \frac{\cos y}{y} dx \right) dy$$

$$= \int_0^1 \left(\frac{\cos y}{y} x \Big|_{x=0}^{x=y} \right) dy = \int_0^1 \cos y \, dy = \sin y \Big|_0^1 = \sin 1.$$

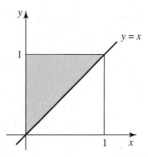

Figure 6.39   Region of Example 6.28.

EXERCISES 6.3   **Exercises 1 to 4:** Evaluate $\iint_D f \, dA$ for the function f and the region $D \subseteq \mathbb{R}^2$.

1. $f(x, y) = ye^x$, D is the triangular region bounded by the lines $y = 1$, $y = 2x$ and $x = 0$

2. $f(x, y) = (x^2 + y^2)^{3/4}$, D is the disk $x^2 + y^2 \le 9$

3. $f(x, y) = y^2$, D is the triangular region bounded by the lines $y = 2x$, $y = 5x$ and $x = 2$

4. $f(x, y) = (2x - x^2)^{-1/2}$, D is the triangular region bounded by the lines $y = -x + 1$, $y = 0$ and $x = 0$

Exercises 5 to 9: Find the volume of the solid in $\mathbb{R}^3$.

5. the solid bounded by the cylinder $y^2 + z^2 = 4$ and the plane $x + y = 2$ in the first octant

6. the solid under the paraboloid $z = x^2 + y^2$ and above the region in the xy-plane bounded by the parabola $y = x^2$ and the line $y = x$

7. the solid bounded by the planes $y = 3x$, $y = 0$, $z = 0$ and $x + y + z = 4$

8. the solid bounded by the cylinders $x^2 + y^2 = 1$ and $x^2 + z^2 = 1$

9. the solid under the surface $z = xy$ and above the triangle in the xy-plane with vertices $(0, 1)$, $(1, 1)$ and $(1, 2)$

10. Compute $\int_0^{\pi/3} \left(\int_0^{\pi/2} \cos(x + y)dx \right) dy$ using $\cos(x + y) = \cos x \cos y - \sin x \sin y$ and separation of variables. Check your result by direct evaluation.

11. Compute $\int_0^1 \left(\int_0^2 (1 - x - y + xy)dx \right) dy$ using separation of variables. Check your result by direct evaluation.

Exercises 12 to 15: Sketch the region of integration and reverse the order of integration. Do not solve the integrals.

12. $\int_0^\pi \left(\int_0^{\sin(x/2)} x^3 y^2 dy \right) dx$

13. $\int_0^1 \left(\int_{\arctan x}^{\pi/4} (y^2 - x)dy \right) dx$

14. $\int_0^1 \left(\int_{x/2}^x x^2 y^2 dy \right) dx + \int_1^2 \left(\int_{x/2}^1 x^2 y^2 dy \right) dx$

15. $\int_1^2 \left(\int_1^{2y} \frac{\ln x}{x} dx \right) dy$

Exercises 16 to 22: Evaluate the following integrals by reversing the order of integration.

16. $\int_0^1 \left(\int_y^1 e^{x^2} dx \right) dy$

17. $\int_0^1 \left(\int_0^{\arccos y} x dx \right) dy$

18. $\int_0^1 \left(\int_{y^{1/3}}^1 e^{x^4} dx \right) dy$

19. $\int_0^3 \left(\int_{x^2}^9 x \cos(2y^2)dy \right) dx$

20. $\int_{1/2}^1 \left(\int_1^{2y} \frac{\ln x}{x} dx \right) dy + \int_1^2 \left(\int_y^2 \frac{\ln x}{x} dx \right) dy$

21. $\int_1^2 \left(\int_1^{\sqrt{y}} 5dx \right) dy + \int_2^4 \left(\int_{y/2}^{\sqrt{y}} 5dx \right) dy$

22. $\int_0^1 \left(\int_0^{\arcsin x} y^2 dy \right) dx$

23. Compute $\iint_D e^{x^3} dA$ over the region bounded by $y = x^2$, $x = 1$ and $y = 0$.

24. Compute the area of the region $x^2 + y^2 \leq 9$ that lies to the left of the line $x = 1/5$.

6.4   CHANGE OF VARIABLES IN A DOUBLE INTEGRAL

Sometimes the evaluation of a double integral $\iint_D f\, dA$ is difficult because either the region D is geometrically complicated or the function f and/or D give rise to an integrand that is hard to handle. One possible way to solve this problem is to use the change of variables technique.

Let us recall how change of variables (also known as the substitution rule) works for functions of one variable. Consider the definite integral $\int_1^2 e^{5x} dx$. Let $u = 5x$, so that $x = u/5$; this means that x is now viewed as a function of u, $x(u) = u/5$. Then

$dx = x'(u)du = (1/5)du$ and

$$\int_1^2 e^{5x}dx = \int_5^{10} e^u \tfrac{1}{5}du,$$

where the limits of integration have been changed accordingly (when $x = 1$, $u = 5$; when $x = 2$, $u = 10$). One more example: consider the integral $\int_1^2 e^{-5x}dx$. Using $u = -5x$, so that $x = -u/5$, we get $dx = (-1/5)du$ and

$$\int_1^2 e^{-5x}dx = \int_{-5}^{-10} e^u \left(-\tfrac{1}{5}\right)du = \int_{-10}^{-5} e^u \tfrac{1}{5}du,$$

where the minus sign was used to switch the limits of integration. In general, to compute $\int_a^b f(x)dx$, we set $x = x(u)$. Then $dx = x'(u)du = (dx/du)du$ and

$$\int_I f(x)dx = \int_{a^*}^{b^*} f(x(u))\frac{dx}{du}du = \int_{I^*} f(x(u))\left|\frac{dx}{du}\right|du,$$

where $I = [a, b]$, $x(a^*) = a$, $x(b^*) = b$ and $I^* = [\min\{a^*, b^*\}, \max\{a^*, b^*\}]$. Whenever we use interval notation, like $[\alpha, \beta]$, we must have $\alpha \leq \beta$. This is what the fuss involving min and max and the absolute value is all about (recall the example of $\int_1^2 e^{-5x}dx$ above).

It follows that the change of variables for functions of one variable can be written as

$$\int_I f(x)dx = \int_{I^*} f(x(u))\left|\frac{dx}{du}\right|du.$$

And this is precisely the formula that we will be able to generalize to functions of two (and later, three) variables. The ingredients in the integral on the right side are the composition of f and x (remember that x is now a function of u) and the transformed interval I^* (the function x maps I^* to I).

Assume that $f = f(x, y)$ is a function of two variables. A *change of variables* is defined by setting

$$x = x(u, v), \qquad y = y(u, v),$$

where x and y are differentiable functions of u and v. In terms of functions, the change of variables can be described as a differentiable map $T: D^* \to D$, where D^* and D are regions in $\mathbb{R}^2$ and

$$T(u, v) = (x(u, v), y(u, v))$$

(instead of the usual notation T_1, T_2 for the components of T we use x and y, to emphasize that we are thinking of them as forming a coordinate system in $\mathbb{R}^2$).

A successful change of variables (that is, a good choice of T) will reduce the integration over a region D to an integration over a simpler region D^*. Before stating the theorem, we have to understand how T works. So, first of all, we study the properties of maps $T: \mathbb{R}^2 \to \mathbb{R}^2$.

A good way to understand functions is to draw their graphs. However, drawing the graph of T would require four dimensions: two for the independent variables and two for the range (a different view of T, that of a vector field in $\mathbb{R}^2$, has been studied before— unfortunately, it cannot be of help to us now). To overcome this problem, we proceed as follows: we use one coordinate system as the domain of T (and call it the *uv-plane* or the *uv-coordinate system*) and another as the range (and call it the *xy-plane* or the *xy-coordinate system*). We visualize T by investigating its effect on different objects (points, lines, rectangles, regions, etc.) in the domain.

Example 6.29

Consider the map $T: \mathbb{R}^2 \to \mathbb{R}^2$ given by $T(u, v) = (u + 2v, 3u - v)$. Find the image $T(D^*)$ of the rectangle $D^* = [0, 1] \times [0, 2]$ under T.

Solution Let us first compute the image of a horizontal line $v = k$ (k is a constant) in the *uv*-plane. Since $T(u, k) = (u + 2k, 3u - k)$, it follows that in the *xy*-plane, $x = u + 2k$ and $y = 3u - k$. Eliminating u (for example, compute u from the first equation and substitute into the second) we get $y = 3x - 7k$. Therefore, horizontal lines $v = k$ map to parallel lines (all with slope 3) $y = 3x - 7k$. Similarly, the image of a vertical line $u = k$ is $T(k, v) = (k + 2v, 3k - v)$. Hence $x = k + 2v$, $y = 3k - v$, and (after eliminating v) $y = -x/2 + 7k/2$. In words, vertical lines $u = k$ map to parallel lines $y = -x/2 + 7k/2$.

The rectangle D^* is bounded by horizontal lines $v = 0$ and $v = 2$ and vertical lines $u = 0$ and $u = 1$. We can now find its image. T maps the line $v = 0$ to the line $y = 3x$ and the line $v = 2$ to the line $y = 3x - 14$. Moreover, any horizontal line $v = k$, $0 < k < 2$ between $v = 0$ and $v = 2$ is mapped to the line $y = 3x - 7k$ (where $0 < 7k < 14$), that lies between the images $y = 3x$ and $y = 3x - 14$ of $v = 0$ and $v = 2$. Therefore, T maps the horizontal strip $0 \le v \le 2$ to the (slanted) strip bounded by $y = 3x$ and $y = 3x - 14$; see Figure 6.40.

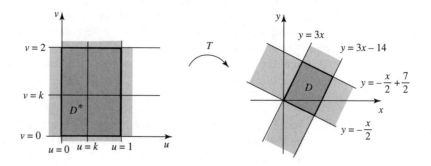

Figure 6.40 Map T of Example 6.29.

Similarly, T maps $u = 0$ to $y = -x/2$, $u = 1$ to $y = -x/2 + 7/2$, and every vertical line $u = k$, $0 < k < 1$, between $u = 0$ and $u = 1$ to the line $y = -x/2 + 7k/2$ between the images $y = -x/2$ and $y = -x/2 + 7/2$ of $u = 0$ and $u = 1$ in the *xy*-plane. Consequently, T maps the vertical strip $0 \le u \le 1$ to the (slanted) strip bounded by $y = -x/2$ and $y = -x/2 + 7/2$.

Therefore, the image D of the rectangle D^* is the parallelogram bounded by $y = 3x$, $y = 3x - 14$, $y = -x/2$ and $y = -x/2 + 7/2$.

Example 6.30   Polar Coordinates.

The change from Cartesian to polar coordinates can be described as

$$x = r \cos \theta, \qquad y = r \sin \theta,$$

or as the mapping

$$T(r, \theta) = (r \cos \theta, r \sin \theta)$$

(following tradition, we use r and θ instead of u and v). Compute the image of the rectangle $[1, \sqrt{2}] \times [0, \pi]$ in the $r\theta$-plane under the map T.

Solution   We proceed as in the previous example: the image of a horizontal line $\theta = k$ (k is a constant) is $T(r, k) = (r \cos k, r \sin k)$; then $x = r \cos k$, $y = r \sin k$ and (divide the two equations) $y/x = \tan k$; i.e., $y = (\tan k)x$. It follows that the horizontal lines $\theta = k$ map to the lines through the origin with slope $\tan k$ (if $k \neq \pi/2$). If $k = \pi/2$, then $x = 0$, $y = r$ and the image is the y-axis (as suspected); see Figure 6.41.

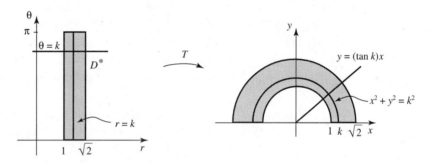

Figure 6.41   Polar mapping of Example 6.30.

The images of vertical lines $r = k \geq 0$ are $T(k, \theta) = (k \cos \theta, k \sin \theta)$; that is, $x = k \cos \theta$, $y = k \sin \theta$ and $x^2 + y^2 = k^2$. In words, vertical lines $r = k$ map to circles of radius k, if $k > 0$. If $k = 0$, the whole line maps to the origin. The rectangle D^* is bounded by $r = 1$, $r = \sqrt{2}$, $\theta = 0$ and $\theta = \pi$. Its image $D = T(D^*)$ is bounded by the image curves: circles of radii 1 and $\sqrt{2}$ and the line $y = 0$. Hence D is the upper half of the annulus of radii 1 and $\sqrt{2}$.

Example 6.31   Find the image of the rectangle $D^* = [1, 2] \times [0, 4]$ under $T(u, v) = (2u, 1)$.

Solution   The image of a horizontal line $v = k$ is $T(u, k) = (2u, 1)$; i.e., $x = 2u$ (u runs over all real numbers) and $y = 1$. Therefore, every horizontal line maps to the same horizontal line, $y = 1$. The vertical line $u = k$, $1 \leq k \leq 2$, maps to $T(k, v) = (2k, 1)$ (k is fixed here); i.e., to the point $(2k, 1)$ on the line $y = 1$. It follows that T "squishes" the rectangle D^* onto the line segment D on the line $y = 1$, from $x = 2$ to $x = 4$.

Not every function $T: \mathbb{R}^2 \rightarrow \mathbb{R}^2$ can represent a change of variables (the map of

Example 6.31 is certainly not likely to be such a map).

■ Definition 6.5   One-to-one and Onto Function.

A function $T: D^* \subseteq \mathbb{R}^2 \to \mathbb{R}^2$ is called *one-to-one* if for each (u, v) and (u', v') in D^*, $T(u, v) = T(u', v')$ implies that $u = u'$ and $v = v'$. A function $T: D^* \subseteq \mathbb{R}^2 \to \mathbb{R}^2$ is called *onto* D if for every point $(x, y) \in D$ there is a point (u, v) in D^* such that $T(u, v) = (x, y)$.

■

According to Definition 6.5, a function or a map (they are synonyms) is one-to-one if whenever two points have the same image, they are actually the same point. Equivalently, a one-to-one function maps different points to different points. The function T of Example 6.31 is not one-to-one, since, for example both $(1, 0)$ and $(1, 1)$ (actually all points on $u = 1$) map onto the point $(2, 1)$. The function T is onto D if every point in D is "hit" by one (or more) points from D^*.

The polar map of Example 6.30 is onto the semi-annulus $D = \{(x, y) \mid 1 \le x^2 + y^2 \le 2, y \ge 0\}$. Let us prove it: pick any point $(x_0, y_0) \in D$. We have to find a point (or points) in D^* that is (are) mapped to (x_0, y_0). The point (x_0, y_0) lies on the circle $x^2 + y^2 = x_0^2 + y_0^2$ of radius $\sqrt{x_0^2 + y_0^2}$ and on the line $y = \arctan(y_0/x_0)x$ through the origin; see Figure 6.42. In Example 6.30 we showed that horizontal lines map to lines through the origin, and vertical lines map to circles. In particular, the vertical line $r = \sqrt{x_0^2 + y_0^2}$ will map to the circle of radius $\sqrt{x_0^2 + y_0^2}$ and the horizontal line $\theta = \arctan(y_0/x_0)$ will map to the line of slope $\arctan(y_0/x_0)$ through the origin. The point A that is the intersection of the two lines in the $r\theta$-plane gets mapped to (x_0, y_0).

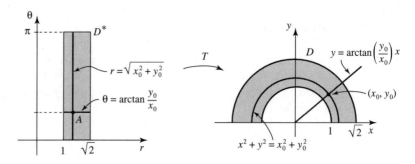

Figure 6.42   The polar map is onto the semi-annulus.

We have also noticed that the function T distorts the region it is applied to. We now introduce the function that will measure that distortion. Its precise meaning will be discussed later in this section.

■ Definition 6.6   Jacobian of a Function $T: \mathbb{R}^2 \to \mathbb{R}^2$.

Let $T(u, v) = (x(u, v), y(u, v))$ be a C^1 function defined on a region $D^* \subseteq \mathbb{R}^2$. The determinant of the derivative DT of T is called the *Jacobian* of T and is denoted by

$J(x, y; u, v)$ or $\partial(x, y)/\partial(u, v)$. Hence

$$\frac{\partial(x, y)}{\partial(u, v)} = \begin{vmatrix} \partial x/\partial u & \partial x/\partial v \\ \partial y/\partial u & \partial y/\partial v \end{vmatrix}.$$

■

Example 6.32

Consider the mapping (of Example 6.30) $T(r, \theta) = (r \cos \theta, r \sin \theta)$ that defines polar coordinates in the plane. Show that it is one-to-one on $D^* = [1, \sqrt{2}] \times [0, \pi]$ and compute its Jacobian.

Solution To prove that T is one-to-one we have to show that $T(r, \theta) = T(r', \theta')$ implies that $r = r'$ and $\theta = \theta'$ (i.e., if two points (r, θ) and (r', θ') were mapped by T into the same point, then (r, θ) and (r', θ') must have been the same point to begin with). Now $T(r, \theta) = T(r', \theta')$ implies that $(r \cos \theta, r \sin \theta) = (r' \cos \theta', r' \sin \theta')$, and hence

$$r \cos \theta = r' \cos \theta' \tag{6.3}$$

and

$$r \sin \theta = r' \sin \theta', \tag{6.4}$$

for $1 \le r, r' \le \sqrt{2}$ and $0 \le \theta, \theta' \le \pi$.

If $\theta = \pi/2$, then (6.3) reads $r' \cos \theta' = 0$, hence $\cos \theta' = 0$ (since $1 \le r' \le \sqrt{2}$, so r' cannot be 0) and therefore $\theta' = \pi/2$ (which is the only solution such that $0 \le \theta' \le \pi$). Now (6.4) with $\theta = \theta' = \pi/2$ gives $r = r'$. The case $\theta' = \pi/2$ is dealt with analogously.

If $\theta, \theta' \ne \pi/2$, then we can divide (6.4) by (6.3), thus getting $\tan \theta = \tan \theta'$. Since $0 \le \theta, \theta' \le \pi$, we conclude that either $\theta = 0$ and $\theta' = \pi$, or $\theta = \pi$ and $\theta' = 0$, or $\theta = \theta'$. If $\theta = 0, \theta' = \pi$ then (6.3) gives $r = -r'$, which is impossible since $1 \le r, r' \le \sqrt{2}$ (i.e., both r and r' are positive). The second case is ruled out in the same way. In the third case, either (6.3) or (6.4) imply that $r = r'$.

Therefore, $(r, \theta) = (r', \theta')$, so T is a one-to-one mapping on $D^* = [1, \sqrt{2}] \times [0, \pi]$. Moreover, T is C^1 (the component functions are C^1), and the Jacobian is computed to be

$$\frac{\partial(x, y)}{\partial(r, \theta)} = \begin{vmatrix} \cos \theta & -r \sin \theta \\ \sin \theta & r \cos \theta \end{vmatrix} = r. \tag{6.5}$$

◄

Example 6.33

Show that the map $T(u, v) = (u + 2v, 3u - v)$ of Example 6.29 is one-to-one and onto D and compute its Jacobian.

Solution From $T(u, v) = T(u', v')$ it follows that $(u+2v, 3u-v) = (u'+2v', 3u'-v')$; i.e., $u + 2v = u' + 2v'$ and $3u - v = 3u' - v'$. Multiply the second equation by 2 and add the two equations, thus getting $7u = 7u'$; i.e., $u = u'$. Either of the two equations now yields $v = v'$. Therefore, T is one-to-one.

To show that T is onto, pick any point (x_0, y_0) in D. We have to find a point (u_0, v_0) in D^* such that $T(u_0, v_0) = (x_0, y_0)$. We could argue geometrically as in the case of the polar coordinates mapping: (x_0, y_0) belongs to the intersection of the two lines that are parallel to the sides of the parallelogram. All we have to do is to identify the two lines in D^* that map to those lines and find their intersection. Here is an alternative way: from $T(u_0, v_0) = (u_0 + 2v_0, 3u_0 - v_0) = (x_0, y_0)$ it follows that $u_0 + 2v_0 = x_0$ and $3u_0 - v_0 = y_0$. Solving for u_0 and v_0 we get $u_0 = (x_0 + 2y_0)/7$ and $v_0 = (3x_0 - y_0)/7$.

To check that, we compute

$$T(u_0, v_0) = T\left(\frac{x_0 + 2y_0}{7}, \frac{3x_0 - y_0}{7}\right)$$

$$= \left(\frac{x_0 + 2y_0}{7} + 2\frac{3x_0 - y_0}{7}, 3\frac{x_0 + 2y_0}{7} - \frac{3x_0 - y_0}{7}\right) = (x_0, y_0).$$

The Jacobian of T is

$$\frac{\partial(x, y)}{\partial(u, v)} = \begin{vmatrix} 1 & 2 \\ 3 & -1 \end{vmatrix} = -7.$$

Our next definition introduces a special class of maps, called affine (and in a special case, linear) maps.

Identify a point (u, v) in $\mathbb{R}^2$ with the tip of the vector $\mathbf{u} = (u, v)$, that is represented as a 2×1 matrix $\begin{bmatrix} u \\ v \end{bmatrix}$. Let A be a 2×2 matrix

$$A = \begin{bmatrix} a_{11} & a_{12} \\ a_{21} & a_{22} \end{bmatrix}$$

and let

$$\mathbf{b} = \begin{bmatrix} b_1 \\ b_2 \end{bmatrix}.$$

■ **Definition 6.7**   Linear and Affine Maps.

A map $T: \mathbb{R}^2 \to \mathbb{R}^2$ defined by

$$T\begin{bmatrix} u \\ v \end{bmatrix} = \begin{bmatrix} a_{11} & a_{12} \\ a_{21} & a_{22} \end{bmatrix}\begin{bmatrix} u \\ v \end{bmatrix} + \begin{bmatrix} b_1 \\ b_2 \end{bmatrix}$$

is called an *affine map*. If $b = \begin{bmatrix} 0 \\ 0 \end{bmatrix}$, then T it is called a *linear map*. ■

With the identifications announced before the definition, we can write T as

$$T(\mathbf{u}) = A\mathbf{u} + \mathbf{b},$$

where the operations on the right side are matrix operations, and the resultant 2×1 matrix is interpreted as a point in $\mathbb{R}^2$. The formula for T can be expanded as

$$T(u, v) = (a_{11}u + a_{12}v + b_1, a_{21}u + a_{22}v + b_2).$$

We have already met a linear map in Example 6.29 (and also in Section 1.4, where we called it a linear vector field) and an affine map in Example 6.31. Our next theorem will simplify computations with affine (and therefore also linear) maps.

■ **Theorem 6.6**   Properties of Affine Maps.

Let $T(\mathbf{u}) = A\mathbf{u} + \mathbf{b}$ be an affine map and assume that $\det(A) \neq 0$. Then

(a) T is one-to-one.

(b) T maps lines to lines, parallel lines to parallel lines and the intersection of two lines to the intersection of their images.

(c) If D^* is a parallelogram, then $T(D^*)$ is a parallelogram.

(d) If D is a parallelogram, and D^* is a region such that $T(D^*) = D$, then D^* is a parallelogram. ∎

The proofs are technical and are left as exercises (with hints).

In the change of variables theorem we will actually have to find D^* from $T(D^*) = D$. In the case when D is a rectangle (or polygon, in general), the theorem will help us find D^*: all we need is to identify the vertices of D^* and connect them with straight lines.

Example 6.34

The change of variables $x = u+2v$, $y = u-v$ can be represented as a map $T: \mathbb{R}^2 \to \mathbb{R}^2$ given by

$$T(u, v) = (u + 2v, u - v).$$

Let D be the square $[0, 1] \times [0, 1]$. Find the region D^* that maps to D and compute the Jacobian of T.

Solution The map T is linear, and therefore in order to find D^* we have to find the points that map to the vertices of the square D, and then join them with straight lines.

Solving $u+2v = 0$ and $u-v = 0$ gives that $(u = 0, v = 0)$ maps to $(x = 0, y = 0)$. Solving $u+2v = 1$ and $u-v = 0$ gives that $(u = 1/3, v = 1/3)$ maps to $(x = 1, y = 0)$. Similarly, we can check that $(2/3, -1/3)$ maps to $(0, 1)$ and that $(1, 0)$ maps to $(1, 1)$, and therefore D^* is the parallelogram with vertices $(0, 0)$, $(1/3, 1/3)$, $(2/3, -1/3)$ and $(1, 0)$.

The fact that T is one-to-one follows from

$$\det(A) = \det \begin{bmatrix} 1 & 2 \\ 1 & -1 \end{bmatrix} = -3 \neq 0$$

and Theorem 6.6(a). The map T is clearly C^1 ($u + 2v$ and $u - v$ are C^1 functions of u and v), and its Jacobian is

$$\frac{\partial(x, y)}{\partial(u, v)} = \begin{vmatrix} 1 & 2 \\ 1 & -1 \end{vmatrix} = -3.$$

◀

The fact that $\det(A)$ is equal to the Jacobian of T is not a coincidence, but holds for all affine maps (the proof is straightforward, and is left as exercise).

Recall that a change of variables $x = x(u, v)$, $y = y(u, v)$, where x and y are C^1 functions of u and v, can be described as a C^1, one-to-one mapping $T(u, v) = (x(u, v), y(u, v))$.

■ **Theorem 6.7**   Change of Variables Formula

Let D and D^* be elementary regions in $\mathbb{R}^2$ and let $T: D^* \to D$ be a C^1, one-to-one map such that $T(D^*) = D$. For any integrable function $f: D \to \mathbb{R}$,

$$\iint_D f(x, y)\, dA = \iint_{D^*} f(x(u, v), y(u, v)) \left| \frac{\partial(x, y)}{\partial(u, v)} \right| dA^*. \qquad (6.6) \ \blacksquare$$

In words, the integral of f over D equals the integral over D^* of the composition $f \circ T$, multiplied by the absolute value of the Jacobian of T. Instead of giving the (technical and somewhat long) proof of the theorem we will explain the geometric meaning of (6.6).

Subdivide the region D^* into small rectangles in the usual way: enclose D^* into a rectangle, form a division of that rectangle into n^2 (n is a large integer) subrectangles and consider only those subrectangles whose intersection with D^* is non-empty (see Figure 6.43). Choose one of those subrectangles and name it R^*. Label its sides by Δu and Δv and assume that one of its vertices is located at (u_0, v_0). Label the diametrically opposite vertex by $(u, v) = (u_0 + \Delta u, v_0 + \Delta v)$. The area of R^* is $\Delta u \Delta v$, and the sum $\sum \Delta u \Delta v$ over all subrectangles that intersect D^* (the others were thrown away) approximates the area of D^*.

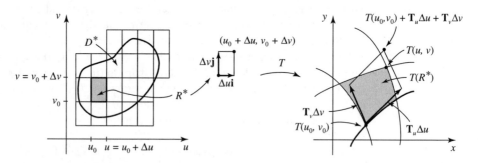

Figure 6.43   Small rectangle R^* and its image $R = T(R^*)$.

The image $R = T(R^*)$ of the rectangle R^* is most probably no longer a rectangle or a parallelogram. It is the region in $\mathbb{R}^2$ bounded by the images by T of the horizontal ($v = v_0$ and $v = v_0 + \Delta v$) and vertical ($u = u_0$ and $u = u_0 + \Delta u$) lines that form the boundary of R^*. We will now approximate the area of R. Recall that a function $T: \mathbb{R}^2 \to \mathbb{R}^2$, $T(u, v) = (x(u, v), y(u, v))$, maps points to points, but its derivative $DT: \mathbb{R}^2 \to \mathbb{R}^2$, given by

$$DT(u, v) = \begin{bmatrix} \dfrac{\partial x}{\partial u} & \dfrac{\partial x}{\partial v} \\[2mm] \dfrac{\partial y}{\partial u} & \dfrac{\partial y}{\partial v} \end{bmatrix},$$

maps tangent vectors to tangent vectors. The vector $\Delta u \mathbf{i}$ is tangent to the line $v = v_0$ at

(u_0, v_0). Therefore, its image

$$DT(u_0, v_0)(\Delta u\mathbf{i}) = \begin{bmatrix} \frac{\partial x}{\partial u}(u_0, v_0) & \frac{\partial x}{\partial v}(u_0, v_0) \\ \frac{\partial y}{\partial u}(u_0, v_0) & \frac{\partial y}{\partial v}(u_0, v_0) \end{bmatrix} \cdot \begin{bmatrix} \Delta u \\ 0 \end{bmatrix}$$

$$= \frac{\partial x}{\partial u}\bigg|_{(u_0,v_0)} \Delta u\mathbf{i} + \frac{\partial y}{\partial u}\bigg|_{(u_0,v_0)} \Delta u\mathbf{j} = \mathbf{T}_u(u_0, v_0)\Delta u,$$

where $\mathbf{T}_u(u_0, v_0) = (\partial x/\partial u)(u_0, v_0)\mathbf{i} + (\partial y/\partial u)(u_0, v_0)\mathbf{j}$, is the vector tangent to the image of the line $v = v_0$ at $T(u_0, v_0)$. All functions involved (T, $\partial x/\partial u$, $\partial x/\partial v$, etc.) are evaluated at (u_0, v_0). We will keep this in mind but, for simplicity, will drop (u_0, v_0) from the notation. Similarly, at (u_0, v_0), the image $DT(\Delta v\mathbf{j})$ of $\Delta v\mathbf{j}$ is computed to be

$$DT(\Delta v\mathbf{j}) = \begin{bmatrix} \frac{\partial x}{\partial u} & \frac{\partial x}{\partial v} \\ \frac{\partial y}{\partial u} & \frac{\partial y}{\partial v} \end{bmatrix} \cdot \begin{bmatrix} 0 \\ \Delta v \end{bmatrix} = \frac{\partial x}{\partial v}\Delta v\mathbf{i} + \frac{\partial y}{\partial v}\Delta v\mathbf{j} = \mathbf{T}_v\Delta v,$$

where $\mathbf{T}_v = (\partial x/\partial v)\mathbf{i} + (\partial y/\partial v)\mathbf{j}$.

On the other hand, we have shown in Section 2.4 that

$$T(u, v) \approx T(u_0, v_0) + DT(u_0, v_0)\begin{bmatrix} u - u_0 \\ v - v_0 \end{bmatrix},$$

where $u = u_0 + \Delta u$, $v = v_0 + \Delta v$ (read formula (2.16) with $\mathbf{F} = T$, $\mathbf{a} = (u_0, v_0)$ and $\mathbf{x} = (u, v)$). Therefore

$$T(u, v) \approx T(u_0, v_0) + \begin{bmatrix} \frac{\partial x}{\partial u} & \frac{\partial x}{\partial v} \\ \frac{\partial y}{\partial u} & \frac{\partial y}{\partial v} \end{bmatrix}\begin{bmatrix} \Delta u \\ \Delta v \end{bmatrix} = T(u_0, v_0) + \begin{bmatrix} \frac{\partial x}{\partial u}\Delta u + \frac{\partial x}{\partial v}\Delta v \\ \frac{\partial y}{\partial u}\Delta u + \frac{\partial y}{\partial v}\Delta v \end{bmatrix}$$

$$= T(u_0, v_0) + \left(\frac{\partial x}{\partial u}\Delta u + \frac{\partial x}{\partial v}\Delta v\right)\mathbf{i} + \left(\frac{\partial y}{\partial u}\Delta u + \frac{\partial y}{\partial v}\Delta v\right)\mathbf{j}$$

$$= T(u_0, v_0) + \mathbf{T}_u\Delta u + \mathbf{T}_v\Delta v.$$

It follows that the area $A(R)$ of R is approximated by the area of the parallelogram spanned by $\mathbf{T}_u\Delta u$ and $\mathbf{T}_v\Delta v$, which is equal to $\|\mathbf{T}_u\Delta u \times \mathbf{T}_v\Delta v\|$. But

$$\mathbf{T}_u\Delta u \times \mathbf{T}_v\Delta v = \begin{vmatrix} \mathbf{i} & \mathbf{j} & \mathbf{k} \\ \frac{\partial x}{\partial u}\Delta u & \frac{\partial y}{\partial u}\Delta u & 0 \\ \frac{\partial x}{\partial v}\Delta v & \frac{\partial y}{\partial v}\Delta v & 0 \end{vmatrix} = \Delta u\Delta v\left(\frac{\partial x}{\partial u}\frac{\partial y}{\partial v} - \frac{\partial x}{\partial v}\frac{\partial y}{\partial u}\right)\mathbf{k}$$

$$= \begin{vmatrix} \frac{\partial x}{\partial u} & \frac{\partial x}{\partial v} \\ \frac{\partial y}{\partial u} & \frac{\partial y}{\partial v} \end{vmatrix}\Delta u\Delta v\,\mathbf{k} = \frac{\partial(x, y)}{\partial(u, v)}\Delta u\Delta v\,\mathbf{k},$$

and hence (Δu and Δv are positive)

$$A(R) = \|\mathbf{T}_u\Delta u \times \mathbf{T}_v\Delta v\| = \left|\frac{\partial(x, y)}{\partial(u, v)}\right|\Delta u\Delta v;$$

i.e., $A(R)$ is equal to the absolute value of the Jacobian multiplied by $\Delta u\Delta v$. It follows that the area of the image R under a map T of a small rectangle R^* is approximately equal to the absolute value of the Jacobian of T multiplied by the area of R^*.

The sum

$$\sum \left|\frac{\partial(x, y)}{\partial(u, v)}\right|\Delta u\Delta v$$

(over all R's) approximates the area of $T(D^*) = D$. Taking the limit as the rectangles become smaller and smaller we get that

$$\int_D \left| \frac{\partial(x, y)}{\partial(u, v)} \right| du\,dv \qquad (6.7)$$

gives the area of D. Hence the (integral of the absolute value of the) Jacobian describes how area changes under the map T.

Example 6.35

Approximate the area of the image R of a small rectangle R^* with sides $\Delta u = 0.1$, $\Delta v = 0.2$ and one vertex at $(u_0, v_0) = (2, 3)$ under the map $T(u, v) = (uv^2, u + v)$.

Solution   The area of R^* is 0.02. The area of R is approximately equal to the product of the absolute value of the Jacobian $\det(DT)$ at $(2, 3)$ and the area of R^*. Therefore

$$A(R) \approx \left| \det \begin{bmatrix} v^2 & 2uv \\ 1 & 1 \end{bmatrix}_{at\ (2,3)} \right| A(R^*) = |v^2 - 2uv|\Big|_{(2,3)}\ 0.02 = 0.06. \qquad \blacktriangleleft$$

Example 6.36

Jacobian for Affine Maps.

If T is an affine map (and, in particular, a linear map), then the above approximate computation becomes exact, since T maps parallelograms to parallelograms (so that there are no curves to be approximated by straight line segments). Let us look at several maps and compute their Jacobians.

(a) Let $T: \mathbb{R}^2 \to \mathbb{R}^2$ be the translation $T(u, v) = (u+1, v)$ in the horizontal direction. The Jacobian is

$$\frac{\partial(x, y)}{\partial(u, v)} = \begin{vmatrix} 1 & 0 \\ 0 & 1 \end{vmatrix} = 1,$$

and hence there is no change in the area; see Figure 6.44.

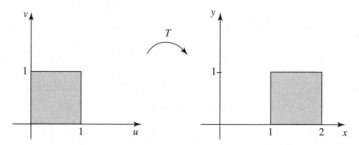

Figure 6.44   The map $T(u, v) = (u+1, v)$ preserves area.

(b) Let $T(u, v) = (au, bv)$, where $a, b > 0$. In words, T is an expansion in the x-direction if $a > 1$ and an expansion in the y-direction if $b > 1$. If $a < 1$ then T is a contraction in the x-direction, and if $b < 1$ a contraction in the y-direction. The

Jacobian of T is

$$\frac{\partial(x, y)}{\partial(u, v)} = \begin{vmatrix} a & 0 \\ 0 & b \end{vmatrix} = ab,$$

and the area changes by the factor ab; see Figure 6.45.

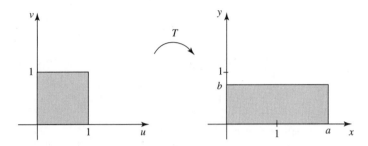

Figure 6.45 The map $T(u, v) = (au, bv)$ changes the area by the factor ab (pictured is a case for which $a > 1$ and $b < 1$).

(c) Let $T(u, v) = (u \cos \phi - v \sin \phi, u \sin \phi + v \cos \phi)$; i.e., T is a rotation about the origin through the angle ϕ in the counterclockwise direction; see Figure 6.46. Then

$$\frac{\partial(x, y)}{\partial(u, v)} = \begin{vmatrix} \cos \phi & -\sin \phi \\ \sin \phi & \cos \phi \end{vmatrix} = 1,$$

so there is no change in the area. ◄

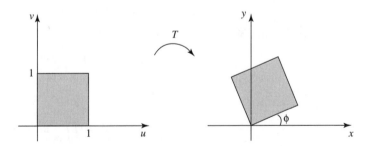

Figure 6.46 The map $T(u, v) = (u \cos \phi - v \sin \phi, u \sin \phi + v \cos \phi)$ preserves area.

Example 6.37 Evaluate

$$\iint_D e^{x^2 + y^2} \, dA$$

where D is the region $\{(x, y) \mid 1 \leq x^2 + y^2 \leq 2, y \geq 0\}$ of Example 6.30.

Solution   Let $x = r \cos \theta$, $y = r \sin \theta$, with $1 \le r \le \sqrt{2}$ and $0 \le \theta \le \pi$. Then

$$\left| \frac{\partial(x, y)}{\partial(r, \theta)} \right| = |r| = r,$$

as in (6.5), and by Theorem 6.7,

$$\iint_D e^{x^2 + y^2} \, dA = \iint_{D^*} e^{r^2} r \, dA^*,$$

where D^* is the rectangle $[1, \sqrt{2}] \times [0, \pi]$ in the $r\theta$-plane. Therefore

$$\iint_D e^{x^2 + y^2} \, dA = \int_0^\pi \left(\int_1^{\sqrt{2}} e^{r^2} r \, dr \right) d\theta$$

(substitute $u = r^2$, $du = 2r \, dr$)

$$= \int_0^\pi \left(\frac{1}{2} e^{r^2} \Big|_1^{\sqrt{2}} \right) d\theta = \left(\frac{1}{2} e^2 - \frac{1}{2} e \right) \int_0^\pi d\theta = \frac{1}{2}(e^2 - e)\pi. \quad \blacktriangleleft$$

Example 6.38   Compute $\iint_D (x + y) \, dA$ where D is the region $0 \le x \le 1$, $0 \le y \le x$

(a) by using the change of variables $x = u + v$, $y = u - v$, and

(b) by direct computation.

Solution   Notice that $T(u, v) = (x, y) = (u + v, u - v)$ is a linear map with the corresponding matrix

$$A = \begin{bmatrix} 1 & 1 \\ 1 & -1 \end{bmatrix}.$$

(a) The Jacobian of the change of variables is

$$\frac{\partial(x, y)}{\partial(u, v)} = \begin{vmatrix} 1 & 1 \\ 1 & -1 \end{vmatrix} = -2,$$

and therefore

$$\iint_D (x + y) \, dA = \iint_{D^*} 2u \, |-2| \, dA^*,$$

where D^* is the region that maps to D under the map $T(u, v) = (u + v, u - v)$.

The region D is the triangular region with vertices $(0, 0)$, $(1, 0)$ and $(1, 1)$. Now $x = u + v = 0$ and $y = u - v = 0$ imply that $u = v = 0$; i.e., the point $(0, 0)$ in the uv-plane maps to the point $(0, 0)$ in the xy-plane. Analogously, $x = u + v = 1$ and $y = u - v = 0$ imply that $u = v = 1/2$; i.e., the point $(1/2, 1/2)$ in the uv-plane maps to the point $(1, 0)$ in the xy-plane. Similarly, the point $(1, 0)$ in the uv-plane maps to $(1, 1)$ in the xy-plane; see Figure 6.47. The fact that triangles map to triangles follows from Theorem 6.6(b).

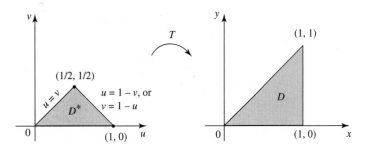

Figure 6.47 The map $T(u, v) = (u + v, u - v)$.

Hence D^* is the triangle with vertices $(0, 0)$, $(1/2, 1/2)$ and $(1, 0)$. The fact that T is one-to-one follows from the fact that T is linear, since $\det(A) \neq 0$ (cf. Theorem 6.6(a)). Hence

$$\iint_D (x + y)\, dA = 4 \int_0^{1/2} \left(\int_v^{1-v} u\, du \right) dv = 2 \int_0^{1/2} \left(u^2 \Big|_{u=v}^{u=1-v} \right) dv$$

$$= 2 \int_0^{1/2} (1 - 2v)\, dv = 2(v - v^2)\Big|_0^{1/2} = \frac{1}{2}.$$

In the reversed order of integration,

$$\iint_D (x + y)\, dA = 4 \left(\int_0^{1/2} \left(\int_0^u u\, dv \right) du + \int_{1/2}^1 \left(\int_0^{1-u} u\, dv \right) du \right)$$

$$= 4 \left(\int_0^{1/2} \left(uv \Big|_{v=0}^{v=u} \right) du + \int_{1/2}^1 \left(uv \Big|_{v=0}^{v=1-u} \right) du \right)$$

$$= 4 \left(\frac{u^3}{3} \Big|_0^{1/2} + \left(\frac{u^2}{2} - \frac{u^3}{3} \right) \Big|_{1/2}^1 \right) = \frac{1}{2}.$$

(b) A direct computation gives

$$\iint_D (x + y)\, dx\, dy = \int_0^1 \left(\int_0^x (x + y)\, dy \right) dx = \int_0^1 \left(xy + \frac{y^2}{2} \Big|_{y=0}^{y=x} \right) dx$$

$$= \frac{3}{2} \int_0^1 x^2\, dx = \frac{3}{2} \frac{x^3}{3} \Big|_0^1 = \frac{1}{2}.$$

Example 6.39   Using the change of variables $x = v$ and $y = u/v$ transform the integral $\iint_D x^2 y^2\, dA$, where D is the region in the first quadrant bounded by the parabolas $y = x^2$ and $y = 2x^2$ and the hyperbolas $xy = 1$ and $xy = 2$.

Solution   The change of variables function T is defined by $T(u, v) = (v, u/v)$. First of all, we have to find the region D^* such that $T(D^*) = D$. From $y = x^2$ we get $u/v = v^2$ and $v = u^{1/3}$. From $y = 2x^2$ we get $u/v = 2v^2$ and $v = (u/2)^{1/3}$. Similarly, $xy = 1$ implies $u = 1$ and $xy = 2$ implies $u = 2$. It follows that D^* is the region of type 1 in the uv-plane, defined by $1 \leq u \leq 2$ and $(u/2)^{1/3} \leq v \leq u^{1/3}$; see Figure 6.48.

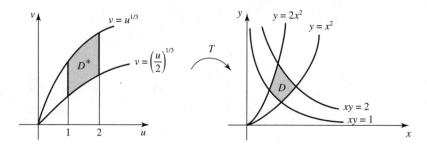

Figure 6.48   The function T maps the region D^* to D.

The function T is C^1 except at $v = 0$ (but that is irrelevant, since D^* is away from the u-axis), and its Jacobian is

$$\frac{\partial(x, y)}{\partial(u, v)} = \begin{vmatrix} 0 & 1 \\ 1/v & -u/v^2 \end{vmatrix} = \frac{1}{v}.$$

Therefore,

$$\iint_D x^2 y^2 \, dA = \iint_{D^*} v^2 \left(\frac{u}{v}\right)^2 \left|\frac{1}{v}\right| \, dA^* = \int_1^2 \left(\int_{(u/2)^{1/3}}^{u^{1/3}} \frac{u^2}{v} \, dv\right) du.$$

◀

EXERCISES 6.4   **Exercises 1 to 5:** Evaluate the given double integral by converting to polar coordinates.

1. $\int_0^2 \left(\int_0^{\sqrt{4-x^2}} e^{x^2+y^2} dy\right) dx$

2. $\iint_D xy \, dA$, where D is the region in the first quadrant bounded by $x^2 + y^2 = 4$, $y = x/\sqrt{2}$ and $y = 0$

3. $\int_{-1}^1 \left(\int_0^{\sqrt{1-x^2}} \arctan(y/x) dy\right) dx$

4. $\iint_D \sqrt{x^2 + y^2} \, dA$, where D is the semi-circle $(x - 1)^2 + y^2 = 1$, $y \geq 0$

5. $\iint_D \sqrt{2x^2 + 2y^2 + 3} \, dA$, where D is the disk $x^2 + y^2 \leq 1$

6. Convert the double integral $\int_0^2 \left(\int_0^{\sqrt{4x-x^2}} (x^2 + y^2)^{3/4} dy\right) dx$ to polar coordinates. Do not evaluate it.

7. Find the volume of the solid under the paraboloid $z = x^2+y^2$, inside the cylinder $x^2+y^2 = 5$ and above the xy-plane.

8. Find the volume of the solid between the paraboloids $z = 3x^2+3y^2$ and $z = 12-3x^2-3y^2$.

9. Find the volume of the solid inside the cylinder $x^2+y^2 = 4$, inside the ellipsoid $4x^2+4y^2+z^2 = 64$ and above the xy-plane.

10. Using a double integral compute the volume of a sphere of radius $a > 0$.

11. Show that if $T(\mathbf{u}) = A\mathbf{u} + \mathbf{b}$ is an affine map, then $\det(A)$ is equal to the Jacobian of T.

12. Consider the map $T(\mathbf{u}) = A\mathbf{u} + \mathbf{b}$, where

$$A = \begin{bmatrix} a_{11} & a_{12} \\ a_{21} & a_{22} \end{bmatrix}, \qquad \mathbf{b} = \begin{bmatrix} b_1 \\ b_2 \end{bmatrix},$$

and assume that $\det(A) \neq 0$.

(a) Show that T is one-to-one (hint: you will need the fact that if $\det(A) \neq 0$ then the 2×2 system $a_{11}X + a_{12}Y = 0$ and $a_{21}X + a_{22}Y = 0$ has a unique solution $X = Y = 0$).

(b) Compute the image of the line $\boldsymbol{\ell}_1(t) = (w_1 + tv_1, w_2 + tv_2)$, $t \in \mathbb{R}$, under T. Next, compute the image of the line $\boldsymbol{\ell}_2(t) = (\overline{w_1} + tv_1, \overline{w_2} + tv_2)$, $t \in \mathbb{R}$, parallel to $\boldsymbol{\ell}_1(t)$. Conclude that parallel lines map to parallel lines.

(c) Consider two lines $\boldsymbol{\ell}_1(t) = (tv_1, tv_2)$, $t \in \mathbb{R}$, and $\boldsymbol{\ell}_2(t) = (tw_1, tw_2)$, $t \in \mathbb{R}$, that intersect at the origin. The origin is mapped to (b_1, b_2) under T. Compute the images of $\boldsymbol{\ell}_1(t)$ and $\boldsymbol{\ell}_2(t)$ and find their point of intersection.

(d) Show that $S(\mathbf{x}) = A^{-1}\mathbf{x} - A^{-1}\mathbf{b}$ is the inverse map of T, where A^{-1} is the inverse matrix of A (i.e., show that $S \circ T(u, v) = (u, v)$ and $T \circ S(x, y) = (x, y)$).

(e) Using (d), prove statement (d) of Theorem 6.6.

13. Approximate the area of the image of a small rectangle with sides $\Delta u = 0.1$ and $\Delta v = 0.05$ and one vertex located at $(2, 4)$, under the mapping T defined by $T(u, v) = (\sqrt{u^2 + v^2}, uv)$.

14. Approximate the area of the image of a small rectangle with sides $\Delta u = 0.03$ and $\Delta v = 0.1$ and one vertex located at $(-2, 1)$, under the mapping T defined by $T(u, v) = (u \sin v, u \cos v)$.

15. Describe in words the map $T: \mathbb{R}^2 \to \mathbb{R}^2$ given by $T(u, v) = (au, v + b)$, where $a > 1$ and $b > 0$. What is the relation between the area of a region D and the area of its image $T(D)$?

16. Consider the map $T: \mathbb{R}^2 \to \mathbb{R}^2$ given by $T(u, v) = (u + v, v)$. Describe the region to which T maps a square whose sides are parallel to the coordinate axes. Compute the Jacobian of T and interpret the result geometrically.

17. Evaluate $\iint_D (5x + y^2 + x^2) \, dA$, where D is the part of the annulus $1 \leq x^2 + y^2 \leq 4$ in the upper half-plane.

18. Using a double integral find the area of the region enclosed by one loop of the curve $r = \cos 2\theta$. Hint: sketch the curve.

19. Find the area of the region inside the cardioid $r = 1 - \sin\theta$, $0 \leq \theta \leq 2\pi$.

20. Express the volume of the right circular cone of radius r and height h as a double integral in polar coordinates.

21. Find the area of the region in the first quadrant bounded by the curves $r = \theta$ and $r = 2\theta$.

22. Compute the integral $\iint_D (4x + 6y) \, dA$, where D is the region bounded by the lines $4y = x - 3$, $4y = x + 2$, $2x + 3y = 6$ and $2x + 3y = 17$ (hint: use the change of variables $x = 4u - 3v$, $y = u + 2v$).

23. Compute the integral $\iint_D (x^2 - y^2) \, dA$, where D is the region bounded by the curves $xy = 1$, $y = x - 1$ and $y = x + 1$ (hint: use the change of variables $x = u + v$, $y = -u + v$).

24. Compute the integral $\iint_D (2x - y) \, dA$, where D is the region bounded by the curves $y = 2x$, $x = 2y$ and $x + y = 6$ (hint: use the change of variables $x = u - v$, $y = u + v$).

25. Compute the volume of the wedge cut from the cylinder $x^2 + y^2 = 9$ by the planes $z = 0$ and $z = y + 3$.

26. Compute the volume of the solid below the plane $z = y + 4$ and above the disk $x^2 + y^2 \leq 1$.

27. Compute the integral $\iint_D xy^3\, dA$, where D is the region in the first quadrant bounded by the lines $x = 1$ and $x = 2$ and the hyperbolas $xy = 1$ and $xy = 3$ (hint: use the change of variables $x = v$, $y = u/v$).

28. Compute the integral $\iint_D 5\, dA$, where D is the region inside the ellipse $4x^2 + 2y^2 = 1$ (hint: define a change of variables so that the region of integration becomes a circle).

29. Evaluate $\iint_D 5(x + y)\, dA$, where D is the region bounded by the lines $3x - 2y = 5$, $3x - 2y = -2$, $x + y = -2$ and $x + y = 1$ using a suitable change of variables.

30. Evaluate $\iint_D x^2\, dA$, where D is the region $0 \leq \frac{1}{9}x^2 + y^2 \leq 1$ using a suitable change of variables.

31. Evaluate $\iint_D e^x\, dA$, where D is the region defined by $x + y = 0$, $x + y = 2$, $y = x$ and $y = 2x$.

32. Evaluate $\iint_D (x^2 - y^2)\, dA$, where D is the region in the first quadrant bounded by the curves $x^2 - y^2 = 1$, $x^2 - y^2 = 2$, $y = 0$ and $y = 2x$, using the change of variables $x = u \cosh v$ and $y = u \sinh v$.

33. Evaluate $\iint_D \sin \frac{x+y}{x-y}\, dA$, where D is the region bounded by the lines $x - y = 1$, $x - y = 5$ and the coordinate axes.

34. A one-to-one C^1 map $T(u, v) = (x(u, v), y(u, v))$ can be viewed as a transformation from Cartesian coordinates x, y to curvilinear coordinates u, v in $\mathbb{R}^2$. The scale factors of T are defined as $h_u = \|\partial T(u, v)/\partial u\|$ and $h_v = \|\partial T(u, v)/\partial v\|$. Show that the Jacobian of T is equal to the product $h_u h_v$ of the scale factors.

View a C^1, one-to-one map $T(u_1, u_2, u_3) = (x(u_1, u_2, u_3), y(u_1, u_2, u_3), z(u_1, u_2, u_3))$ as a transformation of coordinates in $\mathbb{R}^3$; see Section 2.8. Define the scale factors of T, and show that, as in the case of $\mathbb{R}^2$, the Jacobian of T is equal to the product of the scale factors.

6.5   TRIPLE INTEGRALS

The definition, properties and methods of evaluation of triple integrals are analogous to those of double integrals. Nevertheless, for the sake of completeness we will briefly go through the relevant concepts.

Let $f = f(x, y, z)$ be a *bounded* function defined on a closed and bounded solid V in $\mathbb{R}^3$. Recall that a function $f \colon V \to \mathbb{R}$ is bounded if there exists $M \geq 0$ such that $|f(x, y, z)| \leq M$ for all $(x, y, z) \in V$. The fact that V is closed means that it contains the surface that is its boundary. Enclose V with a big rectangular box (this is possible due to the assumption that V is bounded) and divide it into n^3 sub-boxes V_{ijk}, $i, j, k = 1, \ldots, n$, with faces parallel to coordinate planes; see Figure 6.49. Form the *(triple) Riemann sum*

$$\mathcal{R}_n = \sum_i \sum_j \sum_k f(x_i^*, y_j^*, z_k^*)\Delta V_{ijk},$$

where (x_i^*, y_j^*, z_k^*) is any point in V_{ijk}, $\Delta V_{ijk} = \Delta x_i \Delta y_j \Delta z_k$ is the volume of V_{ijk} and the sums run over those V_{ijk} that have a non-empty intersection with V.

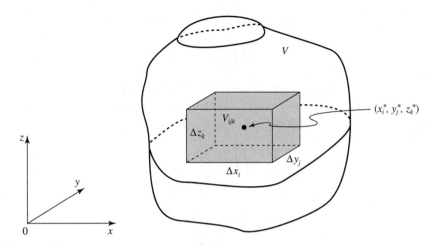

Figure 6.49   A sub-box V_{ijk} from the definition of the Riemann sum of f.

■ Definition 6.8   Triple Integral

The *triple integral $\iiint_V f \, dV$ of f over V* is defined by

$$\iiint_V f \, dV = \lim_{n \to \infty} \mathcal{R}_n,$$

whenever the limit on the right side exists.

The definition does not depend on the way V is divided into sub-boxes V_{ijk} or on the choice of the point (x_i^*, y_j^*, z_k^*) in each V_{ijk}. A function f for which the above triple integral is defined is called *integrable*. Continuous functions, as well as some bounded discontinuous functions (those whose points of discontinuity lie on the graph of a continuous function of two variables) are integrable (compare with the integrability of functions of two variables over regions in $\mathbb{R}^2$ discussed in Section 6.2). Continuous functions defined on a closed and bounded set are bounded (see Appendix A), so there was no need to say "continuous bounded functions" in the previous sentence.

From the construction, it follows that the integral $\iiint_V 1 \, dV$ represents the volume of the solid V.

Various symbols, such as

$$\int_V f \, dV, \qquad \int_V f \, dx \, dy \, dz, \qquad \iiint_V f \, dx \, dy \, dz$$

and some others are used to denote triple integrals.

As in the two-dimensional case, the triple integral $\iiint_V f \, dV$ over the rectangular parallelepiped (i.e., the "rectangular box")

$$V = [a_1, b_1] \times [a_2, b_2] \times [a_3, b_3] = \{(x, y, z) \mid a_1 \le x \le b_1, a_2 \le y \le b_2, a_3 \le z \le b_3\}$$

can be computed as an iterated integral:

$$\iiint_V f\,dV = \int_{a_3}^{b_3} \left(\int_{a_2}^{b_2} \left(\int_{a_1}^{b_1} f(x, y, z)dx \right) dy \right) dz.$$

This is the version of Fubini's Theorem for triple integrals (the function f has to be continuous). Moreover, these integrations can be performed in any order (there are six different combinations). For example,

$$\iiint_V f\,dV = \int_{a_1}^{b_1} \left(\int_{a_3}^{b_3} \left(\int_{a_2}^{b_2} f(x, y, z)dy \right) dz \right) dx$$

$$= \int_{a_3}^{b_3} \left(\int_{a_1}^{b_1} \left(\int_{a_2}^{b_2} f(x, y, z)dy \right) dx \right) dz,$$

etc.

In Section 6.2 we defined elementary regions in $\mathbb{R}^2$ as regions of type 1, 2 or 3. To distinguish between those and their analogues in three dimensions we will add (2D) or (3D) to their name, thus indicating their dimension. A *region of type 1(3D)* is the set of all points (x, y, z) such that:

(a) Points (x, y) belong to an elementary (2D) region D in $\mathbb{R}^2$, and

(b) $\kappa_1(x, y) \leq z \leq \kappa_2(x, y)$, where κ_1 and κ_2 denote continuous functions such that if $\kappa_1(x, y) = \kappa_2(x, y)$ then the point (x, y) belongs to the boundary of D.

In other words, if surfaces that bound a type-1(3D) region intersect, then they intersect at points on the boundary of D, and not in the inside of D; see Figure 6.50.

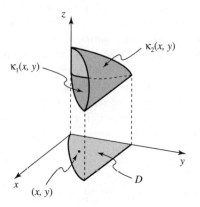

Figure 6.50 A region of type 1(3D)

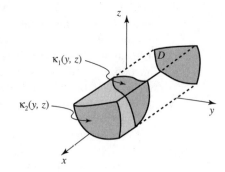

Figure 6.51 A region of type 2(3D)

A *region of type 2(3D)* is defined similarly, with x and z interchanged. That means that the back and the front of a type-2(3D) region are the surfaces $x = \kappa_1(y, z)$ and $x = \kappa_2(y, z)$, and the points (y, z) belong to an elementary (2D) region in the yz-plane. The surfaces $\kappa_1(y, z)$ and $\kappa_2(y, z)$ can only intersect along the boundary of that region; see Figure 6.51.

A *region of type 3(3D)* is defined by interchanging y and z in the definition of a region of type 1 (3D). A region is of *type 4(3D)* if it is of types 1(3D), 2(3D) and 3(3D). A three-dimensional region is called an *elementary 3D region* if it belongs to one (or more) of the four types defined above.

Now assume that V is of type 1(3D). Then either

$$\begin{cases} a \leq x \leq b \quad \text{and} \\ \phi(x) \leq y \leq \psi(x) \quad \text{if } D \subseteq \mathbb{R}^2 \text{ is of type 1(2D), and} \\ \kappa_1(x, y) \leq z \leq \kappa_2(x, y) \end{cases}$$

or

$$\begin{cases} c \leq y \leq d \quad \text{and} \\ \phi(y) \leq x \leq \psi(y) \quad \text{if } D \subseteq \mathbb{R}^2 \text{ is of type 2(2D), and} \\ \kappa_1(x, y) \leq z \leq \kappa_2(x, y). \end{cases}$$

Consequently,

$$\iiint_V f \, dV = \iint_D \left(\int_{\kappa_1(x,y)}^{\kappa_2(x,y)} f(x, y, z) dz \right) dA$$

$$= \int_a^b \left(\int_{\phi(x)}^{\psi(x)} \left(\int_{\kappa_1(x,y)}^{\kappa_2(x,y)} f(x, y, z) dz \right) dy \right) dx$$

or

$$\iiint_V f \, dV = \iint_D \left(\int_{\kappa_1(x,y)}^{\kappa_2(x,y)} f(x, y, z) dz \right) dA$$

$$= \int_c^d \left(\int_{\phi(y)}^{\psi(y)} \left(\int_{\kappa_1(x,y)}^{\kappa_2(x,y)} f(x, y, z) dz \right) dx \right) dy.$$

■ **Theorem 6.8**   **Change of Variables in a Triple Integral.**

Let V and V^* be elementary (3D) regions in $\mathbb{R}^3$, and let

$$T = T(u, v, w) = (x(u, v, w), y(u, v, w), z(u, v, w)): V^* \to V$$

be a C^1, one-to-one function such that $T(V^*) = V$. For an integrable function $f: V \to \mathbb{R}$,

$$\iiint_V f \, dV = \iiint_{V^*} f(x(u, v, w), y(u, v, w), z(u, v, w)) \left| \frac{\partial(x, y, z)}{\partial(u, v, w)} \right| dV^*. \quad ■$$

The integrand on the right side is the composition $f \circ T$ (i.e., f expressed in terms of "new" variables u, v and w) multiplied by the absolute value of the Jacobian

$$\frac{\partial(x, y, z)}{\partial(u, v, w)} = det(DT) = \begin{vmatrix} \partial x/\partial u & \partial x/\partial v & \partial x/\partial w \\ \partial y/\partial u & \partial y/\partial v & \partial y/\partial w \\ \partial z/\partial u & \partial z/\partial v & \partial z/\partial w \end{vmatrix}.$$

Notice that this is a straightforward generalization of the Change of Variables Theorem for double integrals (see Section 6.4).

Example 6.40   Evaluate $\iiint_V f \, dV$, where $f(x, y, z) = z e^{x+y}$ and V is the parallelepiped $0 \le x \le 1$, $0 \le y \le 2$ and $0 \le z \le 3$.

Solution   By Fubini's Theorem for triple integrals (f is continuous), we can compute this integral in any of the six iterated versions. For example,

$$\iiint_V f \, dV = \int_0^1 \left(\int_0^3 \left(\int_0^2 z e^{x+y} dy \right) dz \right) dx.$$

Since $f = z e^{x+y} = z e^x e^y$, we can separate the integrations and proceed as follows:

$$\iiint_V f \, dV = \left(\int_0^1 e^x \, dx \right) \left(\int_0^3 z \, dz \right) \left(\int_0^2 e^y \, dy \right)$$

$$= \left(e^x \Big|_0^1 \right) \left(\frac{z^2}{2} \Big|_0^3 \right) \left(e^y \Big|_0^2 \right) = \tfrac{9}{2}(e-1)(e^2-1). \qquad \blacktriangleleft$$

Example 6.41   Evaluate $\iiint_V 2y \, dV$, where V is the solid in the first octant bounded by the plane $x + 2y + z = 6$; see Figure 6.52.

Solution   The solid V can be viewed as a type-1(3D) region: the corresponding elementary (2D) region D is the triangle bounded by the x-axis, the y-axis and the line $x + 2y = 6$ (which is the intersection of the plane $x + 2y + z = 6$ and the xy-plane). The bottom and the top surfaces are $z = \kappa_1(x, y) = 0$ and $z = \kappa_2(x, y) = 6 - x - 2y$. It follows that

$$\iiint_V 2y \, dV = \iint_D \left(\int_0^{6-x-2y} 2y \, dz \right) dA$$

$$= \int_0^3 \left(\int_0^{6-2y} \left(\int_0^{6-x-2y} 2y \, dz \right) dx \right) dy$$

$$= \int_0^3 \left(\int_0^{6-2y} \left(2yz \Big|_{z=0}^{z=6-x-2y} \right) dx \right) dy$$

$$= \int_0^3 \left(\int_0^{6-2y} (12y - 2xy - 4y^2) dx \right) dy$$

$$= \int_0^3 \left(12xy - x^2 y - 4y^2 x \Big|_{x=0}^{x=6-2y} \right) dy$$

$$= \int_0^3 (36y - 24y^2 + 4y^3) \, dy = (18y^2 - 8y^3 + y^4) \Big|_0^3 = 27.$$

Reversing the order of the outer two integrations, we get

$$\iiint_V 2y \, dV = \iint_D \left(\int_0^{6-x-2y} 2y \, dz \right) dA = \int_0^6 \left(\int_0^{3-x/2} \left(\int_0^{6-x-2y} 2y \, dz \right) dy \right) dx.$$

The solid V can also be described as a type-2(3D) region: points (y, z) belong to the triangle in the yz-plane bounded by the lines $y = 0$ (z-axis), $z = 0$ (y-axis) and $2y + z = 6$. Furthermore $0 \le x \le 6 - 2y - z$; i.e., the sides of V are the surfaces $x = 0$

and $x = 6 - 2y - z$. Hence

$$\iiint_V 2y \, dV = \int_0^6 \left(\int_0^{3-z/2} \left(\int_0^{6-2y-z} 2y dx \right) dy \right) dz$$

$$= \int_0^3 \left(\int_0^{6-2y} \left(\int_0^{6-2y-z} 2y dx \right) dz \right) dy.$$

Two more equivalent integrals can be obtained by noticing that V is also a type-3(3D) region.

◄

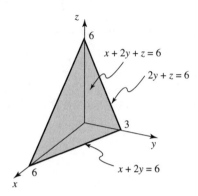

Figure 6.52 Region of example 6.41.

Example 6.42

Compute $\iiint_V \left(x^2 + y^2 \right) dV$, where V is the solid bounded by the cylinder $x^2 + y^2 \leq 4$ and the planes $z = 0$ and $z = 2$.

Solution The solid V can be viewed as a type-1 (3D) region: the corresponding elementary (2D) region is the disk $D = \{(x, y) \mid x^2 + y^2 \leq 4\}$ in the xy-plane, and V is bounded from below and above by the planes $z = \kappa_1(x, y) = 0$ and $z = \kappa_2(x, y) = 2$. Since D is a disk, we pass to cylindrical coordinates

$$x = r \cos \theta, \quad y = r \sin \theta, \quad z = z.$$

The Jacobian is computed to be

$$\frac{\partial(x, y, z)}{\partial(r, \theta, z)} = \begin{vmatrix} \cos \theta & -r \sin \theta & 0 \\ \sin \theta & r \cos \theta & 0 \\ 0 & 0 & 1 \end{vmatrix} = r,$$

and therefore

$$\iiint_V \left(x^2 + y^2 \right) dV = \iiint_{V^*} r^2 \, |r| \, dV^*,$$

where V^* is the rectangular box $[0, 2] \times [0, 2\pi] \times [0, 2]$ (the first interval represents r, the second θ, and the last one z). It follows that

$$\iiint_{V^*} r^2 \, |r| \, dV^* = \iint_{[0,2] \times [0,2\pi]} \left(\int_0^2 r^3 dz \right) dA$$

$$= \int_0^{2\pi} \left(\int_0^2 \left(\int_0^2 r^3 dz \right) dr \right) d\theta$$

$$= \int_0^{2\pi} \left(\int_0^2 2r^3 dr \right) d\theta = 2\pi \left. \frac{r^4}{2} \right|_0^2 = 16\pi.$$

Example 6.43   Express the integral

$$\int_{-1}^1 \left(\int_0^1 \left(\int_{-\sqrt{x}}^{\sqrt{x}} 2xy dz \right) dx \right) dy$$

as an iterated integral in some other order of integration (other than just switching dx and dy).

Solution   The given integral is equal to the triple integral $\iiint_V 2xy\,dV$, where V is determined by $-1 \le y \le 1$, $0 \le x \le 1$, and $-\sqrt{x} \le z \le \sqrt{x}$. It follows that V is a type-1 (3D) region defined by $D = [0, 1] \times [-1, 1]$ and $-\sqrt{x} = \kappa_1(x, y) \le z \le \kappa_2(x, y) = \sqrt{x}$; see Figure 6.53.

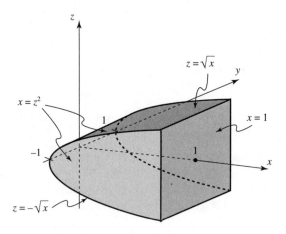

Figure 6.53   The three-dimensional region of Example 6.43.

Think of V as a type-2 (3D) region, where D is the rectangle $D = [-1, 1] \times [-1, 1]$ in the yz-plane (since $-\sqrt{x} \le z \le \sqrt{x}$ and $0 \le x \le 1$ it follows that $-1 \le z \le 1$; that is how the second interval in D was computed). V is bounded on the sides by $x = z^2$ and $x = 1$. Therefore,

$$\iiint_V 2xy\,dV = \iint_D \left(\int_{z^2}^1 2xy dx \right) dA = \int_{-1}^1 \left(\int_{-1}^1 \left(\int_{z^2}^1 2xy \, dx \right) dy \right) dz.$$

Example 6.44   Compute the volume of the solid V that lies inside the sphere $x^2 + y^2 + z^2 = a^2$ and outside the sphere $x^2 + y^2 + z^2 = b^2$, $b < a$.

Solution   We use spherical coordinates

$$x = \rho \sin \phi \cos \theta, \quad y = \rho \sin \phi \sin \theta, \quad z = \rho \cos \phi.$$

The Jacobian is computed to be

$$\frac{\partial(x, y, z)}{\partial(\rho, \phi, \theta)} = \begin{vmatrix} \sin \phi \cos \theta & \rho \cos \phi \cos \theta & -\rho \sin \phi \sin \theta \\ \sin \phi \sin \theta & \rho \cos \phi \sin \theta & \rho \sin \phi \cos \theta \\ \cos \phi & -\rho \sin \phi & 0 \end{vmatrix}$$

$$= \sin \phi \cos \theta (\rho^2 \sin^2 \phi \cos \theta) - \rho \cos \phi \cos \theta (-\rho \sin \phi \cos \phi \cos \theta)$$
$$- \rho \sin \phi \sin \theta (-\rho \sin^2 \phi \sin \theta - \rho \cos^2 \phi \sin \theta)$$
$$= \rho^2 \sin^3 \phi \cos^2 \theta + \rho^2 \cos^2 \phi \cos^2 \theta \sin \phi$$
$$+ \rho^2 \sin^3 \phi \sin^2 \theta + \rho^2 \sin \phi \cos^2 \phi \sin^2 \theta$$

(combine the first and the third, and the second and the fourth terms)

$$= \rho^2 \sin^3 \phi + \rho^2 \sin \phi \cos^2 \phi = \rho^2 \sin \phi (\sin^2 \phi + \cos^2 \phi)$$
$$= \rho^2 \sin \phi. \tag{6.8}$$

There is a way to avoid this computation: recall that the Jacobian of the change of variables is equal to the product of scale factors (see Exercise 34 in Section 6.4), and those were computed in Section 2.8. Since

$$x^2 + y^2 + z^2 = \rho^2 \sin^2 \phi \cos^2 \theta + \rho^2 \sin^2 \phi \sin^2 \theta + \rho^2 \cos^2 \phi$$
$$= \rho^2 (\sin^2 \phi (\cos^2 \theta + \sin^2 \theta) + \cos^2 \phi) = \rho^2,$$

the spheres $x^2 + y^2 + z^2 = a^2$ and $x^2 + y^2 + z^2 = b^2$ have equations $\rho = a$ and $\rho = b$ in spherical coordinates. It follows that

$$\text{volume}(V) = \int_0^{2\pi} \left(\int_0^{\pi} \left(\int_b^a 1 \cdot \rho^2 \sin \phi \, d\rho \right) d\phi \right) d\theta$$

$$= \int_0^{2\pi} \left(\int_0^{\pi} \sin \phi \, d\phi \right) \left(\int_b^a \rho^2 \, d\rho \right) d\theta$$

$$= \left(-\cos \phi \Big|_0^{\pi} \right) \left(\frac{\rho^3}{3} \Big|_b^a \right) \int_0^{2\pi} d\theta = \frac{4\pi}{3} (a^3 - b^3).$$

There is a much faster way to compute the volume in question: subtract the volume of the smaller ball $(4\pi b^3/3)$ from the volume of the larger ball $(4\pi a^3/3)$. However, the point of this example was to illustrate the use of spherical coordinates in integration.

◀

Example 6.45   Find the volume of the solid region ("ice-cream cone with a scoop of ice-cream") that lies inside the sphere $x^2 + y^2 + z^2 = z$ and above the cone $z^2 = x^2 + y^2$, $z \geq 0$, shown in Figure 6.54.

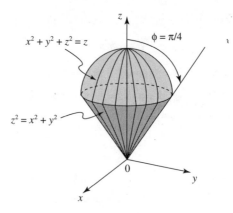

Figure 6.54   "Ice cream cone" of Example 6.45.

Solution   As in the previous example, we use spherical coordinates. In order to compute the limits of integration (and thus obtain the solid V^* that is mapped onto V, see Theorem 6.8) we transform the given equations. The equation of the sphere $x^2 + y^2 + z^2 = z$ transforms to $\rho^2 = \rho \cos \phi$ (since $x^2 + y^2 + z^2 = \rho^2$) or $\rho = \cos \phi$. Hence $0 \le \rho \le \cos \phi$ are the limits for ρ. The equation of the cone $z^2 = x^2 + y^2$ transforms to

$$\rho^2 \cos^2 \phi = \rho^2 \sin^2 \phi \cos^2 \theta + \rho^2 \sin^2 \phi \sin^2 \theta = \rho^2 \sin^2 \phi,$$

or $\rho \cos \phi = \pm \rho \sin \phi$. Hence (divide by $\rho \cos \phi$) $\tan \phi = \pm 1$ or $\phi = \pm \pi/4$. Since $\phi \ge 0$ (by the definition of spherical coordinates) it follows that $0 \le \phi \le \pi/4$ are the limits of integration for ϕ. Finally, $0 \le \theta \le 2\pi$ and

$$
\text{volume}(V) = \int_0^{2\pi} \left(\int_0^{\pi/4} \left(\int_0^{\cos \phi} \rho^2 \sin \phi \, d\rho \right) d\phi \right) d\theta
$$

$$
= \int_0^{2\pi} \left(\int_0^{\pi/4} \sin \phi \left. \frac{\rho^3}{3} \right|_0^{\cos \phi} d\phi \right) d\theta = \frac{1}{3} \int_0^{2\pi} \left(\int_0^{\pi/4} \sin \phi \cos^3 \phi \, d\phi \right) d\theta
$$

$$
= -\frac{1}{3} \int_0^{2\pi} \left(\left. \frac{1}{4} \cos^4 \phi \right|_0^{\pi/4} \right) d\theta = -\frac{1}{3} \frac{1}{4} \left(\left(\frac{\sqrt{2}}{2} \right)^4 - 1 \right) \int_0^{2\pi} d\theta = \frac{\pi}{8}.
$$

EXERCISES 6.5   **Exercises 1 to 9:**   Compute the value of the triple integral $\iiint_V f \, dV$.

1. $f(x, y, z) = 2x - y - z$, V is the parallelepiped defined by the planes $x = 3$, $y = 2$ and $z = 2$ in the first octant

2. $f(x, y, z) = xye^{y+z}$, V is the rectangular box $0 \le x \le 2$, $0 \le y \le 1$, $0 \le z \le \ln 2$

3. $f(x, y, z) = y^2$, V is the tetrahedron in the first octant bounded by the plane $x + y + z = 1$

4. $f(x, y, z) = yz$, V is the three-dimensional solid that lies under the parabolic sheet $z = 4 - y^2$ and above the rectangle $[0, 1] \times [0, 2]$ in the xy-plane

5. $f(x, y, z) = 2z - 5$, V is the three-dimensional solid between the surfaces $z = 2y^2$ and $z = 8 - 2y^2$, for $0 \leq x \leq 1$

6. $f(x, y, z) = x + y$, V is the three-dimensional solid below the paraboloid $z = 1 - x^2 - y^2$, inside the cylinder $x^2 + y^2 = 1$ and above the xy-plane

7. $f(x, y, z) = 4y$, V is the three-dimensional solid bounded by the paraboloids $z = 12 - x^2 - y^2$ and $z = 2x^2 + 2y^2$

8. $f(x, y, z) = 3 + 2x$, V is the three-dimensional solid inside the cone $y^2 = x^2 + z^2$, between the planes $y = 2$ and $y = 5$

9. $f(x, y, z) = xyz$, V is the three-dimensional solid inside the sphere $x^2 + y^2 + z^2 = 2$ and inside the cylinder $x^2 + y^2 = 1$

Exercises 10 to 16: Evaluate the iterated integral and describe the region of integration (parentheses have been dropped from the notation).

10. $\displaystyle\int_0^2 \int_0^x \int_0^3 xy \, dz \, dy \, dx$

11. $\displaystyle\int_0^1 \int_0^{2-2y} \int_0^{4-2x-4y} 3 \, dz \, dx \, dy$

12. $\displaystyle\int_0^1 \int_0^y \int_{-1}^{5y} x \, dz \, dx \, dy$

13. $\displaystyle\int_0^{2\pi} \int_0^2 \int_0^{r^2} r^2 z \, dz \, dr \, d\theta$

14. $\displaystyle\int_{-1}^1 \int_0^{1-x^2} \int_0^{\sqrt{y}} x^2 y^2 z^2 \, dz \, dy \, dx$

15. $\displaystyle\int_{-\sqrt{8}}^{\sqrt{8}} \int_{-\sqrt{8-x^2}}^{\sqrt{8-x^2}} \int_{-3}^{8-x^2-y^2} 2 \, dz \, dy \, dx$

16. $\displaystyle\int_0^1 \int_0^{\sqrt{1-y^2}} \int_0^{\sqrt{1-x^2-y^2}} (2x - y) \, dz \, dx \, dy$

Exercises 17 to 25: Find the volume of the solid in $\mathbb{R}^3$.

17. the tetrahedron with vertices $(0, 0, 0)$, $(1, 0, 0)$, $(0, 1, 0)$, and $(0, 0, 1)$

18. inside $x^2 + y^2 + z^2 = a^2$ and outside $x^2 + y^2 + z^2 = b^2$, $b < a$

19. inside the sphere $x^2 + y^2 + z^2 = 4$ and outside the ellipsoid $4x^2 + 4y^2 + z^2 = 4$

20. above the cone $z^2 = x^2 + y^2$, inside the sphere $x^2 + y^2 + z^2 = 1$ and above the xy-plane

21. inside the cylinder $(x - 1)^2 + y^2 = 1$, outside the cone $z^2 = x^2 + y^2$ and above the xy-plane

22. the part of the cone $2z^2 = x^2 + y^2$ between the horizontal planes $z = 1$ and $z = 2$

23. smaller of the two solids above the xy-plane, bounded by the paraboloid $z = 16 - x^2 - y^2$ and by the vertical plane $x + y = 4$; do not evaluate the integral — just set it up in Cartesian and cylindrical coordinates

24. above the plane $z = a$ and inside the sphere $x^2 + y^2 + z^2 = b^2$, $b > a$

25. inside the sphere $x^2 + y^2 + z^2 = a^2$ and inside the cylinder $x^2 + y^2 = b^2$, $b \leq a$

26. Express the integral $\int_0^1 \int_0^y \int_0^x x^2 yz \, dz \, dx \, dy$ in the remaining 5 orders of integration.

27. Express the integral $\int_{-\sqrt{2}}^{\sqrt{2}} \int_{-\sqrt{2-x^2}}^{\sqrt{2-x^2}} \int_{x^2+y^2-2}^{2-x^2-y^2} (x^2 + y^2 - 2) \, dz \, dy \, dx$ in cylindrical coordinates.

28. Express the integral $\int_0^6 \int_0^{1-x/6} \int_0^{2-x/2-2y} xyz \, dz \, dy \, dx$ in the remaining 5 orders of integration. What is the region of integration?

29. Compute the volume of the solid bounded by the following pairs of parallel planes: $x + y = 1$, $x + y = 3$, $y + 2z = -2$, $y + 2z = 4$, $2x + y + z = -1$ and $2x + y + z = 1$.

30. Find the volume of the three-dimensional solid below $z = x^2 + y^2$ and above the region $xy = 1$, $xy = 3$, $x^2 - y^2 = 1$, $x^2 - y^2 = 4$ in the first quadrant.

31. Consider the triple integral $\iiint_V 2x \, dV$, where V is the solid three-dimensional region bounded by the surfaces $z = x^2 + y^2$, $z = 2(x^2 + y^2)$ and $z = 1$. Express it as an iterated integral in cylindrical coordinates. Do not evaluate it.

CHAPTER REVIEW

Review Questions

Answer/discuss the following questions:

1. Explain how to approximate the volume of a solid under the graph of a positive function $z = f(x, y)$ and above a rectangle R in the xy-plane using double Riemann sums. Suppose that you have used a double Riemann sum to approximate the volume of the solid under the graph of $z = e^{-x}$ and above $[0, 1] \times [-1, 1]$, using the upper left corner of each subrectangle. Is your estimate an overestimate or an underestimate?

2. One of the properties of double integrals is that $\left| \iint_R f \, dA \right| \leq \iint_R |f| \, dA$, where R is a rectangle. Find examples of functions (and rectangles) such that $\left| \iint_R f \, dA \right| = \iint_R |f| \, dA$ and $\left| \iint_R f \, dA \right| < \iint_R |f| \, dA$.

3. State Cavalieri's principle (for the computation of volume). Formulate its analogue in the case of area and use it to prove that any two triangles with the same base and same height have equal areas. Explain how to obtain a formula for the volume of a solid of revolution using Cavalieri's principle.

4. State Fubini's Theorem and explain its meaning.

5. Find examples of type-2 regions. Describe how to extend the definition of the double integral from a rectangle to a region of type 2. Express a double integral over a region of type 2 as an iterated integral.

6. Without integration, find the value of $\iint_D f \, dA$, where $f(x, y) = \sqrt{1 - x^2 - y^2}$ and D is the unit disk $x^2 + y^2 \leq 1$. Again, without integration, find $\iint_R \sin^3 x \, dA$, where $R = [-\pi, \pi] \times [0, 1]$.

7. Is it possible that the average value of $f(x, y) = e^{x+y} \sin(3x - y^4)$ over the square $D = [-1, 1] \times [-1, 1]$ be 9? Explain your answer.

8. Define the Jacobian of the function $T : \mathbb{R}^2 \to \mathbb{R}^2$ and explain its geometric significance. If T is defined by $T(\mathbf{x}) = A\mathbf{x}$, where A is a 2×2 matrix, what is its Jacobian?

9. State the Change of Variables Theorems for double and triple integrals.

Computer Projects

1. **Integral Estimates and Average Value.**
   Consider the function $f(x, y) = e^{x-y} \sqrt{x^2 + y^2}$ defined on the square $D = [0, 1] \times [0, 1]$.

(a) Without the use of a graph or a calculator estimate the minimum and the maximum of f on D. Based on your estimate for f, find an upper bound and a lower bound for $\iint_D f \, dA$.

(b) Plot the graph of the surface $z = f(x, y)$ over D and find better estimates (if possible) for the minimum and the maximum of f on D. Find an upper bound and a lower bound for $\iint_D f \, dA$.

(c) Using a computer, find $\iint_D f \, dA$. Compute the average value $\overline{f}$ of f over D.

(d) Using a computer, plot all points in D where the average value $\overline{f}$ is attained.

2. **Isoperimetric Ratio.**

In this project we will investigate the *isoperimetric ratio* $I(D) = \ell(\mathbf{c})/A(D)^{1/2}$, where D is a bounded region in $\mathbb{R}^2$, $\mathbf{c}$ is the curve that forms its boundary, $A(D)$ denotes the area of D and $\ell(\mathbf{c})$ is the length of $\mathbf{c}$.

(a) Find $I(D)$ for a square.

(b) Find $I(D)$ for a disk of radius a.

(c) Let D_m be the rectangle with sides m and 1. Compute $I(D_m)$ and the limit of $I(D_m)$ as $m \to \infty$ and as $m \to 0$. Find a minimum value of $I(D_m)$ and plot $I(D_m)$ on $(0, 10)$.

(d) Let $\overline{D}_n$ be the region in the first quadrant bounded by the curve $\mathbf{c}_n(t) = (\cos^n t, \sin^n t)$, $t \in [0, \pi/2]$. Let D_n be the region consisting of four copies of $\overline{D}_n$, obtained by reflecting $\overline{D}_n$ with respect to the x-axis, the y-axis and with respect to the origin; see Figure 6.55. Sketch the region D_n and compute $I(D_n)$ for $n = 1$, $n = 2$, $n = 3$ and $n = 1/2$.

(e) What curve (or region) in (a) – (d) has the smallest isoperimetric ratio?

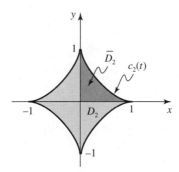

Figure 6.55   Region D_n of Project 2 (case $n = 2$).

Further Explorations

1. Evaluate the iterated integral

$$\int_0^{2\pi} \int_0^{2+\cos\theta} \int_0^{\pi/4} \rho^2 \sin\phi \, d\phi d\rho d\theta$$

and describe the region of integration.

2. The amount of radioactivity at a point (x, y) near a nuclear power plant is given by the function $f(x, y)$. Let D denote some geographical region. What is the meaning of $\iint_D f \, dA$? What is the meaning of $\iint_D f \, dA \Big/ \iint_D dA$?

3. Find the volume of the wedge cut out from the cylinder $x^2 + y^2 = a^2$, $a > 0$, by the planes $z = 0$ and $z = my + am$, $m > 0$.

4. Compute the volume of the region outside the paraboloid $z = x^2 + y^2$, inside the cylinder $x^2 + 4y^2 = 4$ and above the xy-plane using the change of variables $x = 2r \cos \theta$, $y = r \sin \theta$, $z = z$.

5. Let $f(x, y)$ be a continuous function on a rectangle $R \subseteq \mathbb{R}^2$ and assume that $f \geq 0$ on R. Prove that if $\iint_R f \, dA = 0$, then $f(x, y) = 0$ for all (x, y) in R.

6. Figure 6.56 shows several level curves of a function $f(x, y)$. Using Riemann sums, estimate $\iint_D f \, dA$ where D is the rectangle $[0, 4] \times [0, 2]$.

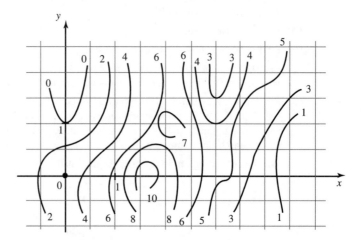

Figure 6.56   Level curves of Exercise 6.

7. Find the area of the region inside both circles $r = 4 \cos \theta$ and $r = 2$.

8. Find the volume of the three-dimensional solid in the first octant bounded by the surfaces $xy = 1$, $xy = 2$, $xz = 1$, $xz = 3$, $y + z = 0$ and $y + z = 2$ (use a suitable change of variables).

9. Let D be a type-1 region defined by $a \leq x \leq b$ and $-\psi(x) \leq y \leq \psi(x)$, where $\psi(x) \geq 0$ is continuous on $[a, b]$. Let $f(x, y)$ be a continuous function on D such that $f(x, -y) = -f(x, y)$ for all $(x, y) \in D$. Using a Riemann sum argument, prove that $\iint_D f \, dA = 0$.

Chapter 7

INTEGRATION OVER SURFACES; PROPERTIES AND APPLICATIONS OF INTEGRALS

By analogy with the desciption of a curve using a function defined on an interval of real numbers, we define a surface as the image of a function (that is also called a parametrization) defined on a subset of $\mathbb{R}^2$. To gain a better feel for parametrizations, we start by examining parametrizations of a sphere, a cylinder, a cone and a surface that is the graph of a function of two variables. We proceed by discussing smoothness, orientation and other concepts relevant for integration.

The surface integrals of real-valued functions and vector fields are defined in terms of integration over elementary regions in $\mathbb{R}^2$. The sections devoted to these topics provide a rich source of worked examples and discuss important applications, such as surface area and the flux of a vector field. A way of constructing surface integrals by projection (needed in the case when a parametrization is not avaliable or not convenient) is also discussed.

In the last section we unify various types of integration defined in the last three chapters into a single concept. Further examples, properties and some physical applications are discussed as well.

7.1 PARAMETRIZED SURFACES

So far we have investigated (double) integrals over various regions in the plane $\mathbb{R}^2$. Our next goal is to define integration over more general regions in space (such as the surface of a sphere, cylinder, torus, etc.). Since this generalization is very similar in spirit to the definition of the path integral, we start by recalling the main idea.

A curve is represented by the equation $\mathbf{c}(t) = (x(t), y(t), z(t))$, $t \in [a, b]$, called the parametric representation. The path integral of a real-valued function of several variables or of a vector field is defined as the definite integral over the interval $[a, b] \subseteq \mathbb{R}$ of a function of (one variable) t— hence integration over a curve is reduced to integration along an interval on the x-axis.

In this section we start developing analogous concepts, by first defining a surface and its parametric representation. In the two following sections, the surface integrals of real-valued functions of several variables and the surface integrals of vector fields will be defined in terms of integration over elementary regions in $\mathbb{R}^2$.

Before giving the definition of a surface, let us examine what objects we would like to call surfaces. We can think of the image of a curve $\mathbf{c}: [a, b] \rightarrow \mathbb{R}^3$ in a mechanical way: assume that the interval $[a, b]$ is made of some material that can be deformed. By bending, stretching and pasting we can deform $[a, b]$ to "fit over" the image of $\mathbf{c}$. Hence we think of $\mathbf{c}$ as being "made" from the interval $[a, b]$ by "deforming" it (without breaking), as shown in Figure 7.1.

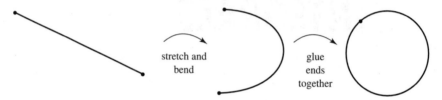

Figure 7.1 Deforming an interval produces a curve.

Similarly, a surface is a geometric object that can be obtained by deforming (i.e., stretching, bending, twisting, pasting, but not breaking) a region in the plane $\mathbb{R}^2$. Figure 7.2 demonstrates the deformation of a rectangle into a helicoid, a cylinder and a torus.

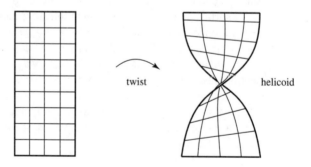

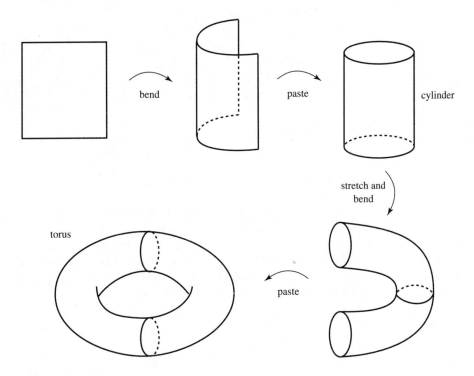

Figure 7.2   Deformation of a rectangle into a helicoid, cylinder and torus.

Definition 7.1   Parametrized Surface and Surface.

A *parametrized surface* is a map $\mathbf{r}: D \rightarrow \mathbb{R}^3$, where D is a region in $\mathbb{R}^2$ and $\mathbf{r}$ is one-to-one except possibly on the boundary of D. The image $S = \mathbf{r}(D)$ is called a *surface*.

In components, a parametrization $\mathbf{r}$ (see Figure 7.3) can be expressed as

$$\mathbf{r}(u, v) = (x(u, v), y(u, v), z(u, v)), \qquad (u, v) \in D.$$

A surface S is *continuous* (respectively, *differentiable, C^1*) if and only if its parametrization $\mathbf{r}(u, v): D \rightarrow \mathbb{R}^3$ is continuous (respectively, differentiable, C^1); i.e., if and only if its components $x(u, v), y(u, v), z(u, v): D \rightarrow \mathbb{R}$ are continuous (respectively, differentiable, C^1).

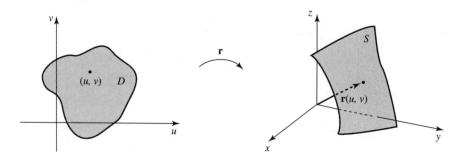

Figure 7.3 S is a surface, and $\mathbf{r}$ is its parametrization (or parametrized surface).

The map $\mathbf{r}$ is the map (described in the introduction) that "deforms" the region D into the surface S. The assumption that $\mathbf{r}$ is one-to-one guarantees that the surface does not intersect itself (a similar requirement ("simple curve") was needed for integration along curves). The fact that on the boundary of D $\mathbf{r}$ does not have to be one-to-one means that we are allowed to "glue" points on the boundary of D together to form a surface (think of making a cylinder from a sheet of paper). Let us examine a few examples.

Example 7.1   Sphere.

A parametric representation of the sphere $x^2 + y^2 + z^2 = a^2$ of radius a centered at the origin is given by (see Figure 7.4)

$$\mathbf{r}(u, v) = (a \cos v \cos u, a \cos v \sin u, a \sin v), \quad 0 \le u \le 2\pi, \quad -\pi/2 \le v \le \pi/2.$$

(Thus $x = a \cos v \cos u$, $y = a \cos v \sin u$ and $z = a \sin v$, and so

$$x^2 + y^2 + z^2 = a^2 \cos^2 v \cos^2 u + a^2 \cos^2 v \sin^2 u + a^2 \sin^2 v$$
$$= a^2 \cos^2 v + a^2 \sin^2 v = a^2.$$

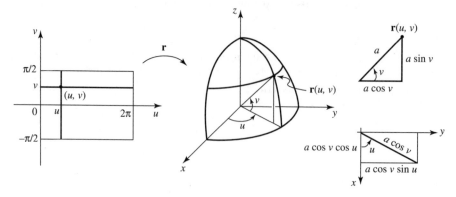

Figure 7.4   Geometric meaning of parameters u and v for the sphere.

The inequalities $0 \leq u \leq 2\pi$ and $-\pi/2 \leq v \leq \pi/2$ state that the domain D is the rectangle $[0, 2\pi] \times [-\pi/2, \pi/2]$ in the uv-plane.)

Let us examine the map $\mathbf{r}$.

The image of the line segment $\{(u, 0) | 0 \leq u \leq 2\pi\}$ is given by

$$\mathbf{r}(u, 0) = (a \cos u, a \sin u, 0),$$

which is the circle of radius a in the xy-plane centered at $(0, 0)$ and represents the "equator" of the sphere. The image of the segment $\{(u, v_0) \mid 0 \leq u \leq 2\pi\}$ (v_0 is fixed) parallel to the u-axis is

$$\mathbf{r}(u, v_0) = (a \cos v_0 \cos u, a \cos v_0 \sin u, a \sin v_0),$$

which is the circle of radius $a \cos v_0$, obtained as the intersection of the plane $z = a \sin v_0$ (parallel to the xy-plane) and the sphere. In other words, it is a "parallel" (of latitude v_0) of the sphere S; see Figure 7.5.

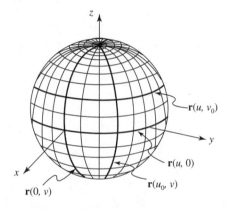

Figure 7.5 Parametric representation of a sphere.

The image of the vertical segment $\{(0, v) \mid -\pi/2 \leq v \leq \pi/2\}$ is given by

$$\mathbf{r}(0, v) = (a \cos v, 0, a \sin v),$$

which is the semi-circle in the xz-plane, a "meridian" of S. In general, the image of the vertical segment $\{(u_0, v) \mid -\pi/2 \leq v \leq \pi/2\}$ (u_0 is fixed) is the curve

$$\mathbf{r}(u_0, v) = (a \cos u_0 \cos v, a \sin u_0 \cos v, a \sin v),$$

which is the "meridian" corresponding to the angle u_0 measured from the positive direction of the x-axis (think of longitudinal lines on the Earth).

There are other representations of the sphere. For example

$$\mathbf{r}(u, v) = (a \cos u \sin v, a \sin u \sin v, a \cos v), \quad 0 \leq u \leq 2\pi, \quad 0 \leq v \leq \pi.$$

In this case, the parameters u and v have interpretations different from those given in Example 7.1.

Example 7.2   Cylinder.

The cylinder $x^2 + y^2 = a^2$, $0 \le z \le b$ of radius a and height b can be represented by

$$\mathbf{r}(u, v) = (a \cos u, a \sin u, v), \qquad 0 \le v \le b, \quad 0 \le u \le 2\pi.$$

(Hence the domain D of $\mathbf{r}$ is the rectangle $D = [0, 2\pi] \times [0, b]$ in the uv-plane.) The curves $u = u_0 = $ constant are vertical line segments (v is the parameter)

$$\mathbf{r}(u_0, v) = (a \cos u_0, a \sin u_0, v) = (a \cos u_0, a \sin u_0, 0) + v(0, 0, 1), \qquad 0 \le v \le b;$$

see Figure 7.6. For $v = v_0 = $ constant we get

$$\mathbf{r}(u, v_0) = (a \cos u, a \sin u, v_0), \qquad 0 \le u \le 2\pi;$$

i.e., the circle that is the intersection of the cylinder and the plane $z = v_0$.

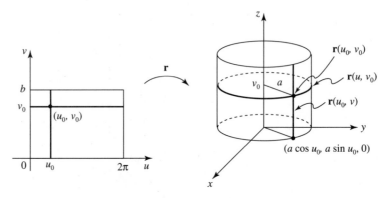

Figure 7.6   Parametric representation of a cylinder.

We could have described the same cylinder as

$$\mathbf{r}(u, v) = (a \cos mu, a \sin mu, nv), \qquad 0 \le v \le b/n, \quad 0 \le u \le 2\pi/m,$$

where $m, n > 0$. This shows that a surface (like a curve) can have infinitely many parametric representations.

Example 7.3   Cone.

The parametric representation of the cone $x^2 + y^2 = z^2$, $0 \le z \le b$, of height b is given by

$$\mathbf{r}(u, v) = (v \cos u, v \sin u, v), \qquad (u, v) \in D = [0, 2\pi] \times [0, b].$$

The curve corresponding to $v = v_0$,

$$\mathbf{r}(u, v_0) = (v_0 \cos u, v_0 \sin u, v_0), \qquad 0 \le u \le 2\pi,$$

is a circle of radius v_0 in the horizontal plane $z = v_0$, if $v_0 > 0$ (when $v_0 = 0$ the circle collapses to the point $(0, 0, 0)$); see Figure 7.7. The curve corresponding to $u = u_0$,

$$\mathbf{r}(u_0, v) = (v \cos u_0, v \sin u_0, v) = v(\cos u_0, \sin u_0, 1), \qquad 0 \le v \le b,$$

is a straight line segment from the origin (when $v = 0$) to the point $(b \cos u_0, b \sin u_0, b)$, when $v = b$.

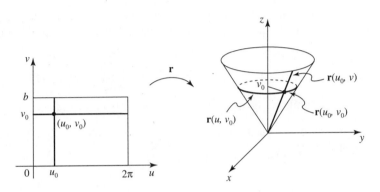

Figure 7.7 Parametric representation of a cone.

In terms of a deformation, the cone of the previous example is obtained in the following way: the rectangle $[0, 2\pi] \times [0, b]$ is first deformed into a triangle: the bottom horizontal line segment $v = 0$ is compressed to a point, and the top segment $v = b$ is expanded or compressed (depending on b) to the length $2\pi b$ (which is the length of the circle that forms the "rim" of the cone); see Figure 7.8. A horizontal line segment $v = v_0$, $0 \le v_0 \le b$ is deformed into a line segment of length $2\pi v_0$. The cone is now obtained by glueing together the two (slanted) sides of the triangle. The map $\mathbf{r}$ thus described is not one-to-one on the left, right and bottom sides of the rectangle. It is one-to-one on the top side, except at its ends.

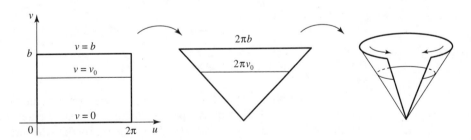

Figure 7.8 Deformation of a rectangle into a cone.

Let S be a surface represented by a parametrization

$$\mathbf{r}(u, v) = (x(u, v), y(u, v), z(u, v)), \qquad (u, v) \in D \subseteq \mathbb{R}^2.$$

Pick a point $\mathbf{r}(u_0, v_0)$ on S. The restriction of $\mathbf{r}$ to the curve $v = v_0$ in $D \subseteq uv$-plane is the curve

$$\mathbf{c}_{v_0}(u) = \mathbf{r}(u, v_0) = (x(u, v_0), y(u, v_0), z(u, v_0)), \qquad (u, v_0) \in D,$$

on S going through the point $\mathbf{r}(u_0, v_0)$; see Figure 7.9 (the parameter of the curve is called u, rather than t; v_0 is fixed). The tangent vector $\mathbf{T}_u$ to $\mathbf{c}_{v_0}$ at $\mathbf{r}(u_0, v_0)$ is given by

$$\mathbf{T}_u(u_0, v_0) = \mathbf{c}'_{v_0}(u_0) = \left(\frac{\partial x}{\partial u}\Big|_{(u_0, v_0)}, \frac{\partial y}{\partial u}\Big|_{(u_0, v_0)}, \frac{\partial z}{\partial u}\Big|_{(u_0, v_0)} \right).$$

Similarly, the tangent to the curve (here u_0 is fixed and v is the parameter)

$$\mathbf{c}_{u_0}(v) = \mathbf{r}(u_0, v) = (x(u_0, v), y(u_0, v), z(u_0, v)), \qquad (u_0, v) \in D,$$

at the point $\mathbf{r}(u_0, v_0)$ is given by

$$\mathbf{T}_v(u_0, v_0) = \mathbf{c}'_{u_0}(v_0) = \left(\frac{\partial x}{\partial v}\Big|_{(u_0, v_0)}, \frac{\partial y}{\partial v}\Big|_{(u_0, v_0)}, \frac{\partial z}{\partial v}\Big|_{(u_0, v_0)} \right).$$

The components of the tangent vector $\mathbf{T}_u(u_0, v_0)$ are the partial derivatives of the components $x(u, v)$, $y(u, v)$ and $z(u, v)$ with respect to u, evaluated at (u_0, v_0). Using the notation introduced in Section 2.4 we write $\mathbf{T}_u(u_0, v_0) = (\partial \mathbf{r}/\partial u)(u_0, v_0)$. Similarly, $\mathbf{T}_v(u_0, v_0) = (\partial \mathbf{r}/\partial v)(u_0, v_0)$.

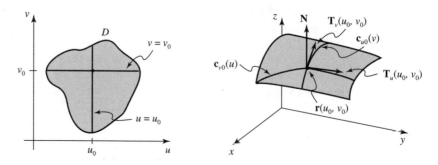

Figure 7.9   Tangent and normal vectors to a surface.

The vector $\mathbf{N}(u_0, v_0) = \mathbf{T}_u(u_0, v_0) \times \mathbf{T}_v(u_0, v_0)$, perpendicular to both $\mathbf{T}_u(u_0, v_0)$ and $\mathbf{T}_v(u_0, v_0)$ (and therefore perpendicular to the plane tangent to the surface at $\mathbf{r}(u_0, v_0)$), is called a *normal vector* (or the *surface normal*) to the surface S at $\mathbf{r}(u_0, v_0)$.

The coordinate expression for $\mathbf{N}$ is given by (drop (u_0, v_0) from the notation to keep it simple)

$$\mathbf{N} = \mathbf{T}_u \times \mathbf{T}_v = \begin{vmatrix} \mathbf{i} & \mathbf{j} & \mathbf{k} \\ \partial x/\partial u & \partial y/\partial u & \partial z/\partial u \\ \partial x/\partial v & \partial y/\partial v & \partial z/\partial v \end{vmatrix} \tag{7.1}$$

$$= \left(\frac{\partial y}{\partial u} \frac{\partial z}{\partial v} - \frac{\partial y}{\partial v} \frac{\partial z}{\partial u}, \frac{\partial z}{\partial u} \frac{\partial x}{\partial v} - \frac{\partial z}{\partial v} \frac{\partial x}{\partial u}, \frac{\partial x}{\partial u} \frac{\partial y}{\partial v} - \frac{\partial x}{\partial v} \frac{\partial y}{\partial u} \right), \tag{7.2}$$

or, using the Jacobian (see Definition 6.6),

$$\mathbf{N} = \left(\frac{\partial(y, z)}{\partial(u, v)}, \frac{\partial(z, x)}{\partial(u, v)}, \frac{\partial(x, y)}{\partial(u, v)} \right). \tag{7.3}$$

■ Definition 7.2   Smooth Parametrization and Smooth Surface.

A parametrization $\mathbf{r} = \mathbf{r}(u, v) \colon D \subseteq \mathbb{R}^2 \to \mathbb{R}^3$ is said to be *smooth at* (u_0, v_0) (or *smooth at a point* $\mathbf{r}(u_0, v_0)$) if $\mathbf{N}(u_0, v_0) \neq \mathbf{0}$. It is *smooth* if it is smooth at all points in D.

A surface is called *smooth* if it has a smooth parametrization. ■

We have already seen that there could be an infinite number of parametrizations with the same image; i.e., representing the same surface. A surface is called smooth if *one* of them turns out to be smooth. Let us examine a few examples.

Example 7.4

Compute the normal vector $\mathbf{N} = \mathbf{T}_u \times \mathbf{T}_v$ to the sphere parametrized by

$$\mathbf{r}(u, v) = (a \cos v \cos u, a \cos v \sin u, a \sin v), \quad 0 \le u \le 2\pi, \quad -\pi/2 \le v \le \pi/2,$$

where $a > 0$.

Solution   From

$$\mathbf{T}_u(u, v) = (-a \cos v \sin u, a \cos v \cos u, 0)$$

and

$$\mathbf{T}_v(u, v) = (-a \sin v \cos u, -a \sin v \sin u, a \cos v)$$

it follows that

$$\mathbf{N}(u, v) = \mathbf{T}_u(u, v) \times \mathbf{T}_v(u, v) = \begin{vmatrix} \mathbf{i} & \mathbf{j} & \mathbf{k} \\ -a \cos v \sin u & a \cos v \cos u & 0 \\ -a \sin v \cos u & -a \sin v \sin u & a \cos v \end{vmatrix}$$

$$= (a^2 \cos^2 v \cos u, a^2 \cos^2 v \sin u, a^2 \cos v \sin v \sin^2 u + a^2 \sin v \cos v \cos^2 u)$$

$$= a \cos v (a \cos v \cos u, a \cos v \sin u, a \sin v) = a \cos v \, \mathbf{r}(u, v).$$

It follows that the vector normal to the sphere is parallel to the position vector and

$$\|\mathbf{N}(u, v)\| = |a \cos v| \|\mathbf{r}(u, v)\| = a^2 \cos v,$$

since $\|\mathbf{r}(u, v)\| = a$ and $\cos v \ge 0$ for $-\pi/2 \le v \le \pi/2$. This parametrization is not smooth when $v = \pm \pi/2$; i.e., at the north and south poles $(0, 0, \pm a)$ of the sphere. ◀

Example 7.5   Consider the cone

$$\mathbf{r}(u, v) = v \cos u\mathbf{i} + v \sin u\mathbf{j} + v\mathbf{k}, \qquad 0 \le u \le 2\pi, \quad 0 \le v \le b$$

of Example 7.3. The tangents are $\mathbf{T}_u = -v \sin u\mathbf{i} + v \cos u\mathbf{j}$ and $\mathbf{T}_v = \cos u\mathbf{i} + \sin u\mathbf{j} + \mathbf{k}$, and the surface normal $\mathbf{N}$ is computed to be

$$\mathbf{N} = \mathbf{T}_u \times \mathbf{T}_v = \begin{vmatrix} \mathbf{i} & \mathbf{j} & \mathbf{k} \\ -v \sin u & v \cos u & 0 \\ \cos u & \sin u & 1 \end{vmatrix} = v \cos u\mathbf{i} + v \sin u\mathbf{j} - v\mathbf{k}.$$

At the vertex of the cone (which corresponds to $v = 0$ and $0 \le u \le 2\pi$), $\mathbf{N}(u, 0) = (0, 0, 0)$; therefore this parametrization is not smooth at the vertex. It is smooth at any other point, since in that case $v > 0$ and hence $\mathbf{N}(u, v) \ne \mathbf{0}$. Notice that, except at the vertex, the $\mathbf{k}$ component of $\mathbf{N}$ is negative. In other words, the normal vector $\mathbf{N}$ to the cone (parametrized as above, not in every case!) points downward; i.e., away from the cone.

◀

Example 7.6   Compute the normal vector $\mathbf{N} = \mathbf{T}_u \times \mathbf{T}_v$ to the surface

$$\mathbf{r}(u, v) = (u, u, v^3), \qquad 0 \le u \le 1, \quad -1 \le v \le 1.$$

Solution   By definition,

$$\mathbf{N} = \mathbf{T}_u \times \mathbf{T}_v = \begin{vmatrix} \mathbf{i} & \mathbf{j} & \mathbf{k} \\ 1 & 1 & 0 \\ 0 & 0 & 3v^2 \end{vmatrix} = 3v^2\mathbf{i} - 3v^2\mathbf{j},$$

and it follows that the parametrization is smooth at all points $\mathbf{r}(u, v)$ for which $v \ne 0$. The same surface (it is the part of the vertical plane that crosses the xy-plane along the line segment $y = x$ (from $(0, 0)$ to $(1, 1)$) and is bounded above and below by the planes $z = 1$ and $z = -1$) can be parametrized by

$$\overline{\mathbf{r}}(u, v) = (u, u, v), \qquad 0 \le u \le 1, \quad -1 \le v \le 1.$$

In this case,

$$\overline{\mathbf{N}} = \overline{\mathbf{T}}_u \times \overline{\mathbf{T}}_v = \begin{vmatrix} \mathbf{i} & \mathbf{j} & \mathbf{k} \\ 1 & 1 & 0 \\ 0 & 0 & 1 \end{vmatrix} = \mathbf{i} - \mathbf{j},$$

which is always a non-zero vector.

◀

This example shows that "looks can be deceiving": a plane does appear to be smooth (it seems we can always draw a non-zero normal vector); but if we parametrize it using the map $\mathbf{r}$ of the previous example, there will be points where the surface normal is zero.

Example 7.7

Compute the surface normal $\mathbf{N}$ to the surface S given by

$$\mathbf{r}(u, v) = (u, v, |u|), \qquad -1 \le u \le 1, \quad 0 \le v \le 1.$$

Solution   Clearly, $\mathbf{T}_v = (0, 1, 0)$. If $u > 0$ then $\mathbf{r}(u, v) = (u, v, u)$ and $\mathbf{T}_u = (1, 0, 1)$, and if $u < 0$ then $\mathbf{r}(u, v) = (u, v, -u)$ and $\mathbf{T}_u = (1, 0, -1)$. It follows that

$$\mathbf{N}(u, v) = (\mathbf{T}_u \times \mathbf{T}_v)(u, v) = (\mathbf{i} + \mathbf{k}) \times \mathbf{j} = \mathbf{k} - \mathbf{i}$$

at points $\mathbf{r}(u, v)$ where $u > 0$, and

$$\mathbf{N}(u, v) = (\mathbf{T}_u \times \mathbf{T}_v)(u, v) = (\mathbf{i} - \mathbf{k}) \times \mathbf{j} = \mathbf{k} + \mathbf{i}$$

at points $\mathbf{r}(u, v)$ where $u < 0$.

Since the function $|u|$ is not differentiable at $u = 0$ it follows that the tangent vector $\mathbf{T}_u$ is not defined at points $\mathbf{r}(0, v)$ for $0 \le v \le 1$. Therefore the surface S has an "edge" $\{(u, v) \mid u = 0, 0 \le v \le 1\}$, so is not smooth at these points; see Figure 7.10.

(To check that the function $f(u) = |u|$ is not differentiable at 0 we use the definition of the derivative

$$f'(0) = \lim_{h \to 0} \frac{f(h) - f(0)}{h} = \lim_{h \to 0} \frac{|h|}{h}$$

and notice that the limit does not exist: the right limit (that is, when $h > 0$, hence $|h| = h$) is 1, whereas the left limit (when $h < 0$, hence $|h| = -h$) is -1.)

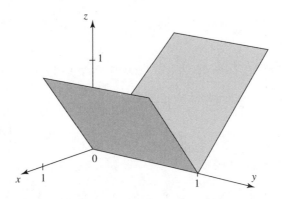

Figure 7.10   Surface $\mathbf{r}(u, v) = (u, v, |u|)$ has an edge along the y-axis.

Example 7.8

Graph of a Function $z = f(x, y)$ is a Surface in $\mathbf{R}^3$.

The graph of a differentiable function $f : D \subseteq \mathbb{R}^2 \to \mathbb{R}$ is a surface in $\mathbb{R}^3$ that can be parametrized by

$$\mathbf{r}(u, v) = (u, v, f(u, v)), \quad (u, v) \in D.$$

Instead of drawing two separate coordinate systems, one for the domain D (the "uv-coordinate system") and one for the surface S (the "xyz-coordinate system") as done in the previous examples, we merge the two together by placing the uv-plane over the xy-plane. Figure 7.11 shows the graph of $z = x^2 y - y^3$ in this newly constructed coordinate system: both the surface and its domain are shown. Keeping the identification $u = x$ and $v = y$ in mind, we sometimes write the parametrization as

$$\mathbf{r}(x, y) = (x, y, f(x, y)), \quad (x, y) \in D$$

(compare with Example 3.5 in Section 3.1, where the graph of $y = f(x)$ was viewed as a parametrized curve).

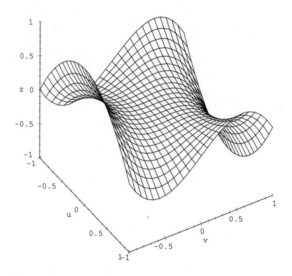

Figure 7.11   Graph of $z = f(x, y) = x^2 y - y^3$ is a smooth surface.

The tangents are given by

$$\mathbf{T}_u = \left(1, 0, \frac{\partial f}{\partial u}\right), \qquad \mathbf{T}_v = \left(0, 1, \frac{\partial f}{\partial v}\right),$$

and therefore

$$\mathbf{N} = \mathbf{T}_u \times \mathbf{T}_v = \left(1, 0, \frac{\partial f}{\partial u}\right) \times \left(0, 1, \frac{\partial f}{\partial v}\right) = \left(-\frac{\partial f}{\partial u}, -\frac{\partial f}{\partial v}, 1\right).$$

Since $\mathbf{N}(u, v) \neq \mathbf{0}$, for all (u, v), it follows that the graph of a differentiable function is a smooth surface. The normal vector $\mathbf{N}$ points upward, since its $\mathbf{k}$ component is positive.

The tangent plane to a smooth surface S at the point $\mathbf{r}(u_0, v_0)$ is the plane spanned by the vectors $\mathbf{T}_u(u_0, v_0)$ and $\mathbf{T}_v(u_0, v_0)$. Its equation is

$$a(x - x_0) + b(y - y_0) + c(z - z_0) = 0,$$

where $\mathbf{N}(u_0, v_0) = (a, b, c)$ is the surface normal $\mathbf{N}(u_0, v_0) = \mathbf{T}_u(u_0, v_0) \times \mathbf{T}_v(u_0, v_0)$, and $\mathbf{r}(u_0, v_0) = (x_0, y_0, z_0)$ is the point of tangency with the surface. A surface that is not smooth at (u_0, v_0) does not have a tangent plane at that point.

Example 7.9

Let S be the surface parametrized by

$$\mathbf{r}(u, v) = (u \cos v, u \sin v, v), \qquad u > 0, \quad v \geq 0.$$

Compute the equation of the plane tangent to S at the point $\mathbf{r}(1, \pi) = (-1, 0, \pi)$.

Solution The tangent vectors to S at $\mathbf{r}(1, \pi)$ are

$$\mathbf{T}_u(1, \pi) = \left.\frac{\partial \mathbf{r}}{\partial u}\right|_{(1,\pi)} = (\cos v, \sin v, 0)\big|_{(1,\pi)} = (-1, 0, 0), \quad \text{and}$$

$$\mathbf{T}_v(1, \pi) = \left.\frac{\partial \mathbf{r}}{\partial v}\right|_{(1,\pi)} = (-u \sin v, u \cos v, 1)\big|_{(1,\pi)} = (0, -1, 1),$$

and therefore

$$\mathbf{N}(1, \pi) = (\mathbf{T}_u \times \mathbf{T}_v)(1, \pi) = (0, 1, 1).$$

The equation of the tangent plane is

$$0(x + 1) + 1(y - 0) + 1(z - \pi) = 0,$$

i.e., $y + z - \pi = 0$. ◀

Example 7.10

Compute the equation of the plane tangent to the graph of $z = f(x, y)$ at (x_0, y_0, z_0).

Solution The normal vector $\mathbf{N}$ was computed in Example 7.8 to be (replace u by x and v by y)

$$\mathbf{N} = \left(-\frac{\partial f}{\partial x}(x_0, y_0), -\frac{\partial f}{\partial y}(x_0, y_0), 1\right).$$

Consequently, the tangent plane has the equation (after multiplying by -1)

$$\frac{\partial f}{\partial x}(x_0, y_0)(x - x_0) + \frac{\partial f}{\partial y}(x_0, y_0)(y - y_0) - (z - z_0) = 0.$$ ◀

A surface may be *one-sided* or *two-sided*. A two-sided surface is a surface whose sides are "separated" in the sense that a person walking along one side of the surface can never reach the other side of it without crossing an edge or breaking through the surface. The sphere, the cone, the plane, the torus, the graph of $z = f(x, y)$, the surface in Figure 7.12— actually all the surfaces we have encountered so far— are two-sided.

Probably the most famous one-sided surface is the *Möbius strip*; see Figure 7.13. It can be made from a rectangular piece of paper, with one side longer than the other: just twist one smaller side by 180 degrees and glue it to the other smaller side.

This time, a person walking along "one side" will suddenly find herself/himself on "the other side" of it. "Replacing" a walking person by a vector normal to the surface, we see that the normal, starting at the point P, returns to P after a continuous motion, but points in the opposite direction. This can only happen on one-sided surfaces.

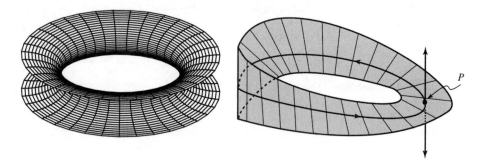

Figure 7.12 Two-sided surface.   **Figure 7.13** Möbius strip has only one side.

On a two-sided surface there are two normal directions, given by the unit normal vectors $\mathbf{n}_1$ and $\mathbf{n}_2$ such that $\mathbf{n}_2 = -\mathbf{n}_1$; see Figure 7.14.

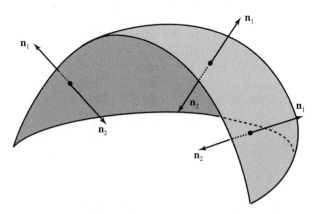

Figure 7.14 Normal directions on a two-sided surface.

■ **Definition 7.3** Orientation of a Surface.

An *orientation* of a two-sided surface is a continuous choice of unit normal vectors. That choice is called the *positive orientation*. It determines the side of the surface (the one unit normal vectors point away from), called the *outside* or the *positive side* of the surface. The other side is called the *inside* or the *negative side*.

■

Example 7.11   The plane $x + 2y + z = 3$ can be parametrized by

$$\mathbf{r}(u, v) = (u, v, 3 - u - 2v), \qquad u, v \in \mathbb{R}.$$

The tangents are $\mathbf{T}_u = (1, 0, -1)$ and $\mathbf{T}_v = (0, 1, -2)$. Hence $\mathbf{N} = \mathbf{T}_u \times \mathbf{T}_v = (1, 2, 1)$, so the unit normal vectors are $\pm(1, 2, 1)/\sqrt{6}$.

By choosing $\mathbf{n}$ to be $(1, 2, 1)/\sqrt{6}$, we have chosen the positive orientation, and the outside of the plane (or the positive side) is the side we see if we stand, say, at the point A in the first octant; see Figure 7.15. We can see the negative side (or the inside) of the plane by standing, for example, at the origin.

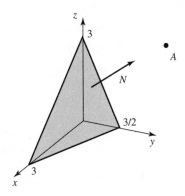

Figure 7.15   From the point A we see the outside of the plane $\mathbf{r}(u, v) = (u, v, 3 - u - 2v)$.

Example 7.12   A normal vector to the sphere S of radius 1 in $\mathbb{R}^3$ (think of the sphere as the level surface of $f(x, y, z) = x^2 + y^2 + z^2$ of value 1) is given by the gradient, $\nabla f = (2x, 2y, 2z)$. Let us choose a unit normal to be

$$\mathbf{n} = \frac{\nabla f}{\|\nabla f\|} = \frac{1}{\sqrt{x^2 + y^2 + z^2}} (x, y, z) = (x, y, z)$$

(clearly, the other choice for a unit normal would be the negative of $\mathbf{n}$).

The vector $\mathbf{n}$ points away from the outside of the sphere, which agrees with our intuition. Vector $-\mathbf{n}$ points into the inside of S. In other words, the side of the sphere that we see if we stand, say, at the point $(10, 10, 0)$ is the positive orientation of S. The side we see standing at the origin is the inside, or the negative orientation.

Let S be an *oriented surface*: that means that S is a two-sided surface and we have decided which side is the outside and which is the inside. Equivalently, an orientation can be prescribed by a continuous selection of a unit normal $\mathbf{n}$ to S. Now consider a parametrization $\mathbf{r}(u, v)$ of S and the normal vector $\mathbf{N} = \mathbf{T}_u \times \mathbf{T}_v$ determined by that parametrization. A unit normal vector $\mathbf{N}/\|\mathbf{N}\| = \mathbf{T}_u \times \mathbf{T}_v/\|\mathbf{T}_u \times \mathbf{T}_v\|$ is either equal to $\mathbf{n}$ or to $-\mathbf{n}$. If $\mathbf{N}/\|\mathbf{N}\| = \mathbf{n}$ we say that the parametrization $\mathbf{r}$ is *orientation-preserving*, and if $\mathbf{N}/\|\mathbf{N}\| = -\mathbf{n}$ then $\mathbf{r}$ is *orientation-reversing*.

Example 7.13   Consider the following parametrization of the unit sphere:

$$\mathbf{r}(u, v) = (\cos u \sin v, \sin u \sin v, \cos v), \qquad 0 \le u \le 2\pi, \quad 0 \le v \le \pi.$$

The surface normal vector $\mathbf{N}$ is given by

$$\mathbf{N} = \mathbf{T}_u \times \mathbf{T}_v = \begin{vmatrix} \mathbf{i} & \mathbf{j} & \mathbf{k} \\ -\sin u \sin v & \cos u \sin v & 0 \\ \cos u \cos v & \sin u \cos v & -\sin v \end{vmatrix}$$

$$= (-\cos u \sin^2 v, -\sin u \sin^2 v, -\sin v \cos v)$$

$$= -\sin v (\cos u \sin v, \sin u \sin v, \cos v) = -\sin v \cdot \mathbf{r}(u, v).$$

It follows that the unit normal

$$\frac{\mathbf{N}}{\|\mathbf{N}\|} = \frac{-\sin v \, \mathbf{r}(u, v)}{|-\sin v| \cdot \|\mathbf{r}(u, v)\|} = \frac{-\sin v}{|-\sin v|} \mathbf{r}(u, v) = -\mathbf{r}(u, v)$$

($\mathbf{r}(u, v)$ represents points on the sphere of raduis 1 and hence $\|\mathbf{r}(u, v)\| = 1$) points in the direction opposite to $\mathbf{r}(u, v)$ (since $0 \le v \le \pi$ it follows that $\sin v \ge 0$ and therefore $|-\sin v| = \sin v$ and $-\sin v / |-\sin v| = -\sin v / \sin v = -1$; this explains the appearance of the minus sign in front of $\mathbf{r}(u, v)$). Therefore, with the choice of the vector $\mathbf{n}$ from Example 7.12, $\mathbf{N}/\|\mathbf{N}\| = -\mathbf{n}$; i.e., the parametrization is orientation-reversing. On the other hand, the parametrization of the sphere

$$\mathbf{r}(u, v) = (\cos v \cos u, \cos v \sin u, \sin v), \quad 0 \le u \le 2\pi, \quad -\pi/2 \le v \le \pi/2,$$

given in Example 7.4 (with $a = 1$) yields the unit normal vector

$$\frac{\mathbf{N}}{\|\mathbf{N}\|} = \frac{\cos v \, \mathbf{r}(u, v)}{\|\cos v \, \mathbf{r}(u, v)\|} = \frac{\cos v}{|\cos v|} \mathbf{r}(u, v) = \mathbf{r}(u, v).$$

This time, $\mathbf{N}/\|\mathbf{N}\|$ has the same direction as $\mathbf{r}(u, v)$, since $\cos v \ge 0$ for $-\pi/2 \le v \le \pi/2$. With the orientation convention of Example 7.12, $\mathbf{N}/\|\mathbf{N}\| = \mathbf{n}$, and it follows that this is an orientation-preserving parametrization.   ◄

The orientation of the graph S of the function $z = f(x, y)$ (see Example 7.8) is defined as follows: the outside of S is the side away from which the unit normal vector

$$\mathbf{n} = \frac{\mathbf{N}}{\|\mathbf{N}\|} = \frac{(-\frac{\partial f}{\partial u}, -\frac{\partial f}{\partial v}, 1)}{\sqrt{\left(\frac{\partial f}{\partial u}\right)^2 + \left(\frac{\partial f}{\partial v}\right)^2 + 1}}$$

points. In other words, the positive orientation is determined by the choice of the normal with $\mathbf{k}$ component equal to $+1$, and the negative orientation corresponds to the normal whose $\mathbf{k}$ component is -1.

EXERCISES 7.1   **1.** Consider the parametric representations of the sphere and the cylinder given in Examples 7.1 and 7.2. Describe how $\mathbf{r}$ maps the boundary of the rectangle D in each case.

2. Consider the parametrization

$$\mathbf{r}(u, v) = (a \cos u \sin v, a \sin u \sin v, a \cos v), \quad 0 \le u \le 2\pi, \quad 0 \le v \le \pi$$

of the sphere of radius a. Give a geometric interpretation of the parameters u and v.

Exercises 3 to 10: Find a parametrization of each surface in $\mathbb{R}^3$.

3. upper hemisphere $x^2 + y^2 + z^2 = a^2$, $z \ge 0$

4. the part of the upper hemisphere $x^2 + y^2 + z^2 = a^2$, $z \ge 0$ cut out by the cone $z^2 = x^2 + y^2$

5. the part of the plane $z - 3y + x = 2$ inside the cylinder $x^2 + y^2 = 4$

6. the graph of $x^2 + y^2 - z^2 = 1$

7. the part of the plane $x + 2y + z = 6$ in the first octant

8. the part of the cone $x^2 + y^2 = z^2$ in the first octant

9. the part of the paraboloid $z = x^2 + y^2$ in the first octant

10. the surface obtained by rotating the circle $(y - 3)^2 + z^2 = 1$, $x = 0$ about the z-axis

Exercises 11 to 18: For each parametrized surface $\mathbf{r}(u, v)$ in $\mathbb{R}^3$,

    (a) find the tangent vectors $\mathbf{T}_u$ and $\mathbf{T}_v$ and the normal $\mathbf{N}$, and

    (b) find all points where $\mathbf{r}(u, v)$ is smooth.

11. $\mathbf{r}(u, v) = (2u, u^2 + v, v^2)$, $u, v \ge 0$

12. $\mathbf{r}(u, v) = (u, e^u \sin v, e^u \cos v)$, $0 \le v \le 2\pi$, $u \in \mathbb{R}$

13. $\mathbf{r}(u, v) = (\sin u \cos v, \sin u \sin v, 2 \cos u)$, $0 \le u, v \le 2\pi$

14. $\mathbf{r}(u, v) = (u^2 + v^2, u^2 - v^2, 2uv)$, $0 \le u, v \le 1$

15. $\mathbf{r}(u, v) = ((1 + \cos v) \cos u, (1 + \cos v) \sin u, \sin v)$, $0 \le u, v \le 2\pi$

16. $\mathbf{r}(u, v) = (u, \cos v, \sin v)$, $0 \le u \le 1$, $0 \le v \le \pi$

17. $\mathbf{r}(u, v) = (u, v, 1 - (u^2 + v^2))$, $0 \le u, v < \infty$

18. $\mathbf{r}(u, v) = (u, |u|, v)$, $-1 \le u \le 1$, $0 \le v \le 2$

19. Find an equation of the plane tangent to the surface $\mathbf{r}(u, v) = (e^u, e^v, uv)$ at the point $(1, 1, 0)$.

20. Let S be the surface $z = 10 - x^2 - 2y^2$. Compute the equation of the plane tangent to it at the point $(1, 2, 1)$

    (a) by using the parametrization $\mathbf{r}(u, v) = (u, v, 10 - u^2 - 2v^2)$;

    (b) by viewing S as the graph of the function $f(x, y) = 10 - x^2 - 2y^2$; and

    (c) by viewing S as the level surface of $f(x, y, z) = z + x^2 + 2y^2$.

21. Find an equation of the plane tangent to the graph of $y = x^2 + 2xz$ at the point $(1, 3, 1)$.

22. Find an equation of the plane tangent to the graph of $y = f(x, z)$ at the point (x_0, y_0, z_0).

23. Show that the plane tangent to the cone $z^2 = x^2 + y^2$ (at any point where it exists) goes through the origin.

24. Consider the following parametrizations.

    (a) $\mathbf{r}_1(u, v) = (u, v, 1)$, $-1 \le u, v \le 1$

    (b) $\mathbf{r}_2(u, v) = (2u, 3v, 1)$, $-1/2 \le u \le 1/2$, $-1/3 \le v \le 1/3$

(c) $r_3(u, v) = (u^3, v^3, 1)$, $-1 \leq u, v \leq 1$

(d) $r_4(u, v) = (\sin u, \sin v, 1)$, $0 \leq u, v \leq 2\pi$

Check that the images of $r_1, \ldots, r_4$ represent the same set. State which parametrizations are continuous, differentiable, C^1. State which parametrizations are smooth at $(0, 0, 1)$. Compute the tangent plane at $(0, 0, 1)$ for those parametrizations.

25. Find a parametrization of the ellipsoid $x^2/a^2 + y^2/b^2 + z^2/c^2 = 1$.

26. Let S be the surface $r(u, v) = (u^2, 2uv, 0)$, $-\infty < u, v < \infty$. Find an orientation-reversing parametrization of S.

27. Find the points (if any) on the surface $r(u, v) = (u^2v, uv^2, 1)$ where the tangent plane is parallel to the plane $z = x - y$.

28. Find all points (if any) (x, y, z) on the paraboloid $z = 2 - x^2 - y^2$ where the normal vector is parallel to the vector joining the origin and the point (x, y, z).

7.2   SURFACE INTEGRALS OF REAL-VALUED FUNCTIONS

The path integral of a real-valued function provides a way of investigating the values of a function along a given curve. It is defined as a limit of approximating sums, each summand being of the form (value of f at a point on the curve)·(length of an approximation of a small part of the curve by a straight line segment). If $f \equiv 1$, then the path integral represents the length of a curve.

The surface integral is a higher-dimensional analogue of the path integral. This time, what interests us are the values of a function f at points that belong to a surface S in $\mathbb{R}^3$. We will build approximating sums in the form (value of f at a point on the surface)·(area of an approximation of a small part of the surface by a parallelogram), and define the surface integral as the limit of such sums as the number of approximating parallelograms approaches infinity. In the special case when $f \equiv 1$, we will obtain a formula for surface area.

Let $r: D \rightarrow \mathbb{R}^3$ be a parametrization of a surface S in $\mathbb{R}^3$ and let D be an elementary region in $\mathbb{R}^2$. Assume, for simplicity, that D is a rectangle (if D is not a rectangle, enclose it with a rectangle (that can be done since D is an elementary region, and therefore bounded), subdivide that rectangle into small subrectangles and consider only those that have a non-empty intersection with D). Divide D into n^2 rectangles, choose one of them, name it R (we drop the subscripts for simplicity, and instead of using R_{ij} we use R to denote a generic rectangle that belongs to a subdivision) and label its sides Δu and Δv. From the definition of the partial derivative

$$\frac{\partial r}{\partial u} = \lim_{\Delta u \to 0} \frac{r(u + \Delta u, v) - r(u, v)}{\Delta u}$$

it follows that, for small Δu,

$$\frac{\partial r}{\partial u} \approx \frac{r(u + \Delta u, v) - r(u, v)}{\Delta u},$$

and therefore

$$\mathbf{r}(u + \Delta u, v) - \mathbf{r}(u, v) \approx \frac{\partial \mathbf{r}}{\partial u} \Delta u.$$

It follows that the image of the lower side Δu of R is a curve (see Figure 7.16) $\mathbf{r}(\Delta u)$ whose length (assuming that R is small) can be approximated as

$$\ell(\mathbf{r}(\Delta u)) \approx \|\mathbf{r}(u + \Delta u, v) - \mathbf{r}(u, v)\| \approx \left\|\frac{\partial \mathbf{r}}{\partial u} \Delta u\right\|$$

Similarly, the image $\mathbf{r}(\Delta v)$ of the left side of the rectangle (labelled as Δv) has length

$$\ell(\mathbf{r}(\Delta v)) \approx \|\mathbf{r}(u, v + \Delta v) - \mathbf{r}(u, v)\| \approx \left\|\frac{\partial \mathbf{r}}{\partial v} \Delta v\right\|.$$

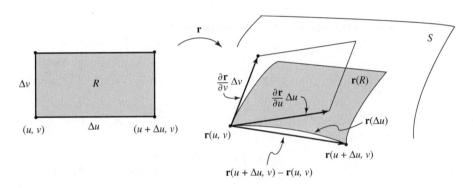

Figure 7.16 Approximating the patch $\mathbf{r}(R)$ by a parallelogram.

Now consider the image $\mathbf{r}(R)$ of R. For small Δu and Δv it can be approximated by the parallelogram spanned by

$$\frac{\partial \mathbf{r}}{\partial u} \Delta u = \mathbf{T}_u \Delta u \qquad \text{and} \qquad \frac{\partial \mathbf{r}}{\partial v} \Delta v = \mathbf{T}_v \Delta v.$$

It follows that the area of the patch $\mathbf{r}(R)$ on S is approximately equal to

$$\|\mathbf{T}_u \Delta u \times \mathbf{T}_v \Delta v\| = \|\mathbf{T}_u \times \mathbf{T}_v\| \Delta u \Delta v$$

(recall that the area of a parallelogram spanned by two vectors equals the magnitude of their cross product).

Form the sum

$$\mathcal{R}_n = \sum \|\mathbf{T}_u \times \mathbf{T}_v\| \Delta u \Delta v$$

of areas of patches $\mathbf{r}(R)$ for all n^2 rectangles R that form a subdivision of D. As $n \to \infty$, the sums $\mathcal{R}_n$ approach the double integral

$$\int_D \|\mathbf{T}_u \times \mathbf{T}_v\| dA.$$

On the other hand, the patches $\mathbf{r}(R)$ approximate the surface S better and better as n keeps increasing. Therefore, we *define* the *surface area* $A(S)$ of S to be

$$A(S) = \int_D \|\mathbf{T}_u \times \mathbf{T}_v\| dA.$$

Next, take any function f defined at the points of S, and form its Riemann sums in the usual way:

$$\mathcal{R}_n = \sum f(\mathbf{r}(u, v)) \|\mathbf{T}_u \times \mathbf{T}_v\| \Delta u \Delta v.$$

The summation goes over n^2 rectangles R that form a subdivision of D. The surface integral of f over S will be defined (as usual) as the limit of $\mathcal{R}_n$ as $n \to \infty$. The assumption on the continuity of f guarantees that this limit exists (we will not prove that). Recall that the cross product $\mathbf{T}_u \times \mathbf{T}_v$ of tangent vectors is the surface normal vector $\mathbf{N}$.

■ **Definition 7.4**   Surface Integral of a Real-valued Function.

Let S be a smooth surface in $\mathbb{R}^3$ parametrized by

$$\mathbf{r}(u, v) = (x(u, v), y(u, v), z(u, v)), \qquad (u, v) \in D,$$

where $D \subseteq \mathbb{R}^2$ is an elementary region and $f: S \to \mathbb{R}$ a real-valued continuous function. The *surface integral of f over S*, denoted by $\iint_S f \, dS$, is defined by the formula

$$\iint_S f \, dS = \iint_D f(\mathbf{r}(u, v)) \|\mathbf{N}(u, v)\| \, dA,$$

where $\mathbf{N}(u, v) = \mathbf{T}_u(u, v) \times \mathbf{T}_v(u, v)$.   ■

Let us emphasize that only the values of f at points on the surface S are relevant in the computation of the surface integral $\iint_S f \, dS$. If $f \equiv 1$, the integral $\iint_S dS$ gives the surface area of S.

Example 7.14   Compute the integral $\iint_S xy \, dS$, where S denotes the surface of the cylinder $x^2 + y^2 = 4$, with $-1 \leq z \leq 1$.

Solution   Parametrize S by (cf. Example 7.2) $\mathbf{r}(u, v) = (2 \cos u, 2 \sin u, v)$, $(u, v) \in D$, where D is the rectangle $[0, 2\pi] \times [-1, 1]$ in the uv-plane. The tangent vectors are $\mathbf{T}_u = (-2 \sin u, 2 \cos u, 0)$ and $\mathbf{T}_v = (0, 0, 1)$, and thus $\mathbf{N}(u, v) = \mathbf{T}_u(u, v) \times \mathbf{T}_v(u, v) = (2 \cos u, 2 \sin u, 0)$. Therefore $\|\mathbf{N}(u, v)\| = 2$ and

$$\iint_S xy \, dS = \iint_D 2 \cos u \cdot 2 \sin u \cdot 2 \, dA$$

(use the double-angle formula $\sin 2u = 2 \sin u \cos u$)

$$= 4 \int_{-1}^1 \left(\int_0^{2\pi} \sin 2u \, du \right) dv = 4 \int_{-1}^1 \left(-\frac{1}{2} \cos 2u \Big|_0^{2\pi} \right) dv = 0.$$ ◀

Example 7.15   Find $\iint_S \sqrt{x^2 + y^2 + 1}\, dS$, where S is the helicoidal surface

$$\mathbf{r}(u, v) = (u \cos v, u \sin v, v), \qquad 0 \le u \le 1, \quad 0 \le v \le 2\pi,$$

shown in Figure 7.17.

Solution   The tangent vectors $\mathbf{T}_u$ and $\mathbf{T}_v$ to S are $\mathbf{T}_u = (\cos v, \sin v, 0)$ and $\mathbf{T}_v = (-u \sin v, u \cos v, 1)$; thus $\mathbf{N} = \mathbf{T}_u \times \mathbf{T}_v = (\sin v, -\cos v, u)$, $\|\mathbf{N}\| = \sqrt{1 + u^2}$, and

$$\iint_S \sqrt{x^2 + y^2 + 1}\, dS = \iint_{[0,1] \times [0, 2\pi]} \sqrt{u^2 + 1}\sqrt{u^2 + 1}\, dA$$

$$= \int_0^{2\pi} \left(\int_0^1 (u^2 + 1)\, du \right) dv = \int_0^{2\pi} \left(\frac{u^3}{3} + u \Big|_0^1 \right) dv = \frac{8\pi}{3}. \qquad \triangleleft$$

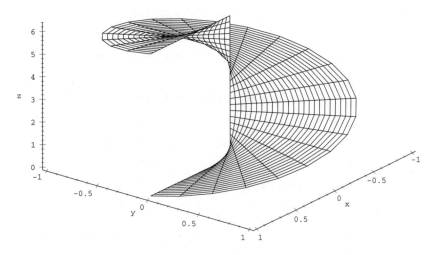

Figure 7.17   Helicoid $\mathbf{r}(u, v) = (u \cos v, u \sin v, v)$, $0 \le u \le 1$, $0 \le v \le 2\pi$.

■ **Theorem 7.1**   Surface Integrals are Independent of Parametrization.

Let S be a smooth surface and let $f: S \to \mathbb{R}$ be a real-valued continuous function. The surface integral $\iint_S f\, dS$ does not depend on the parametrization of S, provided the parametrization is smooth.   ■

The theorem states that if $\mathbf{r}(u, v): D \to \mathbb{R}^3$ and $\mathbf{r}^*(u^*, v^*): D^* \to \mathbb{R}^3$ are smooth parametrizations of S, then

$$\iint_S f\, dS = \iint_D f(\mathbf{r}(u, v)) \|\mathbf{T}_u \times \mathbf{T}_v\|\, dA = \iint_{D^*} f(\mathbf{r}^*(u^*, v^*)) \|\mathbf{T}_{u^*} \times \mathbf{T}_{v^*}\|\, dA^*.$$

Consequently, the notation $\iint_S f\, dS$ for the surface integral is justified— there is no need to mention the parametrization that is used. In particular, if $f \equiv 1$, then

$$A(S) = \iint_D \|\mathbf{T}_u \times \mathbf{T}_v\| \, dA = \iint_{D^*} \|\mathbf{T}_{u^*} \times \mathbf{T}_{v^*}\| \, dA^*;$$

i.e., the surface area $A(S)$ does not depend on a parametrization of the surface (as expected).

The proof of this theorem is similar to the proof of the theorem stating that path integrals of scalar functions are independent of parametrization and will be omitted.

Example 7.16   Find a formula for the integral $\iint_S g \, dS$, where S is the graph of a differentiable function $z = f(x, y)$ defined on an elementary region $D \subseteq \mathbb{R}^2$ and $g(x, y, z): S \subseteq \mathbb{R}^3 \to \mathbb{R}$ is a continuous function.

Solution   Let $x = u$ and $y = v$, so that $z = f(u, v)$; in other words, the map

$$\mathbf{r}(u, v) = (u, v, f(u, v)), \qquad (u, v) \in D,$$

parametrizes the surface S (see Example 7.8). Then $\mathbf{T}_u = (1, 0, \partial f/\partial u)$, $\mathbf{T}_v = (0, 1, \partial f/\partial v)$ and $\mathbf{N}(u, v) = \mathbf{T}_u \times \mathbf{T}_v = (-\partial f/\partial u, -\partial f/\partial v, 1)$, and hence

$$\iint_S g \, dS = \iint_D g(u, v, f(u, v)) \sqrt{1 + \left(\frac{\partial f}{\partial u}\right)^2 + \left(\frac{\partial f}{\partial v}\right)^2} \, dA.$$

Example 7.17   Compute the integral of $g(x, y, z) = \arctan(y/x)$ over the surface S that consists of the part of the graph of $z = x^2 + y^2$ between $z = 1$ and $z = 2$.

Solution   In order to parametrize S we take $x = u$ and $y = v$, so that

$$\mathbf{r}(u, v) = (u, v, u^2 + v^2), \qquad 1 \le u^2 + v^2 \le 2.$$

It follows that $\mathbf{T}_u = (1, 0, 2u)$, $\mathbf{T}_v = (0, 1, 2v)$ and $\mathbf{N} = \mathbf{T}_u \times \mathbf{T}_v = (-2u, -2v, 1)$, so that

$$\iint_S \arctan\left(\frac{y}{x}\right) dS = \iint_D \arctan\left(\frac{v}{u}\right) \sqrt{4u^2 + 4v^2 + 1} \, dA,$$

where D is the annulus $1 \le u^2 + v^2 \le 2$ in the uv-plane (obtained by combining $z = x^2 + y^2$ and $1 \le z \le 2$). Changing to polar coordinates we get (recall that $\arctan(y/x) = \theta$)

$$\iint_S \arctan\left(\frac{y}{x}\right) dS = \int_0^{2\pi} \left(\int_1^{\sqrt{2}} \theta \sqrt{1 + 4r^2} \, r \, dr\right) d\theta$$

$$= \left(\int_0^{2\pi} \theta \, d\theta\right) \left(\frac{1}{12}(1 + 4r^2)^{3/2}\Big|_1^{\sqrt{2}}\right) = \frac{\pi^2}{6}\left(9^{3/2} - 5^{3/2}\right).$$

Example 7.18   Compute the surface area $A(S)$ of the part S of the plane $2x + y + z = 4$ in the first octant.

Solution Parametrize the plane by $x = u$, $y = v$ and $z = 4 - 2u - v$, where (x, y) belongs to the triangular region D in the xy-plane bounded by the x-axis, the y-axis and the line $2x + y = 4$; see Figure 7.18. In the spirit of the definition of a parametrization, we have to describe D as the triangular region bounded by the u-axis, the v-axis and the line $2u + v = 4$ (however, it might be more convenient to imagine D as a subset of the xy-plane). The area of S is given by

$$A(S) = \iint_D \|\mathbf{T}_u \times \mathbf{T}_v\| \, dA.$$

From $\mathbf{r}(u, v) = (u, v, 4 - 2u - v)$ it follows that $\mathbf{T}_u = (1, 0, -2)$, $\mathbf{T}_v = (0, 1, -1)$ and $\|\mathbf{T}_u \times \mathbf{T}_v\| = \|(2, 1, 1)\| = \sqrt{6}$; thus

$$A(S) = \int_0^2 \left(\int_0^{4-2u} \sqrt{6} \, dv \right) du = \sqrt{6} \int_0^2 (4 - 2u) \, du = \sqrt{6} \left(4u - u^2 \right) \Big|_0^2 = 4\sqrt{6}.$$

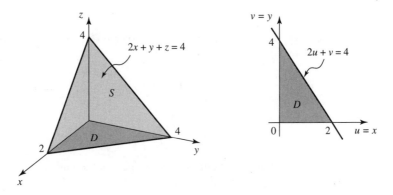

Figure 7.18 Surface S of the plane of Example 7.18.

Example 7.19

Compute the surface area of the torus

$$\mathbf{r}(u, v) = ((R + \rho \cos v) \cos u, (R + \rho \cos v) \sin u, \rho \sin v), \qquad 0 \le u, v \le 2\pi.$$

The geometric meaning of the parameters u and v is illustrated in Figure 7.19.

Solution The surface normal vector $\mathbf{N} = \mathbf{T}_u \times \mathbf{T}_v$ is computed to be

$$\mathbf{N}(u, v) = \begin{vmatrix} \mathbf{i} & \mathbf{j} & \mathbf{k} \\ -(R + \rho \cos v) \sin u & (R + \rho \cos v) \cos u & 0 \\ -\rho \sin v \cos u & -\rho \sin v \sin u & \rho \cos v \end{vmatrix}$$

$$= ((R + \rho \cos v) \rho \cos u \cos v, (R + \rho \cos v) \rho \sin u \cos v, (R + \rho \cos v) \rho \sin v)$$

$$= (R + \rho \cos v) \rho (\cos u \cos v, \sin u \cos v, \sin v),$$

and its norm is given by

$$\|\mathbf{N}(u, v)\|^2 = (R + \rho \cos v)^2 \rho^2 \|(\cos u \cos v, \sin u \cos v, \sin v)\|^2 = (R + \rho \cos v)^2.$$

Consequently, the surface area of the torus is computed to be

$$A(S) = \iint_{[0,2\pi]\times[0,2\pi]} (R + \rho\cos v)\rho\,dA = \rho \int_0^{2\pi} \left(\int_0^{2\pi} (R + \rho\cos v)dv \right) du$$

$$= \rho \int_0^{2\pi} \left(Rv + \rho\sin v \,\Big|_0^{2\pi} \right) du = \rho \int_0^{2\pi} 2\pi R\,du = 4\pi^2 R\rho.$$

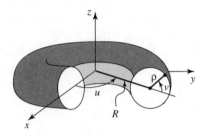

Figure 7.19   Torus $\mathbf{r}(u,v) = ((R + \rho\cos v)\cos u, (R + \rho\cos v)\sin u, \rho\sin v)$.

Example 7.20

The electrostatic potential at $(0, 0, -a)$ induced by a charge of constant charge density σ on the hemisphere S defined by $x^2 + y^2 + z^2 = a^2$, $z \geq 0$ is given by

$$U = c \iint_S \frac{\sigma}{\sqrt{x^2 + y^2 + (z+a)^2}}\,dS,$$

where the value of the constant c depends on the units that are used. Show that $U = 2\pi\sigma ac(2 - \sqrt{2})$.

Solution   Parametrize the hemisphere by

$$\mathbf{r}(u, v) = (a\cos u\sin v, a\sin u\sin v, a\cos v), \qquad 0 \leq u \leq 2\pi, \quad 0 \leq v \leq \pi/2.$$

Then

$$x^2 + y^2 + (z + a)^2 = a^2\cos^2 u\sin^2 v + a^2\sin^2 u\sin^2 v + a^2\cos^2 v + 2a^2\cos v + a^2$$
$$= a^2\sin^2 v + a^2\cos^2 v + 2a^2\cos v + a^2 = 2a^2 + 2a^2\cos v$$
$$= 2a^2(1 + \cos v)$$

and

$$\mathbf{N} = \mathbf{T}_u \times \mathbf{T}_v = \begin{vmatrix} \mathbf{i} & \mathbf{j} & \mathbf{k} \\ -a\sin u\sin v & a\cos u\sin v & 0 \\ a\cos u\cos v & a\sin u\cos v & -a\sin v \end{vmatrix}$$

$$= -a\sin v(a\sin v\cos u, a\sin v\sin u, a\cos v) = -a\sin v\,\mathbf{r}(u,v).$$

It follows that $\|\mathbf{N}\| = |-a\sin v|\,\|\mathbf{r}(u,v)\| = a^2\sin v$ and hence

$$U = c \iint_S \frac{\sigma}{\sqrt{x^2 + y^2 + (z+a)^2}}\,dS = c \int_0^{2\pi} \left(\int_0^{\pi/2} \frac{\sigma}{a\sqrt{2}\sqrt{1 + \cos v}} a^2\sin v\,dv \right) du$$

(using the substitution $t = 1 + \cos v$)

$$= c \int_0^{2\pi} \left(\frac{a\sigma}{\sqrt{2}} \left. (-2(1+\cos v)^{1/2}) \right|_{v=0}^{v=\pi/2} \right) dv$$

$$= c \int_0^{2\pi} \frac{a\sigma}{\sqrt{2}} (-2 + 2\sqrt{2}) \, dv = 2\pi \frac{ac\sigma}{\sqrt{2}} \sqrt{2} (2 - \sqrt{2}) = 2\pi a\sigma c (2 - \sqrt{2}).$$

It is possible to define the surface integral over a more general class of surfaces, as will now be introduced.

A surface S is called a *piecewise smooth surface* if it is a disjoint union of surfaces S_i (that means that the most two S_i's can have in common are points and/or curves), parametrized by $\mathbf{r}_i \colon D_i \to \mathbb{R}^3$, $i = 1, \ldots, n$, where

(a) D_i is an elemetary region in $\mathbb{R}^2$,

(b) $\mathbf{r}_i$ is one-to-one, except possibly on the boundary of D_i,

(c) $\mathbf{r}_i$ is of class C^1, except possibly on the boundary of D_i, and

(d) $S_i = \mathbf{r}_i(D_i)$ is a smooth surface, except possibly at a finite number of points.

The integral of a function over S is defined as a sum of integrals over S_i.

Example 7.21 Compute $\iint_S yz \, dS$, where S consists of the hemisphere $x^2 + y^2 + z^2 = 1$, $z \geq 0$ and the disk $0 \leq x^2 + y^2 \leq 1$, in the xy-plane.

Solution The surface S is piecewise smooth, and

$$\iint_S yz \, dS = \iint_{S_1} yz \, dS + \iint_{S_2} yz \, dS,$$

where S_1 is the surface of the hemisphere and S_2 is the disk. Parametrize S_1 by

$$\mathbf{r}_1(u, v) = (\cos u \sin v, \sin u \sin v, \cos v), \qquad 0 \leq u \leq 2\pi, \quad 0 \leq v \leq \pi/2.$$

Repeating the computation of Example 7.20 with $a = 1$, we get $\|\mathbf{N}_1\| = \sin v$ and hence

$$\iint_{S_1} yz \, dS = \iint_{[0,2\pi] \times [0,\pi/2]} \sin u \sin v \cos v \, \sin v \, dA$$

$$= \int_0^{2\pi} \left(\int_0^{\pi/2} \sin u \sin^2 v \cos v \, dv \right) du$$

$$= \left(\int_0^{2\pi} \sin u \, du \right) \left(\int_0^{\pi/2} \sin^2 v \cos v \, dv \right) = 0,$$

by separation of variables, using the fact that $\int_0^{2\pi} \sin u \, du = 0$.

Paramterize S_2 by

$$\mathbf{r}_2(u, v) = (u, v, 0), \qquad (u, v) \in D,$$

where D is the disk $\{(u, v) \mid u^2 + v^2 \leq 1\}$. From the formula of Example 7.16 (with

$f(u, v) = 0)$ it follows that

$$\iint_{S_2} yz \, dS = \iint_D (y)(0)(1) \, dA = 0.$$

Therefore, $\iint_S f \, dS = 0$.

So far, we have learned how to set up a surface integral if a parametrization of a surface is known explicitly (or if it can be constructed). We have also derived a formula in the case when a surface is given as the graph of a function $z = f(x, y)$. But how do we set up a surface integral if there is no (explicit) parametrization? To be more specific: suppose that a surface is given in the form $F(x, y, z) = C$, where F is a C^1 function and $C \in \mathbb{R}$ (i.e., it is given as a level surface of a C^1 function). We need to find a way to compute its (surface) area and then (as in the beginning of this section) generalize the construction to obtain the surface integral of a continuous function $f : \mathbb{R}^3 \to \mathbb{R}$.

One thing is immediate: since the gradient vector is always perpendicular to a level surface, it follows that either $\mathbf{n} = \nabla F / \|\nabla F\|$ or $\mathbf{n} = -\nabla F / \|\nabla F\|$ is the unit normal vector defining the orientation of the surface. In order to derive a formula for the area, we take a more intuitive approach, based on the following principle (that is sometimes called "the Area Cosine Principle"). Consider a plane region ΔS that makes an angle θ ($0 \leq \theta \leq \pi/2$) with respect to the xy-plane; see Figure 7.20. Let ΔD be the region in the xy-plane that is the orthogonal projection of ΔS. Let us compare the areas of ΔS and ΔD.

The distances in the x-direction remain the same for both ΔS and its projection. However, the distances in the y-direction do not: the distance in the projection ΔD gets distorted (shortened) by the factor of $\cos \theta$. Therefore,

$$\text{area}(\Delta D) = \text{area}(\Delta S) \, \cos \theta$$

(see Exercise 15), where $0 \leq \theta \leq \pi/2$. Notice that θ is also the angle between the upward unit normal $\mathbf{n}$ to ΔS and the vector $\mathbf{k}$ (unit normal to ΔD), so that $\cos \theta = \mathbf{n} \cdot \mathbf{k} / (\|\mathbf{n}\| \, \|\mathbf{k}\|) = \mathbf{n} \cdot \mathbf{k}$ and thus

$$\text{area}(\Delta S) = \frac{\text{area}(\Delta D)}{\mathbf{n} \cdot \mathbf{k}}.$$

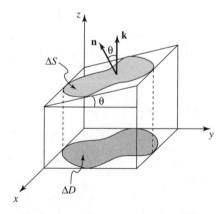

Figure 7.20   Area Cosine Principle.

One technical point: assume that ΔS is oriented by the downward-pointing normal $-\mathbf{n}$. In that case, the angle between the normal $-\mathbf{n}$ and $\mathbf{k}$ is $\pi - \theta$, and their dot product is negative. Therefore, in order to include both orientations in the formula, we need the absolute value, so that

$$\text{area}(\Delta S) = \frac{\text{area}(\Delta D)}{|\mathbf{n} \cdot \mathbf{k}|}.$$

Now let S be a surface oriented by the unit normal $\mathbf{n}$, and assume that every line perpendicular to the xy-plane intersects S in at most one point (so that we can project S onto the xy-plane). Take a small patch ΔS on S (that is so small that it can be assumed flat; i.e., can be approximated by a plane region) and consider its projection ΔD onto the xy-plane; see Figure 7.21.

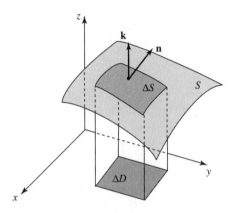

Figure 7.21   The area of ΔS is approximately equal to $\text{area}(\Delta D)/|\mathbf{n} \cdot \mathbf{k}|$.

By the Area Cosine Principle, the area of ΔS is approximately equal to $\text{area}(\Delta D)/|\mathbf{n} \cdot \mathbf{k}|$, and

$$\text{area}(S) \approx \sum \frac{\text{area}(\Delta D)}{|\mathbf{n} \cdot \mathbf{k}|},$$

where the summation goes over all small patches ΔS. In the limit, as the size $\Delta S \to 0$, we get that

$$\text{area}(S) = \iint_D \frac{dA}{|\mathbf{n} \cdot \mathbf{k}|},$$

where D is the projection of S onto the xy-plane, and dA refers to integration with respect to x and y.

Example 7.22   Find the surface area of the part S of the paraboloid $z = 2 - x^2 - y^2$ that lies above the xy-plane.

Solution   View S as the level surface $F(x, y, z) = x^2 + y^2 + z = 2$. Its normal is

$\nabla F = (2x, 2y, 1)$ and hence the (upward) unit normal to S is

$$\mathbf{n} = (2x/\sqrt{4x^2 + 4y^2 + 1}, \, 2y/\sqrt{4x^2 + 4y^2 + 1}, \, 1/\sqrt{4x^2 + 4y^2 + 1}).$$

From $z = 2 - x^2 - y^2 \geq 0$ it follows that $x^2 + y^2 \leq 2$ (i.e., the projection D of S onto the xy-plane is the disk $x^2 + y^2 \leq 2$). Since $|\mathbf{n} \cdot \mathbf{k}| = 1/\sqrt{4x^2 + 4y^2 + 1}$, it follows that the area of S is

$$\text{area}(S) = \iint_D \sqrt{4x^2 + 4y^2 + 1}\, dA.$$

Passing to polar coordinates, we get that (recall that $dA = r\,dr\,d\theta$)

$$\text{area}(S) = \int_0^{2\pi} \left(\int_0^{\sqrt{2}} \sqrt{4r^2 + 1}\, r\,dr \right) d\theta$$

$$= \int_0^{2\pi} \left(\tfrac{1}{12}(4r^2 + 1)^{3/2} \, \Big|_0^{\sqrt{2}} \right) d\theta = \tfrac{2}{12}\pi(9^{3/2} - 1) = \tfrac{13}{3}\pi.$$

◀

Repeating the above construction for projections with respect to the remaining two coordinate planes, we get that

$$\text{area}(S) = \iint_D \frac{dA}{|\mathbf{n} \cdot \mathbf{i}|},$$

where D is the projection of S onto the yz-plane and dA refers to integration with respect to y and z, and

$$\text{area}(S) = \iint_D \frac{dA}{|\mathbf{n} \cdot \mathbf{j}|},$$

where D is the projection of S onto the xz-plane and dA refers to integration with respect to x and z. Of course, in every case we have to make sure that it is possible to project S onto the required plane.

In general, if S is a surface in $\mathbb{R}^3$ oriented by the unit normal $\mathbf{n}$ and $f(x, y, z)$ is a continuous real-valued function on S, then

$$\iint_S f\, dS = \iint_D f(x, y, z)\frac{dA}{|\mathbf{n} \cdot \mathbf{k}|},$$

where D is the projection of S onto the xy-plane. As usual, dA refers to the corresponding integration (in this case, with respect to x and y). By considering the remaining two projections, we obtain two more formulas for $\iint_S f\, dS$.

Example 7.23   Let $f(x, y, z) = 4xz$ and assume that S is the part of the surface $x^2 + y + 2z = 4$ in the first octant oriented by the upward-pointing normal; see Figure 7.22. Set up (do not evaluate) double integrals that would evaluate the surface integral $\iint_S f\, dS$ using projections.

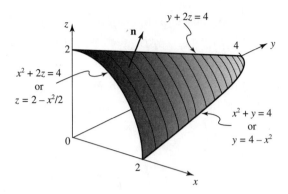

Figure 7.22 Surface $x^2 + y + 2z = 4$ of Example 7.23.

Solution The surface S can be viewed as the level surface $F(x, y, z) = 4$ of the function $F(x, y, z) = x^2 + y + 2z$. From $\nabla F = (2x, 1, 2)$ it follows that the (upward) unit normal (z-component has to be positive) is $\mathbf{n} = \nabla F / \|\nabla F\| = (2x, 1, 2)/\sqrt{4x^2 + 5}$.

The projection D_1 of S onto the xz-plane is the region bounded by $x = 0$, $z = 0$ and (substitute $y = 0$ into the equation for S) $z = 2 - x^2/2$. Since $|\mathbf{n} \cdot \mathbf{j}| = 1/\sqrt{4x^2 + 5}$ it follows that

$$\iint_S f \, dS = \iint_{D_1} f(x, y, z) \frac{dA}{|\mathbf{n} \cdot \mathbf{j}|} = \iint_{D_1} 4xz \frac{dA}{1/\sqrt{4x^2 + 5}},$$

where dA refers to integration with respect to x and z. Hence

$$\iint_S f \, dS = \int_0^2 \left(\int_0^{2-x^2/2} 4xz\sqrt{4x^2 + 5} \, dz \right) dx.$$

The projection D_2 of S onto the yz-plane is the triangle bounded by $y = 0$, $z = 0$ and (substitute $x = 0$ into the equation for S) $y + 2z = 4$. It follows that

$$\iint_S f \, dS = \iint_{D_2} f(x, y, z) \frac{dA}{|\mathbf{n} \cdot \mathbf{i}|},$$

where dA refers to integration with respect to y and z, and $|\mathbf{n} \cdot \mathbf{i}| = |2x/\sqrt{4x^2 + 5}| = 2x/\sqrt{4x^2 + 5}$, since $x \geq 0$. Thus

$$\iint_S f \, dS = \iint_{D_2} 4xz \frac{dA}{2x/\sqrt{4x^2 + 5}} = \iint_{D_2} 2z\sqrt{4x^2 + 5} \, dA.$$

Since the integration is with respect to y and z, we have to eliminate x. From $x^2 + y + 2z = 4$ we get $x^2 = 4 - y - 2z$ and therefore

$$\iint_S f \, dS = \iint_{D_2} 2z\sqrt{21 - 4y - 8z} \, dA = \int_0^4 \left(\int_0^{2-y/2} 2z\sqrt{21 - 4y - 8z} \, dz \right) dy.$$

The projection D_3 of S onto the xy-plane is the region bounded by $x = 0$, $y = 0$

and $y = 4 - x^2$. Since $|\mathbf{n} \cdot \mathbf{k}| = 2/\sqrt{4x^2 + 5}$ it follows that

$$\iint_S f \, dS = \iint_{D_3} f(x, y, z) \frac{dA}{|\mathbf{n} \cdot \mathbf{k}|} = \iint_{D_3} 4xz \frac{dA}{2/\sqrt{4x^2 + 5}},$$

where dA refers to integration with respect to x and y. Eliminating z and setting up the limits of integration, we get

$$\iint_S f \, dS = \iint_{D_3} 2x \left(2 - \frac{x^2}{2} - \frac{y}{2} \right) \sqrt{4x^2 + 5} \, dA$$

$$= \int_0^2 \left(\int_0^{4-x^2} x(4 - x^2 - y)\sqrt{4x^2 + 5} \, dy \right) dx.$$

EXERCISES 7.2   **Exercises 1 to 8:** Compute $\iint_S f \, dS$ in each case.

1. $f(x, y, z) = xy$, S is the part of the paraboloid $z = x^2 + y^2$ that lies inside the cylinder of radius 2 whose axis of rotation is the z-axis

2. $f(x, y, z) = 2z(x^2 + y^2)$, S is the surface parametrized by $\mathbf{r}(u, v) = (\cos u, \sin u, v)$, $0 \le u \le \pi, 0 \le v \le 2$

3. $f(x, y, z) = y+x$, S is the tetrahedron with vertices $(0, 0, 0)$, $(2, 0, 0)$, $(0, 2, 0)$ and $(0, 0, 2)$

4. $f(x, y, z) = x^2 + y^2$, S is the part of the cone $z^2 = x^2 + y^2$ between $z = 1$ and $z = 4$

5. $f(x, y, z) = 2y - x$, S is the part of the cone $x^2 = y^2 + z^2$, $x \le 1$ in the first octant

6. $f(x, y, z) = 8y$, S is the parabolic sheet $z = 1 - y^2$, $0 \le x \le 2$, $0 \le y \le 1$

7. $f(x, y, z) = (4x^2 + 4y^2 + 1)^{-1/2}$, S is the part of the paraboloid $z = 4 - x^2 - y^2$ above the xy-plane

8. $f(x, y, z) = \sqrt{x^2 + y^2}$, S is the helicoidal surface $\mathbf{r}(u, v) = (u \cos v, u \sin v, v)$, $0 \le u \le 1$, $0 \le v \le 4\pi$

9. Compute the surface area of the part of the surface $\mathbf{r}(u, v) = (2u \cos v, 2u \sin v, v)$, where $0 \le u \le 2$, $0 \le v \le \pi$.

10. Compute the surface area of the part of the cylinder $x^2 + z^2 = 1$, $z \ge 0$, between the planes $y = 0$ and $z = y + 1$.

11. Compute the surface area of a cone of radius r and height h, using surface integrals.

12. Find the area of the triangle with vertices $(1, 2, 0)$, $(3, 0, 7)$ and $(-1, 0, 0)$ using a surface integral. Check your answer using the cross product.

13. Let S be the sphere $x^2 + y^2 + z^2 = a^2$. Find $\iint_S x \, dS$, $\iint_S x^2 \, dS$ and $\iint_S x^3 \, dS$ without evaluating surface integrals using a parametrization.

14. Compute the surface area of the part of the plane $z = 0$ defined by $-1 \le x \le 1, -1 \le y \le 1$ using the following parametrizations.

    (a) $\mathbf{r}(u, v) = (u, v, 0)$, $-1 \le u, v \le 1$ (b) $\mathbf{r}(u, v) = (u^3, v, 0)$, $-1 \le u, v \le 1$

    (c) $\mathbf{r}(u, v) = (u^{1/3}, v^{1/3}, 0)$, $-1 \le u, v \le 1$

    (d) $\mathbf{r}(u, v) = (\sin u, \sin v, 0)$, $0 \le u, v \le 2\pi$

The results in (a), (b) and (c) are the same. Why is the result in (d) different?

15. Let S be the rectangle in the plane $z = my$, $m > 0$, lying directly above the rectangle $R = [0, a] \times [0, b]$, $a, b > 0$, in the xy-plane. Show that (area of S) $= \sqrt{m^2 + 1} \cdot$ (area of R). Let α be the angle between $\mathbf{k}$ and the upward normal to S. Conclude that (area of S) $= \sec \alpha \cdot$ (area of R).

16. Consider the integral $\iint_S f(x, y, z) \, dS$, where S is a surface symmetric with respect to the xz-plane. If $f(x, -y, z) = -f(x, y, z)$, what is the value of $\iint_S f \, dS$? Using your result, recompute the surface integral in Example 7.21.

17. Evaluate $\iint_S f \, dS$, where $f(x, y, z) = 4xy$ and S is the parabolic sheet $z = 1 - y^2$ in the first octant, bounded by the plane $x = 2$.

18. Using the Area Cosine Principle, find the formula for the area of an ellipse with semi-axes a and b.

19. Compute $\iint_S y \, dS$, where S is the part of the surface $x + y^2 + z = 4$ in the first octant, using a projection of S onto one of the coordinate planes.

20. Let S be the plane $x + y + 2z = 4$ oriented by the upward-pointing normal. Compute $\iint_S (xy^2 + z^2) \, dS$

    (a) using a parametrization of S,

    (b) by viewing S as the graph of the function $z = 2 - x/2 - y/2$ and using the formula of Example 7.16, and

    (c) by using any of the three projections of S onto the coordinate planes.

21. Find the area of the hemisphere S defined by $x^2 + y^2 + z^2 = a^2$, $a > 0$, $y \geq 0$, using a projection of S onto a coordinate plane.

22. Find the surface area of the strip on the sphere $x^2 + y^2 + z^2 = a^2$ $(a > 0)$, defined by the angles ϕ_1 and ϕ_2, where $\phi_1 < \phi_2$ (ϕ_1 and ϕ_2 are defined in the same way as the angle ϕ in spherical coordinates).

7.3 SURFACE INTEGRALS OF VECTOR FIELDS

The aim of this section is to give a generalization of integrals of scalar functions to integrals of vector functions over surfaces in $\mathbb{R}^3$.

▓ Definition 7.5   Surface Integral of a Vector Field.

Let S be a smooth surface in $\mathbb{R}^3$ parametrized by a differentiable map $\mathbf{r} = \mathbf{r}(u, v): D \to \mathbb{R}^3$ (where D is an elementary region in $\mathbb{R}^2$) and let $\mathbf{F}: S \subseteq \mathbb{R}^3 \to \mathbb{R}^3$ be a vector field on S. The *surface integral* $\iint_S \mathbf{F} \cdot d\mathbf{S}$ *of* $\mathbf{F}$ *over* S is defined by

$$\iint_S \mathbf{F} \cdot d\mathbf{S} = \iint_D \mathbf{F}(\mathbf{r}(u, v)) \cdot \mathbf{N}(u, v) \, dA,$$

where $\mathbf{N}(u, v) = \mathbf{T}_u(u, v) \times \mathbf{T}_v(u, v)$.

The surface integral of a vector field depends only on the values of the vector field at points on the surface. According to the definition, it is reduced to a double integral of the *real-valued* function $\mathbf{F}(\mathbf{r}(u, v)) \cdot \mathbf{N}(u, v)$ over an elementary region D.

Example 7.24

Compute $\iint_S \mathbf{F} \cdot d\mathbf{S}$ where $\mathbf{F} = y\mathbf{i} - x\mathbf{j} + z^2\mathbf{k}$ and S is the helicoid given by $\mathbf{r}(u, v) = (u \cos v, u \sin v, v)$, where $0 \leq u \leq 1$ and $0 \leq v \leq \pi/2$.

Solution   The value of $\mathbf{F}$ at the points on the helicoid S is $\mathbf{F}(\mathbf{r}(u, v)) = u \sin v\mathbf{i} - u \cos v\mathbf{j} + v^2\mathbf{k}$. The vector $\mathbf{N}$ normal to S is given by the cross product

$$\mathbf{N} = \mathbf{T}_u \times \mathbf{T}_v = \begin{vmatrix} \mathbf{i} & \mathbf{j} & \mathbf{k} \\ \cos v & \sin v & 0 \\ -u \sin v & u \cos v & 1 \end{vmatrix} = \sin v\mathbf{i} - \cos v\mathbf{j} + u\mathbf{k},$$

where $\mathbf{T}_u = \partial\mathbf{r}/\partial u$ and $\mathbf{T}_v = \partial\mathbf{r}/\partial v$ are tangent vectors. By definition,

$$\iint_S \mathbf{F} \cdot d\mathbf{S} = \iint_{[0,1]\times[0,\pi/2]} (u \sin v\mathbf{i} - u \cos v\mathbf{j} + v^2\mathbf{k}) \cdot (\sin v\mathbf{i} - \cos v\mathbf{j} + u\mathbf{k})\, dA$$

$$= \int_0^{\pi/2} \left(\int_0^1 (u + uv^2)du \right) dv = \int_0^{\pi/2} \left(\frac{u^2}{2} + \frac{u^2 v^2}{2} \Big|_{u=0}^{u=1} \right) dv$$

$$= \int_0^{\pi/2} \left(\frac{1}{2} + \frac{v^2}{2} \right) dv = \left(\frac{v}{2} + \frac{v^3}{6} \right) \Big|_0^{\pi/2} = \frac{\pi}{4} + \frac{\pi^3}{48}.$$

◀

Example 7.25

Compute the surface integral $\iint_S (y^3\mathbf{i} + x^3\mathbf{j} + 3z^2\mathbf{k}) \cdot d\mathbf{S}$ over the surface S parametrized by $\mathbf{r}: D \to \mathbb{R}^3$, where $\mathbf{r}(u, v) = (u, v, u^2 + v^2)$ and $D = \{(u, v) \mid u^2 + v^2 \leq 4\}$.

Solution   The tangents $\mathbf{T}_u$ and $\mathbf{T}_v$ and the surface normal $\mathbf{N}$ are computed to be $\mathbf{T}_u = (1, 0, 2u)$, $\mathbf{T}_v = (0, 1, 2v)$ and $\mathbf{N} = \mathbf{T}_u \times \mathbf{T}_v = (-2u, -2v, 1)$. Since $\mathbf{F}(\mathbf{r}(u, v)) = (v^3, u^3, 3(u^2 + v^2)^2)$, it follows that

$$\mathbf{F} \cdot \mathbf{N} = (v^3, u^3, 3(u^2 + v^2)^2) \cdot (-2u, -2v, 1)$$

$$= -2uv^3 - 2u^3v + 3(u^2 + v^2)^2$$

$$= -2uv(u^2 + v^2) + 3(u^2 + v^2)^2 = (u^2 + v^2)\left(3(u^2 + v^2) - 2uv\right),$$

and therefore

$$\iint_S \mathbf{F} \cdot d\mathbf{S} = \iint_{\{0 \leq u^2 + v^2 \leq 4\}} \mathbf{F} \cdot \mathbf{N}\, dA$$

$$= \iint_{\{0 \leq u^2 + v^2 \leq 4\}} (u^2 + v^2)\left(3(u^2 + v^2) - 2uv\right) dA$$

(passing to polar coordinates $u = r \cos\theta$, $v = r \sin\theta$)

$$= \int_0^{2\pi} \left(\int_0^2 r^2(3r^2 - 2r^2 \sin\theta \cos\theta)r\,dr \right) d\theta$$

(using $2\cos\theta \sin\theta = \sin 2\theta$)

$$= \int_0^{2\pi} \left(\int_0^2 (3r^5 - r^5 \sin 2\theta) dr \right) d\theta = \int_0^{2\pi} \left(\frac{r^6}{2} - \frac{r^6}{6} \sin 2\theta \Big|_0^2 \right) d\theta$$

$$= \int_0^{2\pi} \left(32 - \frac{32}{3} \sin 2\theta \right) d\theta = \left(32\theta + \frac{32}{6} \cos 2\theta \right) \Big|_0^{2\pi} = 64\pi. \qquad \blacktriangleleft$$

In order to compute the integral of a vector field along a curve we have to specify the orientation on the curve and then choose a parametrization that preserves this orientation. Similarly, the surface integral $\iint_S \mathbf{F} \cdot d\mathbf{S}$ of a vector field $\mathbf{F}$ is an oriented integral: once the orientation of S has been specified (by prescribing the normal direction or by declaring one of the sides of S to be the outside), we have to choose a parametrization that respects our choice of orientation. In the previous two examples the surface was defined using a parametrization, and that implicitly contains the information on the orientation.

Example 7.26 Compute $\iint_S \mathbf{F} \cdot d\mathbf{S}$ if $\mathbf{F} = xyz\mathbf{i}$ and S is the part of the surface of the sphere $x^2 + y^2 + z^2 = 4$ in the first octant, oriented by the outward-pointing normal (i.e., the normal points away from the origin).

Solution Parametrize S by

$$\mathbf{r}(u, v) = (2\cos v \cos u, 2\cos v \sin u, 2\sin v), \qquad 0 \le u \le \pi/2, \quad 0 \le v \le \pi/2.$$

The surface normal $\mathbf{N}$ to S was computed in Example 7.4 to be $\mathbf{N} = 2\cos v\, \mathbf{r}(u, v)$. It points away from the origin, as required. Thus

$$\mathbf{F} \cdot \mathbf{N} = (8\cos^2 v \sin v \cos u \sin u, 0, 0) \cdot 2\cos v(2\cos v \cos u, 2\cos v \sin u, 2\sin v)$$
$$= 32\cos^4 v \sin v \cos^2 u \sin u,$$

and therefore

$$\iint_S \mathbf{F} \cdot d\mathbf{S} = \iint_{[0,\pi/2] \times [0,\pi/2]} \mathbf{F} \cdot \mathbf{N}\, dA$$

$$= \iint_{[0,\pi/2] \times [0,\pi/2]} 32\cos^4 v \sin v \cos^2 u \sin u\, dA$$

$$= 32 \left(\int_0^{\pi/2} \cos^4 v \sin v\, dv \right) \left(\int_0^{\pi/2} \cos^2 u \sin u\, du \right)$$

$$= 32 \left(-\frac{\cos^5 v}{5} \Big|_0^{\pi/2} \right) \left(-\frac{\cos^3 v}{3} \Big|_0^{\pi/2} \right) = \frac{32}{15}. \qquad \blacktriangleleft$$

Example 7.27 Find $\iint_S ((z - x)\mathbf{i} - y\mathbf{j} - 2y^2\mathbf{k}) \cdot d\mathbf{S}$, where S is the surface that is the graph of the function $z = x + 2y^2 - 3$, $0 \le x \le 1$, $-1 \le y \le 1$, oriented by the upward-pointing normal.

Solution   Choose a parametrization

$$\mathbf{r}(u, v) = u\mathbf{i} + v\mathbf{j} + (u + 2v^2 - 3)\mathbf{k}, \qquad 0 \le u \le 1, \quad -1 \le v \le 1.$$

Then $\mathbf{T}_u = \mathbf{i} + \mathbf{k}$, $\mathbf{T}_v = \mathbf{j} + 4v\mathbf{k}$ and $\mathbf{N} = -\mathbf{i} - 4v\mathbf{j} + \mathbf{k}$. Since the $\mathbf{k}$ component of $\mathbf{N}$ is positive, $\mathbf{N}$ points upward and $\mathbf{r}(u, v)$ is an orientation-preserving parametrization of S. By definition,

$$\iint_S ((z - x)\mathbf{i} - y\mathbf{j} - 2y^2\mathbf{k})\, dS \qquad = \iint_{[0,1]\times[-1,1]} \mathbf{F}(\mathbf{r}(u, v)) \cdot \mathbf{N}(u, v)\, dA$$

$$= \iint_{[0,1]\times[-1,1]} ((2v^2 - 3)\mathbf{i} - v\mathbf{j} - 2v^2\mathbf{k}) \cdot (-\mathbf{i} - 4v\mathbf{j} + \mathbf{k})\, dA$$

$$= \iint_{[0,1]\times[-1,1]} 3\, dA = 6,$$

since the last double integral equals three times the area of the rectangle $[0, 1] \times [-1, 1]$.

◀

■ **Theorem 7.2**   Dependence of Surface Integrals on Parametrizations.

Let S be an oriented surface, let $\mathbf{F}$ be a continuous vector field on S and let $\mathbf{r}: D \to \mathbb{R}^3$ and $\mathbf{r}^*: D^* \to \mathbb{R}^3$ be smooth parametric representations of S with corresponding normal vectors $\mathbf{N} = \mathbf{T}_u \times \mathbf{T}_v$ and $\mathbf{N}^* = \mathbf{T}_u^* \times \mathbf{T}_v^*$. Then

$$\iint_D \mathbf{F}(\mathbf{r}(u, v)) \cdot \mathbf{N}(u, v)\, dA = \iint_{D^*} \mathbf{F}(\mathbf{r}^*(u, v)) \cdot \mathbf{N}^*(u, v)\, dA^*$$

if $\mathbf{r}$ and $\mathbf{r}^*$ have the same orientation, and

$$\iint_D \mathbf{F}(\mathbf{r}(u, v)) \cdot \mathbf{N}(u, v)\, dA = - \iint_{D^*} \mathbf{F}(\mathbf{r}^*(u, v)) \cdot \mathbf{N}^*(u, v)\, dA^*$$

if $\mathbf{r}$ and $\mathbf{r}^*$ have opposite orientations.   ■

Theorem 7.2 says that we do not have to worry too much when evaluating surface integrals of vector fields. Given an oriented surface, we can take any smooth parametrization and evaluate $\iint_S \mathbf{F} \cdot d\mathbf{S}$. If that parametrization is orientation-preserving, we have the result. If it is orientation-reversing, the result is the negative of what we obtained.

The proof of the theorem is similar to the proof of the corresponding theorem for path integrals. Its crucial ingredient is the change of variables formula for double integrals.

Example 7.28   Let us compute $\iint_S \mathbf{F} \cdot d\mathbf{S}$ with $\mathbf{F}$ and S as in Example 7.26, but this time with the parametrization

$$\mathbf{r}(u, v) = (2 \cos u \sin v, 2 \sin u \sin v, 2 \cos v), \qquad 0 \le u, v \le \pi/2.$$

Solution   The surface normal $\mathbf{N}$ is $\mathbf{N} = -2 \sin v\, \mathbf{r}(u, v)$; see Example 7.20. Its direction is opposite to the direction of the radius vector $\mathbf{r}(u, v)$; i.e., $\mathbf{N}$ points towards the origin (this follows from the fact that $\sin v \geq 0$ for $0 \leq v \leq \pi/2$). Hence the parametrization given in this example is orientation-reversing, and according to Theorem 7.2, the result should be the negative of the result obtained in Example 7.26. Indeed,

$$\mathbf{F} \cdot \mathbf{N} = 8 \cos u \sin u \sin^2 v \cos v \cdot (-2 \sin v) \cdot 2 \cos u \sin v$$

and

$$\iint_S \mathbf{F} \cdot d\mathbf{S} = \iint_{[0,\pi/2] \times [0,\pi/2]} \mathbf{F} \cdot \mathbf{N} \, dA$$

$$= \iint_{[0,\pi/2] \times [0,\pi/2]} -32 \sin^4 v \cos v \cos^2 u \sin u \, dA$$

$$= -32 \left(\int_0^{\pi/2} \sin^4 v \cos v \, dv \right) \left(\int_0^{\pi/2} \cos^2 u \sin u \, du \right)$$

$$= -32 \left(\frac{\sin^5 v}{5} \bigg|_0^{\pi/2} \right) \left(-\frac{\cos^3 u}{3} \bigg|_0^{\pi/2} \right) = -\frac{32}{15}.$$

◀

Assume that a surface S is smooth; i.e., $\|\mathbf{N}(u, v)\| \neq 0$ for all (u, v). From the definition of the surface integral it follows that

$$\iint_S \mathbf{F} \cdot d\mathbf{S} = \iint_D \mathbf{F}(\mathbf{r}(u, v)) \cdot \mathbf{N}(u, v) \, dA = \iint_D \mathbf{F}(\mathbf{r}(u, v)) \cdot \frac{\mathbf{N}(u, v)}{\|\mathbf{N}(u, v)\|} \|\mathbf{N}(u, v)\| \, dA.$$

This means that the surface integral of the *vector* function $\mathbf{F}$ reduces to the surface integral of the *scalar* function $\mathbf{F}(\mathbf{r}(u, v)) \cdot \mathbf{N}(u, v)/\|\mathbf{N}(u, v)\|$, which is the component of $\mathbf{F}$ in the normal direction. Denoting $\mathbf{N}(u, v)/\|\mathbf{N}(u, v)\|$ by $\mathbf{n}(u, v)$ (so $\mathbf{n}$ is a unit normal vector) we write

$$\iint_S \mathbf{F} \cdot d\mathbf{S} = \iint_D \mathbf{F}(\mathbf{r}(u, v)) \cdot \mathbf{n}(u, v) \|\mathbf{N}(u, v)\| \, dA = \iint_S \mathbf{F} \cdot \mathbf{n} \, dS.$$

This formula can sometimes simplify the computation of a surface integral, as in the case presented in the following example.

Example 7.29   Compute $\iint_S (x\mathbf{i} + y\mathbf{j} + z\mathbf{k}) \, dS$, where S is the surface of the sphere $x^2 + y^2 + z^2 = 1$ oriented with the outward-pointing normal.

Solution   We can solve this problem without the use of a parametrization. Notice that the direction of a normal vector to the sphere is radial; i.e., it has the direction of the line joining the point on the sphere and its center. An outward-pointing normal is given by $\mathbf{n} = x\mathbf{i} + y\mathbf{j} + z\mathbf{k}$. Since $\sqrt{x^2 + y^2 + z^2} = 1$, it follows that $\mathbf{n}$ is actually a unit normal. Therefore

$$\mathbf{F} \cdot \mathbf{n} = (x\mathbf{i} + y\mathbf{j} + z\mathbf{k}) \cdot (x\mathbf{i} + y\mathbf{j} + z\mathbf{k}) = x^2 + y^2 + z^2 = 1,$$

and

$$\iint_S \mathbf{F} \cdot d\mathbf{S} = \iint_S \mathbf{F} \cdot \mathbf{n} \, dS = \iint_S 1 \, dS = 4\pi,$$

since the surface area of a sphere of radius 1 is 4π.

◀

Example 7.30 Consider the surface integral $\iint_S (4x^2 + 4y^2 + 1)\mathbf{k} \cdot d\mathbf{S}$, where S is the part of the surface $z = 1 - (x^2 + y^2)$ that lies above the xy-plane, oriented by an upward-pointing normal. Use the projection of S onto the xy-plane (see end of Section 7.2) to evaluate the integral.

Solution Viewing S as the level surface $F(x, y, z) = 1$ of the function $F(x, y, z) = x^2 + y^2 + z$, we compute the unit normal vector to S to be

$$\nabla F / \|\nabla F\| = \pm(2x, 2y, 1)/\sqrt{4x^2 + 4y^2 + 1}.$$

We need the z-component of $\mathbf{n}$ to be positive, hence $\mathbf{n} = (2x, 2y, 1)/\sqrt{4x^2 + 4y^2 + 1}$ and

$$\iint_S (4x^2 + 4y^2 + 1)\mathbf{k} \cdot d\mathbf{S} = \iint_S (4x^2 + 4y^2 + 1)\mathbf{k} \cdot \mathbf{n} \, dS.$$

The projection D of S onto the xy-plane is the disk $x^2 + y^2 \leq 1$. Therefore, (notice that $\mathbf{n} \cdot \mathbf{k} = 1/\sqrt{4x^2 + 4y^2 + 1} > 0$)

$$\iint_S (4x^2 + 4y^2 + 1)\mathbf{k} \cdot d\mathbf{S} = \iint_D (4x^2 + 4y^2 + 1)\mathbf{k} \cdot \mathbf{n} \frac{dA}{|\mathbf{n} \cdot \mathbf{k}|} = \iint_D (4x^2 + 4y^2 + 1) \, dA,$$

where dA refers to integration with respect to x and y. Passing to polar coordinates, we get

$$\iint_S (4x^2 + 4y^2 + 1)\mathbf{k} \cdot d\mathbf{S} = \int_0^{2\pi} \left(\int_0^1 (4r^2 + 1) \, r \, dr \right) d\theta$$

$$= \int_0^{2\pi} \left((r^4 + \tfrac{1}{2}r^2) \, \Big|_0^1 \right) d\theta = \tfrac{3}{2} 2\pi = 3\pi.$$

◀

Let us now discuss a geometric meaning of the surface integral $\iint_S \mathbf{F} \cdot d\mathbf{S}$ of a vector field $\mathbf{F}$ over a surface S. Suppose that $\mathbf{r}: D \to \mathbb{R}^3$ is a parametrization of S and $\mathbf{F}: S \subseteq \mathbb{R}^3 \to \mathbb{R}^3$ is a continuous vector field. As in the previous section, assume that D is a rectangle and subdivide it into n^2 rectangles. Select one rectangle (name it R) with one vertex at (u, v) and sides Δu and Δv, as in Figure 7.23. The surface integral $\iint_S \mathbf{F} \cdot d\mathbf{S}$ can be written as

$$\iint_S \mathbf{F} \cdot d\mathbf{S} = \iint_D \mathbf{F} \cdot (\mathbf{T}_u \times \mathbf{T}_v) \, dA = \lim_{\text{size}(R) \to 0} \sum \mathbf{F} \cdot (\mathbf{T}_u \times \mathbf{T}_v) \Delta u \Delta v,$$

where $\mathbf{T}_u$ and $\mathbf{T}_v$ are the tangent vectors and the summation goes over all rectangles that form the subdivision of D.

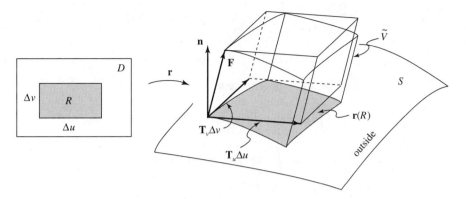

Figure 7.23 Geometric meaning of the surface integral of a vector field.

Each summand

$$\mathbf{F} \cdot (\mathbf{T}_u \times \mathbf{T}_v) \Delta u \Delta v = \mathbf{F} \cdot (\mathbf{T}_u \Delta u \times \mathbf{T}_v \Delta v)$$

is the scalar triple product of $\mathbf{F}$, $\mathbf{T}_u \Delta u$ and $\mathbf{T}_v \Delta v$. Consequently, the absolute value

$$|\mathbf{F} \cdot (\mathbf{T}_u \Delta u \times \mathbf{T}_v \Delta v)|$$

represents the volume of the parallelepiped with sides $\mathbf{F}$, $\mathbf{T}_u \Delta u$ and $\mathbf{T}_v \Delta v$.

Suppose that the orientation of S is given by $\mathbf{n} = +\mathbf{T}_u \times \mathbf{T}_v / \|\mathbf{T}_u \times \mathbf{T}_v\|$, as shown in Figure 7.23. The dot product $\mathbf{F} \cdot (\mathbf{T}_u \times \mathbf{T}_v) \Delta u \Delta v$ is positive if $\mathbf{F}$ points away from the outside of S (since the angle between $\mathbf{F}$ and the normal $\mathbf{n}$ is smaller than $\pi/2$). If $\mathbf{F}$ points away from the inside then $\mathbf{F} \cdot (\mathbf{T}_u \times \mathbf{T}_v) \Delta u \Delta v$ is negative. Therefore,

$$\iint_S \mathbf{F} \cdot d\mathbf{S} = \lim_{\text{size}(R) \to 0} \left(\sum{}^{+} \mathbf{F} \cdot (\mathbf{T}_u \Delta u \times \mathbf{T}_v \Delta v) + \sum{}^{-} \mathbf{F} \cdot (\mathbf{T}_u \Delta u \times \mathbf{T}_v \Delta v) \right),$$

where $\sum^{+}$ denotes the sum over all R's for which $\mathbf{F} \cdot (\mathbf{T}_u \Delta u \times \mathbf{T}_v \Delta v)$ is positive, and $\sum^{-}$ is the sum over all R's for which $\mathbf{F} \cdot (\mathbf{T}_u \Delta u \times \mathbf{T}_v \Delta v)$ is negative.

Think of $\mathbf{F}$ as the velocity vector of a fluid and consider $\sum^{+}$ first. The patch $\mathbf{r}(R)$ on S is approximated by the parallelogram spanned by $\mathbf{T}_u \Delta u$ and $\mathbf{T}_v \Delta v$. Assume that R (and hence $\mathbf{r}(R)$) are so small that $\mathbf{F}$ is (approximately) constant on $\mathbf{r}(R)$. The amount of fluid that flows across the patch $\mathbf{r}(R)$ is equal to the volume of the "twisted parallelepiped" $\tilde{V}$, (see Figure 7.23) and can be approximated by the volume of the parallelepiped spanned by $\mathbf{F}$, $\mathbf{T}_u \Delta u$ and $\mathbf{T}_v \Delta v$. Therefore, $\sum^{+}$ approximates the net volume of fluid that flows outward across S per unit time. Similarly, $\sum^{-}$ gives an approximation for the net volume of fluid that flows inward across S per unit time. Consequently, $\iint_S \mathbf{F} \cdot d\mathbf{S}$ is the net volume of fluid that flows across S per unit time, which is the rate of fluid flow. That is the reason why the integral $\iint_S \mathbf{F} \cdot d\mathbf{S} = \iint_S \mathbf{F} \cdot \mathbf{n} \, dS$ is called the *(outward) flux* of $\mathbf{F}$ across the surface S.

Example 7.31 Compute the flux of the vector field $\mathbf{F} = (\sin x, z, y)$ across the part of the cylinder $y^2 + z^2 = 4$ bounded by $-1/2 \leq x \leq 1/2$, $y \geq 0$ and $z \geq 0$.

Solution   Parametrize the surface of the cylinder (call it S) by $\mathbf{r}(u, v) = (u, 2\cos v, 2\sin v)$, where $-1/2 \le u \le 1/2$ and $0 \le v \le \pi/2$. Then

$$\mathbf{T}_u = (1, 0, 0), \quad \mathbf{T}_v = (0, -2\sin v, 2\cos v), \quad \mathbf{N} = (0, -2\cos v, -2\sin v)$$

and the flux of $\mathbf{F}$ is computed to be

$$\iint_S \mathbf{F} \cdot d\mathbf{S} = \iint_{[-\frac{1}{2},\frac{1}{2}]\times[0,\frac{\pi}{2}]} (\sin u, 2\sin v, 2\cos v) \cdot (0, -2\cos v, -2\sin v) \, dA$$

$$= \int_{-1/2}^{1/2} \left(\int_0^{\pi/2} -8\sin v \cos v \, dv \right) du$$

$$= -4 \int_{-1/2}^{1/2} \left(\int_0^{\pi/2} \sin 2v \, dv \right) du$$

$$= -4 \int_{-1/2}^{1/2} \left(-\frac{1}{2} \cos 2v \Big|_0^{\pi/2} \right) du = -4 \int_{-1/2}^{1/2} 1 \, du = -4.$$

So the rate of fluid flow across S in the direction $\mathbf{N} = (0, -2\cos v, -2\sin v)$ is -4. The normal points downward, towards the x-axis (since the z-component $z = -2\sin v$ is negative).   ◄

As in the case of real-valued functions, the surface integral of a vector field can be defined over a piecewise smooth surface (as the sum of the surface integrals over the disjoint pieces of S that are smooth). Here is an example.

Example 7.32   Compute $\iint_S \mathbf{F} \cdot d\mathbf{S}$, where $\mathbf{F} = x\mathbf{i} + z\mathbf{k}$ and S is the surface of the cube bounded by the six planes $x = 0$, $y = 0$, $z = 0$, $x = 1$, $y = 1$ and $z = 1$ and oriented by an outward normal.

Solution   The surface of a cube is piecewise smooth: it consists of six smooth surfaces that are the faces of the cube (the most that two faces have in common is a common edge, so they are disjoint). We have to integrate $\mathbf{F}$ over all six surfaces and add up the results.

Parametrize the bottom surface by $\mathbf{r}_1(u, v) = (u, v, 0)$, $0 \le u, v \le 1$. Then $\mathbf{n}_1 = -\mathbf{k}$ (see Figure 7.24; no computation for $\mathbf{n}_1$ is needed!) and

$$\iint_{S_1} \mathbf{F} \cdot d\mathbf{S} = \iint_{S_1} \mathbf{F} \cdot \mathbf{n}_1 \, dS = \iint_{[0,1]\times[0,1]} (u\mathbf{i}) \cdot (-\mathbf{k}) \, dA = 0.$$

Parametrize the top surface by $\mathbf{r}_2(u, v) = (u, v, 1)$, $0 \le u, v \le 1$. Then $\mathbf{n}_2 = \mathbf{k}$ and

$$\iint_{S_2} \mathbf{F} \cdot d\mathbf{S} = \iint_{S_2} \mathbf{F} \cdot \mathbf{n}_2 \, dS = \iint_{[0,1]\times[0,1]} (u\mathbf{i} + \mathbf{k}) \cdot \mathbf{k} \, dA = \iint_{[0,1]\times[0,1]} dA = 1$$

(no integration was done here; the last integral was interpreted as area).

Similarly, $\mathbf{r}_3(u, v) = (u, 0, v)$, and $\mathbf{r}_4(u, v) = (u, 1, v)$, $0 \le u, v \le 1$ parametrize the left and the right sides of S. The unit normals are $\mathbf{n}_3 = -\mathbf{j}$ and $\mathbf{n}_4 = \mathbf{j}$, and since

$\mathbf{F} \cdot \mathbf{n}_3 = (u\mathbf{i} + v\mathbf{k}) \cdot \mathbf{j} = 0$ and $\mathbf{F} \cdot \mathbf{n}_4 = (u\mathbf{i} + v\mathbf{k}) \cdot (-\mathbf{j}) = 0$, both integrals $\iint_{S_3} \mathbf{F} \cdot d\mathbf{S}$ and $\iint_{S_4} \mathbf{F} \cdot d\mathbf{S}$ are zero.

Finally, parametrize the front and back sides of S by $\mathbf{r}_5(u, v) = (1, u, v)$, and $\mathbf{r}_6(u, v) = (0, u, v)$, $0 \le u, v \le 1$. Then $\mathbf{n}_5 = \mathbf{i}$ and $\mathbf{n}_6 = -\mathbf{i}$, and

$$\iint_{S_5} \mathbf{F} \cdot d\mathbf{S} = \iint_{S_5} \mathbf{F} \cdot \mathbf{n}_5 \, dS = \iint_{[0,1]\times[0,1]} (\mathbf{i} + v\mathbf{k}) \cdot \mathbf{i} \, dA = 1$$

and

$$\iint_{S_6} \mathbf{F} \cdot d\mathbf{S} = \iint_{S_6} \mathbf{F} \cdot \mathbf{n}_6 \, dS = \iint_{[0,1]\times[0,1]} (v\mathbf{k}) \cdot (-\mathbf{i}) \, dA = 0.$$

Therefore $\iint_S \mathbf{F} \cdot d\mathbf{S} = 0 + 1 + 0 + 0 + 1 + 0 = 2$ is the flux out across S.

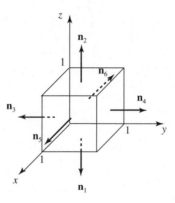

Figure 7.24   Surface of the cube oriented by outward-pointing normals.

We end this section by defining the integral of a 2-form over a surface. Let

$$\alpha = F_1(x, y, z)dydz + F_2(x, y, z)dzdx + F_3(x, y, z)dxdy$$

be a 2-form defined on an open subset $U \subseteq \mathbb{R}^3$ and let

$$\mathbf{r}(u, v) = (x(u, v), y(u, v), z(u, v)): D \to \mathbb{R}^3, \qquad (u, v) \in D,$$

be a parametric representation of a surface $S \subseteq U$ (D is an elementary region in $\mathbb{R}^2$). Define the integral $\int_S \alpha$ of α over S as the double integral

$$\int_S \alpha = \int_S F_1 dydz + F_2 dzdx + F_3 dxdy$$

$$= \iint_D \left(F_1(x(u, v), y(u, v), z(u, v)) \frac{\partial(y, z)}{\partial(u, v)} + F_2(x(u, v), y(u, v), z(u, v)) \frac{\partial(z, x)}{\partial(u, v)} \right.$$

$$\left. + F_3(x(u, v), y(u, v), z(u, v)) \frac{\partial(x, y)}{\partial(u, v)} \right) dA,$$

where $\partial(x, y)/\partial(u, v)$, $\partial(y, z)/\partial(u, v)$ and $\partial(z, x)/\partial(u, v)$ denote the Jacobian determinants

$$\frac{\partial(x, y)}{\partial(u, v)} = \begin{vmatrix} \frac{\partial x}{\partial u} & \frac{\partial x}{\partial v} \\ \frac{\partial y}{\partial u} & \frac{\partial y}{\partial v} \end{vmatrix}, \qquad \frac{\partial(y, z)}{\partial(u, v)} = \begin{vmatrix} \frac{\partial y}{\partial u} & \frac{\partial y}{\partial v} \\ \frac{\partial z}{\partial u} & \frac{\partial z}{\partial v} \end{vmatrix} \qquad \text{and} \qquad \frac{\partial(z, x)}{\partial(u, v)} = \begin{vmatrix} \frac{\partial z}{\partial u} & \frac{\partial z}{\partial v} \\ \frac{\partial x}{\partial u} & \frac{\partial x}{\partial v} \end{vmatrix}.$$

Therefore, $\int_S \alpha$ is evaluated (once an orientation-preserving parametrization of S is chosen) as the double integral of a real-valued function over an elementary region in $\mathbb{R}^2$. That real-valued function is the dot product of the vector field $\mathbf{F} = (F_1, F_2, F_3)$ and the surface normal (see (7.3))

$$\mathbf{N}(u, v) = \mathbf{T}_u(u, v) \times \mathbf{T}_v(u, v) = \left(\frac{\partial(y, z)}{\partial(u, v)}, \frac{\partial(z, x)}{\partial(u, v)}, \frac{\partial(x, y)}{\partial(u, v)} \right),$$

and is therefore equal to

$$\int_S \alpha = \iint_D \mathbf{F}(\mathbf{r}(u, v)) \cdot \mathbf{N}(u, v) \, du dv = \iint_S \mathbf{F} \cdot d\mathbf{S}.$$

It follows that the integral of a 2-form $\alpha = F_1 dy dz + F_2 dz dx + F_3 dx dy$ over a surface S is just the surface integral of the corresponding vector field $\mathbf{F} = (F_1, F_2, F_3)$.

Example 7.33   Compute $\int_S \alpha$ if $\alpha = 2y dx dy - xz dy dz$ and S is the surface

$$\mathbf{r}(u, v) = (u + 2v, u^2, uv), \qquad 0 \le u, v \le 1.$$

Solution   By definition,

$$\int_S \alpha = \int_S 2y dx dy - xz dy dz = \iint_{[0,1] \times [0,1]} \left(2y \frac{\partial(x, y)}{\partial(u, v)} - xz \frac{\partial(y, z)}{\partial(u, v)} \right) dA,$$

where

$$\frac{\partial(x, y)}{\partial(u, v)} = \begin{vmatrix} 1 & 2 \\ 2u & 0 \end{vmatrix} = -4u \qquad \text{and} \qquad \frac{\partial(y, z)}{\partial(u, v)} = \begin{vmatrix} 2u & 0 \\ v & u \end{vmatrix} = 2u^2.$$

Hence

$$\int_S \alpha = \iint_{[0,1] \times [0,1]} \left(2u^2(-4u) - (u + 2v) uv \, 2u^2 \right) dA,$$

$$= -\int_0^1 \left(\int_0^1 (8u^3 + 2u^4 v + 4u^3 v^2) \, du \right) dv$$

$$= -\int_0^1 \left(\left(2u^4 + \frac{2u^5 v}{5} + u^4 v^2 \right) \Big|_{u=0}^{u=1} \right) dv$$

$$= -\int_0^1 \left(2 + \frac{2v}{5} + v^2 \right) dv = -\frac{38}{15}.$$

EXERCISES 7.3   Exercises 1 to 8:   Compute $\iint_S \mathbf{F} \cdot d\mathbf{S}$.

1. $\mathbf{F} = 4y\mathbf{i} + (3x - 1)\mathbf{j} + z\mathbf{k}$, S is the part of the plane $3x + y - z = 1$ (with the upward normal) inside the vertical cylinder of radius 2 whose axis of symmetry is the z-axis

2. $\mathbf{F} = x\mathbf{i} + y\mathbf{j}$, S is the part of the cone $z = \sqrt{x^2 + y^2}$ (oriented with the inward normal) inside the vertical cylinder $x^2 + y^2 = 9$

3. $\mathbf{F} = x^2\mathbf{i} + 2z\mathbf{k}$, S is the hemisphere $x^2 + y^2 + z^2 = 9$, $z \geq 0$, oriented with an outward normal

4. $\mathbf{F} = y\mathbf{i} - x\mathbf{j} + \mathbf{k}$, S is the surface parametrized by $\mathbf{r}(u, v) = (u \cos v, u \sin v, v)$, $0 \leq u \leq 1$, $0 \leq v \leq 4\pi$, and oriented with an upward-pointing normal

5. $\mathbf{F} = z\mathbf{k}$, S is the paraboloid $z = x^2 + y^2$ (oriented with the normal pointing away from it) between the planes $z = 1$ and $z = 2$

6. $\mathbf{F} = 2\mathbf{i} - xy\mathbf{j}$, S is the graph of the function $z = f(x, y) = x^2y^3 - 1$, where $0 \leq x, y \leq 1$, oriented by the upward-pointing normal

7. $\mathbf{F} = x\mathbf{i} + y\mathbf{j} + z\mathbf{k}$, S is the surface parametrized by $\mathbf{r}(u, v) = (e^u \cos v, e^u \sin v, v)$, $0 \leq u \leq \ln 2$, $0 \leq v \leq \pi$, and oriented with an upward pointing normal

8. $\mathbf{F} = x^2y\mathbf{i} - (y + x)\mathbf{j} - z^2x\mathbf{k}$, S is the part of the plane $x + 2y + 8z = 8$ in the first octant with the normal vector pointing upward

9. Let $T(x, y, z) = x^2 + y^2 + 3z^2$ be the temperature at a point (x, y, z) in $\mathbb{R}^3$. Compute the heat flux outward across the surface $x^2 + y^2 = 1$, $-1 \leq z \leq 1$.

10. Let $T(x, y, z) = e^{-x^2 - y^2 - z^2}$ be the temperature at a point (x, y, z) in $\mathbb{R}^3$. Compute the heat flux outward across the sphere $x^2 + y^2 + z^2 = 1$.

11. Consider the vector field $\mathbf{F} = c\mathbf{k}$, where c is a constant.

    (a) Compute the flux $\iint_S \mathbf{F} \cdot \mathbf{n}\, dS$, where S is the hemisphere $x^2 + y^2 + z^2 = a^2$, $z \geq 0$, with the outward-pointing normal.

    (b) Compute the flux of $\mathbf{F}$ across the disk $x^2 + y^2 \leq a^2$ in the xy-plane, with the upward-pointing normal.

    (c) Why are the results in (a) and (b) the same?

Exercises 12 to 17:   Find the flux of $\mathbf{F}$ across the surface S.

12. $\mathbf{F} = x\mathbf{i} + y\mathbf{j} + \mathbf{k}$, out of the closed region bounded by the paraboloid $z = 2x^2 + 2y^2$ and the plane $z = 4$

13. $\mathbf{F} = x\mathbf{i}$, out of the closed region bounded by the paraboloids $z = x^2 + y^2$ and $z = 12 - x^2 - y^2$

14. $\mathbf{F} = x\mathbf{i}$, out of the closed region bounded by the spheres $x^2 + y^2 + z^2 = a^2$ and $x^2 + y^2 + z^2 = b^2$, $a > b$

15. $\mathbf{F} = y^3(\mathbf{j} - \mathbf{k})$, across the part of the plane $2x + y + z = 16$ in the first octant in the direction away from the origin

16. $\mathbf{F} = \mathbf{i} + xy\mathbf{j}$, across the closed cylinder (and in the direction away from it) $x^2 + y^2 = 1$, with the top disk at $z = 2$ and the bottom disk in the xy-plane

17. $\mathbf{F} = x^2y\mathbf{i} + xy^3\mathbf{j} + 2xyz\mathbf{k}$, upward across the surface $z = 2x^2y$, $0 \leq x \leq 1$, $0 \leq y \leq 2$

18. Compute the flux through the surface of the plane $z = 2$, $0 \leq x, y \leq a$ ($a > 0$) of the constant unit vector field $\mathbf{F}$ that makes an angle of α rad ($0 \leq \alpha \leq \pi/2$) with respect to the

plane.

19. Let $\mathbf{F} = F_\rho \mathbf{e}_\rho + F_\theta \mathbf{e}_\theta + F_\phi \mathbf{e}_\phi$ be the representation of the vector field $\mathbf{F}$ in spherical coordinates. Show that the flux of $\mathbf{F}$ out of the sphere $x^2 + y^2 + z^2 = a^2$, $a > 0$, satisfies

$$\iint_S \mathbf{F} \cdot \mathbf{S} = a^2 \int_0^{2\pi} \left(\int_0^\pi F_\rho \sin\phi \, d\phi \right) d\theta.$$

20. Let S be the (closed) surface consisting of the part of the cone $z^2 = x^2 + y^2$, $1 \le z \le 2$ together with the top and bottom disks (in the planes $z = 2$ and $z = 1$). Show that the vector fields $\mathbf{F}_1 = x\mathbf{i} + 2y\mathbf{j} + 3z\mathbf{k}$ and $\mathbf{F}_2 = (y^2 + z)\mathbf{i} + (6y + x)\mathbf{j}$ have the same outward flux.

21. Let $\mathbf{F} = (x + y)\mathbf{i} + \mathbf{j} + z\mathbf{k}$ and assume that S is the part of the plane $x + 2y + 8z = 8$ in the first octant, oriented by the downward-pointing normal. Compute the surface integral $\iint_S \mathbf{F} \cdot d\mathbf{S}$ using a projection of S onto a coordinate plane.

22. Let S be the part of the plane $z = 2$ defined by $0 \le x, y \le a$, $a > 0$. Let c be a positive constant.

   (a) Compute the flux of a vertical field $\mathbf{F} = c\mathbf{k}$ across S.

   (b) Compute the flux of $\mathbf{F} = cz\mathbf{k}$ across S.

   (c) Compute the flux of $\mathbf{F} = cz^2\mathbf{k}$ across S.

   (d) Compute the flux of $\mathbf{F} = c(\mathbf{j} + \mathbf{k})/\sqrt{2}$ across S.

   (e) Compute the flux of $\mathbf{F} = f(x, y, z)\mathbf{i} + g(x, y, z)\mathbf{j}$ across S.

   (f) Interpret the results of (a) – (e).

23. Compute $\iint_S \mathbf{F} \cdot d\mathbf{S}$, where $\mathbf{F}$ and S are as in Exercise 3, using the projection of S onto the xy-plane.

Exercises 24 to 27: Compute $\int_S \alpha$.

24. $\alpha = dxdy$, S is the surface of the sphere $x^2 + y^2 + z^2 = a^2$

25. $\alpha = xdxdy + ydydz + zdzdx$, S is the surface of the cylinder $x^2 + y^2 = 1$, $0 \le z \le 3$

26. $\alpha = xydydz - x^2yzdzdx$, S is the surface $\mathbf{r}(u, v) = (u^2 - v^2, uv, 1 - v)$, $0 \le u, v \le 1$

27. $\alpha = dxdy + zdzdx$, S is the part of the paraboloid $z = x^2 + y^2$ below $z = 4$

7.4   INTEGRALS: PROPERTIES AND APPLICATIONS

Although we have defined all kinds of integrals in the last three chapters, we have to admit that we were in a way repeating the same things over and over again (such as, for example, the construction of Riemann sums). As a conclusion, we will present a unified view of the integrations we have discussed, list their properties and show some applications.

Notation. Throughout this section we will use $\mathcal{M}$ to denote either of the following:

(a) a curve $\mathbf{c}$ (that will be viewed in applications as an approximation of a thin wire);

(b) a plane region D (that will represent a thin flat plate in $\mathbb{R}^2$);

(c) a surface S (that will represent a thin sheet (possibly curved) in $\mathbb{R}^3$); or

(d) a solid V (that will represent a three-dimensional solid in $\mathbb{R}^3$).

We will use $\mathbf{x}$ to denote x, (x, y) or (x, y, z), depending on the context. A common name for geometric objects described in (a) – (d) is a *manifold (with a boundary)*. The integral $\int_{\mathcal{M}} f d\mu$ is interpreted accordingly, as follows:

(a) the path integral $\int_{\mathbf{c}} f ds$ of a real-valued function f. The path integral $\int_{\mathbf{c}} \mathbf{F} \cdot d\mathbf{s}$ of a vector field can be reduced to the path integral of a real-valued function (namely of its tangential component). In the special case when $\mathbf{c}$ is an interval $[a, b]$ on the x-axis, the path integral is the definite integral $\int_a^b f(x)dx$ of a real-valued function of one variable.

(b) the double integral $\iint_D f dA$ of a real-valued function f.

(c) the surface integral $\iint_S f \, dS$ of a real-valued function f.

(d) the triple integral $\iiint_V f \, dV$ of a real-valued function f.

Fundamental Theorem of Calculus. Recall that, if the function $f : [a, b] \to \mathbb{R}$ is continuously differentiable (i.e., if it is C^1), then

$$\int_a^b f'(x)dx = f(b) - f(a).$$

In Section 5.4 we proved the generalization

$$\int_{\mathbf{c}} \nabla f \cdot d\mathbf{s} = f(\mathbf{c}(b)) - f(\mathbf{c}(a))$$

for any C^1 function f and a piecewise C^1 path $\mathbf{c} : [a, b] \to \mathbb{R}^2$ (or $\mathbb{R}^3$). What is common to both is that the integral of the *derivative* of a function is computed by evaluating the function at the endpoints (of an interval, or of a curve). With the proper interpretation of the derivative (and that will be provided by the language of differential forms), we will be able to extend this important fact to more general integrations. That will be the main theme of the last chapter.

Length, Area, Volume. We have already seen that the integral $\mu(\mathcal{M}) = \int_{\mathcal{M}} d\mu$ of the constant function $f(x, y, z) = 1$ (or $f(x, y) = 1$) has a geometric meaning.

(a) If $\mathcal{M} = \mathbf{c}$ is a curve parametrized by $\mathbf{c}(t)$, $t \in [a, b]$, then

$$\int_{\mathbf{c}} ds = \int_a^b \|\mathbf{c}'(t)\| \, dt$$

gives its length $\ell(\mathbf{c})$.

(b) If $\mathcal{M} = D$ is a region in the xy-plane, then

$$\iint_D dA$$

gives the area $A(D)$ of D.

(c) Let $\mathcal{M} = S$ be a surface parametrized by $\mathbf{r}(u, v)$, $(u, v) \in D$. Then

$$\iint_S dS = \iint_D \|\mathbf{N}\| \, dA$$

computes the surface area $A(S)$ of S.

(d) Taking $\mathcal{M}$ to be a three-dimensional solid V, we get the formula

$$\iiint_V dV$$

for its volume $v(V)$.

Average Value of a Function. The *average value* of a real-valued function $f = f(x, y, z)$ (or $f = f(x, y)$) is given by

$$\overline{f} = \frac{1}{\mu(\mathcal{M})} \int_{\mathcal{M}} f \, d\mu,$$

where $\mu(\mathcal{M})$ denotes the length, area or volume, depending on $\mathcal{M}$.

Example 7.34   Compute the average temperature of the cylindrical sheet S described by $x^2 + y^2 = 4$, $0 \le z \le 1$, if the temperature distribution function is $T(x, y, z) = z^2$.

Solution   Parametrize the surface of the cylindrical sheet by

$$\mathbf{r}(u, v) = (2\cos u, 2\sin u, v), \qquad 0 \le u \le 2\pi, \quad 0 \le v \le 1.$$

Then

$$\mathbf{N} = \mathbf{T}_u \times \mathbf{T}_v = (-2\sin u, 2\cos u, 0) \times (0, 0, 1) = (2\cos u, 2\sin u, 0)$$

and hence the average temperature is ($\|\mathbf{N}\| = 2$)

$$\overline{T} = \frac{1}{A(S)} \iint_S z^2 \, dS = \frac{1}{A(S)} \iint_{[0,2\pi] \times [0,1]} v^2 \, 2 \, dA,$$

where $A(S)$ is the surface area of S. We do not need to integrate to compute it: cutting the cylinder vertically and unwrapping it, we get a rectangle of base length (equal to the circumference of the circle) 4π and height 1. Therefore $A(S) = 4\pi$ and

$$\overline{T} = \frac{1}{4\pi} \int_0^{2\pi} \left(\int_0^1 2v^2 \, dv \right) du = \frac{1}{4\pi} \int_0^{2\pi} \frac{2}{3} \, du = \frac{1}{3}. \qquad \blacktriangleleft$$

Properties of Integrals. Assume that functions f and g are integrable, so that $\int_{\mathcal{M}} f \, d\mu$ and $\int_{\mathcal{M}} g \, d\mu$ are defined. Let $\mathcal{M}$ denote a piecewise smooth curve, a piecewise smooth surface (in particular, a plane region) or a solid three-dimensional region. Then

(a) Integrals are *linear* (C denotes a constant):

$$\int_{\mathcal{M}} (f + g) \, d\mu = \int_{\mathcal{M}} f \, d\mu + \int_{\mathcal{M}} g \, d\mu,$$

$$\int_{\mathcal{M}} C f \, d\mu = C \int_{\mathcal{M}} f \, d\mu.$$

(b) Integrals are *additive*: if $\mathcal{M}$ is divided into n (elementary) regions $\mathcal{M}_1, \ldots, \mathcal{M}_n$ that are mutually disjoint, then

$$\int_{\mathcal{M}} f d\mu = \int_{\mathcal{M}_1} f d\mu + \ldots + \int_{\mathcal{M}_n} f d\mu.$$

(c) If $f(\mathbf{x}) \leq g(\mathbf{x})$ for all $\mathbf{x} \in \mathcal{M}$, then

$$\int_{\mathcal{M}} f d\mu \leq \int_{\mathcal{M}} g d\mu.$$

If $m \leq f(\mathbf{x}) \leq M$ for all $\mathbf{x} \in \mathcal{M}$, ($m$ and M are constants) then

$$m \, \mu(\mathcal{M}) \leq \int_{\mathcal{M}} f d\mu \leq M \, \mu(\mathcal{M}),$$

where $\mu(\mathcal{M})$ has a geometric meaning of the length, the area or the volume, depending on $\mathcal{M}$.

(d) The inequality for the absolute value:

$$\left| \int_{\mathcal{M}} f d\mu \right| \leq \int_{\mathcal{M}} |f| \, d\mu.$$

(e) Mean Value Theorem for integrals: If f is a continuous function, then there exists a point $\mathbf{x}_0$ in $\mathcal{M}$ such that

$$\int_{\mathcal{M}} f d\mu = f(\mathbf{x}_0) \, \mu(\mathcal{M}). \tag{7.4}$$

(f) Let $\overline{\mathcal{M}}$ be a collection of all piecewise smooth curves, or all piecewise smooth surfaces or all solid three-dimensional regions (for which it is possible to define the triple integral). Suppose that

$$\int_{\mathcal{M}} f d\mu = 0$$

for *all* $\mathcal{M}$ in $\overline{\mathcal{M}}$ that belong to the domain U of f, and assume that f is continuous on U. Then f is identically zero (i.e., $f(\mathbf{x}) = 0$ for all $\mathbf{x} \in U$).

(g) Assume that $f = f(\mathbf{x}, t)$ is differentiable. Then

$$\frac{\partial}{\partial t} \left(\int_{\mathcal{M}} f d\mu \right) = \int_{\mathcal{M}} \frac{\partial f}{\partial t} d\mu. \tag{7.5}$$

The proofs of all statements except (e) and (f) are based on considering the appropriate Riemann sums (and we have done so in some cases in the last three chapters). Property (e) was proven in the special case of double integrals in Section 6.2. Rather that (re)proving these statements, we are going to make a few comments.

We can rewrite (e) as

$$f(\mathbf{x}_0) = \frac{1}{\mu(\mathcal{M})} \int_{\mathcal{M}} f d\mu,$$

noticing that the right side is the average value of f. Therefore, the Mean Value Theorem for Integrals implies that there must be a point in $\mathcal{M}$ at which a continuous function f attains its average value.

We will use property (f) later, in the following context: assume that f and g are continuous on a set U and

$$\int_{\mathcal{M}} f d\mu = \int_{\mathcal{M}} g d\mu$$

holds for *every* $\mathcal{M} \subseteq U$ in $\overline{\mathcal{M}}$. Then

$$\int_{\mathcal{M}} (f - g) d\mu = 0,$$

for all $\mathcal{M}$, and it follows by (f) that $f = g$ on U. In words, if the integrals of two functions agree for *all* manifolds, (i.e., for all curves or for all surfaces, etc.) then the two functions are equal. To repeat, (f) has to hold for all $\mathcal{M}$ in $\overline{\mathcal{M}}$: it is easy to cook up examples where $\int_{\mathcal{M}} f d\mu = \int_{\mathcal{M}} g d\mu$ for some $\mathcal{M}$, but $f \neq g$. For example,

$$\iint_{[0,1]\times[0,1]} 2x \, dA = \iint_{[0,1]\times[0,1]} 1 \, dA$$

(both are equal to 1), but $2x \neq 1$.

Property (g) will be used in the next chapter in computations dealing with time-dependent electric and magnetic fields; it will allow us to change the order of the time-derivative and the integral over a surface or over a solid three-dimensional region.

Total Mass and Total Charge. Let $\rho = \rho(\mathbf{x})$ denote the *mass density* (i.e., mass per unit length, area or volume, depending on the context) of an object represented as a manifold $\mathcal{M}$. The *total mass* of $\mathcal{M}$ is given by the integral

$$m = \int_{\mathcal{M}} \rho \, d\mu.$$

In the case when $\rho(\mathbf{x})$ represents the *charge density* (i.e., charge per unit length, area or volume, depending on the context), the above formula gives the *total charge* contained in $\mathcal{M}$. If ρ is constant, we say that $\mathcal{M}$ is *homogeneous* (if ρ denotes the mass density) or that it is *uniformly charged* (if ρ denotes the charge density). Then

$$m = \rho \int_{\mathcal{M}} d\mu = \rho \mu(\mathcal{M}),$$

where the meaning of $\mu(\mathcal{M})$ depends on the context.

Example 7.35 Find the mass of a thin-walled conical funnel $z = \sqrt{x^2 + y^2}$, $1 \leq z \leq 2$ (see Figure 7.25) whose density is $\rho(x, y, z) = 2 + z$.

Solution The mass of the funnel is given by $m = \int_{\mathcal{M}} \rho d\mu$, where $\mathcal{M}$ denotes the surface S of the funnel and $\int_{\mathcal{M}}$ represents the surface integral (so that $d\mu = dS$). Therefore,

$$m = \iint_S \rho \, dS = \iint_S (2 + z) \, dS,$$

where S is parametrized by

$$\mathbf{r}(u, v) = (u \cos v, u \sin v, u), \quad 1 \le u \le 2, \quad 0 \le v \le 2\pi.$$

Then $\mathbf{T}_u = (\cos v, \sin v, 1)$ and $\mathbf{T}_v = (-u \sin v, u \cos v, 0)$; the surface normal $\mathbf{N}$ is $\mathbf{N} = \mathbf{T}_u \times \mathbf{T}_v = (-u \cos v, -u \sin v, u)$ and hence ($\|\mathbf{N}\| = u\sqrt{2}$)

$$m = \iint_{[1,2]\times[0,2\pi]} (2 + u) \|\mathbf{N}\| dA$$

$$= \int_0^{2\pi} \left(\int_1^2 (2 + u)\sqrt{2}\, u\, du \right) dv = \sqrt{2} \int_0^{2\pi} (u^2 + \tfrac{1}{3}u^3)\big|_1^2\, dv = \tfrac{32}{3}\pi\sqrt{2}.$$

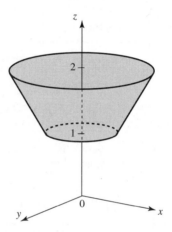

Figure 7.25 Conical funnel of Example 7.35.

Center of mass. Intuitively speaking, the *center of mass* (or the *center of gravity*) of $\mathcal{M}$ is the point CM on which $\mathcal{M}$ balances when supported at that point. However, the center of mass might not be a point of $\mathcal{M}$: the ring $\{1 \le x^2 + y^2 \le 2\}$ of uniform density does not contain the origin, which is its center of mass. In some situations, the object $\mathcal{M}$ behaves as if all of its mass were concentrated at its center of mass (for example in case of motion by translation).

The coordinates of the center of mass of an object $\mathcal{M}$ are

$$\bar{x} = \frac{1}{m} \int_{\mathcal{M}} x\rho d\mu, \qquad \bar{y} = \frac{1}{m} \int_{\mathcal{M}} y\rho d\mu, \qquad \bar{z} = \frac{1}{m} \int_{\mathcal{M}} z\rho d\mu,$$

where m denotes the total mass and ρ is the mass density (if $\mathcal{M}$ represents an object in $\mathbb{R}^2$, then $\bar{z} = 0$ and if it represents an object in $\mathbb{R}$, then $\bar{y} = 0$ and $\bar{z} = 0$). The integral expressions in the above formulas are called *moments*, and are denoted as follows: if $\mathcal{M} \subseteq \mathbb{R}^3$, then

$$M_{yz} = \int_{\mathcal{M}} x\rho(x, y, z)d\mu \quad \text{is the moment with respect to the } yz\text{-plane;}$$

$$M_{xz} = \int_{\mathcal{M}} y\rho(x, y, z)d\mu \quad \text{is the moment with respect to the } xz\text{-plane; and}$$

$$M_{xy} = \int_M z\rho(x, y, z)d\mu \quad \text{is the moment with respect to the } xy\text{-plane.}$$

If $M \subseteq \mathbb{R}^2$, then

$$M_x = \int_M y\rho(x, y)d\mu \quad \text{is the moment about the } x\text{-axis; and}$$

$$M_y = \int_M x\rho(x, y)d\mu \quad \text{is the moment about the } y\text{-axis.}$$

The formulas given here represent a generalization of the center of mass formulas (discussed in Section 1.2) for a finite number of masses to a continuous mass distribution given by the density function. The case of finitely many (say, n) masses can be recovered by replacing the integral with the sum and the density by the masses involved. For example, the expression $\int_M \rho d\mu$ becomes $\sum_{i=1}^n m_i$, and $\int_M x\rho d\mu$ becomes $\sum_{i=1}^n x_i m_i$.

Example 7.36   Find the center of mass of a thin wire in the shape of the helix $\mathbf{c}(t) = (\cos t, \sin t, t+1)$, $t \in [0, 6\pi]$, if the density function is constant and equal to ρ.

Solution   From the parametrization for $\mathbf{c}$ we get $\mathbf{c}'(t) = (-\sin t, \cos t, 1)$, and hence $\|\mathbf{c}'(t)\| = \sqrt{2}$. The mass of the wire is computed to be

$$m = \int_{\mathbf{c}} \rho ds = \rho \int_0^{6\pi} \|\mathbf{c}'(t)\| dt = \rho \int_0^{6\pi} \sqrt{2} dt = 6\sqrt{2}\pi\rho.$$

The moments are computed similarly:

$$M_{yz} = \int_{\mathbf{c}} x\rho ds = \rho \int_0^{6\pi} \cos t \|\mathbf{c}'(t)\| dt = \rho\sqrt{2} \int_0^{6\pi} \cos t \, dt = 0,$$

$$M_{xz} = \int_{\mathbf{c}} y\rho ds = \rho \int_0^{6\pi} \sin t \|\mathbf{c}'(t)\| dt = \rho\sqrt{2} \int_0^{6\pi} \sin t \, dt = 0,$$

and

$$M_{xy} = \int_{\mathbf{c}} z\rho ds = \rho \int_0^{6\pi} (t + 1)\|\mathbf{c}'(t)\| dt = \rho\sqrt{2} \int_0^{6\pi} (t + 1) \, dt = 6\sqrt{2}\pi\rho(3\pi + 1).$$

The coordinates of the center of mass are

$$\bar{x} = \frac{0}{m} = 0, \quad \bar{y} = \frac{0}{m} = 0 \quad \text{and} \quad \bar{z} = \frac{6\sqrt{2}\pi\rho(3\pi + 1)}{6\sqrt{2}\pi\rho} = 3\pi + 1.$$

Example 7.37   Find the mass and the center of mass of the thin plate

$$D = \{(x, y)|0 \le x \le 1, x^2 \le y \le \sqrt{x}\}$$

in the xy-plane, if the density function is $\rho(x, y) = ax$, $a > 0$.

Solution   The mass is

$$m = \iint_D ax \, dA = \int_0^1 \left(\int_{x^2}^{\sqrt{x}} axdy \right) dx$$

$$= a \int_0^1 \left(xy\Big|_{x^2}^{\sqrt{x}} \right) dx = a \int_0^1 \left(x^{3/2} - x^3 \right) dx = a \left(\tfrac{2}{5}x^{5/2} - \tfrac{1}{4}x^4 \right)\Big|_0^1 = \frac{3a}{20}.$$

The moment M_x about the x-axis is

$$M_x = \iint_D axy \, dA = \int_0^1 \left(\int_{x^2}^{\sqrt{x}} axydy \right) dx$$

$$= a \int_0^1 \left(\frac{1}{2}xy^2 \Big|_{x^2}^{\sqrt{x}} \right) dx = \frac{a}{2} \int_0^1 \left(x^2 - x^5 \right) dx = \frac{a}{12}.$$

Similarly, the moment M_y about the y-axis is computed to be

$$M_y = \iint_D ax^2 \, dA = \int_0^1 \left(\int_{x^2}^{\sqrt{x}} ax^2dy \right) dx$$

$$= a \int_0^1 \left(x^2y \Big|_{x^2}^{\sqrt{x}} \right) dx = a \int_0^1 \left(x^{5/2} - x^4 \right) dx = \frac{3a}{35}.$$

Hence the coordinates of the center of mass are

$$\overline{x} = \frac{M_x}{m} = \frac{a/12}{3a/20} = \frac{5}{9} \quad \text{and} \quad \overline{y} = \frac{M_y}{m} = \frac{3a/35}{3a/20} = \frac{4}{7}.$$

Example 7.38   Find the center of mass of the solid region V of constant density a that is inside the sphere $x^2 + y^2 + z^2 = 1$ and above the cone $z^2 = x^2 + y^2$, $z \geq 0$.

Solution   The fact that the solid V is homogeneous (i.e., has constant density) and symmetric with respect to the z-axis implies that the center of mass lies on the z-axis. Consequently, all we have to compute are the mass of V and the moment M_{xy}. Using spherical coordinates

$$x = \rho \sin\phi \cos\theta, \quad y = \rho \sin\phi \sin\theta, \quad z = \rho \cos\phi$$

with $dV = \rho^2 \sin\phi \, d\rho d\phi d\theta$ (see (6.8) in Section 6.5) we compute the mass of V to be

$$m = \iiint_V a \, dV = a \int_0^{2\pi} \left(\int_0^{\pi/4} \left(\int_0^1 \rho^2 \sin\phi d\rho \right) d\phi \right) d\theta.$$

The equation of the sphere $x^2 + y^2 + z^2 = 1$ transforms into $\rho^2 = 1$, i.e., $\rho = 1$; and the limits of integration of ρ are $0 \leq \rho \leq 1$. The equation of the cone $z^2 = x^2 + y^2$ transforms to $\rho^2 \cos^2\phi = \rho^2 \sin^2\phi$, or $\rho \cos\phi = \pm\rho \sin\phi$ and $\tan\phi = \pm 1$ (after dividing by $\rho \cos\phi$). Therefore, $\phi = \pi/4$ (by definition, $\phi \geq 0$) and the limits are $0 \leq \phi \leq \pi/4$. Continuing the computation, we get

$$m = a \int_0^{2\pi} \left(\int_0^{\pi/4} \frac{1}{3} \sin\phi d\phi \right) d\theta$$

$$= \frac{a}{3} \left(\int_0^{2\pi} d\theta \right) \left(\int_0^{\pi/4} \sin\phi \, d\theta \right) = \frac{a}{3} 2\pi \left(1 - \frac{\sqrt{2}}{2} \right) = \frac{a\pi(2 - \sqrt{2})}{3}.$$

Similarly,

$$M_{xy} = \iiint_V az \, dV = a \int_0^{2\pi} \left(\int_0^{\pi/4} \left(\int_0^1 \rho^3 \sin\phi \cos\phi d\rho \right) d\phi \right) d\theta$$

$$= a \int_0^{2\pi} \left(\int_0^{\pi/4} \frac{1}{4} \sin\phi \cos\phi d\phi \right) d\theta = \frac{a}{4} \left(\int_0^{2\pi} d\theta \right) \left(\int_0^{\pi/4} \sin\phi \cos\phi \, d\theta \right)$$

$$= \frac{a}{4} 2\pi \left. \frac{\sin^2\phi}{2} \right|_0^{\pi/4} = \frac{a\pi}{8}.$$

It follows that the coordinates of the center of mass are

$$\bar{x} = 0, \quad \bar{y} = 0, \quad \bar{z} = \frac{M_{xy}}{m} = \frac{a\pi/8}{a\pi(2 - \sqrt{2})/3} = \frac{3}{8(2 - \sqrt{2})}.$$

Moments of inertia. The *moment of inertia* is a measure of the rotational inertia of a body. In other words, it is the "opposition" we feel when we try to change the speed of rotation about an axis. The formulas given below extend the definition of the moments of inertia of a single particle (which is the product of the mass and the square of the distance to the axis) to the moments of inertia of a mass distribution (density) ρ over a manifold (that could be a curve, a plane region, a surface in $\mathbb{R}^3$ or a three-dimensional solid region). Assume that $\mathcal{M} \subseteq \mathbb{R}^2$. The *moment of inertia about the x-axis* is defined by

$$I_x = \int_{\mathcal{M}} y^2 \rho(x, y) d\mu,$$

and the *moment of inertia about the y-axis* is

$$I_y = \int_{\mathcal{M}} x^2 \rho(x, y) d\mu.$$

The *moment of inertia about the origin* (or the *polar moment of inertia*) is given by

$$I_o = \int_{\mathcal{M}} (x^2 + y^2) \rho(x, y) d\mu.$$

If $\mathcal{M} \subseteq \mathbb{R}^3$ then the *moments of inertia about the coordinate axes* are given by

$$I_x = \int_{\mathcal{M}} (y^2 + z^2) \rho(x, y, z) d\mu,$$

$$I_y = \int_{\mathcal{M}} (x^2 + z^2) \rho(x, y, z) d\mu \quad \text{and}$$

$$I_z = \int_{\mathcal{M}} (x^2 + y^2) \rho(x, y, z) d\mu.$$

Example 7.39   Compute the moment of inertia of the homogeneous thin-walled torus S given by (assume that the density is $\rho = 1$)

$$\mathbf{r}(u, v) = ((R + \cos v) \cos u, (R + \cos v) \sin u, \sin v), \qquad 0 \leq u, v \leq 2\pi,$$

with respect to the z-axis.

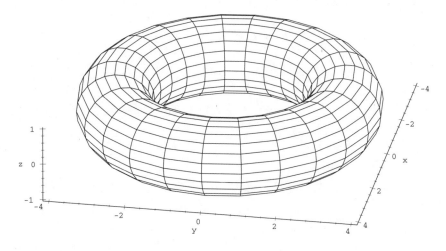

Figure 7.26   Torus of Example 7.39 (with $R = 3$).

Solution   By definition,

$$I_z = \iint_S 1 \cdot (x^2 + y^2)\, dS = \iint_{[0,2\pi] \times [0,2\pi]} (x^2 + y^2) \|\mathbf{N}\| \, dA$$

(the surface normal $\mathbf{N}$ was computed in Example 7.19 (with the inner radius $\rho = 1$) to be $\|\mathbf{N}\| = R + \cos v$; ρ in that example denotes the inner radius of the torus and has nothing to do with the density ρ used in this section). Continuing the computation,

$$I_z = \int_0^{2\pi} \left(\int_0^{2\pi} (R + \cos v)^3 du \right) dv$$

$$= \left(\int_0^{2\pi} du \right) \left(\int_0^{2\pi} (R^3 + 3R^2 \cos v + 3R \cos^2 v + \cos^3 v)\, dv \right)$$

(use $\cos^2 v = 1/2 + (\cos 2v)/2$ for the third integral and $\int \cos^3 v\, dv = \int \cos^2 v \cos v\, dv = \int (1 - \sin^2 v) \cos v\, dv = \int \cos v\, dv - \int \sin^2 v \cos v\, dv = \sin v - \sin^3 v/3$ for the fourth integral)

$$= 2\pi \left(R^3 v + 3R^2 \sin v + \frac{3R}{2} \left(v + \frac{1}{2} \sin 2v \right) + \sin v - \frac{\sin^3 v}{3} \right) \Bigg|_0^{2\pi}$$

$$= 2\pi \left(R^3 2\pi + \frac{3R}{2} 2\pi \right) = 2\pi^2 R(2R^2 + 3).$$

Therefore, the moment of inertia of the thin-walled homogeneous torus S about the z-axis is $2\pi^2 R(2R^2 + 3)$.

◀

Example 7.40

Find the moments of inertia about the coordinate axes of a wire in the shape of the curve $\mathbf{c}(t) = (t^2, 1, -t^2)$, $t \in [0, 1]$, with density $\rho(x, y, z) = y + 1$.

Solution   By definition,

$$I_x = \int_{\mathbf{c}} (y^2 + z^2)\rho(x, y, z)ds$$

(the tangent vector is $\mathbf{c}'(t) = (2t, 0, -2t)$ and hence $\|\mathbf{c}'(t)\| = 2\sqrt{2}\,t$)

$$= \int_0^1 (1 + t^4) \cdot 2 \cdot 2\sqrt{2}\,t\,dt = 4\sqrt{2}\left(\tfrac{1}{2}t^2 + \tfrac{1}{6}t^6\right)\Big|_0^1 = \frac{8\sqrt{2}}{3}.$$

Similarly,

$$I_y = \int_{\mathbf{c}} (x^2 + z^2)\rho(x, y, z)ds = \int_0^1 2t^4 \cdot 2 \cdot 2\sqrt{2}\,t\,dt = 8\sqrt{2}\,\frac{t^6}{6}\Big|_0^1 = \frac{4\sqrt{2}}{3},$$

and

$$I_z = \int_{\mathbf{c}} (x^2 + y^2)\rho(x, y, z)ds = \int_0^1 (t^4 + 1) \cdot 2 \cdot 2\sqrt{2}\,t\,dt = I_x = \frac{8\sqrt{2}}{3}.$$

◀

Example 7.41

Compute the moment of inertia about the y-axis of the solid cylinder $0 \leq x^2 + y^2 \leq 4$, $0 \leq z \leq 1$ of constant density $a = 1$.

Solution   The moment of inertia about the y-axis is computed to be

$$I_y = \iiint_V (x^2 + z^2)a\,dV.$$

Using cylindrical coordinates

$$x = r\cos\theta, \quad y = r\sin\theta, \quad z = z,$$

with $dV = r\,dz\,dr\,d\theta$ (see Example 6.42), we get

$$I_y = \int_0^{2\pi} \left(\int_0^2 \left(\int_0^1 (r^2\cos^2\theta + z^2)r\,dz \right) dr \right) d\theta$$

$$= \int_0^{2\pi} \left(\int_0^2 \left(r^3 z\cos^2\theta + \tfrac{1}{3}rz^3 \right)\Big|_0^1 dr \right) d\theta = \int_0^{2\pi} \left(\int_0^2 \left(r^3\cos^2\theta + \tfrac{1}{3}r \right) dr \right) d\theta$$

$$= \int_0^{2\pi} \left(\tfrac{1}{4}r^4\cos^2\theta + \tfrac{1}{6}r^2 \right)\Big|_0^2 d\theta = \int_0^{2\pi} \left(4\cos^2\theta + \tfrac{2}{3} \right) d\theta$$

$$= \left(4\left(\tfrac{1}{2}\theta + \tfrac{1}{4}\sin 2\theta\right) + \tfrac{2}{3}\theta \right)\Big|_0^{2\pi} = \tfrac{16}{3}\pi.$$

The desired moment of inertia is $I_y = 16\pi/3 \approx 16.76$.

◀

Example 7.42

Steiner's Theorem.

The moment of inertia of an object $\mathcal{M}$ with respect to an axis ℓ is defined by the integral

$$I_\ell = \int_{\mathcal{M}} \rho d^2 d\mu,$$

where d denotes the (perpendicular) distance from a point on $\mathcal{M}$ to the axis ℓ and ρ is the density of $\mathcal{M}$. Let I_{CM} be the moment of inertia of $\mathcal{M}$ with respect to an axis ℓ_{CM} parallel to ℓ that goes through its center of mass.

Prove *Steiner's Theorem,* which states that the moment of inertia with respect to the line ℓ parallel to ℓ_{CM} is

$$I_\ell = k^2 m + I_{CM},$$

where k is the distance between ℓ and ℓ_{CM}, and m is the mass of $\mathcal{M}$; see Figure 7.27.

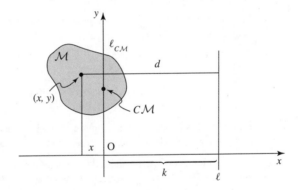

Figure 7.27 Moment of inertia with respect to the line ℓ.

Solution   Assume, for simplicity, that the mass m is contained in $\mathbb{R}^2$ and that the y-axis coincides with the axis ℓ_{CM}. Then

$$I_\ell = \iint_D \rho d^2 \, dA = \iint_D \rho(k - x)^2 \, dA$$

$$= \iint_D \left(\rho k^2 - 2\rho kx + \rho x^2 \right) \, dA$$

$$= k^2 \iint_D \rho \, dA - 2k \iint_D \rho x \, dA + \iint_D \rho x^2 \, dA.$$

The first integral is the product of k^2 and the integral of the density (which is the mass), that is, $k^2 m$. The third one is the moment of inertia with respect to the y-axis, or $I_y = I_{CM}$ in our notation (the y-axis is the same as ℓ_{CM}). The second integral is equal to

$$-2k \iint_D \rho x \, dA = -2km \frac{1}{m} \iint_D \rho x \, dA = -2km\overline{x},$$

where $\bar{x}$ denotes the x-coordinate of the center of mass. By our choice, the center of mass lies on the y-axis and hence $\bar{x} = 0$. Therefore the second integral vanishes, and

$$I_\ell = k^2 m + I_{CM}.$$

◀

EXERCISES 7.4

1. Compute the average pressure on the hemispherical surface $x^2 + y^2 + z^2 = a^2$, $a \leq 1$, $z \geq 0$, if the pressure is given by $p(x, y, z) = 1 - z^2$.

2. Let D be a disk of radius r and let $f(x, y)$ be the distance function from the point (x, y) to the origin. Find the average value of f over D.

3. Let S be the part of the cone $z^2 = x^2 + y^2$ such that $1 \leq z \leq 4$. Compute the average distance from a point on the cone to the z-axis.

4. Find the mass of a thin wire in the form of the helix $\mathbf{c}(t) = \sin t\mathbf{i} - \cos t\mathbf{j} + 4t\mathbf{k}$, $\pi \leq t \leq 6\pi$, made of a material whose density per unit length is given by $\rho(x, y, z) = 3(y^2 + z^2)$.

5. Find the total charge contained in the tetrahedron with vertices $(0, 0, 0)$, $(1, 0, 0)$, $(0, 3, 0)$ and $(0, 0, 4)$, if the charge density is $\rho(x, y, z) = 2x^2 + y$.

6. Find the mass of a metal sheet in the form of the paraboloid $z = x^2 + y^2$, $2 \leq z \leq 3$, if the density is given by $\rho(x, y, z) = 3z$.

7. Find the center of mass of a uniform wire of density ρ, in the form of the semicircle $x^2 + y^2 = a^2$, $y \geq 0$.

8. Find the mass and the center of mass of a uniform wire of density ρ in the form of the helix $\mathbf{c}(t) = (2 \cos t, 2 \sin t, 3t)$, $t \in [0, 6\pi]$.

9. Find the mass and the center of mass of a wire shaped as a quarter circle $x^2 + y^2 = a^2$, $a > 0$, $x, y \geq 0$, with the density $\rho = bx$ (b is a constant).

10. Find the moment of inertia about the z-axis of the homogeneous thin-walled torus of density ρ generated by revolving the circle centered at $(c, 0, 0)$ of radius a ($a < c$) in the xz-plane around the z-axis.

11. Find the center of mass and the moment of inertia about the z-axis of the surface of the paraboloid $z = 2(x^2 + y^2)$, $0 \leq z \leq 8$ of constant density ρ.

12. Find the polar moment of inertia of the spherical surface $x^2 + y^2 + z^2 = a^2$ of constant density ρ.

13. Find the coordinates of the center of mass of the solid upper hemisphere V given by $x^2 + y^2 + z^2 \leq a^2$, $z \geq 0$, of constant density $\rho(x, y, z) = b$.

14. Find the mass of a thin-walled metal funnel in the shape of the cone $z^2 = 4(x^2 + y^2)$, $1 \leq z \leq 4$, with the density $\rho(x, y, z) = 5 - z$.

15. Assume that V is a solid region filled with a liquid and S is a surface in contact with the liquid. The magnitude of the hydrostatic force exerted by the liquid is given by

$$F = \iint_S \mu(z_o - z) \, dS,$$

where μ is the specific weight of the liquid (the units are weight/volume) and z_o is the z-coordinate of the highest point in V.

Assume that a tank in the shape of a hemisphere of radius a with flat bottom is filled with a liquid of constant specific weight μ. Compute the magnitude of the hydrostatic force on the tank.

16. Assume that the tank from Exercise 15 is turned upside down. Compute the magnitude of the hydrostatic force on the tank.

17. Compute the magnitude of the hydrostatic force (see Exercise 15) on a cylindrical tank with flat top and bottom of radius 2 m and of height 10 m. Assume that the liquid has a constant specific weight μ.

18. Compute the magnitude of the hydrostatic force (see Exercise 15) on a cylindrical tank with hemispherical top and flat bottom, if the cylindrical part of it has radius 2 m and the height 10 m. Assume that the liquid has a constant specific weight μ.

19. Find a function f and a curve $\mathbf{c}$ in $\mathbb{R}^3$ so that $\left| \int_{\mathbf{c}} f \, ds \right| < \int_{\mathbf{c}} |f|$.

20. Using $\ln(1 + u) \le u$ (which holds for $u \ge 0$) estimate $\iint_D \ln(1 + \frac{x}{2} + \frac{y}{3}) \, dA$, where D is the triangle in the first quadrant bounded by the line $y = -x + 3$.

21. Estimate $\iint_S (z^2 + 1) \, dS$ from above and below, where S is the upper hemisphere $x^2 + y^2 + z^2 = 1$, $z \ge 0$.

22. Estimate $\iiint_V (x^2 + y^2 + z^2)^{-1} \, dV$ from above and below, where V is the rectangular box $0 \le x, y \le 3, 2 \le z \le 4$.

23. Estimate $\int_{\mathbf{c}} e^{\sin(x+y)} \, ds$, where $\mathbf{c}$ is the helix $\mathbf{c}(t) = (2 \cos t, 2 \sin t, t + 2)$, $\pi \le t \le 4\pi$.

24. Find the center of mass of the rectangle $R = [0, 1] \times [1, 1]$ in $\mathbb{R}^3$ whose density is given by $\rho(x, y) = (1 + y^2)$. Using Steiner's Theorem find the moment of inertia of R about the line $y = 2$.

CHAPTER REVIEW

Review Questions

Answer/discuss the following questions:

1. Describe how to parametrize the curve $\mathbf{c}$ that is the graph of $y = f(x)$, $x \in [a, b]$ and the surface S that is the graph of $z = f(x, y)$, $(x, y) \in D \subseteq \mathbb{R}^2$. Define the positive orientation of S.

2. If you cut a Möbius strip along its middle circle, how many surfaces do you get, and are they one-sided or two-sided?

3. Define the surface integral of a real-valued function f. Write down a parametrization of a surface S that is the graph of a continuous function $z = g(x, y)$ and an expression for the surface integral of f over S.

4. Explain the Area Cosine Principle. Suppose that you are sitting high on the z-axis and looking at a plane region directly below you. If you see a square of side 1, and the actual plane region is a rectangle with sides 1 and 2, under what angle with respect to the xy-plane was the rectangle placed?

5. Is it true that the surface integral of a constant vector field **F** over a sphere is zero? Explain your answer.

6. Suppose that a plate in the shape of the disk $\{(x, y) \mid x^2 + y^2 \leq 2\}$ is made of several materials with different densities. Is it still possible for its center $(0, 0)$ to be the center of mass?

7. What is the flux of $\mathbf{F} = \mathbf{i} + \mathbf{j}$ across the surface of the cube in the first octant bounded by $x = 1$, $y = 1$ and $z = 1$?

8. Define the integral of a 2-form over a surface and relate it to the surface integral of a vector field.

Computer Projects

1. Isoperimetric Ratio.

Let S be a closed surface in $\mathbb{R}^3$ and let V be the three-dimensional solid region enclosed by S. We will investigate the isoperimetric ratio $I(V) = A(S)/v(V)^{2/3}$, where $A(S)$ is the surface area of S and $v(V)$ is the volume of V.

(a) Compute the isoperimetric ratio for a cube of side a.

(b) Compute the isoperimetric ratio $I(m)$ for a rectangular box whose base is a square of side a and whose height is ma, where $m > 0$. Plot the graph of $I(m)$ for $m \in (0, 5)$. What box has the smallest isoperimetric ratio? Describe what happens to $I(m)$ as $m \to \infty$ (i.e., as the box gets higher and higher) and as $m \to 0$ (i.e., as the box gets lower and lower).

(c) Compute the isoperimetric ratio for a ball of radius a.

(d) Compute the isoperimetric ratio $I(n)$ for the family of ellipsoids $x^2 + y^2 + z^2/n^2 = 1$, $n > 1$. Use the formula

$$S = 2\pi \left(1 + \frac{n^2}{\sqrt{n^2 - 1}} \arcsin\left(\sqrt{n^2 - 1}/n\right)\right)$$

for the surface area of an ellipsoid with semi-axes 1, 1 and $n > 1$. Plot the graph of $I(n)$ on $(1, 10)$. What happens to $I(n)$ as $n \to \infty$ and as $n \to 1^+$? Compare your answers to parts (c) and (d).

(e) What solid has the smallest isoperimetric ratio? Compare with Project 2 at the end of Chapter 6.

2. Constructing Parametrizations of Surfaces.

In this project we will construct parametrizations of a torus and of a Möbius strip (that could be used to produce pictures such as those in Figure 7.13 in Section 7.1, or in Figure 7.26 in Section 7.4).

(a) Let us do a torus first. Plot the circle (say, of radius 2) $\mathbf{c}(t) = (2\cos t, 2\sin t, 0)$, $t \in [0, 2\pi]$ in the xyz-coordinate system. For each point A on that circle, construct a smaller circle (say, of radius 1) centered at A, that lies in the plane that is perpendicular to the xy-plane and contains the line segment $\overline{OA}$; see Figure 7.28.

To do that, use the angle u as a parameter for the smaller circle and find the vector $\overrightarrow{OP}$ (your expression will contain two parameters, t and u). What is the range for u? Now plot all vectors $\overrightarrow{OP}$ thus obtained (by specifying the range of the parameters). Adjust the above parametrization so that the larger circle has radius $R > 0$ and the smaller one has radius $r > 0$. Choose different values for R and r and plot the corresponding tori.

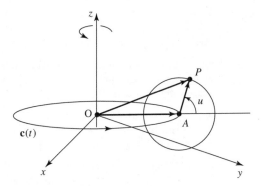

Figure 7.28   Torus of Project 2(a).

(b) Recall that we can make a Möbius strip from a rectangular piece of paper, with one side longer than the other: just twist one smaller side by 180 degrees and glue it to the other smaller side. Let us use this "mechanical" description to construct a parametrization of the Möbius strip. Start with a circle $\mathbf{c}(t) = (\cos t, \sin t, 0)$, $t \in [0, 2\pi]$, and imagine a line segment perpendicular to the xy-plane whose midpoint is at a point A on that circle. As A completes one full revolution around the circle, the corresponding line segments describe a cylinder of height equal to the length of that segment; see Figure 7.29 (that's not exactly what we wanted, but ...).

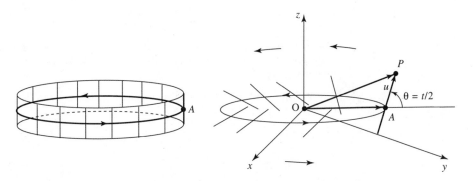

Figure 7.29   Constructing the Möbius strip of Project 2(b).

Now imagine that, as A moves around the circle, the segment moves with A in such a way that its angle with respect to the xy-plane changes — as A completes one full revolution, the line segment rotates through 180 degrees; i.e., ends up upside-down; see Figure 7.29. To describe the rotation of the segment, use $\theta = t/2$ (as t goes from 0 to 2π, θ goes from 0 to π — just what we need). Let u be the distance from A to a point P on the segment, if P is above the xy-plane (if it lies below the xy-plane, take $-u$). Find the vector $\overrightarrow{OP}$ (your expression will contain parameters t and u; choose the range for u so that the segment is of length $1/2$). Plot all vectors $\overrightarrow{OP}$ thus obtained to obtain a Möbius strip. Suppose that the line segment completes one full revolution (360 degrees) instead of half. What surface does it generate?

Further Explorations

1. Find a function f and a surface S in $\mathbb{R}^3$ so that $\left| \iint_S f \, dS \right| < \iint_S |f| \, dS$.

2. Let f be a continuous function defined on a region D that is divided into n mutually disjoint regions $D_1, \ldots, D_n$. Find the average of f over D, if the areas of $D_1, \ldots, D_n$ and the averages of f over each D_i, $i = 1, \ldots, n$ are known.

3. Let S be a level surface of a function $f : \mathbb{R}^3 \to \mathbb{R}$ and D its projection onto the xy-plane. Find an expression for the surface area of S. Then use it to find a formula for the surface area of the graph of $z = g(x, y)$, $(x, y) \in D$.

4. Find an example of a non-constant function defined on the homogeneous disk $D = \{(x, y) \mid x^2 + y^2 \leq 1\}$ with the property that its average value is attained at the center of mass of D.

5. Let S be a surface in $\mathbb{R}^3$ parametrized by $\mathbf{r}(u, v) = (u, v, f(u, v))$, $(u, v) \in D \subseteq \mathbb{R}^2$. Show that

$$\iint_S P(x, y, z) \, dy \, dz + Q(x, y, z) \, dz \, dx + R(x, y, z) \, dx \, dy$$

$$= \iint_D \left(-P(u, v, f(u, v)) \frac{\partial f}{\partial u} - Q(u, v, f(u, v)) \frac{\partial f}{\partial v} + R(u, v, f(u, v)) \right) dA.$$

6. Find the volume of the ellipsoid $x^2/a^2 + y^2/b^2 + z^2/c^2 = 1$ using triple integrals.

7. Let S be a surface in $\mathbb{R}^3$ parametrized by $\mathbf{r}(u, v) : D \subseteq \mathbb{R}^2 \to \mathbb{R}^3$. Prove that

$$\iint_S dS = \iint_D (EG - F^2) \, dA,$$

where $E = \|\partial \mathbf{r}/\partial u\|^2$, $F = (\partial \mathbf{r}/\partial u) \cdot (\partial \mathbf{r}/\partial v)$ and $G = \|\partial \mathbf{r}/\partial v\|^2$. The quantities E, F and G are said to form the *Second Fundamental Form* of S and are used to investigate geometric properties of S.

8. Estimate $\iiint_V (\sin(zx) + e^{x^2+y}) \, dV$ from above and below, where V is the rectangular box $-1 \leq x, y \leq 1$, $0 \leq z \leq 4\pi$.

Chapter 8

CLASSICAL INTEGRATION THEOREMS OF VECTOR CALCULUS

The Fundamental Theorem of Calculus states that the definite integral of the derivative of a function depends not on the whole interval of integration but only on its endpoints. We have managed to generalize this important result to the integral of a gradient vector field along any curve in a plane or in space.

In this chapter we continue our investigation of the relation between the concepts of integration and differentiation. The results, contained in the theorems of Green, Gauss and Stokes (the so-called Classical Integration Theorems of Vector Calculus), are all variations of the same theme applied to different types of integration. Green's Theorem relates the path integral of a vector field along an oriented, simple closed curve in the xy-plane to the double integral of its derivative (to be precise, the *curl*) over the region enclosed by that curve. Gauss' Divergence Theorem extends this result to closed surfaces and Stokes' Theorem generalizes it to simple closed curves in space. Several versions of these theorems are presented, together with a number of worked examples and applications. In particular, we obtain new physical interpretations of *div* and *curl*.

The last section is completely devoted to a discussion of applications of vector calculus in electromagnetism. The emphasis is placed not on explaining the details of the theory of electromagnetism but on identifying physical quantities involved as mathematical objects and showing how to use calculus in manipulating them to obtain meaningful results. The guiding idea is to explain, line by line, all details and intricacies of the mathematical arguments, so that, when studying a text in electromagnetism, the reader will be prepared to go over the mathematical side smoothly and concentrate on understanding the physics of it.

8.1   GREEN'S THEOREM

One of the theorems that establishes a relationship between the concepts of the derivative and the integral is Green's Theorem. It states that the integral of a vector field along a closed curve in a plane is equal to the integral of the derivative of that vector field over the two-dimensional region enclosed by the curve. Before stating the theorem we will identify what curves and regions will be involved and then consider some special cases.

We say that a region $D \subseteq \mathbb{R}^2$ is "good" if it is either an elementary region (those were defined in Section 6.2) or can be divided into disjoint pieces $D_1, \ldots, D_n$ each of which is an elementary region. In the latter case,

$$\iint_D f \, dA = \iint_{D_1} f \, dA + \cdots + \iint_{D_n} f \, dA,$$

for a real-valued function f. The boundary ∂D of D consists of a finite number of simple closed curves, that are oriented by the following rule:

if we walk along the boundary curve in the positive direction (i.e., we follow the positive orientation), then the region is on our left.

For example, let D be the disk $\{(x, y) \mid x^2 + y^2 \leq 1\}$. It is an elementary region (to be precise: a region of type 3) whose boundary consists of the circle $\partial D = \{(x, y) \mid x^2 + y^2 = 1\}$ oriented counterclockwise (that is the positive orientation). The annulus $D = \{(x, y) \mid 1 \leq x^2 + y^2 \leq 4\}$ is not an elementary region, but is "good"— it can be divided into four pieces each of which is an elementary region; see Figure 8.1(a).

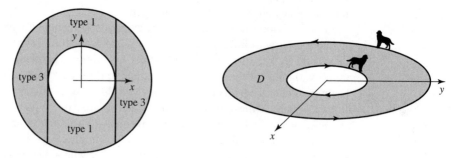

Figure 8.1   Annulus $D = \{(x, y) \mid 1 \leq x^2 + y^2 \leq 4\}$.
(a) D is a "good" region.   (b) Positive orientation of the boundary ∂D.

The boundary ∂D of D consists of two circles (of radii 1 and 2), and the positive orientation is given by the counterclockwise orientation of the outer circle and the clockwise orientation of the inner one, as shown on Figure 8.1(b).

Let D be a region of type 1 and let $\mathbf{c} = \partial D$ be its positively-oriented boundary, as in Figures 8.2 and 8.3. The curve $\mathbf{c}$ is piecewise smooth: it consists of the graphs $\mathbf{c}_1$ and $\mathbf{c}_2$ of continuous functions $y = \phi(x)$ and $y = \psi(x)$ defined on $[a, b]$ and at most two vertical segments: along $x = a$ from $\psi(a)$ to $\phi(a)$ (call it $\mathbf{c}_3$; if $\psi(a) = \phi(a)$, then $\mathbf{c}_3$ collapses to a point) and along $x = b$ from $\phi(b)$ to $\psi(b)$ (call it $\mathbf{c}_4$; if $\psi(b) = \phi(b)$, then $\mathbf{c}_4$ becomes a point; see Figure 8.3).

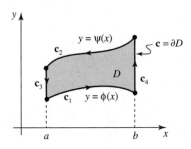

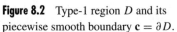

Figure 8.2 Type-1 region D and its piecewise smooth boundary $\mathbf{c} = \partial D$.

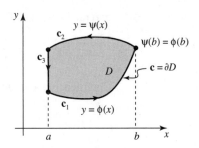

Figure 8.3 Type-1 region D and its piecewise smooth boundary $\mathbf{c} = \partial D$.

Let $P(x, y)$ be a C^1 function. Take the vector field $\mathbf{F}_1(x, y) = (P(x, y), 0)$ and compute its integral along the boundary curve $\mathbf{c}$:

$$\int_{\mathbf{c}} \mathbf{F}_1 \cdot d\mathbf{s} = \int_{\mathbf{c}_1} \mathbf{F}_1 \cdot d\mathbf{s} + \int_{\mathbf{c}_2} \mathbf{F}_1 \cdot d\mathbf{s} + \int_{\mathbf{c}_3} \mathbf{F}_1 \cdot d\mathbf{s} + \int_{\mathbf{c}_4} \mathbf{F}_1 \cdot d\mathbf{s}.$$

Parametrize $\mathbf{c}_1$ by $\mathbf{c}_1(t) = (t, \phi(t))$, $t \in [a, b]$. Then $\mathbf{c}_1'(t) = (1, \phi'(t))$ and

$$\int_{\mathbf{c}_1} \mathbf{F}_1 \cdot d\mathbf{s} = \int_a^b \mathbf{F}_1(\mathbf{c}_1(t)) \cdot \mathbf{c}_1'(t)\, dt$$
$$= \int_a^b (P(t, \phi(t)), 0) \cdot (1, \phi'(t))\, dt = \int_a^b P(t, \phi(t))\, dt.$$

Parametrize the line segment $\mathbf{c}_4$ by $\mathbf{c}_4(t) = (b, t)$, $t \in [\phi(b), \psi(b)]$. Then $\mathbf{c}_4'(t) = (0, 1)$ and

$$\int_{\mathbf{c}_4} \mathbf{F}_1 \cdot d\mathbf{s} = \int_{\phi(b)}^{\psi(b)} \mathbf{F}_1(\mathbf{c}_4(t)) \cdot \mathbf{c}_4'(t)\, dt$$
$$= \int_{\phi(b)}^{\psi(b)} (P(b, t), 0) \cdot (0, 1)\, dt = \int_a^b 0\, dt = 0.$$

An analogous computation would show that $\int_{\mathbf{c}_3} \mathbf{F}_1 \cdot d\mathbf{s} = 0$ (clearly, it does not matter whether $\mathbf{c}_3$ and/or $\mathbf{c}_4$ are segments or points— in any case, the integrals are zero).

Now consider the parametrization $\bar{\mathbf{c}}_2(t) = (t, \psi(t))$, $t \in [a, b]$. The orientation of $\bar{\mathbf{c}}_2$ is wrong (it goes from $(a, \psi(a))$ to $(b, \psi(b))$), but we will fix it in a few lines. Replacing $\phi(t)$ by $\psi(t)$ in the evaluation of $\int_{\mathbf{c}_1} \mathbf{F}_1 \cdot d\mathbf{s}$, we get

$$\int_{\bar{\mathbf{c}}_2} \mathbf{F}_1 \cdot d\mathbf{s} = \int_a^b P(t, \psi(t))\, dt.$$

Therefore,

$$\int_{\mathbf{c}_2} \mathbf{F}_1 \cdot d\mathbf{s} = -\int_{\bar{\mathbf{c}}_2} \mathbf{F}_1 \cdot d\mathbf{s} = -\int_a^b P(t, \psi(t))\, dt,$$

and the integral of $\mathbf{F}_1$ along $\mathbf{c}$ is

$$\int_{\mathbf{c}} \mathbf{F}_1 \cdot d\mathbf{s} = \int_{\mathbf{c}_1} \mathbf{F}_1 \cdot d\mathbf{s} + \int_{\mathbf{c}_2} \mathbf{F}_1 \cdot d\mathbf{s} = \int_a^b \big(P(t, \phi(t)) - P(t, \psi(t))\big)\, dt.$$

Rewrite the above integral using x instead of t:

$$\int_{\mathbf{c}} \mathbf{F}_1 \cdot d\mathbf{s} = \int_a^b \big(P(x, \phi(x)) - P(x, \psi(x))\big)\, dx,$$

and consider the difference $P(x, \phi(x)) - P(x, \psi(x))$ in the integrand. The Fundamental Theorem of Calculus $\int_a^b f'(t)dt = f(b) - f(a)$, applied to a function $f(t) = g(x, t)$, viewed as a function of t (hence x is fixed) reads

$$\int_a^b \frac{\partial}{\partial t} g(x, t)\, dt = g(x, b) - g(x, a).$$

Replacing g by P, t by y and (the limits of integration) a by $\psi(x)$ and b by $\phi(x)$ in the above formula and reading it from right to left, we get

$$P(x, \phi(x)) - P(x, \psi(x)) = \int_{\psi(x)}^{\phi(x)} \frac{\partial}{\partial y} P(x, y)\, dy,$$

and that is exactly what we need! It follows that

$$\int_{\mathbf{c}} \mathbf{F}_1 \cdot d\mathbf{s} = \int_a^b \big(P(x, \phi(x)) - P(x, \psi(x))\big)\, dx$$

$$= \int_a^b \left(\int_{\psi(x)}^{\phi(x)} \frac{\partial P(x, y)}{\partial y} dy \right) dx = - \int_a^b \left(\int_{\phi(x)}^{\psi(x)} \frac{\partial P(x, y)}{\partial y} dy \right) dx.$$

We recognize the result as the iterated integral of $\partial P / \partial y$ over the region D. Hence

$$\int_{\mathbf{c}} \mathbf{F}_1 \cdot d\mathbf{s} = - \iint_D \frac{\partial P}{\partial y}\, dA,$$

where $\mathbf{F}_1(x, y) = (P(x, y), 0)$.

Next, consider a type-2 region D with positively-oriented boundary $\mathbf{c} = \partial D$ and integrate the vector field $\mathbf{F}_2(x, y) = (0, Q(x, y))$ along $\mathbf{c}$ ($Q(x, y)$ is a C^1 function of x and y). Proceeding as in the previous case we obtain

$$\int_{\mathbf{c}} \mathbf{F}_2 \cdot d\mathbf{s} = \iint_D \frac{\partial Q}{\partial x}\, dA.$$

The details of the computation are left as an exercise (with hints— see Exercise 6).

Finally, consider a type-3 region D, its positively-oriented boundary curve $\mathbf{c}$ and a C^1 vector field $\mathbf{F}(x, y) = \mathbf{F}_1(x, y) + \mathbf{F}_2(x, y) = (P(x, y), Q(x, y))$. Adding up the results of the two path integrals of $\mathbf{F}_1$ and $\mathbf{F}_2$ we get

$$\int_{\mathbf{c}} \mathbf{F} \cdot d\mathbf{s} = \int_{\mathbf{c}} \mathbf{F}_1 \cdot d\mathbf{s} + \int_{\mathbf{c}} \mathbf{F}_2 \cdot d\mathbf{s} = \iint_D \left(\frac{\partial Q}{\partial x} - \frac{\partial P}{\partial y} \right) dA.$$

■ **Theorem 8.1**   Green's Theorem.

Let D be a "good" region in $\mathbb{R}^2$ with positively-oriented boundary $\mathbf{c} = \partial D$. If $\mathbf{F}(x, y) = (P(x, y), Q(x, y))$ is a C^1 vector field on D, then

$$\int_{\mathbf{c}} \mathbf{F} \cdot d\mathbf{s} = \iint_D \left(\frac{\partial Q(x, y)}{\partial x} - \frac{\partial P(x, y)}{\partial y} \right) dA.$$

■

Recall that, if $\mathbf{F}(x, y) = (P(x, y), Q(x, y))$ and $\mathbf{c}(t) = (x(t), y(t))$, then (for simplicity, drop (x, y) and t from the notation)

$$\int_{\mathbf{c}} \mathbf{F} \cdot d\mathbf{s} = \int_a^b \mathbf{F} \cdot \mathbf{c}' \, dt$$

$$= \int_a^b (P, Q) \cdot (x', y') \, dt = \int_a^b \left(P \frac{dx}{dt} + Q \frac{dy}{dt} \right) dt = \int_{\mathbf{c}} P \, dx + Q \, dy$$

(see Section 5.3 for definitions); i.e., the path integral of the vector field $\mathbf{F} = (P, Q)$ equals the path integral of the corresponding 1-form $P \, dx + Q \, dy$. With this in mind, we write Green's Theorem in a (probably) more familiar form as

$$\int_{\mathbf{c}} P \, dx + Q \, dy = \iint_D \left(\frac{\partial Q}{\partial x} - \frac{\partial P}{\partial y} \right) dA. \tag{8.1}$$

Proof

We are not going to prove Green's Theorem in its full generality (that is, for an arbitrary "good" region D). The discussion preceding the statement of the theorem actually serves as a proof in the case when D is a region of type 3. To give the flavor of the general case, consider a region D that is not an elementary region, but can be broken into a disjoint union of two type-3 regions D_1 and D_2, as shown in Figure 8.4.

Let $\mathbf{c} = \partial D$ be the positively-oriented boundary of D and assume that D_1 and D_2 intersect along the curve $\boldsymbol{\gamma}$. Orienting the boundary ∂D_1 by our convention (see Figure 8.4) and applying Green's Theorem for type-3 regions, we get

$$\int_{\partial D_1} P \, dx + Q \, dy = \iint_{D_1} \left(\frac{\partial Q}{\partial x} - \frac{\partial P}{\partial y} \right) dA;$$

i.e.,

$$\int_{\mathbf{c}_1} P \, dx + Q \, dy + \int_{\boldsymbol{\gamma}} P \, dx + Q \, dy = \iint_{D_1} \left(\frac{\partial Q}{\partial x} - \frac{\partial P}{\partial y} \right) dA.$$

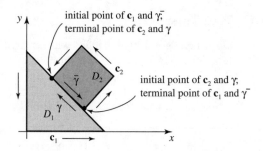

Figure 8.4 D is a disjoint union of type-3 regions D_1 and D_2.

The orientation convention for ∂D_2 requires that we orient the common boundary of D_1 and D_2 in the direction opposite of $\boldsymbol{\gamma}$; see Figure 8.4. Applying Green's Theorem to D_2, we get

$$\int_{\mathbf{c}_2} P\,dx + Q\,dy \; + \int_{\overline{\boldsymbol{\gamma}}} P\,dx + Q\,dy = \iint_{D_2} \left(\frac{\partial Q}{\partial x} - \frac{\partial P}{\partial y} \right) dA.$$

Adding up the two equations (since $\boldsymbol{\gamma}$ and $\overline{\boldsymbol{\gamma}}$ are of opposite orientations it follows that $\int_{\overline{\boldsymbol{\gamma}}} P\,dx + Q\,dy = -\int_{\boldsymbol{\gamma}} P\,dx + Q\,dy$) we get

$$\int_{\mathbf{c}_1} P\,dx + Q\,dy + \int_{\mathbf{c}_2} P\,dx + Q\,dy = \iint_{D_1} \left(\frac{\partial Q}{\partial x} - \frac{\partial P}{\partial y} \right) dA + \iint_{D_2} \left(\frac{\partial Q}{\partial x} - \frac{\partial P}{\partial y} \right) dA$$

and therefore

$$\int_{\mathbf{c}} P\,dx + Q\,dy = \iint_{D} \left(\frac{\partial Q}{\partial x} - \frac{\partial P}{\partial y} \right) dA. \qquad \blacksquare$$

Green's theorem gives us options: we can either compute a path integral directly, using a parametrization, or convert it to a double integral and then evaluate (of course, the curve and the region involved have to satisfty the assumptions of the theorem).

Example 8.1   Evaluate $\int_{\mathbf{c}} \mathbf{F} \cdot d\mathbf{s}$, where $\mathbf{F}(x, y) = e^x \mathbf{i} + 2x \mathbf{j}$ and $\mathbf{c}$ is the boundary of the region D shown in Figure 8.5, oriented counterclockwise.

Solution   The region D is of type 1 (and consequently, it is "good"), the vector field $\mathbf{F}$ is C^1 and the orientation convention has been respected—therefore, we can apply Green's Theorem. It follows that

$$\int_{\mathbf{c}} \mathbf{F} \cdot d\mathbf{s} = \iint_{D} \left(\frac{\partial}{\partial x}(2x) - \frac{\partial}{\partial y}(e^x) \right) dA = \iint_{D} 2\,dA.$$

Using iterated integrals, we get

$$\iint_{D} 2\,dA = \int_{0}^{\pi} \left(\int_{\sin x}^{2+\cos x} 2\,dy \right) dx$$

$$= 2 \int_{0}^{\pi} (\cos x - \sin x + 2)\,dx = 2(\sin x + \cos x + 2x) \Big|_{0}^{\pi} = 4\pi - 4.$$

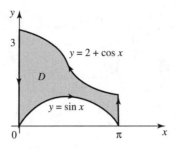

Figure 8.5 Region D of Example 8.1.

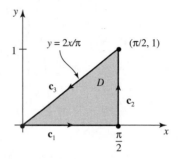

Figure 8.6 Triangle of Example 8.2.

Example 8.2

Evaluate the path integral $\int_c (y - \sin x)dx + \cos x dy$, where c is the triangle with vertices $(0, 0)$, $(\pi/2, 0)$ and $(\pi/2, 1)$, both directly and using Green's theorem.

Solution Orient the curve c counterclockwise, so that the region lies to the left of it; see Figure 8.6. Let $c_1(t) = (t, 0)$, $t \in [0, \pi/2]$. Then

$$\int_{c_1} (y - \sin x)dx + \cos x dy = \int_0^{\pi/2} \left((y - \sin x)x' + \cos x \ y' \right) dt$$

$$= -\int_0^{\pi/2} \sin t \, dt = \cos t \Big|_0^{\pi/2} = -1.$$

Parametrize c_2 by $c_2(t) = (\pi/2, t)$, $t \in [0, 1]$. Then

$$\int_{c_2} (y - \sin x)dx + \cos x dy = \int_0^1 \left((t - 1) \cdot 0 + 0 \cdot 1 \right) dt = 0.$$

Parametrize c_3 by $c_3(t) = (\pi/2, 1) + t(-\pi/2, -1) = (\pi/2 - t\pi/2, 1 - t)$, $t \in [0, 1]$. Then

$$\int_{c_3} (y - \sin x)dx + \cos x dy$$

$$= \int_0^1 \left[\left(1 - t - \sin \left(\tfrac{\pi}{2} - t\tfrac{\pi}{2} \right) \right) \left(-\tfrac{\pi}{2} \right) + \cos \left(\tfrac{\pi}{2} - t\tfrac{\pi}{2} \right) (-1) \right] dt$$

$$= -\frac{\pi}{2} \left(t - \frac{t^2}{2} - \frac{2}{\pi} \cos \left(\tfrac{\pi}{2} - t\tfrac{\pi}{2} \right) \right) \Big|_0^1 + \frac{2}{\pi} \sin \left(\tfrac{\pi}{2} - t\tfrac{\pi}{2} \right) \Big|_0^1 = -\frac{\pi}{4} + 1 - \frac{2}{\pi}.$$

Adding the three integrals we get

$$\int_c (y - \sin x)dx + \cos x dy = -\frac{\pi}{4} - \frac{2}{\pi}.$$

On the other hand, the application of Green's Theorem gives (the equation of c_3 is $y = 2x/\pi$)

$$\int_c (y - \sin x)dx + \cos x dy = \iint_D (-\sin x - 1) \, dA$$

$$= \int_0^1 \left(\int_{\pi y/2}^{\pi/2} (-\sin x - 1) dx \right) dy = \int_0^1 (\cos x - x) \Big|_{\pi y/2}^{\pi/2} dy$$

$$= \int_0^1 \left(-\frac{\pi}{2} - \cos\left(\frac{\pi}{2}y\right) + \frac{\pi}{2}y \right) dy$$

$$= \left(-\frac{\pi}{2}y - \frac{2}{\pi}\sin\left(\frac{\pi}{2}y\right) + \frac{\pi}{2}\frac{y^2}{2} \right) \Big|_0^1 = -\frac{\pi}{2} - \frac{2}{\pi} + \frac{\pi}{4} = -\frac{\pi}{4} - \frac{2}{\pi}. \quad \blacktriangleleft$$

Next, we give a vector-field interpretation of the double integral appearing in Green's Theorem. If we write the vector field $\mathbf{F}$ as $\mathbf{F}(x, y) = P(x, y)\mathbf{i} + Q(x, y)\mathbf{j} + 0\mathbf{k}$, we find its curl $curl\,\mathbf{F}$ to be (P and Q do not depend on z)

$$curl\,\mathbf{F} = \begin{vmatrix} \mathbf{i} & \mathbf{j} & \mathbf{k} \\ \partial/\partial x & \partial/\partial y & \partial/\partial z \\ P & Q & 0 \end{vmatrix} = \left(\frac{\partial Q}{\partial x} - \frac{\partial P}{\partial y} \right) \mathbf{k}.$$

Computing the dot product of both sides by $\mathbf{k}$, we get

$$curl\,\mathbf{F} \cdot \mathbf{k} = \left(\frac{\partial Q}{\partial x} - \frac{\partial P}{\partial y} \right),$$

which is precisely the integrand from the theorem. Hence the right side in Theorem 8.1 is the double integral of the scalar function $curl\mathbf{F} \cdot \mathbf{k}$ over the region D.

Putting the above remarks together, we obtain the vector form of Green's theorem:

$$\int_{\mathbf{c} = \partial D} \mathbf{F} \cdot d\mathbf{s} = \iint_D curl\,\mathbf{F} \cdot \mathbf{k}\, dA.$$

Remember that, in the above statement, D represents a "good" region, $\mathbf{c}$ is the positively oriented boundary of D and $\mathbf{F}$ is a C^1 vector field defined on D.

A direct consequence of Green's Theorem is that if a simple closed curve $\mathbf{c}$ encloses a "good" region D and f is twice continuously differentiable, then, with $\mathbf{F} = \nabla f$,

$$\int_{\mathbf{c}} \nabla f \cdot d\mathbf{s} = \iint_D curl\,(\nabla f) \cdot \mathbf{k}\, dA = 0,$$

since $curl\,(\nabla f) = \mathbf{0}$. In other words, we have re-established the fact that the path integral of a gradient vector field around a simple closed curve is zero.

Example 8.3   Compute $\int_{\mathbf{c}} \mathbf{F} \cdot d\mathbf{s}$, where $\mathbf{F} = e^y \mathbf{i} + \sin x \mathbf{j}$ and $\mathbf{c}$ is the boundary of the rectangle $[0, \pi] \times [0, 1]$.

Solution   Rather than breaking $\mathbf{c}$ into four smooth curves and evaluating $\int_{\mathbf{c}} \mathbf{F} \cdot d\mathbf{s}$ over each curve, we use Green's theorem. Orienting $\mathbf{c}$ counterclockwise (so that the rectangle is on its left) and computing $curl\,\mathbf{F}$ to be

$$curl\,\mathbf{F} = (0, 0, \cos x - e^y),$$

we proceed as follows:

$$\int_c \mathbf{F} \cdot d\mathbf{s} = \iint_{[0,\pi]\times[0,1]} curl\mathbf{F} \cdot \mathbf{k}\, dA = \iint_{[0,\pi]\times[0,1]} (\cos x - e^y)\, dA$$

$$= \int_0^1 \left(\int_0^\pi (\cos x - e^y) dx \right) dy = \int_0^1 \left. (\sin x - xe^y) \right|_0^\pi dy$$

$$= -\int_0^1 \pi e^y\, dy = \pi(1 - e).$$

Example 8.4 Compute $\int_c \mathbf{F} \cdot d\mathbf{s}$, if $\mathbf{F} = xy^2\mathbf{i} - x^2 y\mathbf{j}$ and $\mathbf{c}$ is the boundary of the region $x \geq 0$, $0 \leq y \leq 1 - x^2$, shown in Figure 8.7.

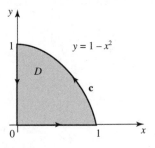

Figure 8.7 Region D and its boundary $\mathbf{c}$ of Example 8.4.

Solution The *curl* of $\mathbf{F}$ is computed to be $(0, 0, -4xy)$, and hence, by Green's Theorem (view D as a type-1 region)

$$\int_c \mathbf{F} \cdot d\mathbf{s} = \iint_D (-4xy\mathbf{k}) \cdot \mathbf{k}\, dA$$

$$= \int_0^1 \left(\int_0^{1-x^2} -4xy\, dy \right) dx = \int_0^1 \left(\left. -2xy^2 \right|_0^{1-x^2} \right) dx$$

$$= \int_0^1 -2x(1-x^2)^2\, dx = \left. \frac{(1-x^2)^3}{3} \right|_0^1 = -\frac{1}{3}.$$

Green's Theorem gives new formulas for computing the area of a region in the plane. Take D to be a "good" region and let $\mathbf{c} = \partial D$ be its positively-oriented boundary. Substituting $P(x, y) = -y$, $Q(x, y) = 0$ in (8.1) we get

$$\int_c -y\, dx = \iint_D 1\, dA = A(D),$$

where $A(D)$ is the area of D. Similarly, with $P(x, y) = 0$, $Q(x, y) = x$ we get

$$\int_c x\, dy = \iint_D 1\, dA = A(D).$$

Adding up the two expressions, we obtain (after dividing by 2)

$$\frac{1}{2}\int_{\mathbf{c}} x\,dy - y\,dx = A(D).$$

These formulas provide three different ways of computing the area of a region as a path integral along its (closed) boundary.

Example 8.5   Using a path integral, find the area of the region D in the first quadrant bounded by $y = x$ and $y = x^3$.

Solution   We will use the first of the three formulas derived above. The boundary $\mathbf{c} = \partial D$ of D consists of the part of the cubic parabola $y = x^3$ from $(0, 0)$ to $(1, 1)$ (call it $\mathbf{c}_1(t)$) and of the straight line segment from $(1, 1)$ to $(0, 0)$ (call it $\mathbf{c}_2(t)$); see Figure 8.8.

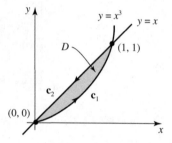

Figure 8.8   Region D of Example 8.5.

The curve $\mathbf{c}_1$ is given by $\mathbf{c}_1(t) = (t, t^3)$, $t \in [0, 1]$, and

$$\int_{\mathbf{c}_1} -y\,dx = \int_0^1 \left(-y\frac{dx}{dt}\right)dt = -\int_0^1 t^3\,dt = -\tfrac{1}{4}.$$

The curve $\mathbf{c}_2$ is given by $\mathbf{c}_2(t) = (1 - t, 1 - t)$, $t \in [0, 1]$, and hence

$$\int_{\mathbf{c}_2} -y\,dx = \int_0^1 -(1 - t)(-1)\,dt = \left(t - \tfrac{1}{2}t^2\right)\Big|_0^1 = \tfrac{1}{2}.$$

Hence the area of D is

$$A(D) = \int_{\mathbf{c}} -y\,dx = \int_{\mathbf{c}_1} -y\,dx + \int_{\mathbf{c}_2} -y\,dx = \tfrac{1}{4}.$$

To check the result, use the double integral:

$$A(D) = \int_0^1 \left(\int_{x^3}^x 1\,dy\right)dx = \int_0^1 \left(y\,\Big|_{x^3}^x\right)dx = \int_0^1 (x - x^3)\,dx = \tfrac{1}{4}.$$

We have already used the fact that the path integral $\int_{\mathbf{c}} \mathbf{F}\cdot d\mathbf{s}$ of the vector field $\mathbf{F} = (P, Q)$ is equal to the path integral $\int_{\mathbf{c}} P\,dx + Q\,dy$ of the corresponding 1-form $\alpha = P\,dx +$

Qdy. Using the definition, we compute the differential of α to be

$$d\alpha = dP \wedge dx + dQ \wedge dy$$

$$= \left(\frac{\partial P}{\partial x}dx + \frac{\partial P}{\partial y}dy\right) \wedge dx + \left(\frac{\partial Q}{\partial x}dx + \frac{\partial Q}{\partial y}dy\right) \wedge dy$$

$$= \left(\frac{\partial Q}{\partial x} - \frac{\partial P}{\partial y}\right) dxdy,$$

hence obtaining yet another form of Green's Theorem:

■ **Theorem 8.2**   Green's Theorem for Differential Forms.

Let $\alpha = P(x, y)dx + Q(x, y)dy$ be a C^1 1-form defined on a "good" region D with positively-oriented boundary $\mathbf{c} = \partial D$. Then

$$\int_{\partial D} \alpha = \int_D d\alpha.$$ ■

The integral on the right side is the integral of a 2-form $d\alpha$, defined in Section 7.3. In words, the integral of a 1-form α over a boundary of a "good" region D equals the integral of its differential $d\alpha$ over D.

We will soon realize that this formulation is a common theme of all integration theorems.

Let us clarify a technical issue: the right side of the formula in Theorem 8.2 is the integral $\int_D f(x, y)dxdy$ of the 2-form $f(x, y)dxdy = (\partial Q/\partial x - \partial P/\partial y)dxdy$ over a region D in the xy-plane. In general, to evaluate such integrals (for any $f(x, y)$), we parametrize D by $\mathbf{r}(u, v) = (u, v, 0)$, where $(u, v) \in D$; then (see the end of Section 7.3)

$$\int_D f(x, y)dxdy = \iint_D f(u, v)\frac{\partial(x, y)}{\partial(u, v)}dA = \iint_D f(u, v)\, dA,$$

since

$$\frac{\partial(x, y)}{\partial(u, v)} = \begin{vmatrix} 1 & 0 \\ 0 & 1 \end{vmatrix} = 1.$$

Now $\iint_D f(u, v)\, dA$ is a double integral over a region in $\mathbb{R}^2$, and is computed as an iterated integral. Replacing u and v by x and y, we get $\iint_D f(u, v)\, dA = \iint_D f(x, y)\, dA$ and hence

$$\int_D f(x, y)dxdy = \iint_D f(x, y)\, dA.$$

This means that an integral of a 2-form $f(x, y)dxdy$ over a region D in the xy-plane can be interpreted as a double integral of $f(x, y)$ over D (i.e., as an iterated integral).

Example 8.6   Let $\alpha = xydx - x^2ydy$ be a 1-form and let $\mathbf{c}$ be the circle $\mathbf{c}(t) = (\cos t, \sin t)$, $t \in [0, 2\pi]$. Compute $\int_{\mathbf{c}} \alpha$, first directly, and then using Green's theorem.

Solution   By definition,

$$\int_{\mathbf{c}} \alpha = \int_c xy\,dx - x^2y\,dy$$

$$= \int_0^{2\pi} \left(xy\frac{dx}{dt} - x^2y\frac{dy}{dt} \right) dt$$

$$= \int_0^{2\pi} \left(-\cos t \sin^2 t - \sin t \cos^3 t \right) dt$$

$$= \left(-\tfrac{1}{3}\sin^3 t + \tfrac{1}{4}\cos^4 t \right) \Big|_0^{2\pi} = \tfrac{1}{4} - \tfrac{1}{4} = 0.$$

Since

$$d\alpha = (y\,dx + x\,dy) \wedge dx - (2xy\,dx + x^2\,dy) \wedge dy = (-x - 2xy)\,dx\,dy,$$

Green's Theorem implies that

$$\int_{\mathbf{c}} \alpha = \int_D d\alpha = -\iint_{\{0 \le x^2 + y^2 \le 1\}} (x + 2xy)\,dA.$$

Passing to polar coordinates we get

$$\int_{\mathbf{c}} \alpha = -\int_0^{2\pi} \left(\int_0^1 \left(r\cos\theta + 2r^2\cos\theta\sin\theta \right) r\,dr \right) d\theta$$

$$= -\int_0^{2\pi} \left(\tfrac{1}{3}r^3\cos\theta + \tfrac{1}{2}r^4\cos\theta\sin\theta \right) \Big|_0^1 d\theta$$

$$= -\int_0^{2\pi} \left(\tfrac{1}{3}\cos\theta + \tfrac{1}{2}\cos\theta\sin\theta \right) d\theta = -\left(\tfrac{1}{3}\sin\theta + \tfrac{1}{4}\sin^2\theta \right) \Big|_0^{2\pi} = 0. \quad \blacktriangleleft$$

Example 8.7   **Double Integral of the Laplacian.**

Let $D \subseteq \mathbb{R}^2$ be a "good" region and let $\mathbf{c} = \partial D$ be its C^1, positively-oriented smooth boundary curve (recall that "smooth" implies that $\|\mathbf{c}'(t)\| \ne 0$). Assume that the function $f: D \to \mathbb{R}$ is twice continuously differentiable (it is also called a C^2 function). By definition, the Laplace operator of f is equal to $\Delta f = \partial^2 f/\partial x^2 + \partial^2 f/\partial y^2$, and therefore

$$\iint_D \Delta f\,dA = \iint_D \left(\frac{\partial^2 f}{\partial x^2} + \frac{\partial^2 f}{\partial y^2} \right) dA = \iint_D \left(\frac{\partial}{\partial x}\left(\frac{\partial f}{\partial x}\right) + \frac{\partial}{\partial y}\left(\frac{\partial f}{\partial y}\right) \right) dA$$

(using Green's Theorem (8.1) with $Q = \partial f/\partial x$ and $P = -\partial f/\partial y$ we convert the double integral into the following path integral)

$$= \int_{\mathbf{c} = \partial D} -\frac{\partial f}{\partial y}\,dx + \frac{\partial f}{\partial x}\,dy$$

(using the definition of the path integral of a 1-form)

$$= \int_a^b \left(-\frac{\partial f}{\partial y}\frac{dx}{dt} + \frac{\partial f}{\partial x}\frac{dy}{dt} \right) dt,$$

where $\mathbf{c}(t) = (x(t), y(t))$, $t \in [a, b]$ is a parametrization of $\mathbf{c}$. Let us interpret the integrand in the above expression: it is the dot product of the vectors $(\partial f/\partial x, \partial f/\partial y)$

and $(dy/dt, -dx/dt) = (y'(t), -x'(t))$. The first factor is the gradient of f. The dot product of the second factor $\mathbf{N} = (y'(t), -x'(t))$ with the tangent $\mathbf{c}'(t) = (x'(t), y'(t))$ is zero. Consequently, $\mathbf{N}$ is a vector normal to $\mathbf{c}$. Notice that $\|\mathbf{N}\| = \|\mathbf{c}'(t)\|$. Moreover, we know that $\mathbf{N}$ is an outward normal, since its x-component coincides with the y-component of the tangent (the x-component of the inward normal equals the negative of the y-component of the tangent); see Figure 8.9.

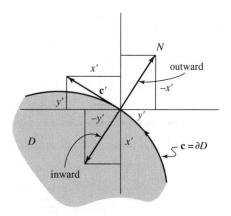

Figure 8.9 Inward and outward normal vectors to a curve $\mathbf{c} = \partial D$.

It follows that

$$\iint_D \Delta f \, dA = \int_a^b \nabla f \cdot \mathbf{N} \, dt = \int_a^b \left(\nabla f \cdot \frac{\mathbf{N}}{\|\mathbf{N}\|} \right) \|\mathbf{N}\| \, dt$$

(since $\mathbf{c}$ is smooth and $\|\mathbf{N}\| = \|\mathbf{c}'(t)\|$ it follows that $\|\mathbf{N}\| \neq 0$)

$$= \int_a^b \left(\nabla f \cdot \frac{\mathbf{N}}{\|\mathbf{N}\|} \right) \|\mathbf{c}'\| \, dt$$

(by definition of the path integral $\int_{\mathbf{c}} g \, ds = \int_a^b g \|\mathbf{c}'\| dt$, with $g = \nabla f \cdot \mathbf{N}/\|\mathbf{N}\|$ read backward and using $\mathbf{n} = \mathbf{N}/\|\mathbf{N}\|$; $\mathbf{n}$ is the unit outward normal)

$$= \int_{\mathbf{c}} \nabla f \cdot \mathbf{n} \, ds = \int_{\mathbf{c}} D_{\mathbf{n}} f \, ds,$$

by definition of the directional derivative ($D_{\mathbf{n}} f = \nabla f \cdot \mathbf{n}$). The directional derivative $D_{\mathbf{n}} f$ is called the *normal derivative of f* and is denoted by $\partial f / \partial n$. Hence

$$\iint_D \Delta f \, dA = \int_{\mathbf{c} = \partial D} \frac{\partial f}{\partial n} ds.$$

◄

Example 8.8 Compute $\int_{\mathbf{c}} (\partial f / \partial n) ds$, where $f(x, y) = x^2 + y^2$ and $\mathbf{c}$ is the circle $x^2 + y^2 = 4$, both directly and using the formula derived in the previous example.

Solution We compute the path integral first. Parametrize $\mathbf{c}$ by $\mathbf{c}(t) = (2 \cos t, 2 \sin t)$, $t \in [0, 2\pi]$. Then $\mathbf{c}'(t) = (-2 \sin t, 2 \cos t)$ and thus $\mathbf{N} = (2 \cos t, 2 \sin t)$ is an outward normal. The normal derivative is computed to be

$$\frac{\partial f}{\partial n} = \nabla f \cdot \mathbf{n} = (2x, 2y) \cdot \frac{\mathbf{N}}{\|\mathbf{N}\|} = (4\cos t, 4\sin t) \cdot \frac{(2\cos t, 2\sin t)}{2} = 4,$$

and hence ($\ell(\mathbf{c})$ denotes the length of $\mathbf{c}$)

$$\int_{\mathbf{c}} \frac{\partial f}{\partial n} ds = \int_{\mathbf{c}} 4 ds = 4\ell(\mathbf{c}) = 16\pi.$$

Alternatively, (the Laplacian is computed to be $\Delta f = 2 + 2 = 4$),

$$\int_{\mathbf{c}} \frac{\partial f}{\partial n} ds = \iint_{\{x^2+y^2 \le 4\}} \Delta f \, dA = 4 \text{ area}(\{x^2 + y^2 \le 4\}) = 16\pi.$$

EXERCISES 8.1

Exercises 1 to 5: Compute $\int_{\mathbf{c}} \mathbf{F} \cdot d\mathbf{s}$ using Green's Theorem.

1. $\mathbf{F} = -2y\mathbf{i} + x\mathbf{j}$, $\mathbf{c}(t) = (2\cos t, \sin t)$, $t \in [0, 2\pi]$

2. $\mathbf{F} = (x^2+1)^{-1}\mathbf{j}$, $\mathbf{c}$ is the boundary of the rectangle $[0, 2] \times [0, 3]$, oriented counterclockwise

3. $\mathbf{F} = e^{x+y}\mathbf{j} - e^{x-y}\mathbf{i}$, $\mathbf{c}$ is the boundary of the triangle defined by the lines $y = 0$, $x = 1$ and $y = x$, oriented counterclockwise

4. $\mathbf{F} = (2 - y^3)\mathbf{i} + (y + x^3 + 2)\mathbf{j}$, $\mathbf{c}$ is the circle of radius 5 centered at the origin and oriented counterclockwise

5. $\mathbf{F} = 2x^2y^2\mathbf{i} - x\mathbf{j}$, $\mathbf{c}$ consists of the curve $y = 2x^3$ from $(0, 0)$ to $(1, 2)$ followed by the straight line segment from $(1, 2)$ back to $(0, 0)$, oriented counterclockwise

6. Let D be a type-2 region given by $c \le y \le d$ and $\phi(y) \le x \le \psi(y)$, let $\mathbf{c}$ be its positively-oriented boundary and let $\mathbf{F}_2(x, y) = (0, Q(x, y))$.

    (a) Show that the integral of $\mathbf{F}_2$ along horizontal line segments $y = c$ and $y = d$ is zero.

    (b) Prove that $\int_{\mathbf{c}} \mathbf{F}_2 \cdot d\mathbf{s} = \int_c^d Q(\psi(y), y) - Q(\phi(y), y) \, dy$.

    (c) Using the Fundamental Theorem of Calculus, show that $Q(\psi(y), y) - Q(\phi(y), y) = \int_{\phi(y)}^{\psi(y)} (\partial Q(x, y)/\partial x) \, dx$.

    (d) Conclude that $\int_{\mathbf{c}} \mathbf{F}_2 \cdot d\mathbf{s} = \iint_D (\partial Q/\partial x) dA$.

Exercises 7 to 11: Compute $\int_{\mathbf{c}} \mathbf{F} \cdot d\mathbf{s}$ directly, or using Green's Theorem.

7. $\mathbf{F} = x^2y^2\mathbf{i} + y^4\mathbf{j}$, $\mathbf{c}$ is the curve $x^2 + y^2 = 1$, oriented counterclockwise

8. $\mathbf{F} = (2x + 3y + 2)\mathbf{i} - (x - 4y + 3)\mathbf{j}$, $\mathbf{c}$ is the ellipse $x^2 + 4y^2 = 4$, oriented clockwise

9. $\mathbf{F} = \cosh y\mathbf{i} + x \sinh y\mathbf{j}$, $\mathbf{c}$ is the boundary of the triangle defined by the lines $y = 4x$, $y = 2x$ and $x = 1$, oriented counterclockwise (recall that $\cosh y = (e^y + e^{-y})/2$ and $\sinh y = (e^y - e^{-y})/2$)

10. $\mathbf{F} = e^x(\mathbf{i}+\mathbf{j})$, $\mathbf{c}$ is the boundary of the triangle with vertices $(0, 0)$, $(1, 2)$ and $(0, 2)$, oriented counterclockwise

11. $\mathbf{F} = \arctan(y/x)\mathbf{i} + \arctan(x/y)\mathbf{j}$, $\mathbf{c}$ is the circle $x^2 + y^2 = 2$ oriented counterclockwise

12. Let $\alpha = x^2y dx - xy^2 dy$ be a 1-form and let D be the annulus $1 \le x^2 + y^2 \le 4$.

(a) Compute $\int_{\mathbf{c}} \alpha$, where $\mathbf{c}$ is the boundary of D, with the outside circle oriented counter-clockwise and the inner circle oriented clockwise.

(b) Compute $\int_{\mathbf{c}} \alpha$, where $\mathbf{c}$ is the boundary of D, with both circles oriented counterclockwise.

13. Using a path integral compute the area of the region D bounded by the curves $y = 2x^2$ and $y = 4x$.

14. Using a path integral compute the area of the region D bounded by the curves $x = y^2$, $x = 2$ and $x = 3$.

15. Using a path integral compute the area of the region D in the first quadrant bounded by the astroid $x^{2/3} + y^{2/3} = 1$.

16. Using a path integral compute the area of the region bounded by the x-axis and the cycloid $\mathbf{c}(t) = (t - \sin t, 1 - \cos t)$, where $0 \leq t \leq 2\pi$.

17. Compute the work of the force $\mathbf{F} = x\mathbf{i} + (x^2 + 3y^2)\mathbf{j}$ done on a particle that moves along the straight line segments from $(0, 0)$ to $(3, 0)$, then from $(3, 0)$ to $(1, 2)$, and then from $(1, 2)$ back to $(0, 0)$.

18. Assume that the curves involved are oriented counterclockwise.

(a) Compute $\displaystyle\int_{\mathbf{c}} \frac{xdy + ydx}{x^2 + y^2}$, where $\mathbf{c}$ is the circle $x^2 + y^2 = 1$.

(b) Compute $\displaystyle\int_{\mathbf{c}} \frac{xdy + ydx}{x^2 + y^2}$, where $\mathbf{c}$ is the circle $(x - 1)^2 + (y + 1)^2 = 1$.

19. Assume that f is a C^2, harmonic function (i.e., $f_{xx} + f_{yy} = 0$) on a set that contains a "good" region D. Show that $\int_{\partial D}(f_x dy - f_y dx) = 0$, where ∂D is the boundary of D oriented counterclockwise.

20. Let D be a "good" region with positively-oriented boundary $\partial D = \mathbf{c}$. Assume that D is of constant density ρ. Express its mass m and moments M_x and M_y (with respect to the y-axis and the x-axis) in terms of path integrals.

21. Let D be a "good" region with positively-oriented boundary $\partial D = \mathbf{c}$. Assume that D is of constant density ρ. Express its moments of inertia about the x-axis and the y-axis in terms of path integrals.

22. Let D be the disk $x^2 + y^2 \leq 1$, let $\mathbf{c}$ be its positively oriented boundary and let $f(x, y) = x^2 + 3y^2$. By computing both sides, check that $\iint_D \Delta f \, dA = \int_{\mathbf{c}} D_{\mathbf{n}} f \, ds$, where $\mathbf{n}$ is the outward normal to $\mathbf{c}$ and $D_{\mathbf{n}} f$ is the directional derivative in the direction of the normal. Δf denotes the Laplacian of f, defined by $\Delta f = f_{xx} + f_{yy}$.

23. Check that (see Exercise 22 for the notation) $\iint_D \Delta f \, dA = \int_{\mathbf{c}} D_{\mathbf{n}} f \, ds$ for the function $f(x, y) = e^x \cos y$, where D is the rectangle $[0, 1] \times [0, 2]$ and $\mathbf{c}$ is its positively-oriented boundary.

24. Check that (see Exercise 22 for the notation) $\iint_D \Delta f \, dA = \int_{\mathbf{c}} D_{\mathbf{n}} f \, ds$ for the function $f(x, y) = e^{x+y}$, where D is the rectangle $[0, 1] \times [0, 1]$ and $\mathbf{c}$ is its positively-oriented boundary.

Exercises 25 to 32: Compute $\int_{\mathbf{c}} \alpha$.

25. $\alpha = y^2 dx + xy dy$, $\mathbf{c}$ is the boundary of the triangle determined by the equations $y = x$, $x = 0$ and $y = 1$, with counterclockwise orientation

26. $\alpha = x dy$, $\mathbf{c}$ is the cardioid $r = 1 + \cos\theta$, with counterclockwise orientation

27. $\alpha = (x - y)^2 dx + 2x dy$, **c** is the closed curve determined by $y = x^2$ and $y = x$, oriented counterclockwise

28. $\alpha = (y^2 + e^{\tan x}) dx + (y \ln y + x^2) dy$, **c** is the closed curve determined by $y = x^3$ and $y = 16x$ from $(0, 0)$ to $(4, 64)$, oriented counterclockwise

29. $\alpha = 2xy(y dx + x dy)$, **c** is the circle $x^2 + y^2 = 1$, oriented counterclockwise

30. $\alpha = x dx + x dy$, **c** consists of the semi-circle $x^2 + y^2 = 1$, $y \geq 0$, followed by the straight line segment from $(-1, 0)$ to $(1, 0)$, with counterclockwise orientation

31. $\alpha = x dx + (x^2 + y^2) dy$, **c** is the boundary of the annulus $1 \leq x^2 + y^2 \leq 2$; the outer circle is oriented counterclockwise, and the inner one has clockwise orientation

32. $\alpha = (2x + 2y^2) dx - 3x dy$, **c** is the boundary of the rectangle $[0, 1] \times [-2, 2]$, with counterclockwise orientation

---

8.2   THE DIVERGENCE THEOREM

The Divergence Theorem (or Gauss' Divergence Theorem) is similar to Green's Theorem: it relates an integral over a closed geometric object (a closed surface) to an integral over the region (in this case a three-dimensional solid region) enclosed by it.

Elementary (3D) regions are regions in $\mathbb{R}^3$ bounded by surfaces that are graphs of real-valued functions of two variables. Depending on which of the variables are involved, the regions are called type 1(3D), type 2(3D) or type 3(3D). A region is of type 1(3D) if its "bottom" and "top" sides are graphs of continuous functions $\kappa_1(x, y)$ and $\kappa_2(x, y)$. A region is of type 2(3D) if its "back" and "front" sides are graphs of continuous functions $\kappa_1(y, z)$ and $\kappa_2(y, z)$, and of type 3(3D) if its "left" and "right" sides are graphs of continuous functions $\kappa_1(x, z)$ and $\kappa_2(x, z)$ (of course, the names "top," "bottom," "left," etc., for sides depend on the point from which we look at the xyz-coordinate system; see Section 6.5 for precise definitions). A region is of type 4(3D) if it is of type 1(3D), type 2(3D) and type 3(3D). For example, a rectangular box whose sides are parallel to coordinate axes is of type 4(3D). The ball $\{(x, y, z) \mid x^2 + y^2 + z^2 \leq 1\}$ and the upper half-ball $\{(x, y, z) \mid x^2 + y^2 + z^2 \leq 1, z \geq 0\}$ are of type 4(3D).

A region $V \subseteq \mathbb{R}^3$ is called "*good (3D)*" if it is either of type-4(3D), or can be broken into pieces each of which is a type 4(3D) region. The solid region between two cubes, one placed inside the other one, is a "good (3D)" region: it can be broken into 6 (or more) parallelepipeds, see Figure 8.10.

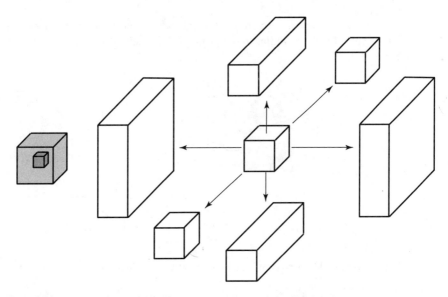

Figure 8.10 The solid region between two cubes is a "good (3D)" region.

A boundary ∂V of a "good (3D)" region is a closed surface or a union of closed surfaces. It can be oriented in two ways: either by choosing an outward normal (that is, a normal that points away from the solid region V, into space) or an inward normal (that points into the region V). We define the *positive* orientation as the choice of an outward normal.

We have seen in Section 7.3 that if $\mathbf{F}$ is the velocity vector of a fluid, then the surface integral

$$\iint_S \mathbf{F} \cdot d\mathbf{S} = \iint_S \mathbf{F} \cdot \mathbf{n}\, dS$$

measures (for S closed and oriented by the (unit) outward normal $\mathbf{n}$) the total volume of fluid leaving the three dimensional region enclosed by the surface S per unit time. On the other hand, the three-dimensional analogue of our interpretation of the divergence given in Section 4.2 relates the total fluid outflow (from the solid region) to the divergence of the vector field that represents the fluid velocity. This observation is formalized in the statement of our next theorem.

■ **Theorem 8.3**   Divergence Theorem of Gauss.

Let V be a "good (3D)" region in $\mathbb{R}^3$ and let ∂V be its positively oriented boundary. Assume that $\mathbf{F}$ is a C^1 vector field on V. Then

$$\iint_{S=\partial V} \mathbf{F} \cdot d\mathbf{S} = \iiint_V div\, \mathbf{F}\, dV.$$ ■

Proof

We will not be able to prove the theorem for a general "good (3D)" region V and will instead concentrate on a special case of a type-4(3D) region. As we will see soon, the proof is very similar to the proof of the special cases of Green's Theorem.

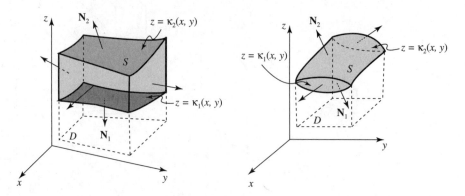

Figure 8.11   Two type-1(3D) regions V with positively-oriented boundary surfaces S.

Consider a type-1(3D) region V defined by

$$V = \{(x, y, z) \mid \kappa_1(x, y) \leq z \leq \kappa_2(x, y), (x, y) \in D\},$$

where D is an elementary region in $\mathbb{R}^2$. The boundary $S = \partial V$ is, in general, a piecewise smooth surface that consists of the "bottom" and "top" surfaces (that are the graphs of $z = \kappa_1(x, y)$ and $z = \kappa_2(x, y)$) and (at most) four vertical sides. Figure 8.11 shows regions V with four and two vertical sides. Orient S by the outward-pointing normal vector field $\mathbf{N}$ (that is, by our convention, the positive orientation). We will compute $\iint_S \mathbf{F} \cdot d\mathbf{S}$, where $\mathbf{F} = R(x, y, z)\mathbf{k}$ is a C^1 vector field defined on V.

On any of the vertical sides, $\mathbf{N}$ is parallel to the xy-plane, and therefore $\mathbf{F} \cdot \mathbf{N} = R(x, y, z)\mathbf{k} \cdot \mathbf{N} = 0$. Consequently, the vertical sides do not contribute anything to the integral $\iint_S \mathbf{F} \cdot d\mathbf{S}$ (which is certainly not a surprise: $\mathbf{F}$ represents a flow in the vertical direction only, and so there is no flux through the sides that are parallel to the flow).

Parametrize the bottom surface S_1 as $\mathbf{r}_1(u, v) = (u, v, \kappa_1(u, v))$, where $(u, v) \in D$. The outward normal to S_1 is $\mathbf{N}_1 = -(-\partial\kappa_1/\partial u, -\partial\kappa_1/\partial v, 1)$. Since the $\mathbf{k}$-component of $\mathbf{N}_1$ is -1, $\mathbf{N}_1$ points downward (as it should); in Section 7.1 this choice of the normal was called the negative orientation of the surface. From

$$\mathbf{F}(\mathbf{r}_1(u, v)) \cdot \mathbf{N}_1(u, v) = R(u, v, \kappa_1(u, v))\mathbf{k} \cdot \left(\frac{\partial\kappa_1}{\partial u}\mathbf{i} + \frac{\partial\kappa_1}{\partial v}\mathbf{j} - \mathbf{k}\right) = -R(u, v, \kappa_1(u, v))$$

it follows that

$$\iint_{S_1} \mathbf{F} \cdot d\mathbf{S}_1 = -\iint_D R(u, v, \kappa_1(u, v))dA = -\iint_D R(x, y, \kappa_1(x, y))dA,$$

after replacing u by x and v by y.

The integral over S_2 is computed analogously, the only difference being the choice of a normal. Parametrize S_2 by $\mathbf{r}_2(u, v) = (u, v, \kappa_2(u, v))$, where $(u, v) \in D$ and choose $\mathbf{N}_2 = +(-\partial\kappa_2/\partial u, -\partial\kappa_2/\partial v, 1)$. Proceeding as above, we obtain

$$\iint_{S_2} \mathbf{F} \cdot d\mathbf{S}_2 = \iint_D R(x, y, \kappa_2(x, y)) dA,$$

and therefore

$$\iint_S \mathbf{F} \cdot d\mathbf{S} = \iint_D (R(x, y, \kappa_2(x, y)) - R(x, y, \kappa_1(x, y))) dA.$$

The Fundamental Theorem of Calculus $\int_a^b f'(t)dt = f(b) - f(a)$, applied to a function $f(t) = g(x, y, t)$, viewed as a function of t (hence x and y are fixed) gives

$$\int_a^b \frac{\partial}{\partial t} g(x, y, t)\, dt = g(x, y, b) - g(x, y, a).$$

Replacing g by R, t by z, a by $\kappa_1(x, y)$ and b by $\kappa_2(x, y)$, we get

$$\int_{\kappa_1(x,y)}^{\kappa_2(x,y)} \frac{\partial}{\partial z} R(x, y, z)\, dz = R(x, y, \kappa_2(x, y)) - R(x, y, \kappa_1(x, y)),$$

and that is the integrand we are looking for! It follows that

$$\iint_S \mathbf{F} \cdot d\mathbf{S} = \iint_D \left(\int_{\kappa_1(x,y)}^{\kappa_2(x,y)} \frac{\partial}{\partial z} R(x, y, z)\, dz \right) dA$$

is equal to the iterated integral of the triple integral of $\partial R/\partial z$ over V; hence

$$\iint_S \mathbf{F} \cdot d\mathbf{S} = \iint_S R\mathbf{k} \cdot d\mathbf{S} = \iiint_V \frac{\partial R}{\partial z}\, dV.$$

Similar computations will prove that

$$\iint_S P\mathbf{i} \cdot d\mathbf{S} = \iiint_V \frac{\partial P}{\partial x}\, dV$$

for a type-2(3D) region V and

$$\iint_S Q\mathbf{j} \cdot d\mathbf{S} = \iiint_V \frac{\partial Q}{\partial y}\, dV$$

for a type-3(3D) region V. Adding up the three expressions we get that

$$\iint_S (P\mathbf{i} + Q\mathbf{j} + R\mathbf{k}) \cdot d\mathbf{S} = \iiint_V \left(\frac{\partial P}{\partial x} + \frac{\partial Q}{\partial y} + \frac{\partial R}{\partial z} \right) dV;$$

i.e.,

$$\iint_S \mathbf{F} \cdot d\mathbf{S} = \iiint_V div\, \mathbf{F}\, dV,$$

where $\mathbf{F} = P\mathbf{i} + Q\mathbf{j} + R\mathbf{k}$ and V is a type-4(3D) region. ∎

Example 8.9 Verify the Divergence Theorem for the vector field $\mathbf{F} = y^2\mathbf{i} + x^2\mathbf{j} + z^2\mathbf{k}$, where S is the surface of the cylinder $x^2 + y^2 = 4$, $0 \leq z \leq 5$, together with the top disk

$\{(x, y) \mid x^2 + y^2 \le 4, z = 5\}$ and the bottom disk $\{(x, y) \mid x^2 + y^2 \le 4, z = 0\}$, oriented by the outward normal.

Solution   Let us first compute $\iint_S \mathbf{F} \cdot d\mathbf{S}$ directly. The top disk S_1 can be parametrized using $\mathbf{r}_1(u, v) = (u, v, 5)$, where $u^2 + v^2 \le 4$. Then $\mathbf{T}_u^1 = (1, 0, 0)$, $\mathbf{T}_v^1 = (0, 1, 0)$, the normal is $\mathbf{N}_1 = \mathbf{T}_u^1 \times \mathbf{T}_v^1 = (0, 0, 1)$ and

$$\iint_{S_1} \mathbf{F} \cdot d\mathbf{S} = \iint_{\{u^2 + v^2 \le 4\}} (v^2, u^2, 25) \cdot (0, 0, 1) \, dA$$
$$= \iint_{\{u^2 + v^2 \le 4\}} 25 \, dA = 25 \ \text{area}(\{u^2 + v^2 \le 4\}) = 100\pi.$$

In words, the total flux out of the cylinder through its top side equals 100π. Similarly, the bottom disk S_2 can be parametrized by $\mathbf{r}_2(u, v) = (u, v, 0)$, $u^2 + v^2 \le 4$. The tangents and the normal are as for the top side. However, to comply with the outward orientation requirement for the surface, we take $\mathbf{N}_2 = (0, 0, -1)$ as the normal; see Figure 8.12. Hence

$$\iint_{S_2} \mathbf{F} \cdot d\mathbf{S} = \iint_{\{u^2 + v^2 \le 4\}} (v^2, u^2, 0) \cdot (0, 0, -1) \, dA = 0.$$

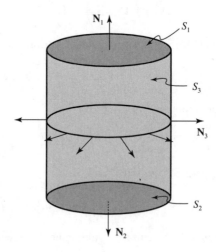

Figure 8.12   Surface of the cylinder oriented by the outward normal.

Finally, parametrize S_3 (the curved surface of the cylinder) by

$$\mathbf{r}_3(u, v) = (2 \cos u, 2 \sin u, v), \qquad 0 \le u \le 2\pi, \quad 0 \le v \le 5.$$

Then $\mathbf{T}_u^3 = (-2 \sin u, 2 \cos u, 0)$, $\mathbf{T}_v^3 = (0, 0, 1)$, $\mathbf{N}_3 = (2 \cos u, 2 \sin u, 0)$ and ($\mathbf{N}_3$ points outward: it is the position vector of a point on the circle in the xy-plane)

$$\iint_{S_3} \mathbf{F} \cdot d\mathbf{S} = \iint_{[0, 2\pi] \times [0, 5]} (4 \sin^2 u, 4 \cos^2 u, v^2) \cdot (2 \cos u, 2 \sin u, 0) \, dA$$

$$= \int_0^5 \left(\int_0^{2\pi} (8 \sin^2 u \cos u + 8 \cos^2 u \sin u) du \right) dv$$

$$= 8 \int_0^5 \left(\tfrac{1}{3} \sin^3 u - \tfrac{1}{3} \cos^3 u \right) \Big|_0^{2\pi} dv = 8 \int_0^5 0 \, dv = 0.$$

Adding up the three integrals we get

$$\iint_S \mathbf{F} \cdot d\mathbf{S} = 100\pi.$$

The Divergence Theorem claims that the same result will be obtained by computing

$$\iiint_V div \mathbf{F} \, dV,$$

where V denotes the *solid* cylinder $\{(x, y, z) \mid x^2 + y^2 \leq 4, 0 \leq z \leq 5\}$. Indeed ($div\, \mathbf{F} = 2z$),

$$\iiint_V div \mathbf{F} \, dV = \iint_{\{x^2+y^2 \leq 4\}} \left(\int_0^5 2z \, dz \right) dA$$

$$= 25 \iint_{\{x^2+y^2 \leq 4\}} dA = 25 \text{area}(\{(x, y) \mid x^2 + y^2 \leq 4\}) = 100\pi. \quad \blacktriangleleft$$

Example 8.10   Evaluate $\iint_S \mathbf{F} \cdot d\mathbf{S}$, where $\mathbf{F} = e^{y+z}\mathbf{k}$ and S is the piecewise smooth surface of the parallelepiped $0 \leq x \leq 1, 0 \leq y \leq 4, 0 \leq z \leq 2$, oriented by the outward normal.

Solution   Let V be the solid parallelepiped $[0, 1] \times [0, 4] \times [0, 2]$. By the Divergence Theorem,

$$\iint_S e^{y+z}\mathbf{k} \cdot d\mathbf{S} = \iiint_V div(e^{y+z}\mathbf{k}) \, dV$$

$$= \int_0^1 \left(\int_0^4 \left(\int_0^2 e^y e^z dz \right) dy \right) dx = \int_0^1 \left(\int_0^4 e^y \left(e^z \Big|_0^2 \right) dy \right) dx$$

$$= (e^2 - 1) \int_0^1 \left(e^y \Big|_0^4 \right) dx = (e^2 - 1)(e^4 - 1) \int_0^1 dx = (e^2 - 1)(e^4 - 1). \quad \blacktriangleleft$$

Example 8.11   Compute the (outward) flux of $\mathbf{F} = xy^2\mathbf{i} + y^3\mathbf{j} + 4x^2z\mathbf{k}$ through the surface of the (solid) cylinder V given by $x^2 + y^2 \leq 4, 0 \leq z \leq 5$.

Solution   The Divergence Theorem applied to the closed surface S enclosing V ($\partial V = S$) implies that

$$\iint_S (xy^2\mathbf{i} + y^3\mathbf{j} + 4x^2z\mathbf{k}) \cdot d\mathbf{S} = \iiint_V (y^2 + 3y^2 + 4x^2) \, dV$$

$$= \iint_{\{x^2+y^2 \leq 4\}} \left(\int_0^5 (4x^2 + 4y^2) dz \right) dA = 20 \iint_{\{x^2+y^2 \leq 4\}} (x^2 + y^2) \, dA$$

(using polar coordinates $x = r \cos\theta, y = r \sin\theta$; hence $dA = r \, dr \, d\theta$)

$$= 20 \int_0^{2\pi} \left(\int_0^2 r^2 \, r \, dr \right) d\theta$$

$$= 20 \left(\int_0^{2\pi} d\theta \right) \left(\int_0^2 r^3 \, dr \right) = 20 \cdot 2\pi \cdot 4 = 160\pi.$$

Example 8.12   Compute $\iint_S (x^2\mathbf{i} - (2x-1)y\mathbf{j} + 4z\mathbf{k}) \cdot d\mathbf{S}$, where S is the surface of the cone $x^2 + y^2 = z^2$, $0 \le z \le 2$, oriented by the outward normal.

Solution S is a closed surface enclosing a solid three-dimensional region V. By the Divergence Theorem,

$$\iint_S (x^2\mathbf{i} - (2x-1)y\mathbf{j} + 4z\mathbf{k}) \cdot d\mathbf{S} = \iiint_V \left(2x - (2x-1) + 4 \right) dV$$

$$= 5 \iint_{\{x^2+y^2 \le 4\}} \left(\int_{\sqrt{x^2+y^2}}^2 dz \right) dA$$

$$= 5 \iint_{\{x^2+y^2 \le 4\}} \left(2 - \sqrt{x^2 + y^2} \right) dA = 5 \int_0^{2\pi} \left(\int_0^2 (2-r)r \, dr \right) d\theta$$

$$= 5 \left(\int_0^{2\pi} d\theta \right) \left(\int_0^2 (2r - r^2) \, dr \right) = 5 \cdot 2\pi \left(r^2 - \tfrac{1}{3}r^3 \right) \Big|_0^2 = \frac{40\pi}{3}.$$

There is a faster way to compute this integral. From the second line in the above computation it follows that the result is 5 volume(V), where V is the cone with base radius 2 and height 2. Therefore the answer is $5(1/3)8\pi = 40\pi/3$.

The Divergence Theorem of Gauss states that the integral $\iint_S \mathbf{F} \cdot d\mathbf{S} = \iint_S \mathbf{F} \cdot \mathbf{n} \, dS$ of the normal component $\mathbf{F} \cdot \mathbf{n}$ of a vector field $\mathbf{F}$ over a surface equals the integral of the divergence of $\mathbf{F}$ over the three-dimensional region enclosed by that surface.

We are going to discuss the analogue of Gauss' Theorem in two dimensions. Let $D \subseteq \mathbb{R}^2$ be a region to which Green's Theorem applies (see Section 8.1; those regions were called "good"). Parametrize its boundary curve by $\mathbf{c}(t) = (x(t), y(t))$, $t \in [a, b]$, so that $\mathbf{c}$ is positively oriented (i.e., D is on its left). A normal vector field $\mathbf{N}$ to the curve $\mathbf{c}$ is found from $\mathbf{N} \cdot \mathbf{c}'(t) = 0$, where $\mathbf{c}'(t) = (x'(t), y'(t))$ is a tangent vector field. It follows that there are two choices: $\mathbf{N} = (y'(t), -x'(t))$ or $\mathbf{N} = -(y'(t), -x'(t))$. From Figure 8.13 it follows that the x-component of the outward normal equals the y-component of the tangent $\mathbf{c}'(t)$ (the x-component of the inward normal equals the negative of the y-component of the tangent). Therefore the outward normal is $\mathbf{N} = (y'(t), -x'(t))$, and the unit outward normal is $\mathbf{n} = \mathbf{N}/\sqrt{(x'(t))^2 + (y'(t))^2}$.

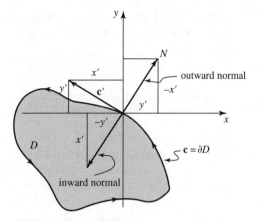

Figure 8.13 Outward and inward normals to a curve.

We are now ready to state the theorem.

■ **Theorem 8.4**   Divergence Theorem in the Plane.

Let $\mathbf{F} = P(x, y)\mathbf{i} + Q(x, y)\mathbf{j}$ be a C^1 vector field on $D \subseteq \mathbb{R}^2$. Then

$$\int_{\mathbf{c}=\partial D} \mathbf{F} \cdot \mathbf{n}\, ds = \iint_D \operatorname{div} \mathbf{F}\, dA,$$

where $\mathbf{n}$ is the outward unit normal vector to $\mathbf{c}$.   ■

Proof

The definition of the path integral implies that

$$\int_{\mathbf{c}=\partial D} \mathbf{F} \cdot \mathbf{n}\, ds = \int_a^b \mathbf{F}(\mathbf{c}(t)) \cdot \mathbf{n}(\mathbf{c}(t))\, \|\mathbf{c}'(t)\|\, dt$$

$$= \int_a^b \Big(P(x(t), y(t))\mathbf{i} + Q(x(t), y(t))\mathbf{j} \Big)$$

$$\cdot \frac{y'(t)\mathbf{i} - x'(t)\mathbf{j}}{\sqrt{(x'(t))^2 + (y'(t))^2}} \cdot \sqrt{(x'(t))^2 + (y'(t))^2}\, dt$$

$$= \int_a^b \Big(P(x(t), y(t))\, y'(t) - Q(x(t), y(t))\, x'(t) \Big)\, dt$$

(applying the definition of the integral of a 1-form; see Section 5.3)

$$= \int_{\mathbf{c}} P(x, y)dy - Q(x, y)dx$$

(using Green's Theorem)

$$= \iint_D \left(\frac{\partial P}{\partial x} + \frac{\partial Q}{\partial y} \right) dA = \iint_D \operatorname{div} \mathbf{F}\, dA.$$ ■

The integral $\int_c \mathbf{F} \cdot \mathbf{n} \, ds$, where $\mathbf{c}$ is a simple closed curve and $\mathbf{n}$ is the outward unit normal to $\mathbf{c}$, is called the *(outward) flux of $\mathbf{F}$ across $\mathbf{c}$* or the *(outward) flux of $\mathbf{F}$ across the region enclosed by $\mathbf{c}$.*

Example 8.13

Compute the integral of the normal component of $\mathbf{F}(x, y) = x^2\mathbf{i} + xy\mathbf{j}$ along the unit circle oriented counterclockwise.

Solution   Let us compute $\int_c \mathbf{F} \cdot \mathbf{n} \, ds$ as a line integral first. Parametrize $\mathbf{c}$ by $\mathbf{c}(t) = (\cos t, \sin t)$, $t \in [0, 2\pi]$. Then $\mathbf{c}'(t) = (-\sin t, \cos t)$ is the tangent field and $\mathbf{n} = (\cos t, \sin t)$ is the outward unit normal field ($\mathbf{n}$ is clearly an outward normal, since it is equal to the position vector of a point on the circle). It follows that ($\|\mathbf{c}'(t)\| = 1$)

$$
\int_c \mathbf{F} \cdot \mathbf{n} \, ds = \int_0^{2\pi} \mathbf{F}(\mathbf{c}(t)) \cdot \mathbf{n}(\mathbf{c}(t)) \|\mathbf{c}'(t)\| \, dt
$$

$$
= \int_0^{2\pi} \left(\cos^2 t, \sin t \cos t\right) \cdot \left(\cos t, \sin t\right) dt = \int_0^{2\pi} \left(\cos^3 t + \sin^2 t \cos t\right) dt
$$

$$
= \int_0^{2\pi} \left(\cos t (1 - \sin^2 t) + \sin^2 t \cos t\right) dt = \int_0^{2\pi} \cos t \, dt = 0.
$$

By the Divergence Theorem in the Plane,

$$
\int_c \mathbf{F} \cdot \mathbf{n} \, ds = \iint_D div \, \mathbf{F} \, dA = \iint_{\{x^2+y^2 \leq 1\}} 3x \, dA
$$

(passing to polar coordinates)

$$
= 3 \int_0^{2\pi} \left(\int_0^1 r^2 \cos \theta dr\right) d\theta
$$

$$
= 3 \left(\int_0^{2\pi} \cos \theta \, d\theta\right) \left(\int_0^1 r^2 \, dr\right) = 3 \cdot 0 \cdot \frac{1}{3} = 0.
$$

◀

Example 8.14

Gauss' Law for Electrostatic Fields.

Consider the electrostatic field

$$
\mathbf{E}(\mathbf{r}) = \frac{1}{4\pi \epsilon_0} \frac{Q}{\|\mathbf{r}\|^3} \mathbf{r},
$$

in $\mathbb{R}^3 - \{(0, 0, 0)\}$ (where $\mathbf{r} = x\mathbf{i} + y\mathbf{j} + z\mathbf{k}$) due to a charge Q located at the origin.

Take a small sphere S_1 (of radius a) centered at the origin and let S_2 be any closed surface containing S_1. Denote by $\mathbf{n}_1$ and $\mathbf{n}_2$ the corresponding unit outward-pointing normal vectors; see Figure 8.14.

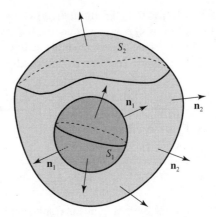

Figure 8.14 Surfaces S_1 and S_2 oriented by outward-pointing normal vectors.

Consider the solid three-dimensional region V between S_1 and S_2: its boundary ∂V consists of S_1 and S_2 and is oriented by $\mathbf{n}_2$ on S_2 and by $-\mathbf{n}_1$ on S_1 (the normal $\mathbf{n}_1$ points into the solid V and is the inward normal for V). By the Divergence Theorem

$$\iiint_V div\,\mathbf{E}\,dV = \iint_{\partial V} \mathbf{E}\cdot d\mathbf{S} = \iint_{\partial V} \mathbf{E}\cdot\mathbf{n}\,dS$$

(∂V consists of S_1 and S_2)

$$= \iint_{S_1} \mathbf{E}\cdot(-\mathbf{n}_1)\,dS + \iint_{S_2}\mathbf{E}\cdot\mathbf{n}_2\,dS.$$

But $div\,\mathbf{E} = 0$ in V (that was computed in Section 4.2) and the above computation implies that

$$\iint_{S_2}\mathbf{E}\cdot\mathbf{n}_2\,dS = \iint_{S_1}\mathbf{E}\cdot\mathbf{n}_1\,dS$$

for *any* closed surface S_2 that contains S_1.

   Let us compute the integral $\iint_{S_1}\mathbf{E}\cdot\mathbf{n}_1\,dS$. Instead of writing down a parametrization, we argue as follows: S_1 is a sphere, so a normal at a point (x, y, z) on S_1 has the same direction as the position vector $\mathbf{r} = x\mathbf{i} + y\mathbf{j} + z\mathbf{k}$ of that point. Hence the unit outward normal is $\mathbf{n}_1 = \mathbf{r}/\|\mathbf{r}\|$. Consequently

$$\iint_{S_1}\mathbf{E}\cdot\mathbf{n}_1\,dS = \iint_{S_1}\frac{1}{4\pi\epsilon_0}\frac{Q}{\|\mathbf{r}\|^3}\mathbf{r}\cdot\frac{\mathbf{r}}{\|\mathbf{r}\|}\,dS = \frac{Q}{4\pi\epsilon_0}\iint_{S_1}\frac{1}{\|\mathbf{r}\|^2}\,dS$$

($\|\mathbf{r}\| = a$, since S_1 is a sphere of radius a)

$$= \frac{Q}{4\pi\epsilon_0}\frac{1}{a^2}\iint_{S_1}dS = \frac{Q}{4\pi\epsilon_0}\frac{1}{a^2}4\pi a^2 = \frac{Q}{\epsilon_0}$$

(recall that $\iint_{S_1}dS = $ (surface) area of $S = 4\pi a^2$). Therefore,

$$\iint_{S_2}\mathbf{E}\cdot\mathbf{n}_2\,dS = \frac{Q}{\epsilon_0};$$

i.e., the electric flux of $\mathbf{E}$ through *any* closed surface that contains the charge Q (located at the origin) is Q/ϵ_0 (consequently, it does not depend on that surface).

This is a special case (a single charge Q is involved) of *Gauss' Law*, which states that the net charge enclosed by a (closed) surface S is

$$Q = \epsilon_0 \iint_S \mathbf{E} \cdot d\mathbf{S},$$

where $\mathbf{E}$ is the electrostatic field due to the charge and ϵ_0 is a constant. From the Divergence Theorem it follows that

$$Q = \epsilon_0 \iint_S \mathbf{E} \cdot \mathbf{S} = \epsilon_0 \iiint_V div\,\mathbf{E}\,dV,$$

where V is the three-dimensional solid enclosed by S (i.e., $\partial V = S$). On the other hand, $Q = \iiint_V \rho\,dV$ (where ρ is the charge density), and therefore

$$\epsilon_0 \iiint_V div\,\mathbf{E}\,dV = \iiint_V \rho\,dV$$

and

$$\iiint_V \left(\frac{\rho}{\epsilon_0} - div\,\mathbf{E} \right) dV = 0.$$

Since V is an arbitrary three-dimensional region, we conclude that (see Section 7.4, part (f) in Properties of Integrals)

$$div\,\mathbf{E} - \frac{\rho}{\epsilon_0} = 0.$$

This equation relates the charge distribution and the resulting electric field; it is called Maxwell's first equation.

◀

■ **Theorem 8.5**   Gauss' Divergence Theorem for Differential Forms.

Assume that $V \subseteq \mathbb{R}^3$ is a "good (3D)" region with boundary ∂V oriented by an outward normal. Let α be a C^1 2-form defined on an open set U containing V. Then

$$\int_{\partial V} \alpha = \int_V d\alpha.$$

■

Proof

This theorem is a straightforward translation of the Divergence Theorem into the language of differential forms. Let $\alpha = F_1 dydz + F_2 dzdx + F_3 dxdy$, where $F_1 = F_1(x, y, z)$, $F_2 = F_2(x, y, z)$ and $F_3 = F_3(x, y, z)$ are C^1 real-valued functions defined on U. The surface integral in Gauss' Theorem,

$$\iint_{S=\partial V} \mathbf{F} \cdot d\mathbf{S} = \iiint_V div\,\mathbf{F}\,dV,$$

where $\mathbf{F} = F_1\mathbf{i} + F_2\mathbf{j} + F_3\mathbf{k}$, is equal to $\int_{\partial V} \alpha$, as demonstrated in Section 7.3. Furthermore (we immediately drop terms that are zero)

$$d\alpha = \frac{\partial F_1}{\partial x}dx \wedge dydz + \frac{\partial F_2}{\partial y}dy \wedge dzdx + \frac{\partial F_3}{\partial z}dz \wedge dxdy$$

$$= \left(\frac{\partial F_1}{\partial x} + \frac{\partial F_2}{\partial y} + \frac{\partial F_3}{\partial z}\right)dxdydz.$$

By definition, the integral $\int_V f dxdydz$ of the 3-form $f dxdydz$ ($f = f(x, y, z)$ is a real-valued function) is equal to $\iiint_V f \, dV$. Therefore

$$\int_V d\alpha = \int_V \left(\frac{\partial F_1}{\partial x} + \frac{\partial F_2}{\partial y} + \frac{\partial F_3}{\partial z}\right)dxdydz = \iiint_V div\,\mathbf{F}\,dV,$$

and the statement of the theorem is established. ∎

Example 8.15 Let V be a "good(3D)" region in $\mathbb{R}^3$. Prove that

$$\int_{\partial V} xdydz + ydzdx + zdxdy = 3v(V),$$

where $v(V)$ denotes the volume of V (compare with area formulas obtained from Green's Theorem in the previous section).

Solution By Theorem 8.5 we obtain

$$\int_{\partial V} xdydz + ydzdx + zdxdy = \int_V d\,(xdydz + ydzdx + zdxdy)$$

$$= \int_V dx \wedge dydz + dy \wedge dzdx + dz \wedge dxdy$$

$$= 3\int_V dxdydz = 3\int_V dV = 3v(V). \quad \triangleleft$$

Example 8.16 Using Gauss' Divergence Theorem evaluate $\int_S \alpha$, where $\alpha = xdydz + ydzdx$ and S is the closed upper hemisphere of radius 1 (i.e., it consists of the upper hemisphere $\{(x, y, z) \mid x^2 + y^2 + z^2 = 1, z \geq 0\}$ together with the disk $\{(x, y, z) \mid x^2 + y^2 \leq 1, z = 0\}$ in the xy-plane). Check the result by direct computation.

Solution Since $d\alpha = dx \wedge dydz + dy \wedge dzdx = 2dxdydz$, Gauss' Divergence Theorem implies that

$$\int_{S=\partial V} xdydz + ydzdx = \int_V 2dxdydz,$$

where V denotes the upper-half ball of radius 1. Therefore,

$$\int_S xdydz + ydzdx = 2\int_V dxdydz = 2\,v(V) = \tfrac{4}{3}\pi.$$

Now let us compute the same integral directly by computing the surface integral of α. Parametrize the upper hemisphere S_1 (cf. Section 7.1) by

$$\mathbf{r}_1(u, v) = (\cos v \cos u, \cos v \sin u, \sin v), \qquad 0 \le u \le 2\pi, \quad 0 \le v \le \pi/2.$$

By the definition of the integral of a 2-form (given in Section 7.3),

$$\int_{S_1} \alpha = \iint_{[0,2\pi]\times[0,\pi/2]} \left(\cos v \cos u \frac{\partial(y, z)}{\partial(u, v)} + \cos v \sin u \frac{\partial(z, x)}{\partial(u, v)} \right) dA,$$

where

$$\frac{\partial(y, z)}{\partial(u, v)} = \begin{vmatrix} \cos v \cos u & -\sin v \sin u \\ 0 & \cos v \end{vmatrix} = \cos^2 v \cos u$$

and

$$\frac{\partial(z, x)}{\partial(u, v)} = \begin{vmatrix} 0 & \cos v \\ -\cos v \sin u & -\sin v \cos u \end{vmatrix} = \cos^2 v \sin u.$$

Hence

$$\int_{S_1} \alpha = \iint_{[0,2\pi]\times[0,\pi/2]} \left(\cos^3 v \cos^2 u + \cos^3 v \sin^2 u \right) dA$$

$$= \int_0^{\pi/2} \left(\int_0^{2\pi} \cos^3 v \, du \right) dv = 2\pi \int_0^{\pi/2} \cos^3 v \, dv$$

$(\int \cos^3 v \, dv = \int \cos v (\cos^2 v) dv = \int \cos v (1 - \sin^2 v) dv = \int \cos v \, dv - \int \cos v \sin^2 v \, dv$
$= \sin v - (\sin^3 v)/3)$

$$= 2\pi \left(\sin v - \tfrac{1}{3} \sin^3 v \right) \Big|_0^{\pi/2} = \frac{4\pi}{3}.$$

Parametrize the lower side S_2 by

$$\mathbf{r}_2(u, v) = (u, v, 0), \qquad u^2 + v^2 \le 1.$$

Then

$$\int_{S_2} \alpha = \iint_{\{u^2+v^2\le 1\}} \left(u \frac{\partial(y, z)}{\partial(u, v)} + v \frac{\partial(z, x)}{\partial(u, v)} \right) dA,$$

where

$$\frac{\partial(y, z)}{\partial(u, v)} = \begin{vmatrix} 0 & 1 \\ 0 & 0 \end{vmatrix} = 0 \quad \text{and} \quad \frac{\partial(z, x)}{\partial(u, v)} = \begin{vmatrix} 0 & 0 \\ 1 & 0 \end{vmatrix} = 0.$$

Hence $\int_{S_2} \alpha = 0$ and

$$\int_S \alpha = \int_{S_1} \alpha + \int_{S_2} \alpha = \frac{4\pi}{3} + 0 = \frac{4\pi}{3},$$

as expected.

With the help of the Divergence Theorem of Gauss we can give an interpretation of divergence related to fluid flow.

Let $\mathbf{W}(x, y, z)$ be the velocity vector field of a fluid. Assume that the flow is *steady,* so that $\mathbf{W}$ does not depend on time. Denote by $\rho(x, y, z)$ the mass density of the fluid. Let P be a point inside a small closed surface S placed in the flow, as in Figure 8.15.

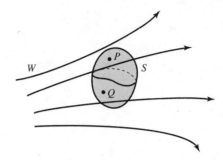

Figure 8.15 Closed surface in a fluid flow.

The outward flux across S is given by the integral

$$\iint_S \rho \, \mathbf{W} \cdot d\mathbf{S},$$

where $\rho \mathbf{W}$ describes the rate of flow of mass per unit area. The Divergence Theorem implies that

$$\iint_S \rho \, \mathbf{W} \cdot d\mathbf{S} = \iiint_V div \, (\rho \, \mathbf{W}) \, dV, \tag{8.2}$$

where V is a three-dimensional solid enclosed by S.

By the Mean Value Theorem for integrals (use (7.4) in Section 7.4 with $f = div \, (\rho \, \mathbf{W})$, $\mathcal{M} = V$ and $d\mu = dV$) it follows that there is a point Q in V (i.e., inside S) such that $(v(V)$ denotes the volume of $V)$

$$div \, (\rho \, \mathbf{W})(Q) = \frac{1}{v(V)} \iiint_V div \, (\rho \, \mathbf{W}) \, dV.$$

Combining the above, we get

$$div \, (\rho \, \mathbf{W})(Q) = \frac{1}{v(V)} \iint_S \rho \, \mathbf{W} \cdot d\mathbf{S},$$

and hence

$$div \, (\rho \, \mathbf{W})(P) = \lim_{V \to P} \frac{1}{v(V)} \iint_S \rho \, \mathbf{W} \cdot d\mathbf{S}. \tag{8.3}$$

The limit is taken as V shrinks to a point, and therefore Q approaches P (since both Q and P are inside S). The left side of (8.3) is called the *source intensity at* P. Equation (8.3) states that the divergence at P is the net rate of outward flux (at P) per unit volume.

A point P is called a *source* if $div \, (\rho \mathbf{W})$ at P is positive (then the net flow is outward, hence the name). If $div \, (\rho \mathbf{W})(P)$ is negative, the net flow is inward and P is called a *sink*.

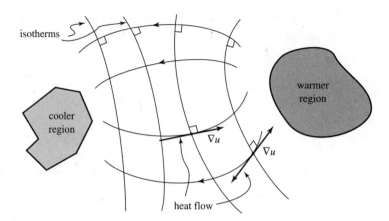

Figure 8.16   Heat flows from warmer regions towards cooler regions along curves perpendicular to isotherms.

Next, we discuss an application of the Divergence Theorem related to *heat flow*. Let $u(x, y, z, t)$ be the temperature at a point (x, y, z) in a solid V, measured at time t. Assume that the function u is twice continuously differentiable. If the temperature inside V is not constant, heat transfer will occur from regions with higher temperature towards regions with lower temperature. Heat transfers are described by the *heat flow equation* (see Example 4.14 in Section 4.1 and Example 4.33 in Section 4.2)

$$\mathbf{F} = -k \, \nabla u, \tag{8.4}$$

where k is a positive constant (called the *heat conductivity*), and ∇u is computed by keeping t fixed.

The gradient of u points in the direction of the largest increase in temperature, and heat flows in the opposite direction, i.e., in the direction of the largest decrease in u; see Figure 8.16. Since a gradient vector field is perpendicular to level curves (in this case, of the temperature function), heat flow occurs in directions perpendicular to isotherms. This explains the appearance of the minus sign in formula (8.4).

Consider a three-dimensional region V with boundary S inside the flow. The rate of heat flow across S out of V is given by

$$\iint_S \mathbf{F} \cdot d\mathbf{S} = \iint_S \mathbf{F} \cdot \mathbf{n} \, dS,$$

where $\mathbf{n}$ is the unit outward normal. From (8.4) and the Divergence Theorem we obtain

$$\iint_S \mathbf{F} \cdot d\mathbf{S} = \iint_S -k \, \nabla u \cdot d\mathbf{S}$$
$$= -k \iiint_V div \, (\nabla u) \, dV = -k \iiint_V \Delta u \, dV, \tag{8.5}$$

where $\Delta u = div \, (\nabla u)$ denotes the Laplacian of u.

The net amount of heat inside S is given by

$$\mathcal{H} = \iiint_V \sigma \rho \, u \, dV,$$

where $\sigma = $ constant is the *specific heat* of the material and ρ denotes its mass density. We assume that $\partial \rho / \partial t = 0$; i.e., that the density remains constant with respect to time. The time rate of change of $\mathcal{H}$ is (the function $\sigma \rho \, u$ is differentiable, and by (7.5) in Section 7.4 we are allowed to switch the time derivative and the triple integral)

$$\frac{\partial \mathcal{H}}{\partial t} = \frac{\partial}{\partial t} \left(\iiint_V \sigma \rho \, u \, dV \right) = \iiint_V \frac{\partial}{\partial t} (\sigma \rho \, u) \, dV$$

(by the product rule $\partial(\sigma \rho u)/\partial t = (\partial \sigma / \partial t)\rho u + (\partial \rho / \partial t)\sigma u + (\partial u / \partial t)\sigma \rho = (\partial u / \partial t)\sigma \rho$, since ρ and σ are constant with respect to time)

$$= \iiint_V \sigma \rho \frac{\partial u}{\partial t} \, dV. \tag{8.6}$$

Since the time rate of change of the heat inside S (which is the boundary of V) equals the rate at which heat "flows" from the outside *into* V, it follows that

$$\frac{\partial \mathcal{H}}{\partial t} = \iint_S \mathbf{F} \cdot (-\mathbf{n}) \, dS = - \iint_S \mathbf{F} \cdot d\mathbf{S},$$

where $-\mathbf{n}$ is the inward normal. Using (8.5) and (8.6) we conclude that

$$\iiint_V \sigma \rho \frac{\partial u}{\partial t} \, dV = k \iiint_V \Delta u \, dV,$$

that is,

$$\iiint_V \left(\sigma \rho \frac{\partial u}{\partial t} - k \Delta u \right) dV = 0,$$

where V is any solid three-dimensional region. Hence (see Properties of Integrals, part (f) in Section 7.4)

$$\sigma \rho \frac{\partial u}{\partial t} = k \Delta u,$$

or, by taking $c^2 = k\sigma^{-1}\rho^{-1}$,

$$\frac{\partial u}{\partial t} = c^2 \Delta u,$$

which is the *heat equation.*

EXERCISES 8.2   **Exercises 1 to 9:** Evaluate the surface integral $\iint_S \mathbf{F} \cdot d\mathbf{S}$, where S is a closed surface oriented by an outward normal.

1. $\mathbf{F}(x, y, z) = (y^2 + \sin z)\mathbf{i} + (e^{\sin z} + 2)\mathbf{j} + (xy + \ln x)\mathbf{k}$, S is the surface of the cube $0 \le x, y, z \le 1$

2. $\mathbf{F}(x, y, z) = (x^2 + z^2)\mathbf{i} + (y^2 + z^2)\mathbf{k}$, S is the surface of the parallelepiped $0 \leq x, y \leq 2$, $0 \leq z \leq 4$

3. $\mathbf{F}(x, y, z) = (x + y^2 + 1)\mathbf{i} + (y + xz)\mathbf{j}$, S consists of the part of the cone $z^2 = x^2 + y^2$ bounded by the disks $0 \leq x^2 + y^2 \leq 1$, $z = 1$ and $0 \leq x^2 + y^2 \leq 4$, $z = 2$

4. $\mathbf{F}(x, y, z) = (2x + 3y)\mathbf{i} - (4y + 3z)\mathbf{j} + 4z\mathbf{k}$, S consists of the paraboloid $z = x^2 + y^2$, $0 \leq z \leq 1$, and the disk $0 \leq x^2 + y^2 \leq 1$, $z = 1$

5. $\mathbf{F}(x, y, z) = -e^x \cos y\mathbf{i} + e^x \sin y\mathbf{j} + \mathbf{k}$, S is the surface of the sphere $x^2 + y^2 + z^2 = 1$

6. $\mathbf{F}(x, y, z) = x^{-1}\mathbf{i} + z^{-1}\mathbf{j} - (yz)^{-1}\mathbf{k}$, S is the surface of the parallelepiped $1 \leq x \leq 2$, $2 \leq y, z \leq 4$

7. $\mathbf{F}(x, y, z) = x^2\mathbf{i} + xy\mathbf{j} + xz\mathbf{k}$, S consists of the upper hemisphere $x^2 + y^2 + z^2 = 1$, $z \geq 0$ and the disk $0 \leq x^2 + y^2 \leq 1$ in the xy-plane

8. $\mathbf{F}(x, y, z) = 2x\mathbf{i} + xy^2\mathbf{j} + xyz\mathbf{k}$, S is the boundary of the three-dimensional solid inside $x^2 + y^2 = 2$, outside $x^2 + y^2 = 1$, and between the planes $z = 0$ and $z = 4$

9. $\mathbf{F}(x, y, z) = ye^z\mathbf{i} + yz\mathbf{k}$, S is the surface of the tetrahedron in the first octant bounded by the plane $x + 2y + z = 4$

10. Use the Divergence Theorem to compute $\iint_S (x + y)\, dS$, where S consists of the (positively oriented) upper hemisphere $x^2 + y^2 + z^2 = 1$, $z \geq 0$, and the disk $0 \leq x^2 + y^2 \leq 1$ in the xy-plane.

11. Use the Divergence Theorem to compute the surface integral $\iint_S xyz\, dS$, where S is the sphere $x^2 + y^2 + z^2 = 1$ oriented by the outward-pointing normal.

12. Compute $\iint_S (x^2 + y^2)\, dS$, where S consists of the part of the paraboloid $z = 2(x^2 + y^2)$ between $z = 0$ and $z = 4$, together with the top disk $0 \leq x^2 + y^2 \leq 2$, $z = 4$, oriented by the outward normal.

13. Let V be a solid three-dimensional region (assumed to be "good" in the sense explained in this section) bounded by a closed, positively oriented surface S. Show that $\iint_S f\nabla g\, d\mathbf{S} = \iiint_V (f\Delta g + \nabla f \cdot \nabla g)\, dV$, where f and g are of class C^2.

14. Compute $\iint_S \mathbf{c} \cdot d\mathbf{S}$, if $\mathbf{c}$ is a constant vector field and S is a closed surface.

15. Let V be a solid three-dimensional region (assumed to be "good") bounded by a closed, positively oriented surface S. Show that $\iint_S D_\mathbf{n} f\, dS = \iiint_V \Delta f\, dV$, where f is of class C^2 and $D_\mathbf{n} f$ denotes the directional derivative of f in the direction of the outward unit normal to S.

16. Let $\mathbf{F}$ be a C^1 vector field in $\mathbb{R}^2$. Assume that $\int_\mathbf{c} \mathbf{F} \cdot \mathbf{n}ds = 0$ for any closed curve $\mathbf{c}$ in $\mathbb{R}^2$ (with the outward normal $\mathbf{n}$). What (if anything) can be said about the divergence of $\mathbf{F}$?

17. Let $\mathbf{F} = y\mathbf{i}/(x^2 + y^2) - x\mathbf{j}/(x^2 + y^2)$. Compute the outward flux $\int_\mathbf{c} \mathbf{F} \cdot \mathbf{n}\, ds$ of $\mathbf{F}$ across the rectangle $R = [-1, 1] \times [-1, 2]$.

Exercises 18 to 22: Find the outward flux $\int_\mathbf{c} \mathbf{F} \cdot \mathbf{n}ds$ and the counterclockwise circulation $\int_\mathbf{c} \mathbf{F} \cdot d\mathbf{s}$ of the vector field $\mathbf{F}$ along the curve $\mathbf{c}$.

18. $\mathbf{F}(x, y) = (2x - 1 + y)\mathbf{i} - (x - 3y)\mathbf{j}$, $\mathbf{c}$ is the square with the vertices $(-1, -1)$, $(1, -1)$, $(1, 1)$ and $(-1, 1)$

19. $\mathbf{F}(x, y) = (x^2 + y^2)\mathbf{i} - xy\mathbf{j}$, $\mathbf{c}$ is the triangle defined by the lines $y = x$, $y = 2x$ and $x = 1$

20. $\mathbf{F}(x, y) = 2xy\mathbf{i} + 3y^2\mathbf{j}$, $\mathbf{c}$ is the boundary of the region in the first quadrant defined by $y = x^2$ and $y = 1$

21. $\mathbf{F}(x, y) = e^x e^y \mathbf{i} + 2e^y \mathbf{j}$, **c** is the boundary of the rectangle $R = [0, 3] \times [0, 4]$ oriented counterclockwise

22. $\mathbf{F}(x, y) = e^x \cos y \mathbf{i} + (xy + e^x \sin y)\mathbf{j}$, **c** is the boundary of the region defined by the curves $y = \ln x$, $y = 0$ and $x = e$

Exercises 23 to 26: Use Gauss' Divergence Theorem to compute $\int_S \alpha$.

23. $\alpha = y\,dydz + xz\,dzdx + z\,dxdy$, S is the boundary of the region inside the cylinder $x^2 + y^2 = 1$, above the xy-plane and below the paraboloid $z = x^2 + y^2$

24. $\alpha = z\,dxdy$, S is the boundary of the ellipsoid $x^2/a^2 + y^2/b^2 + z^2/c^2 = 1$

25. $\alpha = x\,dydz + y\,dzdx + z\,dxdy$, S is the boundary of the region $1 \le x^2 + y^2 + z^2 \le 4$

26. $\alpha = \ln(x^2 + y^2)\,dydz$, S is the boundary of the cylinder $x^2 + y^2 = 4$, $1 \le z \le 2$

8.3 STOKES' THEOREM

Stokes' Theorem is similar in spirit to Green's Theorem: it relates the path integral of a vector field around a closed curve **c** in $\mathbb{R}^3$ to an integral over a surface S whose boundary is **c**. As usual, we have to make precise the assumptions on the curves and surfaces involved. We will do it in two stages: first for a surface that is the graph of a function $z = f(x, y)$ and then for a general parametrized surface.

Let S be a surface defined as the graph of a function $z = f(x, y)$, where $(x, y) \in D$. Assume that the domain $D \subseteq \mathbb{R}^2$ is a region to which Green's Theorem applies (such regions were called "good"; cf. Section 8.1). The boundary ∂D of D is a simple closed curve (that is, a closed curve that does not intersect itself) oriented positively (as we walk along the boundary, the region D is on our left). Parametrize S by (for convenience, we depart from using the standard parameters u and v and use x and y instead)

$$\mathbf{r}(x, y) = (x, y, f(x, y)), \qquad (x, y) \in D,$$

and choose the upward normal $\mathbf{N} = (-\partial f(x, y)/\partial x, -\partial f(x, y)/\partial y, 1)$ as the orientation of S. The positive orientation of the boundary ∂S of S is defined by "lifting" the positive orientation of ∂D, as shown in Figure 8.17.

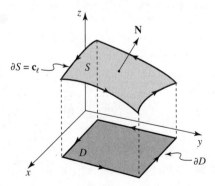

Figure 8.17 "Lifting" the positive orientation to the boundary of the surface.

To be precise, let $\mathbf{c}(t) = (x(t), y(t))$, $t \in [a, b]$, be an orientation-preserving parametrization of the boundary of D. The boundary curve $\mathbf{c}_\ell = \partial S$ can be parametrized as

$$\mathbf{c}_\ell(t) = (x(t), y(t), f(x(t), y(t))), \qquad t \in [a, b].$$

The orientation coming from this parametrization (i.e., the direction of increasing values for t) defines the positive orientation of the boundary ∂S of S. In other words, ∂S is oriented as follows: as we walk on the positive side of S (the outward normal points away from that side) along the boundary, the surface S is on our left.

Now let us look at the case of a parametrized surface S given by $\mathbf{r} = \mathbf{r}(u, v) \colon D \to \mathbb{R}^3$, where D is an elementary region in $\mathbb{R}^2$. Consider the boundary curve $\mathbf{c} = \partial D$ of D. We are tempted to define the boundary of S as the image of $\mathbf{c}$ under $\mathbf{r}$; see Figure 8.18. However, that will not work.

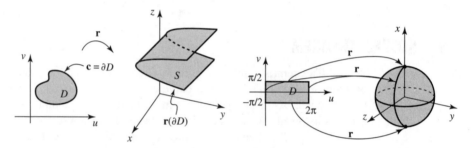

Figure 8.18 An attempt to define the boundary of a parametrized surface.

Figure 8.19 Half-meridian on the sphere is not its boundary.

Take, for example, the parametrization of the sphere (discussed in Example 7.1 of Section 7.1)

$$\mathbf{r}(u, v) = (\cos v \cos u, \cos v \sin u, \sin v), \qquad (u, v) \in D,$$

where D is the rectangle $[0, 2\pi] \times [-\pi/2, \pi/2]$. The horizontal segments that form the boundary ∂D map to the North and South Poles and the vertical segments are both mapped to the same semi-circle in the xz-plane. In other words, the boundary of D gets mapped into the half-meridian of the sphere; see Figure 8.19 (this is certainly not what we would consider as the boundary of a sphere).

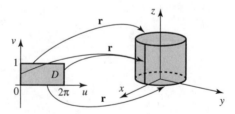

Figure 8.20 "Weird boundary" of the cylinder.

Parametrize the cylinder by

$$\mathbf{r}(u, v) = (\cos u, \sin u, v), \qquad (u, v) \in D = [0, 2\pi] \times [0, 1]$$

as in Example 7.2 in Section 7.1. The image of ∂D under $\mathbf{r}$ consists of the top and bottom circles joined by a vertical segment, as shown in Figure 8.20. This curve (it is not simple!) does not represent our common-sense notion of the cylinder's boundary.

Analyzing these examples, we notice that problems arise when different points on the boundary of D map to the same point. Therefore, to get a meaningful concept of the boundary ∂S of a parametrized surface, we will have to assume that $\mathbf{r}$ is one-to-one on D. In that case, ∂S is defined as the image $\mathbf{r}(\partial D)$ of the boundary ∂D of D under $\mathbf{r}$. If ∂D is parametrized by the map $\mathbf{c}(t) = (x(t), y(t))$, $t \in [a, b]$ (that is orientation preserving in the sense that, for motion along $\mathbf{c}$, the region D is on the left) then the boundary ∂S has the "lifted" parametrization $\mathbf{c}_\ell = \mathbf{r}(\mathbf{c}(t))$ that determines its orientation.

In other words, the situation for one-to-one parametrizations is the same as for surfaces defined as graphs of functions.

We are now ready to give the statement of the theorem.

■ **Theorem 8.6** **Stokes' Theorem.**

Let S be an oriented surface parametrized by a one-to-one parametrization $\mathbf{r}: D \subseteq \mathbb{R}^2 \to \mathbb{R}^3$ and let ∂S be its positively-oriented piecewise smooth boundary curve. If $\mathbf{F}$ is a C^1 vector field on S, then

$$\int_{\partial S} \mathbf{F} \cdot d\mathbf{s} = \iint_S curl\mathbf{F} \cdot d\mathbf{S}.$$

■

Notice that the parametrization $\mathbf{r}(u, v) = (u, v, f(u, v))$ of the graph of the function $f(x, y)$ is always one-to-one.

Proof

We will give a proof of the theorem in the case when S is the graph of a C^2 function $z = f(x, y)$, $(x, y) \in D$, where D is an elementary region in $\mathbb{R}^2$. Let $\mathbf{F}(x, y, z) = (P(x, y, z), Q(x, y, z), R(x, y, z))$ be a C^1 vector field defined on S. Parametrize the boundary of S (as explained in the introduction) by

$$\mathbf{c}_\ell(t) = (x(t), y(t), f(x(t), y(t))), \qquad t \in [a, b],$$

where $\mathbf{c}(t) = (x(t), y(t))$ represents the boundary of D. For simplicity, drop (x, y, z) and t from the notation. The path integral of $\mathbf{F}$ along the boundary of S is

$$\int_{\mathbf{c}_\ell} \mathbf{F} \cdot d\mathbf{s} = \int_a^b \mathbf{F} \cdot \mathbf{c}'_\ell \, dt = \int_a^b (P, Q, R) \cdot \left(\frac{dx}{dt}, \frac{dy}{dt}, \frac{dz}{dt} \right) dt$$

$$= \int_a^b \left(P\frac{dx}{dt} + Q\frac{dy}{dt} + R\frac{dz}{dt} \right) dt.$$

By the chain rule ($z = f(x, y)$, and $x = x(t)$, $y = y(t)$), with the usual convenient sloppiness in notation (dz/dx instead of df/dx, etc.), we get

$$\frac{dz}{dt} = \frac{\partial z}{\partial x}\frac{dx}{dt} + \frac{\partial z}{\partial y}\frac{dy}{dt},$$

and therefore

$$\int_{\mathbf{c}_\ell} \mathbf{F}\cdot d\mathbf{s} = \int_a^b \left(P\frac{dx}{dt} + Q\frac{dy}{dt} + R\left(\frac{\partial z}{\partial x}\frac{dx}{dt} + \frac{\partial z}{\partial y}\frac{dy}{dt} \right) \right) dt$$

$$= \int_a^b \left(\left(P + R\frac{\partial z}{\partial x} \right)\frac{dx}{dt} + \left(Q + R\frac{\partial z}{\partial y} \right)\frac{dy}{dt} \right) dt$$

$$= \int_{\mathbf{c}} \left(P + R\frac{\partial z}{\partial x} \right) dx + \left(Q + R\frac{\partial z}{\partial y} \right) dy;$$

(this was obtained from the definition of the path integral of a 1-form; now proceed by applying Green's Theorem)

$$= \iint_D \left(\frac{\partial}{\partial x}\left(Q + R\frac{\partial z}{\partial y} \right) - \frac{\partial}{\partial y}\left(P + R\frac{\partial z}{\partial x} \right) \right) dA.$$

Consider the integrand in this double integral. Since $Q = Q(x, y, z) = Q(x, y, f(x, y))$, the chain rule implies that

$$\frac{\partial}{\partial x}(Q) = D_1 Q \frac{\partial x}{\partial x} + D_2 Q \frac{\partial y}{\partial x} + D_3 Q \frac{\partial f(x, y)}{\partial x},$$

where $D_i Q$ represents the derivative of Q with respect to its i-th variable ($i = 1, 2, 3$). Writing $D_1 Q$ as $\partial Q/\partial x$, $D_3 Q$ as $\partial Q/\partial z$, and $\partial f/\partial x$ as $\partial z/\partial x$, we get

$$\frac{\partial}{\partial x}(Q) = \frac{\partial Q}{\partial x} + \frac{\partial Q}{\partial z}\frac{\partial z}{\partial x}.$$

Other partial derivatives are computed similarly. It follows that, by the product rule and the chain rule,

$$\frac{\partial}{\partial x}\left(Q + R\frac{\partial z}{\partial y} \right) - \frac{\partial}{\partial y}\left(P + R\frac{\partial z}{\partial x} \right)$$

$$= \frac{\partial Q}{\partial x} + \frac{\partial Q}{\partial z}\frac{\partial z}{\partial x} + \left(\frac{\partial R}{\partial x} + \frac{\partial R}{\partial z}\frac{\partial z}{\partial x} \right)\frac{\partial z}{\partial y} + R\frac{\partial^2 z}{\partial x \partial y}$$

$$- \left(\frac{\partial P}{\partial y} + \frac{\partial P}{\partial z}\frac{\partial z}{\partial y} + \left(\frac{\partial R}{\partial y} + \frac{\partial R}{\partial z}\frac{\partial z}{\partial y} \right)\frac{\partial z}{\partial x} + R\frac{\partial^2 z}{\partial y \partial x} \right)$$

$$= \frac{\partial Q}{\partial x} - \frac{\partial P}{\partial y} + \frac{\partial z}{\partial x}\left(\frac{\partial Q}{\partial z} - \frac{\partial R}{\partial y} \right) + \frac{\partial z}{\partial y}\left(\frac{\partial R}{\partial x} - \frac{\partial P}{\partial z} \right),$$

and consequently,

$$\int_{\mathbf{c}_\ell} \mathbf{F}\cdot d\mathbf{s} = \iint_D \left(\frac{\partial Q}{\partial x} - \frac{\partial P}{\partial y} + \frac{\partial z}{\partial x}\left(\frac{\partial Q}{\partial z} - \frac{\partial R}{\partial y} \right) + \frac{\partial z}{\partial y}\left(\frac{\partial R}{\partial x} - \frac{\partial P}{\partial z} \right) \right) dA.$$

Notice that we used the equality of mixed partials $\partial^2 z/\partial x\partial y = \partial^2 z/\partial y\partial x$ to cancel two terms in the above computation (this is where we need $z = f(x, y)$ to be of class C^2).

On the other hand, since

$$curl\,\mathbf{F} = \left(\frac{\partial R}{\partial y} - \frac{\partial Q}{\partial z}, \frac{\partial P}{\partial z} - \frac{\partial R}{\partial x}, \frac{\partial Q}{\partial x} - \frac{\partial P}{\partial y}\right)$$

and (use z instead of f) $\mathbf{N} = (-\partial z/\partial x, -\partial z/\partial y, 1)$ it follows that

$$\iint_S curl\,\mathbf{F}\cdot d\mathbf{S} = \iint_D curl\,\mathbf{F}\cdot\mathbf{N}\,dA$$

$$= \iint_D \left(\frac{\partial R}{\partial y} - \frac{\partial Q}{\partial z}, \frac{\partial P}{\partial z} - \frac{\partial R}{\partial x}, \frac{\partial Q}{\partial x} - \frac{\partial P}{\partial y}\right)\cdot\left(-\frac{\partial z}{\partial x}, -\frac{\partial z}{\partial y}, 1\right)dA$$

$$= \iint_D \left(-\frac{\partial z}{\partial x}\left(\frac{\partial R}{\partial y} - \frac{\partial Q}{\partial z}\right) - \frac{\partial z}{\partial y}\left(\frac{\partial P}{\partial z} - \frac{\partial R}{\partial x}\right) + \frac{\partial Q}{\partial x} - \frac{\partial P}{\partial y}\right)dA.$$

We are done! Both $\int_{c_\ell}\mathbf{F}\cdot d\mathbf{s}$ and $\iint_S curl\,\mathbf{F}\cdot d\mathbf{S}$ have been shown to be equal to the same integral, and are therefore equal to each other. ∎

Example 8.17

Evaluate the path integral $\int_c\mathbf{F}\cdot d\mathbf{s}$, where $\mathbf{F} = 4z\mathbf{i} - 2x\mathbf{j} + 2x\mathbf{k}$, and $\mathbf{c}$ is the intersection of the cylinder $x^2 + y^2 = 1$ and the plane $z = y + 1$, oriented counterclockwise as seen by a person standing on the plane; see Figure 8.21.

Solution Let us compute $\int_c\mathbf{F}\cdot d\mathbf{s}$ as a path integral first. Parametrize $\mathbf{c}$ by

$$\mathbf{c}(t) = (\cos t, \sin t, \sin t + 1), \quad t \in [0, 2\pi].$$

Then $\mathbf{c}'(t) = (-\sin t, \cos t, \cos t)$ and

$$\int_c\mathbf{F}\cdot d\mathbf{s} = \int_0^{2\pi}(4\sin t + 4, -2\cos t, 2\cos t)\cdot(-\sin t, \cos t, \cos t)\,dt$$

$$= -4\int_0^{2\pi}\sin^2 t\,dt - 4\int_0^{2\pi}\sin t\,dt$$

(use $\sin^2 t = (1 - \cos 2t)/2$)

$$= -4\left(\tfrac{1}{2}t - \tfrac{1}{4}\sin 2t\right)\Big|_0^{2\pi} + 4\cos t\Big|_0^{2\pi} = -4\pi.$$

Since

$$curl\,\mathbf{F} = \begin{vmatrix} \mathbf{i} & \mathbf{j} & \mathbf{k} \\ \partial/\partial x & \partial/\partial y & \partial/\partial z \\ 4z & -2x & 2x \end{vmatrix} = 2\mathbf{j} - 2\mathbf{k},$$

Stokes' Theorem implies that (the assumption on the orientation is satisfied!)

$$\int_c(4z\mathbf{i} - 2x\mathbf{j} + 2x\mathbf{k})\cdot d\mathbf{s} = \iint_S(2\mathbf{j} - 2\mathbf{k})\cdot d\mathbf{S},$$

where S is the part of the surface of the plane $z = y + 1$ cut out by the cylinder $x^2 + y^2 = 1$.

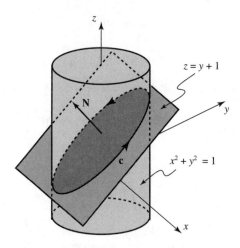

Figure 8.21   Intersection of the cylinder $x^2 + y^2 = 1$ and the plane $z = y + 1$ of Example 8.17.

Parametrize S by

$$\mathbf{r}(u, v) = (u, v, v + 1), \qquad u^2 + v^2 \le 1.$$

Then $\mathbf{T}_u = (1, 0, 0)$, $\mathbf{T}_v = (0, 1, 1)$, $\mathbf{N} = (0, -1, 1)$ and

$$\iint_S (2\mathbf{j} - 2\mathbf{k}) \cdot d\mathbf{S} = \iint_{\{u^2+v^2\le 1\}} (0, 2, -2) \cdot (0, -1, 1)\, dA$$

$$= \iint_{\{u^2+v^2\le 1\}} (-4)\, dA = -4\, \text{area}(\{u^2 + v^2 \le 1\}) = -4\pi. \qquad \blacktriangleleft$$

Example 8.18   Evaluate $\int_{\mathbf{c}} \mathbf{F} \cdot d\mathbf{s}$, where $\mathbf{F} = 2yz\mathbf{i} + xz\mathbf{j} + xy\mathbf{k}$, and $\mathbf{c}$ is the intersection of the cylinder $x^2 + y^2 = 1$ and the parabolic sheet $z = y^2$, with the orientation indicated in Figure 8.22.

Solution   By Stokes' Theorem

$$\int_{\mathbf{c}} \mathbf{F} \cdot d\mathbf{s} = \iint_S \operatorname{curl} \mathbf{F} \cdot d\mathbf{S},$$

where S is the surface $z = y^2$, with $x^2 + y^2 \le 1$. Parametrize S by

$$\mathbf{r}(u, v) = (u, v, v^2), \qquad u^2 + v^2 \le 1.$$

Then $\mathbf{T}_u = (1, 0, 0)$, $\mathbf{T}_v = (0, 1, 2v)$ and $\mathbf{N} = (0, -2v, 1)$. The normal $\mathbf{N}$ points upward, and with the given orientation of $\mathbf{c}$, the surface S lies to its left. Now $\operatorname{curl} \mathbf{F} = (0, y, -z)$ and therefore

$$\int_{\mathbf{c}} \mathbf{F} \cdot d\mathbf{s} = \iint_S \operatorname{curl} \mathbf{F} \cdot d\mathbf{S} = \iint_S \operatorname{curl} \mathbf{F} \cdot \mathbf{N}\, dS$$

$$= \iint_{\{u^2+v^2\le 1\}} (0, v, -v^2) \cdot (0, -2v, 1)\, dA = \iint_{\{u^2+v^2\le 1\}} (-3v^2)\, dA$$

(passing to polar coordinates $u = r\cos\theta$, $v = r\sin\theta$, $dA = r\, dr\, d\theta$)

$$= -3 \int_0^{2\pi} \left(\int_0^1 r^2 \sin^2 \theta \, r \, dr \right) d\theta = -3 \left(\int_0^{2\pi} \sin^2 \theta \, d\theta \right) \left(\int_0^1 r^3 \, dr \right)$$

(using $\int \sin^2 \theta \, d\theta = (1/2) \int (1 - \cos 2\theta) \, d\theta = \theta/2 - (\sin 2\theta)/4$)

$$= -3 \left(\tfrac{1}{2}\theta - \tfrac{1}{4} \sin 2\theta \right) \Big|_0^{2\pi} \left(\tfrac{1}{4} r^4 \right) \Big|_0^1 = -\frac{3\pi}{4}.$$

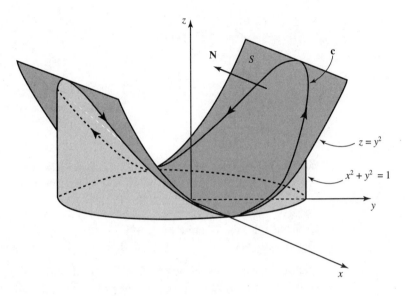

Figure 8.22 Oriented intersection of the cylinder $x^2 + y^2 = 1$ and the parabolic sheet $z = y^2$.

Example 8.19

Evaluate the path integral of the vector field $\mathbf{F} = z^2 \mathbf{i} + x^2 \mathbf{j} + y^2 \mathbf{k}$ along the boundary **c** of the square $0 \le x \le 1$, $0 \le y \le 1$ in the plane $z = 1$, oriented clockwise as seen from the origin; see Figure 8.23.

Solution   Since $curl \, \mathbf{F} = 2y\mathbf{i} + 2z\mathbf{j} + 2x\mathbf{k}$, Stokes' Theorem gives

$$\int_{\mathbf{c}} (z^2 \mathbf{i} + x^2 \mathbf{j} + y^2 \mathbf{k}) \cdot d\mathbf{s} = \iint_S (2y\mathbf{i} + 2z\mathbf{j} + 2x\mathbf{k}) \cdot d\mathbf{S},$$

where S is the square $0 \le x \le 1$, $0 \le y \le 1$, $z = 1$. Parametrizing S by $\mathbf{r}(u, v) = (u, v, 1)$, $0 \le u, v \le 1$, we get $\mathbf{N} = \mathbf{T}_u \times \mathbf{T}_v = (0, 0, 1) = \mathbf{k}$. Next, we check the orientation. The normal $\mathbf{N} = \mathbf{k}$ defines the outside to be the side of the surface that can be seen from a point high on the z-axis, say $(0, 0, 10)$. Alternatively, it is the side away from which $\mathbf{N}$ points. The positive orientation of **c** is therefore the counterclockwise orientation, as seen from the point $(0, 0, 2)$. Seen from the origin, this orientation is clockwise, as required. Hence

$$\iint_S (2y\mathbf{i} + 2z\mathbf{j} + 2x\mathbf{k}) \cdot d\mathbf{S} = \iint_{[0,1] \times [0,1]} (2v\mathbf{i} + 2\mathbf{j} + 2u\mathbf{k}) \cdot \mathbf{k} \, dA$$

$$= \int_0^1 \left(\int_0^1 2u\,du \right) dv = 1.$$

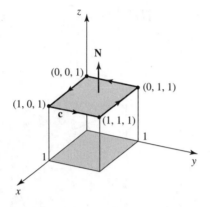

Figure 8.23   The square of Example 8.19

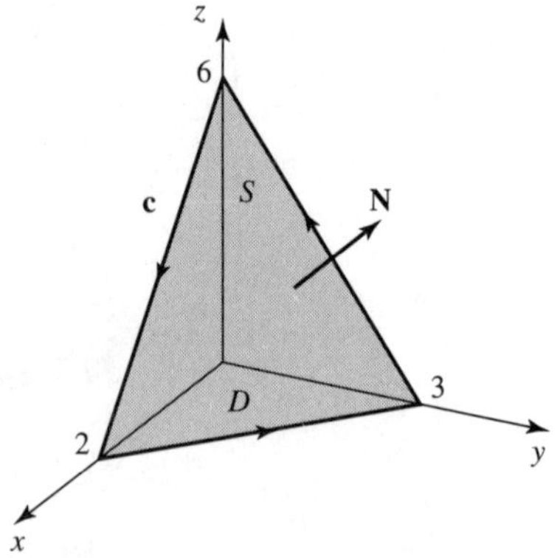

Figure 8.24   Orientation of the triangle in Example 8.20.

Example 8.20   Evaluate $\int_c \mathbf{F} \cdot d\mathbf{s}$, where $\mathbf{F} = (x + y)\mathbf{i} + (2x - z)\mathbf{j} + y\mathbf{k}$ and $\mathbf{c}$ is the boundary of the triangle with vertices $(2, 0, 0)$, $(0, 3, 0)$ and $(0, 0, 6)$, oriented as shown in Figure 8.24.

Solution   Let us take the part of the plane bounded by $\mathbf{c}$ as the surface of integration. Its equation is $x/2 + y/3 + z/6 = 1$, or $z = 6 - 3x - 2y$, and can be parametrized as

$$\mathbf{r}(u, v) = (u, v, -3u - 2v + 6), \qquad \mathbf{u} \in D.$$

D represents the triangle in the xy-plane defined by $x \geq 0$, $y \geq 0$ and (substitute $z = 0$ in $z = 6 - 3x - 2y$ to get) $3x + 2y = 6$. Then $\mathbf{T}_u = (1, 0, -3)$, $\mathbf{T}_v = (0, 1, -2)$, $\mathbf{N} = (3, 2, 1)$ (the orientation convention works!) and $curl\,\mathbf{F} = (2, 0, 1)$, and therefore

$$\int_c \mathbf{F} \cdot d\mathbf{s} = \iint_S curl\,\mathbf{F} \cdot d\mathbf{S}$$

$$= \iint_D (2\mathbf{i} + \mathbf{k}) \cdot (3\mathbf{i} + 2\mathbf{j} + \mathbf{k})\,dA = 7 \iint_D dA = 7\,\mathrm{area}(D) = 21.$$

Example 8.21   Evaluate $\int_c (2\mathbf{i} + x\mathbf{j} + y^2\mathbf{k}) \cdot d\mathbf{s}$ as a path integral, where $\mathbf{c}$ is the circle $x^2 + y^2 = 1$, $z = 1$ oriented counterclockwise as seen from a point $(0, 0, z)$ (with $z > 1$) on the z-axis. Check the result by applying Stokes' Theorem.

Solution   Parametrize $\mathbf{c}$ by

$$\mathbf{c}(t) = (\cos t, \sin t, 1), \qquad t \in [0, 2\pi].$$

Then

$$\int_c (2\mathbf{i} + x\mathbf{j} + y^2\mathbf{k}) \cdot d\mathbf{s} = \int_0^{2\pi} (2, \cos t, \sin^2 t) \cdot (-\sin t, \cos t, 0)\,dt$$

$$= \int_0^{2\pi} (-2\sin t + \cos^2 t)\, dt$$

(using $\cos^2 t = (1 + \cos 2t)/2$)

$$= \left(2\cos t + \tfrac{1}{2}t + \tfrac{1}{4}\sin 2t\right)\Big|_0^{2\pi} = \pi.$$

In order to use Stokes' Theorem we need a surface S whose boundary is $\mathbf{c}$ with the right orientation. Let us take the surface S to be the disk $\{x^2 + y^2 \le 1, z = 1\}$, and parametrize it by

$$\mathbf{r}(u, v) = (u, v, 1), \quad u^2 + v^2 \le 1.$$

Then $\mathbf{T}_u = (1, 0, 0)$, $\mathbf{T}_v = (0, 1, 0)$ and $\mathbf{N} = (0, 0, 1) = \mathbf{k}$. By our conventions, $\mathbf{N}$ is an outward normal (z-component is $+1$) and the outside of S is the top side of the disk. The corresponding orientation of the boundary is the counterclockwise orientation, as needed; see Figure 8.25. It follows that ($curl\, \mathbf{F} = 2y\mathbf{i} + \mathbf{k}$)

$$\int_{\mathbf{c}} \mathbf{F} \cdot d\mathbf{s} = \iint_S curl\, \mathbf{F} \cdot d\mathbf{S} = \iint_{\{u^2+v^2 \le 1\}} (2y\mathbf{i} + \mathbf{k}) \cdot \mathbf{k}\, dA = \iint_{\{u^2+v^2 \le 1\}} 1\, dA = \pi.$$

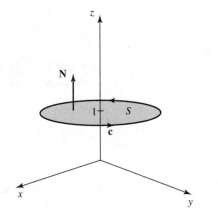

Figure 8.25 The disk of Example 8.21.

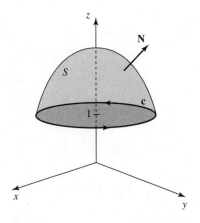

Figure 8.26 The paraboloid $z = 2 - x^2 - y^2$ of Example 8.21.

Although it is simpler to do so, we don't have to use a disk as the surface for integration in Stokes' Theorem. Let us now choose S to be the surface of the paraboloid $z = 2 - x^2 - y^2$ between $z = 1$ and $z = 2$. The boundary of S is the intersection of $z = 2 - x^2 - y^2$ and $z = 1$; i.e., the circle $x^2 + y^2 = 1$ in the plane $z = 1$. Parametrize S by

$$\mathbf{r}(u, v) = (u, v, 2 - u^2 - v^2), \quad u^2 + v^2 \le 1$$

(the condition $u^2 + v^2 \le 1$ was obtained by combining $z = 2 - x^2 - y^2$ and $1 \le z \le 2$). The tangents and the normal are computed to be $\mathbf{T}_u = (1, 0, -2u)$, $\mathbf{T}_v = (0, 1, -2v)$ and $\mathbf{N} = (2u, 2v, 1)$. With this choice of $\mathbf{N}$, the induced orientation on the boundary of

S is the counterclockwise orientation, exactly as needed; see Figure 8.26. Hence

$$\int_c \mathbf{F} \cdot d\mathbf{s} = \iint_S \operatorname{curl} \mathbf{F} \cdot d\mathbf{S} = \iint_{\{u^2+v^2 \le 1\}} (2y\mathbf{i} + \mathbf{k}) \cdot \mathbf{N} \, dA$$

$$= \iint_{\{u^2+v^2 \le 1\}} (2v, 0, 1) \cdot (2u, 2v, 1) \, dA = \iint_{\{u^2+v^2 \le 1\}} (4uv + 1) \, dA$$

(passing to polar coordinates $u = r \cos\theta$, $v = r \sin\theta$, $dA = r \, dr \, d\theta$)

$$= \int_0^{2\pi} \left(\int_0^1 \left(4r^2 \cos\theta \sin\theta + 1 \right) r \, dr \right) d\theta$$

$$= \int_0^{2\pi} \left(r^4 \cos\theta \sin\theta + \tfrac{1}{2} r^2 \right) \Big|_0^1 d\theta = \int_0^{2\pi} \left(\cos\theta \sin\theta + \frac{1}{2} \right) d\theta$$

(using $\cos\theta \sin\theta = (\sin 2\theta)/2$)

$$= \left(-\tfrac{1}{4} \cos 2\theta + \tfrac{1}{2} \theta \right) \Big|_0^{2\pi} = \pi.$$

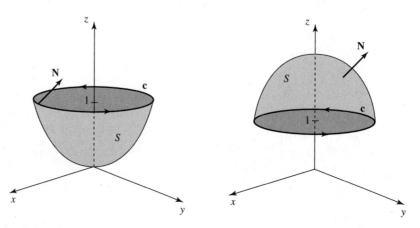

Figure 8.27   The paraboloid $z = x^2 + y^2$ of Example 8.21.

Figure 8.28   The hemisphere of Example 8.21.

Consider yet another surface, the paraboloid S given by $z = x^2 + y^2$, $0 \le z \le 1$; see Figure 8.27. Its boundary is the circle $x^2 + y^2 = 1$, $z = 1$, as required. Parametrize S by

$$\mathbf{r}(u, v) = (u, v, u^2 + v^2), \qquad u^2 + v^2 \le 1.$$

The surface normal $\mathbf{N}$ is $\mathbf{N} = \mathbf{T}_u \times \mathbf{T}_v = (1, 0, 2u) \times (0, 1, 2v) = (-2u, -2v, 1)$. It points inward, into the paraboloid. Once again, it gives the right orientation of the boundary circle ∂S. Hence

$$\int_c \mathbf{F} \cdot d\mathbf{s} = \iint_S \operatorname{curl} \mathbf{F} \cdot d\mathbf{S} = \iint_{\{u^2+v^2 \le 1\}} (2y\mathbf{i} + \mathbf{k}) \cdot \mathbf{N} \, dA$$

$$= \iint_{\{u^2+v^2 \le 1\}} (2v, 0, 1) \cdot (-2u, -2v, 1) \, dA = \iint_{\{u^2+v^2 \le 1\}} (-4uv + 1) \, dA$$

(passing to polar coordinates and continuing as in the previous case)

$$= \left(\tfrac{1}{4} \cos 2\theta + \tfrac{1}{2}\theta \right) \Big|_0^{2\pi} = \pi.$$

Finally, take S to be the upper hemisphere

$$\mathbf{r}(u, v) = (\cos v \cos u, \cos v \sin u, \sin v + 1), \qquad 0 \le u \le 2\pi, \quad 0 \le v \le \pi/2.$$

The surface normal $\mathbf{N}$ was computed in Example 7.4 of Section 7.1 to be

$$\mathbf{N} = \cos v \, (\cos v \cos u, \cos v \sin u, \sin v).$$

Since $\sin v \ge 0$ for $0 \le v \le \tfrac{\pi}{2}$, the normal (has positive z-component and hence) points outward from S into space, and induces counterclockwise orientation on the boundary circle; see Figure 8.28. Hence

$$\int_c \mathbf{F} \cdot d\mathbf{s} = \iint_S curl\mathbf{F} \cdot d\mathbf{S} = \iint_{[0,2\pi] \times [0, \frac{\pi}{2}]} (2y\mathbf{i} + \mathbf{k}) \cdot \mathbf{N} \, dA$$

$$= \iint_{[0,2\pi] \times [0, \frac{\pi}{2}]} (2 \cos v \sin u, 0, 1) \cdot \cos v (\cos v \cos u, \cos v \sin u, \sin v) \, dA$$

$$= \int_0^{2\pi} \left(\int_0^{\pi/2} \left(2 \cos^3 v \sin u \cos u + \cos v \sin v \right) dv \right) du$$

$(\cos^3 v = \cos v(1 - \sin^2 v) = \cos v - \cos v \sin^2 v$, hence $\int \cos^3 v = \sin v - (\sin^3 v)/3$.)

$$= \int_0^{2\pi} \left(2 \sin u \cos u \left(\sin v - \tfrac{1}{3} \sin^3 v \right) + \tfrac{1}{2} \sin^2 v \right) \Big|_0^{\pi/2} du$$

$$= \int_0^{2\pi} \left(\tfrac{4}{3} \sin u \cos u + \tfrac{1}{2} \right) du = \left(\tfrac{4}{3} \tfrac{1}{2} \sin^2 u + \tfrac{1}{2}u \right) \Big|_0^{2\pi} = \pi.$$

◀

Stokes' Theorem states that, in order to compute the surface integral $\iint_S curl\, \mathbf{F} \cdot d\mathbf{S}$, all we really need are the values of $\mathbf{F}$ on the boundary of S, and nowhere else! Therefore, as long as two surfaces S_1 and S_2 have the same boundary $\partial S_1 = \partial S_2$ (with the orientation requirement fulfilled), $\iint_{S_1} curl\, \mathbf{F} \cdot d\mathbf{S}_1 = \iint_{S_2} curl\, \mathbf{F} \cdot d\mathbf{S}_2$, for a C^1 vector field $\mathbf{F}$. Consequently, in computing the path integral around a simple closed curve using Stokes' Theorem, we are free to choose any surface that is bounded by the given curve (with the proper orientation).

We will now use Stokes' Theorem to give a physical interpretation of the curl. Let $\mathbf{F}$ be a velocity vector field of a fluid (assume that $\mathbf{F}$ is C^1). We have seen in Example 5.20 in Section 5.3 (see also the comment following the example) that the path integral $\int_c \mathbf{F} \cdot d\mathbf{s}$ around a simple closed curve c describes the circulation of $\mathbf{F}$; i.e., measures the "turning of the fluid". In other words, $\int_c \mathbf{F} \cdot d\mathbf{s}$ represents the "total velocity" of the fluid around c. We are going to use this description to give an interpretation of $curl\, \mathbf{F}$.

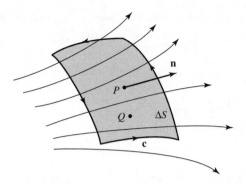

Figure 8.29   Surface ΔS placed in the flow of **F**.

Take a small surface ΔS whose boundary is a positively oriented simple closed curve **c** and place it in the fluid, as shown in Figure 8.29. Choose a point P in ΔS that does not lie on **c**. The surface integral of *curl* **F** over ΔS is equal to

$$\iint_{\Delta S} curl\,\mathbf{F} \cdot d\mathbf{S} = \iint_{\Delta S} curl\,\mathbf{F} \cdot \mathbf{n}\,dS,$$

where **n** is the unit normal to ΔS that satisfies the orientation convention. The average value $\overline{curl\,\mathbf{F} \cdot \mathbf{n}}$ of the *scalar* function *curl* $\mathbf{F} \cdot \mathbf{n}$ over ΔS is given by

$$\overline{curl\,\mathbf{F} \cdot \mathbf{n}} = \frac{1}{A(\Delta S)} \iint_{\Delta S} curl\,\mathbf{F} \cdot \mathbf{n}\,dS,$$

where $A(\Delta S)$ denotes the area of ΔS. The Mean Value Theorem for integrals states that the average value of a continuous function must be attained somewhere— i.e., there is a point Q in ΔS such that

$$\overline{curl\,\mathbf{F} \cdot \mathbf{n}} = curl\,\mathbf{F}(Q) \cdot \mathbf{n}(Q).$$

From Stokes' Theorem we get that

$$\iint_{\Delta S} curl\,\mathbf{F} \cdot \mathbf{n}\,dS = \int_{\partial(\Delta S)=\mathbf{c}} \mathbf{F} \cdot d\mathbf{s},$$

and therefore

$$curl\,\mathbf{F}(Q) \cdot \mathbf{n}(Q) = \overline{curl\,\mathbf{F} \cdot \mathbf{n}} = \frac{1}{A(\Delta S)} \int_{\mathbf{c}} \mathbf{F} \cdot d\mathbf{s},$$

and

$$curl\,\mathbf{F}(P) \cdot \mathbf{n}(P) = \lim_{\Delta S \to P} \frac{1}{A(\Delta S)} \int_{\mathbf{c}} \mathbf{F} \cdot d\mathbf{s}.$$

As ΔS shrinks to the point P, the point Q, being in ΔS, must approach P; this explains the appearance of P on the left side. This equation says that the normal component of the curl (the left side) at P is the limit of the circulation per unit area (the right side).

As an illustration, consider the vector field $\mathbf{F}_1$ of Example 5.20. The counterclockwise circulation around the unit circle was computed to be 2π; dividing by the area (of the disk) enclosed by $\mathbf{c}$, we get 2. On the other hand, $curl\,\mathbf{F}_1 = 2\mathbf{k}$, and (since $\mathbf{c}$ is in the xy-plane) $\mathbf{n} = \mathbf{k}$, so that $curl\,\mathbf{F}_1 \cdot \mathbf{n} = 2$ as well.

Since the circulation $\int_{\mathbf{c}} \mathbf{F} \cdot d\mathbf{s}$ of $\mathbf{F}$ gives the total velocity of the fluid measured around a small closed curve $\dot{\mathbf{c}}$, the normal component $curl\,\mathbf{F} \cdot \mathbf{n}$ can be interpreted as measuring the "total turning" of the fluid around an axis parallel to $\mathbf{n}$.

Next, we translate Stokes' Theorem into the differential-form context.

■ Theorem 8.7   Stokes' Theorem for Differential Forms.

Let $\alpha = P\,dx + Q\,dy + R\,dz$ be a C^1 1-form defined on an open set U in $\mathbb{R}^3$. With the assumptions on $S \subseteq U$ and ∂S as in Theorem 8.6,

$$\int_{\partial S} \alpha = \int_S d\alpha.$$

■

Proof

The statement of this theorem is a rewrite of Stokes' Theorem. To show that, take a vector field $\mathbf{F} = P\mathbf{i} + Q\mathbf{j} + R\mathbf{k}$. The equality

$$\iint_{\partial S} \mathbf{F} \cdot d\mathbf{s} = \int_{\partial S} \alpha$$

holds by definition of the path integral of a 1-form. We have shown earlier (see Section 4.4) that $d\alpha$ corresponds to $curl\,\mathbf{F}$ and hence

$$\int_S d\alpha = \iint_S curl\mathbf{F} \cdot d\mathbf{S}.$$

■

After reading the statements of Green's and Gauss' theorems for differential forms, the statement of Theorem 8.7 comes as no surprise. They are all the same! Using the notation and terminology introduced in Section 7.4, we write all three theorems as

$$\int_{\partial \mathcal{M}} \alpha = \int_{\mathcal{M}} d\alpha, \tag{8.7}$$

where α is a differential form and $\mathcal{M}$ is a manifold (i.e., a curve, a region in a plane, a surface or a three-dimensional solid). And that is all we need! With the correct interpretation, we can recover all three integration theorems from (8.7). For example, if α is a 1-form and $\partial \mathcal{M}$ is a simple closed curve in a plane, then $\int_{\partial \mathcal{M}} \alpha$ represents the path integral of a vector field along the curve. The right side is the integral over the region (in a plane) enclosed by $\partial \mathcal{M}$ (i.e., it is the double integral over $\mathcal{M}$) of the differential $d\alpha$; i.e., of the curl of the vector field. So, in this case we get Green's Theorem.

Now let $\alpha = f$ be a 0-form—i.e., a real-valued function—and let $\mathcal{M} = \mathbf{c}$ be a curve with the initial point A and the terminal point B. In this case, the differential $d\alpha$ is the gradient of f, and $\partial \mathcal{M}$ consists of the two points, A and B. The left side of (8.7) is the "integral" of f over two points A and B, and is interpreted as the real number $f(B) - f(A)$. The right side is the path integral of the gradient, and hence (8.7) reads $\int_{\mathbf{c}} \nabla f \cdot d\mathbf{s} = f(B) - f(A)$. We recognize this equation as the statement of the generalization of the Fundamental Theorem of Calculus discussed in Section 5.4.

The underlying theme (and this is really important) in (8.7) is that the integral of the derivative of a function over a manifold $\mathcal{M}$ does not depend on all of $\mathcal{M}$, but only on its boundary (for example, there are ways of finding the temperature of the core of the Earth that do not require that we actually dig a hole to the core).

Comparing the differential-form versions of Green's and Stokes' theorems we notice that Green's Theorem is a special case of Stokes' Theorem. Let us give another verification of this fact. Assume that $\mathbf{F} = P(x, y)\mathbf{i} + Q(x, y)\mathbf{j}$ is a C^1 vector field in $\mathbb{R}^2$ and $\mathbf{c}$ a simple closed curve that bounds a "good" region $D \subseteq \mathbb{R}^2$ (a "good" region is either an elementary region or a region that can be broken into a disjoint union of elementary regions). Parametrize D by $\mathbf{r}(u, v) = (u, v, 0)$, $(u, v) \in D$. Then $\mathbf{N} = \mathbf{T}_u \times \mathbf{T}_v = (1, 0, 0) \times (0, 1, 0) = (0, 0, 1) = \mathbf{k}$ and it follows that

$$\int_{\mathbf{c}} \mathbf{F} \cdot d\mathbf{s} = \iint_D curl\,\mathbf{F} \cdot d\mathbf{S} = \iint_D curl\,\mathbf{F} \cdot \mathbf{k}\, dA$$

by Stokes' Theorem and the definition of the surface integral of the function $curl\,\mathbf{F}$. The left side is equal to

$$\int_{\mathbf{c}} \mathbf{F} \cdot d\mathbf{s} = \int_a^b (P\mathbf{i} + Q\mathbf{j}) \cdot (x'\mathbf{i} + y'\mathbf{j})\, dt = \int_{\mathbf{c}} P\,dx + Q\,dy,$$

where $\mathbf{c}(t) = (x(t), y(t))$, $t \in [a, b]$, parametrizes the curve $\mathbf{c}$. The right side is computed to be

$$\iint_D curl\,\mathbf{F} \cdot \mathbf{k}\, dA = \iint_D \left(\frac{\partial Q}{\partial x} - \frac{\partial P}{\partial y} \right) \mathbf{k} \cdot \mathbf{k}\, dA = \iint_D \left(\frac{\partial Q}{\partial x} - \frac{\partial P}{\partial y} \right) dA.$$

Combining the above, we get

$$\int_{\mathbf{c}} P\,dx + Q\,dy = \iint_D \left(\frac{\partial Q}{\partial x} - \frac{\partial P}{\partial y} \right) dA,$$

and that is the statement of Green's Theorem.

When talking about gradient vector fields in Section 5.4, we stated the fact that $\int_{\mathbf{c}} \mathbf{F} \cdot d\mathbf{s} = 0$ for any oriented simple closed curve $\mathbf{c}$ is equivalent to $curl\,\mathbf{F} = \mathbf{0}$ if the domain U of $\mathbf{F}$ is simply-connected (read Theorem 5.8, following the equivalences (b) $\Leftrightarrow$ (a) $\Leftrightarrow$ (d)). However, we gave the proof only in the case when U is a star-shaped set. We will now outline the proof in a general case.

Let $\mathbf{F}$ be a vector field that is defined and is C^1 on a simply-connected set $U \subseteq \mathbb{R}^3$, and assume that $curl\,\mathbf{F} = \mathbf{0}$. Find a surface S that does not go through the points where $\mathbf{F}$ is not defined or not C^1 and whose boundary is a closed curve $\mathbf{c}$ (this can always be done; however, the proof is beyond the scope of this book). By Stokes' Theorem,

$$\int_{\mathbf{c}} \mathbf{F} \cdot d\mathbf{s} = \iint_S curl\,\mathbf{F} \cdot d\mathbf{S} = 0,$$

and we are done.

Translated into the language of differential forms, we have shown that if a 1-form α, defined on a simply-connected set $U \subseteq \mathbb{R}^3$, is closed (i.e., $d\alpha = 0$; recall that d for 1-forms is *curl* for vector fields), then its integral $\int_c \alpha$ along any oriented simple closed curve is zero. Interpreting the equivalence (b) $\Leftrightarrow$ (a) of Theorem 5.8, we conclude that there must be a 0-form (i.e., a function) f such that $\alpha = df$. In other words, α is exact, as claimed in Theorem 5.10(a).

EXERCISES 8.3

1. Compute $\int_c \mathbf{F} \cdot d\mathbf{s}$ directly, and then use Stokes' Theorem: let $\mathbf{F} = (x+1)^2 \mathbf{i} - x^2 \mathbf{k}$, and let $\mathbf{c}$ be the intersection of the cylinder $x^2 + 2x + y^2 = 3$ and the plane $z = x$, oriented counterclockwise, as seen from above.

Exercises 2 to 8: Find the circulation $\int_c \mathbf{F} \cdot d\mathbf{s}$ of the vector field $\mathbf{F}$ along the curve $\mathbf{c}$ in the given direction.

2. $\mathbf{F}(x, y, z) = y^2 \mathbf{i} - x \mathbf{j} + z^2 \mathbf{k}$, $\mathbf{c}$ is the ellipse $x^2 + 4y^2 = 4$, $z = 0$, oriented counterclockwise

3. $\mathbf{F}(x, y, z) = (2x + y)\mathbf{i} - (3x - y - x^2 z)\mathbf{k}$, $\mathbf{c}$ is the boundary of the triangle cut out from the plane $x + 4y + 3z = 1$ by the first octant, oriented clockwise as seen from the origin

4. $\mathbf{F}(x, y, z) = x^2 \mathbf{i} + y^2 \mathbf{j} + z^2 \mathbf{k}$, $\mathbf{c}$ is the boundary of the circle $x^2 + y^2 = 4$ in the plane $z = 4$, oriented counterclockwise as seen from the origin

5. $\mathbf{F}(x, y, z) = (x^2 + z^2)\mathbf{i} + y^2 z^2 \mathbf{j}$, $\mathbf{c}$ is the boundary of the rectangle cut out from the plane $y = z$ by the planes $x = 1$, $x = 2$, $y = 0$ and $y = 4$, oriented counterclockwise as seen from above

6. $\mathbf{F}(x, y, z) = -2y \mathbf{i} + z \mathbf{j} - z \mathbf{k}$, $\mathbf{c}$ is the intersection of the cylinder $z^2 + x^2 = 1$ and the plane $y = x + 1$, oriented counterclockwise as seen from the origin

7. $\mathbf{F}(x, y, z) = y^2 (\mathbf{i} + \mathbf{j} + \mathbf{k})$, $\mathbf{c}$ is the circle on the sphere $x^2 + y^2 + z^2 = 1$ defined by $z = 1/2$, oriented clockwise as seen from the origin

8. $\mathbf{F}(x, y, z) = 2x \mathbf{i} + y^2 \mathbf{k}$, $\mathbf{c}$ is the boundary of the paraboloid $z = 4 - x^2 - y^2$ in the first octant, oriented clockwise as seen from the origin

9. Let $\mathbf{F}$ be a constant vector field. A surface S in $\mathbb{R}^3$ and its boundary curve $\mathbf{c}$ are assumed to satisfy the assumptions of Stokes' Theorem. Show that $\iint_S \mathbf{F} \cdot d\mathbf{S} = \frac{1}{2} \int_c (\mathbf{F} \times \mathbf{r}) \cdot d\mathbf{s}$, where $\mathbf{r} = x \mathbf{i} + y \mathbf{j} + z \mathbf{k}$.

Exercises 10 to 17: Compute the circulation $\int_c \mathbf{F} \cdot d\mathbf{s}$ of the vector field $\mathbf{F}$ along the curve $\mathbf{c}$ by direct computation, using the Fundamental Theorem of Calculus or using Stokes' Theorem.

10. $\mathbf{F}(x, y) = 3x e^{-y} \mathbf{i}$, $\mathbf{c}$ consists of the path $y = x^2$ from $(0, 0)$ to $(2, 4)$, followed by the straight line from $(2, 4)$ back to $(0, 0)$

11. $\mathbf{F}(x, y) = 2x \mathbf{i}/(x^2 + y) + \mathbf{j}/(x^2 + y)$, $\mathbf{c}$ is the boundary of the rectangle $[1, 2] \times [0, 1]$, oriented counterclockwise

12. $\mathbf{F}(x, y) = x \sin y \mathbf{i} + y \sin x \mathbf{j}$, $\mathbf{c}$ is the boundary of the triangle defined by the lines $y = x$, $y = \frac{\pi}{2} x$ and $x = 1$, oriented counterclockwise

13. $\mathbf{F}(x, y, z) = y \mathbf{i} + 2z \mathbf{j} + 3x \mathbf{k}$, $\mathbf{c}$ is the intersection of the cylinder $x^2 + y^2 = 1$ and the plane $z = y$, oriented counterclockwise as seen from above

14. $\mathbf{F}(x, y) = (2xy \mathbf{i} + \mathbf{j})e^{x^2}$, $\mathbf{c}$ consists of the straight line segments from $(0, 0)$ to $(1, 1)$, then

from $(1, 1)$ to $(0, 2)$, and then from $(0, 2)$ back to $(0, 0)$

15. $\mathbf{F}(x, y, z) = x\mathbf{i} - yz\mathbf{j} + \mathbf{k}$, $\mathbf{c}$ is the intersection of the paraboloid $z = x^2 + y^2$ and the plane $z = 2y$, oriented counterclockwise as seen from above

16. $\mathbf{F}(x, y, z) = 5\mathbf{i} + 2\mathbf{j} + z\mathbf{k}$, $\mathbf{c}$ is the ellipse $y^2 + 4z^2 = 4$ in the plane $x = 2$, oriented clockwise as seen from the origin

17. $\mathbf{F}(x, y, z) = (2x + y)\mathbf{i} + (2y - x)\mathbf{j}$, $\mathbf{c}$ is the helix $\mathbf{c}(t) = (\cos t, \sin t, t)$, $t \in [0, 3\pi]$, followed by the line segment from $(-1, 0, 3\pi)$ back to $(1, 0, 0)$

18. Show that if the curve $\mathbf{c} = \partial S$ and the surface S satisfy the assumptions of Stokes' Theorem, then $\int_c f\nabla g \cdot d\mathbf{s} = \iint_S (\nabla f \times \nabla g) \cdot d\mathbf{S}$.

19. Show that if the curve $\mathbf{c} = \partial S$ and the surface S satisfy the assumptions of Stokes' Theorem, then $\int_c f\nabla f \cdot d\mathbf{s} = 0$

20. Compute $\int_c (2\mathbf{i} + x\mathbf{j} + y^2\mathbf{k}) \cdot d\mathbf{s}$, where $\mathbf{c}$ is the circle $x^2 + y^2 = 1$, $z = 1$, oriented counterclockwise (as seen from above), by using the fact that $\mathbf{c}$ is the boundary of the cone $z^2 = x^2 + y^2$, $z = 1$.

21. Consider the vector field $\mathbf{F} = -2y\mathbf{i}/(x^2+y^2) + 2x\mathbf{j}/(x^2+y^2)$. Compute the counterclockwise circulation of $\mathbf{F}$ along the circle $x^2+y^2 = 1$, $z = 0$, directly. Can you compute $\iint_S curl\ \mathbf{F}\cdot d\mathbf{S}$, over the disk S in the xy-plane enclosed by $\mathbf{c}$? Explain why your answers do not violate Stokes' Theorem.

22. Set up the integral for the counterclockwise circulation of the vector field $\mathbf{F} = e^x\mathbf{i}/(x^2 + 1)$ around the unit circle in the xy-plane. Then evaluate it using Stokes' Theorem.

8.4 VECTOR CALCULUS IN ELECTROMAGNETISM

The purpose of this section is to explain and illustrate the use of concepts and tools of vector calculus in electromagnetism. We will not attempt to give a presentation covering fully the background needed for the formulas and laws that will be discussed. Instead, we will identify physical quantities as mathematical objects and show how to manipulate them to get meaningful physical quantities.

Formulas from electromagnetism appear in various references in different forms (that differ at most by constants), due to different choices of physical units. The constants that we use are the permittivity of vacuum ϵ_0 (it has appeared already in formulas for the electrostatic field and electrostatic potential) and the *permeability of vacuum* μ_0 (which can be, for example, determined from $\mu_0\epsilon_0 = c^{-2}$, where c is the speed of light in vacuum).

Point Charges. Recall that the electrostatic field $\mathbf{E}(x_0, y_0, z_0)$ at the point $P(x_0, y_0, z_0)$ due to a single charge Q located at $\mathbf{r}_Q = (x_Q, y_Q, z_Q)$ is defined as force per unit charge; i.e.,

$$\mathbf{E}(x_0, y_0, z_0) = \frac{1}{4\pi\epsilon_0} \frac{Q}{\|\mathbf{r}_0 - \mathbf{r}_Q\|^2}\mathbf{u},$$

where $\mathbf{r}_0 = (x_0, y_0, z_0)$ and $\mathbf{u} = (\mathbf{r}_0 - \mathbf{r}_Q)/\|\mathbf{r}_0 - \mathbf{r}_Q\|$ is the unit vector in the direction from the source Q towards the point P.

The electrostatic field at $P(x_0, y_0, z_0)$ due to n charges $Q_1, \ldots, Q_n$ located at $\mathbf{r}_1, \ldots, \mathbf{r}_n$ is the vector sum

$$\mathbf{E}(x_0, y_0, z_0) = \sum_{i=1}^{n} \frac{1}{4\pi\epsilon_0} \frac{Q_i}{\|\mathbf{r}_0 - \mathbf{r}_i\|^2} \mathbf{u}_i,$$

($\mathbf{u}_i = (\mathbf{r}_0 - \mathbf{r}_i)/\|\mathbf{r}_0 - \mathbf{r}_i\|$) of individual electrostatic fields.

Charge Density Function. The above approach, although convenient, is not always satisfactory. There are situations when one has to consider electric charge as being "spread" over some region, rather than concentrated at particular point(s). Such a distribution of charge is described by the *charge density function* $\rho(x, y, z)$. It is defined in the following way: take a region ΔV that contains a point (x, y, z) and assume that it encloses the total charge of ΔQ. The average charge in ΔV is $\Delta Q/\Delta V$ and the limit of these averages as ΔV shrinks to the "point" (x, y, z) is the charge density (by "point" (x, y, z) we actually mean a very small region that contains the point (x, y, z) and is still large enough to contain many charged particles).

Given the charge density function, the total charge contained in a solid region V is given by (this circularity— defining ρ using Q and then defining Q using ρ seems to be unavoidable)

$$Q = \iiint_V \rho \, dV, \tag{8.8}$$

and the electrostatic field is obtained as the integral version of the above summation formula:

$$\mathbf{E}(x_0, y_0, z_0) = \frac{1}{4\pi\epsilon_0} \iiint_V \frac{\rho\mathbf{u}}{\|\mathbf{r}_0 - \mathbf{r}\|^2} \, dV,$$

where $\mathbf{r} = (x, y, z)$ and $\mathbf{u} = (\mathbf{r}_0 - \mathbf{r})/\|\mathbf{r}_0 - \mathbf{r}\|$ (the triple integral of a vector is computed as the triple integral of its components).

Current Density Vector Field. One way to describe *current* is to use the *current density vector field* $\mathbf{J}(x, y, z)$. It is defined as the vector whose magnitude is the current per unit area and whose direction is the direction of the current flow. To be precise: place a small surface ΔS (with a unit normal $\mathbf{n}$) containing the point (x, y, z) in the current. If the total current flowing through ΔS is ΔI, then

$$\Delta I = \mathbf{J} \cdot \mathbf{n} \, A(\Delta S),$$

where $A(\Delta S)$ is the area of ΔS. $\mathbf{J} \cdot \mathbf{n}(x, y, z)$ is now computed as the limit as ΔS collapses to the "point" (x, y, z). If charges have well-ordered motion given by a velocity vector field $\mathbf{v}$, then $\mathbf{J} = \rho\mathbf{v}$. The total current flowing through the surface S placed in the flow is

$$I = \iint_S \mathbf{J} \cdot \mathbf{n} \, dS = \iint_S \mathbf{J} \cdot d\mathbf{S}.$$

Gauss' Theorem. Recall that Gauss' Theorem (see Example 8.14 in Section 8.2) states that the net charge Q enclosed by a closed surface S is

$$Q = \epsilon_0 \iint_S \mathbf{E}(x, y, z) \cdot d\mathbf{S},$$

where $\mathbf{E}(x, y, z)$ is the electrostatic field.

Example 8.22 Find the charge contained in the solid upper hemisphere V of radius 1 if the electric field is given by $\mathbf{E} = x\mathbf{i} + y\mathbf{j} + z\mathbf{k}$.

Solution   By Gauss' law the total charge in V is

$$Q = \epsilon_0 \iint_S \mathbf{E}(x, y, z) \cdot d\mathbf{S},$$

where $S = \partial V$. Using the Divergence Theorem of Gauss we get

$$Q = \epsilon_0 \iiint_V div\, \mathbf{E}(x, y, z)\, dV.$$

Notice that this is the formula for the total charge (8.8), where the charge density is given by the scalar function $\epsilon_0 div\, \mathbf{E}$. In our case, ($v(V)$ denotes the volume of the hemisphere V)

$$Q = \epsilon_0 \iiint_V div\, \mathbf{E}(x, y, z)\, dV = \epsilon_0 \iiint_V 3\, dV = 3\epsilon_0 v(V) = 3\epsilon_0 \tfrac{1}{2}\tfrac{4}{3}\pi = 2\pi\epsilon_0.$$
◀

Let $\mathbf{B}(x, y, z)$ denote a magnetic field at a point (x, y, z) in space.

Ampère's Law. The *magnetic circulation* is defined as the path integral

$$\mathcal{B} = \int_c \mathbf{B}(x, y, z) \cdot d\mathbf{s},$$

where c is a closed contour in space. From standard physical arguments (such as Biot-Savart's Law) it follows that (here presented without proof) $\mathcal{B} = \mu_0 I$, where I is the current

$$I = \iint_S \mathbf{J}(x, y, z) \cdot d\mathbf{S}.$$

The vector field $\mathbf{J}$ is the current density and S is any surface bounded by the contour c. Stokes' Theorem

$$\mathcal{B} = \int_c \mathbf{B}(x, y, z) \cdot d\mathbf{s} = \iint_S curl\, \mathbf{B}(x, y, z) \cdot d\mathbf{S},$$

combined with the above expression for $\mathcal{B}$ gives

$$\iint_S (curl\, \mathbf{B}(x, y, z) - \mu_0 \mathbf{J}(x, y, z)) \cdot d\mathbf{S} = 0.$$

for any S such that $\partial S = \mathbf{c}$. It follows that the integrand is zero; i.e.,

$$curl\,\mathbf{B}(x, y, z) = \mu_0 \mathbf{J}(x, y, z),$$

which is known as *Ampère's Law*.

From this moment on, we assume that the electric field $\mathbf{E}(x, y, z, t)$, the magnetic field $\mathbf{B}(x, y, z, t)$, the charge density $\rho(x, y, z, t)$ and current density $\mathbf{J}(x, y, z, t)$ all change with time. It is assumed that they are continuously differentiable (C^1) functions of the arguments listed. Differential operators $grad$, div and $curl$ are computed by keeping t fixed (i.e., the partial derivatives are taken with respect to "space" variables x, y and z only).

Let $\mathbf{c}$ be a simple closed curve. The *circulation $\mathcal{E}(t)$ of the electric field* $\mathbf{E}(x, y, z, t)$ is given by

$$\mathcal{E}(t) = \int_{\mathbf{c}} \mathbf{E}(x, y, z, t) \cdot d\mathbf{s},$$

and the *magnetic circulation* $\mathcal{B}(t)$ is the path integral

$$\mathcal{B}(t) = \int_{\mathbf{c}} \mathbf{B}(x, y, z, t) \cdot d\mathbf{s}.$$

Let S be a surface in $\mathbb{R}^3$ that satisfies the assumptions of Stokes' Theorem and let ∂S be its positively-oriented boundary. The *magnetic flux* $\Phi(t)$ is defined as

$$\Phi(t) = \iint_{S} \mathbf{B}(x, y, z, t) \cdot d\mathbf{S},$$

and the *flux $\Psi(t)$ of the electric field* is defined as

$$\Psi(t) = \iint_{S} \mathbf{E}(x, y, z, t) \cdot d\mathbf{S}.$$

Conservation of Charge, Continuity Equation. The conservation of charge principle states that if an amount of charge leaves a solid three-dimensional region V enclosed by the surface S (i.e., $S = \partial V$), then the charge inside V must decrease accordingly.

Let V contain a charge density $\rho(x, y, z, t)$, with a current density $\mathbf{J}(x, y, z, t)$ on the boundary surface S. Assume that both ρ and $\mathbf{J}$ are continuously differentiable functions.

The flux integral

$$\iint_{S} \mathbf{J}(x, y, z, t) \cdot d\mathbf{S} = \iint_{S} \mathbf{J}(x, y, z, t) \cdot \mathbf{n}\, dS,$$

with the unit normal $\mathbf{n}$ oriented outward, represents the charge per unit time leaving V through S. The total charge inside V at any time t is

$$Q(t) = \iiint_{V} \rho(x, y, z, t)\, dV,$$

and is changing at the rate

$$\frac{\partial Q(t)}{\partial t} = \frac{\partial}{\partial t}\left(\iiint_V \rho(x, y, z, t)\, dV\right) = \iiint_V \frac{\partial \rho(x, y, z, t)}{\partial t}\, dV. \qquad (8.9)$$

(the function ρ is differentiable, and therefore we are allowed to switch the integration and the time-derivative). By the conservation law

$$\iint_S \mathbf{J}(x, y, z, t) \cdot d\mathbf{S} = -\frac{\partial Q(t)}{\partial t}. \qquad (8.10)$$

If a charge leaves V, then the flux integral on the left is positive; at the same time, the charge inside is decreasing, hence $\partial Q/\partial t < 0$ and $-\partial Q/\partial t$ is positive. Similarly, if a charge enters V, the flux integral is negative (i.e., the outward flux is negative); the charge inside is increasing, hence $\partial Q/\partial t > 0$ and $-\partial Q/\partial t < 0$. This explains the appearance of the minus sign in (8.10).

The left side in (8.10) can be expressed as a volume integral using Gauss' Divergence Theorem:

$$\iint_S \mathbf{J}(x, y, z, t) \cdot d\mathbf{S} = \iiint_V div\, \mathbf{J}(x, y, z, t)\, dV. \qquad (8.11)$$

Substituting this equation and (8.9) into (8.10) we get

$$\iiint_V div\, \mathbf{J}(x, y, z, t)\, dV = -\iiint_V \frac{\partial \rho(x, y, z, t)}{\partial t}\, dV$$

and therefore

$$\iiint_V \left(div\, \mathbf{J}(x, y, z, t) + \frac{\partial \rho(x, y, z, t)}{\partial t}\right) dV = 0.$$

Since this equation holds for any region V, it follows that

$$div\, \mathbf{J}(x, y, z, t) + \frac{\partial \rho(x, y, z, t)}{\partial t} = 0. \qquad (8.12)$$

Equation (8.12) is called the *continuity equation,* and is a basic equation of electromagnetism (similar equations appear in other applications). If $\partial \rho/\partial t = 0$ at all points, the continuity equation gives $div\, \mathbf{J}(x, y, z, t) = 0$, which is the condition for *steady currents.* In that case,

$$\iint_S \mathbf{J}(x, y, z, t) \cdot d\mathbf{S} = \iiint_V div\, \mathbf{J}(x, y, z, t)\, dV = 0;$$

i.e., the total current leaving any closed surface S is zero. In other words, charge does not "accumulate" or "disappear" at some point.

Faraday's Law. Faraday's Law states that the circulation of $\mathbf{E}$ around a simple closed curve $\mathbf{c}$ equals negative the rate of change of magnetic flux through a surface S bounded by $\mathbf{c}$,

$$\mathcal{E}(t) = -\frac{\partial \Phi(t)}{\partial t}.$$

The circulation $\mathcal{E}(t)$ is computed, by Stokes' Theorem, to be

$$\mathcal{E}(t) = \int_{c=\partial S} \mathbf{E}(x, y, z, t) \cdot d\mathbf{s} = \iint_S curl\, \mathbf{E}(x, y, z, t) \cdot d\mathbf{S}.$$

When we substitute this and

$$\frac{\partial \Phi(t)}{\partial t} = \frac{\partial}{\partial t}\left(\iint_S \mathbf{B}(x, y, z, t) \cdot d\mathbf{S} \right) = \iint_S \frac{\partial \mathbf{B}(x, y, z, t)}{\partial t} \cdot d\mathbf{S}$$

(we are allowed to switch the integral and the partial derivative since $\mathbf{B}$ is assumed differentiable) into Faraday's Law we obtain

$$\iint_S curl\, \mathbf{E}(x, y, z, t) \cdot d\mathbf{S} = -\iint_S \frac{\partial \mathbf{B}(x, y, z, t)}{\partial t} \cdot d\mathbf{S},$$

that is,

$$\iint_S \left(curl\, \mathbf{E}(x, y, z, t) + \frac{\partial \mathbf{B}(x, y, z, t)}{\partial t} \right) \cdot d\mathbf{S} = 0.$$

Since this equation holds for any surface S, it follows that

$$curl\, \mathbf{E}(x, y, z, t) = -\frac{\partial \mathbf{B}(x, y, z, t)}{\partial t},$$

which is known as Maxwell's second equation.

It follows that Faraday's Law implies Maxwell's second equation. As a matter of fact, the two are equivalent. To demonstrate it, we start with Maxwell's second equation and will derive Faraday's Law. By Stokes' Theorem,

$$\mathcal{E}(t) = \int_{\partial S} \mathbf{E}(x, y, z, t) \cdot d\mathbf{s} = \iint_S curl\, \mathbf{E}(x, y, z, t) \cdot d\mathbf{S}$$

(using Maxwell's equation and switching the time derivative and the integral)

$$= \iint_S -\frac{\partial \mathbf{B}(x, y, z, t)}{\partial t} \cdot d\mathbf{S} = -\frac{\partial}{\partial t}\left(\iint_S \mathbf{B}(x, y, z, t) \cdot d\mathbf{S} \right) = -\frac{\partial \Phi(t)}{\partial t},$$

where

$$\Phi(t) = \iint_S \mathbf{B}(x, y, z, t) \cdot d\mathbf{S}$$

is the magnetic flux.

Let us point out that a number of laws that we have encountered so far (and there will be more in the remaining part of this section) come in two forms. They either claim something about an integral of a field (circulation or flux) or, (expressed in a differential form), about the properties of a field at a point. For example, the (integral) law $\mathcal{B}(t) = \int_c \mathbf{B}(x, y, z, t) \cdot d\mathbf{s} = \mu_0 I(t)$ has its (differential) counterpart $curl\, \mathbf{B}(x, y, z, t) = \mu_0 \mathbf{J}(x, y, z, t)$, known as Ampère's Law. We showed in Section 8.2 that the integral statement of Gauss' Law $\iint_S \mathbf{E}(x, y, z, t) \cdot d\mathbf{S} = Q/\epsilon_0$ can be written as the formula $div\, \mathbf{E}(x, y, z, t) = \rho(x, y, z, t)/\epsilon_0$ giving the value of $div\, \mathbf{E}$ at a point (it is known as Maxwell's first equation). Furthermore, Maxwell's second equation $curl\,\mathbf{E}(x, y, z, t) = -\partial\mathbf{B}(x, y, z, t)/\partial t$ and Faraday's Law $\int_{\mathbf{c}}\mathbf{E}(x, y, z, t)\cdot d\mathbf{s} = -\partial\Phi(t)/\partial t$ represent two different viewpoints of the same physical fact.

Therefore, there are not that many formulas after all. As a matter of fact, a complete set of laws that relate electric and magnetic fields to each other and to the charges and currents that produce them consists of four equations, known as *Maxwell's equations*.

Maxwell's Equations. We have already discussed two equations: the first one is Gauss' Law

$$div\,\mathbf{E}(x, y, z, t) = \frac{\rho(x, y, z, t)}{\epsilon_0},\tag{8.13}$$

written in differential form (actually all four equations can be written in differential form). The second equation is Faraday's Law

$$curl\,\mathbf{E}(x, y, z, t) = -\frac{\partial\mathbf{B}(x, y, z, t)}{\partial t}.\tag{8.14}$$

The generalized form of Ampère's Law

$$curl\,\mathbf{B}(x, y, z, t) = \mu_0\left(\mathbf{J}(x, y, z, t) + \epsilon_0\frac{\partial\mathbf{E}(x, y, z, t)}{\partial t}\right),\tag{8.15}$$

(earlier in the section we assumed that $\partial\mathbf{E}(x, y, z, t)/\partial t = 0$) and the requirement that there be no magnetic sources present

$$div\,\mathbf{B}(x, y, z, t) = 0.\tag{8.16}$$

complete the list of Maxwell's equations.

In the absence of charges (that is, $\rho(x, y, z, t) = 0$; for example, in the case of electromagnetic waves propagating in a vacuum) and currents (i.e., $\mathbf{J}(x, y, z, t) = \mathbf{0}$) Maxwell's equations read (from now on, we drop the list of variables (x, y, z, t) from the notation)

$$div\,\mathbf{E} = 0\tag{8.17}$$

$$curl\,\mathbf{E} = -\frac{\partial\mathbf{B}}{\partial t}\tag{8.18}$$

$$curl\,\mathbf{B} = \frac{1}{c^2}\frac{\partial\mathbf{E}}{\partial t}\tag{8.19}$$

$$div\,\mathbf{B} = 0.\tag{8.20}$$

Maxwell's equations are not symmetric in $\mathbf{B}$ and $\mathbf{E}$ (i.e., interchanging $\mathbf{B}$ and $\mathbf{E}$ does not yield the same equations). Nevertheless, we are going to show that $\mathbf{B}$ and $\mathbf{E}$ satisfy the same differential equation (in this special case when $\rho = 0$ and $\mathbf{J} = 0$). We will accomplish that by computing the Laplacian of $\mathbf{B}$ and $\mathbf{E}$ (recall that the Laplacian of the vector field $\mathbf{F} = (F_1, F_2, F_3)$ is given by $\Delta\mathbf{F} = (\Delta F_1, \Delta F_2, \Delta F_3)$) using the transformation formula

$$curl\,(curl\,\mathbf{F}) = grad\,(div\,\mathbf{F}) - \Delta\mathbf{F};\tag{8.21}$$

see Section 4.3. We first use (8.18)

$$curl\,(curl\,\mathbf{E}) = curl\left(-\frac{\partial \mathbf{B}}{\partial t}\right) = -curl\left(\frac{\partial \mathbf{B}}{\partial t}\right),$$

then interchange the derivatives $curl$ and $\partial/\partial t$ (this can be done whenever $\mathbf{B}$ is a differentiable vector field), and use (8.19)

$$= -\frac{\partial}{\partial t}(curl\,\mathbf{B}) = -\frac{\partial}{\partial t}\left(\frac{1}{c^2}\frac{\partial \mathbf{E}}{\partial t}\right) = -\frac{1}{c^2}\frac{\partial^2 \mathbf{E}}{\partial t^2}.$$

Substituting this into (8.21) and using (8.17) we get

$$\Delta \mathbf{E} = grad\,(div\,\mathbf{E}) - curl\,(curl\,\mathbf{E}) = \frac{1}{c^2}\frac{\partial^2 \mathbf{E}}{\partial t^2}.$$

Similarly, by (8.19) and (8.18)

$$curl\,(curl\,\mathbf{B}) = curl\left(\frac{1}{c^2}\frac{\partial \mathbf{E}}{\partial t}\right) = \frac{1}{c^2}curl\left(\frac{\partial \mathbf{E}}{\partial t}\right) = \frac{1}{c^2}\frac{\partial}{\partial t}(curl\,\mathbf{E}) = -\frac{1}{c^2}\frac{\partial^2 \mathbf{B}}{\partial t^2},$$

and

$$\Delta \mathbf{B} = grad\,(div\,\mathbf{B}) - curl\,(curl\,\mathbf{B}) = \frac{1}{c^2}\frac{\partial^2 \mathbf{B}}{\partial t^2},$$

since $div\,\mathbf{B} = 0$ by (8.20). Therefore

$$\Delta \mathbf{E} = \frac{1}{c^2}\frac{\partial^2 \mathbf{E}}{\partial t^2} \qquad \text{and} \qquad \Delta \mathbf{B} = \frac{1}{c^2}\frac{\partial^2 \mathbf{B}}{\partial t^2};$$

i.e., both $\mathbf{B}$ and $\mathbf{E}$ satisfy the same *(higher dimensional) wave equation* in the special case when $\rho = 0$ and $\mathbf{J} = \mathbf{0}$.

Poynting Vector. Let us for the moment stay with the special case of Maxwell's equations (8.17)–(8.20). Computing the dot product of (8.19) (with $1/c^2$ replaced by $\mu_0\epsilon_0$)

$$curl\,\mathbf{B} = \mu_0\epsilon_0\frac{\partial \mathbf{E}}{\partial t}$$

with $\mathbf{E}$, and noticing that $(\|\mathbf{E}\|^2)' = (\mathbf{E}\cdot\mathbf{E})' = \mathbf{E}'\cdot\mathbf{E} + \mathbf{E}\cdot\mathbf{E}' = 2\mathbf{E}\cdot\mathbf{E}'$ we obtain

$$\mathbf{E}\cdot curl\,\mathbf{B} = \mu_0\epsilon_0\,\mathbf{E}\cdot\frac{\partial \mathbf{E}}{\partial t} = \frac{1}{2}\mu_0\epsilon_0\frac{\partial}{\partial t}\left(\|\mathbf{E}\|^2\right). \qquad (8.22)$$

Similarly, the dot product of (8.18)

$$curl\,\mathbf{E} = -\frac{\partial \mathbf{B}}{\partial t}$$

with $\mathbf{B}$ gives

$$\mathbf{B}\cdot curl\,\mathbf{E} = -\mathbf{B}\cdot\frac{\partial \mathbf{B}}{\partial t} = -\frac{1}{2}\frac{\partial}{\partial t}\left(\|\mathbf{B}\|^2\right). \qquad (8.23)$$

Now subtract (8.22) from (8.23)

$$\mathbf{B}\cdot curl\,\mathbf{E} - \mathbf{E}\cdot curl\,\mathbf{B} = -\frac{\partial}{\partial t}\left(\frac{1}{2}\|\mathbf{B}\|^2 + \frac{1}{2}\mu_0\epsilon_0\|\mathbf{E}\|^2\right)$$

and use the formula $\mathbf{B} \cdot curl\,\mathbf{E} - \mathbf{E} \cdot curl\,\mathbf{B} = div\,(\mathbf{E} \times \mathbf{B})$ from Section 4.3 to simplify the left side and obtain

$$div\,(\mathbf{E} \times \mathbf{B}) = -\mu_0 \frac{\partial}{\partial t}\left(\frac{1}{2\mu_0}\|\mathbf{B}\|^2 + \frac{1}{2}\epsilon_0\|\mathbf{E}\|^2 \right). \quad (8.24)$$

The expression in parentheses on the right side of (8.24) is called the *total energy density* Ω in an electromagnetic field: it is equal to the sum $\Omega = \Omega_e + \Omega_m$ of the *energy density of the electric field*

$$\Omega_e = \frac{1}{2}\epsilon_0\|\mathbf{E}\|^2$$

and the *energy density of the magnetic field*

$$\Omega_m = \frac{1}{2\mu_0}\|\mathbf{B}\|^2.$$

We can rewrite (8.24) as

$$div\,\mathbf{P} = -\frac{\partial \Omega}{\partial t},$$

where $\mathbf{P} = \mu_0^{-1}\mathbf{E} \times \mathbf{B}$. The vector $\mathbf{P}$ is called the *Poynting vector* and indicates the magnitude and direction of the energy flow (time rate of change of the total energy density) in an electromagnetic field.

Now we go back to the general form of Maxwell's equations (8.13) – (8.16).

Vector and Scalar Potentials. Consider the electrostatic field in $\mathbb{R}^3$

$$\mathbf{E} = \frac{1}{4\pi\epsilon_0}\frac{Q}{\|\mathbf{r}\|^3}\mathbf{r},$$

defined for $\mathbf{r} \neq \mathbf{0}$. Since $curl\,\mathbf{E} = \mathbf{0}$ (we have shown that in Section 4.2) it follows by Theorem 5.8 in Section 5.4 that there is a *scalar potential* ϕ such that

$$\mathbf{E} = -grad\,\phi. \quad (8.25)$$

According to Maxwell's equation (8.16), the divergence of the magnetic field $\mathbf{B}$ vanishes, and consequently (see (5.9) in Section 5.4), there exists a *vector potential* $\mathbf{A}$ such that

$$\mathbf{B} = curl\,\mathbf{A}. \quad (8.26)$$

Now assume that both $\mathbf{E}$ and $\mathbf{B}$ vary with time. Then, in the absence of magnetic charge, (8.26) still holds, but (8.25) is no longer true, since $curl\,\mathbf{E} \neq \mathbf{0}$. Therefore, we have to define a new scalar potential for this (new, time-dependent) situation. By (8.14) and (8.26)

$$curl\,\mathbf{E} = -\frac{\partial \mathbf{B}}{\partial t} = -\frac{\partial}{\partial t}(curl\,\mathbf{A}) = -curl\left(\frac{\partial \mathbf{A}}{\partial t} \right),$$

and thus

$$curl\left(\mathbf{E} + \frac{\partial \mathbf{A}}{\partial t} \right) = \mathbf{0}.$$

This identity implies that the vector field $\mathbf{E} + \partial\mathbf{A}/\partial t$ has a potential function. So we *define* the *scalar potential* ϕ by

$$grad\,\phi = -\left(\mathbf{E} + \frac{\partial\mathbf{A}}{\partial t}\right). \tag{8.27}$$

Substituting (8.27) into (8.13) we get that

$$\frac{\rho}{\epsilon_0} = div\,\mathbf{E} = div\left(-grad\,\phi - \frac{\partial\mathbf{A}}{\partial t}\right)$$

$$= -div\,(grad\,\phi) - div\left(\frac{\partial\mathbf{A}}{\partial t}\right) = -\Delta\phi - \frac{\partial}{\partial t}(div\,\mathbf{A}).$$

In this computation we used the definition of the Laplace operator $\Delta\phi = div\,(grad\,\phi)$ and the fact that for a differentiable function the derivatives $\partial/\partial t$ and div can be interchanged. Rewrite the above as

$$\Delta\phi + \frac{\partial}{\partial t}(div\,\mathbf{A}) = -\frac{\rho}{\epsilon_0}. \tag{8.28}$$

We will now compute both sides in Maxwell's equation (8.15), which states that

$$curl\,\mathbf{B} = \mu_0\mathbf{J} + \mu_0\epsilon_0\frac{\partial\mathbf{E}}{\partial t} = \mu_0\mathbf{J} + \frac{1}{c^2}\frac{\partial\mathbf{E}}{\partial t}. \tag{8.29}$$

The left side can be expressed using (8.21) as

$$curl\,\mathbf{B} = curl\,(curl\,\mathbf{A}) = grad\,(div\,\mathbf{A}) - \Delta\mathbf{A}. \tag{8.30}$$

Substituting (8.27) into the right side of (8.29) we get

$$\mu_0\mathbf{J} + \frac{1}{c^2}\frac{\partial\mathbf{E}}{\partial t} = \mu_0\mathbf{J} + \frac{1}{c^2}\frac{\partial}{\partial t}\left(-grad\,\phi - \frac{\partial\mathbf{A}}{\partial t}\right)$$

$$= \mu_0\mathbf{J} - \frac{1}{c^2}\frac{\partial}{\partial t}(grad\,\phi) - \frac{1}{c^2}\frac{\partial^2\mathbf{A}}{\partial t^2}$$

$$= \mu_0\mathbf{J} - \frac{1}{c^2}grad\,\frac{\partial\phi}{\partial t} - \frac{1}{c^2}\frac{\partial^2\mathbf{A}}{\partial t^2}. \tag{8.31}$$

Identity (8.29), together with (8.30) and (8.31) gives

$$grad\,(div\,\mathbf{A}) - \Delta\mathbf{A} = \mu_0\mathbf{J} - \frac{1}{c^2}grad\,\frac{\partial\phi}{\partial t} - \frac{1}{c^2}\frac{\partial^2\mathbf{A}}{\partial t^2},$$

or, after rearranging terms,

$$\Delta\mathbf{A} - \frac{1}{c^2}\frac{\partial^2\mathbf{A}}{\partial t^2} - grad\left(div\,\mathbf{A} + \frac{1}{c^2}\frac{\partial\phi}{\partial t}\right) = -\mu_0\mathbf{J}. \tag{8.32}$$

Equations (8.28) and (8.32) give the relations between the scalar potential ϕ and the vector potential $\mathbf{A}$.

Lorentz Gauge. Let us first examine how much freedom we have in choosing $\mathbf{A}$ such that $\mathbf{B} = curl\,\mathbf{A}$. In other words: suppose that $\mathbf{B} = curl\,\mathbf{A}_0$ for some $\mathbf{A}_0$— what is the relation between $\mathbf{A}$ and $\mathbf{A}_0$? Do they have to be equal?

Since $\mathbf{B} = curl\,\mathbf{A}$ and $\mathbf{B} = curl\,\mathbf{A}_0$ it follows that $curl\,\mathbf{A} = curl\,\mathbf{A}_0$ and $curl\,(\mathbf{A} - \mathbf{A}_0) = \mathbf{0}$. A vector field whose $curl$ is zero has a potential function. Hence $\mathbf{A} - \mathbf{A}_0 = grad\,f$ for some scalar function f, and the answer to our question is the following: instead of taking $\mathbf{A}$, we could take $\mathbf{A} - grad\,f$ and still keep the equality $\mathbf{B} = curl\,\mathbf{A}$.

Now suppose that we took

$$\mathbf{A}_0 = \mathbf{A} - grad\,f \tag{8.33}$$

instead of $\mathbf{A}$ in (8.26). The only change we have to make is to define a new scalar potential ϕ_0; i.e., the one that corresponds to $\mathbf{A}_0$ by means of (8.27). Hence, by (8.27) and (8.33)

$$grad\,\phi_0 = -\mathbf{E} - \frac{\partial \mathbf{A}_0}{\partial t} = -\mathbf{E} - \frac{\partial}{\partial t}(\mathbf{A} - grad\,f)$$

$$= -\mathbf{E} - \frac{\partial \mathbf{A}}{\partial t} + \frac{\partial}{\partial t}(grad\,f) = grad\,\phi + grad\left(\frac{\partial f}{\partial t}\right);$$

that is,

$$grad\,\phi_0 = grad\left(\phi + \frac{\partial f}{\partial t}\right),$$

and therefore

$$\phi_0 = \phi + \frac{\partial f}{\partial t} + \text{constant} = \phi + \frac{\partial f}{\partial t}, \tag{8.34}$$

(take the constant to be 0, for simplicity).

Therefore, instead of choosing $\mathbf{A}$ and ϕ we could choose $\mathbf{A}_0$ and ϕ_0, given by (8.33) and (8.34), with *any* scalar function f. We are going to make use of this freedom in choosing f to simplify equations (8.28) and (8.32). To be precise, we will try to get rid of the term

$$div\,\mathbf{A} + \frac{1}{c^2}\frac{\partial \phi}{\partial t}$$

in (8.32). Using (8.33) and (8.34) we get

$$div\,\mathbf{A}_0 + \frac{1}{c^2}\frac{\partial \phi_0}{\partial t} = div\,(\mathbf{A} - grad\,f) + \frac{1}{c^2}\frac{\partial}{\partial t}\left(\phi + \frac{\partial f}{\partial t}\right)$$

$$= div\,\mathbf{A} + \frac{1}{c^2}\frac{\partial \phi}{\partial t} - \left(div\,(grad\,f) - \frac{1}{c^2}\frac{\partial^2 f}{\partial t^2}\right),$$

or

$$div\,\mathbf{A} + \frac{1}{c^2}\frac{\partial \phi}{\partial t} = div\,\mathbf{A}_0 + \frac{1}{c^2}\frac{\partial \phi_0}{\partial t} + \left(\Delta f - \frac{1}{c^2}\frac{\partial^2 f}{\partial t^2}\right). \tag{8.35}$$

From the theory of partial differential equations (nonhomogeneous wave equations) it follows that (under general conditions, which are fulfilled in our case) there exists a scalar function f such that

$$\Delta f - \frac{1}{c^2}\frac{\partial^2 f}{\partial t^2} = -\left(div\,\mathbf{A}_0 + \frac{1}{c^2}\frac{\partial \phi_0}{\partial t}\right);$$

i.e., we can find f such that the right side of (8.35) is zero. Consequently, this choice for f implies, by (8.35),

$$div\,\mathbf{A} + \frac{1}{c^2}\frac{\partial\phi}{\partial t} = 0. \tag{8.36}$$

The scalar potential ϕ and vector potential $\mathbf{A}$ satisfying (8.36) are said to satisfy the *Lorentz gauge*. Substituting the Lorentz gauge condition (8.36) into (8.28) and (8.32) gives

$$\Delta\phi + \frac{\partial}{\partial t}\left(-\frac{1}{c^2}\frac{\partial\phi}{\partial t}\right) = \Delta\phi - \frac{1}{c^2}\frac{\partial^2\phi}{\partial t^2} = -\frac{\rho}{\epsilon_0} \tag{8.37}$$

and

$$\Delta\mathbf{A} - \frac{1}{c^2}\frac{\partial^2\mathbf{A}}{\partial t^2} = -\mu_0\mathbf{J}. \tag{8.38}$$

Equations (8.37) and (8.38) are a decoupled (and thus simpler; ϕ and $\mathbf{A}$ are separated, which was not the case in (8.28) and (8.32)) pair of wave equations for ϕ and $\mathbf{A}$.

Next, we will illustrate the use of the calculus of differential forms.

Electromagnetic Potential as a Differential Form. Recall that the vector potential $\mathbf{A} = (A_x, A_y, A_z)$ is defined by

$$\mathbf{B} = curl\,\mathbf{A}, \tag{8.39}$$

where $\mathbf{B}$ is a time-changing magnetic field. Until the end of this section we will use subscripts to denote components of a vector and "∂" notation for partial derivatives.

The scalar potential ϕ is determined from (see (8.27))

$$grad\,\phi = -\mathbf{E} - \frac{\partial\mathbf{A}}{\partial t}, \tag{8.40}$$

where $\mathbf{E}$ denotes a time-changing electric field.

We have to slightly generalize the definition of a differential form. Recall that forms were built of basic forms corresponding to the coordinate functions x, y and z. Our generalization consists of including the time t as a coordinate, so that the basic 1-forms are dt, dx, dy and dz. A (differential) 1-form is an expression

$$\alpha = f(t, x, y, z)dt + g(t, x, y, z)dx + h(t, x, y, z)dy + k(t, x, y, z)dz,$$

where f, g, h and k are real-valued functions. This time there are more forms: there are six basic 2-forms ($dtdx$, $dtdy$, $dtdz$, $dxdy$, $dydz$ and $dzdx$), four basic 3-forms ($dtdxdy$, $dtdydz$, $dtdzdx$ and $dxdydz$), and (a new one!) there is a basic 4-form $dtdxdydz$ (we decided to put dt first in order to obtain correct signs in the formulas that we will derive).

The wedge product and the differential are defined as in Section 4.4, keeping in mind that the degrees go up four and that the differential of a 4-form is zero. For example, the differential of the 1-form α given above is

$$d\alpha = df \wedge dt + dg \wedge dx + dh \wedge dy + dk \wedge dz,$$

where

$$df = \frac{\partial f}{\partial t}dt + \frac{\partial f}{\partial x}dx + \frac{\partial f}{\partial y}dy + \frac{\partial f}{\partial z}dz,$$

with similar expressions for dg, dh and dk.

Define the *electromagnetic potential* to be the 1-form

$$\mathcal{A} = -\phi dt + A_x dx + A_y dy + A_z dz,$$

where A_x, A_y, A_z and ϕ are defined in (8.39) and (8.40). The differential of $\mathcal{A}$ is

$$d\mathcal{A} = -d\phi \wedge dt + dA_x \wedge dx + dA_y \wedge dy + dA_z \wedge dz$$

$$= -\frac{\partial \phi}{\partial x}dxdt - \frac{\partial \phi}{\partial y}dydt - \frac{\partial \phi}{\partial z}dzdt + \frac{\partial A_x}{\partial t}dtdx + \frac{\partial A_x}{\partial y}dydx + \frac{\partial A_x}{\partial z}dzdx$$

$$+ \frac{\partial A_y}{\partial t}dtdy + \frac{\partial A_y}{\partial x}dxdy + \frac{\partial A_y}{\partial z}dzdy + \frac{\partial A_z}{\partial t}dtdz + \frac{\partial A_z}{\partial x}dxdz + \frac{\partial A_z}{\partial y}dydz$$

(combine terms together using $dxdt = -dtdx$, $dydx = -dxdy$, etc.)

$$= \left(\frac{\partial A_x}{\partial t} + \frac{\partial \phi}{\partial x}\right)dtdx + \left(\frac{\partial A_y}{\partial t} + \frac{\partial \phi}{\partial y}\right)dtdy + \left(\frac{\partial A_z}{\partial t} + \frac{\partial \phi}{\partial z}\right)dtdz$$

$$+ \left(\frac{\partial A_y}{\partial x} - \frac{\partial A_x}{\partial y}\right)dxdy + \left(\frac{\partial A_z}{\partial y} - \frac{\partial A_y}{\partial z}\right)dydz + \left(\frac{\partial A_x}{\partial z} - \frac{\partial A_z}{\partial x}\right)dzdx.$$

Let us identify the expression we have obtained. Rewriting (8.40) in components,

$$\left(\frac{\partial \phi}{\partial x}, \frac{\partial \phi}{\partial y}, \frac{\partial \phi}{\partial z}\right) = -\left(E_x, E_y, E_z\right) - \left(\frac{\partial A_x}{\partial t}, \frac{\partial A_y}{\partial t}, \frac{\partial A_z}{\partial t}\right),$$

we realize that the terms in parentheses appearing in the first three summands are the components of $-\mathbf{E}$. Since

$$curl\,\mathbf{A} = \begin{vmatrix} \mathbf{i} & \mathbf{j} & \mathbf{k} \\ \partial/\partial x & \partial/\partial y & \partial/\partial z \\ A_x & A_y & A_z \end{vmatrix}$$

$$= \left(\frac{\partial A_z}{\partial y} - \frac{\partial A_y}{\partial z}, \frac{\partial A_x}{\partial z} - \frac{\partial A_z}{\partial x}, \frac{\partial A_y}{\partial x} - \frac{\partial A_x}{\partial y}\right), \tag{8.41}$$

the remaining three summands contain components $(curl\,\mathbf{A})_z$, $(curl\,\mathbf{A})_x$ and $(curl\,\mathbf{A})_y$ of $curl\,\mathbf{A}$. But $\mathbf{B} = curl\,\mathbf{A}$ by (8.39), so these components are just $\mathbf{B}_z$, $\mathbf{B}_x$ and $\mathbf{B}_y$. Therefore,

$$d\mathcal{A} = -E_x dtdx - E_y dtdy - E_z dtdz + B_z dxdy + B_x dydz + B_y dzdx. \tag{8.42}$$

The differential form $d\mathcal{A}$ carries information on both the electric and magnetic field, and is called the *electromagnetic tensor.*

We have seen in Section 4.4 (see Theorem 4.6) that the differential applied twice to any differential form gives zero. So let us expand $d(d\mathcal{A}) = 0$ to see what will come out of it. Starting from (8.42), we get

$$0 = d(d\mathcal{A}) = -dE_x \wedge dtdx - dE_y \wedge dtdy - dE_z \wedge dtdz$$

$$+ dB_z \wedge dxdy + dB_y \wedge dzdx + dB_x \wedge dydz$$

$$= -\frac{\partial E_x}{\partial y}dydtdx - \frac{\partial E_x}{\partial z}dzdtdx - \frac{\partial E_y}{\partial x}dxdtdy - \frac{\partial E_y}{\partial z}dzdtdy$$

$$- \frac{\partial E_z}{\partial x}dxdtdz - \frac{\partial E_z}{\partial y}dydtdz + \frac{\partial B_z}{\partial t}dtdxdy + \frac{\partial B_z}{\partial z}dzdxdy$$

$$+ \frac{\partial B_y}{\partial t}dtdzdx + \frac{\partial B_y}{\partial y}dydzdx + \frac{\partial B_x}{\partial t}dtdydz + \frac{\partial B_x}{\partial x}dxdydz$$

(use anticommutativity $dydxdt = -dydtdx = dtdydx = -dtdxdy$, etc.)

$$= \left(\frac{\partial E_y}{\partial x} - \frac{\partial E_x}{\partial y} + \frac{\partial B_z}{\partial t}\right)dtdxdy + \left(\frac{\partial E_z}{\partial y} - \frac{\partial E_y}{\partial z} + \frac{\partial B_x}{\partial t}\right)dtdydz$$

$$+ \left(\frac{\partial E_x}{\partial z} - \frac{\partial E_z}{\partial x} + \frac{\partial B_y}{\partial t}\right)dtdzdx + \left(\frac{\partial B_x}{\partial x} + \frac{\partial B_y}{\partial y} + \frac{\partial B_z}{\partial z}\right)dxdydz.$$

The 3-form above is zero, and that implies that all four of its components have to be zero. The last one reads

$$div\, \mathbf{B} = 0,$$

which is Maxwell's equation (8.16)! Computing *curl* **E** exactly as in (8.41), we get that (recall that we use subscripts to denote the components of a vector)

$$\frac{\partial E_y}{\partial x} - \frac{\partial E_x}{\partial y} + \frac{\partial B_z}{\partial t} = 0 \quad \text{implies} \quad (curl\,\mathbf{E})_z + \left(\frac{\partial \mathbf{B}}{\partial t}\right)_z = 0,$$

$$\frac{\partial E_z}{\partial y} - \frac{\partial E_y}{\partial z} + \frac{\partial B_x}{\partial t} = 0 \quad \text{implies} \quad (curl\,\mathbf{E})_x + \left(\frac{\partial \mathbf{B}}{\partial t}\right)_x = 0, \quad \text{and}$$

$$\frac{\partial E_x}{\partial z} - \frac{\partial E_z}{\partial x} + \frac{\partial B_y}{\partial t} = 0 \quad \text{implies} \quad (curl\,\mathbf{E})_y + \left(\frac{\partial \mathbf{B}}{\partial t}\right)_y = 0.$$

In vector notation,

$$curl\,\mathbf{E} = -\frac{\partial \mathbf{B}}{\partial t},$$

which is Maxwell's second equation (8.14).

EXERCISES 8.4

1. Let $\mathbf{A} = 2xz^2\mathbf{i} + xy\mathbf{j} + yz\mathbf{k}$. Find a vector field $\mathbf{A}_0$ defined on $\mathbb{R}^3$ (that differs non-trivially from **A**; i.e., differs by more than just a constant) such that $curl\,\mathbf{A}_0 = curl\,\mathbf{A}$. Describe all such vector fields.

2. Maxwell's equations for a steady-state charge distribution $(d\rho/dt = 0)$ and a divergence-free current distribution $(div\,\mathbf{J} = 0)$ are
$$curl\,\mathbf{E} = \mathbf{0},\ div\,\mathbf{E} = \rho/\epsilon_0,\ div\,\mathbf{B} = 0 \text{ and } curl\,\mathbf{B} = \mu_0\mathbf{J}.$$

   (a) Show that $\mathbf{E} = z\mathbf{j} + y\mathbf{k} + (\rho/\epsilon_0)x\mathbf{i}$ and $\mathbf{B} = -xy\mathbf{i} + x\mathbf{j} + yz\mathbf{k}$ are examples of electric and magnetic fields that satisfy Maxwell's equations and find **J**.

   (b) Compute the Poynting vector $\mathbf{P} = \mu_0^{-1}\mathbf{E} \times \mathbf{B}$.

3. Verify that Maxwell's equations (8.13) – (8.16) imply the equation of continuity for **J** and ρ; i.e., show that $div\,\mathbf{J} + \partial\rho/\partial t = 0$.

4. Show that if a vector field $\mathbf{A}$ and a scalar function ϕ satisfy

$$div\,\mathbf{A} + \frac{\partial\phi}{\partial t} = 0, \quad \Delta\phi - \frac{\partial^2\phi}{\partial t^2} = -\rho\mu_0 \quad \text{and} \quad \Delta\mathbf{A} - \frac{\partial^2\mathbf{A}}{\partial t^2} = -\mu_0\mathbf{J},$$

then

$$\mathbf{E} = c^2\left(-grad\,\phi - \frac{\partial\mathbf{A}}{\partial t}\right) \quad \text{and} \quad \mathbf{B} = curl\,\mathbf{A}$$

satisfy Maxwell's equations (8.13) – (8.16).

5. Show that

$$\mathbf{E} = e^t\left((x+y)\mathbf{i} + (y+z)\mathbf{j} + z\mathbf{k}\right) \quad \text{and} \quad \mathbf{B} = e^t\mathbf{i} + (x^2 - z^2)\mathbf{j} + (e^t + 1)\mathbf{k}$$

satisfy Maxwell's equations (see equations (8.13) – (8.16)) with

$$\rho = 3\epsilon_0 e^t \quad \text{and} \quad \mathbf{J} = \left(\frac{2z}{\mu_0} - \epsilon_0 e^t(x+y)\right)\mathbf{i} - \epsilon_0 e^t(y+z)\mathbf{j} + \left(\frac{2x}{\mu_0} - \epsilon_0 e^t z\right)\mathbf{k}.$$

6. Let $\mathbf{E}(x, y, z, t) = e^t\left(x^2\mathbf{i} + y^2\mathbf{j} + z^2\mathbf{k}\right)$ be a time-dependent electric field, $t \geq 0$.

(a) Find the total charge density $\rho(x, y, z, t)$ from the first Maxwell's equation $div\,\mathbf{E} = \rho/\epsilon_0$.

(b) Find the scalar potential ϕ (recall that $\mathbf{E} = -grad\,\phi$).

(c) Check that the vector field $\mathbf{B} = yi + xz\mathbf{j} + xy\mathbf{k}$ satisfies Maxwell's equations $curl\,\mathbf{E} = -\partial\mathbf{B}/\partial t$ and $div\,\mathbf{B} = 0$.

(d) Find the vector potential $\mathbf{A}$ (recall that $\mathbf{A}$ is determined from $\mathbf{B} = -curl\,\mathbf{A}$).

(e) Check that the scalar and vector potentials satisfy $\Delta\phi + (\partial/\partial t)div\,\mathbf{A} = -\rho/\epsilon_0$.

7. Express Maxwell's equation $curl\,\mathbf{E} = -\partial\mathbf{B}/\partial t$ in cylindrical coordinates.

8. Express Maxwell's equation $curl\,\mathbf{B} = \mu_0\left(\mathbf{J} + \epsilon_0\partial\mathbf{E}/\partial t\right)$ in cylindrical coordinates.

9. Show that $\mathbf{E} = \sin x \sin t\mathbf{j}$ and $\mathbf{B} = \sin x \cos t\mathbf{k}$ satisfy some (but not all) of Maxwell's equations (8.17) – (8.20) if we take $c = 1$. (This means that $\mathbf{E}$ and $\mathbf{B}$ are not realistic electric and magnetic fields.)

CHAPTER REVIEW

Review Questions

Answer/discuss the following questions:

1. Write down different versions of Green's Theorem and list the assumptions needed for the results to hold. What are some advantages and disadvantages of using Green's Theorem (as compared to computing path integrals)?

2. Let $\mathbf{c}_1$ and $\mathbf{c}_2$ be simple closed curves in $\mathbb{R}^2$, both oriented counterclockwise and such that $\mathbf{c}_1$ is completely contained in the region enclosed by $\mathbf{c}_2$. Express the double integral of $curl\,\mathbf{F}$ over the region between $\mathbf{c}_1$ and $\mathbf{c}_2$ in terms of path integrals.

3. The integral of $\mathbf{F} = -y\mathbf{i}/(x^2 + y^2) + x\mathbf{j}/(x^2 + y^2)$ along the circle $x^2 + y^2 = 1$ is 2π. The double integral of $curl\,\mathbf{F}$ over the disk $\{(x, y) \mid x^2 + y^2 \leq 1\}$ seems to be zero. Is that a contradiction to Green's Theorem?

4. Define the normal derivative $D_n f$ of a real-valued function f. Explain how to evaluate the path integral of $D_n f$ in terms of a double integral.

5. Give the statement of the Divergence Theorem of Gauss. Explain why we say that it is a generalization of Green's Theorem to one dimension higher.

6. Explain how to recognize/define the outward normal to a closed plane curve. State the two-dimensional version of the Divergence Theorem.

7. Define the boundary of a parametrized surface. Explain how to define the orientation of its boundary curve(s).

8. Write down the differential-form version of the classical integration theorems. Explain how to obtain particular versions (Green's, Gauss' and Stokes') and the Fundamental Theorem of Calculus and its generalization (see Section 5.4) from it.

9. Let $\mathbf{F} = (\tan z, x, yz)$. Is it true that the path integral of $\mathbf{F}$ along the unit circle $\mathbf{c}$ in the xy-plane must be equal to the surface integral of $curl\,\mathbf{F}$ along *any* surface whose boundary is $\mathbf{c}$?

10. Consider Maxwell's equations (8.17) – (8.20). Write down the corresponding integral versions. Which version would you call "global" and which would you call "local?"

Computer Project

1. **Stokes' Theorem.**
   Consider the vector field $\mathbf{F}(x, y, z) = (xy^2 - 2)\mathbf{i} + xe^{-x^2-y^2}\mathbf{j} + (y - x - 2)\mathbf{k}$.

   (a) Find $\int_\mathbf{c} \mathbf{F} \cdot d\mathbf{s}$, where $\mathbf{c}$ is the circle of radius 1 in the plane $z = 1$, centered at $(0, 0, 1)$.

   (b) Consider the family of paraboloids $\{S_a\}$ defined by $z = (1 - a)(x^2 + y^2) + a$, $z \leq 1$, $a < 1$. Check that the circle $\mathbf{c}$ from (a) is the common boundary of all paraboloids in this family. Compute the surface integral of $curl\,\mathbf{F}$ over S_a, $a < 1$.

   (c) Consider the family of circles $\{\mathbf{c}_a\}$ given by $x^2 + y^2 = 1 - a$, $z = 1$, $a < 1$, and a family of surfaces $\{S_a\}$ given by $z = x^2 + y^2 + a$, $z \leq 1$, $a < 1$. Check that $\mathbf{c}_a$ is a boundary of S_a for each a. Compute $\int_{\mathbf{c}_a} \mathbf{F} \cdot d\mathbf{s}$ and $\iint_{S_a} curl\,\mathbf{F} \cdot d\mathbf{S}$ for $a = 1/2$, $a = 0$, $a = -1$ and $a = -10$.

Further Explorations

1. Compute $\int_\mathbf{c} y\,dx$, where $\mathbf{c}$ consists of the circles $x^2 + y^2 = 16$ (oriented counterclockwise), $(x - 2)^2 + y^2 = 1$ (oriented clockwise), and $(x + 2)^2 + y^2 = 1$ (oriented clockwise).

2. Assume that f is a harmonic function (i.e., $f_{xx} + f_{yy} = 0$) on a set that contains a "good" region D. Let ϕ be any differentiable function. Show that $\int_{\partial D} \phi(f_x dy - f_y dx) = \int_D (\phi_x f_x + \phi_y f_y)\,dx dy$, where ∂D is the boundary of D oriented counterclockwise.

3. Let $\alpha = \dfrac{-y}{1 - (x^2 + y^2)}dx + \dfrac{x}{1 - (x^2 + y^2)}dy$. Evaluate $\int_{\mathbf{c}_\epsilon} \alpha$, where $\mathbf{c}_\epsilon$ is the circle $\mathbf{c}_\epsilon(t) = (\epsilon\cos t, \epsilon\sin t)$, $0 \leq t \leq 2\pi$, and $\epsilon > 0$, $\epsilon \neq 1$. Compute $\lim \int_{\mathbf{c}_\epsilon} \alpha$ as $\epsilon \to 0$, as $\epsilon \to 1$ and as $\epsilon \to \infty$.

4. Assume that $\alpha = x^2 dx + xy\,dy$ and $\mathbf{c}$ is the triangle with vertices $(0, 0)$, $(2, 0)$ and $(0, 1)$

oriented counterclockwise. Evaluate $\int_c \alpha$ first directly, and then using Green's Theorem.

5. Evaluate the surface integral $\iint_S \mathbf{F} \cdot d\mathbf{S}$, where $\mathbf{F} = (x^3 + 3yz)\mathbf{i} + 3z^2y\mathbf{j} + 3y^2z\mathbf{k}$, and S is the boundary of the three-dimensional region between the spheres $x^2 + y^2 + z^2 = 1$ and $x^2 + y^2 + z^2 = 9$ oriented by the outward-pointing normal.

6. Let V be a solid three-dimensional region (assumed to be "good") bounded by a closed, positively-oriented surface S. Show that

$$\iint_S (f\nabla g - g\nabla f) \cdot d\mathbf{S} = \iiint_V (f\Delta g - g\Delta f)\, dV,$$

where f and g are of class C^2.

7. Consider the vector field $\mathbf{F} = x(x^2 + y^2)^{-1}\mathbf{i} + y(x^2 + y^2)^{-1}\mathbf{j}$ in $\mathbb{R}^2$.

   (a) Check that the divergence of $\mathbf{F}$ is zero at all points except at the origin.

   (b) Compute the path integral of $\mathbf{F} \cdot \mathbf{n}$ along the circle $\mathbf{c}_\epsilon$ of radius ϵ, $\epsilon > 0$ ($\mathbf{n}$ is the outward unit normal).

   (c) By (a), $\iint_{D_\epsilon} div\,\mathbf{F}\, dA = 0$, where D_ϵ is the disk $0 < x^2 + y^2 \le \epsilon$. Explain why the fact that the result in (b) is not zero does not violate the Divergence Theorem in the plane.

8. Use Gauss' Theorem to compute $\int_S \alpha$, where $\alpha = (x^2 + 2xy)dydz + (2y + x^2z)dzdx + 4x^2y^3dxdy$ and S is the boundary of the region in the first octant cut out by the cylinder $x^2 + y^2 = 9$ and the plane $z = 1$.

9. Find the circulation of the vector field $\mathbf{F} = e^x yz\mathbf{i} - e^y\mathbf{j} + e^z\mathbf{k}$ along the boundary $\mathbf{c}$ of the triangle with vertices $(0, 0, 1)$, $(0, -2, 0)$ and $(1, 0, 0)$, oriented clockwise as seen from the origin.

10. Let S be a surface and $\mathbf{c} = \partial S$ its boundary curve. Show that if a vector field $\mathbf{F}$ is perpendicular to $\mathbf{c}$, then $\iint_S curl\,\mathbf{F} \cdot d\mathbf{S} = 0$.

11. Consider the integral $\iint_D e^{x^2}\, dA$, where D is the triangle defined by the lines $y = x$, $x = 1$ and $y = 0$. Follow the steps to evaluate it using Stokes' Theorem.

    (a) Write e^{x^2} as the dot product $e^{x^2}\mathbf{k} \cdot \mathbf{k}$ of the vector field $\mathbf{F} = e^{x^2}\mathbf{k}$ and the unit normal $\mathbf{N} = \mathbf{k}$ to D. Check that the triangle D can be parametrized so that the normal is $\mathbf{k}$. Check that $curl\,(-ye^{x^2}\mathbf{i}) = \mathbf{F}$.

    (b) From (a) it follows that $\iint_D e^{x^2}\, dA = \iint_D curl\,(-ye^{x^2}\mathbf{i}) \cdot \mathbf{N} dA$. Now use Stokes' Theorem to evaluate the integral on the right side.

    (c) Check your result in (b) by evaluating the double integral using an appropriate order of integration.

12. Let $\mathcal{B} = B_x dt dx + B_y dt dy + B_z dt dz + c^{-2}(E_x dy dz + E_y dz dx + E_z dx dy)$ and let $\mathcal{D} = J_x dt dy dz + J_y dt dz dx + J_z dt dx dy - \rho dx dy dz$, where B_x, B_y, B_z and E_x, E_y, E_z are the components of time-changing magnetic and electric fields, J_x, J_y and J_z are the components of the total current density and ρ is the total charge density.

    (a) Show that Maxwell's equations $(8.13) – (8.16)$ imply $d\mathcal{B} + \mu_0\mathcal{D} = 0$.

    (b) Conclude from (a) that $d\mathcal{D} = 0$.

    (c) Interpret $d\mathcal{D} = 0$ in physical terms.

    (d) Find α such that $d\alpha = \mathcal{D}$ (hint: use (a)).

Exercises 13 and 14: Consider differential forms corresponding to the coordinates t, x, y and z. There are six basic 2-forms: $dtdx, dtdy, dtdz, dxdy, dydz$ and $dzdx$. We define the operation $*$ (called the Hodge star operator, or just star) that maps 2-forms to 2-forms, in the following way:

first we define $*$ on basic 2-forms and then extend it (using linearity) to all 2-forms:

(i) $*dxdy = dtdz,$ $\qquad$ $*dydz = dtdx,$ $\qquad$ $*dzdx = dtdy,$

$\quad$ $*dtdx = -c^{-2}dydz,$ $\quad$ $*dtdy = -c^{-2}dzdx,$ $\quad$ $*dtdz = -c^{-2}dxdy.$

(ii) Let $\alpha = f\,dtdx + g\,dtdy + h\,dtdz + k\,dxdy + l\,dydz + m\,dzdx$ be a 2-form, where f, g, h, k, l and m are differentiable functions of x, y, z and t. Then

$$*\alpha = -c^{-2}f\,dydz - c^{-2}g\,dzdx - c^{-2}h\,dxdy + k\,dtdz + l\,dtdx + m\,dtdy.$$

13. Let $\alpha = x^2t\,dxdy + zt^2\,dtdz - xy^2zt\,dtdy.$

$\quad$ **(a)** Compute $*\alpha$. $\qquad\qquad\qquad$ **(b)** Show that $*(*\alpha) = -c^{-2}\alpha.$

$\quad$ **(c)** Compute $\alpha \wedge (*\alpha)$.

14. Recall that the electromagnetic tensor $\mathcal{E}$ is given by $\mathcal{E} = -E_x\,dtdx - E_y\,dtdy - E_z\,dtdz + B_z\,dxdy + B_x\,dydz + B_y\,dzdx$. We showed that $\mathcal{E} = d\mathcal{A}$, where $\mathcal{A}$ is the 1-form $\mathcal{A} = -\phi\,dt + A_x\,dx + A_y\,dy + A_z\,dz$, called the electromagnetic potential.

$\quad$ **(a)** Since $\mathcal{E} = d\mathcal{A}$, it follows that $d\mathcal{E} = 0$ (why?). Interpret this differential-form equation by analyzing its components.

$\quad$ **(b)** Compute $*\mathcal{E}$.

$\quad$ **(c)** Interpret the equation $d(*\mathcal{E}) = 0$.

15. Let S be a surface in $\mathbb{R}^3$ and let $\mathbf{c}$ be its boundary curve. Assuming that S and $\mathbf{c}$ satisfy the assumptions of Stokes' Theorem, show that $\int_{\mathbf{c}}(f\nabla g + g\nabla f) \cdot d\mathbf{s} = 0$ for C^2 functions f and g.

Appendix A

Various Results Used in This Book and Proofs of Differentiation Theorems

In this appendix we give (mostly) technical proofs of theorems about properties of derivatives that were stated in Chapter 2. We start by quoting a few results that have been used in various situations in this book. Some are needed again in the proofs presented here.

■ **Theorem 1**   Intermediate Value Theorem.

Assume that $g: [a, b] \to \mathbb{R}$ is a continuous function defined on the closed interval $[a, b]$ and let N be any number between $g(a)$ and $g(b)$. Then there exists a number $c \in [a, b]$ such that $g(c) = N$.

■

■ **Theorem 2**   Mean Value Theorem.

Assume that $g: [a, b] \to \mathbb{R}$ is a function continuous on the closed interval $[a, b]$ and differentiable on the open interval (a, b). Then there is a number $c \in (a, b)$ such that $g(b) - g(a) = g'(c)(b-a)$.

■

■ **Theorem 3**   Extreme Value Theorem.

Let $f: V \subseteq \mathbb{R}^m \to \mathbb{R}$ be a continuous function defined on a closed and bounded set $V \subseteq \mathbb{R}^m$, $m \geq 1$. There is a point $\mathbf{a}_1$ in V such that $f(\mathbf{a}_1) \geq f(\mathbf{x})$ for all $\mathbf{x} \in V$, and there is a point $\mathbf{a}_2$ in V such that $f(\mathbf{a}_2) \leq f(\mathbf{x})$ for all $\mathbf{x} \in V$.

■

In words, a continuous function defined on a closed and bounded set has a minimum value and a maximum value. It follows that a continuous function defined on a closed and bounded set is bounded.

The following two inequalities will be used repeatedly in the proofs in this appendix.

■ **Theorem 4** Triangle Inequality.

Let **v** and **w** be vectors in $\mathbb{R}^m$, $m \geq 1$. Then $\|\mathbf{v} + \mathbf{w}\| \leq \|\mathbf{v}\| + \|\mathbf{w}\|$. ■

■ **Theorem 5** Cauchy-Schwarz Inequality.

Let **v** and **w** be vectors in $\mathbb{R}^m$, $m \geq 1$. Then $|\mathbf{v} \cdot \mathbf{w}| \leq \|\mathbf{v}\| \, \|\mathbf{w}\|$. ■

The Cauchy-Schwarz Inequality implies that $|\mathbf{v} \cdot \mathbf{w}|^2 \leq \|\mathbf{v}\|^2 \, \|\mathbf{w}\|^2$ for $\mathbf{v}, \mathbf{w} \in \mathbb{R}^m$. Consequently, if $\mathbf{v} = (v_1, \ldots, v_m)$ and $\mathbf{w} = (w_1, \ldots, w_m)$, then

$$(v_1 w_1 + \cdots + v_m w_m)^2 \leq (v_1^2 + \cdots + v_m^2)(w_1^2 + \cdots + w_m^2). \tag{1}$$

See Exercise 10 in Section 1.3 for the versions of this inequality in $\mathbb{R}^2$ and in $\mathbb{R}^3$.

Let A be an $n \times m$ matrix and let **x** be a vector in $\mathbb{R}^m$. By $A \cdot \mathbf{x}$ we mean a matrix product of A and **x**, where **x** is thought of as an $m \times 1$ matrix. In that case $A \cdot \mathbf{x}$ is an $n \times 1$ matrix, or a vector in $\mathbb{R}^n$; we use $\|A \cdot \mathbf{x}\|$ to denote its norm.

The norm of an $n \times m$ matrix $A = [a_{ij}]$ is defined by

$$\|A\| = \left(\sum_{i=1}^{n} \sum_{j=1}^{m} a_{ij}^2 \right)^{1/2}.$$

■ **Theorem 6** Inequality for the Norm of a Matrix.

Let A be an $n \times m$ matrix and let $\mathbf{x} \in \mathbb{R}^m$ be any vector. Then $\|A \cdot \mathbf{x}\| \leq \|A\| \, \|\mathbf{x}\|$. ■

Proof

Let $\mathbf{x} = (x_1, \ldots, x_m)$; the product $A \cdot \mathbf{x}$ is a vector whose components are

$$A \cdot \mathbf{x} = \begin{bmatrix} a_{11} & a_{12} & \cdots & a_{1m} \\ a_{21} & a_{22} & \cdots & a_{2m} \\ \vdots & \vdots & & \vdots \\ a_{n1} & a_{n2} & \cdots & a_{nm} \end{bmatrix} \cdot \begin{bmatrix} x_1 \\ x_2 \\ \vdots \\ x_m \end{bmatrix} = \begin{bmatrix} a_{11}x_1 + a_{12}x_2 + \cdots + a_{1m}x_m \\ a_{21}x_1 + a_{22}x_2 + \cdots + a_{2m}x_m \\ \vdots \\ a_{n1}x_1 + a_{n2}x_2 + \cdots + a_{nm}x_m \end{bmatrix}.$$

The square of its magnitude is

$$\|A \cdot \mathbf{x}\|^2 = (a_{11}x_1 + a_{12}x_2 + \cdots + a_{1m}x_m)^2 + (a_{21}x_1 + a_{22}x_2 + \cdots + a_{2m}x_m)^2$$
$$+ \cdots + (a_{n1}x_1 + a_{n2}x_2 + \cdots + a_{nm}x_m)^2.$$

Using (1) with $v_1 = a_{11}, v_2 = a_{12}, \ldots, v_m = a_{1m}$ and $w_1 = x_1, w_2 = x_2, \ldots, w_m = x_m$ we get

$$(a_{11}x_1 + a_{12}x_2 + \cdots + a_{1m}x_m)^2 \leq (a_{11}^2 + a_{12}^2 + \cdots + a_{1m}^2)(x_1^2 + x_2^2 + \cdots + x_m^2).$$

In a similar way we estimate the remaining terms in the expression for $\|A \cdot \mathbf{x}\|^2$, thus getting

$$\|A \cdot \mathbf{x}\|^2 \leq (a_{11}^2 + a_{12}^2 + \cdots + a_{1m}^2)(x_1^2 + x_2^2 + \cdots + x_m^2)$$
$$+ (a_{21}^2 + a_{22}^2 + \cdots + a_{2m}^2)(x_1^2 + x_2^2 + \cdots + x_m^2)$$
$$+ \cdots + (a_{n1}^2 + a_{n2}^2 + \cdots + a_{nm}^2)(x_1^2 + x_2^2 + \cdots + x_m^2)$$
$$= (a_{11}^2 + a_{12}^2 + \cdots + a_{nm}^2)(x_1^2 + x_2^2 + \cdots + x_m^2)$$

$$= \left(\sum_{i=1}^{n} \sum_{j=1}^{m} a_{ij}^2 \right) \|\mathbf{x}\|^2.$$

Consequently,

$$\|A \cdot \mathbf{x}\| \leq \left(\sum_{i=1}^{n} \sum_{j=1}^{m} a_{ij}^2 \right)^{1/2} \|\mathbf{x}\| = \|A\| \, \|\mathbf{x}\|. \qquad \blacksquare$$

■ **Theorem 7**   An Estimate for $\|\mathbf{F}(\mathbf{x}) - \mathbf{F}(\mathbf{a})\|$.

Let $\mathbf{F}: U \subseteq \mathbb{R}^m \to \mathbb{R}^n$ be differentiable at $\mathbf{a} \in \mathbb{R}^m$. Then

$$\|\mathbf{F}(\mathbf{x}) - \mathbf{F}(\mathbf{a})\| \leq (1 + \|D\mathbf{F}(\mathbf{a})\|) \, \|\mathbf{x} - \mathbf{a}\|,$$

for $\mathbf{x}$ near $\mathbf{a}$, such that $\mathbf{x} \neq \mathbf{a}$. $D\mathbf{F}(\mathbf{a})$ denotes the derivative of $\mathbf{F}$ evaluated at $\mathbf{a}$.   ■

Proof

By Definition 2.12, $\mathbf{F}$ is differentiable at $\mathbf{a}$ if

$$\lim_{\mathbf{x} \to \mathbf{a}} \frac{\|\mathbf{F}(\mathbf{x}) - \mathbf{F}(\mathbf{a}) - D\mathbf{F}(\mathbf{a})(\mathbf{x} - \mathbf{a})\|}{\|\mathbf{x} - \mathbf{a}\|} = 0.$$

Interpret this definition in terms of ϵ and δ: choose $\epsilon = 1$; then there is a $\delta > 0$ such that $0 < \|\mathbf{x} - \mathbf{a}\| < \delta$ implies

$$\frac{\|\mathbf{F}(\mathbf{x}) - \mathbf{F}(\mathbf{a}) - D\mathbf{F}(\mathbf{a})(\mathbf{x} - \mathbf{a})\|}{\|\mathbf{x} - \mathbf{a}\|} < \epsilon = 1,$$

i.e.,

$$\|\mathbf{F}(\mathbf{x}) - \mathbf{F}(\mathbf{a}) - D\mathbf{F}(\mathbf{a})(\mathbf{x} - \mathbf{a})\| < \|\mathbf{x} - \mathbf{a}\|. \qquad (2)$$

By the Triangle Inequality and (2),

$$\begin{aligned}
\|\mathbf{F}(\mathbf{x}) - \mathbf{F}(\mathbf{a})\| &= \|\mathbf{F}(\mathbf{x}) - \mathbf{F}(\mathbf{a}) - D\mathbf{F}(\mathbf{a})(\mathbf{x} - \mathbf{a}) + D\mathbf{F}(\mathbf{a})(\mathbf{x} - \mathbf{a})\| \\
&\leq \|\mathbf{F}(\mathbf{x}) - \mathbf{F}(\mathbf{a}) - D\mathbf{F}(\mathbf{a})(\mathbf{x} - \mathbf{a})\| + \|D\mathbf{F}(\mathbf{a})(\mathbf{x} - \mathbf{a})\| \\
&\leq \|\mathbf{x} - \mathbf{a}\| + \|D\mathbf{F}(\mathbf{a})\| \, \|\mathbf{x} - \mathbf{a}\|,
\end{aligned}$$

since, by Theorem 6,

$$\|D\mathbf{F}(\mathbf{a})(\mathbf{x} - \mathbf{a})\| \leq \|D\mathbf{F}(\mathbf{a})\| \, \|\mathbf{x} - \mathbf{a}\|.$$

It follows that

$$\|\mathbf{F}(\mathbf{x}) - \mathbf{F}(\mathbf{a})\| \leq \left(1 + \|D\mathbf{F}(\mathbf{a})\| \right) \|\mathbf{x} - \mathbf{a}\|,$$

for $0 < \|\mathbf{x} - \mathbf{a}\| < \delta$.   ■

Next, we turn to proofs of Theorems in Sections 2.4, 2.5 and 2.6. For convenience, we recall their statements.

■ **Theorem 2.4**   Differentiable Functions are Continuous.

Let $\mathbf{F}: U \subseteq \mathbb{R}^m \to \mathbb{R}^n$ be a vector-valued function and let $\mathbf{a} \in U$. If $\mathbf{F}$ is differentiable at $\mathbf{a}$ then it is continuous at $\mathbf{a}$.   ■

Proof

We have to show that $\lim_{x\to a} \mathbf{F}(x) = \mathbf{F}(a)$, or, equivalently, $\lim_{x\to a}\|\mathbf{F}(x) - \mathbf{F}(a)\| = 0$. Since $\mathbf{F}$ is differentiable at a, it follows from Theorem 7 that there exists $\delta > 0$ such that

$$\|\mathbf{F}(x) - \mathbf{F}(a)\| \leq \left(1 + \|DF(a)\|\right)\|x - a\|, \tag{3}$$

where $0 < \|x - a\| < \delta$. We will now use the definition of a limit: choose *any* $\bar{\epsilon} > 0$ and let $\bar{\delta} < \min\{\delta, \bar{\epsilon}(1 + \|DF(a)\|)^{-1}\}$. Because $\bar{\delta} < \delta$, (3) holds for $0 < \|x - a\| < \bar{\delta}$, so

$$\|\mathbf{F}(x) - \mathbf{F}(a)\| < (1 + \|DF(a)\|)\,\bar{\delta} < (1 + \|DF(a)\|)\frac{\bar{\epsilon}}{1 + \|DF(a)\|} = \bar{\epsilon},$$

since $\bar{\delta} < \bar{\epsilon}(1 + \|DF(a)\|)^{-1}$. ∎

■ Theorem 2.5   Continuity of Partial Derivatives Implies Differentiability.

Let $\mathbf{F}\colon U \subseteq \mathbb{R}^m \to \mathbb{R}^n$ be a vector-valued function with components $F_1, \ldots, F_n\colon U \subseteq \mathbb{R}^m \to \mathbb{R}$. If all partial derivatives $\partial F_i/\partial x_j$ ($i = 1, \ldots, n$, $j = 1 \ldots, m$) are continuous at a, then $\mathbf{F}$ is differentiable at a. ∎

Proof

Consider the case $m = 2$ and $n = 1$; i.e., let $f(x, y)\colon U \subseteq \mathbb{R}^2 \to \mathbb{R}$ and assume that $\partial f/\partial x$ and $\partial f/\partial y$ are continuous at $a = (a, b) \in U$. According to Definition 2.12, we have to show that

$$\lim_{x\to a}\frac{|f(x, y) - f(a, b) - Df(a, b)(x - a, y - b)|}{\|(x - a, y - b)\|} = 0,$$

where $Df(a, b) = [\,(\partial f/\partial x)(a, b) \quad (\partial f/\partial y)(a, b)\,]$. Write $f(x, y) - f(a, b)$ as $f(x, y) - f(a, b) = f(x, y) - f(a, y) + f(a, y) - f(a, b)$. By the Mean Value Theorem (see Theorem 2) applied to $g(x) = f(x, y)$ (y is kept fixed) it follows that there is a number c_1 between x and a such that

$$f(x, y) - f(a, y) = \frac{\partial f}{\partial x}(c_1, y)(x - a).$$

Similarly, there is a number c_2 between y and b such that

$$f(a, y) - f(a, b) = \frac{\partial f}{\partial y}(a, c_2)(y - b).$$

It follows that

$$f(x, y) - f(a, b) = \frac{\partial f}{\partial x}(c_1, y)(x - a) + \frac{\partial f}{\partial y}(a, c_2)(y - b)$$

and

$$|f(x, y) - f(a, b) - Df(a, b)(x - a, y - b)|$$

$$= \left|\frac{\partial f}{\partial x}(c_1, y)(x - a) + \frac{\partial f}{\partial y}(a, c_2)(y - b) - \frac{\partial f}{\partial x}(a, b)(x - a) - \frac{\partial f}{\partial y}(a, b)(y - b)\right|$$

$$= \left|\left(\frac{\partial f}{\partial x}(c_1, y) - \frac{\partial f}{\partial x}(a, b)\right)(x - a) + \left(\frac{\partial f}{\partial y}(a, c_2) - \frac{\partial f}{\partial y}(a, b)\right)(y - b)\right|$$

(continue using the Triangle Inequality and the inequalities $|x - a| \leq \sqrt{(x-a)^2 + (y-b)^2} = \|(x-a, y-b)\|$ and $|y - b| \leq \sqrt{(x-a)^2 + (y-b)^2} = \|(x-a, y-b)\|$)

$$\leq \left| \frac{\partial f}{\partial x}(c_1, y) - \frac{\partial f}{\partial x}(a, b) \right| |x - a| + \left| \frac{\partial f}{\partial y}(a, c_2) - \frac{\partial f}{\partial y}(a, b) \right| |y - b|$$

$$\leq \left(\left| \frac{\partial f}{\partial x}(c_1, y) - \frac{\partial f}{\partial x}(a, b) \right| + \left| \frac{\partial f}{\partial y}(a, c_2) - \frac{\partial f}{\partial y}(a, b) \right| \right) \|(x-a, y-b)\|.$$

Finally,

$$\frac{|f(x, y) - f(a, b) - Df(a, b)(x-a, y-b)|}{\|(x-a, y-b)\|}$$

$$\leq \left| \frac{\partial f}{\partial x}(c_1, y) - \frac{\partial f}{\partial x}(a, b) \right| + \left| \frac{\partial f}{\partial y}(a, c_2) - \frac{\partial f}{\partial y}(a, b) \right|.$$

As $x \to a$ (hence $c_1 \to a$) and $y \to b$,

$$\frac{\partial f}{\partial x}(c_1, y) - \frac{\partial f}{\partial x}(a, b) \to 0,$$

by the continuity of $\partial f / \partial x$ at (a, b). Similarly, as $x \to a$ and $y \to b$,

$$\frac{\partial f}{\partial y}(a, c_2) - \frac{\partial f}{\partial y}(a, b) \to 0,$$

and we are done.

The technique of this proof can be applied to any function $f : \mathbb{R}^m \to \mathbb{R}$ with $m \geq 2$. The general case of a vector-valued function $\mathbf{F} : \mathbb{R}^m \to \mathbb{R}^n$ is dealt with componentwise. ∎

■ **Theorem 2.6**   **Properties of Derivatives.**

(a) Assume that the functions $\mathbf{F}, \mathbf{G} : U \subseteq \mathbb{R}^m \to \mathbb{R}^n$ are differentiable at $\mathbf{a} \in U$. Then the sum $\mathbf{F} + \mathbf{G}$ and the difference $\mathbf{F} - \mathbf{G}$ are differentiable at $\mathbf{a}$ and

$$D(\mathbf{F} + \mathbf{G})(\mathbf{a}) = D\mathbf{F}(\mathbf{a}) + D\mathbf{G}(\mathbf{a}) \qquad \text{and} \qquad D(\mathbf{F} - \mathbf{G})(\mathbf{a}) = D\mathbf{F}(\mathbf{a}) - D\mathbf{G}(\mathbf{a}).$$

(b) If the function $\mathbf{F} : U \subseteq \mathbb{R}^m \to \mathbb{R}^n$ is differentiable at $\mathbf{a} \in U$ and $c \in \mathbb{R}$ is a constant, then the product $c\mathbf{F}$ is differentiable at $\mathbf{a}$ and

$$D(c\mathbf{F})(\mathbf{a}) = c\, D\mathbf{F}(\mathbf{a}).$$

(c) If the real-valued functions $f, g : U \subseteq \mathbb{R}^m \to \mathbb{R}$ are differentiable at $\mathbf{a} \in U$ then their product fg is differentiable at $\mathbf{a}$ and

$$D(fg)(\mathbf{a}) = g(\mathbf{a})Df(\mathbf{a}) + f(\mathbf{a})Dg(\mathbf{a}).$$

(d) If the real-valued functions $f, g : U \subseteq \mathbb{R}^m \to \mathbb{R}$ are differentiable at $\mathbf{a} \in U$ then their quotient f/g is differentiable at $\mathbf{a}$ and

$$D\left(\frac{f}{g} \right)(\mathbf{a}) = \frac{g(\mathbf{a})Df(\mathbf{a}) - f(\mathbf{a})Dg(\mathbf{a})}{g(\mathbf{a})^2},$$

if $g(\mathbf{a}) \neq 0$.

(e) If the vector-valued functions $\mathbf{v}, \mathbf{w} \colon U \subseteq \mathbb{R} \to \mathbb{R}^n$ are differentiable at $a \in U$, then their dot (scalar) product $\mathbf{v} \cdot \mathbf{w}$ is differentiable at a and

$$(\mathbf{v} \cdot \mathbf{w})'(a) = \mathbf{v}'(a) \cdot \mathbf{w}(a) + \mathbf{v}(a) \cdot \mathbf{w}'(a).$$

(f) If the vector-valued functions $\mathbf{v}, \mathbf{w} \colon U \subseteq \mathbb{R} \to \mathbb{R}^3$ are differentiable at $a \in U$, their cross (vector) product $\mathbf{v} \times \mathbf{w}$ is differentiable at a and

$$(\mathbf{v} \times \mathbf{w})'(a) = \mathbf{v}'(a) \times \mathbf{w}(a) + \mathbf{v}(a) \times \mathbf{w}'(a). \qquad \blacksquare$$

Proof

(a) Let $\mathbf{H} = \mathbf{F} + \mathbf{G}$; we have to show that $D\mathbf{H}(\mathbf{a}) = D\mathbf{F}(\mathbf{a}) + D\mathbf{G}(\mathbf{a})$, i.e.,

$$\lim_{\mathbf{x} \to \mathbf{a}} \frac{\|\mathbf{H}(\mathbf{x}) - \mathbf{H}(\mathbf{a}) - (D\mathbf{F}(\mathbf{a}) + D\mathbf{G}(\mathbf{a}))(\mathbf{x} - \mathbf{a})\|}{\|\mathbf{x} - \mathbf{a}\|} = 0.$$

Using the Triangle Inequality we get

$$
\begin{aligned}
& \frac{\|\mathbf{H}(\mathbf{x}) - \mathbf{H}(\mathbf{a}) - (D\mathbf{F}(\mathbf{a}) + D\mathbf{G}(\mathbf{a}))(\mathbf{x} - \mathbf{a})\|}{\|\mathbf{x} - \mathbf{a}\|} \\
& = \frac{\|\mathbf{F}(\mathbf{x}) - \mathbf{F}(\mathbf{a}) - D\mathbf{F}(\mathbf{a})(\mathbf{x} - \mathbf{a}) + \mathbf{G}(\mathbf{x}) - \mathbf{G}(\mathbf{a}) - D\mathbf{G}(\mathbf{a})(\mathbf{x} - \mathbf{a})\|}{\|\mathbf{x} - \mathbf{a}\|} \\
& \leq \frac{\|\mathbf{F}(\mathbf{x}) - \mathbf{F}(\mathbf{a}) - D\mathbf{F}(\mathbf{a})(\mathbf{x} - \mathbf{a})\|}{\|\mathbf{x} - \mathbf{a}\|} + \frac{\|\mathbf{G}(\mathbf{x}) - \mathbf{G}(\mathbf{a}) - D\mathbf{G}(\mathbf{a})(\mathbf{x} - \mathbf{a})\|}{\|\mathbf{x} - \mathbf{a}\|}.
\end{aligned}
$$

By assumption, both terms approach 0 as $\mathbf{x} \to \mathbf{a}$, and we are done. The proof of the formula for the derivative of the difference is analogous.

(b) This statement follows immediately from

$$\frac{\|c\mathbf{F}(\mathbf{x}) - c\mathbf{F}(\mathbf{a}) - cD\mathbf{F}(\mathbf{a})(\mathbf{x} - \mathbf{a})\|}{\|\mathbf{x} - \mathbf{a}\|} = |c| \frac{\|\mathbf{F}(\mathbf{x}) - \mathbf{F}(\mathbf{a}) - D\mathbf{F}(\mathbf{a})(\mathbf{x} - \mathbf{a})\|}{\|\mathbf{x} - \mathbf{a}\|}$$

and the fact that $\mathbf{F}$ is differentiable.

(c) We have to prove that

$$\lim_{\mathbf{x} \to \mathbf{a}} \frac{|(fg)(\mathbf{x}) - (fg)(\mathbf{a}) - (g(\mathbf{a})Df(\mathbf{a}) + f(\mathbf{a})Dg(\mathbf{a}))(\mathbf{x} - \mathbf{a})|}{\|\mathbf{x} - \mathbf{a}\|} = 0.$$

The numerator can be written as

$$|fg(\mathbf{x}) - fg(\mathbf{a}) - (g(\mathbf{a})Df(\mathbf{a}) + f(\mathbf{a})Dg(\mathbf{a}))(\mathbf{x} - \mathbf{a})|$$

(add and subtract $f(\mathbf{x})g(\mathbf{a})$)

$$
\begin{aligned}
= |& f(\mathbf{x})g(\mathbf{x}) - f(\mathbf{a})g(\mathbf{a}) - g(\mathbf{a})Df(\mathbf{a})(\mathbf{x} - \mathbf{a}) - f(\mathbf{a})Dg(\mathbf{a})(\mathbf{x} - \mathbf{a}) \\
& + f(\mathbf{x})g(\mathbf{a}) - f(\mathbf{x})g(\mathbf{a})|
\end{aligned}
$$

(add and subtract $f(\mathbf{x})Dg(\mathbf{a})(\mathbf{x} - \mathbf{a})$)

$$
\begin{aligned}
= |& g(\mathbf{a})(f(\mathbf{x}) - f(\mathbf{a}) - Df(\mathbf{a})(\mathbf{x} - \mathbf{a})) + f(\mathbf{x})(g(\mathbf{x}) - g(\mathbf{a}) - Dg(\mathbf{a})(\mathbf{x} - \mathbf{a})) \\
& + (f(\mathbf{x}) - f(\mathbf{a}))Dg(\mathbf{a})(\mathbf{x} - \mathbf{a})|
\end{aligned}
$$

(use the Triangle Inequality)

$$
\begin{aligned}
\leq & \, |g(\mathbf{a})| \, |f(\mathbf{x}) - f(\mathbf{a}) - Df(\mathbf{a})(\mathbf{x} - \mathbf{a})| + |f(\mathbf{x})| \, |g(\mathbf{x}) - g(\mathbf{a}) - Dg(\mathbf{a})(\mathbf{x} - \mathbf{a})| \\
& + |f(\mathbf{x}) - f(\mathbf{a})| \, |Dg(\mathbf{a})(\mathbf{x} - \mathbf{a})|. \qquad (4)
\end{aligned}
$$

By assumption, f and g are differentiable, and therefore

$$\frac{|f(\mathbf{x}) - f(\mathbf{a}) - Df(\mathbf{a})(\mathbf{x} - \mathbf{a})|}{\|\mathbf{x} - \mathbf{a}\|} \to 0 \quad \text{and} \quad \frac{|g(\mathbf{x}) - g(\mathbf{a}) - Dg(\mathbf{a})(\mathbf{x} - \mathbf{a})|}{\|\mathbf{x} - \mathbf{a}\|} \to 0$$

as $\mathbf{x} \to \mathbf{a}$. Finally, from Theorem 6 it follows that

$$\frac{|f(\mathbf{x}) - f(\mathbf{a})| \, |Dg(\mathbf{a})(\mathbf{x} - \mathbf{a})|}{\|\mathbf{x} - \mathbf{a}\|} \le \frac{|f(\mathbf{x}) - f(\mathbf{a})| \, \|Dg(\mathbf{a})\| \, \|\mathbf{x} - \mathbf{a}\|}{\|\mathbf{x} - \mathbf{a}\|} = |f(\mathbf{x}) - f(\mathbf{a})| \, \|Dg(\mathbf{a})\|.$$

Since f is differentiable, it is continuous, and therefore $|f(\mathbf{x}) - f(\mathbf{a})| \to 0$ as $\mathbf{x} \to \mathbf{a}$. So all three terms in (4) divided by $\|\mathbf{x} - \mathbf{a}\|$ approach 0 as $\mathbf{x} \to \mathbf{a}$.

(d) Proof is similar to (c).

(e) If $\mathbf{v}, \mathbf{w}: U \subseteq \mathbb{R} \to \mathbb{R}^n$, then their dot product $\mathbf{v} \cdot \mathbf{w}$ is a function from U into $\mathbb{R}$; therefore, "to be differentiable" means "to have a derivative (as a single-variable function)." Using the definition, we get

$$(\mathbf{v} \cdot \mathbf{w})'(a) = \lim_{x \to a} \frac{(\mathbf{v} \cdot \mathbf{w})(x) - (\mathbf{v} \cdot \mathbf{w})(a)}{x - a}$$

(add and subtract $\mathbf{v}(x) \cdot \mathbf{w}(a)$)

$$= \lim_{x \to a} \frac{\mathbf{v}(x) \cdot \mathbf{w}(x) - \mathbf{v}(a) \cdot \mathbf{w}(a) + \mathbf{v}(x) \cdot \mathbf{w}(a) - \mathbf{v}(x) \cdot \mathbf{w}(a)}{x - a}$$

$$= \lim_{x \to a} \frac{\mathbf{v}(x) \cdot (\mathbf{w}(x) - \mathbf{w}(a))}{x - a} + \frac{\mathbf{w}(a) \cdot (\mathbf{v}(x) - \mathbf{v}(a))}{x - a}$$

$$= \mathbf{v}(a) \cdot \mathbf{w}'(a) + \mathbf{w}(a) \cdot \mathbf{v}'(a).$$

(f) Proceed as in (e).

■

■ Theorem 2.7   Chain Rule.

Suppose that $\mathbf{F}: U \subseteq \mathbb{R}^m \to \mathbb{R}^n$ is differentiable at $\mathbf{a} \in U$, U is open in $\mathbb{R}^m$, $\mathbf{G}: V \subseteq \mathbb{R}^n \to \mathbb{R}^p$ is differentiable at $\mathbf{F}(\mathbf{a}) \in V$, V is open in $\mathbb{R}^n$, and $\mathbf{F}(U) \subseteq V$ (so that the composition $\mathbf{G} \circ \mathbf{F}$ is defined). Then $\mathbf{G} \circ \mathbf{F}$ is differentiable at $\mathbf{a}$ and

$$D(\mathbf{G} \circ \mathbf{F})(\mathbf{a}) = D\mathbf{G}(\mathbf{F}(\mathbf{a})) \cdot D\mathbf{F}(\mathbf{a}),$$

where $\cdot$ denotes matrix multiplication.

■

Proof

Denote the composition $\mathbf{G} \circ \mathbf{F}$ by $\mathbf{H}$. We have to prove that

$$\lim_{\mathbf{x} \to \mathbf{a}} \frac{\|\mathbf{H}(\mathbf{x}) - \mathbf{H}(\mathbf{a}) - D\mathbf{G}(\mathbf{F}(\mathbf{a})) \cdot D\mathbf{F}(\mathbf{a})(\mathbf{x} - \mathbf{a})\|}{\|\mathbf{x} - \mathbf{a}\|} = 0.$$

Write the numerator as

$$\|\mathbf{H}(\mathbf{x}) - \mathbf{H}(\mathbf{a}) - D\mathbf{G}(\mathbf{F}(\mathbf{a}))(\mathbf{F}(\mathbf{x}) - \mathbf{F}(\mathbf{a}))$$
$$+ D\mathbf{G}(\mathbf{F}(\mathbf{a}))(\mathbf{F}(\mathbf{x}) - \mathbf{F}(\mathbf{a}) - D\mathbf{F}(\mathbf{a})(\mathbf{x} - \mathbf{a}))\|$$

(use the Triangle Inequality)

$$\le \|\mathbf{H}(\mathbf{x}) - \mathbf{H}(\mathbf{a}) - D\mathbf{G}(\mathbf{F}(\mathbf{a}))(\mathbf{F}(\mathbf{x}) - \mathbf{F}(\mathbf{a}))\|$$
$$+ \|D\mathbf{G}(\mathbf{F}(\mathbf{a}))(\mathbf{F}(\mathbf{x}) - \mathbf{F}(\mathbf{a}) - D\mathbf{F}(\mathbf{a})(\mathbf{x} - \mathbf{a}))\|. \tag{5}$$

We analyze each term separately. Since $\mathbf{F}$ is differentiable, Theorem 7 implies that for some $\delta_1 > 0$

$$\|\mathbf{F}(\mathbf{x}) - \mathbf{F}(\mathbf{a})\| \leq M \|\mathbf{x} - \mathbf{a}\|, \tag{6}$$

where $0 < \|\mathbf{x} - \mathbf{a}\| < \delta_1$; the constant $(1 + \|D\mathbf{F}(\mathbf{a})\|)$ is denoted by M. Hence

$$\|\mathbf{F}(\mathbf{x}) - \mathbf{F}(\mathbf{a})\| < M\delta_1. \tag{7}$$

Let $\epsilon > 0$. Since $\mathbf{G}$ is differentiable at $\mathbf{F}(\mathbf{a})$, there exists $\delta_2 > 0$ such that

$$\frac{\|\mathbf{G}(\mathbf{y}) - \mathbf{G}(\mathbf{F}(\mathbf{a})) - D\mathbf{G}(\mathbf{F}(\mathbf{a}))(\mathbf{y} - \mathbf{F}(\mathbf{a}))\|}{\|\mathbf{y} - \mathbf{F}(\mathbf{a})\|} < \frac{\epsilon}{2} \tag{8}$$

whenever $0 < \|\mathbf{y} - \mathbf{F}(\mathbf{a})\| < \delta_2$. We can assume that $\delta_2 < 1$. (We took $\epsilon/2$ intead of ϵ for strategic reasons.)

If $M\delta_1 < \delta_2$ then from (7) we get $\|\mathbf{F}(\mathbf{x}) - \mathbf{F}(\mathbf{a})\| < M\delta_1 < \delta_2$. If $M\delta_1 \geq \delta_2$ then instead of taking $\mathbf{x}$ such that $0 < \|\mathbf{x} - \mathbf{a}\| < \delta_1$, take $\mathbf{x}$ that satisfies $0 < \|\mathbf{x} - \mathbf{a}\| < \delta_2/M \leq \delta_1$. In that case (6) implies that $\|\mathbf{F}(\mathbf{x}) - \mathbf{F}(\mathbf{a})\| \leq M\|\mathbf{x} - \mathbf{a}\| < \delta_2$. Therefore, if $0 < \|\mathbf{x} - \mathbf{a}\| < \min\{\delta_2/M, \delta_1\}$ then $\|\mathbf{F}(\mathbf{x}) - \mathbf{F}(\mathbf{a})\| < \delta_2 < 1$. But in that case (read (8) with $\mathbf{y} = \mathbf{F}(\mathbf{x})$),

$$\frac{\|\mathbf{G}(\mathbf{F}(\mathbf{x})) - \mathbf{G}(\mathbf{F}(\mathbf{a})) - D\mathbf{G}(\mathbf{F}(\mathbf{a}))(\mathbf{F}(\mathbf{x}) - \mathbf{F}(\mathbf{a}))\|}{\|\mathbf{F}(\mathbf{x}) - \mathbf{F}(\mathbf{a})\|} < \frac{\epsilon}{2},$$

or

$$\|\mathbf{H}(\mathbf{x}) - \mathbf{H}(\mathbf{a}) - D\mathbf{G}(\mathbf{F}(\mathbf{a}))(\mathbf{F}(\mathbf{x}) - \mathbf{F}(\mathbf{a}))\| < \frac{\epsilon}{2}\|\mathbf{F}(\mathbf{x}) - \mathbf{F}(\mathbf{a})\| < \frac{\epsilon}{2}.$$

Now look at the last term in (5). By Theorem 7 (with $A = D\mathbf{G}(\mathbf{F}(\mathbf{a}))$) it follows that

$$\|D\mathbf{G}(\mathbf{F}(\mathbf{a}))(\mathbf{F}(\mathbf{x}) - \mathbf{F}(\mathbf{a}) - D\mathbf{F}(\mathbf{a})(\mathbf{x} - \mathbf{a}))\|$$
$$\leq \|D\mathbf{G}(\mathbf{F}(\mathbf{a}))\| \|\mathbf{F}(\mathbf{x}) - \mathbf{F}(\mathbf{a}) - D\mathbf{F}(\mathbf{a})(\mathbf{x} - \mathbf{a})\|.$$

Since $\mathbf{F}$ is differentiable, there exists $\delta_3 > 0$ such that (instead of ϵ, take $\epsilon/[2\|D\mathbf{G}(\mathbf{F}(\mathbf{a}))\|]$)

$$\|\mathbf{F}(\mathbf{x}) - \mathbf{F}(\mathbf{a}) - D\mathbf{F}(\mathbf{a})(\mathbf{x} - \mathbf{a}))\| < \frac{\epsilon}{2\|D\mathbf{G}(\mathbf{F}(\mathbf{a}))\|},$$

whenever $0 < \|\mathbf{x} - \mathbf{a}\| < \delta_3$.

Let $\delta = \min\{\delta_2/M, \delta_1, \delta_3\}$. Then for all $\mathbf{x}$, $0 < \|\mathbf{x} - \mathbf{a}\| < \delta$, (5) is less than

$$\frac{\epsilon}{2} + \|D\mathbf{G}(\mathbf{F}(\mathbf{a}))\| \frac{\epsilon}{2\|D\mathbf{G}(\mathbf{F}(\mathbf{a}))\|} = \epsilon,$$

and we are done. ∎

■ Theorem 2.8   Equality of Mixed Partial Derivatives.

Let f be a real-valued function of m variables $x_1, \ldots, x_m$ with continuous second-order partial derivatives (that is, of class C^2). Then

$$\frac{\partial^2 f}{\partial x_i \partial x_j} = \frac{\partial^2 f}{\partial x_j \partial x_i},$$

for all $i, j = 1, \ldots, m$. ∎

Proof

Assume that $f = f(x, y)$; the general case is proven analogously. Consider the expression

$$G(h, k) = f(x + h, y + k) - f(x, y + k) - f(x + h, y) + f(x, y) = \overline{f}(x + h) - \overline{f}(x),$$

where $\overline{f}(x) = f(x, y + k) - f(x, y)$. The function $\overline{f}$ is a function of one variable; by the Mean Value Theorem (see Theorem 2) there exists a number c_x between $x + h$ and x such that

$$\overline{f}(x + h) - \overline{f}(x) = \overline{f}'(c_x)h = \left(\frac{\partial f}{\partial x}(c_x, y + k) - \frac{\partial f}{\partial x}(c_x, y) \right) h.$$

Now view $\partial f / \partial x$ as a function of its second variable and use the Mean Value Theorem again; so there there exists a number c_y between $y + k$ and y such that

$$\frac{\partial f}{\partial x}(c_x, y + k) - \frac{\partial f}{\partial x}(c_x, y) = \frac{\partial}{\partial y}\left(\frac{\partial f}{\partial x} \right)(c_x, c_y)k.$$

It follows that

$$G(h, k) = \frac{\partial^2 f}{\partial y \partial x}(c_x, c_y)hk \qquad \text{and} \qquad \frac{\partial^2 f}{\partial y \partial x}(c_x, c_y) = \frac{G(h, k)}{hk}.$$

As $h \to 0$ and $k \to 0$, $c_x \to x$ and $c_y \to y$ and therefore

$$\frac{\partial^2 f}{\partial y \partial x}(x, y) = \lim_{k,h \to 0} \frac{G(h, k)}{hk}.$$

Starting with $G(h, k) = \overline{\overline{f}}(y + k) - \overline{\overline{f}}(y)$, where $\overline{\overline{f}}(y) = f(x + h, y) - f(x, y)$ and , proceeding as before, we arrive at

$$\frac{\partial^2 f}{\partial x \partial y}(x, y) = \lim_{k,h \to 0} \frac{G(h, k)}{hk}.$$

It follows that

$$\frac{\partial^2 f}{\partial y \partial x}(x, y) = \frac{\partial^2 f}{\partial x \partial y}(x, y).$$

∎

Appendix B
Answers to Odd-Numbered Exercises

CHAPTER 1

SECTION 1.1

1. For example, $\mathbf{v} = \mathbf{i}$ and $\mathbf{w} = 4\mathbf{i}$ satisfy $\|\mathbf{v} + \mathbf{w}\| = \|\mathbf{v}\| + \|\mathbf{w}\|$; if $\mathbf{v} = \mathbf{i}$ and $\mathbf{w} = \mathbf{i} + \mathbf{j}$, then $\|\mathbf{v} + \mathbf{w}\| = \sqrt{5} < \|\mathbf{v}\| + \|\mathbf{w}\| = 1 + \sqrt{2}$; vectors $\mathbf{v} = -\mathbf{i} + \mathbf{j}$ and $\mathbf{w} = \mathbf{i}$ are such that $\|\mathbf{v} + \mathbf{w}\| = 1 < (\|\mathbf{v}\| + \|\mathbf{w}\|)/2 = (\sqrt{2} + 1)/2$.

3. Take $\mathbf{v} = (v_1, v_2) \in \mathbb{R}^2$ (same proof works in $\mathbb{R}^n$, $n \geq 2$); if $\|\mathbf{v}\| = 0$, then $\sqrt{v_1^2 + v_2^2} = 0$ implies $v_1 = v_2 = 0$. If $\mathbf{v} = (0, 0)$, then $\|\mathbf{v}\| = 0$.

5. $(\sqrt{8}, \pi/4)$, $(\sqrt{8}, 3\pi/4)$, $(\sqrt{8}, 7\pi/4)$, $(\sqrt{8}, 5\pi/4)$.

7. The difference of lengths of two sides in a triangle is smaller than or equal to the length of the third side; equality holds in the case when $\mathbf{v}$ and $\mathbf{w}$ are parallel, point in the same direction and $\|\mathbf{v}\| \geq \|\mathbf{w}\|$.

9. The smallest value of $\|\mathbf{v} + \mathbf{w}\|$ is 0, and its largest value is 2.

11. $\sqrt{5}$.   **13.** 1.

15. Let $A(a_1, a_2)$, $B(b_1, b_2)$ be points in $\mathbb{R}^2$. Construct the right triangle whose hypothenuse is $\overline{AB}$ and the sides are parallel to the coordinate axes and use the Pythagorean Theorem (consider the cases when A and B lie on the same horizontal or on the same vertical line separately). Use a similar approach for a proof in $\mathbb{R}^3$.

17. Representatives of $\mathbf{v}$ are $\overrightarrow{A_1B_1}$, $\overrightarrow{A_2B_2}$, $\overrightarrow{A_3B_3}$ and $\overrightarrow{A_4B_4}$, where $A_1(0, 1, 1)$, $B_1(0, 3, 0)$ $A_2(0, 3, 0)$, $B_2(0, 5, -1)$, $A_3(8, 9, -4)$, $B_3(8, 11, -5)$, $A_4(10, -1, 4)$ and $B_4(10, 1, 3)$.

19. $\mathbf{a} - 2\mathbf{b} = 8\mathbf{i} - \mathbf{j} - \mathbf{k}$, $\mathbf{a} - \mathbf{c}/\|\mathbf{c}\| = \mathbf{i} - \mathbf{j} + \mathbf{k}$ and $3\mathbf{a} + \mathbf{c} - \mathbf{j} + \mathbf{k} = 8\mathbf{i} - 4\mathbf{j} + 4\mathbf{k}$; the unit vector in the direction of $\mathbf{b} + 2\mathbf{a}$ is $(\mathbf{i} - 2\mathbf{j} + 3\mathbf{k})/\sqrt{14}$.

21. $-3\mathbf{i} = 3(\cos \pi \, \mathbf{i} + \sin \pi \, \mathbf{j})$, $\mathbf{i}/2 - \mathbf{j} \approx 1.11803(\cos 5.17604 \, \mathbf{i} + \sin 5.17604 \, \mathbf{j})$ and $\mathbf{i} - 4\mathbf{j} \approx 4.12311(\cos 4.95737 \, \mathbf{i} + \sin 4.95737 \, \mathbf{j})$.

23. Let $\mathbf{v} = (v_1, v_2, v_3)$ and compute both sides using definitions of vector operations. The fact that they are equal follows from properties of real numbers.

SECTION 1.2

1. $\ell(t) = (1 - 3t, 3 - 15t)$, $t \in \mathbb{R}$; to get infinitely many parametrizations, replace $3\mathbf{v}$ by $m\mathbf{v}$, $m \neq 0$.

3. In all three cases, $\ell(t) = (1 - 3t, 1 + 3t)$. For the line, $t \in \mathbb{R}$; for the half-line, $t \geq 0$; for the line segment, $0 \leq t \leq 1$.

5. $\ell(t) = (2, 1) + t(-3, 4)$, $t \in \mathbb{R}$; $\ell'(t) = (2, 1) + t(-3, 4)$, $t \geq 0$.

7. Let $\mathbf{p}$ be the position vector of a point in the rectangle or on its boundary; then $\mathbf{p} = (1 + 3\alpha)\mathbf{i} + (1 + \beta)\mathbf{j}$, where $0 \leq \alpha, \beta \leq 1$.

9. Relative position is $\pm(\mathbf{i} + 2\mathbf{j} - 3\mathbf{k})$; distance is $\sqrt{14}$.

11. The particle will cross the xy-plane at $(15, 2, 0)$, when $t = 4$.

13. $\mathbf{F} = 5\sqrt{3}\mathbf{i} + 5\mathbf{j}$.   **15.** $(1, -1/2)$.

17. The center of mass is located on the axis of symmetry of the triangle; i.e., on the line through one of its vertices perpendicular to the opposite side, $\sqrt{3}/3$ units away from that side.

19. Approximately $5.861\mathbf{i} + 5.439\mathbf{j}$.

SECTION 1.3

1. Write $\mathbf{v} = (v_1, \dots, v_n)$ and $\mathbf{w} = (w_1, \dots, w_n)$ and use the definition of the dot product and properties of real numbers.

3. Let $\mathbf{u} = (u_1, u_2, u_3)$, $\mathbf{v} = (v_1, v_2, v_3)$ and $\mathbf{w} = (w_1, w_2, w_3)$, and compute both sides of each formula using the definition of the dot product. The identities follow from properties of real numbers.

5. Write $\mathbf{a} = a_\mathbf{u}\mathbf{u} + a_\mathbf{v}\mathbf{v} + a_\mathbf{w}\mathbf{w}$, where $a_\mathbf{u}$, $a_\mathbf{v}$ and $a_\mathbf{w}$ are real numbers. To get $a_\mathbf{u}$ compute the dot product of $\mathbf{a}$ with $\mathbf{u}$ and use the assumptions. The remaining two coefficients are obtained analogously.

7. Approximately 1.6515, 1.1867 and 0.3034 rad.

9. The dot product of the two vectors is zero.

11. All three angles are the same, approximately equal to 0.9553 rad.

13. Use the formula for the angle between two vectors; the assumption guarantees that the two angles are equal.

15. $\mathbf{i} + 2\mathbf{j} = \frac{3}{2}(\mathbf{i} + \mathbf{j}) - \frac{1}{2}(\mathbf{i} - \mathbf{j})$.

17. $3x - z + 2 = 0$.   **19.** $3x + 2y - 8z = 0$.

21. Orient the sides $\mathbf{p}_1, \dots, \mathbf{p}_n$ of a polygon so that the terminal point of one side is the initial point of the neighboring one. The work of $\mathbf{F}$ is $W = \mathbf{F} \cdot \mathbf{p}_1 + \dots + \mathbf{F} \cdot \mathbf{p}_n$. Since $\mathbf{p}_1 + \dots + \mathbf{p}_n = \mathbf{0}$, it follows that $W = 0$.

23. $\mathbf{i} = (1/6)\mathbf{u} + (1/6)\mathbf{w}$.

25. Let $\mathbf{a} \in \mathbb{R}^3$ be orthogonal to $\mathbf{u}$, $\mathbf{v}$ and $\mathbf{w}$. Using $\mathbf{a} = a_\mathbf{u}\mathbf{u} + a_\mathbf{v}\mathbf{v} + a_\mathbf{w}\mathbf{w}$ and the assumptions show that $\mathbf{a} = \mathbf{0}$.

SECTION 1.4

1. $\begin{bmatrix} -16 & 10 \\ 8 & -16 \end{bmatrix}$.

3. Not defined.

5. $\begin{bmatrix} 1 & -3 \\ 7 & -13 \end{bmatrix}$.

7. $\begin{bmatrix} 0 & 25 & -20 \\ 16 & -33 & 28 \\ -8 & -71 & 56 \end{bmatrix}$.

9. $\begin{bmatrix} 59 & 42 \\ -98 & 255 \end{bmatrix}$.

11. $\begin{bmatrix} -5/3 & 7/3 \\ -8/3 & 1/3 \end{bmatrix}$.

13. $\begin{bmatrix} 0 & 0 \\ -10 & -1 \end{bmatrix}$.

15. $\mathbf{F}_C$ assigns to a vector its symmetric image with respect to the line $y = x$; $\mathbf{F}_{I_2}$ maps a vector into itself.

17. -7.   **19.** r.   **21.** -20.

23. Let $A = [a_{ij}]$, $B = [b_{ij}]$, $(i, j = 1, 2)$, and show that both $\det(AB)$ and $\det(A)\det(B)$ are equal to the same number. Then $\det(AB) = \det(A)\det(B) = \det(B)\det(A) = \det(BA)$.

25. Let $A = \begin{bmatrix} a_{11} & a_{12} \\ a_{21} & a_{22} \end{bmatrix}$; then $B = \begin{bmatrix} a_{11} & a_{12} \\ \alpha a_{11} & \alpha a_{12} \end{bmatrix}$ and $\det(B) = 0$.

27. Every time we interchange two rows or two columns in a matrix, its determinant changes sign; consequently, $\det(B) = \det(A)$.

29. The expression for $\det(A)$ consists of six terms. Each term contains *exactly one* entry from each row of A. If we multiply all elements in one row of A by α, each of the six terms will contain the factor α, and therefore $\det(B) = \alpha\det(A)$.

31. $\mathbf{F}_{A+B} = \mathbf{F}_A + \mathbf{F}_B$; $\mathbf{F}_{2AB} = 2(\mathbf{F}_A \circ \mathbf{F}_B)$ ($\circ$ denotes composition); $\mathbf{F}_{7B} = 7\mathbf{F}_B$.

SECTION 1.5

1. $\mathbf{v} \times \mathbf{w} = 12\mathbf{i} - 5\mathbf{j} + 8\mathbf{k}$, $(\mathbf{v} + \mathbf{w}) \times \mathbf{k} = 4\mathbf{i} - 3\mathbf{j}$, $(2\mathbf{v} - \mathbf{w}) \times (\mathbf{v} + \mathbf{w}) = 36\mathbf{i} - 15\mathbf{j} + 24\mathbf{k}$ and $\mathbf{i} \times (\mathbf{v} \times \mathbf{w}) = -8\mathbf{j} - 5\mathbf{k}$.

3. Expand both sides using the definition of the cross product.

5. $\pm(\mathbf{i} - \mathbf{j})/\sqrt{2}$.   **7.** For example, $\mathbf{u} = \mathbf{i}$, $\mathbf{v} = \mathbf{i}$ and $\mathbf{w} = \mathbf{j}$.

9. 1.

11. Let $\mathbf{v}$ be the vector from $(0, 2)$ to $(3, 2)$ and let $\mathbf{w}$ be the vector from $(0, 2)$ to $(1, 1)$. The area of the parallelogram spanned by $\mathbf{v}$ and $\mathbf{w}$ is $\|\mathbf{v} \times \mathbf{w}\| = 3$.

13. The four points do not belong to the same plane.

15. Let $\mathbf{v}$ be the vector from $(1, 0, 0)$ to $(-3, 2, 2)$, and let $\mathbf{w}$ be the vector from $(1, 0, 0)$ to $(3, -1, -1)$; show that $\mathbf{v} \times \mathbf{w} = \mathbf{0}$.

17. $y = 1$.   **19.** $\sqrt{8/3}$.

21. The magnitude of the torque is the largest on the equator, and the smallest on the North Pole and on the South Pole.

23. The magnitude of $\mathbf{v}$ is the largest on the edge of the disk and the smallest at its center.

CHAPTER REVIEW

Computer Project

1. (a) Car A: $(10 - 50t)\mathbf{i}$; car B: $80t\mathbf{j}$ (b) $d(t) = 10\sqrt{89t^2 - 10t + 1}$ (d) approximately 8.47998 km, reached when $t \approx 0.05618$ h   (e) after approximately 2.17427 h.
(c)

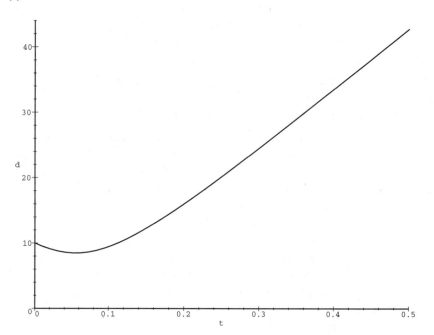

Further Explorations

1. The sum of the squares of lengths of the diagonals in a parallelogram is equal to the sum of the squares of lengths of its four sides.

3. $\cos \alpha = \mathbf{v} \cdot \mathbf{i} / \|\mathbf{v}\|$, $\cos \beta = \mathbf{v} \cdot \mathbf{j} / \|\mathbf{v}\|$ and $\cos \gamma = \mathbf{v} \cdot \mathbf{k} / \|\mathbf{v}\|$; $\mathbf{v} = \|\mathbf{v}\|(\cos \alpha \mathbf{i} + \cos \beta \mathbf{j} + \cos \gamma \mathbf{k})$.

5. Equation of the plane Π is $8x - 10y - 7z + 12 = 0$. Planes perpendicular to Π that contain the given point are represented by $(t - 2s)x - (2t + 3s)y + (4t + 2s)z + 3t + 8s = 0$, where $t, s \in \mathbb{R}$ and at least one of t or s is not zero.

7. Interpret the determinant as a scalar triple product.

9. (a) For example, $A = \begin{bmatrix} 2 & -1 \\ 4 & -2 \end{bmatrix}$ and $\mathbf{v} = \begin{bmatrix} 3 \\ 6 \end{bmatrix}$ (b) $\mathbf{F}_A(\mathbf{v}) = \mathbf{0}$, written in components, gives a system of equations for the components of $\mathbf{v}$. Use the fact that $\det(A) \neq 0$ to show that the only solution is $\mathbf{v} = 0$.

CHAPTER 2

SECTION 2.1

1. Domain is $\mathbb{R}^2$; range is $\mathbb{R}$.

3. The domain of f consists of all $(u, v, t, z) \in \mathbb{R}^4$ such that $u + v \neq \pi/2 + k\pi$ (k integer) and $t, z \in \mathbb{R}$; range is $\mathbb{R}$.

5. Domain is the set $\mathbb{R}^2 - \{(0, 0)\}$; range is $[0, 3]$.

7. Domain is the set $\{(x, y) \mid x > 0 \text{ and } y > 0\}$; range is $\{(c, d) \mid c \in \mathbb{R} \text{ and } d \geq 0\}$.

9. Domain is $\mathbb{R}^2$; range is $[0, \infty)$.

11. Domain is $\{(x, y) \mid x^2 - y^2/4 \leq 1\}$; range is $[0, 2]$.

13. Domain is the set $\{(x, y) \mid x \neq 0, y \in \mathbb{R}\}$; range is $\mathbb{R}$.

15. The range consists of all unit vectors. Identify vectors in $\mathbb{R}^2$ with points in $\mathbb{R}^2$ — the range of $\mathbf{F}$ is the circle of radius 1 centered at the origin.

17. $f(x, y, z) = 42/(x^2 + y^2 + z^2)$.

19. There is no unique answer, since there is no information on the values of the temperature. If we assume that, say, $-100 \leq T \leq 60$, the domain of W is the set $\{(T, v) \mid -100 \leq T \leq 60, 5 \leq v \leq 45\}$.

21. Domain is the set $\{(x, y, z) \mid x \neq 0, y \neq 0 \text{ and } z \neq 0\}$; it represents $\mathbb{R}^3$ with the three coordinate planes removed.

23. Domain consists of all $(r, \theta) \in \mathbb{R}^2$.

25. The domain is the set $\{(x, y) \mid x^2 - y^2 \geq 1\}$.

SECTION 2.2

1. There are no level curves of value $c \neq 1$; the "level curve" (or, better yet, the level set) of value $c = 1$ is the xy-plane.

3. There are no level curves of value $c > 3$; the "level curve" of value $c = 3$ is the origin; if $c < 3$, the level curve is a circle centred at the origin, of radius $\sqrt{3 - c}$.

5. There are no level curves of value $c \leq 0$; the level curve of value $c > 0$ is the hyprebola $y = (\ln c)/x$ if $c \neq 1$ and the x-axis if $c = 1$.

7. The level curve of value $c \neq 0$ is the line $y = x/c$ with the origin removed. If $c = 0$, the level curve is the y-axis without the origin.

9. The level curve of value c is the graph of $y = \sin x$ moved up c units if $c \geq 0$ or down $|c|$ units if $c < 0$.

11. The level curve of value $c > 0$ is the hyperbola with asymptotes $y = \pm x$ and x-intercepts at $(\pm\sqrt{c}, 0)$; the level curve of value $c < 0$ is the hyperbola with asymptotes $y = \pm x$ and y-intercepts at $(0, \pm\sqrt{-c})$; the level curve of value $c = 0$ consists of two lines, $y = x$ and $y = -x$, that intersect at the origin.

13. The level surface of value c is a parabolic sheet $y = x^2 + c$. Figure below shows parabolic sheets with $c = -1.5$, $c = 0$ and $c = 1$.

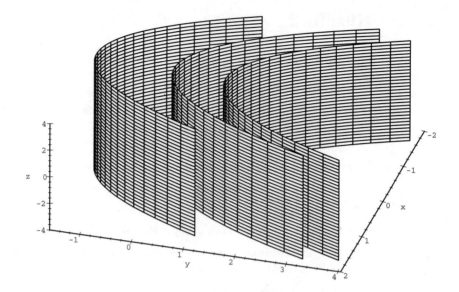

15. There are no level surfaces for $c < 1$; the "level surface" of value $c = 1$ is the origin; if $c > 1$, the level surface is the ellipsoid with semiaxes $\sqrt{c-1}/2$ (in the x-direction), $\sqrt{c-1}/2$ (in the y-direction) and $\sqrt{c-1}$ (in the z-direction), symmetric with respect to the origin.

17. The level surface of value c is the plane parallel to the yz-plane that crosses the x-axis at $((c-4)/3, 0, 0)$.

19. There are no isotherms of value c if $c \leq 0$ or $c > 50$. The isotherm of value $0 < c < 50$ is an ellipse with semi-axes $\sqrt{50/c-1}$ and $\sqrt{50/c-1}/\sqrt{3}$. If $c = 50$ the isotherm is the point $(0, 0)$.

21. (a) In $\mathbb{R}^2$, $x = a$ is the line, parallel to the y-axis, going through $(a, 0)$. In $\mathbb{R}^3$, $x = a$ is the plane, parallel to the yz-plane, going through $(a, 0, 0)$ (b) In $\mathbb{R}^2$, $y = b$ is the the line, parallel to the x-axis, going through $(0, b)$. In $\mathbb{R}^3$, $y = b$ is the plane, parallel to the xz-plane, going through $(0, b, 0)$.

23. (a) Sphere, centered at the origin, of radius a (b) Sphere, centered at (m, n, p), of radius a.

25. Upper hemisphere (i.e., the part of the sphere centered at the origin of radius $\sqrt{2}$, above and in the xy-plane).

27. Cylinder of radius 3 whose axis of (rotational) symmetry is the z-axis.

29. Plane, parallel to the xy-plane, 4 units above it.

31.

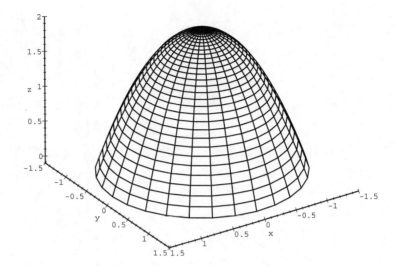

33.

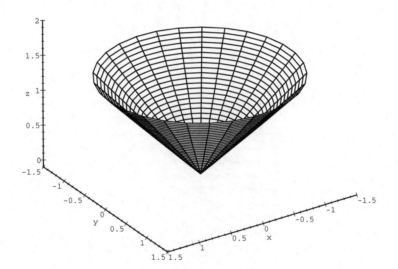

35.

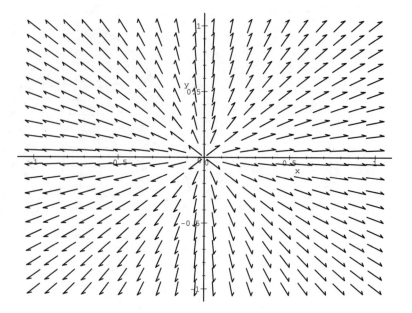

37.

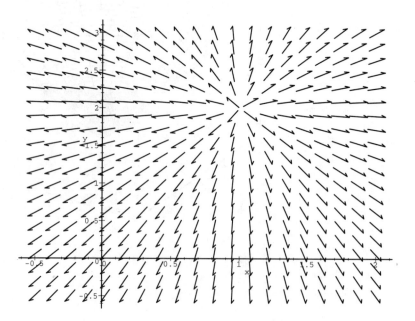

39.   **41.**

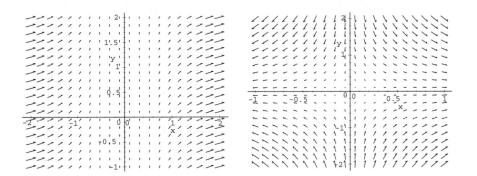

SECTION 2.3

1. The radius has to be smaller than $\sqrt{-\ln 0.99}$.

3.

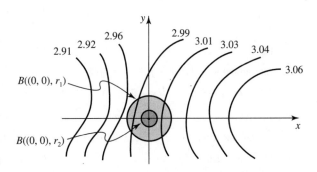

5. 0.   **7.** Does not exist.   **9.** 0.

11. Does not exist.   **13.** Does not exist.   **15.** Does not exist.

17. Does not exist.   **19.** $\mathbf{F}$ is not continuous at $(0, 0, 0)$.

21. $f(x, y)$ is continuous for all $(x, y) \in \mathbb{R}^2$.

23. f is not continuous at $\mathbf{x} = \mathbf{x}_0$.

25. It is impossible to define $f(0, 0)$ so as to make f continuous at $(0, 0)$.

27. $\lim\limits_{(x,y)\to(0,0)} f(x, y)$ does not exist, so f cannot be made continuous at $(0, 0)$.

29. All points in U are interior points; the boundary of U consists of the x-axis and the y-axis.

31. Let $\mathbf{x} = (x_1, \ldots, x_m)$ and $\mathbf{a} = (a_1, \ldots, a_m)$; then $f(\mathbf{x}) = x_1 a_1 + \ldots + x_m a_m$ is a first degree polynomial and therefore continuous.

33. Defining $F(0, 2) = (2, 2)$ will make F continuous at $(0, 2)$.

35. Defining $F(1, 0) = (\sin 1, 0, 1)$ will make F continuous at $(1, 0)$.

SECTION 2.4

1. U is open in $\mathbb{R}^2$.   **3.** U is not open in $\mathbb{R}^2$.

5. U is open in $\mathbb{R}^3$.   **7.** $f_x = yx^{y-1} + y/x$; $f_y = x^y \ln x + \ln x$.

9. $f_x = 1/(x + y + z^2)$; $f_z = 2z/(x + y + z^2)$.

11. $f_x = (x^4 - 3x^2y^2 - 2xy^3)/(x^2 - y^2)^2$; $f_y = (3x^2y^2 + 2yx^3 - y^4)/(x^2 - y^2)^2$.

13. $f_x = e^{xy} \sin y(y \cos x - \sin x)$; $f_y = e^{xy} \cos x(x \sin y + \cos y)$.

15. $\partial f/\partial x_i = x_i/\sqrt{x_1^2 + \cdots + x_m^2}$.   **17.** $f_x = xe^{-x^2}$; $f_y = 0$.

19. $z_x = f'(x)$; $z_y = g'(y)$.   **21.** $z_x = f'(x)/g(y)$; $z_y = -f(x)g'(y)/g(y)^2$.

23. In the northern direction.

25. (a) $f_y(2, 3) = 24e^{-22}$ (b) the slope is $24e^{-22}$ (c) $f_y(2, 3)$ is the slope of the tangent line (at the point where $y = 3$) to the curve $z = f(2, y)$ that is the intersection of the graph of $z = f(x, y)$ and the vertical plane $x = 2$.

27. $\begin{bmatrix} 0 & 1 \\ 1 & 0 \\ 0 & 0 \end{bmatrix}$.   **29.** $\begin{bmatrix} 1 & 1 & 0 \\ 2 & 2 & 1 \end{bmatrix}$.

31. $[2a_1 \quad 2a_2 \quad 2a_3]$.   **33.** $[1 \quad -1]$.

35. Interpreted as a vector, $\nabla f(\mathbf{x}) = \mathbf{x}/\|\mathbf{x}\|$; its domain is $\mathbb{R}^3 - \{(0, 0, 0)\}$.

37. $L_{(2,-1)}(x, y) = \ln 4 + \frac{3}{4}(x - 2) + \frac{1}{2}(y + 1)$.

39. $L_{(3,2)}(x, y) = 4x - y - 2$.   **41.** $L_{(0,1,1)}(x, y, z) = (y + z)/\sqrt{2}$.

43. Use the fact that, for (x, y) near $(2, 3)$, $f(x, y) \approx L_{(2,3)}(x, y)$.

45. Use the fact that $f(x, y) = \sqrt{x^3 + y^3} \approx L_{(1,2)}(x, y)$, where $L_{(1,2)}(x, y)$ is the linear approximation of f at $(1, 2)$; it follows that $f(0.99, 2.02) \approx 3.035$; the calculator value is 3.0352441 (accuracy depends on the calculator used).

47. $7.95 \ln 1.02 \approx 0.16$; the calculator value is 0.1574309.

49. Approximate $f(x, y) = \int_x^y e^{-t^2} dt$ using the linear approximation $L_{(1,1)}(x, y) = e^{-1}(y - x)$; it follows that $f(0.995, 1.02) \approx L_{(1,1)}(0.995, 1.02) = 0.025e^{-1}$.

51. $\Delta f \approx 0.2950836$; $df \approx 0.2456344$.   **53.** $\Delta f \approx -0.080384$. $df = -0.08$.

55. Error in computing the volume V is approximately 4.5% (i.e., $\Delta V \approx 0.045V$).

57. Approximately 5%.

59. $\Delta R \approx dR = 0.44$; the calculator value is $R(11, 12, 19) - R(10, 10, 20) \approx 0.4077329$.

61. $\mathbf{c}'(2) = (4, -1/4)$, $\mathbf{c}''(2) = (2, 1/4)$; $\mathbf{c}'(1) = (2, -1)$, $\mathbf{c}''(1) = (2, 2)$; $\mathbf{c}'(1/10) = (1/5, -100)$ and $\mathbf{c}''(1/10) = (2, 2000)$; as $t \to 0$, both $\|\mathbf{c}'(t)\|$ and $\|\mathbf{c}''(t)\|$ approach ∞.

63. $2x + 4y + z - 11 = 0$.

65. f_x is given by $f_x(x, y) = 2xy/(x^2 + y^2)$ if $(x, y) \neq (0, 0)$ and $f_x(0, 0) = 0$. Since the limit of f_x as $(x, y) \to (0, 0)$ does not exist, f_x is not continuous at $(0, 0)$.

67. All partial derivatives of the components of $\mathbf{F}$ exist at $(0, 0)$; and $DF = \begin{bmatrix} 1 & 0 \\ 0 & 0 \end{bmatrix}$. Using polar coordinates, prove that $\lim\limits_{(x,y) \to (0,0)} \|\mathbf{F}(x, y) - \mathbf{F}(0, 0) - D\mathbf{F}(0, 0) \cdot (x, y)\| / \|(x, y)\| = 0$.

SECTION 2.5

1. Using $D_i g$ for the derivative of g with respect to its i-th variable, we get $f_x = 2xyD_1g + 2D_2g + D_3g$ and $f_y = x^2D_1g + 5D_2g + D_4g$, where D_ig, $i = 1, 2, 3, 4$, are evaluated at $(x^2y, 2x + 5y, x, y)$.

3. $F_x(x, y) = (D_1 f) h'(x) + (D_3 f) k_x(x, y)$, $F_y(x, y) = (D_2 f) g'(y) + (D_3 f) k_y(x, y)$, where $D_1 f$, $D_2 f$ and $D_3 f$ are computed at $(h(x), g(y), k(x, y))$.

5. $\nabla(fg)(x, y) = [\,(2x + y) \ln(xy) + x + y \quad x \ln(xy) + (x^2 + xy)/y\,]$; the derivative of f/g at $(2, 2)$ is $D(f/g)(2, 2) \approx [\,2.24672 \quad -0.63867\,]$.

7. $D(f/x)(1, \pi, -1) = [\,4 \quad 1 \quad -\pi\,]$; $D(x^2yf)(2, 0, 1) = [\,0 \quad 4 \quad 0\,]$.

9. $\partial w/\partial \rho = f_x \sin\phi \cos\theta + f_y \sin\phi \sin\theta + f_z \cos\phi$; $\partial w/\partial\theta = -\rho \sin\phi(f_x \sin\theta - f_y \cos\theta)$; $\partial w/\partial\phi = f_x\rho \cos\phi \cos\theta + f_y\rho \cos\phi \sin\theta - f_z\rho \sin\phi$.

11. $(\mathbf{v} \times \mathbf{w})'(t) = 2te^t(2 + t)\mathbf{i} - 8t^3\mathbf{k}$.   **13.** $D(g \circ \mathbf{F})(0, 0) = [\,1 \quad 1\,]$.

15. $\partial w/\partial x = D_1 f + D_2 f\, g_x$; $\partial w/\partial z = D_2 f\, g_z + D_3 f$; all partial derivatives $D_i f$, $i = 1, 2, 3$ are computed at $(x, g(x, z), z)$.

17. $D\mathbf{F}(\mathbf{x}) = A$; to prove differentiability, use Definition 2.12 or Theorem 2.5.

19. $(df/dt)(0) = 8$.

SECTION 2.6

1. $z_{xx} = y^2e^{xy} - 2/x^2$; $z_{yy} = x^2e^{xy} - 3/y^2$; $z_{xy} = z_{yx} = e^{xy}(1 + xy)$.

3. $z_{xx} = 5(x^2+y^2)^{1/2}(4x^2+y^2)$; $z_{yy} = 5(x^2+y^2)^{1/2}(x^2+4y^2)$; $z_{xy} = z_{yx} = 15xy(x^2+y^2)^{1/2}$.

5. $z_{xx} = z_{xy} = z_{yx} = z_{yy} = 2\cos(2x + 2y)$.

7. $z_{xx} = a^2 f''(ax + by) + a^2y^{-2}g''(ax/y)$; $z_{xy} = z_{yx} = abf''(ax + by) - a^2xy^{-3}g''(ax/y) - ay^{-2}g'(ax/y)$; $z_{yy} = b^2 f''(ax + by) + a^2x^2y^{-4}g''(ax/y) + 2axy^{-3}g'(ax/y)$.

9. $w_{xyzx} = 48xyz^3$.

11. (a) $u_x = 3x^2 - 3y^2 = v_y$; $u_y = -6xy = -v_x$ (b) $u_x = e^x \cos y = v_y$; $u_y = -e^x \sin y = -v_x$.

13. Both sides are equal to $z = xe^y + ye^x$.

15. A C^2 function of m variables has $m(m + 1)/2$ different second-order partial derivatives.

17. Use f', f'', g' and g'' to denote the derivatives of f and g; substituting $u_{xx} = 2f'+xf''+yg''$, $u_{xy} = f' + xf'' + g' + yg''$ and $u_{yy} = 2g' + xf'' + yg''$ into $u_{xx} - 2u_{xy} + u_{yy}$ we get 0.

19. The domain of z is $\mathbb{R}^2 - \{(0, 0)\}$. From $z_{xx} = (2y^2 - 2x^2)/(x^2 + y^2)^2$ and $z_{yy} = (2x^2 - 2y^2)/(x^2 + y^2)^2$ it follows that $z_{xx} + z_{yy} = 0$.

21. Multiply $\partial^2 R/\partial R_1^2 = -2R_2^2(R_1 + R_2)^{-3}$ and $\partial^2 R/\partial R_2^2 = -2R_1^2(R_1 + R_2)^{-3}$ and simplify.

23. $V_{xx} = GMm(y^2 + z^2 - 2x^2)(x^2 + y^2 + z^2)^{-5/2}$; $V_{yy} = GMm(x^2 + z^2 - 2y^2)(x^2 + y^2 + z^2)^{-5/2}$ and $V_{zz} = GMm(x^2 + y^2 - 2z^2)(x^2 + y^2 + z^2)^{-5/2}$.

SECTION 2.7

1. $(4, \pi, 0)$; $(0, \theta, 3)$ for $0 \le \theta < 2\pi$; $(2, \pi/2, 4)$; $(3.60555, 5.30039, -1)$.

3. T maps the given cube onto a rectangular box whose sides are $2a$ and the height is a and then rotates it for π radians about the z-axis.

5. Paraboloid: $z = 4 - r^2$ (in cylindrical coordinates), $\rho \cos \phi = 4 - \rho^2 \sin^2 \phi$ (in spherical coordinates); plane: $r \cos \theta + 2r \sin \theta - z = 0$ (in cylindrical coordinates), $\sin \phi \cos \theta + 2 \sin \phi \sin \theta - \cos \phi = 0$ (in spherical coordinates).

7. $r = C$ is the cylinder of radius C (if $C > 0$) whose axis of rotation is the z-axis; $\theta = C$ is the plane perpendicular to the xy-plane that contains the z-axis and whose intersection with the xy-plane makes the angle θ with respect to the positive x-axis. $z = C$ is the plane parallel to the xy-plane. The coordinate curve $r = C_1$, $\theta = C_2$ is the line perpendicular to the xy-plane, crossing it at the point with polar coordinates (C_1, C_2); the coordinate curve $r = C_1$, $z = C_2$ is the circle of radius C_1 in the plane $z = C_2$, centered at $(0, 0, C_2)$; the coordinate curve $\theta = C_1$, $z = C_2$ is the line in the plane $z = C_2$ crossing the z-axis at $(0, 0, C_2)$; when that line is projected onto the xy-plane, it makes the angle θ with respect to the positive x-axis.

9. $\mathbf{i} = \sin \phi \cos \theta \mathbf{e}_\rho - \sin \theta \mathbf{e}_\theta + \cos \phi \cos \theta \mathbf{e}_\phi$, $\mathbf{j} = \sin \phi \sin \theta \mathbf{e}_\rho + \cos \theta \mathbf{e}_\theta + \cos \phi \sin \theta \mathbf{e}_\phi$, $\mathbf{k} = \cos \phi \mathbf{e}_\rho - \sin \phi \mathbf{e}_\phi$.

11. $\mathbf{F}(r, \theta, z) = (\cos \theta + \sin \theta) \mathbf{e}_r + (\cos \theta - \sin \theta) \mathbf{e}_\theta$ (in cylindrical coordinates); $\mathbf{F}(\rho, \theta, \phi) = \sin \phi (\cos \theta + \sin \theta) \mathbf{e}_\rho + (\cos \theta - \sin \theta) \mathbf{e}_\theta + \cos \phi (\cos \theta + \sin \theta) \mathbf{e}_\phi$ (in spherical coordinates).

13. $\mathbf{F}(r, \theta, z) = -r \mathbf{e}_\theta$ (in cylindrical coordinates); $\mathbf{F}(\rho, \theta, \phi) = -\rho \sin \phi \mathbf{e}_\theta$ (in spherical coordinates).

15. $d\mathbf{e}_\theta/dt = -\sin \phi (d\theta/dt) \mathbf{e}_\rho - \cos \phi (d\theta/dt) \mathbf{e}_\phi$; $d\mathbf{e}_\phi/dt = -(d\phi/dt) \mathbf{e}_\rho + \cos \phi (d\theta/dt) \mathbf{e}_\theta$.

17. In cylindrical coordinates $ds^2 = dr^2 + r^2 d\theta^2 + dz^2$; in spherical coordinates, $ds^2 = d\rho^2 + \rho^2 \sin^2 \phi d\theta^2 + \rho^2 d\phi^2$.

SECTION 2.8

1. (a) $h_u = h_v = \sqrt{u^2 + v^2}$, $h_z = 1$; $\mathbf{e}_u = u\mathbf{i}/\sqrt{u^2 + v^2} + v\mathbf{j}/\sqrt{u^2 + v^2}$, $\mathbf{e}_v = -v\mathbf{i}/\sqrt{u^2 + v^2} + u\mathbf{j}/\sqrt{u^2 + v^2}$, $\mathbf{e}_z = \mathbf{k}$ (b) Follows from $\mathbf{e}_u \cdot \mathbf{e}_v = \mathbf{e}_u \cdot \mathbf{e}_z = \mathbf{e}_v \cdot \mathbf{e}_z = 0$ (c) $\mathbf{F} = F_u \mathbf{e}_u + F_v \mathbf{e}_v + F_z \mathbf{e}_z$, where $F_u = (\frac{1}{2}u(u^2 - v^2) + u^2v^3)(u^2 + v^2)^{-1/2}$, $F_v = (-\frac{1}{2}v(u^2 - v^2) + u^3v^2)(u^2 + v^2)^{-1/2}$ and $F_z = -2uv$ (d) $u = C$ is the parabolic sheet perpendicular to the xy-plane, whose trace in the xy-plane is $y^2 = C^4 - 2C^2x$; $v = C$ is the parabolic sheet $y^2 = C^4 + 2C^2x$; $z = C$ is the plane parallel to the xy-plane   (e) The z-curve $u = C_1$ and $v = C_2$ is the vertical line that crosses the xy-plane at $(\frac{1}{2}(C_1^2 - C_2^2), C_1C_2)$; the u-curve $v = C_2$ and $z = C_3$ is the parabola $y^2 = 2C_2^2x + C_2^4$ in the plane $z = C_3$; the v-curve $u = C_1$ and $z = C_3$ is the parabola $y^2 = -2C_1^2x + C_1^4$ in the plane $z = C_3$.

3. (a) $h_\xi = h_\eta = a\sqrt{\sinh^2 \xi + \sin^2 \eta}$, $h_\phi = a \sinh \xi \sin \eta$; unit coordinate vectors are given by $\mathbf{e}_\xi = (a \cosh \xi \sin \eta \cos \phi \mathbf{i} + a \cosh \xi \sin \eta \sin \phi \mathbf{j} + a \sinh \xi \cos \eta \mathbf{k})/h_\xi$, $\mathbf{e}_\eta = (a \sinh \xi \cos \eta \cos \phi \mathbf{i} + a \sinh \xi \cos \eta \sin \phi \mathbf{j} - a \cosh \xi \sin \eta \mathbf{k})/h_\eta$ and

$\mathbf{e}_\phi = -\sin\phi\mathbf{i} + \cos\phi\mathbf{j}$ (b) Follows from $\mathbf{e}_\xi \cdot \mathbf{e}_\eta = \mathbf{e}_\xi \cdot \mathbf{e}_\phi = \mathbf{e}_\eta \cdot \mathbf{e}_\phi = 0$
(c) $\mathbf{F} = F_\xi\mathbf{e}_\xi + F_\eta\mathbf{e}_\eta + F_\phi\mathbf{e}_\phi$, where $F_\xi = (\sinh^2\xi\,\sin\eta\cos\eta)(\sinh^2\xi + \sin^2\eta)^{-1/2}$,
$F_\eta = -\sinh\xi\cosh\xi\sin^2\eta)(\sinh^2\xi + \sin^2\eta)^{-1/2}$ and $F_\phi = 0$ (d) The coordinate surface
$\phi = C$ is the plane perpendicular to the xy-plane that crosses it along the line of slope
$\tan C$. If $\cos C = 0$ then it is the yz-plane. The coordinate surface $\xi = C$ is the ellipsoid $x^2/\sinh^2 C + y^2/\sinh^2 C + z^2/\cosh^2 C = a^2$. The coordinate surface $\eta = C$ is the
hyperboloid $x^2/\sin^2 C + y^2/\sin^2 C - z^2/\cos^2 C = -a^2$.

5. (a) $h_u = h_v = a/(\cosh v - \cos u)$, $h_z = 1$; the corresponding unit vectors are given
by $\mathbf{e}_u = (-\sinh v\sin u\mathbf{i} + (\cosh v\cos u - 1)\mathbf{j})/(\cosh v - \cos u)$, $\mathbf{e}_v = (-(\cosh v\cos u - 1)\mathbf{i} - \sinh v\sin u\mathbf{j})/(\cosh v - \cos u)$ and $\mathbf{e}_z = \mathbf{k}$ (b) Follows from $\mathbf{e}_u \cdot \mathbf{e}_z = \mathbf{e}_v \cdot \mathbf{e}_z = \mathbf{e}_u \cdot \mathbf{e}_v = 0$ (c) $\mathbf{F} = F_u\mathbf{e}_u + F_v\mathbf{e}_v + F_z\mathbf{e}_z$, where $F_u = -z\sinh v\sin u/(\cosh v - \cos u)$,
$F_v = -z(\cosh v\cos u - 1)/(\cosh v - \cos u)$, $F_z = 0$.

CHAPTER REVIEW

Computer Projects

1. (a) $\mathbb{R}^2 - \{(0,0)\}$ (b) does not exist   (c) approximately 0   (d) approximately 0   (e) along
$y = x$ (see $g_1(x)$) the limit at 0 does not exist   (f) (the plot suggests that $\lim\limits_{(x,y)\to(0,0)} f(x,y) \approx$
0, which is wrong).

(b), (c), (d)

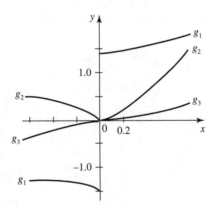

(f)

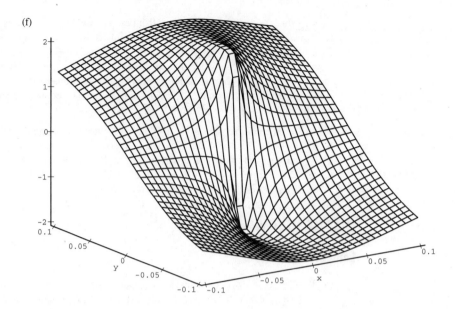

3. (a) Square each inequality and simplify   (d) the surface is built of lines that are parallel to the xy-plane and intersect the z-axis at various heights between $-1/2$ and $1/2$; since different approaches to $(0, 0)$ give different results, the limit does not exist.

(b)

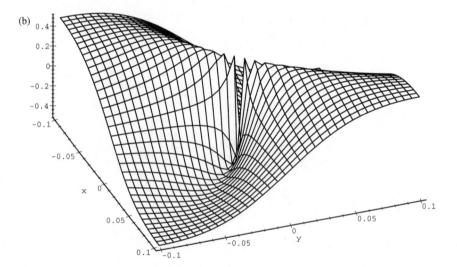

(c)

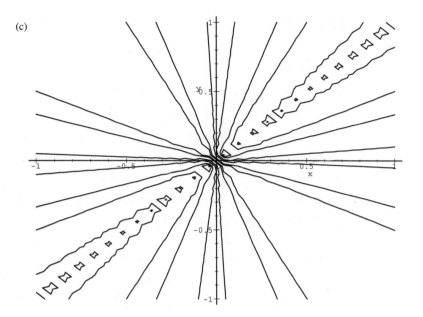

Further Explorations

1. Limit is zero; define $f(0, 0) = 0$.

3. Use the "ϵ-δ definition" of continuity.

5. There are no level curves if $c > 1$; when $c \le 1$, a level curve consists of: the circle $x^2 + y^2 = 9$ (if $c = 1$); the circles $x^2 + y^2 = 9 \pm \sqrt{1-c}$ (if $-80 < c < 1$); the circle $x^2 + y^2 = 18$ and the point $(0, 0)$ (if $c = -80$); the circle $x^2 + y^2 = 9 + \sqrt{1-c}$ (if $c < -80$).

7. (a) $(\partial T/\partial x)(3/2, 2) \approx -0.6103$; the cross-section is a sine curve of period 4 and amplitude $30e^{-4}$; as we move along the rod from $x = 3/2$ forward, we will experience a decrease in temperature of approximately 0.6103 degrees/unit distance   (b) $(\partial T/\partial t)(3/2, 2) \approx -0.7771$; the cross-section is the curve $y(t) = 15\sqrt{2}e^{-2t}$; at time $t = 2$, the temperature decreases at a rate of approximately 0.7771 degrees/unit of time.

9. Using the assumption, show that $f(0, 0) = 0$ and $f_x(0, 0) = f_y(0, 0) = 0$. To verify part (b) of Definition 2.12, use the assumption once again.

11. (a) yes   (b) yes   (c) yes   (d) no.

13. (a) no   (b) no   (c) no   (d) no.

15. $\partial F/\partial t = g R^2 (R + r)^{-2}(\partial m/\partial t) - 2mg R^2 (R + r)^{-3}(\partial r/\partial t)$.

CHAPTER 3

SECTION 3.1

1. $\mathbf{c}(t) = (3 - 3t, 1 + 4t, -2 + 2t),\ t \in \mathbb{R}$.   **3.** $\mathbf{c}(t) = (\sqrt{5}\cos t, \sqrt{5}\sin t),\ t \in [0, 2\pi]$.

5. $\mathbf{c}(t) = (-2 + 3\cos t, -1 + \sin t),\ t \in [0, 2\pi]$.

7. $\mathbf{c}(t) = (1 + t^2, t),\ 0 \le t \le 1$.   **9.** $\mathbf{c}(t) = (\cos^3 t, \sin^3 t),\ t \in [0, 2\pi]$.

11. $\mathbf{c}(t) = (2\sin 2t, 2\cos t, 2\sin t),\ t \in [0, 2\pi]$.

13. $\mathbf{c}(t) = (\sqrt{2}\sin t, \pm\sqrt{2}\sin t, \sqrt{2}\cos t),\ t \in [0, 2\pi]$.

15. $\mathbf{c}(t)$ is the part of the parabola $y = (x + 3)^2$ between $(-3, 0)$ and $(-1, 4)$.

17. $\mathbf{c}(t)$ is the right branch of the hyperbola $x^2 - y^2 = 4$; as $t \to \infty$, both components of $\mathbf{c}(t)$ approach $+\infty$.

19. $\mathbf{c}(t)$ is the part of the graph of $y = e^{3x}$ from $(0, 1)$ to $(\ln 2, 8)$.

21. $\mathbf{c}(t)$ is the circle of radius 1 in the plane $z = 3$ with the center at $(0, 0, 3)$. The initial and the terminal points are at $(1, 0, 3)$, and the orientation is counterclockwise, as seen from high up the z-axis (say, from the point $(0, 0, 10)$).

23. $\mathbf{c}(t)$ represents a circular helix with the initial point $(1, 0, 0)$ and the terminal point $(-1, 0, \pi^3)$.

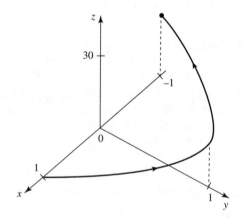

25. $\mathbf{c}(t)$ is the part of the graph of $y = \arctan x$ from $(-1, -\pi/4)$ to $(1, \pi/4)$.

27. $\mathbf{c}(t)$ is the part of the right branch of the hyperbola $x^2 - y^2 = 4$, from $(2, 0)$ to $(5/2, 3/2)$.

29. $\mathbf{c}(t)$ is a clockwise spiral — it starts at $(0, 1)$ and ends at $(0, e^{\pi/2})$.

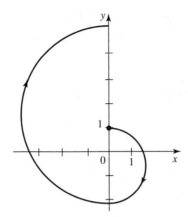

31. In all four cases, $x^2 + y^2 = 4$; c_1, c_3 and c_4 are oriented clockwise, and c_2 is oriented counterclockwise; c_1, c_2 and c_4 wind around the circle once, while c_3 winds around it three times. To get new parametrizations, adjust the existing ones, like $c_5(t) = (2\cos 5t, 2\sin 5t)$, $t \in [0, 4\pi]$; or, invent more "exotic" ones, like $c_6(t) = (\sqrt{2}(\sin t + \cos t), \sqrt{2}(\sin t - \cos t))$, $t \in [0, 2\pi]$.

33. For example, $c(t) = ((t+1)^{2/3}, 2(t+1)^{2/3})$ is not differentiable at $t = -1$.

35. $c(t)$ is continuous, not differentiable and not C^1.

37. $c(t)$ is C^1, hence also continuous and differentiable.

SECTION 3.2

1. $v(t) = (3t^2, -t^{-2}, 0)$; speed $= \sqrt{9t^4 + t^{-4}}$; $a(t) = (6t, 2t^{-3}, 0)$.

3. $v(t) = -\tan t\mathbf{i} + \cot t\mathbf{j}$; speed $= \sqrt{\tan^2 t + \cot^2 t}$; $a(t) = -\sec^2 t\mathbf{i} - \csc^2 t\mathbf{j}$.

5. $v(t) = 2e^{2t}(\sin(2t) + \cos(2t))\mathbf{i} + 2e^{2t}(\cos(2t) - \sin(2t))\mathbf{j}$; speed $= 2\sqrt{2}e^{2t}$; the acceleration is $a(t) = 8e^{2t}\cos(2t)\mathbf{i} - 8e^{2t}\sin(2t)\mathbf{j}$.

7. $v(t) = (t^{-1/2}/2, 1, 3t^{1/2}/2)$; speed $= (4 + 9t + t^{-1})^{1/2}/2$; $a(t) = (-t^{-3/2}/4, 0, 3t^{-1/2}/4)$.

9. $v(t) = (-t + 1, t + 2, 0)$; $c(t) = (t - t^2/2, 2 + 2t + t^2/2, 0)$.

11. $v(t) = (t^2/2, t + 1, t)$; $c(t) = (t^3/6 - 2, t^2/2 + t, t^2/2 + 3)$.

13. $v(t) = (t^2/2)\mathbf{i} + (2 + t^3/3)\mathbf{j} + (-3 + t^2/2)\mathbf{k}$; $c(t) = (4 + t^3/6)\mathbf{i} + (2 + 2t + t^4/12)\mathbf{j} + (-6 - 3t + t^3/6)\mathbf{k}$.

15. The particle reaches its maximum speed of approximately 8.0002 (units) at $t = 4$.

17. The particle reaches its highest position when $t = 12$.

19. The range of the projectile is approximately $43, 302$ m; maximim height ($\approx 18, 750$ m) is reached when $t \approx 61.86$ s; the speed at the time of impact is 700 m/s.

21. $\ell(t) = (\sqrt{3}, t)$, $t \in \mathbb{R}$.   **23.** $\ell(t) = (-3t, 3, 2\pi + 4t)$, $t \in \mathbb{R}$.

25. $\ell(t) = (-1, 1 + t)$, $t \in \mathbb{R}$.

27. Use the product rule and the chain rule.

29. $v(t) = -e^{-t}(\cos t + \sin t, \sin t - \cos t)$; it is horizontal at $c(\pi/4)$, $c(5\pi/4)$ and $c(9\pi/4)$ and vertical at $\mathbf{c}(3\pi/4)$, $\mathbf{c}(7\pi/4)$ and $\mathbf{c}(11\pi/4)$.

31. The vector $-\mathbf{j}$ is tangent to the image of $\mathbf{c}(t)$ under $\mathbf{F}$ at $t = 0$.

33. The required vector is $(a_{11}c_1 + a_{12}c_2)\mathbf{i} + (a_{21}c_1 + a_{22}c_2)\mathbf{j}$.

SECTION 3.3

1. $\ell(p_5) \approx 1.17488$.   **3.** π.   **5.** $\sqrt{2}(e^\pi - 1)$.

7. Approximately 2.08581.   **9.** $\sinh 1$.   **11.** 12.

13. It is not possible to evaluate the integrals for the lengths of the given curves; the idea is to compare the integrands.

15. $a\pi/4$.   **17.** $8^{3/2} - 5^{3/2}$.

19. 4; integration is a bit tricky; hint: multiply and divide by $\sqrt{1 - \sin\theta}$.

21. $s(t) = t^2 + t$, $0 \le t \le 2\pi$.

23. $s(t) = 13t$, $t \in [0, \pi/4]$; $\mathbf{c}(s) = 5\cos(s/13)\mathbf{i} + 5\sin(s/13)\mathbf{j} + (12s/13)\mathbf{k}$, $s \in [0, 13\pi/4]$.

25. $s(t) = \sqrt{2}(e^t - 1)$, $0 \le t \le 1$; $\mathbf{c}(s) = (1 + s/\sqrt{2})[\cos(\ln(1 + s/\sqrt{2}))\mathbf{i} + \sin(\ln(1 + s/\sqrt{2}))\mathbf{j}]$, $s \in [0, \sqrt{2}(e - 1)]$.

27. Since $\mathbf{c}_2(t) = \mathbf{c}_1(t/2)$ and $\mathbf{c}_3(t) = \mathbf{c}_1(-t)$, it follows that $\mathbf{c}_1$, $\mathbf{c}_2$ and $\mathbf{c}_3$ are reparametrizations of each other, and so represent the same curve; its length is $\pi\sqrt{5}$.

29. $\mathbf{T}(1) = -\mathbf{i}$.   **31.** No.

SECTION 3.4

1. $\mathbf{a}_T = (16t^2, 8t, 16t^2)/(8t^2 + 1)$; $\mathbf{a}_N = (2, -8t, 2)/(8t^2 + 1)$.

3. $\mathbf{a}_T = 0$; $\mathbf{a}_N = \mathbf{a} = -12\sin t\,\mathbf{j} - 12\cos t\,\mathbf{k}$.

5. $\mathbf{a}_T = (\sin t(1 - \cos t)\mathbf{i} + \sin^2 t\mathbf{j})/(2 - 2\cos t)$; and $\mathbf{a}_N = (\sin t(1 - \cos t)\mathbf{i} + (2\cos t - 2\cos^2 t - \sin^2 t\mathbf{j})/(2 - 2\cos t)$.

7. $\|\mathbf{c}'\| = \sqrt{(x')^2 + (y')^2}$; $\mathbf{T}' = ((x')^2 + (y')^2)^{-3/2}\left(x''(y')^2 - x'y'y'', y''(x')^2 - x'y'x''\right)$; $\|\mathbf{T}'\| = ((x')^2 + (y')^2)^{-1}|x''y' - x'y''|$; so $\kappa = \|\mathbf{T}'\|/\|\mathbf{c}'\| = |x''y' - x'y''|/((x')^2 + (y')^2)^{3/2}$.

9. $\mathbf{c}(t)$ is a line; its curvature is zero.

11. $\kappa(t) = 2(4t^2 + 1)^{-3/2}$; maximum is 2, occurs at $\mathbf{c}(0) = (0, 3)$; as $t \to \infty$, $\kappa(t) \to 0$.

13. $\mathbf{T}(t) = (\sin t + \cos t, 0, \cos t - \sin t)/\sqrt{2}$; $\mathbf{N}(t) = (\cos t - \sin t, 0, -\sin t - \cos t)/\sqrt{2}$; curvature is $\kappa(t) = \sqrt{2}e^{-t}/2$; $\mathbf{a}_N = e^t(\cos t - \sin t, 0, -\sin t - \cos t)$.

15. $\mathbf{T}(t) = (1, -\sin t, -\cos t)/\sqrt{2}$; $\mathbf{N}(t) = (0, -\cos t, \sin t)$; $\kappa(t) = 1/2$; $\mathbf{a}_N = (0, -\cos t, \sin t)$.

17. $\mathbf{T}(t) = (-\cos t - \sin t, -\sin t + \cos t, -1)/\sqrt{3}$; $\mathbf{N}(t) = (\sin t - \cos t, -\sin t - \cos t, 0)/\sqrt{2}$; $\kappa(t) = e^t\sqrt{2}/3$; $\mathbf{a}_N = e^{-t}(\sin t - \cos t, -\sin t - \cos t, 0)$.

19. $(x - 241/12)^2 + (y + 143)^2 = 145^3/144$.

21. $x + 2z - \pi = 0$.   **23.** $\kappa(x_0) = 2(1 + 4x_0^2)^{-3/2}$.

25. Maximum curvature occurs at $x = 1/\sqrt{2}$; its value is $\kappa(1/\sqrt{2}) \approx 0.3849$.

27. $2y + z - 2 = 0$.   **29.** $(x - \pi/2)^2 + y^2 = 1$.

SECTION 3.5

1. $d(\mathbf{T}(s) \cdot \mathbf{T}(s))/ds = 0$; $(d\mathbf{c}(t)/dt) \cdot \mathbf{T}(t) = \|\mathbf{c}'(t)\|$; $d\mathbf{N}(s)/ds \cdot \mathbf{B}(s) = \tau(s)$.

3. Yes.

5. $\mathbf{T}(\pi/2) = (-\mathbf{i} + \mathbf{k})/\sqrt{2}$; $\mathbf{N}(\pi/2) = (-\mathbf{i} - \mathbf{k})/\sqrt{2}$; $\mathbf{B}(\pi/2) = -\mathbf{j}$.

7. $\mathbf{T}(t) = (\cos t/\sqrt{2}, \cos t/\sqrt{2}, -\sin t)$; $\mathbf{N}(t) = (-\sin t/\sqrt{2}, -\sin t/\sqrt{2}, -\cos t)$; $\mathbf{B}(t) = \mathbf{T}(t) \times \mathbf{N}(t) = (-1, 1, 0)/\sqrt{2}$.

9. Since $d\mathbf{N}/ds + \kappa\mathbf{T}$ is perpendicular to both $\mathbf{T}$ and $\mathbf{N}$, it must be parallel to $\mathbf{B}$. We can define τ so that $d\mathbf{N}/ds + \kappa\mathbf{T} = \tau\mathbf{B}$.

11. Differentiate $\mathbf{c}'(t) = (ds/dt)\mathbf{T}$ with respect to t and use formula (3.6).

13. Use the formula of Exercise 11 and the fact that $\mathbf{c}'(t) = \|\mathbf{c}'(t)\|\mathbf{T}(t) = (ds/dt)\mathbf{T}(t)$.

15. $b/(a^2 + b^2)$.

17. The torsion is zero; the curvature $\kappa(t) = 1/(2a(t^2 + 1)^{3/2})$ $k(t)$ is largest when $t = 0$.

19. $\kappa(t) = (3 + 2\sin t \cos t - 2\sin t - 2\cos t)^{1/2}(4 - 2\sin t - 2\cos t)^{-3/2}$; $\tau(t) = -(3 + 2\sin t \cos t - 2\sin t - 2\cos t)^{-1}$.

SECTION 3.6

1. The flow lines of $\mathbf{F}$, $\mathbf{F}_1$ and $\mathbf{F}_2$ are parabolas $y = Cx^2$, $C = $ constant. $\mathbf{F}_1$ has the "fastest" flow lines, while those of $\mathbf{F}$ have the smallest speed; flow lines of $\mathbf{F}_1$ "flow" in the same direction as those of $\mathbf{F}$, while the flow lines of $\mathbf{F}_2$ "flow" in the opposite direction.

3. $\mathbf{c}(t) = t(6/\sqrt{13}, 4/\sqrt{13})$, $t \geq 0$.

5.

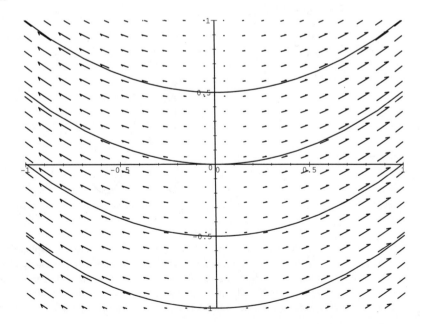

7.

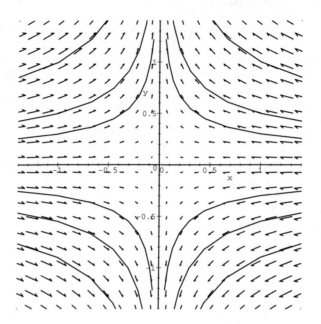

9. There are infinitely many answers. For example, $\mathbf{F}(x, y, z) = (y, y/z, 2z/y)$.

11. To get the flow lines of $-\mathbf{F}$, take the flow lines of $\mathbf{F}$ and reverse their orientation.

CHAPTER REVIEW

Computer Projects

1. (a) $\kappa(t) = 2(\sin^2 t + 4\cos^2 t)^{-3/2}$; $\tau(t) = 0$ (b) curvature is the largest at $(0, \pm 2)$ and smallest at $(\pm 1, 0)$ (c) $(x + 3)^2 + y^2 = 16$.

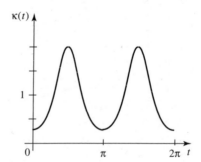

3. (a) $\mathbf{c}(t) = (11at^3/2 - 12at^2 + 15at/2, at^3 - a)$ (b) no airplane would choose a route that we suggest! Although the curvature does change continuously from 0 to $1/a$, it does not assume only the values between them, but grows much larger. Obviously our requirements on the trajectory did not suffice — additional conditions have to be imposed (like curvature assuming only the values between 0 and $1/a$, probably some assumptions on the speed, etc.).

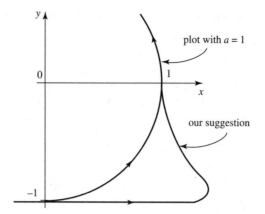

plot with $a = 1$

our suggestion

Further Explorations

1. $\mathbf{W} = \tau \mathbf{T} + \kappa \mathbf{B}$.

3. Recall that $\kappa(s) = \|d\mathbf{T}(s)/ds\| = \lim_{\Delta s \to 0} \|\mathbf{T}(s + \Delta s) - \mathbf{T}(s)\|/|\Delta s|$. To compute the limit use $\|\mathbf{T}(s + \Delta s) - \mathbf{T}(s)\| = 2\sin(|\theta(s + \Delta s) - \theta(s)|/2)$, where θ is the angle between the tangent and the positive x-axis, and the approximation $\sin a \approx a$ for a close to 0.

5. Use Newton's Second Law and Exercise 27 in Section 3.2 to show that the derivative of $r^2(d\theta/dt)$ with respect to t is zero.

7. At $x = -\ln 8/4$.

9. The speed is $e^t \sqrt{3}$; the magnitude of the acceleration is $e^t \sqrt{5}$.

CHAPTER 4

SECTION 4.1

1. $-3/\sqrt{5}$.   3. $(3\ln 4 + 12)/5$.   5. 0.

7. $\nabla f(2, 3) = (81, 2)$; the directional derivative is $79/\sqrt{2}$.

9. $\nabla f(0, \pi) = (-1, 0)$; the directional derivative is $1/\sqrt{1 + \pi^2}$.

11. $\nabla f(0, -1, 2) = 2e^{-5}\mathbf{j} - 4e^{-5}\mathbf{k}$; the directional derivative is $-2e^{-5}/\sqrt{3}$.

13. Maximum rate of change of is $\sqrt{10}$; the direction is $(\sqrt{2}, 2\sqrt{2})$.

15. Maximum rate of change equals $\sqrt{77}/4$; the direction is $3\mathbf{i}/2 - 5\mathbf{j}/4 - \mathbf{k}$.

17. Maximum rate of change equals $\sqrt{13}$; the direction is $(2, -3)$.

19. (a) $-400e^{-2}/\sqrt{2}$ (b) Pressure increases most rapidly in the direction of $\nabla P(0, 1) = (0, -400e^{-2})$; it decreases most rapidly in the opposite direction   (c) $400e^{-2}$ (d) $\pm\mathbf{i}$.

21. In the direction of the vector $(3/5, 4/5)$ and in the direction of the vector $(1, 0)$.

23. $24/\sqrt{10}$.   25. Use the definition of the gradient.

27. Use the definition of the gradient and the quotient rule.

29. Approximately 1.1698 rad.

31. $\pi y + 3z - 2\pi = 0$.   **33.** $2x - 3y - 4\sqrt{2}z + 6 = 0$.

35. Normal line: $\ell_N(t) = (2, 4 + 2t, \sqrt{3} + 2t\sqrt{3})$, $t \in \mathbb{R}$; tangent plane: $y + \sqrt{3}z - 7 = 0$.

37. Normal line: $\ell_N(t) = (0, e + t, 1)$, $t \in \mathbb{R}$; tangent plane: $y = 1$.

39. Normal line: $\ell_N(t) = (3t, -2 - 2t)$, $t \in \mathbb{R}$; tangent line: $\ell_T(t) = (2t, -2 + 3t)$, $t \in \mathbb{R}$.

41. Normal line: $\ell_N = (2t + \ln 2, \pi/2)$, $t \in \mathbb{R}$; tangent line: $\ell_T(t) = (\ln 2, t + \pi/2)$, $t \in \mathbb{R}$.

43. $(1/2, 3/2, -5/2)$.

45. Unit normal vectors are $\pm(\pi, 2, 2)/\sqrt{\pi^2 + 8}$.

47. Using the gradient, find a parametrization of a line normal to the sphere. Show that that line contains the center of the sphere.

49. Show that the normal vectors of the two families of curves are perpendicular.

51. Use the fact that the gradient vector is perpendicular to a level surface.

53. $V(x, y) = -xe^{xy} + C$, where C is a constant.

55. $V(x, y, z) = x^2y^2 + x^3z - yz^3 + C$, where C is a constant.

57. $V(x, y) = -x^2y^2/2 - x^3y + C$, where C is a constant.

SECTION 4.2

1. The expression is meaningless.   **3.** Vector field.

5. Vector field.   **7.** Scalar function.

9. $curl\, \mathbf{F} = (xz + x)\mathbf{i} - (yz - y^2)\mathbf{j} - (z + 2yz)\mathbf{k}$; $div\, \mathbf{F} = xy$.

11. $curl\, \mathbf{F} = -e^{-y}\mathbf{j} + (e^y - ze^{-y})\mathbf{k}$; $div\, \mathbf{F} = xe^y$.

13. $curl\, \mathbf{F} = -2(y + z)\mathbf{i} + 2(x + 3z)\mathbf{j} + 2(x - 3y)\mathbf{k}$; $div\, \mathbf{F} = 6x + 2y - 2z$.

15. $\mathbf{F}$ is not conservative.

17. $\mathbf{F}(x, y)$ is conservative; $V(x, y) = -x^3y - y^4/4 + C$, where C is a constant.

19. $\mathbf{F}(x, y, z)$ is conservative; $V(x, y, z) = xy + 3z + C$, where C is a constant.

21. Use definitions and the chain rule.

23. No, since $div\,(curl\, \mathbf{F}) \neq 0$.   **25.** Show that $curl\, \mathbf{F} = \mathbf{0}$.

27. $\mathbf{F}(x, y) = (x^3 - 3xy^2, -3x^2y + y^3, 0)$; check that $div\, \mathbf{F} = 0$ and $curl\, \mathbf{F} = \mathbf{0}$.

29. $\mathbf{F} = \mathbf{F}_1 + \mathbf{F}_2$, where $\mathbf{F}_1 = z\mathbf{i} + \mathbf{j}$ is incompressible and $\mathbf{F}_2 = \mathbf{j} - z\mathbf{k}$ is irrotational (there are infinitely many decompositions).

31. $\mathbf{F} = \mathbf{F}_1 + \mathbf{F}_2$, where $\mathbf{F}_1 = -4\mathbf{i}$ is incompressible and $\mathbf{F}_2 = e^{2y}\mathbf{j} + \arctan z\mathbf{k}$ is irrotational (there are infinitely many decompositions).

33. Use $curl\,(grad\, f) = \mathbf{0}$ and the definition of Δf.

35. $div\, \mathbf{F} = 4x + 8y^2z + 3x^3 - 3x - 8y^2z + 2x^3 \neq 0$; $div\,(xyz^2\mathbf{F}) = 0$.

37. Use the chain rule to show that $curl\, \mathbf{F} = \mathbf{0}$.

39. Use definitions to show that both sides are equal to the same vector; the identity holds if both f and $\mathbf{F}$ are differentiable.

41. $div\,(x\mathbf{i} + y\mathbf{j} + z\mathbf{k}) = 3.$

43. Write $\|\mathbf{r}\|\mathbf{r} = \sqrt{x^2 + y^2 + z^2}\,(x\mathbf{i} + y\mathbf{j} + z\mathbf{k})$ and compute the divergence; alternatively, use Exercise 38 and then Exercises 41 and 42.

45. Use definitions; f and g must be of class C^2.

47. $div\,(\mathbf{F} \times \mathbf{r}) = 0.$

49. $\mathbf{r}$ is a radial vector field; since there are no rotations within the flow, $curl\,\mathbf{r} = \mathbf{0}$.

51. $-2\|\mathbf{r}\|^{-3}\mathbf{r}$.

SECTION 4.3

1. $grad\,(\mathbf{F}\cdot\mathbf{G}) = ((F_1)_x G_1 + F_1(G_1)_x + (F_2)_x G_2 + F_2(G_2)_x + (F_3)_x G_3 + F_3(G_3)_x)\,\mathbf{i} + A\mathbf{j} + B\mathbf{k}$, where A and B contain six terms each; A is obtained from the coefficient of $\mathbf{i}$ by replacing all partial derivatives with respect to x with partial derivatives with respect to y, and B is obtained from the coefficient of $\mathbf{i}$ by replacing all partial derivatives with respect to x with partial derivatives with respect to z.

$$(\mathbf{F} \cdot \nabla)\mathbf{G} = \big(F_1(G_1)_x + F_2(G_1)_y + F_3(G_1)_z\big)\,\mathbf{i} + \big(F_1(G_2)_x + F_2(G_2)_y + F_3(G_2)_z\big)\,\mathbf{j}$$
$$+ \big(F_1(G_3)_x + F_2(G_3)_y + F_3(G_3)_z\big)\,\mathbf{k}.$$

The expression for $(\mathbf{G} \cdot \nabla)\mathbf{F}$ is obtained from $(\mathbf{F} \cdot \nabla)\mathbf{G}$ by interchanging $\mathbf{F}$ and $\mathbf{G}$.

$$\mathbf{F} \times curl\,\mathbf{G} = \big[F_2(G_2)_x - F_2(G_1)_y + F_3(G_3)_x - F_3(G_1)_z\big]\,\mathbf{i} + \big[-F_1(G_2)_x + F_1(G_1)_y$$
$$+ F_3(G_3)_y - F_3(G_2)_z\big]\,\mathbf{j} + \big[-F_1(G_3)_x + F_1(G_1)_z - F_2(G_3)_y + F_2(G_2)_z\big]\,\mathbf{k}.$$

The expression for $\mathbf{G} \times curl\,\mathbf{F}$ is obtained from $\mathbf{F} \times curl\,\mathbf{G}$ by interchanging $\mathbf{F}$ and $\mathbf{G}$.

3. The left side is equal to

$$curl\,(f\mathbf{F}) = \big(F_3(f)_y + f(F_3)_y - F_2(f)_z - f(F_2)_z\big)\,\mathbf{i}$$
$$+ (F_1(f)_z + f(F_1)_z - F_3(f)_x - f(F_3)_x)\,\mathbf{j} + \big(F_2(f)_x + f(F_2)_x - F_1(f)_y - f(F_1)_y\big)\,\mathbf{k},$$

and the right side is

$$f\,curl\,\mathbf{F} + grad\,f \times \mathbf{F} = f\,\big[((F_3)_y - (F_2)_z)\,\mathbf{i} + ((F_1)_z - (F_3)_x)\,\mathbf{j} + ((F_2)_x - (F_1)_y)\,\mathbf{k}\big]$$
$$+ \big(F_3(f)_y - F_2(f)_z\big)\,\mathbf{i} + \big(F_1(f)_z - F_3(f)_x\big)\,\mathbf{j} + \big(F_2(f)_x - F_1(f)_y\big)\,\mathbf{k},$$

and the identity follows.

5. $\Delta(fg) = f_{xx}g + 2f_x g_x + fg_{xx} + f_{yy}g + 2f_y g_y + fg_{yy}$; $g\Delta f = g(f_{xx} + f_{yy})$; $f\Delta g = f(g_{xx} + g_{yy})$; $grad\,f \cdot grad\,g = f_x g_x + f_y g_y$.

7. An alternative to a somewhat long computation is to simplify the expression using product rules of the form $div\,(\mathbf{F} \times \mathbf{G})$ and $curl\,(f\mathbf{F})$, together with the fact that the scalar triple product of vectors with two equal factors is zero.

9. $div\,(f\,grad\,g) = f\,div\,(grad\,g) + (grad\,g) \cdot (grad\,f)$; interchange f and g to obtain the expression for $div\,(g\,grad\,f)$ and subtract.

11. Use the product rule for $div\,(f\mathbf{F})$ with $f = \|\mathbf{r}\|^{-3}$ and $\mathbf{F} = \mathbf{r}$ and the fact that (check it!) $grad\,\|\mathbf{r}\|^{-3} = -3\|\mathbf{r}\|^{-5}\mathbf{r}$.

13. $grad\, f = (D_1 g\, u_x + D_2 g\, v_x + D_3 g,\ D_1 g\, u_y + D_2 g\, v_y + D_4 g)$.

15. $\|\mathbf{r}\|^{-2}\mathbf{r}$.

17. $\|\mathbf{r}\|^{-2}$.

19. $div\,\mathbf{F} = 3r;\ curl\,\mathbf{F} = \frac{1}{r}(\cos\theta - r^2)\mathbf{e}_r + 2z\mathbf{e}_z$.

21. $div\,\mathbf{F} = 2\theta/\rho - (\sin\theta\cot\phi)/\rho - \cot\phi;\ curl\,\mathbf{F} = \cos\theta\cos(2\phi)\mathbf{e}_\rho/(\rho\sin\phi) - (\frac{1}{2}\cos\theta\sin(2\phi) - 1)\mathbf{e}_\phi/(\rho\sin\phi) - 2\mathbf{e}_\theta$.

23. $(\cosh^2 u - \cos^2 v)^{-1}(v\sinh u\cos v - u\cosh u\sin v)$.

25. $curl\,\mathbf{F} = A^{-2}\begin{vmatrix} A\mathbf{e}_u & A\mathbf{e}_v & \mathbf{e}_z \\ \partial/\partial u & \partial/\partial v & \partial/\partial z \\ AF_u & AF_v & F_z \end{vmatrix}$, where $\mathbf{F} = F_u\mathbf{e}_u + F_v\mathbf{e}_v + F_z\mathbf{e}_z$ and $A = a/(\cosh v - \cos u)$.

27. $\frac{\partial\phi}{\partial t} = c(\sinh^2 u + \sin^2 v)^{-1}\left(\frac{\partial^2\phi}{\partial u^2} + \frac{\partial^2\phi}{\partial v^2}\right) + c\frac{\partial^2\phi}{\partial z^2}$.

29. (a) $\frac{\partial U}{\partial t} = c\left(\frac{\partial^2 U}{\partial\rho^2} + 2\rho^{-1}\frac{\partial U}{\partial\rho} + \rho^{-2}\frac{\partial^2 U}{\partial\phi^2} + \rho^{-2}\cot\phi\frac{\partial U}{\partial\phi}\right)$ (b) $\frac{\partial U}{\partial t} = c\left(\frac{\partial^2 U}{\partial\rho^2} + 2\rho^{-1}\frac{\partial U}{\partial\rho}\right)$ (c) $\frac{\partial^2 U}{\partial\rho^2} + 2\rho^{-1}\frac{\partial U}{\partial\rho} = 0$ (d) $\rho^{-2}\sin^{-2}\phi\frac{\partial^2 U}{\partial\theta^2} + \rho^{-2}\frac{\partial^2 U}{\partial\phi^2} + \rho^{-2}\cot\phi\frac{\partial U}{\partial\phi} = 0$.

SECTION 4.4

1. $e^{x+y}(x^2 + y^2)dz$.

3. $3x(x^2 + y^2)dxdz + yz(x^2 + y^2)dydz$.

5. Not defined.

7. 0 (zero 2-form).

9. $(2x^2 + 2y^2 - \sin x)dxdydz$.

11. 0 (zero 4-form).

13. (a) Both sides are equal to $-x^2 e^z dxdydz$ (b) Both sides are equal to $x^2 dxdy + x^2 dxdz$.

15. $e^{xyz}(yzdx + xzdy + xydz)$.

17. $2xdxdydz$.

19. $2\sinh x\cosh x\, dxdy$.

21. $(1 + x)dxdydz$.

23. $(1 + x^2)^{-1}dx$.

25. 0 (zero 3-form).

27. $d\alpha = (3x^2 + 2)dxdy;\ d(d\alpha) = 0$.

29. Both sides are equal to $e^z((4xy - 2xyz - y^3)dx + (2x^2 - 3xy^2 - x^2 z)dy + (x^2 y - xy^3 - x^2 yz)dz)$.

31. 0 (zero 3-form).

33. $div\,\mathbf{F} = 2xyz - y;\ d\alpha = (2xyz - y)dxdydz$.

35. $d(df) = 0$ represents $curl\,(\nabla f) = \mathbf{0}$.

CHAPTER REVIEW

Computer Project

1. (a) maximum rate of change is approximately 10.18105; the direction is approximately $(3.07843, 9.70450)$ (b) $1.24485 < \alpha \le \pi$, where α is the angle between measured from $\nabla f(1, 2)$ (c) $g(\theta) \approx 3.07843\cos\theta + 9.70450\sin\theta$; maximum at $\theta \approx 1.26362$; minimum at $\theta \approx 4.40521$.

(d)

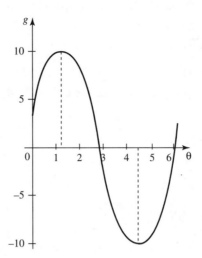

Further Explorations

1. First show that $grad \, \|\mathbf{r}\|^{-2} = -2\|\mathbf{r}\|^{-4}\mathbf{r}$ and $div \, (\|\mathbf{r}\|^{-2}\mathbf{r}) = \|\mathbf{r}\|^{-2}$; from the definition of the Laplace operator and a product rule for div it follows that $\Delta(div \, (\|\mathbf{r}\|^{-2}\mathbf{r})) = div \, (grad \, \|\mathbf{r}\|^{-2}) = -2div \, (\|\mathbf{r}\|^{-4}\mathbf{r}) = 2\|\mathbf{r}\|^{-4}$.

3. Compute the derivative of $f(t\mathbf{x}) = t^p f(\mathbf{x})$ with respect to t and evaluate for $t = 1$.

5. (a) $2\mathbf{i} + 8\mathbf{j}$ (b) $-2\mathbf{i} - 8\mathbf{j}$; the angle is $\arccos(1/\sqrt{69}) \approx 1.4502$ rad   (c) there are two directions, $-0.9730\mathbf{i} + 0.2308\mathbf{j}$ and $-0.9671\mathbf{i} + 0.2543\mathbf{j}$.

7. Show that $\left(f(\mathbf{c}(t)) \right)' = -\|\mathbf{c}'(t)\|^2 \le 0$.

9. (a) $\nabla V(1, 1, -3) \approx -0.01618\mathbf{i} - 0.01618\mathbf{j} + 0.04854\mathbf{k}$ (b) in directions perpendicular to $\nabla V(1, 1, -3)$.

CHAPTER 5

SECTION 5.1

1. Yes.

3. No, since ϕ is not differentiable at 0.

5. Yes.

7. No, since ϕ is not bijective.

9. Not simple; closed; not simple closed.

11. Simple; not closed; not simple closed.

13. Simple; not closed; not simple closed.

15. $\mathbf{c}(t) = (t, \sqrt{t^2 + 1})$, $t \in [-1, 1]$, is C^1 (hence differentiable and continuous).

17. $\mathbf{c}_1$, $\mathbf{c}_2$ and $\mathbf{c}_4$ are C^1 paths; $\mathbf{c}_3$ is continuous, but not piecewise C^1 and not C^1; $\mathbf{c}_5$ is piecewise C^1, but not continuous, and not C^1.

19. $\phi(t) = \pm\sqrt{Ct + D}$, $t \in [1, 3]$; the constants C and D are chosen so that ϕ is defined.

21. $(\cos(St), -\sin(St))$, $t \in [0, 2\pi/S]$, is orientation-preserving of speed S; $(\cos t, \sin t)$, $t \in [0, 2\pi]$, is orientation-reversing of speed 1.

SECTION 5.2

1. $11\sqrt{2}/2$.

3. $\sqrt{3}/3$.

5. $16 \ln 4 + (\ln 4)^2/2 - 547.5$.

7. $5\sqrt{29}/2$.

9. $-48\pi\sqrt{5}$.

11. $5(1 - e^{-9})/9 \approx 0.5556$.

13. -16.

15. Yes, that is possible.

17. 8π.

19. $(2^{3/2} - 1)/3 \approx 0.6095$.

21. $8\pi e^{16}$.

23. No.

25. $-6/\pi$.

SECTION 5.3

1. $2/5$.

3. $e^2 - 2e + 1$.

5. 3π.

7. $(2/3)(\pi/2)^6 \approx 10.0145$.

9. $e + 8$.

11. Approximately 5.2940.

13. The direction of $\mathbf{F}$ is orthogonal to all circles centered at the origin.

15. (a) 0   (b) 1/3   (c) 1/5   (d) 1/2   (e) $2/\pi \approx 0.6366$ (f) 1; sketch the vector fields and all paths; give an interpretation in terms of "alignment" of the curves with the vector field.

17. $12/7$.

19. $5/34$.

21. 0.

23. 0.

25. (a) $4/3$ (b) $4/3$ (c) $-4/3$; path integral of a 1-form depends on the orientation.

27. Express the path integral along a curve as the sum along its pieces that are smooth and apply Theorem 5.3 to each piece.

29. The circulation is 0; the flux is $2\pi r$.

31. The circulation is 0; the flux is πr.

SECTION 5.4

1. Not connected; not simply-connected; not star-shaped.

3. Connected; not simply-connected; not star-shaped.

5. Not connected; not simply-connected; not star-shaped.

7. Connected; simply-connected; not star-shaped.

9. Connected; simply-connected; star-shaped.

11. $8 \sin 1$.

13. Integral along $\mathbf{c}_1$ is π, whereas the integral along $\mathbf{c}_2$ is $-\pi$; the domain of $\mathbf{F}$ is not simply-connected, and Theorem 5.8 does not apply.

15. $\mathbf{F}$ is not a gradient vector field.

17. $\mathbf{F}$ is a gradient vector field on $U = \{(x, y) \mid y > 0\}$; $f = x^2 \ln y + y^2 + C$, where C is a constant.

19. $\mathbf{F}$ is a gradient vector field on $\mathbb{R}^3$; $f = \sin(xy) + z \cos y + C$, where C is a constant.

21. $\pi/2$.

23. (a) $curl\ \mathbf{F} = \mathbf{0}$ (b) $V(x, 0) = 0$ (c) $V(0, y) = 0$.

25. (a) $-18e^{-2}$ (b) $-18e^{-2}$.

27. $f = \|\mathbf{r}\|^4/4 + C$, where C is a constant.   **29.** $\int_c \mathbf{F} \cdot d\mathbf{s} = \ln 2178$.

31. Use the Fundamental Theorem of Calculus and the interpretation of $\int_c \alpha$ as a path integral of a vector field.

CHAPTER REVIEW

Computer Project

1. (a) $W(\theta) = (e^{\sin\theta\cos\theta} - 1)/2 + \sin^3\theta/3$ (b) minimum work : $\theta \approx 5.04291$ rad; maximim work: $\theta \approx 1.03951$ rad; zero work: $\theta = 0, 2\pi$ rad; $\theta \approx 2.17310$ rad; $\theta \approx 4.25790$ rad   (c) give an interpretation in terms of alignment of the vector filed with lines that make an angle θ with respect to the positive x-axis.

(b)

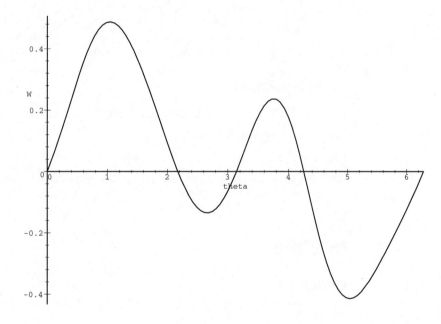

(d)

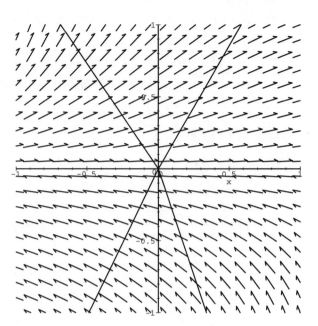

Further Explorations

1. $\phi(t) = (Ct + D)^{2/3} - 4/9$, where $C > 0$ and D are constants.

3. $\int_{C_\epsilon} \mathbf{F} \cdot d\mathbf{s} = \epsilon \ln \epsilon$; the limit is 0.

5. $-a\|\mathbf{r}\|^3/3$.

7. Using the chain rule and Newton's Second Law, show that $dE(t)/dt = 0$; this equation is the Conservation of Energy Law.

CHAPTER 6

SECTION 6.1

1. $448/9$.   3. $-75/2$.   5. $(1 + \sqrt{e})/4$.

7. Area of R.   9. 5.

11. Conclude that $1 \leq e^{x^2+y^2} \leq e^2$ and integrate over R.

13. $2\pi^2$.   15. f is integrable; $\iint_R f\, dA = 11$.

17. Not true if $R = [0, 1] \times [0, 1]$; true if $R = [1, 2] \times [2, 3]$.

19. No.

SECTION 6.2

1. $\iint_D f \, dA$ is the negative of the volume of the solid region below D and above f. $\iint_D (f-g) \, dA$ is the volume of the solid region between f and g and above $D \subseteq \mathbb{R}^2$.

3. $r^2 h \pi / 3$.   **5.** $e^2 - 3$.   **7.** $e^3 - e^2 + e - 5$.

9. 0.   **11.** 1/6.   **13.** Approximately -32.3135.

15. 0.   **17.** Approximately 23.0906.   **19.** $4e^{-3} \le \iint_D e^{-x-y} \, dA \le 4e$.

21. 22.   **23.** 1/12.

25. Use the remark immediately following the statement of Theorem 6.5.

27. $ab\pi$.   **29.** $8\sqrt{2}/3$.

31. Points in R that lie on the circle centered at $(0, 0)$ of radius $\sqrt{5/3}$.

SECTION 6.3

1. $-2e^{1/2} + 7/2$.   **3.** 156.   **5.** $2\pi - 8/3$.

7. 8/3.   **9.** 11/24.   **11.** 0.

13. $\int_0^{\pi/4} \left(\int_0^{\tan y} (y^2 - x) dx \right) dy$.

15. $\int_1^2 \left(\int_1^2 \frac{\ln x}{x} dy \right) dx + \int_2^4 \left(\int_{x/2}^2 \frac{\ln x}{x} dy \right) dx$.

17. $-1 + \pi/2$.   **19.** $(\sin 162)/8$.   **21.** 10/3.   **23.** $(e - 1)/3$.

SECTION 6.4

1. $\pi(e^4 - 1)/4$.   **3.** $\pi^2/4$.   **5.** $\pi(5^{3/2} - 3^{3/2})/3$.

7. $25\pi/2$.   **9.** Approximately 93.9578.   **11.** Follows from $DT = A$.

13. Approximately 0.1342.

15. T is an expansion by the factor a in the u-direction and a translation by b in the v-direction; the area of the image of D is equal to $a \cdot \text{area}(D)$.

17. $15\pi/4$.   **19.** $3\pi/2$.   **21.** $\pi^3/2^4$.

23. 0.   **25.** 27π.   **27.** 15/2.

29. $-21/2$.   **31.** $1 + 2e - 3e^{2/3}$.

33. 0; use the change of variables $x = \frac{1}{2}(u + v)$, $y = \frac{1}{2}(u - v)$.

SECTION 6.5

1. 12.   **3.** 1/60.   **5.** $32\sqrt{2}$.

7. 0.   **9.** 0.

11. 4; the region of integration is the three-dimensional solid in the first octant bounded by the plane $2x + 4y + z = 4$.

13. $128\pi/7$; the region of integration is the three-dimensional solid inside the cylinder $x^2+y^2=4$, above the xy-plane and below the paraboloid $z=x^2+y^2$.

15. 112π; the region of integration is the three-dimensional solid inside the cylinder $x^2+y^2=8$, bounded from below by the plane $z=-3$ and from above by the paraboloid $z=8-x^2-y^2$.

17. $1/6$.   19. 8π.   21. $32/9$.

23. In Cartesian coordinates, $\int_0^4 \left(\int_{4-x}^{\sqrt{16-x^2}} 16 - x^2 - y^2 dy \right) dx$; in cylindrical coordinates,
$\int_0^{\pi/2} \left(\int_{4/(\sin\theta+\cos\theta)}^4 (16-r^2)r\,dr \right) d\theta$.

25. $4\pi(a^3-(a^2-b^2)^{3/2})/3$.

27. $\int_0^{2\pi} \left(\int_0^{\sqrt{2}} \left(\int_{r^2-2}^{2-r^2} (r^2-2)r\,dz \right) dr \right) d\theta$.

29. 8.

31. $\int_0^{2\pi} \left(\int_0^{\sqrt{1/2}} \left(\int_{r^2}^{2r^2} 2r^2 \cos\theta\,dz \right) dr \right) d\theta + \int_0^{2\pi} \left(\int_{\sqrt{1/2}}^1 \left(\int_{r^2}^1 2r^2 \cos\theta\,dz \right) dr \right) d\theta$.

CHAPTER REVIEW

Computer Project

1. (a) $0 \le \iint_D f\,dA \le e\sqrt{2}$ (b) $0 \le \iint_D f\,dA \le 2.8$ (c) $\iint_D f\,dA = \overline{f} \approx 0.83748$.
(b)

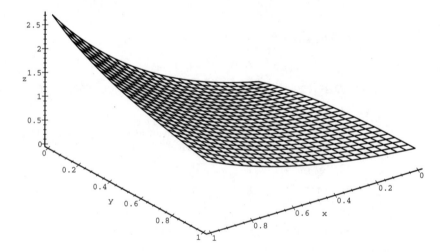

(d)

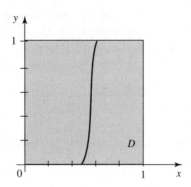

Further Explorations

1. $11\pi(2-\sqrt{2})/3$. The region of integration is the solid inside the inverted cone (with vertex at $(0, 0, 0)$ and angle $\pi/4$ with respect to the positive z-axis with the z-axis as axis of rotation) bounded from above by the graph of $\rho = 2 + \cos\theta$.

3. $a^3 m\pi$.

5. Let $\iint_R f \, dA = 0$ and assume that $f(x_0, y_0) > 0$ for some (x_0, y_0). Use the fact that a continuous function with $f(x_0, y_0) > 0$ must be positive on a ball centered at (x_0, y_0) to prove that $\iint_R f \, dA > 0$, thus getting a contradiction.

7. $(8\pi/3) - 2\sqrt{3}$.

9. Use the idea of Example 6.3 in Section 6.1.

CHAPTER 7

SECTION 7.1

1. Sphere: the top and the bottom line segments are mapped to the north and the south poles respectively, while the vertical boundary line segments are mapped to the meridian that is the intersection of the sphere and the xz-plane with $x \geq 0$. Cylinder: the vertical boundary line segments are mapped to the line that is the intersection of the cylinder and the xz-plane with $x \geq 0$. Horizontal lines $v = 0$ and $v = b$ are mapped to the bottom and the top boundary circles.

3. $\mathbf{r}(u, v) = (a \cos v \cos u, a \cos v \sin u, a \sin v)$, $0 \leq u \leq 2\pi$, $0 \leq v \leq \pi/2$.

5. $\mathbf{r}(u, v) = (u, v, 2 + 3v - u)$, $(u, v) \in D$, where D is the disk $u^2 + v^2 \leq 4$.

7. $\mathbf{r}(u, v) = (u, v, 6 - u - 2v)$, $(u, v) \in D$, where D is the triangular region bounded by the coordinate lines and the line $u + 2v = 6$.

9. $\mathbf{r}(u, v) = (u, v, u^2 + v^2)$, $u, v \geq 0$.

11. (a) $\mathbf{T}_u = (2, 2u, 0)$, $\mathbf{T}_v = (0, 1, 2v)$; $\mathbf{N} = (4uv, -4v, 2)$ (b) S is smooth for all $u, v \geq 0$.

13. (a) $\mathbf{T}_u = (\cos u \cos v, \cos u \sin v, -2 \sin u)$, $\mathbf{T}_v = (-\sin u \sin v, \sin u \cos v, 0)$; the surface

normal is $\mathbf{N} = \sin u (2 \sin u \cos v, 2 \sin u \sin v, \cos u)$ (b) S is not smooth at $(0, 0, \pm 2)$.

15. (a) $\mathbf{T}_u = (1 + \cos v)(-\sin u, \cos u, 0)$, $\mathbf{T}_v = (-\sin v \cos u, -\sin v \sin u, \cos v)$; $\mathbf{N} = (1 + \cos v)(\cos u \cos v, \sin u \cos v, \sin v)$ (b) S is not smooth at $(0, 0, 0)$.

17. (a) $\mathbf{T}_u = (1, 0, -2u)$, $\mathbf{T}_v = (0, 1, -2v)$; $\mathbf{N} = (2u, 2v, 1)$ (b) S is smooth for all $u, v \geq 0$.

19. $z = 0$.   **21.** $4x - y + 2z - 3 = 0$.

23. The cone is not smooth only at $\mathbf{r}(u, 0) = (0, 0, 0)$. At any other point (call it $\mathbf{r}(u_0, v_0)$) the tangent plane has the equation $(v_0 \cos u_0)x + (v_0 \sin u_0)y - v_0 z = 0$.

25. $\mathbf{r}(u, v) = (a \cos v \cos u, b \cos v \sin u, c \sin v)$, $0 \leq u \leq 2\pi$, $-\pi/2 \leq v \leq \pi/2$ (of course, this is not the only possible parametrization).

27. There are no such points.

SECTION 7.2

1. 0.   **3.** $(16 + 8\sqrt{3})/3$.   **5.** $(4 - \pi)\sqrt{2}/6$.

7. 4π.   **9.** Approximately 29.1966.   **11.** $\pi r \sqrt{h^2 + r^2}$.

13. $\iint_S x \, dS = \iint_S x^3 \, dS = 0$; $\iint_S x^2 \, dS = 4\pi a^4/3$.

15. The sides of S are a and $b\sqrt{1 + m^2}$.

17. $4(5^{3/2} - 1)/3$.   **19.** Approximately 10.4652.   **21.** $2\pi a^2$.

SECTION 7.3

1. 0.   **3.** 36π.   **5.** $-3\pi/2$.

7. $3\pi^2/4$.   **9.** -8π.

11. (a) $\pi a^2 c$ (b) $\pi a^2 c$ (c) The flow is vertical and the projections of both surfaces onto the xy-plane are the same.

13. 36π.   **15.** 0.   **17.** -2.

19. Use $\mathbf{r}(\theta, \phi) = a \cos \theta \sin \phi \mathbf{i} + a \sin \theta \sin \phi \mathbf{j} + a \cos \phi \mathbf{k}$, where $0 \leq \theta \leq 2\pi$ and $0 \leq \phi \leq \pi$; the surface normal is $a \sin \phi \, \mathbf{r}(\theta, \phi) = a^2 \sin \phi \mathbf{e}_\rho$, see (2.36) in Section 2.7; now use the definition to compute the given surface integral.

21. $-52/3$.   **23.** 36π.   **25.** 0.   **27.** 4π.

SECTION 7.4

1. $1 - a^2/3$.   **3.** $42/15$.   **5.** $19/10$.

7. $(0, 2a/\pi)$.   **9.** Mass is $a^2 b$; the center of mass is at $(a\pi/4, a/2)$.

11. The center of mass is at $(0, 0, 4.6695)$; the moment of inertia about the z-axis is approximately 84.4635ρ.

13. $(0, 0, 3a/8)$.   **15.** $a^3 \mu \pi$.   **17.** $100\mu\pi$.

19. For example, $f(x, y, z) = z$ and $\mathbf{c}(t) = (0, 0, t)$, $-1 \leq t \leq 1$.

21. $2\pi \leq \iint_S (z^2 + 1) \, dS \leq 4\pi$.   **23.** $3\pi \sqrt{5}/e \leq \iint_c e^{\sin(x+y)} ds \leq 3\pi e\sqrt{5}$.

CHAPTER REVIEW

Computer Project

1. (a) 6   (b) $I(m) = (2 + 4m)m^{-2/3}$; the cube of side a has the smallest isoperimetric ratio of all rectangular boxes considered; as $m \to 0$ and as $m \to \infty$, $I(m) \to \infty$;   (c) $(4\pi)^{1/3}3^{2/3}$ (d) $I(n) = 3^{2/3}(4\pi)^{1/3}(1/2)n^{-2/3}\left(1 + (n^2/\sqrt{n^2 - 1})\arcsin\left(\sqrt{n^2 - 1}/n\right)\right)$; $I(n)$ approaches ∞ as $n \to \infty$; as $n \to 1^+$, $I(n)$ approaches $(4\pi)^{1/3}3^{2/3}$ (e) sphere.
(b)

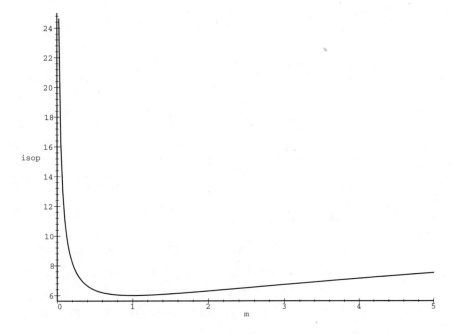

(d)

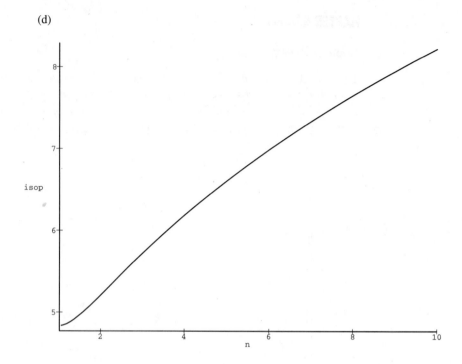

isop

n

Further Explorations

1. For example, $f(x, y, z) = z$, and S is the part of the plane $z = x$, $-1 \le x \le 1$, $0 \le y \le 1$.

3. $A(S) = \iint_D |f_z|^{-1}(f_x^2 + f_y^2 + f_z^2)^{1/2}\, dA$; $A(S) = \iint_D (g_x^2 + g_y^2 + 1)^{1/2}\, dA$.

5. Use the definition of the surface integral of a 2-form.

7. Use formula (7.2) in Section 7.1 to show that $\|\mathbf{N}\| = EG - F^2$.

CHAPTER 8

SECTION 8.1

1. 6π.	3. $-2e + (e^2 + 5)/2$.	5. $-109/90$.
7. 0.	9. 0.	11. 0.
13. $8/3$.	15. $3\pi/32$.	17. 8.

19. Use Theorem 8.2.

21. $I_x = \rho \int_c (C_1(x)\mathbf{i} + (xy^2 + C_2(y))\mathbf{j}) \cdot d\mathbf{s}$, $I_y = \rho \int_c (D_1(x)\mathbf{i} + (\frac{1}{3}x^3 + D_2(y))\mathbf{j}) \cdot d\mathbf{s}$, where $C_1(x)$, $C_2(y)$, $D_1(x)$ and $D_2(y)$ are functions of the variables indicated (there are infinitely many answers).

23. Both sides are equal to 0.

25. $-1/3$.	27. $11/30$.	29. 0.	31. 0.

SECTION 8.2

1. 0.   **3.** $14\pi/3$.   **5.** 0.

7. 0.   **9.** $8/3$.   **11.** 0.

13. Using a product rule from Section 4.3 show that $div\,(f\nabla g) = f\Delta g + \nabla f \cdot \nabla g$.

15. Start with $D_{\mathbf{n}}f = \nabla f \cdot \mathbf{n}$, integrate over S and use the Divergence Theorem.

17. 0.   **19.** Flux: $1/3$; circulation: $-3/2$.

21. Flux: $(e^4 - 1)(e^3 + 5)$; circulation: $-(e^3 - 1)(e^4 - 1)$.

23. $\pi/2$.   **25.** 28π.

SECTION 8.3

1. 0.   **3.** $5/12$.   **5.** -16.   **7.** 0.

9. Show that $curl\,(\mathbf{F} \times \mathbf{r}) = 2\mathbf{F}$ and use Stokes' Theorem.

11. 0.   **13.** 2π.   **15.** 0.   **17.** -3π.

19. Show that $curl\,(f\nabla f) = \mathbf{0}$ and use Stokes' Theorem.

21. The circulation is 4π; Stokes' Theorem does not apply.

SECTION 8.4

1. For example, $\mathbf{A}_0 = (2xz^2 + f(x))\mathbf{i} + (xy + g(y))\mathbf{j} + (yz + h(z))\mathbf{k}$, where f, g and h are differentiable functions; $\mathbf{A}_0 = \mathbf{A} + grad\,f$, where $f(x, y, z)$ is a differentiable function.

3. Compute $div\,\mathbf{J}$ from (8.15) and then use (8.13).

5. Use definitions of div and $curl$.

7. $\frac{1}{r}\left(\frac{\partial E_z}{\partial \theta} - r\frac{\partial E_\theta}{\partial z}\right) = -\frac{\partial B_r}{\partial t}$; $\frac{1}{r}\left(-\frac{\partial E_z}{\partial r} + \frac{\partial E_r}{\partial z}\right) = -\frac{\partial B_\theta}{\partial t}$; $\frac{1}{r}\left(E_\theta + r\frac{\partial E_\theta}{\partial r} - \frac{\partial E_r}{\partial \theta}\right) = -\frac{\partial B_z}{\partial t}$.

9. Equation (8.19) does not hold.

CHAPTER REVIEW

Computer Project

1. (a) $\int_{\mathbf{c}} \mathbf{F} \cdot d\mathbf{s} = \pi/e$ (b) $\int_{\mathbf{c}} \mathbf{F} \cdot d\mathbf{s} = \pi/e \approx 1.15573$ (must be the same due to Stokes' Theorem)   (c) $\int_{\mathbf{c}_{1/2}} \mathbf{F} \cdot d\mathbf{s} = \int_{S_{1/2}} curl\,\mathbf{F} \cdot d\mathbf{S} = e^{-1/2}\pi/2$, $\int_{\mathbf{c}_0} \mathbf{F} \cdot d\mathbf{s} = \int_{S_0} curl\,\mathbf{F} \cdot d\mathbf{S} = e^{-1}\pi$, $\int_{\mathbf{c}_{-1}} \mathbf{F} \cdot d\mathbf{s} = \int_{S_{-1}} curl\,\mathbf{F} \cdot d\mathbf{S} = 2e^{-2}\pi$ and $\int_{\mathbf{c}_{-10}} \mathbf{F} \cdot d\mathbf{s} = \int_{S_{-10}} curl\,\mathbf{F} \cdot d\mathbf{S} = 11e^{-11}\pi$.

Further Explorations

1. -14π.

3. $\iint_{\mathbf{c}_\epsilon} \alpha = 2\pi\epsilon^2(1 - \epsilon^2)^{-1}$; as $\epsilon \to 0$, $\iint_{\mathbf{c}_\epsilon} \alpha \to 0$; as $\epsilon \to 1^+$, $\iint_{\mathbf{c}_\epsilon} \alpha \to -\infty$; as $\epsilon \to 1^-$, $\iint_{\mathbf{c}_\epsilon} \alpha \to \infty$; as $\epsilon \to \infty$, $\iint_{\mathbf{c}_\epsilon} \alpha \to -2\pi$.

5. $2904\pi/5$.

7. (a) Follows from $(\partial/\partial x)(x(x^2+y^2)^{-1}) = (y^2-x^2)(x^2+y^2)^{-2}$ and $(\partial/\partial y)(y(x^2+y^2)^{-1}) = (x^2 - y^2)(x^2 + y^2)^{-2}$ (b) 2π (c) $\mathbf{F}$ is not C^1 at the origin.

9. 0.

11. (a) $\mathbf{r}(u, v) = (u, v, 0)$, $(u, v) \in D$ (b) $(e - 1)/2$ (c) $(e - 1)/2$.

13. (a) $*\alpha = x^2 t \, dt dz - c^{-2} z t^2 dx dy + c^{-2} x y^2 z t \, dz dx$ (b) use the definition of $*$ (c) $\alpha \wedge (*\alpha) = (x^4 t^2 - c^{-2} z^2 t^4 - c^{-2} x^2 y^4 z^2 t^2) dx dy dz dt$.

15. Show that $curl \, (f \nabla g + g \nabla f) = \mathbf{0}$.

Index

TABLE OF DERIVATIVES

1. $(f(x) \pm g(x))' = f'(x) \pm g'(x)$

2. $(Cf(x))' = Cf'(x)$

3. $(f(x)g(x))' = f'(x)g(x) + f(x)g'(x)$

4. $\left(\dfrac{f(x)}{g(x)}\right)' = \dfrac{f'(x)g(x) - f(x)g'(x)}{g^2(x)}$

5. $(f(x)^{g(x)})' = g(x)f(x)^{g(x)-1}f'(x) + f(x)^{g(x)}g'(x)\ln f(x)$

6. $f(g(x))' = f'(g(x))g'(x)$

7. $C' = 0$

8. $(x^n)' = nx^{n-1}$

9. $|x|' = \dfrac{|x|}{x}$ (if $x \neq 0$)

10. $(\sin x)' = \cos x$

11. $(\cos x)' = -\sin x$

12. $(\tan x)' = \sec^2 x$

13. $(\csc x)' = -\cot x \csc x$

14. $(\sec x)' = \sec x \tan x$

15. $(\cot x)' = -\csc^2 x$

16. $(e^x)' = e^x$

17. $(a^x)' = a^x \ln a$

18. $(\ln x)' = \dfrac{1}{x}$

19. $(\arcsin x)' = \dfrac{1}{\sqrt{1 - x^2}}$

20. $(\arccos x)' = -\dfrac{1}{\sqrt{1 - x^2}}$

21. $(\arctan x)' = \dfrac{1}{x^2 + 1}$

22. $(\sinh x)' = \cosh x$

23. $(\cosh x)' = \sinh x$

24. $(\tanh x)' = \text{sech}^2 x$

TABLE OF INTEGRALS

1. $\displaystyle\int (f(x) \pm g(x))\, dx = \int f(x)\, dx \pm \int g(x)\, dx$

2. $\displaystyle\int Cf(x)\, dx = C\int f(x)\, dx$

3. $\displaystyle\int f(x)g'(x)\, dx = f(x)g(x) - \int f'(x)g(x)\, dx$ (Integration by Parts)

4. $\displaystyle\int_a^b f(g(x))\, dx = \int_{g(a)}^{g(b)} f(u)\, du$ (Change of Variables or the Substitution Rule)

5. $\displaystyle\int a\, dx = ax + C$

6. $\displaystyle\int x^n\, dx = \frac{1}{n+1}x^{n+1} + C \ (n \neq -1)$

7. $\displaystyle\int \frac{1}{x}\, dx = \ln|x| + C$

8. $\displaystyle\int \sin x\, dx = -\cos x + C$

9. $\displaystyle\int \cos x\, dx = \sin x + C$

10. $\displaystyle\int \tan x\, dx = -\ln|\cos x| + C$

11. $\displaystyle\int \cot x\, dx = \ln|\sin x| + C$

12. $\displaystyle\int \csc x\, dx = \ln|\csc x - \cot x| + C$

13. $\displaystyle\int \sec x\, dx = \ln|\sec x + \tan x| + C$

14. $\displaystyle\int \sin^2 x\, dx = \frac{1}{2}x - \frac{1}{4}\sin 2x + C$

15. $\displaystyle\int \cos^2 x\, dx = \frac{1}{2}x + \frac{1}{4}\sin 2x + C$

16. $\displaystyle\int \sin^n x\, dx = -\frac{1}{n}\sin^{n-1} x \cos x + \frac{n-1}{n}\int \sin^{n-2} x\, dx + C$

17. $\displaystyle\int \cos^n x\, dx = \frac{1}{n}\cos^{n-1} x \sin x + \frac{n-1}{n}\int \cos^{n-2} x\, dx + C$

18. $\displaystyle\int \sec^2 x\, dx = \tan x + C$

19. $\displaystyle\int \csc^2 x\, dx = -\cot x + C$

20. $\displaystyle\int \sec x \tan x\, dx = \sec x + C$

21. $\displaystyle\int \csc x \cot x\, dx = -\csc x + C$

22. $\displaystyle\int \arcsin x\, dx = x\arcsin x + \sqrt{1 - x^2} + C$

23. $\displaystyle\int \arctan x\, dx = x\arctan x - \frac{1}{2}\ln(1 + x^2) + C$